## MARTIN FROBISHER, Sc.D.

Formerly Special Consultant, Laboratory Branch, Communicable Disease Center, United States Public Health Service. Formerly, Associate Professor of Bacteriology, Emory University Medical School, Atlanta, Georgia; Special Member, International Health Division, Rockefeller Foundation; Associate Professor of Bacteriology, Johns Hopkins University; Chief, Bacteriology Section, Communicable Disease Center, United States Public Health Service; Professor and Head, Department of Bacteriology, University of Georgia.

**8**th edition

# FUNDAMENTALS OF

# *Microbiology*

## An Introduction to the Microorganisms with Special Reference to the Procaryons

## W. B. SAUNDERS COMPANY
### PHILADELPHIA · LONDON · TORONTO

W. B. Saunders Company: West Washington Square
Philadelphia, Pa. 19105

12 Dyott Street
London W. C. 1

1835 Yonge Street
Toronto 7, Ontario

Reprinted December, 1968
Fundamentals of Microbiology

# Preface to the Eighth Edition

In this new edition this book has been largely rewritten and is designed to present, within the spatial and temporal limitations of an elementary textbook for college students, as complete and broad an introductory survey of the field of microbiology as possible. Supplementary reading for each chapter has been suggested to open additional approaches to those interested in more detailed discussions. As indicated in the new subtitle, the presentation is now directed mainly toward the procaryotic Protista or, more accurately, the Monera, i.e., the bacteria (including the rickettsias, PPLO and chlamydias) and, to a lesser extent, the Cyanophyceae. The eucaryotic Protista (Protozoa, Eumycetes and Chlorophyta) are described briefly as an introduction for beginning students or as a review for students who have already had a course in elementary biology. Though neither cellular nor living, viruses are included as Protista or Monera "by courtesy." We now stand in admiring awe of the man-made viruses and their creators. We may predict that evolution will become computerized and Darwin astonished, not to say scandalized.

The first portion of the new edition begins the subject with magic and empiricism and leads through the beginnings of scientific biology and microbiology. For the convenience of instructor and class some basic details of microscopic and cultural techniques and growth phenomena are presented in early chapters along with some historical sidelights. Data on enzymes and bioenergetics, being of such a very fundamental nature, are also given early in the book.

A second approach to the general subject starts with the structure of atoms and carries through molecules and the synthesis of macromolecules, detailing especially the synthesis and structure of the nucleic acids and their role in genetics, mutation and evolution. Hypothetical evolutionary relationships of eucaryotic and procaryotic Protista are then discussed and the types described and compared. The three chapters on viruses are preceded by chapters on genetics and mutation and the role, in them, of the nucleic acids, the "living" substance of viruses.

The mid-portion of the book presents fundamental data on communicable disease and its transmission, immunology, the effects of environmental factors, disinfection and sterilization, antibiotics, and methods of systematic study and classification. These are all essential to intelligent reading of the final portion of the book that describes mainly the bacteria (including rickettsias, chlamydias and PPLO), their activities in nature and their role for good or evil in human affairs.

As in the past, the author has welcomed criticism, especially that which could be used to make the book more accurate and useful to others. He acknowledges the frequent validity of criticism and extends his sincere thanks to those who took the time to cooperate in this facet of microbiological pedagogy. He is especially grateful to Dr. Antonio Romano, who read the entire manuscript of this edition, and to Dr. Clyde Goodheart, who read the chapters on the viruses. Their recommendations have proved very useful indeed and any errors of omission or commission in spite of good advices are entirely the responsibility of the author.

Thanks are also due to the many scientists who gave permission and materials for illustrations. Acknowledgments of sources are given with each illustration. Lack of space has prevented the use of many exceedingly valuable contributions.

Finally, grateful acknowledgment is made of the indulgent, untiring and expert assistance of the entire staff of W. B. Saunders Company, without whom this edition would not have been possible; to Alice P. Snyder, who typed the manuscript, and to Amy W. Frobisher, who read and checked the final draft and helped the author over some very rough trails.

MARTIN FROBISHER
*Chatham, Massachusetts*

# Contents

1    *The Origins of Microbiology and the Chemical Basis of Microbial Life*

*Chapter 5*

ENZYMES........................................................ 56

*Chapter 6*

CHEMICAL BASIS OF MICROBIAL LIFE: Atoms, Ions, Isotopes.............. 70

*Chapter 7*

CHEMICAL BASIS OF MICROBIAL LIFE: Structure of Compounds............ 79

*Chapter 8*

CHEMICAL BASIS OF MICROBIAL LIFE: Macromolecules.................... 85

*Chapter 9*

BIOENERGETICS...................................................103

# 2  *The Protista: Eucaryotic and Procaryotic; The Viruses*

# 3   *Microbiology, the Patchwork Quilt*

# 4  *The Parade of the Procaryons*

# 5   *Microorganisms at Work*

# 1

# The Origins of Microbiology and the Chemical Basis of Microbial Life

The fascination of mankind with the wonders of Nature, and especially with the nature and origin of life, is as old as *Homo sapiens* himself and perhaps *H. neanderthalensis* and his ancestors. The ancients, and the not-so-ancients, were, in addition, much concerned with, and to a great extent governed by, mysteries beyond life; the occult and the supernatural. Only in comparatively recent times have some of the dark clouds of ignorance, superstition and fear surrounding the nature of life and natural phenomena been dissipated by intelligence, thought, experimentation and learning, i.e., by Science, the search for experimentally demonstrable truth.

During the centuries since thought, questioning and experimentation began Science has grown enormously. In the last three or four decades the scope of scientific investigation has become so extensive that today Biological Science is no longer the concern of only a few hundred scholars; numerous large groups of specialists devote themselves to scores of growing segments of what was formerly a single, relatively limited area of thought. Among the most absorbing and rapidly expanding of these segments of the science of Biology is the field of Microbiology; a relatively new segment that developed only as a result of, and concomitantly with, the invention and improvement of microscopes and the science of Micros-

1

copy. As knowledge in other fields grew, Microbiology was more and more nurtured and fostered by related sciences such as Chemistry, Physics and Mathematics.

Accordingly, the first part of this book presents several chapters of introductory material related to the beginnings and development of the sciences of Microscopy and Microbiology. It describes, for beginning students, some of the methodologies of Microscopy and Microbiology, the general nature of microorganisms, and the chemical basis of microbial life as revealed by those avuncular sciences, Physics and Chemistry. The paths of knowledge thus pointed out then lead into more detailed descriptions of the types of microorganisms that make up the Kingdom Protista as outlined in Part 2.

# Chapter 1

## ORIGINS OF BIOLOGY AND MICROBIOLOGY

Before the dawn of civilization in the Mesopotamian regions and farther east some 7000 to 8000 years ago there was little exact knowledge of either the causes or nature of natural phenomena. However, scholarly thinkers and their works were not wholly lacking. By the time writing and written history had been "invented" 5000 to 6000 years ago in Sumeria, Egypt, Syria and adjacent regions, many keen and ambitious minds in the ancient priesthoods, secular upper classes and royal families had learned of the medicinal and poisonous properties of certain plants and of the venoms of certain snakes and insects. They knew how to exploit nature for political and other purposes. For thousands of years after the beginnings of civilization magic, incantation, abracadabra and witchcraft passed for science and usually also for religion. Even as recently as the Middle Ages (c. 500–1400 A.D.) and later in the European Renaissance (c. 1400–1700 A.D.) astrology (aided by imaginative charlatans, with weird grimaces and impressive passes) passed for astronomy; alchemy (strongly flavored with wizardry) masqueraded as chemistry; the most outrageous quackery was accepted, even by royalty, as medicine.

As always, however, honest, imaginative and inquisitive men here and there were still capable of analytical and creative thought and the proposing of working hypotheses to be tested experimentally. They were sometimes reviled, persecuted and tortured for their supposed dealings with "The Evil One." Century after century these pioneer scientists (seekers after experimentally demonstrable truth) began to establish a system of knowledge based on accurate, purposeful observation; logical inference; imaginative hypothesis; and ingenious experiments designed to establish indisputable fact or destroy fallacy.

Because of great difficulties in travel and communications, ancient scholars shared little of one another's learning. As the centuries passed, exploration began and travel became more common, populations increased, and vast interminglings of peoples occurred because of wars and trade. Scientific information thus began to spread from country to country and, more recently, from continent to continent. Instead of a few great scholars who were thought (even by themselves!) to know everything, men began to realize that there were boundless deserts and plains and illimitable dark forests of ignorance only awaiting the axe and plow of the devoted researcher to yield rich crops of wonderful, golden knowledge. Men also realized the awesome truth that knowledge is power—to create or to destroy utterly. Eventually scientific thought, experimentation and communications became permissible and even respectable. They also became incalculably profitable and frightening.

Scientists interested in the mysteries of life collected, over the centuries, a considerable mass of reasonably accurate information about such living things as could be seen with the naked eye, and even with "magnifying glasses" (magnifications of about 10 diameters). By 350 B.C. Aristotle and his students had drawn up a systematic, though limited and (as we now know) often erroneous classification of hundreds of plants and animals. Accumulating knowledge of living organisms slowly became arranged into a more or less orderly system and the study of life was eventually dignified with a given name: *biology* (Gr. *bios* = life; *logos* = study or descrip-

3

tion). Most of biology was at first largely descriptive of outward form and macroscopic (Gr. *makros* = large; *skopion* = to see) anatomy. These descriptions became the basis of classifications and taxonomy—major preoccupations of most early botanists and zoologists. Until the seventeenth and eighteenth centuries chemistry and physics were almost completely separate fields of study and little used in biology. Life and living substance were commonly thought of as mysterious and beyond physical and chemical analysis.

## 1.1   BEGINNINGS OF MICROSCOPY

Until about 1660 A.D. all knowledge of the form, structure and life processes of plants and animals was narrowly restricted to what could be seen with the naked (or very feebly assisted) human eye. Microorganisms were merely "fabulous monsters." Visual limitations of the pitiably restricted eye of man had always stood, like an impenetrable curtain, between man and the fantastic and glittering cosmos of the microscopic world.

Unaided human vision fails to see objects less than about 100 $\mu$ (0.004 or $\frac{1}{254}$ inch) in diameter or to perceive as separate objects (i.e.,

**TABLE 1.1   SOME LINEAR MEASURES COMMONLY USED IN MICROBIOLOGY**

| |
|---|
| 1 inch = 2.54 cm. |
| 1 cm. = 10 mm. |
| 1 mm. = 1000 $\mu$ |
| 1 $\mu$ = 0.001 mm. = 0.00003937 or 1/25,400 inch<br>    = 1000 m$\mu$ |
| 1 m$\mu$ = 0.001 $\mu$ = 10.0 Angstrom (Å) |
| 1 Å = .0001 $\mu$ = 0.0000001 mm. = 1/254,000,000 inch |

*resolve*) particles separated by distances less than about 100 $\mu$. Microscopic linear units are shown in Table 1.1. The development of practical, relatively high-power microscopy about the middle of the seventeenth century was like turning on a 500-watt lamp in a pitch-dark curiosity shop. It gave men the power to see a universe of objects, living and inanimate, so minute that their very existence had never before even been suspected.

**The First Microscopes.**   By the end of the thirteenth century simple lenses (magnifying glasses) had already been used in various ways for many years. Such lenses, however, did not magnify very highly. About 1590, a Dutch spectacle maker, Zacharias Janssen, used a second lens to magnify the image produced by a primary lens. This is the basic principle of the compound microscope used by every micro-

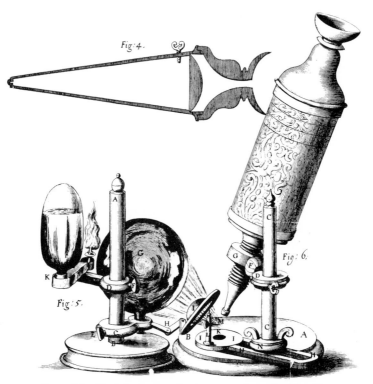

**Figure 1.1**   Hooke's compound microscope; drawn by himself.

**Figure 1.2**   Drawing of "white mould" by Robert Hooke.

biologist today. Galileo invented an improved compound microscope in 1610. Robert Hooke (1635–1703) made and used a compound microscope in the 1660's and described his fascinating explorations of the newly discovered universe of the microscopic in his classic "Micrographia" (1665), published at request of the Royal Society in London (Fig. 1.1). Although Hooke's highest magnifications were possibly enough to reveal bacteria, he apparently made no observations of them, probably because he studied mainly opaque objects in the dry state by reflected light, conditions that, as will be explained, are not optimal for observation of microorganisms. However, his pictures of "white mould" (probably a *Mucor* species) are very informative and accurate (Fig. 1.2).

A contemporary of Hooke, and the man mainly responsible for revealing the hitherto unknown and unseen world of microorganisms, did not use a compound microscope. He was the Dutch investigator, Antonj van Leeuwenhoek (1632–1723), a linen merchant by trade and a man of public and commercial affairs in the city of Delft (Fig. 1.3). He was not a trained scientist but was self-educated, and amused himself by means of his skill and craftsmanship in glass blowing and fine metal work. He lived in relatively easy circumstances with leisure time for his avocation of making minute, simple but powerful lenses. With these he delighted in examining a great variety of objects: saliva, pepper decoctions, cork, the leaves of plants, circulating blood in the tail of a salamander, seminal fluid, urine, cow dung, scrapings from the teeth and so on. In many of these he saw living creatures, some of which we now know were protozoa and bacteria but all of which he called "animalcules."

In spite of the fact that his microscopes were not compound he obtained remarkable results with them.

. . . he showed rare ingenuity and expert craftsmanship in the grinding and mounting of his simple lenses, a skill which he zealously kept to himself; and in spite of the requests of his learned friends, he refused to disclose the secret of his success.

. . . Leeuwenhoek's instruments are not true microscopes at all in the sense in which we think of microscopes,

**Figure 1.3**   Antonj van Leeuwenhoek. A fanciful delineation based on a famous portrait. The picture shows accurately the size and shape of the first microscopes, the manner in which they were used, and the simple laboratory apparatus of the "Father of Bacteriology." (Courtesy of Lambert Pharmacal Co.)

but rather simple magnifying glasses generally consisting of a small, single, biconvex lens. The object, and not the lens, was moved into focus by means of screws [Fig. 1.4].

To adjust the lens to the object was so long and tedious a task that it is not surprising that Leeuwenhoek used an individual lens for each object. . . . The magnification varied and at best did not exceed two hundred to three hundred diameters. . . . The size of objects which Leeuwenhoek examined was determined by comparison. For this purpose he used at various times a grain of sand, the seed of millet or mustard, the eye of a louse, a vinegar eel,

and still later hair or blood corpuscles. In this way he secured fairly accurate measurements of a great variety of objects. . . . he was forced to admit that the sand grain was more than one million times the size of one of the animalcules.*

Leeuwenhoek was so interested in the things he observed that, like Hooke, he wrote minutely detailed reports about them to the Royal Society in London, beginning in 1674. He was later elected a fellow of the Royal Society. Some of his observations are at once quaint and epoch-making. For example, after examining material which he scraped from between his teeth, he said:

Though my teeth are kept usually very clean, nevertheless when I view them in a Magnifying Glass, I find growing between them a little white matter as thick as wetted flour; in this substance, though I could not perceive any motion, I judged there might probably be living Creatures.

I therefore took some of this flour and mixt it either with pure rain water wherein were no Animals; or else with some of my Spittle (having no Air bubbles to cause a motion in it) and then to my great surprise perceived that the aforesaid matter contained very small living animals, which moved themselves very extravagantly. The biggest sort had the shape of A. Their motion was strong and nimble, and they darted themselves through the water or spittle, as a Jack or Pike does through the water. These were generally not many in number. The second sort had the shape of B. These spun about like a top, or took a course sometimes on one side, as is shown at C and D. They were more in number than the first. In the third sort I could not well distinguish the Figure, for sometimes it seem'd to be an Oval, and other times a Circle. These

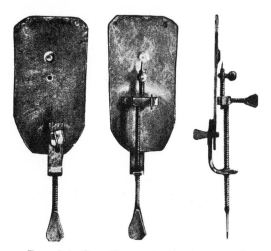

**Figure 1.4**   One of Leeuwenhoek's microscopes: front, back and side views. The tiny spherical or hemispherical lens is held in the slightly raised structure in the upper part of the metal plate. The object to be examined was mounted at the tip of the sharp-pointed mounting pin. Focusing was accomplished by means of the three thumbscrews to which the mounting pin is attached. These are approximately actual size.

---

*Fred, E. B.: Antonj van Leeuwenhoek. J. Bact., *25*:1, 1933.

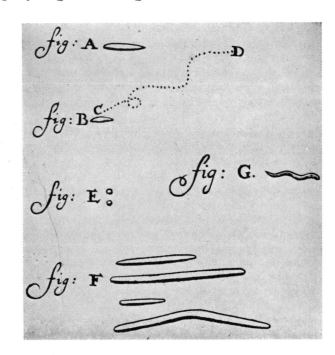

**Figure 1.5** Leeuwenhoek's drawings of bacteria. Here may be seen cocci, bacilli and (probably) a spirochete. The motion of one of the bacilli is clearly indicated. Today such observations are commonplace. But Leeuwenhoek was seeing them for the first time in the history of the human race! It was as momentous a discovery as that of Columbus —a new world!

were so small they seem'd no bigger than E and therewithal so swift, that I can compare them to nothing better than a swarm of Flies or Gnats, flying and turning among one another in a small space* [Figure 1.5].

Note that, unlike Hooke, Leeuwenhoek made many of his observations by light transmitted *through* the object and that the microorganisms were suspended in various fluids, not immobilized or otherwise altered by drying.

## 1.2  MICROORGANISMS AND THE ORIGIN OF LIFE

The ancients knew nothing of microorganisms, of evolution, or of the fact that only living things could beget living things. They believed that creatures like frogs, mice, bees and other animals sprang fully formed from fertile mud, decaying carcasses, warm rain or fog and the like. Van Helmont (1577–1644) devised a method for *manufacturing* mice. He recommended putting some wheat grains with soiled linen and cheese into an appropriate receptacle and leaving it undisturbed for a time in an attic or stable. Mice would then appear. This observation may still be experimentally confirmed but the conclusions drawn from it differ today.

Belief in spontaneous generation lived on

*Fred, E. B.: Antonj van Leeuwenhoek. J. Bact., *25*:1, 1933.

for years, as it had for centuries. For example, an elderly lady of the writer's early acquaintance complained bitterly that she had been cheated by a merchant who sold her a woolen coat which was of such a quality that it turned entirely into moths when left undisturbed in a closet for some months!

In the earlier years, in the absence of exact knowledge of microorganisms or chemistry, there had arisen much skepticism and bitter feeling over the question of the origin of life. One "scientist" who still held to the ancient ideas says of the views of another who doubted,

So may we doubt whether, in cheese and timber, worms are generated, or if beetles and wasps in cow dung, or if butterflies, locusts, shell-fish, snails, eels, and such life be procreated of putrefied matter which is to receive the forms of that creature to which it is by formative power disposed. To question this is to question reason, sense and experience. If he doubts this let him go to Egypt and there he will find the fields swarming with mice begot of the mud of Nylus, to the great calamity of the inhabitants.

There was a great deal of such acrid discussion by wordy savants of the times, who tried to settle everything by argument. Experimentation was regarded as rather undignified and even smacking of relations with the devil.

**Francesco Redi (1626–1679).**   The experimental method was, however, being invoked here and there. For example, it had always been supposed that the maggots in decaying meat were derived spontaneously from transformations of the putrid meat itself. Francesco Redi, a physician of Arezzo, questioned this hypothesis. He placed meat and fish in jars covered with very fine gauze and saw flies approach the jars and crawl on the gauze. He saw the eggs of the flies caught on the gauze and observed that the meat then putrefied without maggot formation. Maggots developed only when the flies' eggs were deposited on the meat itself. Obviously the meat itself did not turn into maggots. Redi's work was not widely noted, however, and it was not until much later that another series of experiments was made.

**Louis Joblot (1645–1723).** After Leeuwenhoek's discovery of microorganisms it was thought by many who believed in the Aristotelian doctrine concerning spontaneous generation of life that animal or vegetable matter contained a "vital or vegetative force," capable of converting such matter into new and different forms of life. A popular notion was that geese and lambs could grow from certain kinds of trees. Leeuwenhoek's animalcules were hailed by many as proof of this. In 1710, Louis Joblot observed that hay, when infused in water and allowed to stand for some days, gave rise to countless animalcules, or infusoria (bacteria and protozoa). The hay was thought by some to change into animalcules; anyone today can observe the development of these for himself. Joblot, however, boiled hay infusion and divided it into two portions, placing one in a carefully baked (sterilized) and closed vessel, which he heated thoroughly and kept closed. The other portion was not heated and was kept in an open vessel. The infusion in the open vessel teemed with microorganisms in a few days. In the closed vessel no life appeared as long as it remained closed, thus showing that the infusion alone, once freed of life by heat, was incapable of generating new life spontaneously.

**John Needham (1713–1781).** Similar experiments carried out by an English scientist, John Needham, gave conflicting results. Life developed in Needham's heated closed vessels as well as in the open unheated ones. He therefore believed in spontaneous generation. We shall see later that this result was due to insufficient heating which failed to kill heat-resistant forms of bacteria called *spores*. But nothing was known about spores at that time.

**Lazzaro Spallanzani (1729–1799).** Spallanzani, an Italian naturalist, published the results of a whole series of the same type of experiments which disagreed with those of Needham. He showed that if heating was prolonged sufficiently and the vessels kept closed to exclude dust and air, no animalcules developed in hay infusions or in any other kind of organic matter, such as urine and beef broth. Needham, in reply, said that the prolonged heating destroyed the "vegetative force" of the organic matter which, he said, was necessary for the spontaneous generation of life. Spallanzani answered Needham's objections by showing that the heated infusions in the closed flasks could still develop animalcules when exposed to air (i.e., when microorganisms were introduced with dust).

In 1775 Lavoisier discovered oxygen and the relation between air and life. This renewed the controversy about spontaneous generation, the objection to Spallanzani's results being that it was the exclusion of air (oxygen) from the flasks which prevented the development of life.

**Schulze and Schwann.** New experiments were performed in which unheated air was admitted freely to the previously heated infusions of meat or hay, but only after passing through sulfuric acid or potassium hydroxide solutions (Schulze, 1836) or through very hot glass tubes (Schwann, 1836), the idea being that the air itself introduced the germs of life into the infusions. When the infusions exposed to air so treated failed to develop any life, it was claimed by others that this was not due to a destruction of any germs of life in the air by the sulfuric acid or hot glass, but that the "life-giving" power of the air had been destroyed by these methods, thus preventing spontaneous generation.

**Schröder and von Dusch.** This objection was overcome by Schröder and von Dusch (1854–1861) who performed similar experiments in which the air was not heated or passed through acid or alkali but merely filtered through cotton wool. This method prevented the appearance of animalcules in the heated broth or infusions until the vessels were opened. It was therefore apparent that the method of treatment of the air had nothing to do with the development of animalcules and that these did not develop spontaneously, but that there were particles of living matter floating on dust in the air which not only were killed by heat, acids and alkalis but which could be caught and withheld by the cotton wool alone. The presence of the microorganisms in the cotton wool was later proved by Pasteur. The experiments of Schröder and von Dusch were the origin of our present-day use of cotton plugs for bacteriological culture tubes and flasks.

In spite of these demonstrations, long and bitter controversies still raged. Schröder and von Dusch were not convinced by their own experiments and admitted the possibility that spontaneous generation might occur under natural conditions.

**Louis Pasteur (1822–1895).** Pasteur, one of the most famous French scientists, was born in Dôle, December 27, 1822. Son of a moderately prosperous tanner who had fought for and been decorated on the battlefield by Napoleon, Pasteur had a great admiration for his father's soldierly accomplishments. He later was moved to many of his best scientific achievements by his patriotic zeal. In his boyhood he was an indifferent student but later became an enthusiastic scholar, devoting his energies to a study of chemistry. He discovered the relationship of the stereoisomeric forms of tartrate crystals and revealed a whole new series of possibilities in physical chemistry.

"DISEASES" OF WINES. Pasteur, however, was not one to gloat over such successes and rest on his laurels. He sought for other fields of investigation. His choice was guided largely by patriotic motives. An Englishman had written to him:

People are astonished in France that the sale of French wines should not have become more extended here [in England] since the Commercial Treaties. The reason is simple enough. At first we eagerly welcomed those [French] wines, but we soon had the sad experience that there was too much loss occasioned by the diseases [souring] to which they are subject.*

Germany was at that time making a much better beer than France, and Pasteur undertook to make France a successful rival in that respect. In order to do so he made a long study of beer manufacture and of the cause of souring and spoilage ("diseases") of beer and wines. As a result of these studies he arrived at far-reaching conclusions. He said at the Académie des Sciences in January, 1864:

Might not the diseases of wines be caused by organized ferments, microscopic vegetations [yeasts, molds, bacteria], of which the germs would develop when certain circumstances of temperature, of atmospheric variations, of *exposure to air* [author's italics], would favour their evolution or their introduction into wines? . . . I have indeed reached this result that the alterations ["diseases"] of wines are co-existent with the presence and multiplication of microscopic vegetations.†

Pasteur had found that acid wines, "ropy" wines, bitter wines, sour beer and so on were caused by the growth in them of undesirable contaminating organisms which produced these so-called diseases.

The solution of the problem, as later proved

**Figure 1.6** Pasteur in his laboratory. Dr. Pasteur is examining a specimen of spinal cord from a rabid animal. The material at the bottom of the jar is sodium hydroxide (drying agent).

by Pasteur (Fig. 1.6), lay in preventing the growth of foreign organisms, "wild" yeasts and bacteria, which caused the undesirable conditions. After considerable experimentation along these lines he discovered that the wine did not spoil in transit if it were held for some minutes at a temperature between 50° and 60° C. He said,

I have . . . ascertained that wine was never altered by that preliminary operation [heating], and as nothing prevents it afterwards from undergoing . . . improvement with age—it is evident that this process [heating] offers every advantage.

His experiments were so successful that a practical test of the efficacy of his methods was made. He wrote to a friend:

. . . experiments on the heating of wines will be made by the Minister of the Navy. Great quantities of heated and of non-heated wine are to be sent to Gabon so as to test the process; at present our colonial crews have to drink mere vinegar.

Pasteur laid down three great principles:

1. Every alteration, either of beer or of wine, depends on the development in it of microorganisms which are ferments or "diseases" of the beer or wine.

2. These "germs or ferments" are brought by the air, by the ingredients or by the apparatus used in breweries.

3. Whenever beer or wine contains no *living* microorganisms it remains unchanged.

PASTEURIZATION. In the same way that wines could be preserved by heating from

---

*From "The Life of Pasteur," by René Vallery-Radot, reprinted with permission from Doubleday Company, Inc.
†*ibid.*

various causes of alteration, bottled beer could escape the development of disease ferments by being brought to a temperature of 50° to 55° C. The application of this process soon gave rise to the new word, *"pasteurized"* beer, which became current in technical language. Today, pasteurization of milk (heating at 63° C. for 30 minutes) is routine. The heating kills pathogenic (disease-producing) microorganisms.

PASTEUR ON SPECIFICITY OF DISEASE.   Pasteur foresaw the consequences of his studies, and wrote in his book on beer:

When we see beer and wine subjected to deep alterations because they have given refuge to micro-organisms invisibly introduced and now swarming within them, it is impossible not to be pursued by the thought that similar facts may, *must,* take place in animals and in man.*

It was obvious from Pasteur's studies that each special kind of fermentation or disease of beer or wine was the result of the growth and activity in it of a special, distinct form of yeast or other microorganism, depending on the type of fermentation or disease under investigation. This furthered an idea, already old, of the *specificity* of biological action, and supported the view that animal and human diseases also, like different sorts of putrefaction and fermentation, were each caused by a single, specific type of microorganism.

PASTEUR ON SPONTANEOUS GENERATION. After Pasteur's views of the nature of fermentation had been made public he became involved in the bitter quarrel over the apparently mysterious appearance of "germs" in fermentable or putrescible liquids like wine, beer, urine and broth. Pasteur carried out many ingenious experiments to answer the various objections and fallacies of previous workers and to show that the animalcules in spoiled beer and wine were merely descendants of microorganisms that had gained access to the fluids from dust in the air and that, by their growth and metabolism, caused fermentation and putrefaction. First, he redemonstrated that living creatures float in the air attached to particles of dust. Then he showed, as Schulze and Schwann had done, that when they could be excluded from various substances such as sterilized broth and urine, these substances did not ferment or putrefy. By using flasks with long open necks having several vertical bends in them, he showed that although unheated, untreated and unfiltered air communicated freely with the interior, the dust was caught by gravity in the bends of the neck, and no life appeared in the infusions. Not until

_____
* *ibid.*

the flask was tilted so that the fluid came into contact with this dust and was allowed to run back into the flask, or until the neck of the flask was broken off close to the body, did growth occur in the fluids. Some of Pasteur's flasks which were sterile in 1864 have been preserved and are still sterile (if they have not been destroyed by wars) after over a century!

## 1.3   SPONTANEOUS GENERATION— MODERN STYLE

In 1864 Pasteur received a prize from the French Academy of Science for his studies that conclusively disproved the Aristotelian doctrine of spontaneous generation. Since that time, studies of organic chemistry have produced a mass of evidence to revive the doctrine of spontaneous generation in a modern form called *chemical evolution*. There is now good reason to believe that life evolved during many millions of years from combinations of a few elements (chiefly C, H, O, N, S and P) by a series of reactions that were compatible with natural laws (second law of thermodynamics or law of entropy) and were actually inevitable under what are called "primitive earth" or *prebiotic* conditions. These are conditions that are thought to have existed during the later stages of the formation of the earth over 4,000,000,000 years ago (Fig. 1.7), eons before the Cambrian period that began as recently as 600,000,000 years ago—practically yesterday, geologically speaking (Fig. 1.8).

### CHEMICAL EVOLUTION

Prior to 1828 the formation of organic compounds was believed to be absolutely restricted to living organisms (hence *organic*). In 1828 Friedrich Wöhler, a German chemist, produced urea, $O{=}C{=}(NH_2)_2$, an organic substance common in the wastes of many animals, by the simple process of evaporating an aqueous solution of ammonium cyanate, $O{=}C{=}N(NH_4)$, an inorganic substance.* The old-time distinction between *organic* and *inorganic* evaporated with the water from Wöhler's solution; Wöhler had demonstrated that "spontaneous generation" of

_____
*The term organic chemistry is commonly used to mean the chemistry of the compounds of carbon or of the hydrocarbons and their derivatives. Some exclude certain simple carbon compounds, e.g., oxides, sulfides and metallic carbonates, cyanides and cyanates. Here, for convenience, $CO_2$ and metallic and ammonium carbonates and cyanates are treated as inorganic.

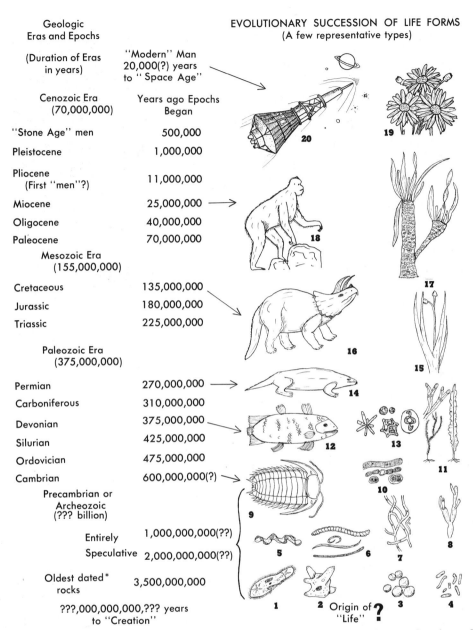

| Geologic Eras and Epochs | EVOLUTIONARY SUCCESSION OF LIFE FORMS (A few representative types) |
|---|---|
| (Duration of Eras in years) | "Modern" Man 20,000(?) years to "Space Age" |
| Cenozoic Era (70,000,000) | Years ago Epochs Began |
| "Stone Age" men | 500,000 |
| Pleistocene | 1,000,000 |
| Pliocene (First "men"?) | 11,000,000 |
| Miocene | 25,000,000 |
| Oligocene | 40,000,000 |
| Paleocene | 70,000,000 |
| Mesozoic Era (155,000,000) | |
| Cretaceous | 135,000,000 |
| Jurassic | 180,000,000 |
| Triassic | 225,000,000 |
| Paleozoic Era (375,000,000) | |
| Permian | 270,000,000 |
| Carboniferous | 310,000,000 |
| Devonian | 375,000,000 |
| Silurian | 425,000,000 |
| Ordovician | 475,000,000 |
| Cambrian | 600,000,000(?) |
| Precambrian or Archeozoic (??? billion) | |
| Entirely | 1,000,000,000(??) |
| Speculative | 2,000,000,000(??) |
| Oldest dated* rocks | 3,500,000,000 |
| ???,000,000,000,??? years to "Creation" | |

**Figure 1.7**   Geologic time scale (left) showing ancient origin of bacteria and other microorganisms in pre-Cambrian times (entirely speculative) at foot of evolutionary scale. Pictures 1, 2, protozoa; 3, 4, bacteria; 5, spirochete (protozoa-like bacterium); 6, marine worms; 7, mold-like bacteria; 8, aquatic fungus (*Saprolegnia*); 9, trilobite (fossil marine arthropod); 10, 13, bacteria-like algae (Cyanophyceae, desmids); 11, higher algae; 12, fossil fish; 14, cotylosaur (fossil reptile); 15, *Psilopsida,* first vascular land plants (Silurian); 16, *Triceratops,* a dinosaur; 17, cycad tree (Jurassic); 18, fossil man-like ape; 19, hybrid (1968) daisies; 20, man in space. *Oldest rocks dated by modern measurements of radioactivity. (From Frobisher, Sommermeyer and Blaustein: Microbiology for Nurses, 11th ed. W. B. Saunders Co., 1964.)

organic substances from inorganic ones could occur. Everyone was naturally excited with the implications for the spontaneous generation of life. If urea could be made to appear "spontaneously," what about other organic substances? Could living substance, or anything like it, be made to appear?

Without recounting the research studies dealing with these points during the decades since Wöhler's discovery, we may say that the "spontaneous" or artificial formations of numerous organic compounds (thiourea, thioacetamide, alcohols, aldehydes, amino acids) from a few elements and simple, naturally occurring

**Figure 1.8**    Reconstruction of a Middle Cambrian sea floor about 600,000,000 years ago. The fauna includes siliceous sponges (the upright cones), jellyfish, and two genera of trilobites (*Paradoxides,* the large form, and *Ellipsocephalus,* the small form). Bacteria had probably already been in existence for millions of years. (Drawing by Z. Burian under the supervision of Prof. J. Augusta. From Kummel: History of the Earth. W. H. Freeman and Co., 1961.)

inorganic substances like $NH_4$, $H_2S$, $H_2O$ and $CO_2$ and CO, using naturally occurring energy sources (electrical discharges, ultraviolet [solar] light, intense sonic and supersonic vibrations, hot compressed steam) that undoubtedly were present under prebiotic conditions have actually been accomplished. The five-carbon sugars (pentoses), ribose and deoxyribose, appear to have been synthesized from such naturally occurring materials as acetaldehyde or formaldehyde under the influence of ultraviolet and gamma rays. These sugars are, as will be detailed later, parts of the most important and absolutely essential materials, ribonucleic and deoxyribonucleic acids (RNA and DNA, respectively), of all living cells and also of viruses. Certain purines and pyrimidines, other essential parts of DNA and RNA, are also reported to have appeared under experimental prebiotic conditions: adenine in solutions of ammonium cyanide, uracil in mixtures of $CH_4$, $H_2$ and $H_2O$, and so on.

Thus we see actually demonstrated the "spontaneous" formation of the organic molecules like amino acids, simple sugars, purines and pyrimidines and a number of others that are the "building stones" of the enormously complex macromolecules (fats, proteins, polysac-

charides, nucleic acids, conjugates such as apoenzymes, lipoproteins, respiratory metalloproteins and so on) that make up living cells.

Unfortunately (or fortunately!) human attempts, even by the most advanced methods, to combine these "building stones" into complex macromolecules as they occur in living cells have failed. Some sugars, some enzyme-like complexes and some genelike structures have been made synthetically in minute quantities at great cost. The last steps, the formation of the type of integrated colloidal complexes that are found in living cells, are still far in the future. (It would be so profitable if we could cheaply synthesize cane sugar or beef!)

## SUPPLEMENTARY READING

Barghoorn, E. S., and Tyler, S. A.: Microorganisms from the Gunflint chert. Science, *147*:563, 1965.

Bulloch, W.: The History of Bacteriology. Oxford University Press, London. 1938.

Ceram, C. W. (Translated by E. B. Garside): Gods, Graves and Scholars. Alfred A. Knopf, New York. 1952.

Cloud, Jr., P. E.: Significance of the Gunflint (Precambrian) microflora. Science, *148*:27, 1965.

Cohen, B.: On Leeuwenhoek's method of seeing bacteria. J. Bact., *34*:343, 1937.

Cohen, B.: The Leeuwenhoek Letter. The Williams and Wilkins Co., Baltimore. 1937.

Cohn, F. (Translated by C. S. Dolley): Bacteria: The Smallest of Living Things. The Johns Hopkins University Press, Baltimore. 1939.

Dobell, C.: Antonj van Leeuwenhoek and His Little Animals. Russell & Russell, Inc., New York. 1958.

Fred, E. B.: Antonj van Leeuwenhoek, J. Bact., *25*:1, 1933.

Haggard, H. W.: Devils, Drugs and Doctors. Garden City Publishing Co., Garden City, N. Y. 1929.

Hooke, R.: Micrographia. Royal Society, London, 1665. Dover Publications, New York. 1961.

Keosian, J.: The Origin of Life. Reinhold Publishing Corp., New York. 1964.

Kummel, B.: History of the Earth. W. H. Freeman and Co., San Francisco. 1961.

Lechevalier, H., and Solotorovsky, M.: Three Centuries of Microbiology. McGraw-Hill Book Co., New York. 1965.

Oró, J., Nooner, D. W., Zlatkis, A., Wikström, S. A., and Barghoorn, E. S.: Hydrocarbons of biological origin in sediments about two billion years old. Science, *148*:77, 1965.

Rush, J. H.: The Dawn of Life. Doubleday & Co., New York. 1958.

Stinchcomb, B. L., Levin, H. L., and Echols, D. J.: Precambrian graphitic compressions of possible biologic origin from Canada. Science, *148*:75, 1965.

Studier, M. H., Hayatsu, R., and Anders, E.: Organic compounds in carbonaceous chondrites. Science, *148*:1455, 1965.

Tilton, G. R., and Steiger, R. H.: Lead isotopes and the age of the earth. Science, *150*:1805, 1965.

# Chapter 2

# MICROBIOLOGY AND MICROSCOPY

## 2.1 OPTICAL MICROSCOPES

The basic principle of modern compound microscopes is the same as that used by Janssen in 1590: the use of a second lens, the *eyepiece,* to magnify the already enlarged image produced by a first lens, or *objective.* Microscopes in which the magnified image is seen directly by the eye through glass lenses and illuminated by visible light are spoken of as *optical microscopes* in contrast to electron microscopes, in which the image is formed on a fluorescent screen by invisible electron streams focused by magnets instead of by glass lenses. In many modern optical microscopes, light is reflected upward by an adjustable mirror at the foot of the instrument (Fig. 2.1). The light is *refracted* in a *condenser,* just above the mirror, to bring the rays to a central point at the plane of the object (Figs. 2.2 and 2.3). The condenser is equipped with an *iris diaphragm,* which is used to eliminate excessive light and reduce the aperture of the condenser for various lenses. The mirror and condenser are now commonly replaced by a built-in adjustable electric light.

Usually the light rays emerge from the top surface of the slide as a cone of light with the apex downward. Those rays that are not too divergent pass through the object. If they do not diverge at too wide an angle they enter the first and most "powerful" lens of the microscope—the *objective.* The wider the scope (numerical aperture, or N.A.) of this lens (or the wider the angle it can survey), the more of the divergent rays (those at the periphery of the cone of rays) it can admit.*

A good camera lens, for example, is a wide lens and brings in much light (it is "fast"). Such lenses have an N.A. of about f2.5 and a relatively short focal length: $1\frac{1}{2}$ to 2 or 3 inches. An oil-immersion objective lens in a compound microscope, on the contrary, has a focal length of only a few millimeters and an N.A. of about 1.3 (i.e., it is a very "short-sighted" lens with a limited N.A.). It works only a millimeter or two from the object in order to get as many as possible of the divergent rays from the object within its narrow scope. Because of its narrow aperture, strong illumination of the object is necessary. Provision of adequate illumination was one of Hooke's great difficulties.

**Oil-Immersion Lens.** When the rays of light emerge from the upper surface of the condenser, some (especially peripheral rays) are refracted beyond the scope of the objective and lost. Others are reflected away from the underside of the glass slide on which the object is mounted, and lost. Others are refracted and reflected from its upper surface. Others are lost by refraction and reflection in the object and at the surface of the objective lens. A considerable part of these various losses and distortion of the image can be prevented by eliminating the

---

*N.A. = $\eta$ sin $\theta$, in which $\eta$ = refractive index of the substance (air, water, immersion oil, etc.) between the object and the front surface of the objective lens. The $\eta$ of air = 1; that of immersion oil and of glass in lenses = 1.52. The angle $\theta$ is that between the most oblique rays traversing the objective lens and the optical axis of the lens.

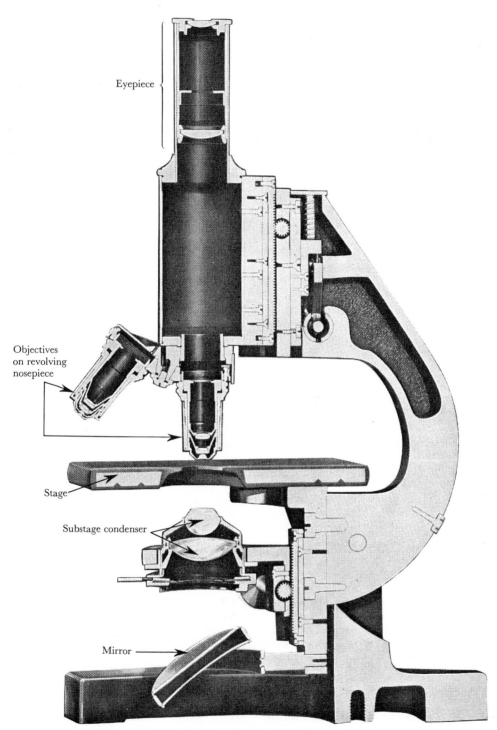

Eyepiece

Objectives
on revolving
nosepiece

Stage

Substage condenser

Mirror

**Figure 2.1**    Modern compound microscopes are merely improved models of the microscopes devised by Janssen in 1590, by Galileo in 1610 and by Hooke about 1660. (Courtesy of Bausch and Lomb Optical Co.)

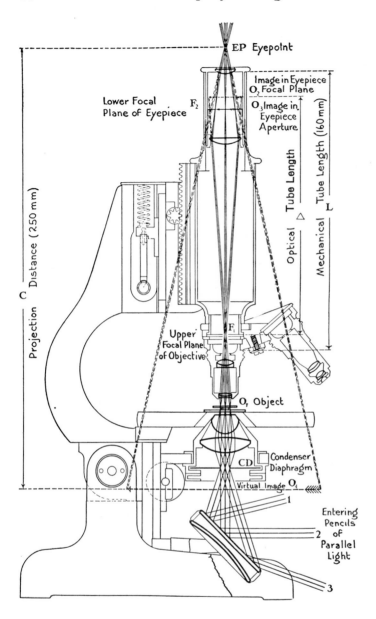

**Figure 2.2**  Chart showing path of light through laboratory microscope. The entering pencils of light (seen at 1, 2, 3) are reflected upward by the mirror through the diaphragm (CD) opening. In passing through the condenser lenses they are focused on the object ($O_1$) on a glass slide. Passing through the object they are refracted by the lenses in the objective. They are brought to a focus at, and then diverge from, the upper focal plane of the objective ($F_1$). Refracted by the lower lens of the eyepiece they form a series of real and virtual images ($O_3$, $O_2$) in the eyepiece focal plane ($F_2$) and eyepiece aperture. These are magnified by the upper lens of the eyepiece and focused at the eyepoint (EP). The object on the glass slide is then seen by the eye as an enlarged, virtual image ($O_4$) which seems to be at a level a little below the condenser. (Courtesy of Bausch and Lomb Optical Co.)

optical effect of these surfaces. This is done by placing a clear, colorless fluid (*immersion oil*), having the same refractive index as glass, between condenser and slide and between slide and objective lens. For high-power microscopy the objective lens is made for oil immersion. Immersion oil, in effect, can increase the N.A. of a lens because it brings in more light rays (Fig. 2.4).

Several lenses placed above the objective are used to correct difficulties inherent in such objectives, namely, spherical and chromatic aberration (distortions of image due to lens curvature). They improve the clarity and distinctness of the magnified image but not the magnification itself. The basic principle of the compound microscope is not altered.

**Real and Virtual Image.**   The *real image* produced by the objective is brought to a focus within the eyepiece, which is a system of two or three lenses at the top of the microscope. This real image is magnified by the topmost lens (ocular) and appears as a greatly enlarged *virtual image*, seeming to be projected to a position just above the reflecting mirror (Fig. 2.2).

**Resolving Power.**   The real measure of a microscope is its *resolving power*. The resolving power of the human eye is relatively limited, because the sensory endings (receptors) of the

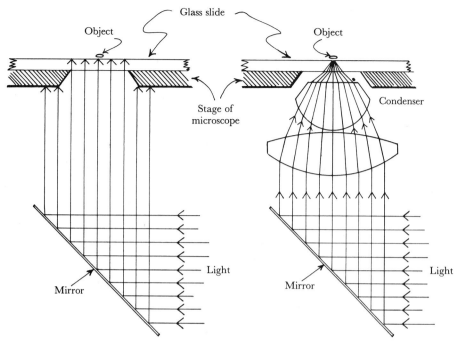

**Figure 2.3**   Illumination of microscopic object without and with substage condenser. The condenser focuses all the light from the mirror on the object.

optic nerve in the retina of the eye are relatively large (i.e., they have dimensions of several $\mu$). If two tiny objects are very close together—say, 0.2 $\mu$—separate rays from each can impinge on one of these retinal receptors; the unaided eye does not perceive that the objects are separate (i.e., it does not *resolve* them). By magnification,

resolving power of the eye is increased. However, as we shall see later, there are definite limitations to resolution by optical microscopes (about 2000×) due to the nature of visible light rays. A simple demonstration of the limited resolving power of the human eye may be made by observing the faces in Figure 2.6 with a 2×

**Figure 2.4**   Effect of immersion oil on light rays in compound microscope. Light rays enter the condenser from below. Light ray A shows path of light if oil is placed *only* between slide and objective lens (the common practice). Broken line A′ shows loss of rays A if oil is not used. Light ray B shows path of light if oil is placed between slide and objective, as above, *and also* between slide and condenser (the practice in darkfield microscopy). Broken line B′ shows loss of rays B if oil is not used. Arrows R,R,R show additional loss of light by reflection from top and bottom surfaces of slide if oil is not used. In summary, use of oil prevents loss of light by refraction and reflection.

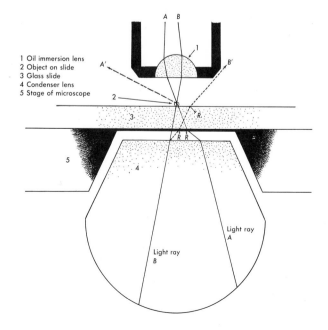

hand lens. The imperceptible photoengraver's "screen" at once becomes readily visible as well-separated (*resolved*) dots.

An oil-immersion objective lens magnifying the object about 90 to 100 diameters is generally used in microbiology. The ocular, or eyepiece, should magnify the real image, formed by the objective, 10 to 20 diameters. The total magnification of 900 to 2000 diameters thus obtained is most useful, higher magnifications tending to give "fuzzy" outlines due in part to poor resolution.

## 2.2   METHODS IN MICROSCOPY

**Hanging-Drop Preparations.**   As Leeuwenhoek discovered, many microorganisms, especially bacteria in a natural living state, are best viewed when suspended in a clear fluid of some sort, usually water, saline solution or broth. The cells are transparent, colorless, refractile and so tiny that they are often difficult to find and even to identify in the drop of fluid. This is especially true of the spherical types (cocci), which may be only 1 or 2 $\mu$ in diameter.

To observe bacteria and similar microorganisms in this state it is necessary to put a loopful of the fluid in which they are suspended in the center of a thin cover slip.* On each of the four corners place a tiny droplet of mineral oil. Hold a hollow-ground slide, depression down, over the slip and bring the two into contact. Invert the slide quickly so that the drop cannot run off to one side. A tiny additional drop of clear mineral oil may now be run under the edges of the cover slip at each corner if needed. This spreads under the cover slip and prevents drying of the drop (Fig. 2.5).

In the hanging drop we may see the size, shape and arrangement of microorganisms and their motion if they are motile. Sometimes bright refractile granules and spores may be seen within the living cells. Since cells of yeasts, molds, protozoa and bacteria are generally colorless and transparent, it is often extremely difficult to study them because this lack of density prevents details from showing clearly. Further, when suspended in fluid they move about, because of either their own motility, currents in the fluid, or brownian movement. They often

*By a *loop* is meant the space included by a tiny ring or loop made at the end of a thin wire. The wire is fixed into some sort of handle so that it may be sterilized in a flame. Loops are usually about 2 mm. in diameter; a loopful is a small drop.

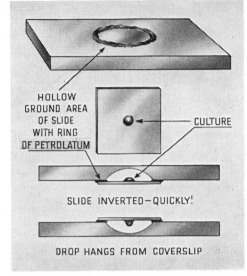

**Figure 2.5**   Hanging drop preparation. (From Thompson: Microbiology and Epidemiology, 5th ed. W. B. Saunders Co., 1962.)

have almost the same refractive index as the fluid in which they are suspended, which makes them nearly invisible, like a splinter of ice immersed in water. The observation of microorganisms in hanging-drop preparations, therefore, yields limited though valuable information.

## DEVELOPMENT OF STAINING METHODS

**Robert Koch (1843–1910).**   Robert Koch was a German physician who became a Nobel Prize winner for his studies in microbiology. Early in his career (about 1870) he was provincial health officer in Wollstein. He had occasion in an official capacity to investigate anthrax (a disease of animals and man caused by *Bacillus anthracis*, a species of cylindrically shaped bacteria). He decided to study the disease in his laboratory during his spare time.

At first Koch and other microbiologists examined all their specimens of microorganisms in the living state, usually in drops of fluid mounted on a bit of glass. They thus became familiar with motility, when present, and they observed refractile granules inside various microorganisms. But their transparency and the constant motion of some of the bacteria (either that purposeless oscillation due to molecular impact, known as *brownian movement*, or real progressive motion due to the action of flagella) made accurate and prolonged study difficult. Koch

**Figure 2.6**   One of the groups of famous scientists who studied microbiology under Koch. Standing, left to right: Alphonse Laveran (1845–1922), discoverer of the malarial parasite; Emile Roux (1853–1933), codiscoverer of diphtheria toxin; Edmund Étienne Nocard (1850–1903), French veterinarian and mycologist; George H. F. Nuttall (1862–1937), British microbiologist. Sitting, left to right: Robert A. Koch (1843–1910), discoverer of the tubercle bacillus and pioneer microbiologist; Karl Joseph Eberth (?) (1835–1926), discoverer of the typhoid bacillus; Elie Metchnikoff (1845–1916), Russian zoologist and discoverer of phagocytes and phagocytosis. (Courtesy of Wiley A. Penn, Director of Laboratories, Department of Health, Savannah, Georgia.)

realized that it would be much better for his drawings and especially for his photographs (both of which, by the way, were excellent) if the bacteria could be made to remain still. He tried spreading out his drops of anthrax-infected fluid in thin films (commonly called *smears*) and allowing them to dry, and met with immediate success. Not only were the anthrax bacilli motionless, but they apparently had not shriveled or changed in any visible way. However, the bacteria were transparent and colorless. It was very difficult to observe the fine details of their structure and equally difficult to photograph them. He obtained ideas from other workers, a procedure commended to all investigators.

Weigert, a German scientist contemporary with Koch, had observed the use by Cohn and others of various dyes to make clear the details of cell structures in histological preparations (histology, i.e., microscopic anatomy). The natural dyes *carmine* and *hematoxylin* were widely used. Ehrlich, a renowned chemist and Nobel Prize winner, had recently improved methods discovered by William Perkin, a brilliant British chemist, of preparing very fine dyes from coal tar distillates. These were the first coal tar, or aniline, dyes. Weigert, the bacteriologist, tried the methods of the histologists with the dyes invented by the chemist. His first success was in

1875, when he found that the dye *methyl violet* could be used to reveal bacteria in histological preparations. This method of making bacteria easy to find and study, when before they had been colorless and transparent and therefore almost invisible, was adopted by Koch and soon came into wide use.

Koch, using the methods of Ehrlich, Weigert, Cohn, Gram, Petri and others, became one of the foremost bacteriologists and teachers of his day. His discoveries attracted scholars from all over the world (Fig. 2.6).

## NATURE OF DYES

Most of the dyes used in microbiology may be thought of as salts of two kinds: (1) acidic, those in which the color-bearing ion, the *chromophore*, is the anion, e.g., sodium$^+$ eosinate$^-$ (the dye, *eosin*) and (2) basic, those in which the chromophore is the cation, e.g., methylene blue$^+$ chloride$^-$ (the dye, *methylene blue*). The first type of dye is acidic in the sense that as an acid the chromophore combines with a base (NaOH) to form the dye salt; the second is basic because the chromophore acts like a base, combining with an acid (HCl) to form the dye salt.

In general, acidic dyes combine more

strongly with cytoplasmic (basic) elements of cells; the basic dyes combine best with nucleic (acidic) elements of cells.

Some dyes do not depend on forming salts or chemical combinations with the stained material. They merely coat the surface by the process of adsorption, or they may merely dissolve or precipitate in the surrounding material. Probably both physical and chemical interactions occur during staining, and probably different processes are involved in staining different species. None is fully explained or understood.

**Simple Stains.**   For most microbiological studies basic stains are used. Bacteria react toward stains as though composed principally of nucleic acid, which takes basic dyes most readily. Methylene blue, crystal violet, basic fuchsin and thionin are very widely used. All belong to the group of aniline (coal tar) dyes. Any simple aniline dye solution may be applied by flooding the smear with it. Löffler's methylene-blue solution is very widely used and reveals many details of form and structure.* The dye is allowed to remain in contact with the smear for about one minute and is then washed off with a gentle stream of cool water. The slide is then blotted (not rubbed) between two pieces of filter or blotting paper. When dry it is ready for examination with the oil-immersion lens as previously described.

**Gram's Stain.**†   Now a simple stain such as Löffler's is of great value for many purposes. But another staining procedure, devised by the Danish scholar, Gram, in 1884, is more valuable because it enables us to differentiate between kinds of bacteria which are morphologically indistinguishable yet of different species. It is therefore called a *differential stain.*

To the smear which, for purposes of discussion, we shall assume to contain a variety of bacteria (e.g., saliva), crystal violet solution‡ is

applied for 30 seconds. This is gently rinsed off and an iodine solution* is applied for 30 seconds. This, in turn, is rinsed off. All of the cells are deeply stained (Fig. 2.7, *A* and *B*). Ninety-five per cent ethyl alcohol is applied and renewed until all but the thickest parts of the smear have ceased to give off dye. (This usually takes from 20 seconds to one minute.)

The differential feature of the method is now apparent. Examination with the microscope will reveal the fact that, as Gram found, while many bacteria retain the violet-iodine combination, others will have yielded it largely to the alcohol and are almost as nearly invisible as before (Fig. 2.7, *C*). Those species of bacteria which retain the stain are called *gram-positive.* Those which yield it to the alcohol are called *gram-negative.*

But the staining process is not yet complete. There is still the important final step of applying the *counterstain*†—a dye of some contrasting color, usually eosin (red), safranin (red), brilliant green or Bismarck brown. Any one of these dyes colors the gram-negative species; they become as visible as the gram-positive ones but are readily differentiated by their color (Fig. 2.7, *D*).

Thus, by applying Gram's stain, which takes but five or six minutes, we can learn a great deal about any bacterium. We make visible not only form, size and certain other structural details, but we can at once assign the organisms to one of two great artificial groups of bacteria: gram-negative or gram-positive.

Some organisms are "borderline" cases in respect to Gram's stain, sometimes being positive, other times negative; and sometimes, both positive and negative cells of the same organism are seen in the same culture. As a rule, repeated tests will reveal the true nature of the bacterium. Slight variations in cultural conditions or staining technique can affect the result. For example, many bacteria are not definitely gram-positive unless cultivated in the presence of at least 5 per cent blood or serum. The acidity or alkalinity (pH) of the fluid in which the bacteria are suspended, as well as the age of the micro-

---

* **Löffler's stain** (Soc. Am. Bact., "Manual of Methods")

Solution A

| | |
|---|---|
| Methylene blue | 0.3 gm. |
| Ethyl alcohol (95 per cent) | 30.0 ml. |

Solution B

| | |
|---|---|
| KOH (0.01 per cent) | 100.0 ml. |

Mix solutions A and B. The mixture keeps well.

† **Gram's stain (Hucker's modification.** Soc. Am. Bact., "Manual of Methods")

‡               Solution A

| | |
|---|---|
| Crystal violet (85 per cent dye content) | 2.0 gm. |
| Ethyl alcohol (95 per cent) | 20.0 ml. |

Solution B

| | |
|---|---|
| Ammonium oxalate | 0.8 gm. |
| Distilled water | 80.0 ml. |

Dilute solution A about 1 in 5 with distilled water and mix with an equal volume of solution B.

---

* **Lugol's iodine**

| | |
|---|---|
| Iodine | 1 gm. |
| Potassium iodide | 2 to 5 gm. |
| Distilled water | 300 ml. |

Allow to stand 24 hours for the iodine to dissolve. It may be necessary to add a few more crystals of potassium iodide.

† **Counterstain**

| | |
|---|---|
| Safranin (2.5 per cent solution in 95 per cent alcohol) | 25 ml. |
| Distilled water | 75 ml. |

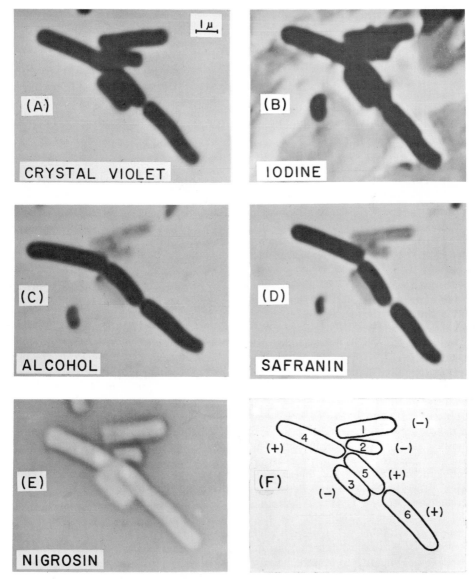

**Figure 2.7** Appearance of gram-positive and gram-negative bacteria following each step of the Gram stain. The gram-positive and gram-negative cells are identified by + and − signs in diagram in *F*. After applying crystal violet and iodine all cells are deeply stained (dark), *A* and *B*. After decolorizing with alcohol (*C*) the gram-negative cells are very light; the gram-positive cells retain the stain (dark). Counterstaining with the transparent red dye, safranin, colors the gram-negative cells but they remain relatively light and translucent (*D*). The nigrosin preparation at *E* illustrates negative staining (see text). (From Bartholomew and Finkelstein: J. Bact., vol. 75.)

organisms, will also markedly affect their reaction to the Gram stain. In acid media, gram-negativeness is the rule.

MECHANISM OF THE GRAM STAIN.   The property of gram-positiveness appears to reside in the cell wall or cytoplasmic membrane. In gram-positive bacteria the cell wall or cytoplasmic membrane appears to have some special affinity for the crystal violet–iodine complex. The cell walls of gram-negative bacteria do not have this affinity or have it to a much lesser degree. The chemical composition and physical structure of the cell walls of gram-positive bacteria differ markedly from those of gram-negative bacteria (Chapter 13). These differences play some role in the differential staining effect, though just how is not yet entirely clear.

The crystal violet and iodine of the Gram stain penetrate both gram-positive and gram-negative cells. The dye and iodine seem to form a compound in the cell, which is removed from the gram-positive cell with difficulty. Removal of various components of the gram-positive cell wall (lipids, carbohydrates) by various agents (ribonuclease, hot water, ether) make the cell gram-negative.

That the cell wall, and possibly the cytoplasmic membrane, plays a decisive role in the Gram stain is shown by the fact that mechanical disruption of gram-positive cells makes the entire cell gram-negative. No part of the disrupted cell retains gram-positiveness.

CORRELATION OF GRAM REACTION WITH OTHER PROPERTIES.   Whatever the explanation of the Gram reaction it is important to note that there are characteristic differences between most gram-positive and gram-negative bacteria. Several of the most obvious of these are shown in Table 2.1. It is evident that the property of gram-positiveness is related to very fundamental physiological properties.

**Ziehl-Neelsen (Acid-Fast) Stain.**   Another differential stain is that of Ziehl-Neelsen. It is used especially for staining tuberculosis bacilli (*Mycobacterium tuberculosis*) and related organisms (genus *Mycobacterium*) having an abundance of a particular waxy material in the cell. Such organisms are gram-positive, but the Gram stain method does not give as useful information about them as the Ziehl-Neelsen, or *acid-fast,* stain.

In using this stain a smear of the material to be examined (e.g., tuberculous sputum) is made as usual, dried and fixed by heat. The smear is then flooded with a special solution of carbolfuchsin and heated to 90° C. over a steam bath for four minutes. This softens the wax and

**TABLE 2.1**   SOME DIFFERENCES BETWEEN GRAM-POSITIVE AND GRAM-NEGATIVE BACTERIA

| Property | Gram-positive | Gram-negative |
|---|---|---|
| Susceptibility to sulfonamide drugs and penicillin | Marked | Much less |
| Inhibition by basic dyes such as crystal violet | Marked | Much less |
| Susceptibility to low surface tension | Marked | Much less |
| Susceptibility to anionic detergents | Marked | Much less |
| Digestion by trypsin or pepsin (dead cells) | Resistant | Susceptible |
| Cell wall digestible by lysozyme | Many species | Requires pre-treatment of the cell wall |
| Dissolved by one per cent NaOH | Resistant | Susceptible |
| Ratio of RNA to DNA in the cell (approx.) | 8 : 1 | Almost equal |
| Aromatic and S-containing amino acids in cell wall | None | Numerous |
| Fat-like substance (lipid) in cell wall | Little | Much |
| Resistance to sodium azide | Marked | Much less |

the dye supposedly penetrates. After washing off the excess dye, the smear is treated for five minutes with cold 95 per cent alcohol containing 5 to 10 per cent hydrochloric acid. The organisms retain the red dye in spite of the acid-alcohol, which removes the color from everything else. Organisms retaining the red stain are said to be acid-fast. If methylene blue or brilliant green is now applied as a counter-stain, the acid-fast bacilli stand out as bright red objects in a blue or green field. The Ziehl-Neelsen stain* is a *differential* stain because it differentiates acid-fast organisms from nonacid-fast ones.

MECHANISM OF THE ACID-FAST STAIN.   It has been suggested that acid-fastness is a matter of

---

*Ziehl-Neelsen (acid-fast) stain (carbolfuchsin)

Solution A
Basic fuchsin                    0.3 gm.
Ethyl alcohol (95 per cent)     10.0 ml.

Solution B
Phenol (melted crystals)         5.0 ml.
Distilled water                 95.0 ml.

Mix solutions A and B. The mixture keeps well. A counterstain of Löffler's methylene blue is generally used, although some workers use brilliant green or saturated aqueous solution of picric acid for better contrast.

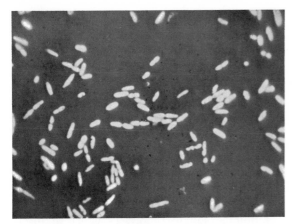

**Figure 2.8** Negative staining or relief demonstration. The background is darkened by nigrosin. The bacilli (agriculturally important *Azotobacter chroococcum*) are unstained and transparent (× 978). (Starkey.)

relative solubilities. The red dye, fuchsin, is more soluble in phenol than in water or acid-alcohol. Phenol, in turn, is more soluble in lipids or waxes, such as are present in tubercle bacilli, than in water. In the acid-fast staining procedure the phenol, with red fuchsin in it, enters the cell lipids and remains because it is there more soluble than in the decolorizing agent (acid-alcohol). The intact cell coatings prevent the red-stained lipids from leaving the cell. If the cell coatings are broken, the lipids leave the cell and the acid-fast property disappears.

**Negative Staining.** This is not really a method of staining bacteria, but of staining the background a solid black, usually with nigrosin.* The dye fails to penetrate the microorganisms at all, and leaves them unstained to appear as light areas in the darkened field (Figs. 2.7, *E* and 2.8). Only the outlines of the organism are made apparent by this method. Consequently, it has a limited application, being used mainly for species that, like spirochetes, cannot be satisfactorily stained by ordinary methods.

A source of error in this method is shrinkage and distortion of the cells of many microorganisms during the drying process.

---

*\*Dorner's method for negative staining*

(Grease-free slides must be used)
Nigrosin   10 gm.
Water     100 ml.

Boil for 30 minutes and add 0.5 ml. formalin. Filter through paper and store in 2 ml. amounts in sterile tubes. Place a loopful of the suspension to be examined on a slide. Immediately add an equal amount of the nigrosin solution, mix and spread out in a thin film (thick films will crack and peel).

Dry in air. Do not wet the slide; do not heat it!

**Special Stains.** In addition to the stains described, there are others designed to bring out special details such as spores, capsules and flagella. Description of each of these methods will be reserved to the discussion of the structural features to which they apply.

## 2.3   DARKFIELD MICROSCOPY

The ordinary compound microscope may easily be equipped for darkfield illumination by substituting a darkfield condenser for the ordinarily used Abbé condenser, or by using a centrally placed *stop* with the Abbé condenser.

A darkfield condenser is designed to prevent the entrance of central rays of light straight upward into the tube of the microscope. All peripheral rays are reflected obliquely to the center of the upper surface of the microscope

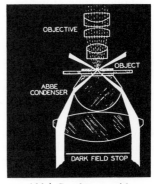

Abbé Condenser with
Dark Field Stop

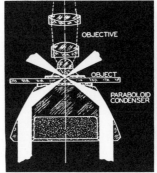

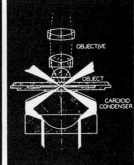

Paraboloid            Cardioid
Condenser            Condenser

**Figure 2.9** Various forms of condensers for oblique illumination of the darkfield. In the upper picture some object on the slide is reflecting light up through the objective lens. In each arrangement note that only peripheral light rays pass the condenser. (Courtesy of Bausch and Lomb Optical Co.)

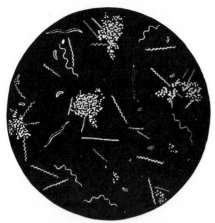

**Figure 2.10**   Darkfield preparation (× 900). A group of spirochetes and other bacteria from a lung abscess. Note that the thicker bacteria are seen only as luminous outlines. This is because they are visible only by means of light reflected from their outer surfaces.

outward form but motility, since the organisms, covered with a cover slip, are examined in a moist, living state.

## 2.4   FLUORESCENCE MICROSCOPY

By *fluorescence* is meant the property of reflecting rays having a wave length different from that of the incident rays. Thus, substances having a certain color by ordinary light appear of a totally different color by ultraviolet ("black") light. For example, objects invisible by ultraviolet light may become brilliantly luminous if painted with a fluorescent substance such as quinine sulfate (fluoresces violet in ultraviolet light) or the dye auramine (fluoresces yellow in ultraviolet rays). Bacteria stained with a fluorescent dye and then observed through an ordinary microscope, using ultraviolet light, appear as luminous objects readily seen and differentiated from nonfluorescent objects. A special, ultraviolet-opaque filter must be placed in the microscope tube to protect the eyes from ultraviolet rays.

One adaptation of fluorescence microscopy has been in the study of tuberculosis. The fluorescent dye, auramine, has a strong affinity for waxlike substances in tubercle bacilli. The hard-to-find bacilli are stained with auramine. All the dye is washed from everything else. The slide is then examined in the dark by ultraviolet light. The tubercle bacilli fluoresce with a brilliant yellow glow and a diagnosis can be quickly made (Fig. 2.11). More widely used applications of fluorescence in microscopy are described in Chapter 24 (fluorescent antibody staining).

slide. They emerge from the upper surface of the slide as a hollow cone of light, apex down and centered on the object. The oblique rays forming this inverted cone do not reach the eye unless some object is present to reflect them upward (Fig. 2.9). The empty field, therefore, appears dark. When a fluid containing any particles such as dust or microorganisms is placed on the slide at the focal point of these oblique rays, each particle becomes visible as a brightly illuminated speck because of the light reflected upward from its surface into the barrel of the microscope (Fig. 2.10). The remainder of the field appears dark, hence the term *darkfield*. Unlike the process of negative staining, the darkfield shows not only

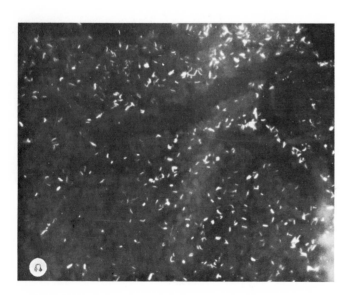

**Figure 2.11**   Fluorescence microscopy of tubercle bacilli in lung tissue treated with auramine. (Courtesy of Society of American Bacteriologists.)

## 2.5   PHASE MICROSCOPY

If one examines the smaller microorganisms such as bacteria in their living state suspended in a hanging drop of fluid, not only is it difficult to see the organisms but it is almost impossible to discern clearly any of the internal structures. This is because there is almost no difference in refractive index or density between the internal structures and their surrounding fluids. The situation is almost like trying to see a tiny fragment of glass in a bowl of water. However, in biological materials there are slight differences in refractive index and density. By means of special optical devices, these differences can be greatly enhanced so that readily perceptible contrast (phase contrast) is produced between these objects and their surroundings.

An ordinary microscope is equipped with a special *annular diaphragm* (Fig. 2.12) which permits only a ring of light to pass upward through the condenser and object. Inside the objective mounting, a transparent disk (*phase-shifting plate,* Fig. 2.12) is placed. This has upon it a ring of optical material on which the ring of light from the annular diaphragm is focused. The ring has the property of advancing or retarding (depending on the material used on the ring) the *phase* of the light waves traversing it.

Now, for each transparent particle in the object, consider a single ray of incident light. From this, two rays result. One, the direct or *undiffracted* ray (Fig. 2.12, *A*), comes from the annular diaphragm, passes through the object, and is focused on the phase-shifting ring. The second ray is derived from the incident ray by being scattered and diffracted in passing around the margin of—not through—the object (Fig. 2.12, *B*). There is thus an optical difference between light waves passing through the object and those scattered (*diffracted*) in passing around it.

The unaided eye fails to detect this difference. However, the phase-shifting plate greatly enhances the difference between the undiffracted and diffracted light waves. As a result the object appears much brighter (or dimmer, depending on the kind of phase-shifting plate used) than

**Figure 2.12**   Image formation by phase contrast. An *annular aperture* in the diaphragm, placed in the focal plane of the substage condenser, controls the illumination on the object. The aperture is imaged by the condenser and objective at the *rear focal plane* of the objective. In this plane the *phase-shifting disk* (diffraction or phase plate) is placed.

With the particular plate shown, light waves, *A* (solid lines), are *transmitted* through the object and pass through the phase-altering ring on the phase plate. At this point they acquire a one-quarter–wave-length advance over light waves, *B* (broken lines), which do not pass through the object but are partly *diffracted* around it. Waves (*B*) do not pass through the phase-altering ring on the phase plate. The resultant *interference* or *resonance* effects of the two portions of light form the final image. Altered *phase* relations in the illuminating rays, induced by otherwise invisible elements in the specimen, are translated into brightness differences (*contrast*) by the phase-altering plate; hence, phase contrast. (Courtesy of Dr. J. R. Benford, Bausch and Lomb Scientific Bureau.)

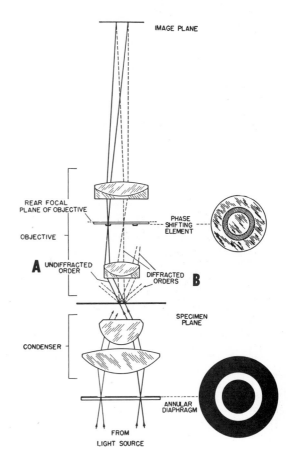

the surrounding material. The contrast between the two, called *phase contrast,* is thus made readily visible to the eye, enabling the observer to see objects otherwise invisible. The contrast may be dark (dark-phase contrast) or light (light-phase contrast), depending on the phase-shifting ring (Fig. 2.13).

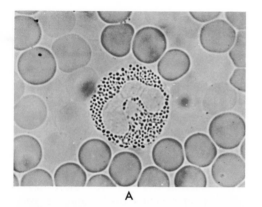

A

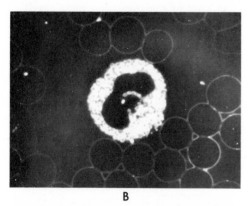

B

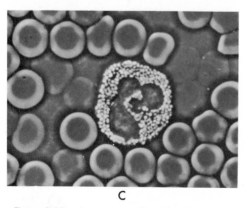

C

**Figure 2.13**   Appearance of a white blood corpuscle or leukocyte (eosinophil) (large, granular, central object) and red blood corpuscles or erythrocytes, unstained and magnified about 1500 times, as seen by three different methods of microscopy; *A*, visible transmitted light (ordinary type of microscopy); *B*, darkfield; *C*, phase microscopy. (From Scope; courtesy of the Upjohn Company.)

## 2.6   ELECTRON MICROSCOPY

The difficulty with optical microscopes lies not with the lens makers but in the fact that the wave lengths of visible light are between about 400 m$\mu$ and 700 m$\mu$. This is relatively *long!* Particles with a diameter of less than one half of the shortest wave length of visible light (violet = 400 m$\mu$), or lines separated by a distance less than about 200 m$\mu$ cannot be *resolved.* Light waves longer than about 700 m$\mu$ (red) entirely "skip over" the individual particles (Fig. 2.14).

Although it has long been known that electromagnetic radiations such as electron beams of high energy (60 kv. or more) have very short wave lengths (around 0.5 m$\mu$), their use in ordinary (optical) microscopes has been impossible because glass is opaque to electrons. However, electrons are deflected from their line of propagation by magnetic fields. This discovery made possible the use of electron beams in microscopy; circular or ring-shaped magnetic fields could be used for *focusing* electron beams (much as a glass lens focuses light rays), thus forming electron images. The first practical electron microscope was constructed by Knoll and Ruska in Berlin in 1931. Improved commercial instruments first came into general use around 1940.

From these basic discoveries the modern electron microscope has evolved (Fig. 2.15). The units in this instrument are analogous to units in an ordinary compound microscope turned upside down, but deal with electron beams rather than light rays. A comparison of the refractive system of an electron microscope with that of a compound optical microscope is seen in Figure 2.16.

**Operation.**   The electron source is commonly a tungsten filament at 30 to 150 kv. potential. The electron beams pass through the center of the ringlike magnetic condenser (analogous to an ordinary microscope condenser) and are converged on the specimen. After passing through the specimen, the magnetic objective-lens coil focuses the electrons into a first (real) image of the object enlarged; in modern instruments this may be up to 2000 times. The magnetic intermediate-image projector (analogous to an optical eyepiece or ocular lens) then magnifies a portion of the first image, producing magnifications up to 250,000 or more. The final enlarged image can be viewed by causing it to strike a fluorescent screen which makes it visible. The image can also be thrown upon a photographic plate for permanent record. Portions of the photographs may be enlarged four

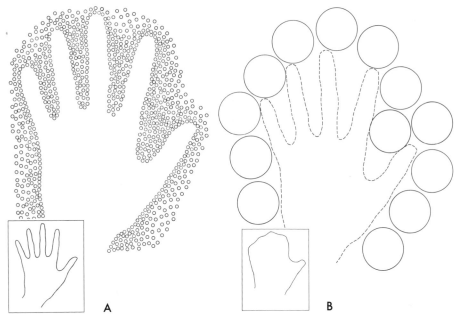

**Figure 2.14**   Effect of wave length on resolution by microscope. In each sketch the circles represent wave lengths: in *A*, electrons; in *B*, visible light. The difference is actually enormously greater than shown. In *A* the projected image reveals all of the details of the form of the object. Each finger is clearly resolved. In *B* the image lacks detail; the long waves yield poor resolution.

to six times without undue loss of detail, thus giving pictures in the range of two million times as large as the object (Fig. 2.17). This degree of magnification is inconceivably tremendous. (The lower-case letter o on this page, say 2 mm. in diameter, if magnified 2 million times would be an area 4 million mm. [over 2.5 miles] in diameter—large enough for several football fields, complete with stadiums, to be lost in.) Direct magnifications up to several millions are available by amplification with an ordinary TV monitor.

Because the motion of electrons is impeded by air, the interior of the electron microscope must be maintained at a vacuum by means of suitable pumps. This necessitates air locks for the insertion and removal of objects and photographic plates. The operator can look into the main tube by means of portholes or magnifying binocular glasses and can scan the images on the fluorescent screen, manipulate the object and make suitable adjustments of alignment and of field strength of the focusing magnets. Some of the external control devices concerned with these details are seen in Figure 2.15.

Under present conditions of electron microscopy, living organisms cannot survive and physiological processes in live cells cannot be studied because of the destructive action of the stream of electrons.

Unlike images that are produced by reflected or transmitted visible light, electron images are produced mainly by the scattering of electrons. Scattering is produced when electrons pass atoms. Heavy atoms (lead, tin, gold) produce more scattering than light atoms (sodium, carbon, nitrogen). Hence there is more contrast in the image. Some materials may also absorb electrons and thus appear as contrast in the final pictures. Objects that are opaque to electrons (electron dense) are not necessarily opaque to light, and vice versa.

The techniques and problems of electron microscopy are many and complex, and are beyond the scope of this discussion. Special laboratory courses are essential to the effective use of these complicated and expensive (from $15,000 to over $100,000) instruments. However, electron lenses suffer from difficulties similar to those found in optical glass lenses, though of electrical rather than of refractive origin: *spherical* and *chromatic aberration* caused by irregularities in "refraction" (i.e., axial and peripheral electrons come to focus at different distances from the lens) and "wave length" (i.e., electron velocities), and distortions like astigmatism resulting from irregularities in field strengths of the magnets and various extraneous magnetic influences. A constant difficulty is contamination of the specimen by volatilized

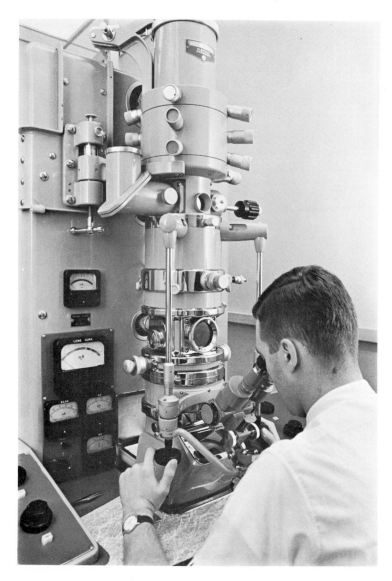

**Figure 2.15** A modern type of electron microscope. The source of electrons is at the top of the large central cylinder. The object to be magnified is inserted through an ingenious air lock about one third of the way down from the top. The operator views the electronic image on a fluorescent screen at the foot of the column through a binocular scanning microscope, which may also be arranged for photography. Note the dials indicating strength of the lens (circular magnet) currents, the beam intensity and magnetic field strengths. There are openings for interior inspection, levers and handles for focusing and for adjusting magnetic lens field intensities, operating the vacuum pumping system and numerous other adjustments and accessories. (Courtesy of the Perkin-Elmer Corporation.)

impurities such as oils, solvents and other materials from various sources within the instrument itself. This is caused by the intense bombardment by electrons within a high vacuum. These contaminations form blurring and obscuring films over the object within a matter of seconds or minutes.

**Specimens for Electron Microscopy.** The preparation of specimens for electron microscopy is a science and an art in itself. The films of plastic or other material on which objects are mounted must not only be extremely thin but free from electron-scattering or absorbing materials, and sufficiently strong to stand necessary manipulation and not volatilize under electron bombardment *in vacuo.* Objects like bacteria and viruses that are to be examined

by transmitted electrons are allowed to settle from a suspension or sprayed onto a suitable electron-transparent film and allowed to dry.

SHADOWING.  Topographical details of surfaces can be accurately reproduced by pouring dilute collodion or Formvar over the material to be examined and then allowing it to dry. The topographical details are replicated in the plastic film or *replica.* The film is removed and placed face up on a slide. It is cleaned, if necessary, and then coated with a thin (a few atoms thick), coherent film of carbon vaporized and deposited vertically on the replica in a vacuum chamber. The carbon-coated plastic replica is then placed, replica down, on an extremely fine-meshed copper supporting grid. After removal of the plastic with an appropri-

**Figure 2.16**   Diagrammatic outline of the path of electron beams in the RCA electron microscope (*A*) as compared with the path of light rays in an ordinary light microscope (*B*). The similarity of the two is clearly evident. In *A* a beam of electrons traveling from the filament at high velocity corresponds to the light rays from the lamp in *B*. The electron rays (*A*) or light rays (*B*) are focused on the specimen (*S* in *B*) by condensing systems. In *A* this is a circular electromagnetic condenser; in *B* it is the lens system, $L_1$. After passing through the specimen the magnetic objective lens coil (corresponding to the objective lens system, $L_2$, of the light microscope) forms a first image (corresponding to *I* in *B*), enlarged about 1000 times. The magnetic intermediate image projector (corresponding to the ocular lens system, $L_3$, of the light microscope) then magnifies this image about 250 times, corresponding to the virtual image ($I_2$ in *B*), producing an overall magnification of 250,000. The final enlarged electronic image can be viewed directly by causing it to strike a fluorescent screen which makes it visible (corresponding to the eye of the observer using a light microscope), or it can be made to record the image on a photographic plate for permanent record and for enlargement up to 1,500,000 or more. (*A*, courtesy of the Radio Corporation of America; *B*, courtesy of the American Society of Microbiology.)

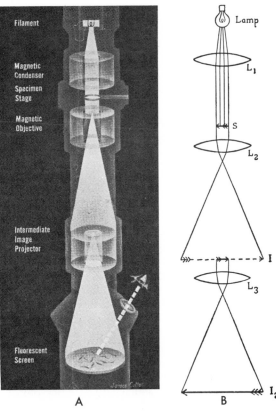

**A**                    **B**

ate solvent, e.g., amyl acetate, vaporized metal (e.g., gold) is applied at an oblique angle. Faces of raised portions of the object that are toward the source of vaporized metal will be more heavily coated with the electron-dense deposit than areas facing away from the source of vapor and hence will appear as highlights in the final picture; the less heavily coated areas will appear as dark "shadows." The length, form and locations of the shadows permit three-dimensional measurements of the objects to be made (Fig. 2.18).

THIN SECTIONS.   For the study of animal and plant tissues with optical microscopes the tissues are first soaked in appropriate fixing (coagulating) and dehydrating solutions, then in water and afterward in dehydrating fluids and paraffin solvents and then allowed to soak in warm paraffin. When fully impregnated with paraffin and cooled in small "blocks," the embedded tissues are cut into thin slices or sections (0.05–0.2 mm.) with a specially sharpened steel blade in an instrument called a *microtome*. The thin section is mounted on a glass slide,

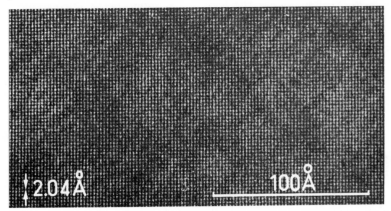

**Figure 2.17**   Lattice image of single gold crystal ($\times$ 5,500,000). In this astonishing picture details of the molecular lattice only 2.04 Å (about 2/254,000,000 inch) apart (opposing arrows) are clearly resolved. The white line at lower right shows the extent of 100 Å (1/2,540,000 inch) at this enormous magnification. (Courtesy of Jeolco, Inc.)

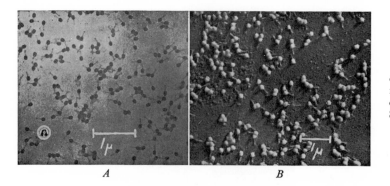

*A*            *B*

**Figure 2.18**  Electron micrographs of a virus (bacteriophage). *A*, Without metal shadowing. *B*, With metal shadowing. (Courtesy of Dr. D. Gordon Sharp, Duke University.)

paraffin is removed from the section and the tissues are then stained with appropriate differential dyes (commonly hematoxylin and eosin) and examined with a microscope.

An analogous procedure is used for making thin sections of bacteria and other microorganisms for electron microscopy. But since bacteria are at most only 3 or 4 $\mu$ in diameter and since electrons have so little penetrating power, the sections must be exceedingly thin: of the order of 20 m$\mu$—almost invisible. The embedding material instead of paraffin is at first a liquid plastic (methacrylate). After mixing with the bacteria it is caused to solidify (polymerize) by warming to about 40° C. There are many difficulties in cutting such materials— the knives themselves are a problem. They are usually a very small segment of the edge of a fragment of broken glass or of diamond. Specially designed microtomes are necessary to eliminate irregularities due to vibrations of the building, the "thick" films of lubricating oils in the instrument, variations due to a few degrees of change in temperature and so on. Further details can be found in appropriate literature. In spite of problems, electron microscopy is making visible to the human eye the very molecules of which Leeuwenhoek's dimly seen animalcules were constituted.

IMPROVEMENTS AND RESULTS.  Modern instruments have devices to simplify maintenance of vacuum, align the beam and adjust its brightness, reduce contamination, alter lens aperture, change magnification, compensate for astigmatism and other lens irregularities, ease focusing, facilitate handling of specimens and photographing the images, regulate temperatures and so on (Fig. 2.15).

The electron microscope shows that protoplasm, once thought to be a single, mysterious living substance, is a complex mechanism containing many distinct parts never before seen.

Such gross structures as nuclei and plastids were found to have elaborate inner mechanisms involving whole systems of interlocking molecules, many actually visible with high-power electron microscopes. The word *protoplasm* as the name of a single substance is now obsolete, although often used loosely to mean any sort of living matter.

## 2.7   OTHER METHODS OF MICROSCOPY

For research and various advanced applied purposes, other methods of microscopy are available. These need not be detailed here but three will be mentioned, with references to literature for those interested in extending the range of human vision "far back among the atoms and electrons."

**X-ray Microscopes.**  X-rays provide a source of even shorter wave lengths than electrons and may be used for various optical purposes. They also have a much greater penetrating power than electrons and thus can serve to make observations which are impossible with electrons.

**Interference Microscopes.**  An additional means of studying transparent objects like living cells is the interference microscope. This combines a double-beam interferometer and a polarizing microscope. The object is seen as in phase contrast but the polarization and wave interference produce greater contrast—and color. It is also possible to measure optical-path differences between different parts of the object.

**Ultraviolet and Television Color-Translating Microscopes.**  One value of ultraviolet light is that it is passed by some parts of a cell but is more or less completely absorbed by other parts, thus creating contrasts between otherwise indistinguishable intracellular structures. Unfortunately, direct vision by ultraviolet light is

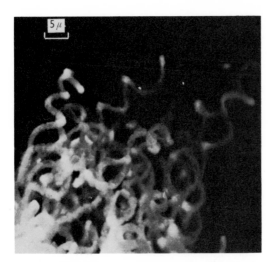

**Figure 2.19**  Coils of conidia of a species of actinomycete as pictured by a scanning electron microscope. In an ordinary electron microscope pictures are made by electrons passing *through* the object, i.e., by transmitted electrons. In the scanning electron microscope the pictures are made by electrons reflected from the surface of the object (compare Leeuwenhoek's and Hooke's microscopes, respectively). Note the topographical details and the three-dimensional effect. (From Williams and Davies: J. Gen. Microbiol., *48*:171, 1967.)

not feasible and, as we have seen, the object can therefore be studied only by means of photographs.

The ultraviolet television microscope permits continuous observation of the object under ultraviolet illumination without the intermediation (with consequent distortion, blurring and delay) of photographs. Without going into the many very complex electronic and optical problems which have been solved, one may say that by means of the ultraviolet television color-translating microscope one may sit in an armchair and observe on his television screen, not a stale Western, but a highly magnified colored picture of a microscope object *inside a living creature.* The colors in the picture represent, not the colors of the object, which may indeed be colorless, but, within certain limits, the chemical composition of the object. This is surely push-button analytical microchemistry!

**Scanning Microscopes.** Although the common type of electron microscope previously described permits very great resolution, interpretation of many electronic images and electron micrographs remains difficult because of lack of contrast and perspective and of other properties inherent in ordinary electron microscopes. Methods are being found that greatly improve electronic images, giving much clearer detail and

perspective effect (Fig. 2.19). In one system an extremely fine (50  Å) pencil of electrons is projected in a moving, scanning manner (like a TV camera) on the surface of the specimen. Synchronized with this is a second beam that is modified by "information" (disturbed impulses) from the first. This second beam is directed to a standard television tube. Instruments based on this principle are called *scanning electron microscopes* (SEM). The operation of such microscopes is a technical specialty in itself.

## SUPPLEMENTARY READING

Bartholomew, J. W., Tucker, F. L., and Finkelstein, H.: The effect of moisture on Gram differentiation, and its relation to proposed gram-positive substrates in yeast and other organisms. J. Gen. Bact., *36*:257, 1964.

Bartholomew, J. W., Cromwell, T., and Gan, R.: Analysis of the mechanism of Gram differentiation by use of a filter-paper chromatographic technique: J. Bact., *90*:766, 1965.

Bradley, D. E.: A study of the negative staining process. J. Gen. Microbiol., *29*:503, 1962.

Conn, H. J., Darrow, M. A., Emmel, V. M., and others: Staining Procedures used by the Biological Stain Commission. The Williams & Wilkins Co., Baltimore. 1960.

Cosslett, V. E.: Modern Microscopy or Seeing the Very Small. Cornell University Press. Ithaca, N. Y. 1966.

Darken, M. A.: Absorption and transport of fluorescent brighteners by microorganisms. Appl. Microbiol., *10*:387, 1962.

Dobell, C.: Antonj van Leeuwenhoek and His Little Animals. Dover Publications, Inc., New York. 1932.

Dondero, N. C.: Simple and rapid method for demonstrating microbial capsules by phase-contrast microscopy. J. Bact., *85*:1171, 1963.

Freeman, J. A., and Geer, J. C.: Cellular Fine Structure. McGraw-Hill Book Co., New York. 1964.

Freundlich, M. M.: The origin of the electron microscope. Science, *142*:185, 1963.

Gilkerson, S. W., and Kanner, O.: Improved technique for the detection of acid-fast bacilli by fluorescence. J. Bact., *86*:890, 1963.

Hooke, R.: Micrographia. 1665. Dover Publications, Inc., New York. 1961.

Kay, D. H.: Techniques for Electron Microscopy. F. A. Davis Co., Philadelphia. 1965.

Martin, L. C.: The Theory of the Microscope. Elsevier Publishing Co., Inc., New York. 1966.

Normore, W. M., and Umbreit, W. W.: Ribonucleates and the Gram stain. J. Bact., *90*:1500, 1965.

Salton, M. R. J.: The relationship between the nature of the cell wall and the Gram stain. J. Gen. Microbiol., *30*:223, 1963.

Scherrer, R.: Cell structure and quantitative Gram stain of *Bacillus megaterium*. J. Gen. Microbiol., *31*:135, 1963.

Seeger, R. J.: Galileo Galilei, His Life and His Works. Pergamon Press, New York. 1966.

Williams, S. T., and Davies, F. L.: Use of a scanning electron microscope for the examination of actinomycete. J. Gen. Microbiol., *48*:171, 1967.

Wren, L. A., and Corrington, J. D.: Understanding and Using the Phase Microscope. Unitron Instrument Co., Newton Highlands, Mass. 1963.

# Chapter 3

## NUTRITION OF MICROORGANISMS

**Metabolism.** Metabolism (Gr. *metabole* = change) refers to all of the essential chemical changes that occur in living organisms. These changes may be divided into two groups:

*Catabolism*—the decomposition or degradation of food substances (*substrates*) into their constituent atoms, molecules or molecular groups to yield (a) *materials* for synthesis of the cell itself or (b) *energy* to carry on these syntheses as well as all other activities of the cell such as motility, reproduction, sporulation and luminosity.

*Anabolism*—comprising all of the *synthetic* or cell-building activities of the cell.

In normally growing cells catabolism and anabolism are continuous, simultaneous and linked processes: anabolism constantly replacing "worn out" or used-up constituents of the cell and synthesizing new cell substance; catabolism constantly furnishing the necessary materials and energy from foodstuffs. The two processes are interdependent. One implies the other. Metabolism ceases absolutely and permanently only with death. Under some conditions—lack of nutrient, freezing, drying, chemical microbistasis, in dormant spores, etc.—metabolism of many unicellular organisms may be brought to a virtual standstill without loss of *viability* (ability to live and develop) for many decades.

## 3.1 FOODS AND ESSENTIAL NUTRIENTS

Napoleon Bonaparte is reputed to have said, "An army marches on its stomach." In establishing this military aphorism he missed the opportunity to become a biological immortal. He could have stated the obvious truth that all life depends on food. To Bonaparte, food meant army rations. To the biologist food might be defined as any substrate that can be metabolized to provide assimilable material or energy for the cell.

### ELEMENTS IN NUTRITION

For all forms of nutrition and active metabolism there are two universal requirements. One is water. The presence of water in adequate amounts will be assumed in all discussions of nutrition and will not be discussed further.

The second universal requirement is for the elements C, H, O, N, P, S and K. These are the major component elements of all living matter. Their presence in the same sorts of compounds (proteins, fats, carbohydrates, etc.) in the same or analogous structures in all cells and also in viruses attests the evolutionary relationship of all living organisms.

Because of minor differences between species of plants, animals and protists* there are, in addition to the elements just mentioned, quantitatively differing requirements for Na, Ca, and Cl. Iron is commonly required by aerobic organisms, including humans. Other special requirements include Mg, which is essential to all photosynthetic organisms since it is the active metal in chlorophyll. Most vertebrates require iodine for the manufacture of thyroxin, and diatoms (Chapter 12) must have silicon for their "valves." Still other elements

---

*Unicellular organisms of the Kingdom *Protista*: protozoa, algae, fungi (Eumycetes), bacteria (Schizomycetes, rickettsias, PPLO, Chlamydiaceae). Viruses, although not cellular organisms, are included for convenience.

are necessary for the coenzymes or prosthetic groups of certain cells: Mo, Cu, Mn, Zn. An exact list of other elemental requirements is difficult to formulate, especially a list of metallic elements, since some are present in only a few species or occur in such minute amounts (*trace elements*) that it is very difficult to detect them or to be sure that, when found, they are functional and not present merely as impurities.

## Accessory Nutrients

Accessory foods are substances that do not yield energy to the cell or contribute materially to its bulk, but which are effective in very minute quantities and absolutely essential to growth. They are often called essential *nutrilites,* growth factors or *micronutrients*. They range in structure from simple ions such as $Fe^{+++}$, $Mn^{++}$ and $Co^{++}$ to complex organic compounds. Vitamins are good examples of complex organic micronutrients. Any normal diet or, at unnecessary expense, a single, small vitamin capsule taken each day supplies most vitamin needs of the human body as well as mineral accessory foods. In our fundamental food requirements we are remarkably like certain very common bacteria, though our digestions are not so inclusive!

In addition to vitamins, certain amino acids have the status of organic micronutrients; that is, they are absolutely essential in minute amounts to the growth of a number of bacteria and human beings. A good example of such an essential amino acid is *tryptophan,* without which the typhoid bacillus (*Salmonella typhi*), the lockjaw organism (*Clostridium tetani*), the diphtheria bacillus (*Corynebacterium diphtheriae*) and several others cannot grow, even though their culture medium is complete in all other respects. Humans require some 22 amino acids. On the other hand, there are many microorganisms that can synthesize their own tryptophan and so do not need to have it fed to them.

The role of such compounds in all cell nutrition was described by Fildes. Assume that an organism (a bacterium, or you or I) requires pantothenic acid. This is a vitamin essential to the synthesis of coenzyme A (Chapter 9). Assume that the organism is able to carry out all but one of the synthetic steps necessary to the formation of pantothenic acid. Beginning with simple ammonia it synthesizes $\beta$-alanine, an essential amino acid (Fig. 3.1). However, it is unable to synthesize pantoic acid, which is

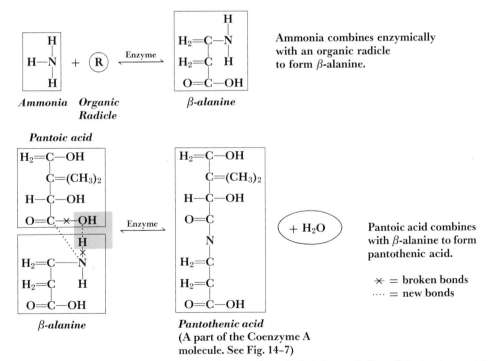

Ammonia combines enzymically with an organic radicle to form $\beta$-alanine.

Pantoic acid combines with $\beta$-alanine to form pantothenic acid.

✳ = broken bonds
···· = new bonds

*Ammonia   Organic Radicle*

*β-alanine*

*Pantoic acid*

*β-alanine*

*Pantothenic acid*
*(A part of the Coenzyme A molecule. See Fig. 14–7)*

**Figure 3.1**   Role of an essential metabolite (in this case beta-alanine) in metabolism. $\beta$-alanine is essential to the formation of pantothenic acid, which is essential to coenzyme A (Fig. 9.7), which is essential to the Krebs cycle, which is essential to life! For explanation see text.

absolutely essential to the complex pantothenic acid molecule. Given only a few micrograms of pantoic acid, completion of the pantothenic acid is provided for and growth occurs. Without pantoic acid no growth is possible. Another organism able to synthesize pantoic acid as well as the other components of pantothenic acid encounters no such difficulty and we say that it does not require pantoic acid. Both organisms may require pantoic acid, but one can manufacture it internally; the other cannot.

## 3.2    NUTRITIONAL TYPES

**Holozoic and Holophytic Nutrition.**    In spite of the universality of major elemental requirements there are striking differences between various species of plants, animals and protists in the form in which the required elements can be utilized. For example, a primary difference between typical plants and animals is their manner of taking food: *holozoic* or *holophytic.*

With a few exceptions such as malaria parasites and tapeworms, animals, from man to protozoa, can ingest solid foods. The ingested solid particles may be of microscopic size, such as bacteria and other protozoa as food for protozoans; or they may be whole antelopes for anacondas. Regardless of size, nutrition involving ingestion of solid foods is said to be *holozoic* (Gr. *holo* = all; *zoic* = like animals) nutrition. On the other hand, with a few possible exceptions such as "carnivorous" plants like sundew or Venus fly trap, plants typically lack the ability to ingest solid food particles.* The food of all typical plants, including bacteria, must be in the form of relatively small molecules, in solution, capable of passing through the cell membrane by diffusion or by certain other mechanisms to be discussed. This sort of nutrition is spoken of as *holophytic* (Gr. *phytic* = like plants).† The nutrition of viruses differs basically from that of all cellular forms and will be discussed with the viruses.

The holophytic mode of taking in foods might seem to impose severe dietary restrictions. In the case of most of the higher plants this is so. However, many true fungi and species

of bacteria can use the same solid foods that soldiers, horses and protozoa enjoy, and other foods besides. This is accomplished by what has been called "extracorporeal digestion," i.e., digestion outside the body.

## 3.3    DIGESTION

As mentioned elsewhere (Chapter 5), physiological digestion is commonly catalyzed by hydrolytic enzymes. Digestion results in the decomposition of complex food materials such as polysaccharides, fats and proteins into their constituent molecules of various soluble substances. These may be amino acids (from proteins), alcohols, glycerol and fatty acids (from fats), and various monosaccharides such as glucose (from polysaccharides). Unlike the original solid food masses, the molecules produced by digestion are small enough to pass through the cell membrane (or the vacuole membrane in some protozoa) into the living cell substance. There they are further changed by other enzyme systems and are used as sources of energy, cell substance or both (Fig. 3.2).

In the higher animals digestion occurs in the gastrointestinal tract. The soluble, molecular

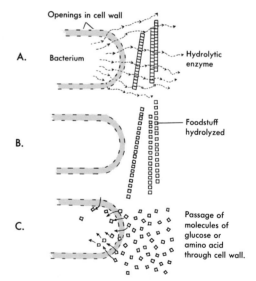

**Figure 3.2**    Utilization of grossly large and insoluble food particles by extracellular digestion. Sketch *A* shows the bacterium secreting hydrolytic enzyme which attacks the food particle (cellulose, protein, fat). In *B* the foodstuff is hydrolyzed and its constituent molecules (glucose, amino acids, fatty acids) are separated from one another. In *C* the molecules derived by hydrolysis of the food pass (or are actively passed by permease enzymes) readily through the bacterial cell wall and cell membrane into the cytoplasm to be further metabolized.

---

*The phenomenon of pinocytosis may be an exceptional case (see page 35).

†If we consider the *tissue cells* of large animals, this difference between plants and animals largely disappears because the tissue cells (except certain phagocytic cells) of all large animals depend on food in solution in the blood.

digestion products are taken from the lumen of the gut into the cells lining the intestine through the cell membranes and thence to the blood and lymph. Among the lower fungi, blue-green algae and bacteria, digestive enzymes are to a large extent excreted aimlessly into the surrounding fluid where they may or may not come into contact with food. They may be wholly dissipated by dilution, convection currents or other factors.

### PINOCYTOSIS

This term is derived from Greek words meaning the process of drinking or swallowing by the cell. In the cell membranes of cells (mainly animal cells) showing this phenomenon, there appear myriads of tiny indentations that seem to act like minute mouths. They take in fluids and solid particles of minute or colloidal size, engulf and close upon them and introduce them into the cell contents through the cell membrane. Pinocytosis is thus a means of ingestion by cells without other means of taking in solid food. It is probably not common in bacteria though certain bacteria of the soil may pass colloidal sulfur through the cell membrane by a process resembling pinocytosis. Certain viruses that infect animal cells appear to gain entrance to the cells through the cell membranes by the mechanism of pinocytosis (Chapter 17).

After complex organic materials have been digested and made assimilable, the processes of utilizing the molecules inside the cells are astonishingly alike in animals, plants and protists though by no means identical. Like the mechanical principles in the automobile, the various metabolic processes and mechanisms are all obviously modifications of the same fundamental plan, yet each species of plant, animal and protist differs metabolically, and therefore in structure and function, to some degree from every other species of plant, animal and protist.

### 3.4   TYPES OF FOODS

Regardless of their unorganized and hit-or-miss digestive systems, an interesting advantage possessed by Protista over sensate animals is their indifference in matters of taste. For example, certain species of bacteria and molds, given time and numbers (and the proper enzymic equipment), may use as food, with equal avid-

ity, railroad ties, crab shells, animal hoofs and horns, feces, paper, leather, sulfur, transmission grease (not silicone), sawdust and old rubber tires. Few if any bacteria or molds are actually so very versatile as to use all these foods, but some approach this degree of enzymic versatility. All the substances mentioned, plus hundreds of others equally distasteful or poisonous to us (such as carbon monoxide, carbolic acid, paraffin, soap, hydrogen gas, aviation gasoline, house paint), serve as at least part of the food for one or another species of microorganisms or, more often perhaps, for combinations of bacteria acting together with molds (see *Syntrophism*). In contrast, other microorganisms are highly restricted and fastidious in the matter of food and can thrive only with the aid of certain particular compounds, such as various derivatives of human blood or living tissue cells. On the basis of their distinctive nutritional requirements, microorganisms may be divided into several groups.

### CLASSIFICATION OF ORGANISMS ACCORDING TO SOURCES OF CARBON AND ENERGY

**Autotrophs and Heterotrophs.** Two definite types of organisms were for years differentiated on the basis of whether (a) they were restricted to an entirely *inorganic* diet, including carbon dioxide (or carbonates) as a sole source of carbon or whether (b) in addition to a mineral diet they also required one or more *organic* substances, i.e., carbon in organic combination. The former (a) were designated true or strict *autotrophs* (Gr. *autos* = self; *trophe* = nourishing); the latter (b) were called *heterotrophs* since it was originally supposed that carbon in organic form could only have been prepared by other living forms (Gr. *hetero* = other).

*Autotrophs.* These typically possess the enzymic equipment to catalyze the direct combination of two carbon atoms or the combination of carbon from carbon dioxide with an organic complex already existing in the cell. Typical autotrophs are represented by familiar green plants and by a number of species of bacteria important in agriculture and industry.

*Heterotrophs.* Heterotrophic organisms (i.e., those that cannot live without organically combined carbon) are the commonest and most widely distributed types. They are represented by *Homo sapiens* and all other animals, and by most species of Eumycetes and bacteria.

With advances in knowledge, the differentiation between autotrophs and heterotrophs lost much of its usefulness because various overlappings, exceptions and borderline cases have come to light that blur the lines of demarkation. For example, some soil-inhabiting bacteria (Genus *Hydrogenomonas*) and others of the Family Athiorhodaceae are capable of living either autotrophically or heterotrophically. Some species living on an otherwise completely inorganic diet must have certain vitamin-like (i.e., organic) substances. Certain common intestinal bacilli can grow well in a simple and completely inorganic solution if provided with sodium citrate as a source of carbon.

Another question arose when it was found that many supposedly typical heterotrophs require carbon dioxide in addition to organic carbon. Although it is not surprising that in the course of billions of years of organic evolution some metabolic aberrations have occurred, it makes classification difficult.

**Chemotrophs and Phototrophs.** The primeval earth is believed (by some) to have been completely dark because of the heavy clouds of water vapor in the skies. It may (or may not*) be a result of their origin and evolution in the dark, but most species of bacteria and higher fungi do not depend on sunlight as their source of energy. On the contrary they thrive in complete darkness, and many species are injured and killed by direct sunlight. These primitive organisms obtain the energy to live and synthesize themselves from *chemical* reactions (oxidations) that are independent of the sun. They are therefore said to be *chemosynthetic* or *chemotrophs.* Organisms that obtain their energy for life and self-synthesis from the sun (or artificial radiant sources) are said to be *photosynthetic* or *phototrophs.*

**Lithotrophs and Organotrophs.** Among the chemotrophs differentiations are made on the basis of the kinds of substrates that are used as electron donors (*oxidized*) as sources of energy. Among the chemotrophs some species oxidize only inorganic substances as sources of energy. For example:

$$NaNO_2 + \tfrac{1}{2}O_2 \longrightarrow NaNO_3 + energy$$
$$H_2S + 2O_2 \longrightarrow H_2SO_4 + energy$$
$$CO + \tfrac{1}{2}O_2 \longrightarrow CO_2 + energy$$

These are mainly strictly autotrophic bacteria of the soil. When the oxidized substrates (electron donors) are entirely *inorganic* or "mineral," the chemotrophic organisms using them

are called *chemolithotrophs* (Gr. *lithos* = stone or mineral).

Chemotrophs that obtain energy by oxidizing *organic* substrates like glucose are said to be *chemoorganotrophs.*

Typical phototrophic organisms use only radiant energy, but they differ in respect to the hydrogen donors that they can use in their photosynthetic processes. Green plants use water as the hydrogen donor for the reduction of carbon dioxide in the synthesis of their cellular organic compounds (see Photosynthesis). They do not require organic carbon. Such organisms are said to be *photolithotrophic* or *photolithotrophs.* Some species of bacteria are photolithotrophic but, unlike all other photosynthetic organisms, they use hydrogen sulfide as hydrogen donor, not water (Chapter 38). Some phototrophic bacteria utilize as hydrogen donors neither water nor hydrogen sulfide but certain specific organic compounds. Such bacteria are said to be *photoorganotrophs.*

The viruses have been omitted from the discussions of nutritional types because their nutrition is of a separate and distinct type, unlike that of any other kind of organism. Viruses have been called *paratrophic;* their energy, and some materials, being extorted from the host cells in which viruses must live.

The relationships of the various nutritional types may be tabulated as follows:

A. As to carbon source:
 1. Autotrophs: can use carbon dioxide as sole source of carbon.
 2. Heterotrophs: require organic source of carbon.
B. As to energy source:
 3. Chemotrophs: obtain energy from oxidation; independent of sunlight for energy.
 4. Phototrophs: obtain energy from sunlight.
 5. Lithotrophs: obtain energy from oxidation of inorganic substrates.
 6. Organotrophs: obtain energy from oxidation of organic substrates.

Terms 3 through 6 are commonly combined as:

 I. Chemolithotrophs: obtain energy only from oxidation of inorganic substrates; most are autotrophic soil bacteria.
 II. Chemoorganotrophs: obtain energy only from oxidation of organic substrates. All are heterotrophs: all animals and Eumycetes and most bacteria.
 III. Photolithotrophs: obtain energy from radiant sources; use inorganic hydrogen

---

*You may argue on either side with equal profit!

donors in photosynthesis; all green plants, blue-green algae and a small group of bacteria.

IV. Photoorganotrophs: obtain energy from radiant sources; use organic hydrogen donors in chemosynthesis; heterotrophs: bacteria of Families Thiorhodaceae and Athiorhodaceae.

(Note that chemotrophs are differentiated on the basis of substrate oxidized for energy. Phototrophs are differentiated on the basis of type of donor of the hydrogen used for reduction of carbon dioxide.)

**Saprophytes.** Presumably most of the earliest heterotrophic fungi, including bacteria, obtained their carbon from inert organic compounds—either those occurring spontaneously around them or those available from the wastes and dead remains of other organisms. Whatever may have been their origin, such heterotrophic forms are commonplace today among both microorganisms and macroorganisms. Many are exceedingly important as scavengers. Among the microorganisms, most "molds" and bacteria are scavengers. They are spoken of as *saprophytes* because they are involved in organic decomposition (Gr. *sapros* = rotten, decaying).

**Parasites.** Probably still later than saprophytes there appeared, either through progressive or regressive evolution or both, types of heterotrophic microorganisms, both plants and animals, that could metabolize not only dead and waste organic matter but also the substances inside other living cells or tissues. They caused disturbances of the delicate physical and chemical equilibria of the organisms in which they lived, injuring and destroying their cells and, if their victims were multicellular, their tissues. This was *disease* and often resulted in the death of the invaded organisms. Such disease-producing organisms, both microscopic and macroscopic, are said to be *parasitic* and *pathogenic.** A woefully long list of pathogenic microorganisms may be cited including the amebae of dysentery, the bacilli of whooping cough, bubonic plague and brucellosis and leprosy bacilli, and so on and on.

Obligate Parasites. In the course of organic evolution some of the parasitic organisms presumably became so fully adapted to a parasitic existence that they became partly or wholly dependent on this mode of life and on the organisms that they parasitized. They apparently lost the ability to live saprophytically and could not multiply in the outer world. Since they are obliged to live a wholly or partly parasitic existence they are said to be *obligate parasites.* Shining examples of obligate parasites are all of the viruses; rickettsias such as those that cause Rocky Mountain spotted fever; animals such as hook- and tapeworms, malaria parasites, spirochetes of syphilis and bacilli that cause leprosy.

## SUPPLEMENTARY READING

Bisset, K. A., and Grace, J. B.: The nature and relationships of autotrophic bacteria. Fourth Symposium, page 28. Soc. Gen. Microbiol., London, 1954.

Butlin, K. R., and Postgate, J. R.: The economic importance of autotrophic micro-organisms. Fourth Symposium, page 271. Soc. Gen. Microbiol., London, 1954.

Committee on Bacteriological Technique, Soc. of Amer. Bacteriologists (now Amer. Soc. for Microbiol.): Manual of Microbiological Methods. McGraw-Hill Book Co., New York. 1957.

Giorgio, A. J., Cartwright, G. E., and Wintrobe, M. M.: Preparation of a copper-deficient medium for yeast growth. J. Bact., *86*:1037, 1963.

Harris, A. H., and Coleman, M. B. (editors): Diagnostic Procedures and Reagents, 4th edition. American Public Health Association, New York. 1963.

Lester, G.: Requirements for potassium by bacteria. J. Bact., *75*:426, 1958.

Lichstein, H. C.: Microbial nutrition. Ann. Rev. Microbiol., *14*:17, 1960.

Miller, S., and Avi-Dor, Y.: The effect of inorganic ions on respiration in *Pasteurella tularensis* and *Escherichia coli.* J. Gen. Microbiol., *18*:221, 1958.

Proom, H., and Knight, B. C. J. G.: The minimal nutritional requirements of some species in the genus *Bacillus.* J. Gen. Microbiol., *13*:474, 1955.

Spitznagel, J. K., and Sharp, D. G.: Magnesium and sulfate ions as determinants in the growth and reproduction of *Mycobacterium bovis.* J. Bact., *78*:453, 1959.

Stamer, J. R., Albury, M. N., and Pederson, C. S.: Substitution of manganese for tomato juice in the cultivation of lactic acid bacteria. Appl. Microbiol., *12*:165, 1964.

Starkey, R. L., and others: Symposium on Autotrophy. J. Bact., *26*:142, 1962.

Sykes, G. (editor): Constituents of Bacteriological Culture Media. Cambridge University Press, New York. 1956.

Weinberg, E. D.: Manganese requirement for sporulation and other secondary biosynthetic processes in *Bacillus.* Appl. Microbiol., *12*:436, 1964.

Woods, D. D., and Lascelles, J.: The No Man's Land between the autotrophic and heterotrophic ways of life. Fourth Symposium, page 1, Soc. Gen. Microbiol., 1954.

---

*Parasitic* is from Greek roots meaning to eat the food of another; *pathogenic* is from Greek roots meaning to produce disease. Parasitism may be of so slight a degree as to be nonpathogenic and verge on commensalism.

# Chapter 4

# CULTIVATION AND GROWTH OF BACTERIA

By the cultivation of microorganisms is meant the process of inducing them to grow. For most purposes of microbiology they are cultivated *in vitro,* i.e., in glass (L. *vitro* = glass) flasks, test tubes and other vessels. Today the term *in vitro* includes containers made of plastic or steel, as in the huge tanks (Fig. 22.2) used for commercial purposes. Cultivation *in vitro* necessitates the preparation of substances that the microorganisms can use as food. Such nutrient preparations are called *culture media.*

## 4.1 CULTURE MEDIA

There are three main types of culture media: natural or empirical, synthetic or "defined," and living. They vary widely in form and composition, depending on the species of organism to be cultivated and the purposes of the cultivation. Here we shall describe only a few representative types of the more commonly used natural or empirical and synthetic culture media used mainly for bacteria, yeasts and molds. Methods for cultivating PPLO, viruses, the P-L-T group or chlamydias and rickettsias are described in the discussions of those forms.

### EMPIRICAL AND SYNTHETIC CULTURE MEDIA

**Natural or Empirical Culture Media.** Empirical media are those used on the basis of experience and not on the basis of exact knowledge of their composition and action. In the early days of microbiology, natural culture media were widely used: milk, urine, diluted blood, vegetable juices and the like. Some media were artificially prepared, such as beef or vegetable broths and meat *infusions,* and are still widely used. They contain a rich assortment of soluble organic and inorganic compounds, comprising all of the elements and accessory substances for many (but not all) microorganisms. Such media are convenient and inexpensive and serve many routine purposes. However, their exact composition is unknown and variable.

Numerous culture media, now widely used, were developed as a result of more exact knowledge of the nutritional requirements of microorganisms. These media consist wholly of dilute, reproducible solutions of chemically pure, known inorganic or organic compounds. They have special uses in research and industry. Artificial media of exactly known, reproducible composition are called *synthetic media* or *chemically defined* media. In order to use one of them it is necessary to know the exact nutritional requirements of the organism. Such knowledge is now available for a number of medically or commercially important microorganisms. Synthetic media are not so commonly used for routine purposes as empirical media because (1) they are often expensive and time consuming to prepare, and (2) the organism to be cultivated is often unknown, for example, when attempting to identify an unknown bacterium that is causing an infection in the blood or spinal fluid. It is therefore customary in most laboratories to use empirical organic media for routine purposes. Many useful empirical media are commercially available in dehydrated ("add water, heat and serve") tablet or powder form.

PEPTONE. Most such media contain about 2 per cent of partly digested or hydrolyzed protein or meat derivatives such as *peptone.* Peptones have in them all the phosphorus, sulfur and basic mineral content of living material, as well as organic carbon and organic nitrogen in numerous complex and soluble forms. Such media furnish a wide variety of substances derived from living material and satisfy a wide range of nutritional requirements.

MEAT EXTRACTS AND INFUSIONS. *Beef tea* (beef extract) and an aqueous extract made by soaking (*infusing*) ground meat in water are common ingredients of culture media useful for a wide variety of microorganisms as well as for people. They are rich in minerals, vitamins, proteins and carbohydrates. They are often mixed with 1 per cent peptone, "adjusted" to a suitable degree of pH* (see Chapter 6) and are then dispensed in tubes or flasks, plugged with cotton and *autoclaved*.† Media made with beef tea are called *extract* media; those made from fresh meat are called *infusion* media. All such media are sometimes loosely included in the general terms *nutrient broth* or *nutrient solution.*

Meat is not the only useful source of organic matter. Fresh extracts of vegetables of various kinds are often used. Canned tomato and orange juices make excellent media for numerous bacteria, yeasts and molds. Some workers use the flesh or juices of shellfish, while those interested in the microbiology of milk sometimes use whey or skim milk. Eggs are

---

*pH and pOH are symbols used to express degrees of acidity and alkalinity. They are factors of critical importance in cell life (Chapter 19).

† Sterilized with compressed steam (Chapter 21).

often used also, especially for tubercle and diphtheria bacilli. Peptones made of partly digested soybeans or of casein have been shown to be as good as meat infusion for many purposes.

Some media are made by adding bits of kidney, spleen or other tissues freshly removed from dead animals under aseptic precautions (i.e., in the absence of contaminating microorganisms) to tubes of broth. Extracts of yeast are often included.

**Adsorption of Nutrients at Surfaces.** The incorporation in bacteriological culture media of small amounts of some solid substance such as ground meat or even sand is often advantageous, as many microorganisms seem to grow best in the crevices of, or in contact with, the surfaces of such matter, forming little nests or *niduses* there. It is probable that oxygen and food substances concentrate at such points by adsorption. Digestive enzymes secreted by the microorganisms into their environment do not diffuse away so quickly in such protected niduses (Fig. 4.1). Indeed, in very dilute media, growth may occur only at such surfaces.

SPECIAL MEDIA. To any of the media we have mentioned, various test and experimental or nutrient substances may be added. Certain carbohydrates may be included to test the fermentative powers of various organisms. Organic esters, blood, glucosides and many other compounds are put into the medium for a great variety of experimental purposes. The medium is then referred to by the name of the special

**Figure 4.1** *A*, A free-floating bacterial cell surrounded by a few suspended particles of food (dark circles) which must be hydrolyzed by the exoenzyme (helicoidal lines) before the resulting hydrolysates (dots) can be assimilated. *B*, Particles of food concentrated in a monomolecular layer on a solid surface. *C*, Food particles are more available to the cell on the solid surface where the interstices at the tangent of the bacterial cell and the solid surface retard the diffusion of exoenzymes and hydrolysates away from the cell. *D*, Multiple cells form additional interstitial spaces. (From ZoBell: J. Bact., vol. 46.)

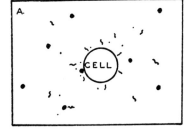
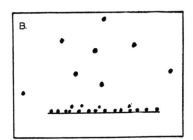
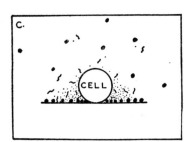
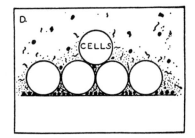

substance, for instance, *lactose-broth, blood-infu-sion-broth, serum-dextrose-extract-agar, starch-carrot-whey-agar* and so on.

## SYNTHETIC CULTURE MEDIA

**Organic Synthetic Media.**   These are often very complicated. A synthetic medium devised for a rather fastidious pathogenic bacterium, *Corynebacterium diphtheriae* (cause of diphtheria), is as follows:

*Solution A*
| | |
|---|---|
| glycine | 0.5 gm. |
| valine | 1.0 gm. |
| leucine | 0.5 gm. |
| glutamic acid | 5.0 gm. |
| methionine | 0.2 gm. |
| tyrosine | 0.1 gm. |
| NaCl | 5.0 gm. |
| $K_2HPO_4$ | 2.0 gm. |
| $H_2O$ | 500.0 ml. |

*Solution B* (add to *A*)
| | |
|---|---|
| Cystine | 0.2 gm. |

(in 30 per cent HCl, minimal quantity to dissolve)

*Addition 1* (add to *A* after adding *B*)
Vitamins:
| | |
|---|---|
| pimelic acid | 1 mg. |
| beta alanine | 1 mg. |
| nicotinic acid | 2 mg. |

Adjust to pH 7.8 (done by adding dilute NaOH to the desired pH).

*Solution C* (add 0.3 ml. of this to the above, after pH adjustment)
Source of $Ca^{++}$:
| | |
|---|---|
| $CaCl_2$ | 33 gm. |
| $H_2O$ | 100 ml. |

Boil gently for 10 minutes. Filter through paper.

*Addition 2* (add to the above)
Sources of $Mg^{++}$, $Cu^{++}$, S:
| | |
|---|---|
| $MgSO_4 \cdot 7H_2O$ | 0.3 gm. |
| $CuSO_4 \cdot 5H_2O$ | 5.0 gm. |
| tryptophan | 100.0 mg. |
| $H_2O$ to make | 1000.0 ml. |

Dispense in flasks and autoclave.

Just before inoculation, to each 100 ml. add aseptically 2 ml. of:

*Solution D*
Organic sources of energy and carbon:
| | |
|---|---|
| sodium lactate | 37.0 ml. |
| glucose | 7.5 gm. |
| maltose (purified) | 15.0 gm. |
| $CaCl_2$ | 0.3 gm. |
| $H_2O$ to make | 100.0 ml. |

Autoclave.

One advantage of synthetic media is that they are exactly reproducible. In rare instances they may be less expensive and troublesome to prepare than media made with meat and meat products such as peptone (especially at current meat prices!). Also, they can be prepared, if necessary, without proteins and therefore without *antigenic* or *allergenic* properties when in-

jected into man or animals in vaccines or for experimental purposes. By virtue of these properties they lend themselves well to exact experimental research and to medical and commercial uses. (See also sections on vitamin assay, Chapter 47.) A great difficulty is that a solution suitable for one species is often not suitable for another, and it is usually difficult to determine the exact requirements for a given species.

**Inorganic Synthetic Media.**   These are among the simplest of media. A medium used for a common, sulfur-oxidizing, strictly autotrophic, chemolithotrophic species of bacteria found in the soil (*Thiobacillus thiooxidans*) is as follows:

| | | |
|---|---|---|
| $(NH_4)_2SO_4$ | 0.2 | gm. |
| $MgSO_4 \cdot 7H_2O$ | 0.5 | gm. |
| $KH_2PO_4$ | 3.0 | gm. |
| $CaCl_2$ | 0.25 | gm. |
| Powdered sulfur | 10.0 | gm. |
| Distilled $H_2O$ to make | 1000.0 | ml. |

The phosphate in the medium is a *buffer* (i.e., it maintains a suitable pH; Chapter 6). It also serves as a source of phosphorus and potassium for the physiological requirements of the cell. Additional trace elements (i.e., micronutrients; Cu, Fe, Mg, Na and others) are usually present as impurities in the water or ingredients. The powdered sulfur is the source of energy. It is oxidized to $H_2SO_4$! (See Chapter 43.) Incubation is at about 25° C.—a temperature common in the soil in summer. Carbon is obtained in inorganic form as carbon dioxide from the atmosphere. Nitrogen is provided in an inorganic form as an ammonium salt. This is a typical synthetic or *chemically defined inorganic* medium.

## 4.2   EVOLUTION OF PURE CULTURE METHODS

If one studies the properties of some substance—say, ferric chloride—and over a period of months performs a series of laborious, time-consuming and expensive tests, carefully noting all the properties of $FeCl_3$ revealed by the tests, it is discouraging to find afterward that a little copper sulfate was inadvertently mixed with the iron salt, completely vitiating the whole set of data. So also one may spend time, energy and money determining the exact and absolute properties of, say, *Saccharomyces cerevisiae,* the brewers' yeast. The findings must be thrown out the window if it is afterward found that the culture of yeast cells was *contaminated* (inadvertently mixed) with some bacteriological weed like *Bacillus subtilis,* a common dust bacterium found, like dandelions, almost everywhere. When studying $FeCl_3$ we must have the pure substance; when studying a microorganism we must have a pure culture, i.e., material containing a single species of microorganism.

**Difficulties with Contaminated Cultures.** Early microbiologists had to contend with the difficulty that, as Leeuwenhoek had observed, the natural habitats (market milk, feces, sewage, the skin, soil, river water, air, dust and so on) of microorganisms generally contain scores of different species living together. The occurrence of a pure culture of any single species in natural materials is rare, though it does happen under certain circumstances such as "blood poisoning" (infection of the blood stream or *septicemia*). In the late 1860's, as soon as anyone attempted to cultivate organisms from a particular source (blood, soil, a lesion) or to handle them with instruments, the microorganisms under study, if not already accompanied by other species, became mixed with a variety of extraneous microorganisms from the instruments, from dust or from some other source. But no good method of separation or *isolation* of organisms in pure culture was then known.

**Origin of Pure Culture Technique.** In 1872 a microbiologist named Schroeter had observed the growth of different sorts of bacteria in isolated masses (*colonies*) of various colors on slices of decaying potato. He thrust a sterile platinum wire into one of the gray bacterial masses and put a bit of it in a little water under his microscope. He saw that all the bacteria in this particular colony looked exactly alike. He examined the bacteria from a yellow colony on the potato, and then those of a red one and a violet one. The organisms from one colony were all round; those from another all had the appearance of tiny, immobile cylinders; organisms from a third looked like minute, living, highly motile, spiral springs; but all the microorganisms in any one colony were always exactly the same. It was obvious that by cultivating microorganisms on *solid* nutrient surfaces it was possible to obtain isolated colonies of any single kind—each a pure culture!

THE USE OF GELATIN. Extending this principle, Koch in 1880 used a 5 to 10 per cent gelatin solution to prepare a transparent, solid jelly with a moist, sticky nutrient surface on flat pieces of glass. In addition, various nutrient solutions and test substances could be added to the gelatin before it was allowed to set. Here was a very important advance—a revolutionary advance, one that has become the basis of all our present-day bacteriology. Modified in technical details, it is currently used in the pure-culture study of viruses, of cells of cancer and of humans, plants and insects. The isolation of microorganisms in *pure culture* and their study by relatively exact methods is one of the pillars of modern microbiology.

In summer, however, and when held in body-temperature incubators, the gelatin melted. Being a protein it was often digested and liquefied by the metabolic processes of the microorganisms, especially molds. Besides that, particles of dust settled on it with various microorganisms from the air or soil, which contaminated it, obscuring and confusing the results as badly as ever.

FIRST USE OF AGAR-AGAR. Many students flocked to Koch's laboratory from all over the world to learn his methods. One of these was W. Hess. To the wife of this man the science of microbiology is indebted for suggesting, in 1881, as a substitute for gelatin the vegetable gum, agar-agar (commonly called *agar*). This gum is a polysaccharide derived from seaweed (*Gelidium* sp.) and was used at that time in making jellies. Agar is transparent and colorless, is not digested or liquefied by man or by most bacteria, melts only at boiling temperature and, once melted, does not set again until approximately body temperature (39° C.). Agar has not been improved upon as a solidifying agent for culture media and is in general use for this purpose today. It is added in 1.5 to 3.0 per cent concentrations to nutrient solutions.

ORIGIN OF THE PETRI PLATE. In order to prevent contamination of the pure cultures by dust, another student in Koch's laboratory, R. J. Petri, suggested the simple expedient of pouring the melted nutrient agar into circular, shallow dishes and immediately covering them with a glass cover. This permitted prolonged examination of the cultures but excluded dust. Such dishes are widely used today and are called *Petri plates.*

After 1883 the preparation and study of pure cultures proceeded at a great rate all over the world (Figs. 4.2 and 4.3).

For many years the use of glass Petri dishes and other culture vessels imposed a burden of cost and dishwashing on microbiological laboratories. Plastic disposable dishes of this type and many other vessels and instruments such as syringes are now available and for many purposes solve many knotty and long-standing problems of cleaning and sterilization.

SILICA GELS. A short time afterward it was discovered that many important species of

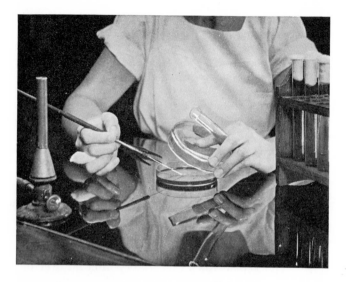

**Figure 4.2**   Subculturing bacteria. Transfer of bacterial colonies from Petri dish to tubes containing sterile culture media. By this method the desired strains of bacteria are isolated in pure culture. Note the type of needle used and the Bunsen burner for flaming (sterilizing) its point. (Courtesy of Parke, Davis Co.)

strictly autotrophic microorganisms of the soil are "poisoned" or inhibited by the presence of an organic substance such as agar. Silica ($SiO_2$) is an acceptable substitute when it is made to assume a jelly-like state. A representative procedure follows: *

> Mix equal volumes of ortho-silicic acid tetraethyl ester and ethyl alcohol.
> Add 6 volumes of boiled distilled water, slowly, with constant stirring.
> Centrifuge to remove turbidity.
> Dispense in tubes or plates.
> Autoclave at 120° C. for 30 to 40 minutes; gel formation occurs.
> Remove alcohol by flooding surface with sterile distilled water.
> Replace water with sterile nutrient solution.
> Reautoclave if necessary to insure sterility.

---

*Manual of Microbiological Methods. Society of American Bacteriologists (American Society for Microbiology). New York, McGraw-Hill Publishing Co., 1957.

A number of species of heterotrophic microorganisms of the sea and soil readily digest and liquefy agar, hence the need for an inorganic medium like silica-gel in cultivating such species. Preparation of silica-gel is not difficult but requires meticulous attention to details such as pH, temperature, concentration of silica and the presence of various ions. Further details of materials and mode of preparation will be found in the literature cited on this page.

OTHER SOLIDIFYING AGENTS.   Several substances other than agar, gelatin or silica are widely used to prepare solid microbiological media. Serum, blood and whole mixed eggs, which coagulate readily on heating, are often used either alone or as the basis for mixtures. In addition, slices of potato, bread, carrot and the like, as well as pieces of meat, can serve as solid media for numerous species of microorganisms.

**Figure 4.3**   Pure culture preparation on a commercial scale. Incubation of pure cultures in special bouillon for preparation of toxins, polio vaccine, and so on. This photograph shows a portion of a large incubator used for various types of culture growth. The temperature of this room is kept at exactly 35° C. (Courtesy of Parke, Davis Co.)

## Cultivation on Fine-Pore Membrane Filters.

A means of cultivating microorganisms, especially bacteria, on a solid surface without the use of a special solidifying agent has been developed through the use of very thin, highly porous membranes of cellulose acetate, collodion or similar materials.* Such membranes can be prepared with pores of the magnitude of 0.5 $\mu$ or smaller. Mounted on a perforated plate to support it in a funnel-shaped apparatus (Fig. 4.4), such a membrane acts as a sieve to filter microorganisms from any fluid: drinking water; dilute feces; blood; digested, centrifuged sputum; dilute broth cultures. After the fluid has passed through, depositing its microorganisms on the surface of the previously sterilized membrane, the membrane is removed from the supporting device with sterile forceps and laid on a disk or pad of sterile blotting paper saturated with any desired nutrient solution. The nutrients from the saturated pad diffuse through the membrane and support growth of colonies on its surface just as though these were on an agar surface (Fig. 4.5). Various selective or special media are used to cultivate special sorts of bacteria. The disks of cellulose acetate or collodion are sometimes sterilized by exposure to sporicidal gases or irradiation with ultraviolet light or gamma rays, but may also be sterilized

---

* Available commercially.

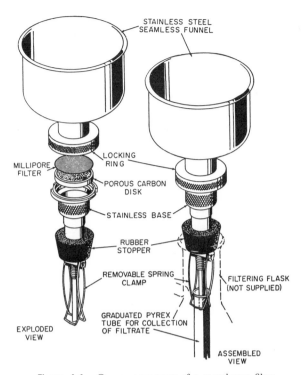

**Figure 4.4**   One arrangement of a membrane filter for removing microorganisms from fluids. The porous carbon disk serves merely to support the fragile membrane (Millipore) filter. It plays no role in the filtering process. The whole assembly, mounted in a receiving filtering flask, is sterilized before use. The microorganisms are held on the filter membrane, there to be cultivated (Fig. 4.5) and counted. (Courtesy of the Millipore Filter Corporation.)

**Figure 4.5**   Plastic Petri-type dish containing a broth selective for bacteria (*Escherichia coli*) which indicate sewage pollution of water. The membrane filter through which the water was filtered was removed from an apparatus like that shown in Figure 4.4 and laid in the dish on the surface of the thin film of broth, which the membrane absorbed. After incubation for 18 hours at 37° C. the distinctively colored, glistening colonies of *E. coli* had developed. (Approximately actual size.) (Courtesy of the Millipore Filter Corporation.)

by heat, with suitable precautions recommended by the manufacturers.

Interesting deviations from the standard procedures of cultivating bacteria are possible. One may incubate organisms on a membrane laid on a pad moistened with one solution for a time, and then transfer the membrane with its colonies to a different medium, or to a stain or to a pad saturated with a reagent to test for some particular growth product or property of the organisms growing on the membrane. One may easily filter a liter of river water through a membrane, place the membrane on a pad containing a special selective medium or a general-purpose nutrient broth, and isolate typhoid bacilli from the water, enumerate spores of pathogenic fungi or count the cultivable organisms in the total sample.

## 4.3   GROWTH AND MULTIPLICATION

**Multiplication and Fission.**   With only a few exceptions such as some gametocytes and

certain modified bacteria, e.g., PPLO and chlamydias (Chapter 41), all living cells* multiply by the *asexual* process of cell *fission*, i.e., by division of the cell into two or more complete individuals that can continue this asexual reproductive process indefinitely, provided food is available and conditions remain favorable. Most bacteria multiply by *binary fission*—division into two equal parts (Fig. 4.6, *A*). The factors that initiate fission and the exact means by which it is achieved are still under investigation. There is evidence that a particular form of nucleic acid (tRNA) referred to as *cytokinin* may promote cell division and growth (Chapters 8 and 14).

Among the autonomously living, *unicellular* organisms (Protista) fission is multiplication, since each fission leads to two new, independent individuals. Among *multicellular* plants and animals, fission of body (*somatic*) cells results

---

*Not viruses, which are noncellular as cells are currently defined.

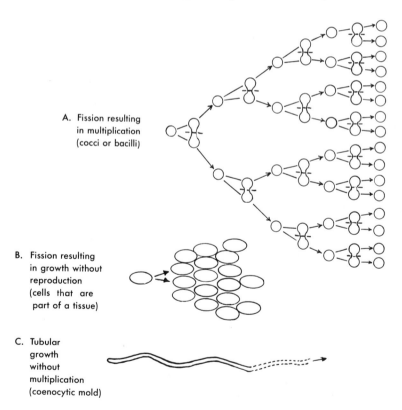

A. Fission resulting in multiplication (cocci or bacilli)

B. Fission resulting in growth without reproduction (cells that are part of a tissue)

C. Tubular growth without multiplication (coenocytic mold)

D. Tubular growth with septation and fragmentation resulting in reproduction (septate mold)

**Figure 4.6**   Various relationships in growth and reproduction. In *A*, growth results in fission, which in turn results in reproduction of many new individual microorganisms. In *B*, fission results in reproduction of the initial cell, but only an increase in size of the multicellular creature of which the cell is a part. In *C*, growth of a coenocytic tube appears only in length of the tube, not in numbers of new organisms as shown by fragmentation of a septate filament in *D*.

only in growth (increase in size) of the individual (Fig. 4.6, *B*), not in multiplication (increase in numbers of complete individuals).

CELL WALL, CELL MEMBRANE AND CELL DIVISION. Electron microscopy shows clearly that in many species of bacteria, when cell fission is to occur, centripetal growth or invagination of *cell membrane* is initiated at a right angle to the long axis of the cell (if the organism is rod shaped).

The cytoplasmic membrane thus forms a double-layered partition or *cell plate* between the two cells-to-be. Two layers of cell-wall material are synthesized between the two layers of membrane as fast as the latter are formed. A separation of the cells then results from a split between the two new cell walls. In some species the cell membrane appears to partition the cell first, followed by the cell wall. The sequence of events may vary in different species and under different environmental conditions.

GROWTH WITHOUT FISSION. Growth of microorganisms does not necessarily involve fission. Many species of normally rod-shaped bacteria, under the influence of numerous extraneous influences, may fail to undergo fission although growth may continue. As a result, instead of numerous individual cells, long nonseptate filaments are formed (Fig. 4.6, *C*). Some fission-inhibiting agents are soap and bile salts; certain sources of food energy, such as glucose; D-forms of various amino acids, such as D-serine and D-histidine; ultraviolet irradiations; certain conditions of improper nutrition, and so on. These factors inhibit *septum formation* but not growth. The exact mechanisms are not yet entirely clear.

**Multiplication and Sex.** Among the "higher" microorganisms (i.e., eucaryotic Protista; Chapter 10), both sexual and asexual reproductive processes are usually readily demonstrable under proper conditions of growth and observation. In these microorganisms a major role of the reproductive process in addition to multiplication is the transfer and recombination of genes (genetic recombination) between male and female cells. Genetic recombination, as biology students know, is one of the main factors in organic evolution. Among bacteria, sex has no role in multiplication; multiplication is entirely asexual. However, genetic recombination is brought about by several mechanisms that do not involve sex at all. A form of conjugation is observed in some species, in which the "sexes" are to some extent interchangeable, and are morphologically indistinguishable. Recombination by such

conjugation is commonly only partial. These genetic phenomena are more fully discussed in Chapter 14.

## 4.4 POPULATIONS OF MICROORGANISMS

Regardless of the possible sex life of microorganisms, the Protista find no difficulty in multiplying enormously asexually under optimal conditions. For example, certain common bacteria (e.g., *Escherichia coli*) if left to their own devices can, within 24 hours or so, produce inside of a thimble-full of broth a population of astronomical proportions, running into the billions.*

It may seem extraordinary—like oxidation without oxygen (Chapter 9), life in a vacuum at 400° below zero F. (Chapter 19) and reproduction without sex—but we can count these billions with reasonable accuracy, in duplicate or quadruplicate, quite easily within a few hours or even minutes!

The numbers (or *populations*) of microorganisms present in various natural materials such as soil or river water vary constantly because of changing conditions. In an ideal situation such as a pure laboratory culture under uniform, optimal physical and chemical conditions the numbers of organisms vary in a perfectly regular and predictable way in accord with general biological laws.

## 4.5 ENUMERATION OF MICROORGANISMS

To illustrate phenomena of growth, multiplication and enumeration of microorganisms we shall use bacteria as our model because they are convenient to work with, the methods are well developed and the principles they illustrate are fairly generally applicable in microbiology. The basic laws hold even in the "special cases" of viral growth, multiplication by conidiospores, and sexual reproduction in which there are sudden releases of large numbers of new cells or growth units. The calculations are adjusted with respect to the peculiar relations between time and numbers.

We generally measure growth (multiplica-

---

*The term population (L. *populus* = people) is generally used to mean all the microbial cells living in the same material or environment; perhaps "*microbu*lation" would be more exact.

tion) of bacteria and other microorganisms by measuring increases in numbers in relation to time.

As an illustration we may select a culture flask containing 50 ml. of sterile infusion broth at 35° C.

Let us introduce by means of a sterile pipette a drop of fluid containing about 10 cells of the common, harmless bacterium of the intestinal tract—*Escherichia coli.* Let us assume that these 10 cells are from an inactive or *dormant* stock culture on an agar slant held for weeks in the refrigerator. The newly inoculated broth culture is held at 35° C. The problem before us is to measure the population at regular intervals by counting the numbers of living cells present. The numbers present at the different periods are then plotted in relation to time, and a *growth curve* is obtained. Enumeration may be carried out by several methods, none of which is exact. Methods may be direct or indirect.

## DIRECT METHODS

CELL COUNTS.   In the *hemacytometer* or counting-chamber method a minute drop of the fluid is placed in a tiny, shallow, rectangular glass vessel called a *hemacytometer* (because it was devised originally for counting hemocytes or blood corpuscles). The counting chamber is partitioned off by ridges into regular, cubical chambers of exactly known volume (Fig. 4.7). By counting the individual cells in each chamber under a microscope and adding them, the numbers of

organisms per milliliter may be computed. This is a total count of live and dead organisms. The method is applicable to any suspension of microscopic particles.

SMEAR COUNTS.   *Direct.*   Another procedure is to smear an exact volume of the culture over an exact area on a slide, stain with methylene blue or other appropriate dye and count the organisms in a known portion of the total area. Knowing the diameter of the microscopic field from previous measurements (by means of a stage micrometer), one can calculate the numbers of organisms per milliliter of culture. This is a total count also, since no distinction is readily made between living and dead organisms. (See Breed Counts of Milk, Chapter 45.) This method is applicable to any suspension of microscopic particles that can be stained with a dye.

*Comparative.*   If 1 ml. of blood and 1 ml. of culture are well mixed and a stained smear of the mixture prepared, an estimate of the numbers of bacteria may be obtained by counting both blood and bacterial cells in a certain number of fields and noting their relative proportions. Since we know that male human blood contains about five million erythrocytes per cubic millimeter, an estimate of the numbers of bacteria is merely a matter of arithmetic. This is a total estimate.

MEMBRANE FILTER COUNTS.   Measured samples of fluid may be passed through sterile, porous-membrane filters and the microorganisms on the filter then counted directly (Fig. 4.5). The organisms must not be too numerous and must be uniformly distributed. They are first

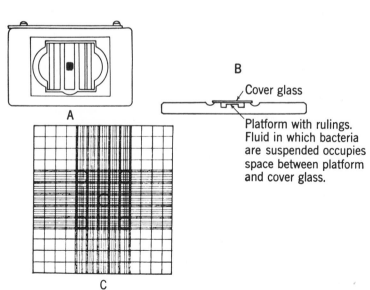

B

Cover glass

A

Platform with rulings. Fluid in which bacteria are suspended occupies space between platform and cover glass.

C

**Figure 4.7**   A hemacytometer (Petroff-Hausser type) adapted for counting bacteria and other microorganisms. *A,* Plan view, showing the area (dark central square) covered by the ruled chambers which are seen enlarged at *C. B,* A vertical section, about two thirds actual size, with cover glass in place. It is customary to count only the cells in the representative areas encircled in *C,* though all may be counted for greater accuracy. (Courtesy of Arthur H. Thomas Co., Philadelphia, Pa.)

stained *in situ* on the membrane and then counted in calibrated fields. Before counting, the filter is made transparent by saturating it with immersion oil. This is a total count of dead and live organisms.

## INDIRECT METHODS

DETERMINATION OF TOTAL VOLUME. Still another method is to place a fixed volume—say, 10 ml.—of the culture in a kind of test tube, called a Hopkins tube, having a narrow, hollow, cylindrical column projecting from the bottom and graduated in millimeters. The organisms are packed into the column by centrifugation at a standard speed and for an exactly measured time, and their total volume is read on the graduated scale. From a knowledge of the average volume of the individual cells an estimation of numbers is possible. This also is a total estimate. In a modified form it is commonly used in medical diagnostic studies to measure the total volume of blood corpuscles in a *hematocrit determination*.

TURBIDOMETRIC METHODS. A widely used technique measures turbidity in the fluid due to the accumulation of cells in it. A measured volume of the culture is placed in a special, clearglass tube of known diameter. This is interposed between a unit source of light and a photoelec-

tric unit, which is attached to a galvanometer. The reading on the galvanometer depends on the passage of light through the culture from the unit source. Of the total light from the unit source, the percentage transmitted through the tube will be diminished in proportion to the turbidity (numbers) (Fig. 4.8). The method is subject to errors due to variation in size and shape and clumping of cells, as well as to different degrees of translucency of various species and other materials in cultures. However, the method is one of the quickest and simplest and is reasonably accurate. Turbidity readings may be standardized in terms of numbers of cells by hemacytometer counts or electronically.

ELECTRONIC COUNTERS. These instruments are capable of accurately counting thousands of cells in a few seconds. Most are based on the principle of electronic gating, which is roughly analogous to the "electronic eye" that operates the familiar automatic door in a supermarket. Basically, it depends on interruptions of an electron beam that traverses a space between two electrodes. Each particle as it passes between the two electrodes causes an interference with the electron beam. The interruption is taken up by instruments and recorded electronically (Fig. 4.9). Other instruments with complex circuitry are based on high-speed scanning beams like TV cameras.

CHEMICAL METHODS. Quantitative deter-

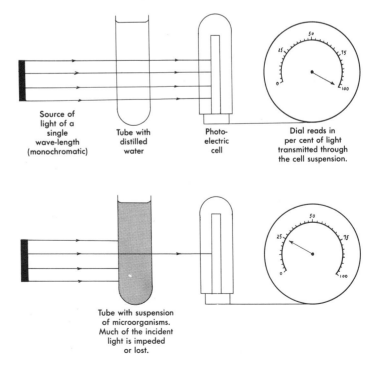

**Figure 4.8** Use of a photoelectric turbidimeter to estimate numbers of microorganisms. Virtually 100 per cent of the light from the source at left passes through the tube with distilled water (top); less than 25 per cent through the tube turbid with suspended microorganisms (bottom).

Source of light of a single wave-length (monochromatic)

Tube with distilled water

Photoelectric cell

Dial reads in per cent of light transmitted through the cell suspension.

Tube with suspension of microorganisms. Much of the incident light is impeded or lost.

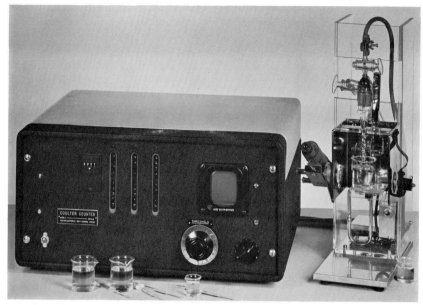

**Figure 4.9**   Estimation of numbers of microorganisms by an electronic "gating" method. For explanation see text. (Courtesy of Coulter Electronics, Chicago, Ill.)

minations of substances that are always present in fairly constant amounts in living cells are sometimes used as equivalents of total cell growth, with or without fission. One is total nitrogen determination by the Kjeldahl method. Since nitrogen is always present in protein in the proportion of about 16 per cent, Kjeldahl values can easily be converted to protein values. Protein may also be measured directly by means of the *Folin reagent,* which gives a color reaction with tyrosine and tryptophan, two amino acids always present in protein in constant amounts. Other chemical methods involve determinations of nucleic acids (DNA and RNA) or the phosphorus of these acids, and so on.

DRY WEIGHT MEASUREMENTS.   These are not much used for measuring bacteria but are a useful method of measuring growth of molds in certain phases of industrial work. The procedures differ with different materials but all depend on effective washing; complete, or at least constant, degrees of dehydration; and accurate weighing. The increase in weight represents biological synthesis and, with data on cell volume available, can be used to calculate cell numbers.

## DILUTION METHODS

**Serial Dilutions.**   The method of serial dilutions is widely used to estimate numbers of

bacteria in various fluids: water, milk, cultures, etc. Into tubes of broth are placed 1 ml. quantities of the sample (of, let us say, milk) diluted in decimal, four-fold, two-fold or other convenient series. After incubation of the tubes of broth, numbers of organisms are recorded by noting presence or absence of growth. For example, in a ten-fold dilution series suppose there is growth in the tube that received the 1:1000 dilution but no growth in the tube receiving the 1:10,000 dilution. Then there were (theoretically) between 1000 and 10,000 organisms per milliliter of the sample of milk tested.

INDICATED NUMBER.   This number of organisms per milliliter is spoken of as the *indicated number* (the reciprocal of the highest dilution showing growth). But it is not a very exact estimate. It measures only live cells that are viable (capable of growth) under the conditions provided and ignores chance variations.

MOST PROBABLE NUMBER.   In the example just cited, *theoretically* there should be 1000 organisms but there may be, *theoretically,* any number up to 9999 per milliliter in the sample. What is the true number? This cannot be stated. However, mathematicians have shown that the number most probably present may be calculated if the results from duplicate or triplicate simultaneous determinations are known. Tables are available showing the most probable number calculable from all possible combinations of results in such series. These tables are much

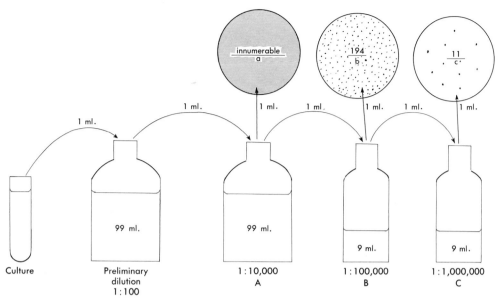

**Figure 4.10**    A colony count of a young culture of *Escherichia coli*. One milliliter of culture was transferred to 99 ml. of buffered diluting fluid in the preliminary dilution. After gentle mixing, 1 ml. of this was transferred to 99 ml. of fluid in bottle *A*. One milliliter of this dilution, after mixing, was placed in plate *a* and 1 ml. was transferred to bottle *B* and so on through plate *c*. After adding agar to the plates and incubating (see text) the plates were examined. Plate *a* contained too many colonies to count; they were confluent and crowded each other out. Plate *b* contained 194 well-distributed, well-separated and easily counted colonies. Plate *c* contained only 11 of a theoretical 19 or 20. The percentage error in each colony in such a high dilution makes such a count unreliable, and such plates are disregarded. It is customary to make colony counts in duplicate and triplicate to minimize such error. This culture contained approximately 20,000,000 viable cells of *E. coli* per milliliter.

used in examination of water. Tables are found in "Standard Methods for the Examination of Water and Wastewater" * with directions for use. It is to be borne in mind that these are most probable numbers, not exact numbers.

This method can be made qualitative as well as quantitative by adding special indicator substances to the broth. For example, it is standard practice to add lactose and to note the highest dilution of sample in which *lactose-fermenters* are found, as indicated by production of acid and gas in the broth. (See Chapter 42.)

COLONY COUNTS. The colony count is a widely applicable procedure used daily for determining approximate numbers of microorganisms in milk, water and many other materials. It is applicable to any microorganisms that will grow as colonies on solid laboratory media. These media must, of course, provide good nutrition for the microorganisms under investigation.

Continuing the examination of our flask of culture inoculated with *Escherichia coli*, mentioned on page 46, we may, at any desired mo-

ment, withdraw exactly 1 ml. of the culture from the flask with a sterile measuring pipette and transfer it to a sterile Petri dish. Immediately afterward, about 15 ml. of nutrient agar, previously melted (and cooled to about 40° C. so as not to kill the bacteria), is poured into the dish. The culture is thoroughly mixed with the still-fluid agar by a gentle horizontal rotation of the dish. In a few minutes the agar will have solidified. This plate culture is held in an incubator at about 35° C. for 24 hours and is then examined for the presence of colonies distributed throughout the agar.

As, with continued incubation, the number of bacteria in the sample increases toward several hundred or thousand per milliliter, the 1 ml. of material removed for the plate count is diluted so that plates are obtained that show only about 50 to 300 colonies (Fig. 4.10). This is easy after a little experience. It avoids lethal crowding of the colonies and separates the colonies so that counting is easier. The number of colonies, multiplied by the reciprocal of the dilution, gives the indicated number per milliliter.

*Roller Tube.* Samples or dilutions of fluid specimens may be placed in nutrient agar (of

---

*12th ed., New York, American Public Health Association, 1965.

**Figure 4.11**   Tubes containing warm, melted agar, inoculated with fluid in which bacteria are to be counted, are spun until cool in the Astell roller-tube spinner. (Courtesy of Consolidated Laboratories, Inc., Chicago Heights, Ill.)

composition appropriate to the organisms expected to grow in it) in cylindrical vials called *roller tubes,* instead of in Petri dishes. While the agar is still fluid these vials are spun in an electric *spinner* until the agar solidifies in a thin film evenly distributed over the inside surface of the tube (Fig. 4.11). After incubation, colonies are easily counted in the film of agar (Fig. 4.12). The method is especially convenient for taking samples of milk and water on field trips, since an indefinite number of sealed roller tubes with warm, fluid, sterile agar in them can be carried along and inoculated on the spot.

**Figure 4.12**   Colonies in agar in one Astell tube as shown in Figure 4.11, after incubation. (Courtesy of Consolidated Laboratories, Inc., Chicago Heights, Ill.)

Whatever the method used for obtaining colonies, each represents, theoretically, the progeny of a single cell that was in the original inoculum and that was imprisoned in or on the agar at that point. Actually, several organisms, if stuck together in a clump, will give rise to only a single colony. The colony count, therefore, does not give a wholly accurate enumeration of the live *individual* cells present in the material under investigation. However, the errors in the plating or roller-tube methods are fairly well known, and, within limitations, such counts are among our most useful means of enumerating microorganisms. The basic principle is widely used and should be fully understood at this point. It measures *only organisms viable under the conditions of growth* (medium, temperature) provided.

COLONY COUNTING.   The counting of colonies in agar is greatly facilitated by the use of a 2× or 3× stereoscopic microscope with both direct and indirect illumination.

Electronic colony counters are used in examining relatively small numbers of plates in which each colony is marked with an electric needle as it is automatically counted (Fig. 4.13).

## 4.6   GROWTH CURVES

Let us suppose that we make colony counts of our culture of *Escherichia coli* every two hours at first, and plot the numbers and logarithms of the numbers of colonies (roughly, live organisms per milliliter) against time. If we were to continue to plot actual numbers instead of logarithms, we should need a sheet of paper

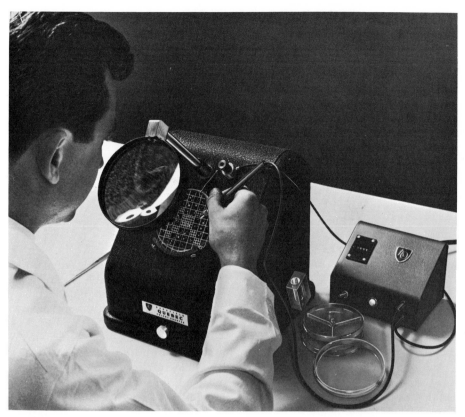

**Figure 4.13**   Electronic colony counter. The probe (actually an electrode) is used to mark the location of each counted colony on a transparent, electrically conductive agar plate. Note the corresponding electrode that completes the circuit near the upper rim of the dish. Each mark is automatically recorded on the electronic counter. (Courtesy of American Optical Company.)

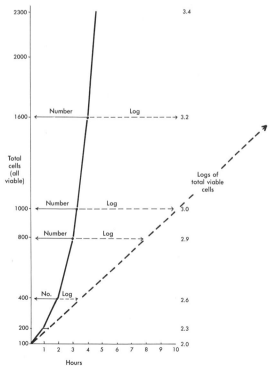

several miles long, because the numbers may run into billions per milliliter (Fig. 4.14). We may continue making counts until no further significant changes in numbers occur. At the end of this time a curve will have been obtained which will look somewhat like that seen in Figure 4.15.

A totally different type of curve would be obtained if we were to count the bacteria in the fluid by means of one of the *total* count methods we have described. This is because many of the bacteria die in the culture during the period of incubation. While appearing in the total count, they cannot produce growth in the dilution-tube series or colonies in Petri plates

**Figure 4.14**   Arithmetic (——) and logarithmic (————) curves of growth in a flask of *Escherichia coli* incubated at 35° C. and inoculated with 100 viable cells from another culture also in the logarithmic phase of growth. The numbers double every hour (assuming that none die). Note that the *total* number of viable cells goes up like a rocket! The logarithms of these numbers proceed in a straight line.

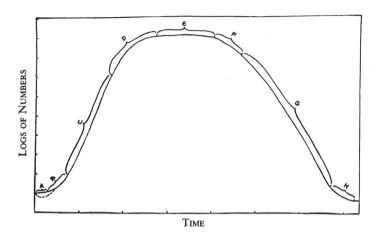

**Figure 4.15** Growth curve of unicellular organisms under optimal conditions of growth. For explanation see text.

since these enumerate only organisms viable under the growth conditions provided. A curve showing total counts as compared with viable counts is seen in Figure 4.16.

## PHASES OF THE GROWTH CURVE

The curve shown in Figure 4.15 has several portions that deserve discussion. These are shown by brackets and labels in the figure.

**Initial Phases.**  Portion *A*, usually called the *latent* or *initial stationary* (or *lag*) *phase*, represents a period during which the dormant organisms are probably imbibing water and swelling, or becoming adjusted to the new environment, much as might occur when a dormant tree is set out in the spring. The exact details of this "awakening" or "reanimation" process are not yet known, although they are under investigation. There is no immediate increase in numbers. The dotted line indicates that some few of the cells may actually die off during this period, only the more vigorous going on to multiplication.

INITIATION OF GROWTH.  When *dormant* cells are used as inoculum, factors of critical impor-

tance in initiating growth are pH, temperature, the presence of suitably high or low oxygen concentrations (oxidation-reduction potential) and favorable concentrations of carbon dioxide. Certain nutrient substances must also be present, especially those which the cell forms slowly or with difficulty for itself.

**Phase of Accelerated Growth.**  Once growth begins it is soon manifested in the rising inflection of portion *B*, which is commonly called the *phase of accelerated growth.* The first two phases together are often called the *lag phase.* During this early period, when fission is slow, the size of the cells is large: near the maximum for the species. This probably represents imbibition of water with consequent swelling and the beginning of metabolic activity before fission has occurred.

ALLELOCATALYSIS.  It is a common experience that an original inoculum of thousands of cells is more likely to result in vigorous growth of the new colony than an inoculum of one or perhaps a dozen cells. There are various explanations of this, mainly to the effect that, with a large inoculum, minute but effective quantities of certain essential food substances, enzymes and

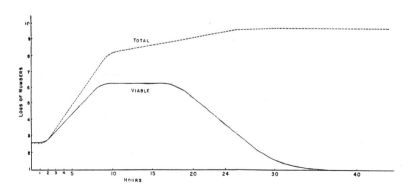

**Figure 4.16**   Relation of total to viable counts of bacteria in a pure culture under optimal conditions of growth. For explanation see text.

other necessary materials (some known, others unknown) are either transported with the inoculum from its previous site of growth or quickly synthesized or released at the new site by the many cells present. One such agent has been called *"schizokinin"* or fission activator. A term sometimes used to describe the mutual support and stimulation among cells in a large inoculum is *allelocatalysis* (Gr. *allelo* = to act together or reciprocally).

During the phase of accelerated growth the time required for each cell to divide gradually decreases, cell size diminishes and fission rate reaches a maximum determined by the species of microorganism and growth conditions.

**Exponential or Logarithmic Phase.** As growth continues, the cells reach their maximum rate of fission. Numbers increase in linear relationship to time. Fission may become so rapid that the number of organisms doubles within 10 minutes. The average size of the cells is at its minimum for the species during this time. It is also conceivable that cell membranes or walls are thinnest and metabolic activities at their highest rate during this period; hence, in part, the vulnerability of young cells to numerous deleterious influences that do not affect mature, less active cells. Fission rate varies greatly with different species and under different conditions of growth. Tubercle bacilli, for example, probably divide only about once a day at the highest rate of growth on solid media, every hour or less in certain fluid media.

During this period of most active multiplication (*C*) the logarithms of the numbers of live organisms counted at short intervals, plotted against time, produce a straight line as shown in Figure 4.14. This period is spoken of as the *logarithmic phase* of multiplication or as the *phase of exponential increase*. Were this to continue uninterrupted, the culture would become a solid mass of bacteria in a few hours. A single cell of *Escherichia coli* allowed to continue such growth unchecked for a year or so would (it is said) produce a mass weighing more than the sun!

During this phase most of the cells are physiologically young and biologically active. If a subculture is made from the flask to a new flask of the same sort of warm sterile broth, growth continues at the logarithmic rate; there is no lag or dormant phase. The lag and dormant phases become evident to some degree in subcultures made during any other phase of the growth cycle. Biochemical peculiarities used for identification of organisms are usually most manifest during the logarithmic period.

**Growth Rate and Generation Time.** The time for a single cell to undergo fission is called the *generation time* of that cell. This varies with species of microorganism, nutrient, environmental conditions and growth phase.

By making one count ($C_1$) at a specified time and a second count ($C_2$) after an interval during the logarithmic phase of growth and knowing the number of time units (tu) we can calculate the total number of organisms (or) produced, the total number of fissions (f) and both growth rate (gr) and generation time (gt).

$C_2 - C_1$ gives the number of new cells. Since each fission produces two organisms or (theoretically) a doubling of total numbers in the culture, the exponent of cell increase per unit of time is 2. At any moment the number of organisms present can be expressed as the log to the base 2 ($\log_2$) of that number. The difference between $\log_2$ of the initial count ($\log_2 C_1$) and the second count ($\log_2 C_2$) gives the total number of generations or fissions (f) during the total number of time units (tu):

$$f = \log_2 C_2 - \log_2 C_1.$$

By substituting common logs ($\log_{10}$ or, simply, log) for logs to the base 2, and using 0.301 as the value of log 2:

$$f = \frac{\log C_2 - \log C_1}{0.301}.$$

The rate at which fissions (generations) occur per time unit (growth rate or gr) can be calculated as:

$$gr = \frac{f}{tu}.$$

In this case let each time unit (tu) equal 1 hour. The time required for each generation to occur (generation time or gt) is found as:

$$gt = \frac{1 \ tu}{f}.$$

Thus, if $C_1 = 50$ and $C_2 = 8{,}935{,}000$ and each tu = 1 hour:

$$f = \frac{6.95109 - 1.69897}{0.301} = 17.45$$

$$gr = \frac{17.45}{18} = 0.96 \text{ generations per hour (allowing a growth period of 18 hours)}$$

and

$$gt = \frac{1}{0.96}$$

$$= 1.04 \text{ hours (62.4 min.) per generation.}$$

**Phase of Negative Growth Acceleration.**
Within a few hours after the commencement of the logarithmic phase, the organisms begin to encounter difficulties. Food begins to run out, poisonous waste products accumulate, pH changes, hydrogen acceptors are used up, energy transfers are diminished, and the cells interfere with each other. The rate of fission begins to decline and the organisms die in increasing numbers, so that the increase in number of live cells slows, as shown in the portion of the curve labeled *D* of Figure 4.15. This is spoken of as the *phase of negative growth acceleration.*

A number of workers have tried to prevent the development of this phase by arranging the culture apparatus so that waste products and exhausted medium may be drawn off at regular intervals without removing the bacteria. New, fresh medium is added at the same times. Theoretically, a solid mass of cells should finally result. Actually, growth eventually ceases far short of this, and, unless very special "steady state" conditions are maintained, the population curve develops as usual with only temporary changes.

IMMORTALITY (?) OF MICROORGANISMS.   It is interesting to speculate upon the relationships between the age of cells, their multiplication and their continued existence without fission. Let us compare the fate of two cells just produced by the fission of their "parent." Under favorable conditions one of the new cells undergoes certain unknown physical and chemical changes,

which are the equivalent of *maturation.* After a few minutes or hours it undergoes fission like its predecessor. What are the relative ages of the new daughter cells? Are the two cells resulting from fission "sisters" or is one the daughter of the other, and which? How can a cell undergo the mysterious changes of maturation and aging and yet by the process of fission produce two "young" cells? Theoretically, such organisms never grow "old" or undergo senescence. Are they, by virtue of continual renewal of youth, immortal?

The other of our two original cells fails to reach a state in which fission occurs, and remains intact. What is its physiological age status? If transferred to a new culture it may begin multiplication at once and become "young" or it may die. It may die even if left in the original culture. Does it die of "old age"? The explanation of its fate is quite obscure. It is evident that chronological age and physiological age may be very different matters among microorganisms.

**Final Phases.**   Eventually (the time depending on the temperature, the size of the flask and volume of fluid, the composition of the medium and numerous other factors) the number of cells dying balances the rate of increase, and the total viable population remains unchanged for a time. The *total* count continues to increase, but not as rapidly as at first. This phase, the *maximum stationary phase,* is shown at *E.*

As conditions become more and more in-

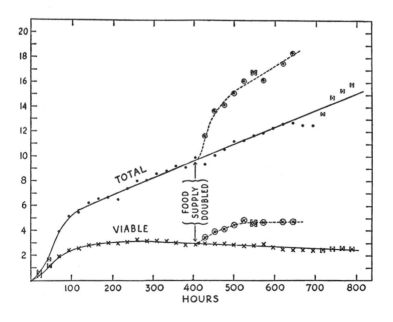

**Figure 4.17**   Growth curves of *Escherichia coli* with a constantly renewed food supply, neither wastes nor dead cells being removed. An increase in food supply stimulates growth temporarily, but death continues and the culture eventually declines and dies. (From Jordan and Jacobs: J. Bact., vol. 48.)

imical to the bacteria, the cells reproduce more slowly, and death overtakes them in ever-increasing numbers, as shown at *F*. This is the phase of accelerated decrease or *accelerated death phase.*

This progresses into the *logarithmic death phase* (*G*), during which decrease in number occurs at a regular, unchanging rate.

Finally, conditions begin to reach an equilibrium such that both rate of death and rate of increase tend to balance each other again at a very low population level, and the *phase of readjustment* (*H*) and a *final dormant phase* are attained. Complete sterility of the culture may not ensue for weeks or months, depending on the kind of organism, whether or not the culture is very acid and so forth.

**Factors Affecting Growth Phases.** The form of the growth curve may be affected by many factors. For example, if the culture is suddenly plunged into ice water, the curve at once ceases its upward trend, remains flat for a time and then begins to decline. If the culture is held at 22° C. instead of 35° C. (for *E. coli*) the rise in the positive phases is much less abrupt and much more extended. Other factors such as pH, concentration of food and so on have their effects also (Fig. 4.17).

## COLONY GROWTH

The obvious limitations to colony expansions are the following: (a) Nutrient solution can diffuse from the agar to the uppermost cells in the colony to only a limited extent. (b) The available nutrient and moisture in the agar in the immediate area are soon exhausted. (c) Wastes do not readily diffuse away and therefore accumulate in the colony and in the agar beneath. The cells at the top of the heap are obviously at a disadvantage, and soon the upper and central portions of the colony undergo the effects of aging and senescence and other effects of unfavorable nutrition and nonremoval of wastes. (d) Colonies that are too crowded compete with and overgrow one another.

## SUPPLEMENTARY READING

Berkley, C.: Potentials for automatic control methods in defined media studies. Ann. N. Y. Acad. Sci., *139* (Art. 1):1, 1966.

Choudhary, A. Q., and Pirt, S. J.: Metal-complexing agents as metal buffers in media for the growth of *Aspergillus niger.*: J. Gen. Microbiol., *99*:41, 1965.

Christie, A. O., and Porteus, J. W.: The cultivation of a single strain of *Actinomyces israelii* in a simplified and chemically defined medium. J. Gen. Microbiol., *28*:443, 1962.

Dean, A. C. R., and Hinshelwood, Sir C.: Growth, Function and Regulation in Bacterial Cells. Oxford University Press, New York. 1966.

Eagon, R. G.: *Pseudomonas natriegens,* a marine bacterium with a generation time of less than 10 minutes. J. Bact., *83*:736, 1962.

Glaser, D. A., and Wattenburg, W. H.: An automated system for the growth and analysis of large numbers of bacterial colonies using an environmental chamber and a computer-controlled flying-spot scanner. Ann. N. Y. Acad. Sci., *139* (Art. 1):243, 1966.

Grula, E. A.: Cell division in a species of *Erwinia.* J. Bact., *84*:599, 1962.

Grula, E. A., and Smith, G. L.: Cell division in a species of *Erwinia,* IX. Electron microscopy of normally dividing cells. J. Bact., *90*:1054, 1965.

Hoffman, H., and Frank, M. E.: Temperature limits, genealogical origin, developmental course, and ultimate fate of heat-induced filaments in *Escherichia coli* microcultures. J. Bact., *85*:1221, 1963.

Knisely, R. F., Swaney, L. M., and Friedlander, H.: Selective media for the isolation of *Pasteurella pestis.* J. Bact., *88*:491, 1964.

Lankford, C. E., Walker, J. R., Reeves, J. B., Nabbut, N. H., Byers, B. R., and Jones, R. J.: Inoculum-dependent division lag of *Bacillus* cultures and its relation to an endogenous factor(s) ("Schizokinen"). J. Bact., *91*:1070, 1966.

Malligo, J. E.: Evaluation of an automatic electronic device for counting bacterial colonies. Appl. Microbiol., *13*:931, 1965.

Mayer, G. D., and Traxler, R. W.: Action of metal chelates on growth initiation of *Bacillus subtilis.* J. Bact., *83*:1281, 1962.

Mickelson, M. N.: Chemically defined medium for growth of *Streptococcus pyogenes.* J. Bact., *88*:158, 1964.

Sinclair, N. A., and Stokes, J. L.: Factors which control maximum growth of bacteria. J. Bact., *83*:1147, 1962.

Swanton, E. M., Curby, W. A., and Lind, H. E.: Experiences with the Coulter counter in bacteriology. Appl. Microbiol., *10*:480, 1962.

Wessman, G. E.: Cultivation of *Pasteurella haemolytica* in a chemically defined medium. Appl. Microbiol., *14*:597, 1966.

# Chapter 5

# ENZYMES

In a foregoing chapter we gained some idea of the nutrition of microorganisms but little notion of those mechanisms that carry on the processes of nutrition: digestion, synthesis of cell substances, release and utilization of energy available in foodstuffs—in short, the processes that constitute *metabolism*. All of these reactions are aided by agents called *catalysts* or *catalytic agents*. The reactions are said to be *catalyzed*.

## 5.1 CATALYSIS

Catalysis is the speeding up of chemical reactions that, although they can theoretically proceed spontaneously if at nearly the same energy level, in the absence of the catalyst would do so only at a very (even infinitely) slow rate. Catalytic agents may be organic or inorganic. Many inorganic catalysts consist of sheets or "sponges" of various inert metals (platinum, lead). They are widely used in industry.

Catalyzed reactions typically occur at the *surface* of the catalytic agent. Therefore, the greater the surface area or state of subdivision of the catalyst, the more the reaction can occur.

For example, a cube of catalyst 1 cm. on each edge has a surface area of 6 sq. cm. Cut into two parts the catalyst has a surface area of 8 sq. cm. Cut into 100 slices each 0.1 mm. thick it presents 204 sq. cm. Divided into millions of colloidal particles it presents a surface area measuring many hundreds of square centimeters.

Substances are in the colloidal state when they are in the form of ultramicroscopically minute particles stably suspended in a fluid (gas or liquid). For example, smoke is a colloidal suspension of minute particles of carbon, tars and other substances in air; milk is a colloidal suspension of casein and fat in whey. Enzymes are colloidal proteins.

Colloidal particles generally have negative, mutually repellent electric charges. These help to keep the particles suspended and prevent their coalescing and precipitating as floc, or coagulating, as in the souring of milk. Unicellular microorganisms, because of their minute size, generally have many of the properties of colloids.

A common industrial inorganic catalyst is finely divided or colloidal platinum. Among its catalytic potentialities is the oxidation of ethyl alcohol. Alcohol and oxygen at room temperature do not combine to a readily perceptible degree. In the presence of finely divided platinum they are greatly concentrated on its surfaces by *ad*sorption (Chapter 19) (not *ab*sorption). A reaction then occurs between alcohol and oxygen, which is facilitated and controlled by the nature and extent of the catalyst, by temperature and by moisture. The alcohol is rapidly oxidized to acetic acid. The platinum does not enter into the reaction, but remains to adsorb more oxygen and more alcohol on its surface. It continues the process of oxidizing the alcohol, first to acetic acid and then to water and carbon dioxide, as long as the products of the reaction, or extraneous side products, are continuously removed and do not remain to block or "poison" the surfaces of the catalyst.

In a simple system of this kind we can predict, from a knowledge of the substances and surfaces involved, what the result of a given combination will be. Stable, inorganic catalysts such as platinum are simple and constant, and are extensively used in industry. In living systems the situation is more complex: numerous physically and chemically complex organic catalysts act simultaneously or in rapid succession.

Enzymes are organic catalysts—colloidal protein complexes. Unlike inorganic catalysts, enzymes act mainly by forming transitory chemical combinations with one or both of the *sub*-

*strates* (substances altered by the enzyme). Following the reaction that is catalyzed between the substrates, the enzyme separates from them. Theoretically it remains unchanged; actually enzymes "wear out" (chemically deteriorate) after prolonged activity.

Partly because of their colloidal structure enzymes usually act exceedingly rapidly and efficiently. Properly concentrated and in contact with optimum amounts of substrates under suitable conditions (temperature, pH), a very small quantity of enzyme, probably of the order of a few molecules, can bring about a relatively large amount of catalyzed reaction in a comparatively short time. For example, 5 ml. of an aqueous extract of pig's pancreas contains perhaps 1 mg. of the enzyme *trypsin* that hydrolyzes (digests)* protein in the intestinal tract. This can decompose 5 lb. of beef (protein) within about 5 hours at 37° C. at a pH of about 7.5. The ratio of specific substrate (in this case beef protein) to pure enzyme (trypsin) probably exceeds one million to one.

## 5.2 DISCOVERY OF ENZYMES

Before the time of Pasteur the nature of the fermentations that produce beers and wines was virtually unknown. Since it is the basis of very large industries the process of fermentation has been the subject of much study. Fermentation was thought by Liebig and many other brilliant chemists to be a spontaneous chemical change entirely independent of life. However, after many ingenious experiments and demonstrations it was made clear by Pasteur around 1860 that fermentation does not occur spontaneously but is wholly dependent on living microorganisms, notably brewers' yeast. Microorganisms were often called "living ferments." Pasteur also showed that true fermentation occurs only in the *absence* of free oxygen. In Pasteur's words, "La fermentation est la vie sans l'air." He called life without air *anaerobiosis.*

It was soon realized that beer and wine fermentations were not caused by the yeast cells themselves, but by some active principle associated with them. The active principle was thought to be inside the cells and was first called an *enzyme* (Greek: *en* = in; *zyme* = yeast or leaven) by Kuhne in 1878. Buchner (Nobel Prize win-

ner), in 1897, found that filtered, cell-free juice of crushed yeast cells would cause sugar to ferment. Thus the fermentative enzyme of yeast, and later a great variety of other sorts of enzymes from many other kinds of living cells, were found to be distinct, nonliving entities mechanically separable from the cells that produced them. We now know that, in a sense, Liebig was right, since fermentation can occur in the absence of living cells. However, the necessary enzymes are produced only by living cells.

## 5.3 STRUCTURE OF ENZYMES

### COENZYMES

In 1905 Buchner and others dialyzed cell-free yeast juice. Dialysis is carried out by enclosing the fluid to be dialyzed in a sac of *selectively permeable* material (i.e., material permeable to some substances but not to others), such as cellophane or animal membrane. The sac is then suspended in water. Ions and small molecules that are soluble in water (salts, glucose, amino acids) pass out of the sac, through the ultramicroscopic pores in the membrane, into the water surrounding the sac. Large molecules, such as those of proteins and complex polysaccharides, cannot pass through the membrane but remain inside the sac. In Buchner's experiments with yeast juice it was found that neither the *dialyzate* (i.e., the material that passed out of the sac) nor the *residue* (i.e., the material that remained inside the sac) could alone produce fermentation. When mixed together, however, they produced normal fermentation. Obviously each contained something essential to the fermentation.

It was soon demonstrated that the essential substance in the residue was a nondialyzable, colloidal protein, readily destroyed by heat (100° C.): i.e., it was thermolabile, as are virtually all proteins. Such a protein moiety of an enzyme is now called an *apoenzyme* (Gr. *apo* = part of).

The essential material in the dialyzate was found to be nonprotein, noncolloidal, of small molecular weight and thermostable. This part of an enzyme, easily separable from the protein part, is now called a *coenzyme*. Apoenzyme and coenzyme together constitute the complete enzyme, called a *holoenzyme* (Gr. *holos* = entire). The term enzyme is generally used to mean holoenzyme.

The molecular structure of many coenzymes is now well known, and some have been syn-

---

*In hydrolysis the bond between two units of a complex molecule is broken by splitting a molecule of water between the two units; $H^+$ is added to one residue, $^-OH$ to the other. (See page 61.)

thesized *in vitro.* Coenzyme molecules generally carry the distinctive, reactive portion of an enzyme. Acting with the apoenzyme, the coenzyme brings about the specific substrate reaction that is characteristic of that particular enzyme. In many coenzymes the distinctive, reactive portion is a familiar vitamin: nicotinic acid or its popular derivative "niacin," or vitamins of the B complex, such as thiamin (vitamin $B_1$) or riboflavin (vitamin $B_2$). In fact, all vitamins that function physiologically have been found to act as the reactive group of one or another coenzyme.

## PROSTHETIC GROUPS

In some enzymes the nonprotein, specifically reactive portion, unlike the coenzyme, is not readily dissociated from the protein portion. The nonprotein portion, analogous to a coenzyme, is then called a *prosthetic group;* the combination of the protein portion and the prosthetic group is called a *conjugated protein.* A familiar example of a conjugated protein is *hemoglobin.* This is a combination of the red, iron-bearing, porphyrin pigment *heme* (the prosthetic group) (Fig. 5.1) with

the globular protein, *globin.* Hemoglobin is the oxygen-carrying pigment of vertebrate red blood corpuscles. The iron of the prosthetic heme group of hemoglobin is readily oxidized and reduced. It combines with oxygen in the air via the lungs, releases oxygen to the body tissues and returns to the lungs for more oxygen.

Although not generally classed as an enzyme, hemoglobin closely resembles some enzymes in both structure and function. There are several metal-bearing, enzyme-like proteins (*metalloproteins*) other than hemoglobin. Generally the active metal is carried in a porphyrin residue much like heme. The metal in the green, sunlight-utilizing pigment *chlorophyll* in higher plants is magnesium instead of iron (Fig. 38.4). In the Crustacea the active metal is copper though it is not carried in porphyrin.

Many common bacteria use atmospheric oxygen, which is combined directly with yellow hemoproteins (closely analogous to hemoglobin) called *cytochromes* (Fig. 5.2). The combination is mediated by an oxidizing enzyme called *cytochrome oxidase.* Some details of these reactions will be given later. All such metalloprotein pigments that are involved in biological oxidations, or respirations, are often called *respiratory pigments.*

## COFACTORS

Some enzymes are first produced by the cell in an incomplete or inactive form. They are called *zymogens* or *pre-enzymes.* These must then be activated or completed by contact outside the cell with another agent called a *kinase,* an *activator* or a *cofactor.* Cofactors may be hydrogen ions or ions of iron, magnesium, copper, molybdenum, cobalt or zinc; they also may be coenzymes, vitamins or other enzymes, depending on the particular enzyme involved. Trypsin, for example, exists in the pancreas as inactive trypsinogen, which becomes activated in the intestine when in contact with a substance called enterokinase. Phosphatase, an enzyme that hydrolyzes organic phosphates, must be activated by magnesium ions. The exact function of some activators, especially vitamins and certain metallic ions, is well known; of others it is not so clear. The seemingly curious and often very specific requirements of many living cells, including our own body cells, for minute quantities of certain metals or vitamins (i.e., micronutrients) are evidence of the fact that these are absolutely essential parts of various coenzymes or prosthetic groups.

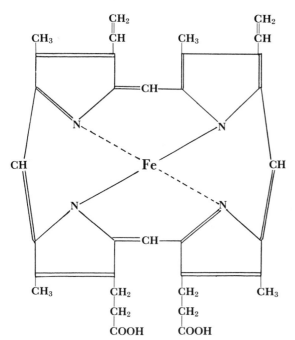

**Figure 5.1**   The heme molecule. Note the position of the iron in this ringlike or clawlike iron-porphyrin molecule. Heme is part of the red coloring matter of the blood. Chelating agents, such as the porphyrins, by combining with (chelating) harmful metallic ions, perform a function analogous to that served by buffers in combining with $H^+$ to maintain a favorable pH. Some pH buffers also act as metal chelating agents.

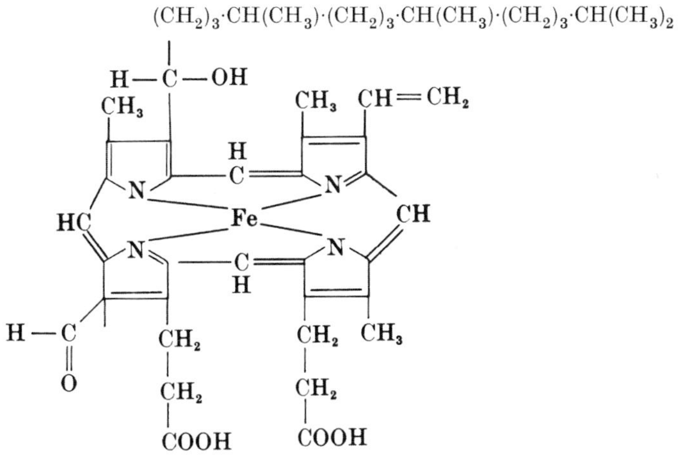

$$(CH_2)_3 \cdot CH(CH_3) \cdot (CH_2)_3 \cdot CH(CH_3) \cdot (CH_2)_3 \cdot CH(CH_3)_2$$

**Figure 5.2**   Iron-porphyrin of cytochrome *a*. (From Harrow and Mazur: Textbook of Biochemisty, 9th ed. W. B. Saunders Co., 1966.)

## 5.4   SPECIFICITY OF ENZYMES

The protein moiety (apoenzyme) of each enzyme is characterized by a property called *specificity* that is typical of proteins in general. Specificity of a protein molecule depends upon the physicochemical configuration of its *surface*. This, in turn, is determined by the number, kind and sequence of amino acids that constitute the peptide chains making up the protein (i.e., its *primary structure*), by the distinctive coiling or helical structure of the peptide chains (*secondary structure*) and by the manner of folding of the long peptide chains of proteins upon themselves (*tertiary structure*) (Chapter 8). Now, since an almost infinite number of permutations and combinations of the approximately 22 amino acids that make up the protein chains (i.e., the primary structure of the proteins) is possible, and since the chains can be twisted (secondary structure) and then folded like long skeins of wool yarn (tertiary structure) in billions of different arrangements, it is evident that there can be an astronomical number of different enzyme proteins (apoenzymes). Each protein is a macromolecule that may consist of hundreds of the 22 to 24 amino acid residues linearly linked in different arrangements. Each is different from all others in respect to molecular configuration; i.e., each enzyme is unique or *specific*. Each enzyme can react only with certain particular substrates that have a corresponding stereochemical structure (Fig. 5.3). This correspondence between enzyme and substrate is of a reciprocal nature such, for example, as the correspondence of a plaster cast to its mold. Exact details of enzyme-substrate interactions remain to be elucidated.

Be it noted that the correspondence between enzymes and substrates extends beyond mere physical form of the molecules involved, and includes the correspondence of mutually attractive electrostatic forces, hydrogen and sulfur bondings, van der Waals forces, and so on.

Specificity of enzymes varies greatly in degree. For example, one enzyme that catalyzes the oxidation of L-amino acids cannot oxidize the corresponding D-amino acids. A certain enzyme that destroys the carboxyl group of (*decarboxylates*) pyruvic and related keto acids will not decarboxylate fatty acids like acetic acid. Some enzymes (e.g., trypsin of the intestine) are more broadly specific and hydrolyze many dif-

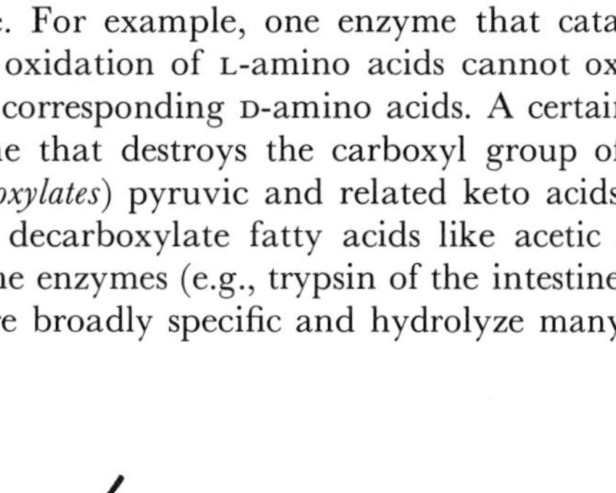

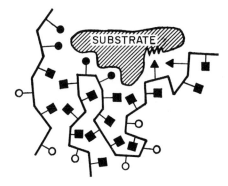

**Figure 5.3**   A schematic representation of an active site of enzyme-substrate interaction. ●, amino acid residues whose fit with substrate determines specificity; ▲, catalytic residues acting on substrate bond, indicated by a jagged line; ○, nonessential residues on the surface; ■, residues whose interaction maintains three-dimensional structure of the enzyme protein. (From Koshland: Science, *142*:1533, 1963.)

ferent proteins, because these enzymes attack peptide bonds between any linked amino acids. These are common to all proteins. Such enzymes do not attack carbohydrates, fats or other classes of substrates not having peptide bonds. Some enzymes, however, can attack only peptide bonds at the end of a peptide chain. Other enzymes attack only carbohydrates. For example amylase, an enzyme in saliva, attacks glycosidic bonds and splits starch into simpler sugars: dextrins, disaccharides and monosaccharides. Such enzymes do not act on proteins and fats.

It is worth noting at this point that many biological phenomena other than enzyme actions involve specific proteins. *Specificity* therefore characterizes many nonenzymic protein functions. Other examples of specificity will be seen in the sections on antigens and antibodies, microbial poisons (toxins), virus infections and certain industrial processes.

### Isoenzymes (Isozymes)

Studies of enzymes by physicochemical methods have shown that numerous enzymes occur in several forms, even in the same tissue or cell. These variant forms are called *isoenzymes* or *isozymes*. They appear to represent different structural arrangements of the same protein subunits, since all forms of a single enzyme have the same molecular weight. All appear also to have the same specificity as to substrate, though they may act in slightly different ways depending on the arrangement of the subunits in the apoenzyme. These structural variations may explain certain hitherto puzzling irregularities in enzyme action and may relate also to obscure immunological discrepancies or actions.

## 5.5   HOW ENZYMES ACT

### Mechanism of Enzyme Action

In most enzymic catalyses, the specific apoenzyme involved appears first to attach to the substrate at certain specific sites. These sites represent reciprocally corresponding physical structure and anionic and cationic groups in the molecule of the substrate (Fig. 5.3). This preliminary combination appears to place certain bonds in the substrate under stress. The coenzyme, because of its appropriate molecular structure, then combines with (*accepts*) a part of the substrate: for example, a hydrogen ion or glycosyl or amino group. This ion or group is then

either passed by the coenzyme to another coenzyme, or to a different substrate molecule, or it may be liberated as waste into the surrounding fluid. The final result depends on the nature of the reaction being catalyzed. The enzyme, freed of the altered substrate residue, is then ready to combine with another substrate molecule and repeat the process. If any energy is released by the reaction it is partly lost as heat and in part taken up into the cell substance by the formation of "energy-rich" compounds that contain certain types of bonds (e.g., organic phosphate bonds, thioester bonds and some others) in certain coenzymes (see Chapter 9). The energy stored in such energy-rich compounds is later used by the cell in motility and cell synthesis.

### Enzyme Induction

Each species of living cells has a genetically determined (inherited) natural endowment with certain functioning enzymes. These are constantly present in, and distinctive of, all of the cells in that species of cell. Such inherited enzymes, part of the normal constitution of the cell, are called *constitutive enzymes*. In addition many cells possess genetic determinants (genes) for the synthesis of numerous enzymes that, curiously, do not ordinarily appear. The mechanisms for the synthesis of such enzymes are genetically repressed. (This is more fully explained in Chapter 14.) Each such repressed genetic determinant finds expression only when a corresponding or *inducing* substrate (or related substance; see next paragraph) enters the cell. In the presence of the inducer the repressor of the appropriate synthetic mechanism is removed and the enzyme specific for the inducer substrate is synthesized. Such enzymes are said to be *inducible*. They were formerly called "adaptive" enzymes. Thus, although genes (i.e., genetically functional units) determine the full enzymic potentialities of a cell, environmental factors in the form of inducers, for example, determine just which of the latent enzymic potentialities of a cell shall appear under any given circumstances. The cell is evidently not under the necessity of synthesizing all its potential enzymes all the time but only such as may be needed from time to time. This is an important economy of the food and energy resources of the cell, since enzyme synthesis requires energy and food substance.

In a number of cases an enzyme may be induced in a cell by any one of several substances that are not themselves substrates but are merely chemically related to a specific metabolizable substrate. A much-studied example is the induction of the enzyme β-galactosidase in a common bacterium, *Escherichia coli.* Synthesis of this enzyme is inducible by not only its normal substrate, lactose (milk sugar; a β-galactoside readily metabolized by *E. coli*) but also by melibiose (an α-galactoside *not* metabolizable by *E. coli*) and also by several thio-β-galactosides. In another bacterium, *Proteus vulgaris,* the enzyme *leucine decarboxylase* is induced by the amino acids alanine (*not* a substrate for *P. vulgaris*) and valine, chemically similar to leucine.

## ENZYME EQUILIBRIA AND REVERSIBILITY

The action of many enzymes is demonstrably reversible. For this reason the symbols used in equations involving enzyme action often indicate reversibility. For example, if we place in a solution of amyl butyrate (an organic salt or *ester*\*) a little *esterase* (an enzyme from the pancreas that hydrolyzes amyl butyrate under the proper conditions of temperature and pH), the amyl butyrate is hydrolyzed to its constituents, butyric acid and amyl alcohol. The decomposition automatically ceases when a certain concentration of the acid and alcohol has been reached, i.e., at a definite *equilibrium point:*

$$C_9H_{18}O_2 + H_2O \underset{\text{Enzyme}}{\overset{}{\rightleftharpoons}} C_4H_8O_2 + C_5H_{12}O$$

*Amyl butyrate*   +   *Butyric acid* + *Amyl alcohol*

Conversely, if we put the acid and alcohol together in a beaker with esterase, amyl butyrate and water are re-formed, ceasing at a definite concentration of end products. This is an excellent example of two of the most important catalyzed reactions in all living forms: *hydrolysis* (separating with water) and *anhydrosynthesis* (joining by withdrawing water). (See also Chapter 8.) This also illustrates the important point that, in general, accumulation of end products inhibits the action of any enzyme in either direction, i.e., at the same equilibrium point. Under any set of constant conditions, the equilibrium point for an enzyme-catalyzed reaction is constant.

There is clearly a constant relationship be-

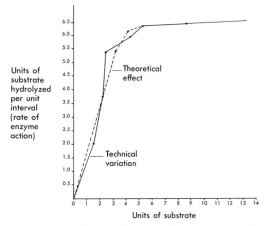

**Figure 5.4**  Relation between substrate concentration and rate of enzyme action with a fixed enzyme concentration. Beyond a certain point (in this illustration about 4 units of substrate) a fixed amount of enzyme becomes saturated with substrate and will not act any faster no matter how much substrate is added. The activity of the enzyme may be inhibited.

tween concentration of enzyme and concentration of substrate. Up to the point of saturation, the rate of reaction increases with increase of ratio of one component to the other. With a constant amount of enzyme, increase of substrate increases rate of reaction until every molecule of enzyme is fully occupied (saturated) with substrate. Further additions of substrate cannot increase the rate of reaction (Fig. 5.4). Conversely, with a fixed amount of substrate, rate of reaction increases with additions of enzyme until all molecules of substrate are in contact with enzyme. Further additions of enzyme do not affect the rate of reaction (Fig. 5.5).

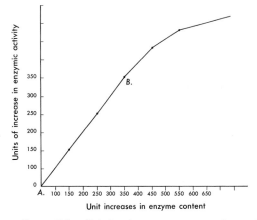

**Figure 5.5**  Relation between enzyme action and enzyme concentration with fixed amount of substrate. The relationship is linear within limits: i.e., between points *A* and *B*. Beyond *B*, all of the substrate eventually comes into contact with enzyme, and no increase in enzyme action occurs regardless of how much enzyme is added.

---

\*An ester is an organic salt formed by the combination of an organic acid with an organic base. For example, the ester, ethyl acetate, is formed by combining acetic acid with ethyl alcohol.

In many instances enzyme-catalyzed reactions appear to proceed in only one direction because the equilibrium point is very far in that direction. In other cases one or more of the end products may be removed constantly by some mechanism so that equilibrium is never reached. Under normal conditions in the living cell, enzyme reactions are constantly pushed in this manner toward the one or the other side of the reactions.

When markedly different *energy levels* are involved, theoretically reversible reactions cannot actually reverse. In the hydrolysis $\rightleftharpoons$ synthesis reaction of amyl butyrate just given very little energy is lost in the hydrolysis or required to complete the resynthesis. The reaction proceeds in either direction because both are at very nearly the same energy level. When a great deal of energy is released, as in the complete enzymic oxidative decomposition of glucose (688,500 calories), resynthesis cannot be brought about by the same enzymes because they cannot restore the lost energy. To reverse the reaction requires that "work" be done by *other* systems of enzymes that capture new energy derived from solar or other radiant sources by green plants or the biooxidation of foodstuffs by nonphotosynthetic species.

As an analogy, compare the stepwise, theoretically reversible process of raising and lowering a car with a jack. The jack may be thought of as an enzyme system. Lowering the car is like the enzymic decomposition of glucose: potential energy is liberated. Raising the car is like resynthesizing the glucose: new energy is required. The two processes take place at totally different energy levels. To complete the analogy, the new energy for raising the car is also derived (ultimately) from biooxidation of the glucose in the muscles of the man (or girl!) operating the jack.

## 5.6   ENZYME CONTROL

**"Feed-back" Controls.**   Inside a living cell most enzymes do not act individually but as parts of well organized, coordinated and sequentially operating systems. Whatever affects one portion of the intracellular enzymic system has some effect on all parts, like the parts of a spider web. As pointed out before, the activity of an enzyme is inhibited by accumulation of the end products of the catalyzed reaction. In a step-wise sequence of cooperating enzymes (a "biological production line") excessive accumulation of a reaction product at the end of the

line may inhibit the action not only of the enzyme at the end of the line but of all the enzymes in that sequence, all the way back to the beginning of the line. This is an important form of automatic control called *feed-back inhibition.*

Eventually, in the presence of excessive amounts of end products, not only is enzyme activity inhibited but the actual synthesis of the enzymes themselves may be repressed. For example, if a cell normally synthesizing a certain substance, say the amino acid alanine, is artificially abundantly supplied with that substance (the end product of the enzyme) from an extraneous source, not only is the enzyme inhibited, but synthesis of some or all of the enzymes in the production line for that substance is repressed until the enzymes are needed again. This is called *feed-back repression.* Note that it is necessary to differentiate between (a) inhibition of the *action* of enzymes by their end products (feed-back inhibition) and (b) feed-back repression of the *synthesis* of the enzymes themselves by the accumulation of end products, especially in enzyme series.

Contrary to its repressive action, the end product of each enzyme in a series or production line can be the *inducer* of the next enzyme in the series and the inhibitor or repressor of the preceding enzyme, thus carrying forward the work of the enzyme machine. Various such start-stop, induce-repress-inhibit mechanisms of enzyme control result in amazingly complex and efficient "automation."

**Energy Controls.**   An important aspect of enzyme control is that related to the liberation of energy from foodstuffs. Clearly, in any regulated mechanism using energy, including living cells, if the energy supply is uninhibited and uncontrolled it can soon become injurious and, in cells, fatal. Conversely, failure to provide energy at a sufficient rate would prevent the normal functioning of the cell. In the cell, as in the machine shop, there must be a "stop-go" mechanism to control the energy supply.

In the machine shop, energy for the power source is supplied by the burning (i.e., the *oxidation*) of fuels or the use of water power. The energy from the power source is transmitted to the machines by belts, shafts and gears. In living machines (e.g., the living cell) energy is also derived from the burning (i.e., the enzymic *biooxidation*) of foods. In the cell the energy liberated by biooxidation is transmitted not by gears and shafts but via high-energy compounds as noted elsewhere, notably certain organic phosphates: e.g., phosphoenol pyruvic acid, acetyl phosphate and, most importantly, adenosine triphosphate

(ATP). The energy of these compounds appears to relate to the special phosphate bonds. Now, ATP is derived during oxidative phosphorylation by addition of a phosphate group + energy (Chapter 9) to adenosine diphosphate (ADP). ADP is derived from adenosine monophosphate (AMP):

$$(AMP + \text{ }^-OPO_3H_2 \longrightarrow$$

$$ADP + \text{ }^-OPO_3H_2 \longrightarrow ATP).$$

ATP is a high-energy compound. The exact manner in which the energy is transferred from the low-energy-level oxidized foods into the high-energy ATP is not yet fully clarified.

From the standpoint of energy control in the cell, ADP is an essential factor because it is needed to accept the energy of foodstuffs and become phosphorylated to high energy ATP in the process. But if the energy stored in the ATP is not used up as fast as it is derived from the biooxidation of foodstuffs, ATP accumulates to excess. None is broken down to replace the supply of ADP that was used in its formation. The supply of ADP is thus depleted. The depletion of the ADP supply prevents its further acceptance of high-energy phosphate. This, in turn, inhibits the entire succession of oxidative enzymes that "collect" the energy from the foodstuffs. The supply of energy is thus automatically cut off until utilization of the energy stored in the excess ATP changes it back to ADP, which at once begins to accept more phosphate and energy. The whole effect is analogous to the backing up of a long line of traffic behind a stoppage far ahead, or the old fable: "Water, water, please quench fire, because fire won't burn stick, stick won't beat dog, dog won't bite pig, pig won't get over the stile and I shan't get home tonight."

The kind of energy control described might be considered a form of feed-back inhibition of an enzyme series due to concentration of an end product, in this case ATP. However, the mechanism differs from feed-back inhibition since it is not the concentration of ATP that blocks the enzyme system, but deprivation of the ATP-forming mechanism of the necessary ADP.

## LOCATION OF ENZYMES IN THE CELL

EXOENZYMES. Probably many enzymes exist free in colloidal suspension in the fluid matrix of the cell. Some of these are secreted to the exterior. They are called *exoenzymes*. Exoenzymes are mainly digestive in function. By hydrolysis they decompose complex organic matter in the outer world, such as proteins, cellulose and fats, to simple, soluble molecules of amino acids (from proteins), glucose (from polysaccharides) and glycerol and fatty acids (from fats). These relatively small molecules can pass through the cell membranes of many microorganisms, there to be utilized as food.

ENDOENZYMES. Foodstuffs, once they get inside the cell, are acted upon by whole systems of enzymes that act only inside the cell. These are *endoenzymes*. Endoenzymes of many kinds cooperate in two general types of process inside the cell: (a) *synthesis* of cell components and food reserves and (b) *bioenergetics*—i.e., the release of energy from foodstuffs. The energy is either stored in reserve nutrients like starch, fats or beta-hydroxybutyric acid inside the cell or is immediately used for any of the active processes of the cell. It is evident that synthetic and energizing mechanisms are closely knit (*coupled*) into a definite and very efficient organization that carries on the complex chemistry of life but whose most intimate interreactions still escape us.

Endoenzymes concerned in the synthesis of proteins are, as noted in Chapter 8, intimately associated with *ribosomes*. In the cells of animals and higher plants endoenzymes concerned in energy production are organized into granular and membranous structures inside organelles called *mitochondria* and, in green plants, are closely associated with the light-absorbing organelles called *chloroplasts*. In bacterial cells the energy-mediating mechanisms appear to be closely associated with the cell membrane from which the more highly evolved *endoplasmic reticulum* of cells of animals and higher plants is derived. Energizing endoenzymes may also possibly be associated with *mesosomes* in bacterial cells that show these structures (Chapter 13). The appearance of mesosomes in bacteria suggests primitive stages in the evolution of endoplasmic reticula.

The term exoenzyme must be used with care, because enzymes that are found in the medium surrounding cells may actually be endoenzymes that have been liberated by rupture of the cells.

## 5.7   FACTORS THAT AFFECT ENZYMES

Since enzymes are protein complexes, they are sensitive to all the various precipitating and coagulating (denaturing) factors that affect proteins in general: i.e., temperatures over 80° C., excessive concentrations of ions of heavy metals or of hydrogen ($H^+$) or hydroxyl ($^-OH$) ions. Active chemicals like chlorine and corrosive agents

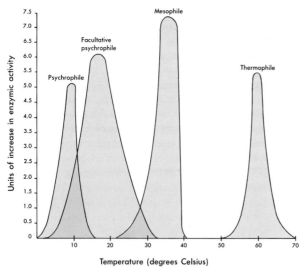

**Figure 5.6**    Relation between temperature and activity of a certain hydrolytic enzyme from different species of microorganisms. If obtained from species growing best in a cold environment (psychrophiles), the enzyme has its maximum activity at around 7° C. In species capable of growing over a wider range of low temperatures (facultative psychrophiles) it acts well over a wider range but has its maximum activity at around 20° C. In species preferring a middle range (mesophiles), the enzyme is most effective at around 37° C. Note that it is rather sharply limited above 37° C. In species growing only at temperatures above 50° C. (thermophiles) it has a rather narrow range with maximum at about 60° C.

like strong alkalis quickly destroy all types of proteins. Any substance or physical agent that destroys protein can act as a *disinfectant*. (See Chapter 21.) At temperatures below 75° C. (boiling point = 100° C.; human body temperature = 37° C.) each enzyme has an *optimal* temperature at which it functions best. This varies considerably with different enzymes and different organisms. Extreme limits range from about −2° C. to 70° C. Most cells thrive from about 20° C. to 40° C., their optimal range (Fig. 5.6). Temperatures below optimal are usually not destructive; they merely slow or inhibit enzyme action. Temperatures much above 75° C. destroy even the most resistant enzymes, except enzymes in bacterial endospores (Chapter 31). Specific temperatures in relation to species will be mentioned farther on.

In addition to being sensitive to deviations in temperature, enzymes are very sensitive to variations in pH or pOH. Different enzymes and different organisms have different requirements but, with a few striking exceptions, optima generally range from about pH 4.5 to pH 8.5 (Fig. 5.7). The optimal pH for most cells is near 7.0 (neutrality). Optimal temperatures and pH's for various species will be cited later. Some are very narrowly restricted.

Other factors of importance in enzyme functioning are hydrostatic and osmotic pressures and ultraviolet light and other radiations. Some enzymes in order to function require high concentrations of salt. Such factors will be discussed farther on (Chapter 19). In general, whatever affects enzymes also affects microorganisms, including the individual cells of our own bodies,

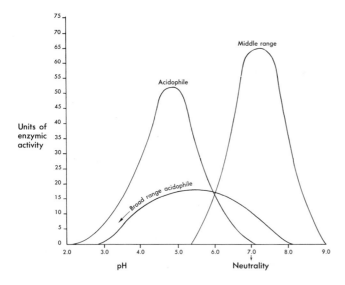

**Figure 5.7**    Relation between pH and activity of a certain type of proteolytic enzyme. In microorganisms that grow best in an acid medium (pH 5.5 to 4.5 or lower; acidophiles) the enzyme has maximum activity around pH 4.8. In certain species that grow best in a near-neutral or middle range of pH (mesophiles as to pH) it has its maximum activity at about pH 7.4. In species capable of growth over a broader range of pH its activity is not so sharply restricted by pH. Probably the enzyme differs chemically in the different species but has the same specific function in each.

since all of the normal activity of life depends on unhampered action of enzymes. The enzyme equipment of any cell is a major expression of its *genetic constitution* (DNA structure; Chapter 8).

**Enzyme Inhibitors.** In addition to chemicals that totally destroy all enzymes, there are many substances (disinfectants and sterilizing agents) that can combine chemically with certain particular enzymes or classes of enzymes, or with their coenzymes, and thus suppress their activity without destroying them or affecting others nearby. Some of these inhibitors combine with, or *attack,* the sulfhydryl group ($^-SH$) that occurs in most proteins, regardless of whether the protein is enzymic or not.

Other enzyme inhibitors are more specific in that they affect only certain particular coenzymes, or even certain parts of certain coenzymes. For example, each molecule of hemoglobin, an enzyme-like metalloprotein, contains an atom of iron that is the essential part of the prosthetic group heme. It is this atom that carries oxygen from the lungs to the tissues. The iron in hemoglobin can combine more readily with the deadly poisons carbon monoxide (CO) and cyanide (HCN) than it can with oxygen. The combining site of the iron in the hemoglobin, normally occupied by oxygen, is pre-empted by the poisons. The oxygen is thus excluded; it is said to be *antagonized.* In this state the hemoglobin can no longer function as an oxygen carrier. The animal so poisoned dies, essentially of anoxia. A parallel example is poisoning of cytochrome oxidase of bacteria by HCN, CO and azides ($Na \cdot CO \cdot N_3$). As shown in a foregoing paragraph, cytochrome is a hemelike oxygen carrier vitally important in many aerobic cells. In either case, hemoglobin or cytochrome, the iron of the prosthetic group is said to have been poisoned.

## 5.8  METABOLITE ANTAGONISM

Enzymes may be inhibited by certain nonmetabolizable substances whose molecular structure is like (or *analogous* to) that of a true, metabolizable substrate (*metabolite*). Such metabolite-like inhibitory agents are called *metabolite antagonists* or *metabolite analogs.* A metabolite analog or antagonist, because of its molecular structure, can pre-empt the specific combining site on a particular enzyme protein (or in its coenzyme) to the exclusion of the true metabolite. The enzyme or coenzyme is not necessarily destroyed, but it can then no longer function. The cell involved may soon die or may remain

for days or years in a state of suspended animation called *microbistasis.* It is a static microbe! The phenomenon is called *metabolite antagonism.* The metabolite antagonist is not acted upon by the enzyme but remains attached to it, a "monkey wrench in the machinery." The antagonist prevents further action of the enzyme.

For example, the dehydrogenase enzyme of lactic acid is inhibited by such compounds as hydroxy malonic acid and oxalic acid.

$$
\begin{array}{lll}
\mathrm{CH_3} & \mathrm{COOH} & \\
| & | & \\
\mathrm{HCOH} & \mathrm{HCOH} & \mathrm{O{=}C{-}OH} \\
| & | & | \\
\mathrm{COOH} & \mathrm{COOH} & \mathrm{O{=}C{-}OH}
\end{array}
$$

*Lactic acid*      *Hydroxy malonic acid*      *Oxalic acid*

These antagonize the lactic acid because they possess, in their structure, the combination

$$
\begin{array}{l}
| \\
\mathrm{{-}C{-}OH.} \\
| \\
\mathrm{COOH}
\end{array}
$$

Lactic acid is not antagonized by malonic acid or ethyl malonic acid:

$$
\begin{array}{ll}
\mathrm{COOH} & \mathrm{COOH} \\
| & | \\
\mathrm{CH_2} & \mathrm{HC{-}CH_3} \\
| & | \\
\mathrm{COOH} & \mathrm{COOH}
\end{array}
$$

*Malonic acid*           *Ethyl malonic acid*

These non-antagonists, while somewhat resembling lactic acid in structure, lack the specific molecular combination requisite for antagonistic attachment to the enzyme. They have instead

$$
\begin{array}{l}
| \\
\mathrm{{-}C{-}H.} \\
| \\
\mathrm{COOH}
\end{array}
$$

Be it noted, however, that oxalic and malonic acids are readily metabolized by some other organisms while lactic acid is not; the metabolite antagonist of one may be the food of another.

Metabolite antagonism is often reversible when there is an excess of the true metabolite. The antagonist and the true metabolite are said to compete for the specific combining site on the enzyme.

It is worth making a special note of these basic principles of metabolite antagonism and of enzyme inhibition by specific poisons because they underlie the action of numerous antimicrobial drugs such as sulfonamides and antibiotics.

## 5.9  CLASSIFICATION AND NOMENCLATURE OF ENZYMES

Early students of plant and animal physiology who discovered new enzymes often gave them descriptive names without consideration of any systematic scheme of nomenclature. Such names as *pepsin* (the protein-digesting enzyme of the stomach), *trypsin,* a proteolytic enzyme from the pancreas, and *ptyalin,* the starch-digesting enzyme in human saliva, are time-honored examples of the early method of naming enzymes. Later it became necessary to systematize nomenclature. It is now customary to name an enzyme by adding the suffix "ase" to the name of the substance acted upon (the substrate) or to the name of the activity of the enzyme. This simple scheme is used in the following outline, in which it can be seen that most enzymes can be gathered into four main groups on the basis of their overall functions—hydrolyzing, transferring, oxidizing and reducing, and adding and removing. The list contains only a few representative examples of each type of enzyme. Hundreds more are known; probably there are thousands yet to be discovered. Numerous enzymes are not readily classifiable, and the exact position and nomenclature of several in this listing are debatable.

A new system of nomenclature based on the reactions catalyzed was drawn up and published as "Enzyme Nomenclature" by the International Union of Biochemistry in 1965. Since this system has not had time to come into full use everywhere, we shall here use some older designations that are still in current use.

**Hydrolyzing Enzymes (Hydrolases).** The hydrolases catalyze reactions involving hydrolysis as shown in Table 5.1.

**Transferring Enzymes (Transferases).** The transferases catalyze transfer, from one molecule to another, of various groups that are not in the free state during the transfer (Table 5.2).

**Oxidizing and Reducing Enzymes (Oxidoreductases).** These enzymes catalyze the transfer of electrons, oxygen or hydrogen. They are basically electron transferases.

ELECTRON-TRANSFER OXIDASES (formerly aerobic dehydrogenases or oxidases).

(a) *Oxygen-obligative Oxidases.* These enzymes remove hydrogen atoms, and concomitantly their electrons ($H^+e^-$), from the substrate, thus oxidizing it (see Chapter 9). The hydrogen is transferred to an intermediate coenzyme or carrier and then to oxygen. These enzymes are restricted to systems using free oxygen as final acceptor for the substrate $H^+e^-$, hence are said to be oxygen-obligative.

$$O_2 + (4e^- + 4H^+) \longrightarrow 2H_2O.$$

(b) *Oxygen-facultative Oxidases* (or aerobic dehydrogenases). These enzymes remove substrate hydrogen like the foregoing but are not restricted to free oxygen as ($H^+e^-$) acceptor. The reduced carrier coenzyme can react with either free oxygen to form $H_2O_2$ or with other ($H^+e^-$) acceptors:

$$O_2 + (2e^- + 2H^+) \longrightarrow H_2O_2.$$

The $H_2O_2$ is commonly decomposed immediately by catalase (see Hydroperoxidases).

*Oxygenases* (or oxygen transferases). These enzymes catalyze transfer of free oxygen directly to the substrate: $O_2 + 2Subs \longrightarrow 2SubsO$. (Subs = substrate, commonly inorganic.)

*Hydroxylases* (or mixed-function oxidases). These catalyze a direct oxidation of the substrate with $\frac{1}{2}O_2$ instead of with $O_2$. Of a molecule of free oxygen ($O_2$), one atom is combined with an organic substrate while the other is reduced to $H_2O$ by a separate or "auxiliary" ($H^+e^-$) donor; commonly an adjacent reduced coenzyme (Coenz H):

$$Subs + \begin{cases} \frac{1}{2}O_2 \longrightarrow SubsO \\ \end{cases}$$
$$2CoenzH + \begin{cases} \frac{1}{2}O_2 \longrightarrow 2Coenz + H_2O \end{cases}$$

*Dehydrogenases* (or anaerobic dehydrogenases). Unlike oxidases, the coenzymes of neither dehydrogenases nor of the first carrier to which they transfer hydrogen can be directly reoxidized by free oxygen, hence the term anaerobic formerly used for these dehydrogenases. To be reoxidized these dehydrogenase coenzymes must pass the substrate ($H^+e^-$) to a second coenzyme

**TABLE 5.1   SOME HYDROLYZING ENZYMES**

| Substrate types | Substrates | Kind of linkage attacked |
|---|---|---|
| Carboxylesterases | Esters of carboxylic acids | Simple ester |
| Lipases | Fats (triglycerides) | Lipid ester |
| Phosphatases | Esters of phosphoric acid | Phosphate ester |
| "Nucleases" (phosphodiesterases) | Nucleic acids | Phosphate diester |
| Peptidases | Proteins, polypeptides | Peptide |
| Glycosidases | Polysaccharides, oligosaccharides | Glycosidic |

**TABLE 5.2   SOME TRANSFERRING ENZYMES**

| Types | Group transferred | Coenzyme |
|---|---|---|
| Transaminases | Amino ($^-NH_2$) | Pyridoxal phosphate |
| Transphosphorylases | Phosphate ($H_2PO_4^-$) | |
| Transpeptidases | Entire peptide units: | |
| | (peptide structure) | |
| Transglycosylases (formerly phosphorylases) | Entire glycosidic units: (glucose ring structure) | In synthetic processes, uridine diphosphate |
| Transacylases | Acetyl ($-C(=O)-CH_3$) or other acyl groups | CoA |

and, in some cells, to a series of others and to the cytochrome system (see Chapter 9).

In some bacteria (facultative anaerobes) the substrate ($H^+e^-$) may, in the absence of free oxygen (i.e., under anaerobic conditions), be combined with oxygen from some readily reduced substance like $NaNO_3$, $Na_2SO_4$ or $Na_2CO_3$ to form $NaNO_2$, $H_2S$ or $CH_4$. All the dehydrogenases can operate in the presence of free oxygen but they cannot use it as an ($H^+e^-$) acceptor.

In this connection differentiate carefully between bacteria whose dehydrogenases may act in the presence of free oxygen or in its total absence (i.e., under *strictly anaerobic* conditions; e.g., facultative bacteria) and bacteria that, while they may contain similar dehydrogenases, are *strictly anaerobic* in the sense that they are poisoned by free oxygen and die in its presence (see Chapter 32).

Dehydrogenases are divided on the basis of their coenzymes: *NADP-linked* are those linked to the cytochrome system by a pyridine nucleotide, nicotinamide-adenine-dinucleotide phosphate (NADP), and *FAD-linked* are those linked to the cytochrome system by a flavin coenzyme, flavin-adenine dinucleotide (FAD), or alloxazine adenine dinucleotide.

HYDROPEROXIDASES. As we have noted, oxygen-facultative, electron-transfer oxidases usually produce hydrogen peroxide as an end product. Many cells are very sensitive to hydrogen peroxide, including many medically and industrially important bacteria. Many peroxide-sensitive cells produce a hydroperoxidase called *catalase*, the coenzyme of which is a hemelike molecule. This decomposes $H_2O_2$ to oxygen and water:

$$2H_2O_2 \longrightarrow 2H_2O + O_2.$$

Catalase activity of human salivary gland cells is easily demonstrated by mixing a few drops of drug store hydrogen peroxide with saliva.

**Adding and Removing Enzymes.**   These enzymes do not catalyze hydrolysis, oxido-reduction or transfer of chemical groups from one molecule to another. Groups are *added* to molecules from the free state in the surrounding medium or *released from* molecules to the surrounding medium in the free state.

CARBOXYLASES.   These adding enzymes catalyze addition of $CO_2$ to organic acids to form carboxyl groups (require preliminary phosphorylation):

$$CH_3 \cdot CO \cdot COOH + CO_2 \longrightarrow$$

*Pyruvic acid*

$$COOH \cdot CH_2—CO \cdot COOH$$

*Oxalacetic acid*

NONOXIDATIVE DECARBOXYLASES.   These removing enzymes are divided into two groups:

(a) Those that catalyze removal of $CO_2$ from carboxyl groups of keto acids (coenzyme, thiamine pyrophosphate):

$$CH_3 \cdot CO \cdot COOH \longrightarrow CH_3CHO + CO_2$$

*Pyruvic acid*          *Acetaldehyde*

(b) Those that catalyze removal of $CO_2$ from carboxyl groups of amino acids (coenzyme, pyridoxal phosphate):

$$R—CHNH_2 \cdot COOH \longrightarrow$$
*any amino acid*

$$R—CH \cdot NH_2 + CO_2$$
*any amine*

HYDRASES AND DEHYDRASES. As their names imply, these enzymes catalyze addition of water to, or removal of water from:

$$COOH \cdot CH{=}CH \cdot COOH \overset{\longleftarrow}{\underset{\longrightarrow}{\pm H_2O}}$$
*Fumaric acid*

$$COOH \cdot CH_2 \cdot CHOH \cdot COOH$$
*Malic acid*

ISOMERASES. These enzymes catalyze isomerization by intramolecular rearrangements of $H^+$ and $^-OH$:

$$\text{Glucose-6-phosphate} \xrightarrow{\underset{\text{isomerase}}{\text{phospho-hexose}}}$$

Fructose-6-phosphate

In addition to the enzymes in the listing there are numerous others not readily classifiable. Among these are the permeases.

**Permease Enzymes.** Cell membranes are said to have a *selective permeability,* i.e., they are highly selective and discriminatory in regard to the substances that may pass through them, inward or outward. Selective permeability is related to molecular structure of both membrane and substance passing through it. Many of the seemingly great physiological differences between various species of cells exist merely because of differences between (1) the molecular structures of their cell membranes or (2) certain enzymes.

Passage of various substances through cell membranes may be accomplished by at least two mechanisms: passive transport and active transport.

PASSIVE TRANSPORT. The substance (or substrate), especially if it is an electrolyte or a relatively small molecule, may diffuse passively through the membrane (a) by diffusion (osmosis), (b) because of solubility in certain components, especially lipids, of the cell membrane or (c) because the substrate is in higher concentration outside the cell membrane than inside. The substrate tends to move with the concentration gradient, i.e., from higher to lower concentration. When the inner and outer concentrations are in equilibrium or when the inner concentration is physiologically ideal for that particular species of cell, inward diffusion either ceases or is balanced by equal outward diffusion. This solubility-diffusion type of mechanism is called *passive transport.* The ionic and solubility relationships are extremely complex.

ACTIVE TRANSPORT. Substrates may also be transported through cell membranes *counter* to concentration gradient. Since this requires added energy, the process is called *active transport.* Active transport may be accomplished by one or both of two systems: enzymic and nonenzymic.

*Enzymic System.* The substrates, including large molecules such as proteins that could not passively diffuse through the membrane, are transported through by the action of one or more enzymes or enzyme systems called *permeases.* The permeases, like other enzymes, are specific for the substrate involved, they are inducible and they are therefore genetically controlled. The exact mechanisms of permease action are still under investigation.

*Nonenzymic System.* Not all active transport is necessarily enzymic. For example, some seaweeds (e.g., kelp) concentrate such large quantities of iodine (as potassium iodide) from the minute quantities in sea water that these algae have served as valuable commercial sources of potassium and iodine. Presumably there is some active transport system that acts counter to concentration gradient, but it is not clear that any enzyme system could be specific for either potassium or iodine or potassium iodide. No enzyme has been demonstrated. Many organisms other than seaweeds similarly concentrate other elements or molecules, apparently by nonenzymic active transport.

## SUPPLEMENTARY READING

Atkinson, D. E.: Regulation of enzyme activity. Ann. Rev. Biochem., *35*:85, 1966.

Ayliffe, G. A. J.: Cephalosporinase and penicillinase activity of gram-negative bacteria. J. Gen. Microbiol., *40*:119, 1965.

Britten, R. J.: The concentration of small molecules within the microbial cell. Fifteenth Symposium, Function and Structure in Microorganisms, page 57. Soc. Gen. Microbiol., London. 1965.

Cantarow, A., and Schepartz, B.: Biochemistry, 4th edition. W. B. Saunders Co., Philadelphia. 1967.

Cohen, G. N.: Regulation of enzyme activity in microorganisms. Ann. Rev. Microbiol., *19*:105, 1965.

Commission of Editors of Biochemical Journals: Enzyme nomenclature. Science, *150*:719, 1965.

Commission on Enzymes of the International Union of

Biochemistry.: Classification and nomenclature of enzymes. Science, *137*:405, 1962.

Dunican, L. K., and Seeley, H. W. Jr.: Temperature-sensitive dextransucrase synthesis by a *Lactobacillus*. J. Bact., *86*:1079, 1963.

Harrow, B., and Mazur, A.: Textbook of Biochemistry, 9th edition. W. B. Saunders Co., Philadelphia. 1966.

Holter, H.: Passage of particles and macromolecules through cell membranes. Fifteenth Symposium, Function and Structure in Micro-organisms, p. 89. Soc. Gen. Microbiol., London. 1965.

Holmes, P. K., Dundas, I. E. D., and Halvorson, H. O.: Halophilic enzymes in cell-free extracts of *Halobacterium salinarium*. J. Bact., *90*:1159, 1965.

Lampen, J. O.: Secretion of enzymes by micro-organisms. Fifteenth Symposium, Function and Structure in Micro-organisms, page 115. Soc. Gen. Microbiol., London. 1965.

Langridge, P., and Morita, R. Y.: Thermolability of malic dehydrogenase from the obligate psychrophile *Vibrio marinus*. J. Bact., *92*:418, 1966.

Nord, F. F. (editor): Advances in Enzymology, Vol. 28. Interscience Publishers, New York. 1966.

Okada, H., and Halvorson, H. O.: Comparison of the active transport systems for α-thioethyl-D-glucopyranoside and maltose in *Saccharomyces cerevisiae*. J. Bact., *86*:966, 1963.

Pardee, A. B.: Response of enzyme synthesis and activity to environment. Eleventh Symposium, Microbial Reaction to Environment, page 19. Soc. Gen. Microbiol., London. 1961.

Shaw, C. R.: Electrophoretic variation in enzymes. Science, *149*:936, 1965.

Shugart, L., and Beck, R. W.: Occurrence and distribution of proteinase of *Streptococcus faecalis* var. *liquefaciens*. J. Bact., *92*:338, 1966.

Umbarger, H. E.: Intracellular regulatory mechanisms. Science, *145*:674, 1964.

Wagner, A. F., and Folkers, K.: Vitamins and Coenzymes. Interscience Publishers, New York. 1964.

Wilkerson, J. H.: Isoenzymes. Chapman and Hall, Publishers, London. 1966.

Williams, J., and Payne, W. J.: Enzymes induced in a bacterium by growth on sodium dodecyl sulfate. Appl. Microbiol., *12*:360, 1964.

# Chapter 6

## CHEMICAL BASIS OF MICROBIAL LIFE
### Atoms, Ions, Isotopes

The myriad different species of living cells, plant, animal, or protist, microbic or human, are obviously variations on a single basic theme —the cell theme. Some cells, like different makes of bicycles, have features not possessed by all, but all are obviously derived from the same fundamental pattern.

All cells, however they may differ in physical and physiological characteristics, are composed of essentially identical elements combined in similar or identical compounds which, with small modifications from species to species, constitute similar or homologous cellular structures. Chemical reactions of the same general (often identical) types underlie the processes by which foodstuffs are utilized in different species of cells as sources of energy and of cell substance. And, finally, it is now known that all of the variations in structure and physiology, including enzymic activities, that characterize different species can be ascribed to relatively small variations in the structure of certain complex molecular groups that are common to all cells; i.e., the heredity-determining nucleic acids. Thus virtually all of the phenomena of life may be explained in terms of molecular biology and referred ultimately to the molecular structure of nucleic acids: deoxyribonucleic acid (DNA) and ribonucleic acid (RNA).

## 6.1  STRUCTURE OF ATOMS

From the foregoing it is obvious that a knowledge of molecular structure is essential to a modern appreciation of biology, especially microbiology. Therefore we shall, for the convenience of the reader, recapitulate some basic concepts concerning atoms, molecules, their structure and their roles in the phenomenon that we call life. It is assumed that the reader has at least a speaking acquaintance with physics and chemistry.

Molecules, as the reader will doubtless remember, are made up of atoms. Each atom, in turn, consists of a heavy, central nucleus surrounded by one or more negatively charged, weightless particles called *electrons* that encircle the nucleus in various inner and outer orbits. Both nucleus and electrons are minute, yet the distance between them is so vast, relative to their sizes, that the spatial relationship of nucleus to orbiting electrons suggests the relationship of the sun to the orbiting planets.

The *atomic nucleus* consists of several kinds of particles, of which protons and neutrons are the most important in this discussion. Each *proton* has a positive electrical charge. *Neutrons* have no electrical charge; they represent a combined proton and electron. Each uncombined proton and each uncombined neutron is assigned an arbitrary weight of 1 unit. The electron weighs about $\frac{1}{1848}$ of this unit—not very heavy! Atoms of different substances have different numbers of protons and neutrons and of orbiting electrons (Fig. 6.1). It is these differences, and especially the differences in number and arrangement of the electrons, that create the differences between substances.

Under usual conditions the negative charges on the electrons of an atom are balanced by the positive charges of the protons in the

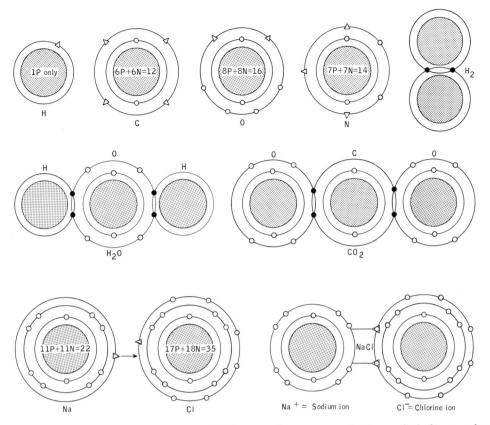

**Figure 6.1**   Diagrammatic structures of atoms of hydrogen, carbon, oxygen and nitrogen, the hydrogen molecule and the molecules of $H_2O$ and $CO_2$. In each diagram the atomic nucleus is shown as a relatively solid central portion with protons and neutrons surrounded by electrons in various shells and orbitals. Electrons indicated as open circles are *paired;* those shown as open triangles are not paired, i.e., they are *valence electrons;* those shown as closed circles are *shared*, i.e., in *covalent bonds.* NaCl is shown as an *ionic pair* held together by weak *electrovalent bonds* (——◁), the single valence electron of Na having been taken over by the seven-electron, unsaturated outer shell of Cl.

nucleus of that atom: i.e., the numbers of protons and of electrons are alike. Such atoms are electrically neutral. The number of electrons (or of protons, since their numbers are equal) in any given type of atom is called the *atomic number* of that atom. The number of protons plus the number of neutrons is the *atomic weight* of that atom. Atomic weight is a relative quantity. It is usually expressed as the number of times heavier a given atom is than an atom of some other substance taken as a standard. This is now commonly carbon (6 protons + 6 neutrons = at. wt. 12; 6 electrons = at. no. 6).

The hydrogen atom is unique in having in its nucleus only one proton; atomic weight = 1.00⁺. A single electron, spinning on its own axis like the earth, orbits the nucleus with extreme rapidity, always at nearly the same distance from the nucleus. The centrifugal force of this whirling motion might cause the electron

to fly off into space, were it not balanced by the constant attraction of the positively charged proton. So rapid is the motion and so strong and generalized is the influence of the electron around the proton that it forms a continuous spherical shell, or cloud, around the nucleus. The continuous zone of distribution of an electron around its nucleus is called a *shell* or *orbital.* Spherical orbitals are designated *s* orbitals; orbitals with patterns other than spherical (commonly figure-eight patterns) are called patterned or *p* orbitals. Depending on the element there may be one or several shells, the series of shells from within outward being designated by the letters *k* to *p.* Carbon, for example, has two shells, an inner or *k* shell containing two *paired* electrons in an *s* orbital close to the nucleus, and an outer or *l* shell with four electrons in modified (hybrid) *p* orbitals.

The six protons in the nucleus of the carbon atom balance the six electrons. The six electrons give it an atomic number of 6. The two electron shells give it a position in the periodic table of the elements in Period 2.

**The Periodic Table of the Elements.** This is a descriptive tabulation of all elements according to atomic structure. (See Table 6.1.) Arrangements vary, but in all tables the numbers of the *periods* (first column) represent the numbers of electron shells per atom. The *group* numbers represent numbers of electrons in the outermost shell. Of these outermost electrons all or, depending on patterns and arrangements of the orbitals, only certain outermost electrons can enter into the formation of compounds with other atoms. The outermost electrons available for the formation of bonds with other atoms or radicals are called *valence electrons* and their number is the valence number (*valence*) of that atom or element.

Elements with one, two or three electrons in the outermost shell (Groups I, II and III of the table) tend to become stabilized by giving these electrons up, elements with five, six or seven outermost electrons (Groups V, VI and VII) tend to achieve stability by accepting electrons. Thus the elements of Groups I, II or III have a tendency to combine in particular with elements of Groups V, VI or VII. The readiness of an element to lose or gain electrons is expressed as *activity*, and the degree of activity is dependent in great part on the distance of the electrons from the nucleus. In general, those changes in electronic structure which achieve greater stability tend to occur and usually release energy.

The outermost shells of elements in Group O are "saturated" with electrons; helium with two, the others with eight, the maximum for *any* outermost shell. This is a condition of complete stability; there is no tendency either to give up or to accept electrons. These are the *inert elements:* helium, neon, argon, krypton, xenon and radon. The transitional elements are subgroups of Periods 4, 5 and 6 and generally have two valence electrons, except Cu, Ag, Pt and Au, which have only one. The rare earth elements (lanthanide series, Period 6, and actinide series, Period 7) concern us but little in biology. Indeed, of over 100 known elements, only about 19 are of demonstrated importance in biology: Ca, *C*, Cl, Co, Cu, *H*, I, *Fe*, *Mg*, Mn, Mo, *N*, *O*, *P*, K, Na, Rb, *S*, Si. Those italicized are most abundant in living cells, although several of the others are absolutely essential in minute amounts. Some of those not listed may be essential, although present only in trace amounts.

**Valence and Compounds.**   It is clear that the numbers of outermost electrons and their positions in regard to the nucleus are of critical importance in regard to combinations of any element with other elements, i.e., in the formation of compounds. Electrons in the inner or *k* shell are generally very strongly held by the nucleus and, except for the hydrogen electron, are not involved in chemical reactions. Outer-shell structures are least stable because outer electrons are less strongly attracted to the nucleus. The strength of the attraction decreases in proportion to the distance of the electron from the nucleus; the outermost electrons are therefore more easily removed and the outermost shells are most readily added to. Although the outermost electrons of atoms are those farthest removed from the strong attraction of the nuclear protons and therefore most involved in combinations between atoms, as a general rule only those outer electrons that are *unpaired* tend to form bonds. For example, oxygen has six outer electrons and is therefore in Group VI of the periodic table; but only two of these six electrons are unpaired, giving oxygen a valence of 2. Similarly, nitrogen has five outer electrons but only three are unpaired. Nitrogen therefore has a valence of 3. Under some circumstances it may exhibit a valence of 4 or 5. Some other elements show this variation of valency.

In general, atoms tend to enter into combinations by which they can approach the stability that, for still obscure reasons, results from the presence of eight (four pairs) outer electrons. This is the structure of most inert elements of Group O. Hydrogen is an exception in that it has only one shell that requires only one more electron to saturate it. It then achieves the stability (and identity) of the inert helium atom with a pair of electrons. Because of its single electron, hydrogen is extremely active. It even reacts with itself to form $H_2$, a diatomic molecule. The halogens, nitrogen and oxygen also generally occur as diatomic molecules.

The capacity of each shell to contain electrons is limited, varying from the *k* shell (capacity two electrons) to the outermost shell (eight electrons). Intermediate shells may have up to 32 electrons. The outermost shell never contains more than eight electrons. A shell with eight electrons is a very stable structure and strongly resists alteration: i.e., it is an inert element (Group O).

Valence electrons cannot long be free or floating in the air, as it were; they tend to be attached to something else. For example carbon, with a valence of 4, cannot form such a com-

**TABLE 6.1 LONG FORM OF THE PERIODIC TABLE OF THE ELEMENTS\*†**

Transition Elements

| Period | IA | IIA | IIIB | IVB | VB | VIB | VIIB | VIII | | | IB | IIB | IIIA | IVA | VA | VIA | VIIA | O Inert Gases |
|---|---|---|---|---|---|---|---|---|---|---|---|---|---|---|---|---|---|---|
| 1 | 1 H 1.008 | | | | | | | | | | | | | | | | | 2 He 4.003 |
| 2 | 3 Li 6.939 | 4 Be 9.012 | | | | | | | | | | | 5 B 10.81 | 6 C 12.011 | 7 N 14.007 | 8 O 15.999 | 9 F 19.00 | 10 Ne 20.183 |
| 3 | 11 Na 22.990 | 12 Mg 24.31 | | | | | | | | | | | 13 Al 26.98 | 14 Si 28.086 | 15 P 30.974 | 16 S 32.064 | 17 Cl 35.453 | 18 Ar 39.948 |
| 4 | 19 K 39.102 | 20 Ca 40.08 | 21 Sc 44.956 | 22 Ti 47.90 | 23 V 50.94 | 24 Cr 51.996 | 25 Mn 54.94 | 26 Fe 55.85 | 27 Co 58.93 | 28 Ni 58.71 | 29 Cu 63.54 | 30 Zn 65.37 | 31 Ga 69.72 | 32 Ge 72.59 | 33 As 74.92 | 34 Se 78.96 | 35 Br 79.909 | 36 Kr 83.80 |
| 5 | 37 Rb 85.47 | 38 Sr 87.62 | 39 Y 88.91 | 40 Zr 91.22 | 41 Nb 92.91 | 42 Mo 95.94 | 43 Tc 99 | 44 Ru 101.07 | 45 Rh 102.91 | 46 Pd 106.4 | 47 Ag 107.870 | 48 Cd 112.40 | 49 In 114.82 | 50 Sn 118.69 | 51 Sb 121.75 | 52 Te 127.60 | 53 I 126.90 | 54 Xe 131.30 |
| 6 | 55 Cs 132.91 | 56 Ba 137.34 | 57-71 La-Lu Rare Earths | 72 Hf 178.49 | 73 Ta 180.95 | 74 W 183.85 | 75 Re 186.2 | 76 Os 190.2 | 77 Ir 192.2 | 78 Pt 195.09 | 79 Au 196.97 | 80 Hg 200.59 | 81 Tl 204.37 | 82 Pb 207.19 | 83 Bi 208.98 | 84 Po 210 | 85 At 210 | 86 Rn 222 |
| 7 | 87 Fr 223 | 88 Ra 226.05 | 89-103 Ac-Lw Actinides | | | | | | | | | | | | | | | |

| Rare Earths | 57 La 138.91 | 58 Ce 140.12 | 59 Pr 140.91 | 60 Nd 144.24 | 61 Pm 145 | 62 Sm 150.35 | 63 Eu 151.96 | 64 Gd 157.25 | 65 Tb 158.92 | 66 Dy 162.50 | 67 Ho 164.93 | 68 Er 167.26 | 69 Tm 168.93 | 70 Yb 173.04 | 71 Lu 174.97 |
|---|---|---|---|---|---|---|---|---|---|---|---|---|---|---|---|
| Actinides | 89 Ac 227 | 90 Th 232.04 | 91 Pa 231 | 92 U 238.03 | 93 Np 237 | 94 Pu 242 | 95 Am 243 | 96 Cm 247 | 97 Bk 249 | 98 Cf 251 | 99 Es 254 | 100 Fm 253 | 101 Md 256 | 102 No 253 | 103 Lw 257 |

\*From Routh, 20th Century Chemistry, 3rd ed., W. B. Saunders Co., 1963.

†Note that of all the elements only about 19 are of known significance in relation to microbiology. The darker shading indicates those elements that are of the most general importance as constituents of living cells, and the lighter shading those elements that are not so widely distributed among species or that occur in lesser amounts generally.

pound as CH as a distinct and stable compound because three of the carbon valences would be left free; the simplest stable compound of carbon with hydrogen is $CH_4$ or methane, the principal constituent of marsh and sewer gas.

Among the elements carbon, the basis of all organic compounds and therefore the key to life as we know it, is unique and most versatile. In the first place, carbon atoms are ambivalent, i.e., they can combine with positive or negative ions or groups simultaneously. They also have the rare property of combining with other carbon atoms. They thus can form almost indefinitely long chains of linked carbon atoms— straight, bent, branched or cyclic. This property is the basis of the large group of aliphatic compounds that underlie many structural parts of living cells. These will be mentioned later.

**Ionization.**   In Chapter 5 we mentioned some properties of aqueous suspensions of large molecules (e.g., proteins) or groups of molecules such as *colloids*. Colloids conduct relatively little electricity.

ELECTROLYTES.   Substances whose aqueous solutions readily conduct electricity are called *electrolytes*. If they are very active in this respect they are said to be strong electrolytes. Generally these are inorganic compounds: salts like sodium chloride, acids like sulfuric acid, bases like potassium hydroxide. Except carbon monoxide, carbon dioxide, carbonates and cyanides, *inorganic* compounds characteristically lack carbon, carbon-to-carbon or carbon-to-hydrogen bonds. These bonds are always found in *organic* compounds, which typically are *not* strong electrolytes.

Substances whose aqueous solutions do not readily conduct electricity are called *nonelectrolytes*. They are generally organic compounds. Organic colloids like protein and fat emulsions are virtually nonelectrolytes. Organic acids like citric (of lemons), acetic (of vinegar) and lactic (of sour milk) are weak electrolytes, that is, their aqueous solutions conduct electricity to a slight degree.

Electrolytes have several other properties that distinguish them from nonelectrolytes. Compared with nonelectrolytes, electrolytes markedly affect the colligative properties of water: i.e., they (a) lower the freezing point, (b) raise the boiling point, (c) increase the osmotic pressure and (d) lower the vapor pressure of their aqueous solutions.

DISSOCIATION.   Electrolytes are electrically conductive because their molecules in aqueous solutions split (*dissociate*) into positively and negatively charged particles called *ions*. They dissociate in this way because: (a) pure water

has a high dielectric constant; i.e., it has practically no conductance for electricity and (if pure!) is therefore a very good insulating material*; (b) water molecules are *polar* because in each molecule the oxygen has attracted the electrons of the hydrogen unequally, giving it unbalanced negativity. These seemingly unrelated facts are easily integrated as follows.

If an electrolyte, for example HCl, $(H^+Cl^-)$ is dissolved in water $\left(\begin{matrix} H^+ \\ {\phantom{H}} \\ H^+ \end{matrix}\!\!\!\searrow O^-\right)$ the positively charged hydrogen ion $(H^+)$ (a *cation*) attracts around itself swarms of water molecules, each with its negative pole (oxygen) nearest the $H^+$ (see Figure 6.2). In a like manner, on electrolytic dissociation the negatively charged chlorine ion $(Cl^-)$ (an *anion*) attracts other water molecules with their positive poles (hydrogen) nearest the $Cl^-$. The two ions ($H^+$ and $Cl^-$) are thus well insulated from each other by the dielectric action of the water molecules. The $H^+$ and $Cl^-$ move about freely in the water. If two oppositely charged, chemically inert electrodes from a battery (e.g., platinum electrodes) are immersed in the solution at opposite sides of the vessel, any cations in the solution migrate to the negative electrode (the *cathode*), accepting electrons therefrom; any anions in the solution migrate to the positive electrode (the *anode*), yielding electrons thereto and thus demonstrating the conductivity of the solution. Each pair of $H^+$ ions, accepting electrons, becomes a hydrogen molecule, and passes off in hydrogen bubbles at the cathode. Each pair of $Cl^-$ ions, yielding electrons, becomes a chlorine molecule, and passes off in bubbles at the anode: an example of *electrolysis*. Various other reactions may occur at the electrodes, depending on the electrolyte in solution, the nature of the electrodes, the solvent, the voltage applied and other factors. The water itself is concomitantly decomposed into $2H_2$ and $O_2$. If the forces of attraction between ions in aqueous solution are great enough to overcome the insulating effect of the water molecules, then those ions will combine or react together.

RADICALS (GROUPS).   A *radical* is a group of atoms held together by strong bonds but containing an excess (or deficiency) of electrons. The group commonly acts as an ion, the valence number of which depends on the net charge of the group; e.g., ammonium, valence $= +1$ $(NH_4^+)$; hydroxyl, valence $= -1$ $(OH^-)$; nitrate, valence $-1$ $(NO_3^-)$; sulfate, valence $-2$ $(SO_4^{--})$; phosphate, valence, $-3$ $(PO_4^{---})$.

---

*Actually it has a very slight though measurable conductance that is extremely important. See under pH.

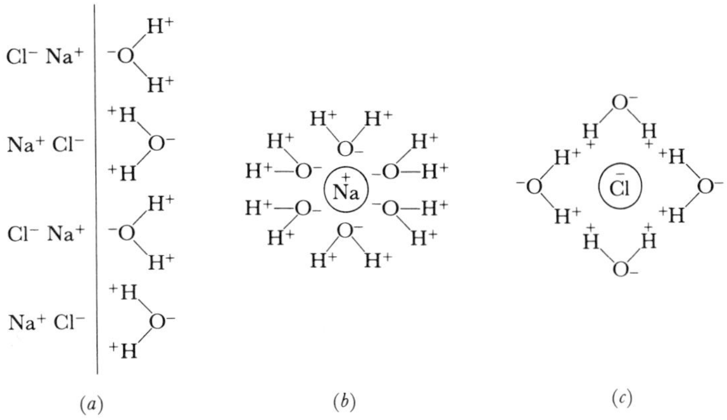

**Figure 6.2**   Dissociation of sodium chloride in water.

(a)                    (b)                    (c)

## HYDROGEN AND HYDROXYL IONS

Hydrogen and hydroxyl ions ($H^+$ and $OH^-$) are extremely important in biology because they are the constituents of water and the basis of the properties of acidity and alkalinity. These influence all aspects of cell life. Degree of *acidity* is commonly expressed as pH, with a number representing the concentration of hydrogen ions, since it is ionized hydrogen that determines the immediate acidic activity of any solution. *Alkalinity* of solutions may be expressed as concentration of hydroxyl ions (pOH) (not hydroxyl groups attached to C). However, since concentrations of hydrogen ions and of hydroxyl ions are reciprocally related, as will be shown, degrees of either are commonly given in terms of pH only.

**pH.**   Since H ions determine acidity, acids or alkalies may be strong or weak, depending on their degree of dissociation. This is always a fixed value for any given electrolyte and is generally expressed as the *dissociation constant.*

Strong acids are those which, when dissolved in water, dissociate largely into positively charged hydrogen ions and negatively charged ions. For example, sulfuric acid dissociates into two hydrogen ions and a sulfate ion. Weak acids like acetic or citric also dissociate, but to a lesser degree. The acidic activity of any acid solution depends upon the concentration of ions of hydrogen, and this is obviously dependent upon the ability of the acid to give them off into the solution or to dissociate. Thus, two acid solutions may be of the same concentration with respect to the total amounts of hydrogen available, yet have widely differing activities due to differences in the amount of active or ionized or dissociated hydrogen. Here we deal with a capacity effect, i.e., total available (dissociated plus undissociated) acid, as contrasted with an intensity or activity effect (dissociated acid or hydrogen ions alone).

As an example, let us compare acetic acid and hydrochloric acid. A liter of a normal solution of each contains exactly 1 gm. of total available hydrogen, yet the activity of the N/1 acetic acid is slight while that of the N/1 hydrochloric acid is great. Of the gram of available hydrogen in the acetic acid solution only 1.36 per cent is in an ionized state, so that there is, in the liter of solution, only 0.0136 gm. of hydrogen ions. The gram of hydrogen in the liter of N/1 HCl solution is 91.4 per cent ionized, giving 0.914 gm. of hydrogen ions per liter. The N/1 HCl, therefore, is about 67 times as active or "strong" as the N/1 acetic acid.

If one were to titrate the solutions, i.e., add N/1 NaOH solution until each became neutral, the total amount of alkali required would be the same in each case. This is due to the fact that, as the alkali combines with the hydrogen ions, more hydrogen ions take their place from the undissociated acid, which strives to maintain a constant hydrogen ion concentration consistent with its dissociation constant. Each acid finally gives up all its available hydrogen and, since each of the solutions by definition (N/1) contained exactly 1 gm. of available hydrogen to start with, each requires the same amount of alkali for its neutralization.

A measurement of hydrogen ion concentration differs from such a titration, in that the former determines the actual concentration of ionized hydrogen at the moment, without calling out any of the reserve, undissociated acid.

In acidimetry the term "normal" refers to the presence of 1 gm. of *total available* hydrogen per liter (dissociated* plus undissociated). By

---

*The concept of hydronium (hydrated hydrogen) ions ($H_3O^+$) in the dissociation of water, while indispensable in advanced studies, is omitted here to simplify discussion.

contrast, a solution normal only with respect to *ionized* hydrogen contains 1 gm. of hydrogen ions per liter. This implies the presence of 1 gm.-equivalent of a completely (100 per cent) dissociated acid; a N/10 solution would contain 0.1 gm.-equivalent of a completely dissociated acid, and so on. (See Table 6.2.)

As shown in Table 6.2, if we were to express hydrogen ion concentrations or normality in terms of grams of hydrogen ions per liter we should have to deal with long words and long rows of zeros; a confusing and laborious system of nomenclature. In 1909 Sorensen devised a simpler system based on the fact that water is itself a very weak electrolyte. As noted previously the extent of dissociation of any electrolyte is a physical constant (K) for that electrolyte under standard conditions. A liter of pure, neutral water at 20° C. always contains 0.0000001 gm. ($1 \times 10^{-7}$ moles) of $H^+$ and, reciprocally, since water is actually $H^+ + OH^-$, 0.0000001 gm. ($1 \times 10^{-7}$ moles) of $OH^-$. In Sorensen's system, the term "grams of hydrogen ions per liter" is replaced by the symbol pH, while the number of moles of $H^+$ per liter ($1 \times 10^{-7}$ in the neutral water under discussion) is expressed as the logarithm of the reciprocal of the fraction, i.e., the positive number 7. The reaction of neutral water, and of any neutral solution, is therefore expressed as pH 7.

Now the product of the concentration of $H^+$ and of $OH^-$ in neutral water is always $10^{-14}$ ($H^+ \times OH^- = K_w = 10^{-7} \times 10^{-7} = 10^{-14}$). Since the product of the two is always the same (i.e., since the two are reciprocally related), the term pH is commonly used to express either. For example, the pH of a solution containing 1 gm. of $H^+$ per liter (i.e., normal [N/l] with respect to hydrogen ions or 1 gm.-equivalent of a completely dissociated acid) is 0 ($\log 1 = 0$). Reciprocally, this is also pOH 14; the smallest fraction of a gram of $OH^-$ per liter possible on the Sorensen scale. Similarly, pH 6 implies pOH 8; pH 2 implies pOH 12, and so on.

Since the number representing pH is derived from a fraction, the larger the fraction the smaller the pH number. Therefore pH numbers between 7 and 0 represent increasing degrees of acidity, and numbers between 7 and 14, increasing degrees of alkalinity (see Table 6.2). Unless one is familiar with the numbers they can at first be misleading. For example, a change in pH from 7 to 6 represents a 10-fold increase in concentration of hydrogen ions since the 7 and 6 are logarithms; a change from pH 7.0 to 7.3 represents a 50 per cent decrease in the concentration of hydrogen ions ($\frac{1}{2} \times 10^{-7} = \log 2 + 7 = 0.3 + 7 = $ pH 7.3).

## 6.2 ISOTOPES

All atoms of a given element have the same number of electrons and the same number of protons to balance those electrons. Atoms thus remain electrically neutral. But not all atoms of a given element necessarily have the same number of neutrons; i.e., different atoms of a given element may have different numbers of neutrons and therefore different atomic weights. Such atoms are called *isotopes*.

**TABLE 6.2** RELATIONSHIPS OF HYDROGEN ION CONCENTRATIONS EXPRESSED IN VARIOUS WAYS

| Reaction | Fraction of Normality* | Hydrogen Ions per Liter (grams) | Logarithms of H Ion Concentrations | Expressed as pH |
|---|---|---|---|---|
| Acid | N/1 | 1.0 | − 0 | 0.0 |
| Acid | N/10 | 0.1 | − 1 | 1.0 |
| Acid | N/100 | 0.01 | − 2 | 2.0 |
| Acid | N/1,000 | 0.001 | − 3 | 3.0 |
| Acid | N/10,000 | 0.000,1 | − 4 | 4.0 |
| Acid | N/100,000 | 0.000,01 | − 5 | 5.0 |
| Acid | N/1,000,000 | 0.000,001 | − 6 | 6.0 |
| Neutral | Pure water | 0.000,000,1 | − 7 | 7.0 |
| Alkaline | N/1,000,000 | 0.000,000,01 | − 8 | 8.0 |
| Alkaline | N/100,000 | 0.000,000,001 | − 9 | 9.0 |
| Alkaline | N/10,000 | 0.000,000,000,1 | −10 | 10.0 |
| Alkaline | N/1,000 | 0.000,000,000,01 | −11 | 11.0 |
| Alkaline | N/100 | 0.000,000,000,001 | −12 | 12.0 |
| Alkaline | N/10 | 0.000,000,000,000,1 | −13 | 13.0 |
| Alkaline | N/1 | 0.000,000,000,000,01 | −14 | 14.0 |

*With respect to hydrogen or hydroxyl *ions*.

In any given sample of an element there is usually a mixture of isotopes. The international atomic weight of any element is listed as an average of the weights of all the various isotopes normally (commonly) present. For example, the weight of a single atom of normal (the most common isotope) chlorine is 35. But any considerable quantity of the element also contains about 25 per cent of heavy chlorine, $Cl^{37}$. The international atomic weight of chlorine as an element is therefore given as 35.457. Similarly, the atomic weight of normal hydrogen is 1 but the international atomic weight is 1.00814. Three isotopes of hydrogen are known: $H^1$, mass (at. wt.) 1.00814; deuterium ($H^2$), mass 2.01474; tritium ($H^{3*}$), mass 3.01701. Tritium is radioactive; it is so designated by the asterisk (*).

There are isotopes of nearly every element; not all are radioactive. Chlorine has two principal (most common) isotopes with atomic weights of 35 and 37. The atomic weight of an isotope is generally indicated by a superscript number ($Cl^{35}$, $Cl^{37}$). Lead has at least 16 isotopes, carbon five or six, and so on. In the periodic table all of the isotopes of an element are placed together, since the position of each element in the table depends only on the number of its *electrons* (at. no.), not its nuclear structure (at. wt.). Isotopes of an element are *chemically* similar since it is mainly the electrons that determine the chemical properties. However, since isotopes have different numbers of neutrons, they may differ markedly in *physical* properties because these are affected by their atomic weights. For example, of the four principal carbon isotopes $C^{11*}$, $C^{12}$, $C^{13}$, and $C^{14*}$ one ($C^{11*}$) is lighter and two are heavier ($C^{13}$ and $C^{14*}$) than the "normal" $C^{12}$ carbon atom. The radioactive isotopes may be detected by means of a Geiger counter.

**Radioactivity and Transmutations of Substance.** Radioactivity is the emanation of various atomic particles and rays (energy) from certain elements that have unstable atomic structures (e.g., isotopes). The emanations of radium (chiefly $Ra^{226*}$), for example, are: (1) alpha rays (particles) that are actually helium nuclei ($2P^{++}$ plus $2N^{00}$) traveling at about one fifth the speed of light; (2) beta rays or particles (actually streams of electrons) moving at nearly the speed of light; and (3) gamma rays. The last are nonparticulate radiant energy somewhat like hard (i.e., short and penetrating) X-rays. They move at the speed of light (186,000 mi./sec.). Radioactivity of isotopes is derived

from instability of their nuclei only, and is fully manifested and detectable with a Geiger counter whether the isotopes are free or combined in compounds.

Stability of an atomic nucleus is greatest when the numbers of protons and neutrons are equal; a ratio of 1:1. If too great a discrepancy exists in this ratio, in either direction, the nucleus is unstable and tends to adjust the ratio to greater stability by giving off energy in the form of various radioactive emanations.

Adjustments are made toward greater stability by alterations in structure of the nucleus such as transformation of neutrons into protons by splitting off electrons from the neutrons. For example, the unstable (radioactive) carbon isotope $_6C^{14}$, with 6 protons and 8 neutrons (a proton:neutron ratio of 3:4), loses an electron from one neutron and thus gains one proton, becoming the stable form of nitrogen ($_7N^{14}$) with 7 each of protons and neutrons. The electron escapes with its energy; a beta particle. Transmutation of one element into another has occurred.

Radioactive isotopes of a number of elements are commonly manufactured by shooting their nuclei with high-velocity atomic particles: neutrons, protons, alpha particles or gamma rays. For example, bombarding normal nitrogen atoms (at. wt. 14) with neutrons made to travel at extremely high speeds by means of an *accelerator* (*cyclotron* or *synchrotron*) splits the nitrogen nucleus, yielding radioactive heavy carbon ($C^{14*}$).

$C^{14*}$ is produced in considerable amounts in atomic bomb explosions. Because carbon enters into organic compounds, $C^{14*}$ eventually gains entrance into the cells and tissue of living human beings. As will be detailed later, radioactivity is an important cause of genetic mutations (altered inherited characteristics) and of cancer, hence isotopes in fallout are of intense interest not only to biologists but to everyone else.

Since the nuclei of radioactive isotopes constantly give off nuclear particles and energy, the nuclei eventually become altered: i.e., they decay. The element finally changes into another element of lower atomic number. For example, the nucleus of uranium (at. no. = 92; or $_{92}U^{238}$) becomes a thorium nucleus (at. no. = 90; i.e., $_{90}Th^{232}$) by losing an alpha particle; the radium nucleus (at. no. = 88) becomes a radon nucleus (at. no. = 86) in the same way.

When a beta particle is given off in radioactivity, a neutron (an electron combined with a proton) splits, permitting the electron to leave the decomposing nucleus. The neutron residue remains in the nucleus as a proton. The atomic number (number of orbital electrons) is thus increased and the element changes into another; for example, uranium (at. no. 92) becomes first neptunium (at. no. 93) and then plutonium (at. no. 94).

The emanation of gamma rays involves only loss of energy, which does not cause alteration in either atomic weight or number although it occurs during both alpha and beta radiations.

All of these nuclear modifications result in the transmutation of substances—the mysterious change that medieval alchemists, wholly ignorant of atomic structure or the true nature of matter, tried so long and so hard to achieve with the aid of abracadabra and other incantations in order to make gold from lead! Many an ambitious prince of bygone centuries subsidized a court alchemist who never in his life came nearer to the secret of "the philosopher's stone" than the causing of weird lights and horrible odors! Often, instead of gaining a fortune, he lost his head.

USES OF ISOTOPES.   Isotopes are of special interest to the biologist because he can use them to study many biological phenomena, such as determining exactly what a living cell does with any given element or compound that it takes in with its food; for example, carbon assimilation. By the use of carbon dioxide made with $C^{14*}$ ($C^{14*}O_2$) it has been shown that, in photosynthesis, carbon dioxide is not combined directly with any organic compound in the cell. It is first reduced by transfer of electrons of hydrogen split from water (Chapter 38). The carbon ($C^{14*}$) is then found in a number of compounds formed during the synthetic process: e.g., phosphoglyceric acid:

$$C^{14}O_2 \xrightarrow[\text{synthesis}]{\text{Photo-}} \begin{array}{c} H_2C-O-PO_3H_2 \\ | \\ HC-OH \\ | \\ C^{14}OOH \end{array}$$

*3-Phosphoglyceric acid*

If $H_2O^{18}$ is provided in photosynthesis, all of the free oxygen given off is $O_2{}^{18}$. No $O^{18}$ is found in the synthesized products. In many species of chemosynthetic bacteria carbon dioxide combines directly with already formed organic molecules. For example, Werkman, Wood, and their colleagues have "fed" carbon dioxide made with $C^{14*}$ to propionic acid bacteria. The radioactive carbon can be followed, like a tracer bullet, through its course in the synthetic processes of the bacterial cell. For each molecule of $C^{14*}$ one molecule of succinic acid or propionic acid is formed, probably from pyruvic acid via oxalacetic acid, or from glycerol:

$$\begin{array}{c} H_2COH \\ | \\ HCOH \\ | \\ H_2COH \end{array} + C^{14}O_2 \rightleftharpoons \begin{array}{c} COOH \\ | \\ CH_2 \\ | \\ CH_2 \\ | \\ C^{14}OOH \end{array} + H_2O$$

*Glycerol*                   *Succinic acid*

A common soil saprophyte, *Aerobacter indologenes,* produces acetic, lactic and succinic acids as waste products of glucose utilization. When $C^{14*}O_2$ is added, $C^{14*}$ is found in these acids. *Proteus vulgaris,* another common saprophyte of soil and water, produces lactic and succinic acids. The $C^{14*}O_2$ is found mainly in the carboxyl group of the acids. The pathway to the formation of these acids is via pyruvic acid according to the *Wood-Werkman reaction:*

$$\begin{array}{c} CH_3 \\ | \\ C=O \\ | \\ COOH \end{array} + C^{14}O_2 \rightleftharpoons \begin{array}{c} C^{14}OOH \\ | \\ CH_2 \\ | \\ C=O \\ | \\ COOH \end{array}$$

*Pyruvic acid*              *Oxalacetic acid*

## SUPPLEMENTARY READING

(See Supplementary Reading at end of Chapter 8.)

# Chapter 7

# CHEMICAL BASIS
# OF MICROBIAL LIFE
## Structure of Compounds

Compounds are substances consisting of atoms of two or more different elements in fixed proportions and steric relations, held together by chemical bonds. Molecules may be combinations of atoms of the same element (e.g., $H_2$, $Cl_2$, $O_2$) or of different elements (e.g., $CH_4$). A molecule is that minimal amount of a substance which, if further subdivided, ceases to be that substance.

## 7.1 CHEMICAL BONDS IN COMPOUNDS

The manner in which atoms are bonded together is of critical importance in all biochemical reactions. Three kinds of bond may be briefly considered here: electrovalent, covalent and hydrogen.

**Inorganic Compounds: Electrovalence.** An electrovalent bond is formed by the *transfer* (not sharing) of one or more electrons from the outer shell of one element, say sodium, to another, say chlorine. Sodium (periodic table Group I) has a single ("extra") outer electron; it lacks seven of the eight electrons needed for stability of the outer shell. Chlorine (periodic table Group VII) has seven outermost electrons; its outermost shell is one electron short of complete stability. Each atom would gain greater stability by combining with the other. The sodium tends to give up its single electron; the chlorine tends to saturate its outer electron shell by accepting the electron. Each becomes ionized thereby. The two ions therefore combine, the sodium transferring its electron to the chlorine, to form sodium chloride (NaCl), common table salt. The bond holding the two ions together is electrostatic and is therefore called an *electrovalent* or *ionic bond.* Such bonds are not very strong. Electrovalent bonds are typical of *inorganic* compounds. Since electrovalence results in aggregations of ions, the compounds thus formed are actually *ion aggregates,* not true molecules. However, the term molecule is commonly used for them. Unlike "true" molecules (see covalence) ions held together by electrovalence are readily separated; i.e., such compounds readily ionize or dissociate in aqueous solutions.

**Organic Compounds: Covalence.** By *covalence* is meant the merging or linking together by *sharing* unpaired outermost electrons of two atoms so that the shared electrons are attracted by each nucleus. *Paired* inner electrons such as the two in the *k* (inner) shell of carbon are very strongly held by the nucleus and are not shared. It is the *unpaired* outer (valence) electrons that tend to be shared; unpaired electrons seek "mates." In the carbon atom there are four unpaired outer (valence) electrons; in hydrogen, one; in nitrogen, three; in oxygen, two. When electron pairs are shared (not transferred), the shared electrons are strongly held by each nucleus. Each pair of shared electrons is called a *covalent bond* or *electron-pair bond:* a strong and stable type of bond. Covalent bonds are most common in organic compounds. If two or three pairs of electrons are shared between two atoms, double and triple covalent bonds, respectively, are formed (see previous discussion of carbon). Instead of being stronger, however, double and triple bonds are progressively less stable.

ANHYDRO BONDS. Among the most important covalent bonds are those formed by the removal of the elements of water from two adjacent molecules: a hydrogen ion from one, a hydroxyl ion from the other. The two ions combine to form water. The residues of the two altered molecules combine by what is sometimes called an *anhydro bond,* a type of covalent bond. The process is sometimes called *anhydrosynthesis.* For example:

$$H_3C-\overset{H_2}{C}-O\boxed{H \ + \ HO}-\overset{O}{C}-CH_3 \rightleftharpoons$$

*Ethyl alcohol*         *Acetic acid*

$$CH_3\overset{H_2}{C}-O-\underset{\uparrow}{\overset{O}{C}}-CH_3$$

Ester bond
(an anhydro bond);

*Ethyl acetate*

Anhydro bonds are extremely important in the process of *polymerization,* the mechanism by which complex *macromolecules* (proteins, polysaccharides, nucleic acids) containing thousands of smaller subunits (e.g., glucose, amino acids, nucleotides), are put together by living cells. Anhydro bonds are important also because they can be readily made or disconnected by enzymic action. Anhydrosynthesis, polymers and their functions in living cells are more fully discussed farther on.

Some common and important anhydro bonds that will be mentioned again are here illustrated:

*Ester Bonds:* Between the carboxyl $(R-\overset{O}{C}-OH)$ group of an organic acid and the hydroxyl group $(R-OH)$ of an alcohol, forming an ester (organic salt). These bonds occur in fats, oils and waxes and related compounds:

$$R^*-\overset{O}{C}-\boxed{OH \ + \ H}O-\overset{H_2}{C}-R \rightleftharpoons$$

$$R-\overset{O}{C}-O-\underset{\uparrow}{\overset{H_2}{C}}-R$$

*Ester bond*

*Phosphate-ester Bonds:* Between phosphoric acid and a hydroxyl group of a sugar, forming a phosphorylated sugar: these bonds are important in polymerization and the storage and transfer of energy in the cell:

$$R-\overset{H_2}{C}-\boxed{OH \ + \ H}O\cdot P\cdot O_3H_2 \rightleftharpoons$$

$$R-\overset{H_2}{C}-\underset{\uparrow}{O}\cdot P\cdot O_3H_2$$

*Phosphate ester bond*

*Thioester Bonds:* Between the carboxyl group of an organic acid and a sulfhydryl ($^-SH$) group in a sulfhydryl-containing compound; important in the storage and transfer of energy in the cell:

$$R-\overset{O}{C}-\boxed{OH \ + \ H}S-R \rightleftharpoons R-\overset{O}{\underset{\uparrow}{C}}-S-R$$

*Thioester bond*

*Peptide Bonds:* Between the carboxyl group of one amino acid and the amino $(R-NH_2)$ group of another, forming peptides, polypeptides and proteins; basic to the synthesis of living matter:

$$R-\overset{O}{C}-\boxed{OH \ + \ H}-\overset{H}{N}-R \rightleftharpoons$$

$$R-\overset{O}{C}-\underset{\uparrow}{\overset{H}{N}}-R$$

*Peptide bond*

*Glycoside Bonds:* Between hydroxyl or related groups in simple sugar molecules (e.g., glucose) to form various disaccharides, and polysaccharides (polymers) like starch and cellulose. The glycoside bond is basic to the synthesis of many structural materials and energy-storing compounds in the cell:

*Glycoside bond* (intersaccharidic)

---

*R symbolizes any *R*adical to which the particular group mentioned (e.g., carboxyl or hydroxyl) is attached. R may range in complexity from $CH_3$ to an enormously complicated structure.

Note that all five reactions are indicated as being reversible. This is because most enzymic reactions are reversible unless too much energy is released by the reaction in one direction (see Chapters 5 and 9).

HYDROLYSIS.   When the anhydrosynthetic process is reversed, the elements of water are reinstated and the constituent residues or subunits are separated and released in their original form. This process, called *hydrolysis,* is exceedingly important in biology because it is the basic reaction of virtually all processes of digestion of proteins, fats, polysaccharides (e.g., starches) and many other compounds with anhydro bonds.

**Hydrogen Bonds.**   As previously noted, hydrogen is unique in having only one electron, one proton and no neutron. The single proton exerts a strong, electrostatic, attractive force that extends beyond its single electron. Hydrogen therefore tends to exert an unbalanced electropositive effect in certain molecules or groups containing it. Such molecules or groups tend to be polarized. Strongly polarized groups or molecules (dipoles), like magnets, attract other polarized groups or molecules. When sufficiently strong the attraction results in the formation of a hydrogen bond through the sharing of a hydrogen atom (not an electron) between adjacent polarized groups or molecules; especially those containing oxygen or nitrogen in polarized groupings. For example, water molecules as well as ammonia molecules, all polarized groupings, become *associated* through hydrogen bonding:

$$+\diagdown \atop + \diagup \; H_2O^- \cdots \qquad +\diagdown \atop + \diagup \; H_2O^- \cdots \qquad +\diagdown \atop + \diagup \; H_2O^- \cdots$$

$$+\diagdown \atop + \diagup \; {-}H_3N^- \cdots \qquad +{-}\diagdown \atop + \diagup \; H_3N^- \cdots \qquad +{-}\diagdown \atop + \diagup \; H_3N^- \cdots$$

Similarly, ammonia and hydrogen chloride form ammonium chloride through hydrogen bonding:

$$+{-}\diagdown \atop + \diagup \; H_3N^- + \; +HCl \longrightarrow \; +{-}\diagdown \atop + \diagup \; H_3N^-$$

$$\cdots +HCl^- \text{ or } NH_4Cl.$$

(In the above diagrams hydrogen bonds are indicated by ·····) In many combinations the proton of hydrogen is actually transferred to the other atom and the bonds are called proton bonds. As will appear, hydrogen bonds, although

relatively weak, are essential in the phenomenon of inheritance and the reproduction of living cells. This is because they help to support the structure of genes (DNA) (Chapter 8).

## 7.2   STRUCTURE OF ORGANIC MOLECULES

Most of the organic molecules or compounds found in living cells are more or less complex derivatives of one large family of compounds, the alkanes or saturated hydrocarbons (hydrogen + carbon). These are the basis of the great series of *aliphatic* (Gr. *aleiphatos* = from fats or oils, e.g., petroleum or hydrocarbon) compounds. The simplest saturated hydrocarbon is methane ($CH_4$), principal constituent of marsh and sewer gas. It is said to be saturated because all of its four valences are linked to hydrogen atoms. Hydrogen-carbon and carbon-carbon bonds are characteristic of organic compounds and are rare in inorganic compounds. Except methane, saturated hydrocarbons are straight chains of from two to scores of carbon atoms linked together by covalent bonds, each with its remaining valences saturated by a hydrogen atom:

$$H{-}\underset{\underset{H}{|}}{\overset{\overset{H}{|}}{C}}{-}\underset{\underset{H}{|}}{\overset{\overset{H}{|}}{C}}{-}\underset{\underset{H}{|}}{\overset{\overset{H}{|}}{C}}{-}\underset{\underset{H}{|}}{\overset{\overset{H}{|}}{C}}{-}\underset{\underset{H}{|}}{\overset{\overset{H}{|}}{C}}{-}\underset{\underset{H}{|}}{\overset{\overset{H}{|}}{C}}{-}H = \quad Hexane = C_6H_{14}$$

Compounds with this type of structure are termed *normal* hydrocarbons. They have the general formula $C_nH_{2n+2}$.

Simple modifications of this form are seen in branched chains or *isomers* (Gr. *isos* = like; *meros* = part):

$$H{-}\underset{\underset{H}{|}}{\overset{\overset{H}{|}}{C}}{-}\underset{\underset{\underset{\underset{H}{|}}{H{-}C{-}H}}{|}}{\overset{\overset{H}{|}}{C}}{-}\underset{\underset{H}{|}}{\overset{\overset{H}{|}}{C}}{-}\underset{\underset{H}{|}}{\overset{\overset{H}{|}}{C}}{-}\underset{\underset{H}{|}}{\overset{\overset{H}{|}}{C}}{-}H = \quad Isohexane = C_6H_{14}$$

Isomers are compounds having the same empirical formula but different chemical or physical properties. Saturated hydrocarbon isomers also have the general formula $C_nH_{2n+2}$.

A second modification of the straight chain is the cyclic form in which the two ends of a chain are joined covalently:

$$H_2C \underset{\underset{C}{\overset{}{\underset{H_2}{|}}}}{\overset{\overset{H_2}{\overset{C}{|}}}{\cdots}} CH_2 = \textit{Cyclohexane} = C_6H_{12}$$

Two of the hydrogens are not needed in such molecules, and thus the general formula of the cyclic form is $C_nH_{2n}$. This molecule is suggestive of the six-sided ring compound, benzene:

$$= \textit{Benzene} = C_6H_6$$

Benzene, however, is the basis of the enormous family of *aromatic* compounds, e.g., phenols. For convenience, benzene may be thought of as resembling cyclohexane in form but unsaturated, with three double bonds alternating with single bonds between the carbon atoms. Double and triple bonds between carbon atoms are also found in many hydrocarbons. Such hydrocarbons are said to be *unsaturated*. The double and triple bonds are increasingly unstable and easily broken. Hydrogen atoms of hydrocarbons may be replaced with hydrogen, hydroxyl, or with halogens: i.e., *substitution compounds*.

**Functional Groups.** The organic compounds that occur in protoplasm generally contain certain groups of atoms that are always linked together and are attached as a group, by covalent bonds, to the molecule of which they are a part. Such groups function as distinct entities. They are spoken of as radicals or functional groups, and they have an electric charge, positive or negative. Their charge is derived from the fact that when the covalent bonds that hold such a group to its molecule are broken, paired, shared electrons are separated. Both the molecular residue and the separated group then have unshared and unpaired electrons and are "free" radicals or ions. These, like electrons, under normal conditions exist free only theoretically or under special conditions. They tend to combine immediately with something else. The combining valence of a group, radical or ion, depends on the net charge of the group. Examples from inorganic chemistry are the ammonium "radical" ($^+NH_4$), valence 1; the sulfate radical ($^=SO_4$), valence 2; the phosphate radical ($^{\equiv}PO_4$), valence 3. A free organic radical would be the methyl group: $^-CH_3$.

In organic chemistry different substances often have similar chemical potentialities because they contain the same functional groups. For example, glucose, a sugar, has at one end of the molecule a *hydroxyl* ($^-OH$) group, an arrangement that is characteristic of alcohols or organic *bases:*

$$CH_3-\overset{\overset{H_2}{\|}}{C}-OH$$
*Ethyl alcohol*

At the other end is a carbonyl ($=C=O$) group, an arrangement that is distinctive of *aldehydes:*

$$CH_3-\overset{\overset{H}{|}}{C}=O$$
*Acetaldehyde*

Glucose therefore, with its curious structure, has the combining properties both of an alcohol and of an aldehyde because its molecule contains those functional groups. Glucose is sometimes called an *aldose* (aldehyde-sugar). In a glucose isomer, fructose (fruit sugar), the carbonyl oxygen is attached to a carbon atom *within* the carbon chain rather than at the end of it:

| | | |
|---|---|---|
| 1 | $C=O$ (H) | $H_2COH$ |
| 2 | $HCOH$ | $C=O$ |
| 3 | $HOCH$ | $HOCH$ |
| 4 | $HCOH$ | $HCOH$ |
| 5 | $HCOH$ | $HCOH$ |
| 6 | $H_2COH$ | $H_2COH$ |
| | D-*Glucose* | D-*Fructose* |

When arranged in this way the group is called a *keto group* ($R-\overset{\overset{O}{\|}}{C}-R$), and sugars containing it are called ketoses. Note that the carbon atoms in the glucose chain are numbered, for reference, from 1 through 6.

If we oxidize the aldehyde group of glucose it changes to the carboxyl group ($R\overset{\overset{O}{\diagup\!\!\diagup}}{C}-OH$). This is characteristic of all organic acids. These ionize to yield a hydrogen ion. By thus replacing the aldehyde group in glucose with the carboxyl group we form the *monocarboxylic sugar acid,* gluconic acid. If we also oxidize the alcoholic group at the other end of the glucose molecule we form a *dicarboxylic sugar acid* (a saccharic or glycaric acid).

Any basic alcoholic hydroxyl group usually reacts readily with any acidic carboxyl group to form an ester or organic salt, plus water. The formation of an ester is analogous to the reaction between the hydroxyl ion of an alkali (e.g., $Na^+OH^-$) and the hydrogen ion of an acid (e.g., $H^+Cl^-$) to form the salt, NaCl, and $H_2O$. Although alcoholic $^-OH$ generally acts as a group

and acidic $R-\overset{\overset{O}{\|}}{C}-OH$ generally ionizes to give $H^+$ as above, in forming an ester it is the hydroxyl (not the H ion) of the $-\overset{\overset{O}{\|}}{C}-OH$ group that combines with the alcoholic hydrogen:

$$CH_3 \cdot \overset{\overset{O}{\|}}{C} - \boxed{OH + H}O - CH_2 \cdot CH_3 \longrightarrow$$

$$CH_3 \cdot \overset{\overset{O}{\|}}{C} - O - CH_2 \cdot CH_3 + H_2O$$

This illustrates a difference between the organic hydroxyl group and the inorganic hydroxyl ion. It also illustrates the principle that the way an atom or group acts depends to a great extent on what other atoms it is combined with.

Using the glucose molecule again as our model, we may replace the hydroxyl group of carbon atom 2 with an amino group ($^-NH_2$), producing *glucosamine:*

*Glucosamine*

D-*Glucose*
(Haworth cyclic formula)*

D-*Glucose*
(cyclic form; see above)

This is an *amino sugar* and is found in the polysaccharide *chitin,* the rigid, structural sub-

stance in the skeletons of insects and Crustacea and in the cell walls of fungi, protozoa and some other protists. The large chemical family of amines, of which glucosamine is only one example, may be thought of as ammonia molecules ($NH_3$) with one or more of the hydrogen atoms replaced by organic groups (e.g., methyl amine: $H_3C-NH_2$). The *amino group* ($^-NH_2$) is the ammonia residue. If the amino group is attached to the alpha carbon atom* of a carboxylic acid, such as propionic acid, we have

an *alpha amino acid, alanine:* $CH_3\overset{\overset{NH_2}{|}}{C}HCOOH$. In alanine and, indeed, in all of the amino acids that occur in protoplasm, the amino group is attached to the *alpha carbon atom,* i.e., next to the carboxyl carbon. Thus the general formula for amino acids that occur in nature is $R-\overset{\overset{NH_2}{|}}{C}H \cdot COOH$. The R may be very simple or very complex and may contain additional amino and carboxylic groups and cyclic and other groups. The amino group is basic and, with the acidic carboxyl group, makes amino acids *amphoteric* (able to react with acids or bases).

Since all amino acids have at least one basic amino group and at least one acidic carboxylic group, they can form bonds between the acidic and basic groups of adjacent amino acid molecules, producing long chains or polymers called *polypeptides,* the basis of protein structure. The bonds between the amino groups and the carboxylic groups are called peptide bonds (see Anhydro Bonds).

Other molecules with both acidic and basic groups may react similarly. For example, the molecules of a fatty acid like beta-hydroxybutyric acid ($\beta$-hba), having acidic carboxyl groups and basic hydroxyl groups, can join, forming ester bonds between the carboxylic and hydroxyl groups of adjacent molecules. Long chains of the polymer, poly-$\beta$-hba, are formed:

$$\underset{\beta\text{-}hydroxybutyric\ acid}{\overset{\overset{CH_3}{|}}{HOCH} \cdot CH_2 \cdot \overset{\overset{O}{\|}}{C} - \boxed{OH \pm H}\overset{\overset{H_2O}{\|}}{O}\overset{\overset{CH_3}{|}}{C} \cdot CH_2 \cdot \overset{\overset{O}{\|}}{C} - OH} \longrightarrow$$

$$\underset{poly\text{-}\beta\text{-}hydroxybutyric\ acid}{\overset{\overset{CH_3}{|}}{HOCH} \cdot CH_2 \cdot \overset{\overset{O}{\|}}{C} \cdot O \cdot \overset{\overset{CH_3}{|}}{C} \cdot CH_2 \cdot \overset{\overset{O}{\|}}{C} - OH}$$

---

*The straight-chain formula of the aldose is bent, as shown by long, outer, circular arrow, into a closed hexagon by bringing the $^-OH$ group of carbon atom 5 into combination with the aldehyde group of carbon number 1 (shorter arrow):

---

*First carbon atom in the chain after the carboxyl carbon atom.

Another important functional group in protoplasmic substances is the sulfhydryl or mercapto group (⁻SH). It may be thought of as analogous to a hydroxyl group in which the oxygen has been replaced by sulfur. The ⁻SH group is found in the amino acids cystine, cysteine and methionine, all of which are extremely important in the formation of enzymes and other essential structures in the cell. Other important functional groups will be mentioned in the appropriate place.

## SUPPLEMENTARY READING

(See Supplementary Reading at end of Chapter 8.)

# Chapter 8

## CHEMICAL BASIS OF MICROBIAL LIFE

## Macromolecules

### 8.1 POLYMERS

As mentioned elsewhere, most of the essential substances of living cells are built up of macromolecules. These are made of smaller molecules that are combined into macromolecules mainly by the process of anhydrosynthesis or *polymerization* (Gr. *polys* = many; *meros* = parts). By polymerization is meant the formation of compounds of high molecular weight by the combination of many small molecules that have identical or similar structures and functional groups that permit interlinkages. Each of the small molecules entering into any polymerization is called a *monomer* (Gr. *monos* = single). When two such molecules are joined chemically the result is a *dimer;* when three are joined they constitute a *trimer.* A combination of more than three molecules in this way is called a *polymer*—a macromolecule. Polymerization is one of the commonest synthetic reactions occurring in living cells, and living cells consist largely of various kinds of polymers. If all of the units in a polymer are identical the polymer is called a *homopolymer* (Gr. *homos* = the same). Examples of homopolymers are starch, made of α-glucose units, and cellulose, made of β-glucose units—two very different substances, both made up of glucose isomers that differ slightly (Fig. 8.1). If the units in a polymer are related but not identical substances, for example the various amino acids in proteins (see Protein Synthesis, this chapter), the substance is said to be a *heteropolymer* (Gr. *hetero* = different). This illustrates the important point that in any given polymer all the *linkages* between the units are identical, though the *units* may be very different (as in a heteropolymer) provided they have the appropriate functional groups to form the linkage characteristic of that kind of polymer, e.g., polysaccharide or polypeptide.

**Polymerization.** There are two general types of polymerization: (a) *addition polymerization* or *polymerization by association* and (b) *anhydro polymerization* or *polymerization by condensation.*

ADDITION POLYMERIZATION. Addition polymerization commonly occurs spontaneously or under the activating (catalytic) action of oxygen or a few ions of hydrogen or hydroxyl or some metal. Addition polymerization is one of

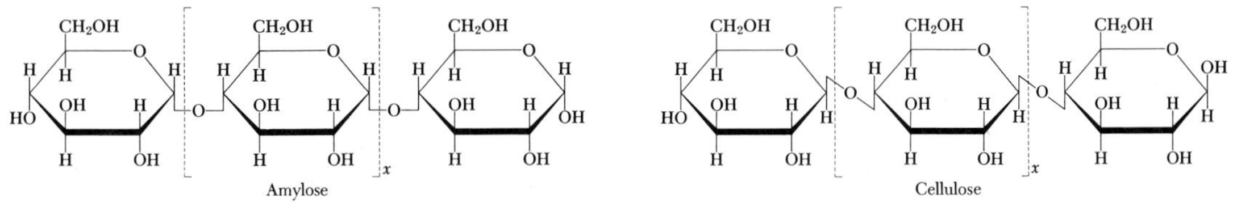

**Figure 8.1** Starch and cellulose formulas, showing marked similarities.

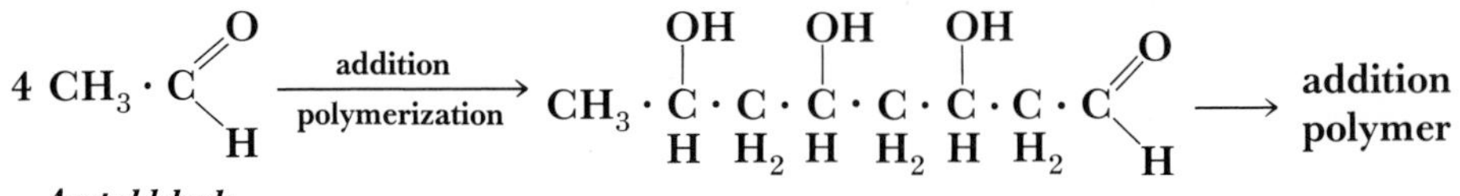

**Figure 8.2**   In addition polymerization, molecules of acetaldehyde link together to form long polymers.

the important processes in chemical evolution (Chapter 1). Nothing is added to or removed from any one of the combining monomers. Thus, the empirical formula of an addition polymer (if a homopolymer) is theoretically a multiple of the empirical formula of the monomer; actually, the terminal groups may differ slightly.

A simple example of addition polymerization is *aldol addition* or aldol condensation. (Do not confuse aldol condensation with condensation polymerization, which is here called *anhydro* polymerization to avoid confusion.) Molecules of aldehydes like formaldehyde and acetaldehyde (with alpha hydrogens), in the presence of $H^+$ or $^-OH$, can link together to form dimers, trimers and long polymers with high molecular weights (Fig. 8.2). By addition polymerization, formaldehyde forms solid *paraformaldehyde;* molecules of acetaldehyde may polymerize to form cyclic *metaldehyde:*

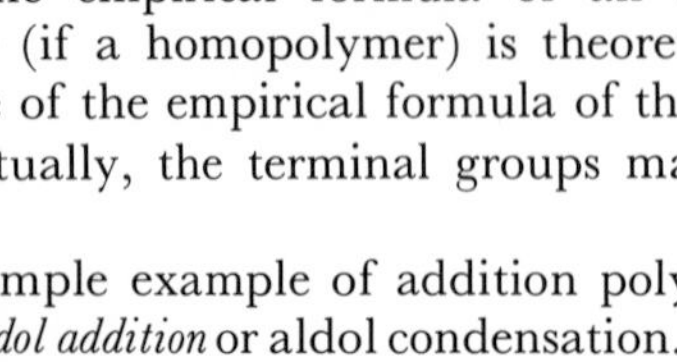

Ketones, alkenes and alkynes can also undergo addition polymerizations. It is evident that many complex and varied substances can be formed by simple addition reactions between relatively simple substances and under *prebiotic* conditions (spontaneously). Most addition polymers are easily depolymerized by heat.

ANHYDRO POLYMERIZATION (CONDENSATION POLYMERIZATION). In anhydro polymerization each monomer is combined with the next by removing $H^+$ from one and $^-OH$ from the other, forming water and causing the two residues to combine (polymerize). Because water is formed the process is sometimes called "anhydrosynthesis" (Chapter 5). Unlike addition polymers, the empirical formula of the anhydro

polymer is not a simple multiple of that of the monomer since x number of molecules of water have been withdrawn in the process of polymerization.

Anhydro polymerization generally involves at least two kinds of enzymes: one or more to activate the units and one to withdraw the $H^+$ and $^-OH$ and cause the residues to combine. The process also requires energy. This is derived from elsewhere in the cell via the ADP-ATP and similar energy-transfer systems (Chapter 9) and is used in forming the bonds between the units of the polymer.

ENERGY MECHANISMS IN POLYMERIZATION. Condensation polymerization (anhydrosynthesis), whether of glucose, amino acids or other units, requires an input of energy; i.e., polymerization is an endothermic process. The energy is derived ultimately from biooxidations of foodstuffs (Chapter 9).

Energy derived from foodstuffs is transferred first into the phosphate bonds of ATP and similar compounds and stored there. These phosphate bonds are said to be energy-rich. When hydrolysis occurs during the process of polymerization, the energy is released.

In polymerization the energy released by breaking the energy-rich phosphate bonds is not lost. For example, in the polymerization of glucose molecules, each hexose molecule (or other monomer) is first activated or energized by combination with one energy-rich phosphate group. The transfer of the phosphate to the monomer is achieved via several intermediate steps involving transphosphorylases and phosphokinases (Gr. *kinema* = activity) or *synthetases.* In the case of starch formation glucose-1-phosphate is formed by uridine diphosphate (UDP) via uridine triphosphate (UTP). UDP and UTP constitute a nucleotide energy-transferring system working via, and analogous to, ADP and ATP. As each glucose-1-phosphate unit is added to the polymer chain, UDP is liberated and the energy of the phosphate bond goes into the making of the glycoside linkage between the glucosyl groups. UDP then receives energy-rich phosphate from ATP, becoming UTP; ATP becomes ADP. The ADP then receives new phosphate from substrate-level and oxidative-chain phosphorylations (and from photophosphorylations in photosynthetic cells) and is re-energized as ATP.

The role of ATP-ADP and UTP-UDP in the formation of starch furnishes an illustration of one common way in which energy from foodstuffs is transferred, by means of energy-rich bonds, into polymers. With some modifications to be discussed, the starch model holds also for the synthesis of proteins, RNA, DNA and lipids as described in the following paragraphs.

## 8.2   MONO-, DI-, TRI- AND POLYSACCHARIDES

A sugar consisting of single molecules (e.g., glucose) is called a *monosaccharide*. Some sugars consist of two sugar molecules joined by glycosidic linkages. They are called *disaccharides*. Examples of familiar disaccharides are *lactose* (a molecule of glucose linked with a molecule of galactose), *sucrose* or ordinary cane sugar (one molecule of glucose and one of fructose) and *maltose*, the sugar in malted barley (two molecules of glucose) (Fig. 8.3). Three-unit sugars are called *trisaccharides* or *trioses*. Trioses are of vital importance in glucose metabolism (Chapter 9) and in photosynthesis (Chapter 38).

In plants "higher" than fungi the carbohydrate polymers starch and cellulose are among the most important structural and nutritional substances. Starch consists of masses of long chains of alpha glucosyl residues. By releasing glucose on hydrolysis starch functions as a reserve food, furnishing both energy and carbon. In the formation of cellulose, beta glucosyl residues are used instead of alpha residues. The strength of wood depends greatly on the tensile strength of the covalent bonds in the chains of glucosyl units. These cellulose fibrils are bundled together lengthwise with a tough "glue," a very complex substance called *lignin*.

In all of the "higher" plants the cell walls are cellulose. Masses of these, with lignin, constitute wood. In many bacteria the cell walls are heteropolymers made up of several amino acids and amino sugars. They are more fully discussed in the section on cell walls (Chapter 13). Glycogen (animal starch), found mainly in animal livers and only rarely in plants, is also a homopolymer of glucose, but the polymer chains are branched.

Several polysaccharides of biological importance are heteropolymers. Some of these, conjugated with lipids (lipopolysaccharides) and other substances, are major constituents of the cell walls of many species of bacteria. Most important of all, perhaps, are the polymers made up of phosphated molecules of the *pentoses* (sugars with five linked carbon atoms) *ribose* and *deoxyribose*. Ribose and deoxyribose phosphate polymers form the very backbone of the chains of nucleotides that make up the nucleic acids RNA and DNA described farther on in this chapter. These control and direct all heredity and all of the enzymic activities and resulting properties of every living cell.

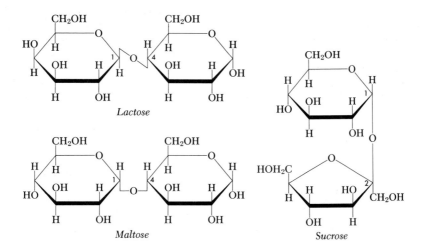

**Figure 8.3**   Three disaccharides. These are common and important components in and sources of energy for living cells.

## 8.3   LIPIDS

This term includes fats, oils, waxes (not petroleum waxes), some fatty acids and polymerized fatty acids. Nearly all are complex esters or similar compounds of the higher fatty acids. Lipids are characteristically insoluble in water but soluble in organic solvents like ether, acetone, alcohol and chloroform. They are important constituents of cells, especially of cell walls and membranes.

Most natural fats are mixtures of triglycerides. A glyceride is a molecule of the tribasic (three replaceable $^-$OH groups) alcohol, glycerol, combined by ester linkages with three molecules of fatty acid: commonly palmitic, stearic (both saturated), and oleic or linoleic (both unsaturated). Usually there are two or three different fatty acids per molecule (Fig. 8.4). Melting points of fats are determined by the fatty acids. The longer chain fatty acids, e.g., carnaubic acid (24 carbon atoms), produce tallow-like and harder fats and waxes. Fats that are fluid at about 22° C. are commonly called "oils," though the term oil has no exact chemical meaning.

Esters, including lipids, are produced by reversible anhydrosynthesis or acid-base reactions; i.e., the withdrawing (or restoring) of the elements of water (hydroxyl from the acid, hydrogen from the alcohol) and combination of the acid and alcohol residues as an ester. When fats are hydrolyzed in the presence of alkali (e.g., potassium hydroxide) *saponification* occurs (Fig. 8.5). The glyceryl receives the hydroxyl group; the fatty acid forms a salt with the potassium and becomes a soluble soap (e.g., toilet soap). Soaps of calcium (e.g., formed in hard water) and of most heavy metals form insoluble curds. In living cells fats serve mainly as reserve fuel globules. (See also poly-beta-hydroxybutyric acid.) In higher animals fats in large deposits also serve as thermal insulation.

Some waxes that are constituents of living cells are fatty acid esters of complex, mono-

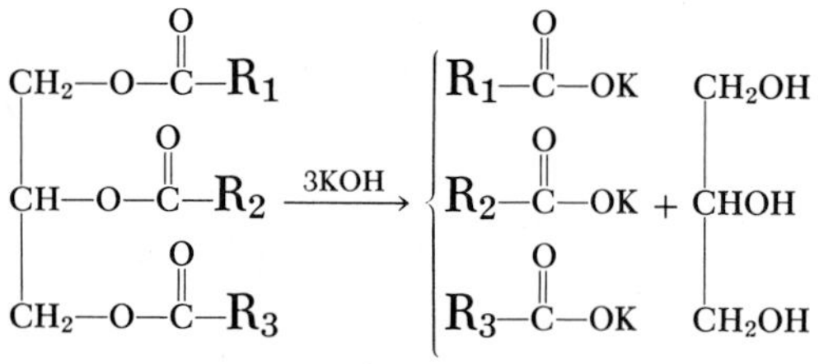

**Figure 8.5**  Saponification of a triglyceride. Note that glycerol is liberated by saponification of any triglyceride.

hydric (one $^-$OH group) alcohols other than glycerol. Some of these waxes, such as *cholesterol esters,* are important in the physiology of higher animals; e.g., humans sometimes worry about cholesterol in the blood and arterial walls. In microorganisms, however, waxes are of lesser (known!) importance. In one group, *Mycobacterium,* which includes the tubercle bacillus, waxes are present in considerable amounts, though their exact physiological function has not yet been fully clarified. Waxes are important in methods of medical diagnosis (see acid-fast stain) and may confer some pathogenicity on acid-fast organisms like the tubercle bacillus.

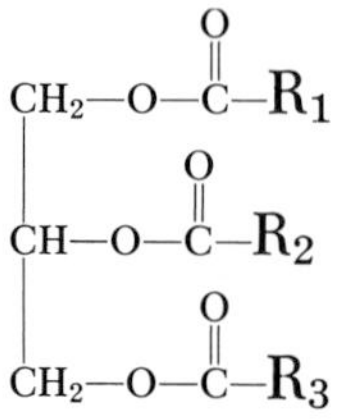

**Lecithins.**   Many triglycerides are not true fats but *lecithins.* Unlike fats, lecithins have a phosphate group attached to glycerol, with two fatty acid groups. Thus, lecithins belong to the group of *phospholipids.* Various additional groups may be attached to the phosphate group: inositol (the *phosphoinositides*), ethanolamine (the *cephalins*) and so on. Many bacteria produce enzymes (*lecithinases*) that destroy lecithins. Several important diagnostic tests are based on this property.

**Lipoproteins.**   A large number of compounds called *lipoproteins,* and others called *proteolipids,* that occur in living cells are lipids combined with proteins by linkages that are very little understood. Lipids are also often combined with carbohydrate complexes or polysaccharides (*lipopolysaccharides*). Lipoproteins are important constituents of the cell membranes of many types of cells, including important species of bacteria. They also occur in the outer coverings of some viruses that infect animals. In viruses the lipoproteins confer special and distinctive properties that will be mentioned in the section on viruses. In certain bacteria such as typhoid bacilli the lipopolysaccharides of the cell walls, complexed with polypeptides, have important pathogenic properties to be mentioned later (see endotoxins).

**Figure 8.4**  Formula of a triglyceride.

One of the most important fatty-acid compounds is poly-beta-hydroxybutyric acid, a polymer of $\beta$-hydroxybutyric acid:

$$\underset{\text{HO}}{}\overset{\text{CH}_3}{\underset{|}{\text{CH}}}-\text{CH}_2-\overset{\overset{\text{O}}{\parallel}}{\text{C}}-\text{OH} \quad \text{(phba)}.$$

The units are joined by ester linkages between the alcoholic hydroxyl group of one molecule and the carboxyl group of the next, a molecule of water being eliminated (anhydrosynthesis) as in all typical ester groupings. Enzymes involved in such polymerizations are sometimes called synthases or synthetases. Poly-beta-hydroxybutyric acid is found as granules and globules in the cells of a number of important and common species of bacteria. It serves a purpose like that of fat or starch, or inorganic metaphosphates (*volutin*), i.e., as a reserve food. Like starch, fat and volutin, it is insoluble and compactly stored as a polymer but readily hydrolyzed to release soluble, readily metabolizable, individual units: beta-hydroxybutyric acid, from its polymer. Similarly, soluble glucose is released from insoluble starch, soluble phosphorous compounds from insoluble volutin, fatty acids and glycerol from water-insoluble fats and oils.

In the synthesis of lipid polymers, energy for the linkages is derived from ATP as in polysaccharide synthesis, though not by direct formation of energy-rich phosphate bonds with the monomers. In lipid polymers the energy appears in an energy-rich acyl ($\text{R}-\overset{\overset{\text{O}}{\parallel}}{\text{C}}-\text{R}$) bond introduced into the fatty acid by combination with coenzyme A (CoA) (see Krebs cycle). The acyl group is then transferred from the fatty acid, leaving the acyl-bond energy. The energy is used in forming the ester linkage between the activated fatty acid and the alcohol (or alcoholic group) with which it combines.

## 8.4  NUCLEIC ACIDS

Unlike carbohydrates, lipids and proteins, nucleic acids (NA's) contribute little as energy sources or structural members of cells. Nucleic acids are like the pilothouse of a ship, contributing nothing as fuel or cargo, hull or superstructure, yet they guide the entire vessel, its contents and crew. As the name implies, NA's were formerly thought to occur only in the nucleus of cells. As will be explained, some NA's are strictly intranuclear, some are not. In the nucleus (or the bacterial nucleoid) NA's are loosely combined (conjugated) with proteins as *nucleoproteins*. The NA's are easily separated from their protein conjugates by mild hydrolytic processes. Structurally, NA's are long-chain heteropolymers. Unlike polymers made up of simple molecules like glucose or amino acids, NA's are made up of complex units called *nucleotides*: i.e., they are *polynucleotides*. Each nucleotide in NA is made up of three components: one molecule of phosphoric acid, one of the pentose ribose (or deoxyribose) and either a purine base (*adenine* or *guanine*) or a pyrimidine base (*cytosine, thymine* or *uracil*) (Fig. 8.6). Alternate forms of cytosine (*methyl cytosine* or *hydroxymethyl cytosine*) may occur in some forms of nucleotides (see farther on). The nucleotide units are joined by phosphate diester bonds between alternating phosphate and sugar groups: sugar–phosphate–sugar–phosphate–sugar and so on. To each sugar group a purine

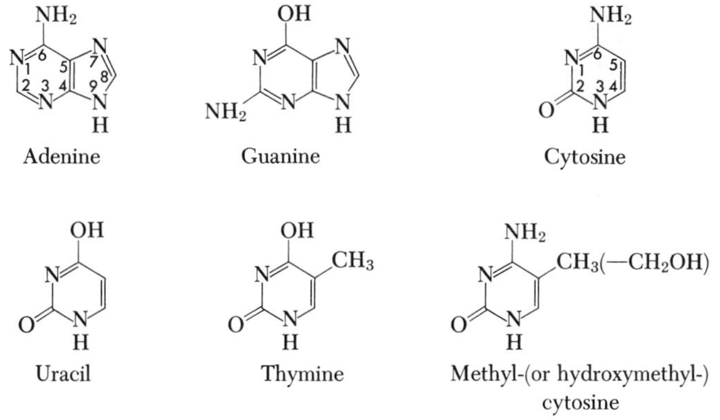

**Figure 8.6**   Formulas of nucleotide bases. For discussion see text.

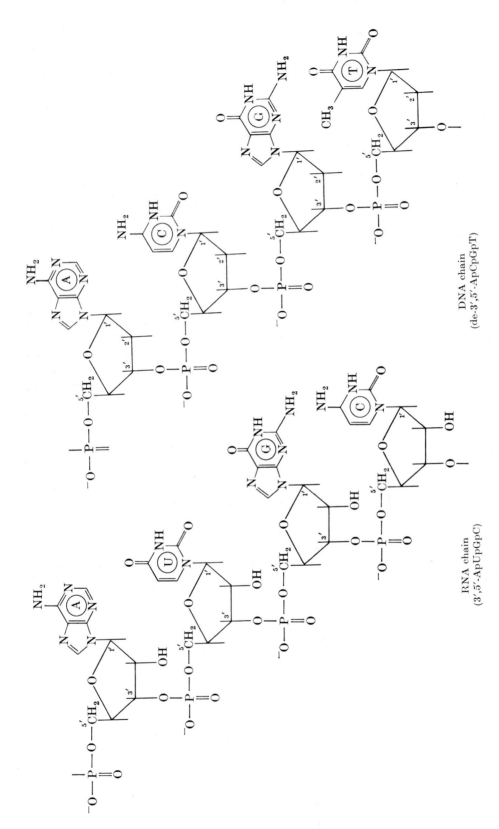

**Figure 8.7** Structure of sections of RNA and DNA chains. Ⓐ = adenine; Ⓣ = thymine; Ⓖ = guanine; Ⓒ = cytosine; Ⓤ = uracil. (From Harrow and Mazur: Textbook of Biochemistry, 9th ed. W. B. Saunders Co., 1966.)

DNA chain
(de-3′,5′-ApCpGpT)

RNA chain
(3′,5′-ApUpGpC)

or pyrimidine base is attached by covalent C to N bonds (Fig. 8.7). The chains of nucleotides in NA's are immensely long. In mammalian cells the number of nucleotides per chain is thought to be of the order of $10^9 = 1$ billion.

**DNA and RNA.** There are two kinds of NA. One, ribonucleic acid (RNA), is so called because its sugar moiety is the pentose *ribose.* In the other, the sugar moiety is very similar but has one less oxygen atom than ribose and is called deoxyribose. This NA is called DNA. In RNA the purine bases may be adenine or guanine and the pyrimidine bases, cytosine or uracil. The bases in DNA are the same except that thymine occurs in place of uracil.

The nucleotides (base + pentose + phosphate) in RNA are adenylic acid (or adenosine-5'-monophosphate, familiar as AMP and in NAD), guanylic acid, cytidylic acid and uridylic acid; in DNA: deoxyadenylic, deoxycytidylic, deoxyguanylic and deoxythymidylic acids. All are *nucleoside phosphates.* While discussing nucleotides it is of interest to note that nucleotides other than adenylic acid also serve as coenzymes. Among these are uridylic acid or uridine-5'-monophosphate or UDP (see starch synthesis); guanylic acid or guanosine-5'-monophosphate or GDP (see Krebs cycle). Adenylic acid is also found in FAD and CoA (see biooxidation and Krebs cycle).

The full story of synthesis of the NA macromolecules logically begins with synthesis of the nucleotides and of the ribose, purines and pyrimidines of which they are composed. These details are not essential to the present discussion; we stipulate the ready formed nucleotides. The formation of the diester bonds linking the pentose-phosphate groups of the various nucleotides into a long chain, the backbone of NA, occurs by the familiar anhydrosynthesis. The free nucleotides occur as triphosphates. In the presence of a NA polymerase enzyme system they join, each giving off pyrophosphate, leaving the energy of the phosphate bond in the polymer chain.

DNA, as is generally known, is the substance of genes, chromosomes and inheritance. In all "higher" cells DNA is confined to the chromosomal structures inside the nuclear membrane. In all bacterial cells DNA is confined to the chromosomal *equivalent,* the fibrillar nucleoid material which is *not* enclosed in a nuclear membrane. In both "higher" as well as in bacterial cells RNA appears in both nuclear and cytoplasmic regions. As will be explained, RNA does not determine heredity, but it acts as an intermediary between the DNA of the nucleus and all synthetic functions in the cell, which are carried on mainly in the cytoplasm. With regard to viruses, in any true virus (i.e., excluding the bacterium-like "large viruses") there is only one kind of NA, either RNA or DNA, never both. (See Chapters 16, 17 and 18.)

The importance of DNA or RNA in all forms of life can hardly be overstated. In all forms of life it is the DNA (or RNA) of the genes and chromosomes that undergoes the alterations called *mutations.* Mutations, with natural selection, are the basis of the great pageant of evolution of all forms of life on this earth, from primeval specks of subvital marine slime to modern astronauts and, who knows, to "moon men." An understanding of the structure, replication and alterations in NA's is the key to the *real* "facts of life."

**Structure of DNA.** The DNA macromolecules that constitute genetic material are intertwined *pairs* of very long chains (strands) of nucleotides. The two nucleotide polymer chains are connected together by weak hydrogen bonds between opposite or complementary purine and pyrimidine bases, much as the two uprights of a ladder are connected by rungs. In the famous Watson-Crick model of DNA, the ladder-like structure is twisted into a double helix (Figs. 8.8 and 8.9).

A most important feature of DNA structure is the *pairing* of the purine and pyrimidine bases to each other. Adenine (A) of one chain is always connected by two hydrogen bonds with thymine (T) of the complementary strand; guanine (G) always is connected by three bonds with cytosine (C). The pairings occur in this way because this diminishes the energy associated with the structure to the greatest extent; hence, they are thermodynamically directed. The two chains of nucleotides in the double helix of DNA "run" in opposite directions: i.e., they have opposite polarity; the deoxyribose residues are oppositely oriented. The pairs of bases, while always A to T and G to C, are highly irregular as to numbers and sequences. Any number or sequence is possible. Since the chains of DNA may contain many thousands of nucleotide units, it is evident that the number of possible combinations and arrangements of nucleotide pairs is virtually unlimited; we may have a sequence of pairs such as G—C, A—T, A—T, C—G, G—C, T—A, with many other sequences, almost ad infinitum. The helical form is maintained by electrostatic attractions between adjacent nucleotides.

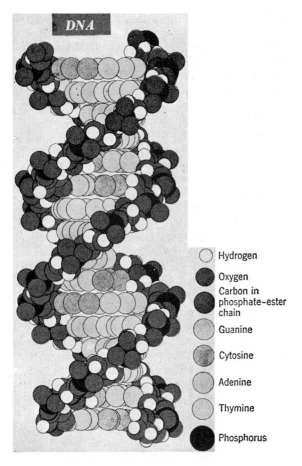

Hydrogen

Oxygen

Carbon in phosphate-ester chain

Guanine

Cytosine

Adenine

Thymine

Phosphorus

**Figure 8.8**   A drawing of the DNA molecule, using solid circles to illustrate atoms. It can be seen that there are two helical grooves of unequal size on the outside of the DNA molecule. (After M. Feughelman et al., in Biophysical Science—A Study Program, edited by J. L. Oncley. John Wiley & Sons.)

**Genetic Significance of DNA.**   The DNA of every species of cell has its own distinctive, invariable (except for rare *mutations,* as will be explained) and specific arrangement of nucleotides. The importance of this lies in the fact that each nucleotide, or any *genetically functional group* of from two to thousands of nucleotides, constitutes a *gene.* Thus your entire admirable self, fair reader, is merely an expression of the arrangement of nucleotides in the DNA of the sex cells (gametocytes) that have carried forward the genetic DNA from one generation of your family to the next from time immemorial. In brief, the helix of DNA is the basis of heredity; indeed, there is no (cellular) life without DNA. It has been called "The Thread of Life." Not the least remarkable feature of this unique vital machine is the fact that it is self-replicating both inside the cell and also outside the cell under laboratory conditions. So far as we are aware, without the replication of DNA life soon ceases.

**Replication of DNA.**   Very briefly, when the process of duplication of the DNA double helix begins, the H-bonds between the A—T and G—C base pairs at a particular point in the double helix break, and the two individual helices separate at that point. This leaves unattached the H-bonding sites of the purine or pyrimidine bases in each separate chain, A, T, G or C. Therefore, each nucleotide residue in each separate strand of the unraveled helix immediately attracts, and combines with, a ready-formed nucleotide from the "pool" of nucleotides in solution in the fluid matrix of the cell; each A combines with a new T nucleotide; each G combines with a new C nucleo-

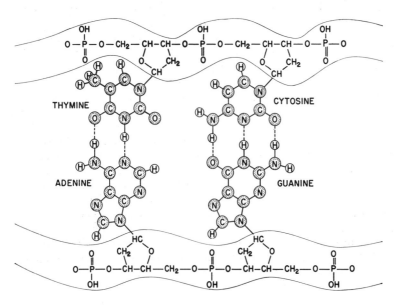

**Figure 8.9**   Molecular drawing of components of DNA. (From Calvin and Calvin: Amer. Sci., *52:*163, 1964.)

tide and so on. The new nucleotides, thus selected and arranged side-by-side according to the existing arrangement and sequence of bases in the strand to which they are attached, then join to form a nucleotide polymer by formation of diester bonds between the ribophosphate residues. This process continues along the length of the double helix from one end to the other. Thus each strand of the original double helix builds up a new complementary strand attached to itself by H-bonds as before. The nucleotide pairs of the new strand are necessarily in the same order and arrangement as before, since the order and arrangement of nucleotides in the old half of the new double helix was conserved and A could combine only with T, and G only with C. Thus the original double helix has now produced two complete, double helices, each an exact replica of the original. Each of the two new double helices consists of one chain of the old double helix and a new complementary chain (Fig. 8.10). This mode of replication of DNA is spoken of as semiconservative.

**Chromosome Replication.**   The mechanism of replication of DNA as a substance may be thus simply and superficially described, but the manner of replication of a bacterial chromosome, made up of DNA, presents many problems. The bacterial chromosome is a long thread of DNA formed into a closed circle (Fig. 8.11). It consists of thousands of nucleotides. The opened circle of thread is estimated to be about 1 mm. (1000 $\mu$) long. It is packed into a cell only about 2 by 8 $\mu$ in dimensions and it constitutes a single, doubly helical macromolecule with a molecular weight of the order of two billion.

When it replicates, one or more still obscure mechanisms, called *replicators,* proceed along the chromosome from a certain fixed point, separating the two strands of the helix as it (they?) go(es) and permitting the formation of complementary strands as previously described. A number of problems still exist concerning the mechanism. For example, what is the mechanism that triggers replication? How does the replicator unwind the helix through some 300,000 turns during the fission period of a cell like *Escherichia coli* that can mature and divide within 20 minutes? This involves some 15,000 turns per minute—a dizzy spin indeed! Further, the chromosome at one point is attached to the cell membrane and, if it unwinds, it involves some sort of swivel to permit the turning. Bear in mind also that the two helices run in opposite directions (have opposite polarities).

RNA commonly differs structurally from DNA in being single stranded. The exact mode of synthesis of RNA is still under investigation. However, double-stranded RNA and single-stranded DNA occur in some viruses (Chapter 18). The single-stranded RNA in cellular organisms is of vital importance in protein synthesis and therefore in inherited characteristics, as explained in the following paragraphs.

Since about 1964 it has been observed that in some bacterial viruses the replication of RNA involves the formation, at least transitorily, of two double-stranded forms of RNA in addition to the single-stranded form. One is spoken of as a replicative form (RF), the other as replicative intermediate (RI). The significance of these findings is clearly of fundamental importance though complete elucidation awaits further investigation.

## 8.5   PROTEINS

**Amino Acids; Peptides.**   Amino acids are organic acids that have an amino group ($^-NH_2$) attached to the alpha carbon atom, i.e., the carbon atom next to the carboxyl ($^-COOH$) group (e.g., alanine):

$$CH_3$$
$$|$$
$$C-NH_2$$
$$|$$
$$COOH$$

D-*alanine*

The alpha carbon atom is asymmetrical. Thus, as among carbohydrates, D and L steric forms of amino acids exist. They are referred to D- and L-serine:

| COOH | COOH |
|---|---|
| NH$_2$CH | HCNH$_2$ |
| CH$_2$OH | CH$_2$OH |
| L-*serine* | D-*serine* |

instead of to D- and L-glyceraldehyde, as are glucose and other carbohydrates.

It is of interest that the amino acids in natural proteins are nearly all of the L form. Some D amino acids, once regarded as "unnatural" because they had never been found in natural substances, occur only in bacteria and molds, notably in antibiotics produced by those organisms and in cell walls of bacteria. Not all of the amino acids that occur in cells are as simple as alanine: e.g., see tryptophan and thyroxine on page 96.

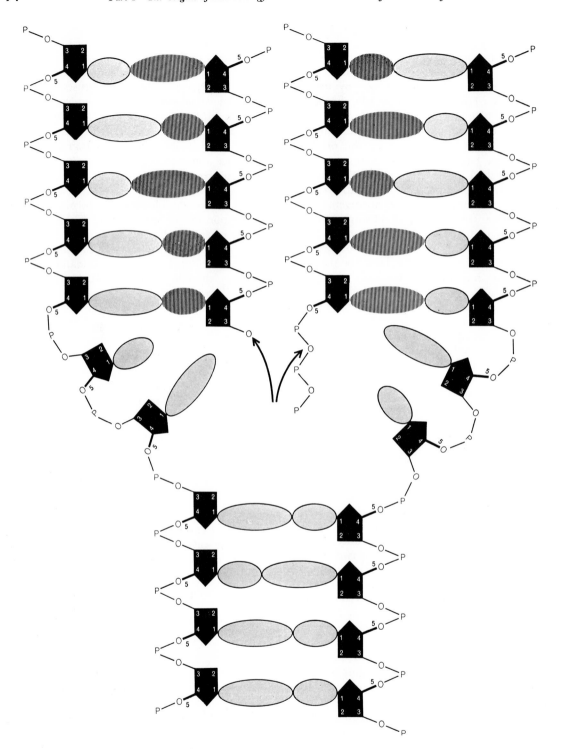

**Figure 8.10** Diagram of the form and mode of replication of the DNA double helix. The still-connected chains of nucleotides of the old double helix are at the lower part of the diagram; their separation is at the center. New nucleotides (bases shaded) are joining the nucleotides of the separated right and left parental (outermost) old chains as fast as the old chains separate. Note that pyrophosphate is split from each new nucleotide triphosphate as it joins the nucleotide chain. Note also the opposite polarities of the nucleotide arrangements in the complementary chains. (From the Bacterial Chromosome, by John Cairns. Copyright © 1966 by Scientific American, Inc. All rights reserved.)

**Figure 8.11**  Replication of bacterial
DNA molecule. The two chains of the
molecule, represented by concentric
circles, are joined at a "swivel" (spot).
DNA labeled with radioactive (isotope-
containing) thymine is shown by dotted
lines; part of one chain of the parent
molecule is labeled by having taken up
the isotopic thymine, as are two generations of newly synthesized DNA. Duplication starts at the swivel and proceeds
counterclockwise. The arrowheads mark
the points at which the two parental
strands are being separated and new DNA
is being synthesized in each chromosome.
Two complete replications are represented.
(From The Bacterial Chromosome, by
John Cairns. Copyright © 1966 by Scientific American, Inc. All rights reserved.)

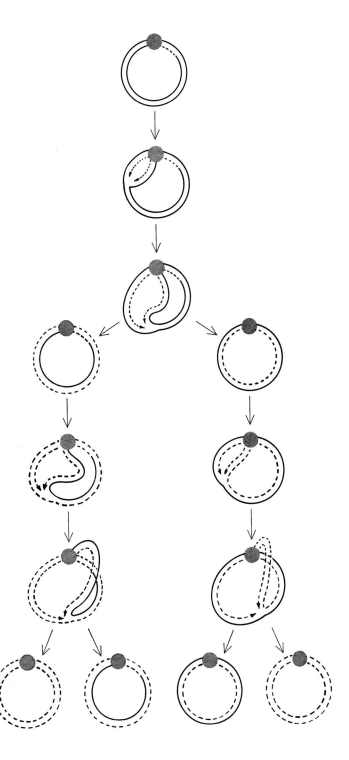

$$H_2N-CH \cdot COOH$$

*tryptophan*

$$CH_2 \cdot CH(NH_2) \cdot COOH$$

*thyroxine*

Like various monosaccharides, amino acids can join together by anhydro polymerization to form *peptides*. A combination of two amino acids constitutes a *dipeptide;* three make a *tripeptide;* many make a *polypeptide*. Proteins are enormously long-chain polypeptides. When protein macromolecules are broken, as by hydrolysis, into large groups of amino acids these are called *peptones* and *proteoses*. Complete hydrolysis of protein yields only amino acids.

The linkage between the amino acid residues in peptides including all proteins is between the carboxyl group of one and the amino group of the other—a peptide bond or linkage:

$$R-C-N-C-R$$

*peptide bond*

This is exemplified in the formation of glycylglycine, a dipeptide:

*glycine*          *glycine*

*glycylglycine*

Formation of the very long peptide chains that constitute proteins is a more complex process than the formation of a glucose homopolymer like starch, because all proteins are complex heteropolymers. Each of the score or more of the amino acids that go to form proteins is structurally different.

**Protein Structure.**   The different amino acids that are joined to form proteins occur in innumerable sequences. The amino-acid sequence of a protein is said to constitute its *primary structure* (Fig. 8.12). Secondly, the peptide chains may be held parallel to each other by H-bonds between adjacent $R-NH$ and $O=C-R$ groups $(R-NH \cdots O=C-R)$ and by disulfide $(R-S-S-R)$ bonds between adjacent sulfur-containing amino acids. Many parallel fibers thus joined can form protein sheets that may be flat or pleated. In another type of arrangement the polypeptide chains are twisted into helices such as the alpha helix. The helices are held in their coiled form chiefly by H-bonds between adjacent coils. A protein is said to be *denatured* when these bonds are broken, as by heating: the coil "unfolds" or straightens out. Many biologically extremely important substances (like keratins of hair, horn and fingernails) consist of protein complexes with such helical forms. These parallelings in sheets, twistings into helices and similar such arrangements of polypeptide chains constitute their *secondary structure* (Fig. 8.13). A *tertiary structure* results when the sheets, helices or bundles are folded and twisted on themselves like the twisted yarn in a skein of wool or a bundled-up towel. The forms of the skeins or sheets are maintained largely by hydrogen and sulfide bonds (Fig. 8.14). Because of tertiary structures we find proteins in the forms of globules, ropes, coiled fibers and many other arrangements. A quaternary structure results from aggregation of units that are in tertiary form. The subunits in quaternary structures are held together by disulfide bonds.

Specificity.   The primary, secondary, tertiary and quaternary structural arrangements of protein molecules are not hit-or-miss. They depend on certain amino-acid sequences. Therefore they are genetically determined and relatively constant. Each protein has its own peculiar, distinctive and specific inherited structure; i.e., it possesses the property of *specificity* (each protein differs from all others).

The number of different proteins possible from different arrangements of some 24 amino acids in the primary, secondary, tertiary and quaternary structures is obviously astronomical.

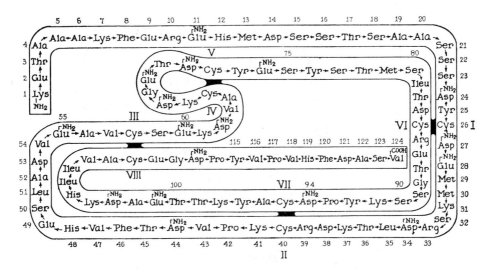

**Figure 8.12**   The complete amino acid sequence of the enzyme ribonuclease. Standard three-letter abbreviations are used to indicate individual amino acid residues. Four disulfide bonds are seen, symbolizing a secondary structure. (From Smyth et al.: J. Biol. Chem., *238*:227, 1963.)

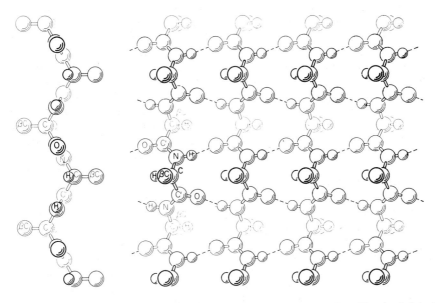

**Figure 8.13**   The parallel-chain pleated sheet structure. (From Pauling and Corey: Proc. Nat. Acad. Sci., *37*:729, 1951.)

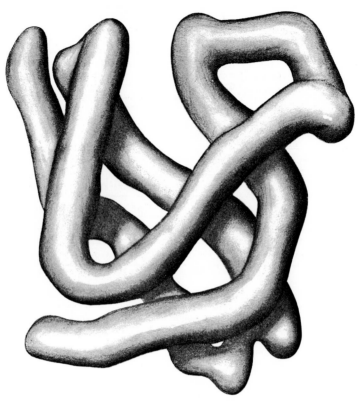

**Figure 8.14**  Typical conformation of peptide chain in a globular protein, after myoglobin structure of Kendrew et al. and hemoglobin structure of Perutz et al. (From Cantarow and Schepartz: Biochemistry, 4th ed. W. B. Saunders Co., 1967.)

When proteins are conjugated with other substances, e.g., metals, lipids and polysaccharides, the number of possible permutations and variations is virtually infinite. The property of specificity is of the greatest importance in all enzymic functions, in resistance to disease, in an individual's identity or in inheritance. Specificity will be discussed again in later sections. Denaturation breaks H-bonds and this results in loss of specificity and other properties of proteins.

## PROTEIN SYNTHESIS

As previously explained, all essential biochemical reactions in the cell are catalyzed by *specific* enzymes, the specificity of which resides in the primary, secondary, tertiary and quaternary structures of their protein moieties (apoenzymes). In the preceding discussion it was stated that the structure of all proteins in the living cell, including enzymes, is determined by the nucleotide units in the DNA of each cell. The obvious question is, how? The answer, drawn from Nature only after years of the most exquisitely incisive, inductively imaginative and toilsome researches by hundreds of highly ingenious biochemists, molecular biologists, microbial geneticists and associated scientists, lies in: (a) the sequence of nucleotides (called the *genetic code*) that make up the DNA chains and (b) the mechanism by which this *code* or *genetic information* or *message* is transferred from the DNA polynucleotide in the nucleus to the protein-synthesizing mechanisms in the cytoplasm. These protein-synthesizing mechanisms are ultramicroscopic granules called *ribosomes* that consist of ribonucleoprotein (40 per cent protein, 60 per cent RNA). Ribosomes make up a great part of the finely granular, apparently diffuse substance of cytoplasm that is seen in specially prepared electron micrographs of cross-sections of cells. In "higher" cells, ribosomes are attached to membranous structures, the endoplasmic reticulum; in bacteria they seem to be diffusely scattered or attached to the cytoplasmic membrane and mesosomes (Chapter 13).

**rRNA and tRNA.**  The RNA of the ribosomes (rRNA) plays a basic role in the synthesis of proteins by providing a place for the work of specific *selection, arrangement* and *joining* of the amino acids to be done. Another form of RNA, called *transfer RNA* (tRNA) consists of relatively small molecules (70 to 100 nucleotides). It exists in solution in the fluid matrix of the cell and is therefore sometimes called *soluble RNA* (sRNA).* Each molecule of tRNA has a terminal nucleotide sequence that enables it to accept a single molecule of an *activated* amino acid and transfer it to a ribosome.

**mRNA and the Genetic Code.** Each ribosome has attached to it a third form of RNA that appears to be formed only by an enzyme, RNA-polymerase, under the direct influence of DNA. The exact details of its formation are not yet fully clarified. It might possibly be a derivative of DNA. However this may be, it exists as a single strand. This carries the identical sequence of nucleotides as a single strand of the DNA; i.e., it is a one-sided transcription of the genetic code. This RNA, formed like a template of the DNA code, acts like a messenger to carry the DNA code or genetic message to the ribosomes. This RNA is called *messenger RNA* (mRNA).

**Transcription of the Genetic Code.** By the use of these three forms of RNA (tRNA, mRNA and rRNA), the construction of a protein polypeptide chain proceeds (in much simplified form) as follows:

Since each amino acid ($NH_2R$) that goes into a polypeptide (protein) chain has a different structure, a different specific enzyme is required to activate each. The energy for activation is derived from ATP bonds by the formation of the complex: $Enz + ATP + NH_2R$. Pyrophosphate is liberated from the ATP (yielding AMP) and the bond energy is left in the complex.

The enzyme then catalyzes combination between the activated amino acid and a molecule of tRNA that has a sequence of three nucleotides (a *nucleotide triplet*) that is specific for that amino acid. Each molecule of tRNA has a distinctive triplet of nucleotides that enables it to combine with one, single, specific amino acid.†

The activated amino acid is then transferred by its specific tRNA molecule, with energy derived from the high-energy compound, guanidine triphosphate (GTP; analogous in function to ATP), to a ribosome where the actual synthesis of the protein occurs. Probably many ribosomes act together in groups called *poly-somes* or *polyribosomes*. These bodies are visible only with electron microscopes (Chapter 13).

The rRNA itself appears to be nonspecific but it acts as a working place for the tRNA and the mRNA. As mentioned before, mRNA is a long, single chain of nucleotides whose sequence is the same as that of the nucleotide sequence (genetic code) in the DNA. Each activated amino acid brought by tRNA to the mRNA becomes attached to the strand of mRNA at a place in which the sequence of the three nucleotides in the tRNA corresponds exactly with that of a triplet of nucleotides in the mRNA. The tRNA triplet is thus oriented opposite the mRNA nucleotides as though the tRNA triplet were part of a complementary strand of DNA. For convenience in visualizing the relationships we may imagine that the tRNA is a three-nucleotide fragment of a single DNA strand while the mRNA is the complementary strand. This complementary relationship between the tRNA and the mRNA necessitates the pairing of the nucleotide triplets in the tRNA and mRNA according to the DNA code of which mRNA is a copy.

Each molecule of tRNA, with its attached amino acid, recognizes its place on the mRNA strand (which carries the DNA code). Thus the sequence of amino acids that are attached to the strand of mRNA by the tRNA is determined by the DNA code.

FINAL SYNTHESIS. Once the activated amino acids are properly aligned in the coded order along the strand of mRNA, the polypeptide bonds are enzymically formed to join the amino acids. The now complete polypeptide chain is released from the ribosome or polysome as a fully fledged protein of highly specific structure (Fig. 8.15). The protein probably then acts with some coenzyme in the daily work of the cell. The tRNA and the activating enzyme are liberated and repeat the process. The mRNA appears to remain attached to the ribosomes to act repeatedly as a template for the ordering of more polypeptide chains when the tRNA's shall bring the activated amino acids to it (see enzyme control).

**The Codon.** Because of the almost infinite number of possible arrangements of the four kinds of nucleotides (letters or digits: A—T, C—G) in the DNA, and considering that one DNA macromolecule contains perhaps 100,000 nucleotides, an almost infinite number of three-letter "words" or nucleotide triplets, each representing an amino acid, can be arranged. Each word thus constructed of three nucleotides in DNA is called a *codon*.

---

*tRNA has been said to "adapt" amino acids to the rRNA and is therefore sometimes also called *adaptor RNA* (aRNA).

†There are some exceptions that need not be considered at this point (see farther on).

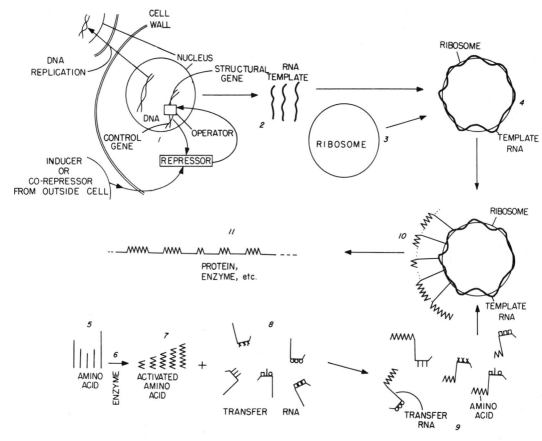

**Figure 8.15**  Diagram of protein synthesis. At the upper left, DNA in the nucleus of the cell is seen forming and liberating strands of template RNA (mRNA; *2*) under genetic control involving inducer, repressor, structural gene, etc. (see enzyme induction and control, Chapters 5 and 14). The mRNA (*2*) becomes associated with ribosomes (*3* and *4*). Different amino acids (*5*, lower left), each activated by its specific enzyme (*6*, *7*), become associated with specific nucleotide triplets that constitute transfer RNA (tRNA; *8*). Each specific nucleotide triplet, with its specific amino acid (*9*) finds its corresponding nucleotide triplet on the strand of mRNA at the ribosome and attaches there (*10*). The amino acids thus ordered along the mRNA at the ribosome (*10*) are enzymically (polymerase) linked through peptide bonds (anhydrosynthesis) to form the polypeptide of protein (*11*) which may be a functional enzyme or a structural member of the cell. (From Calvin [Nobel Prize winner]: Amer. Inst. Biol. Sci. Bulletin, *12*:38, 1962.)

Each protein thus bears an inherited structure and, because of its enzymic or other activities, confers an inherited characteristic on the cell of which it is a part.

**Universality of the Genetic Code.**  A thought-provoking aspect of the genetic code as a biological mechanism is that DNA is constructed on the same general form throughout the living universe. Genes, codons, triplets, amino acids and nucleotide "words" are all involved in the same way and in the same process, though the nucleotide sequences occur in endless variations. The code, i.e., the language of heredity, is said to be universal. The tRNA and mRNA from a bacterial cell will serve the same function and direct the synthesis of the same protein from the same amino acids in an arti-

ficial enzyme mixture derived from a mammalian cell.

Does this universality of the genetic language and mechanism point toward DNA as the common, primeval starting point of all life? There is evidence indicating that various amino acids, the purine and pyrimidine bases and other constituents of RNA and DNA could have been formed in lightning flashes under prebiotic conditions in vapors of water, ammonia and methane.* Thus a single, primeval DNA helix, spontaneously formed, could, in the course of thousands of millions of years, by mutations, genetic recombinations and natural selection,

_____

*Did life begin "in thunder, lightning [and] or in rain?" ("Macbeth," modified)

account for ourselves and all of the living things that now surround us. It is interesting to realize that each helix of DNA in each person was derived from ancestral DNA and that these ancestral strands of DNA have successively produced each other by helix replication without interruption over eons of time. The DNA in each person has been "immortal," although the bodies of the individuals carrying the ceaselessly replicating strands from one generation to another have in time disintegrated. We may draw an analogy with a lighted torch carried for billions of miles and years since life began by successive relay runners who, having handed the torch on to the next runner, themselves drop panting or lifeless by the wayside. It is also conceivable that different forms of primeval DNA helices could have originated at different times and in different places on the earth, thus accounting for various types of animals and different human "races."

**Deciphering the Genetic Code.**   One of the most magnificent pieces of decoding in human history, including Champollion and the Rosetta stone, was not done by international spies or supersleuths in Washington but by Benzer, Watson and Crick and others when they discovered in 1961 that each DNA code word consists of a sequence of three nucleotides (nucleotide triplets). These have been called codons. Each codon occurring in tRNA specifies one amino acid. Also in 1961 Nirenberg and Matthaei mixed, *in vitro,* ribosomes (separated from sonically disrupted cells by high speed differential centrifugations) with a suspension of cytoplasmic materials from the same sort of cells. The mixture contained, among other materials, enzymes, amino acids, tRNA, ribosomes and energy-transfer coenzymes such as ATP and GTP. Here were found all, except one, of the many elements necessary for the synthesis of polypeptides. The one missing ingredient was mRNA.

Now Nirenberg and Matthaei had synthesized a simple form of mRNA in which the entire chain was made up of only one kind of nucleotide, uridylic acid (U). This historic polynucleotide is now often called "poly-U." Be it noted that, although in RNA uracil replaces thymine, uracil and thymine are equivalent in respect to pairing (Fig. 8.6). When U was added to the cellular "purée" just described, the cellular elements in the purée cooperated as they do in a living cell to form a polypeptide chain. But since there was only one kind of triplet or codon, UUU in the synthetic mRNA, the poly-

peptide formed consisted of only one kind of amino acid, phenylalanine.

$$\text{NH}_2$$
$$\bigcirc\!\!-\!\!\text{CH}_2\text{CHCOOH}$$

*phenylalanine*

It was thus revealed that the codon UUU meant phenylalanine; the first genetic code word ever to be deciphered! Of course, many eager researchers were at work deciphering other code words. The huge mass of data resulting from these studies fills many long shelves in libraries and carries the names of scores of brilliant scientists. Suffice it to say here that, in the same or similar ways, codons have been found since then for all the amino acids that occur in natural proteins. AAA means lysine, AGA means arginine, UUU means phenylalanine, UUA means leucine, and so on. It was found also that several amino acids have more than one codon, for example, leucine is specified by CUC, CUU, UUA and UUG. The code is therefore said to be *degenerate* in that each amino acid is not restricted to only one codon. This is true *in vitro,* but the code appears not to act degenerately *in vivo.*

**Genetic Punctuation.**   In reading the entire sequence of triplets in a long chain of DNA (about $10^5$ units) it became difficult to determine where one triplet ended and another began, i.e., to know how the genetic message was punctuated. One might have a series of nucleotides like ACTGATGAGCAT. If we mark off triplets from the left, we find that they are ACT, GAT, GAG and CAT. They make "sense" words (in English). But if we overlook the first A we find CTG, ATG, AGC and so on, i.e., nonsense words. English words are used as an example but of course the triplet letters could be arranged in any sequence in a polypeptide.* In the above example using English words, a single error at the beginning would clearly result in making nonsense words such as CTG of many or all of the succeeding triplets and, in any case, in producing a faulty message (polypeptide) or none at all. After many hypotheses and experiments had been made it was found that a genetic message may be decoded by beginning at a point where the first triplet is not a nonsense word (i.e., is an estab-

---

*After all, when genetic words were devised, there wasn't any English language.

lished codon [genetic word] for a known amino acid) and reading in triplets from there in both directions.

## SUPPLEMENTARY READING

Bigeleisen, J.: Chemistry of isotopes. Science, *147*:463, 1965.

Bodanszky, M., and Bodanszky, A. A.: From peptide synthesis to protein synthesis. Amer. Sci., *55*:185, 1967.

Cantarow, A., and Schepartz, B.: Biochemistry. 4th ed. W. B. Saunders Co., Philadelphia. 1967.

Cold Spring Harbor Symposia on Quantitative Biology, XXXI: The Genetic Code. Cold Spring Harbor Laboratory, Cold Spring, N.Y. 1966.

Gray, H.: Electrons and Chemical Bonding. W. A. Benjamin, New York. 1964.

Hayashi, T., and Szent-Gyorgi, A. G.: Molecular Architecture in Cell Physiology. Prentice-Hall, Inc., Englewood Cliffs, N. J. 1966.

Harrow, B., and Mazur, A.: Textbook of Biochemistry. 9th ed. W. B. Saunders Co., Philadelphia. 1966.

Horecker, B. L.: The biosynthesis of bacterial polysaccharides. Ann. Rev. Microbiol., *20*:253, 1966.

Iglewski, W. J., and Franklin, R. M.: Denaturation and renaturation of viral nucleic acid; II. J. Virol. *1*:804, 1967.

Kasting, R., and McGinnis, A. J.: Radioisotopes and the determination of nutrient requirements. Ann. N. Y. Acad. Sci. *139*(Art. 1):98, 1966.

Kendrew, J. C.: The Thread of Life. Harvard University Press, Cambridge, Mass. 1967.

Luder, W. F., Shepard, R. A., Vernon, A. A., and Zuffanti, A.: General Chemistry. 3rd ed. W. B. Saunders Co., Philadelphia. 1965.

McQuillen, K.: The physical organization of nucleic acid and protein synthesis. Fifteenth Symposium, Function and Structure in Micro-organisms, p. 134. Soc. Gen. Microbiol., London. 1965.

Mulliken, R. S.: Spectroscopy, molecular orbitals, and chemical bonding. Science, *157*:13, 1967.

Neidhardt, F. C.: Roles of amino acid activating enzymes in cellular physiology. Bact. Rev., *30*:701, 1966.

Noller, C. R.: Textbook of Organic Chemistry. 3rd ed. W. B. Saunders Co., Philadelphia. 1966.

O'Leary, W. M.: The fatty acids of bacteria. Bact. Rev., *26*:421, 1962.

Pauling, L., and Hayward, R.: The Architecture of Molecules. W. H. Freeman and Co., San Francisco. 1964.

Philips, D. C.: The three-dimensional structure of an enzyme molecule. Sci. Amer., *215*:78, 1966.

Stacey, K. A.: The biosynthesis of nucleic acids and their roles in protein synthesis. Fifteenth Symposium, Function and Structure in Micro-organisms, p. 159. Soc. Gen. Microbiol., London. 1965.

Steiner, R. F., and Edelhoch, H.: Molecules and Life. Van Nostrand, Princeton. 1967.

Wang, C. H., and Willis, D. L.: Radiotracer Methodology in Biological Science. Prentice-Hall, Inc., Englewood Cliffs, N. J. 1965.

Watson, J. D.: Molecular Biology of the Gene. W. A. Benjamin, New York. 1964.

Wolf, G.: Isotopes in Biology. Academic Press, New York. 1964.

# Chapter 9

# BIOENERGETICS

Chemical reactions that yield heat or energy are said to be *exothermic* or *exergonic* (Gr. *ex* = out from; *therme* = heat; *ergon* = work or energy). In microbiology, the most important exergonic reactions are concerned with the oxidation of nutrients as sources of energy. Such reactions, if they occur in the presence of available oxygen, are often called *respiration*. However, the term respiration seems to imply the presence of lungs, gills or other complex breathing mechanisms. In dealing with unicellular organisms the term biological oxidation or biooxidation is preferable, because it implies only the type of chemical reaction and not the machinery. Perhaps a still more accurate term would be "biological electron transfer" or, for brevity, "bioelectronics" since, as will be explained, all processes of oxidation, bio- or otherwise, and whether or not available oxygen is present, are fundamentally transfers of electrons from the oxidized food substance or *substrate*.

## 9.1 OXIDATION AND REDUCTION

Physiologically, the term biooxidation is associated with an old idea that free or atmospheric oxygen is necessary to life. This view was eclipsed when Pasteur showed that there are numerous species of microorganisms, e.g., yeasts, that can thrive without free oxygen—a phenomenon that Pasteur called *anaerobiosis:* "life without air." As now defined, any biological oxidation is fundamentally the removal of electrons from various substrates.

Now electrons cannot, in the living cell, remain in a free state. If removed from a substrate (an *electron donor* in this context) which is thereby oxidized, there must be something (an *electron acceptor*) immediately present to which the electrons can attach themselves. The elec-

tron acceptor is thereby reduced. Thus when we speak of the oxidation of something we imply the concomitant reduction of something else. Oxidations are always, therefore, coupled reactions and are actually oxidation-reduction or *"redox"* reactions. Oxidation is loss of electrons; reduction is gain of electrons. An electron acceptor is an oxidizing agent; an electron donor is a reducing agent.

In the "traditional" form of oxidation, i.e., addition of oxygen to the substrate, electron transfer is not obvious, but is based on the fact that the oxygen accepts two electrons from the substrate: e.g., $Cu + O = Cu^{++}O^{--}$, an ionic crystal. There are several species of soil bacteria that obtain energy from the enzymic oxidation of such strange nutrients as molecular hydrogen, sulfur and carbon monoxide. In such oxidations free oxygen is combined with the substrate:

$$H_2 + \tfrac{1}{2}O_2 \longrightarrow H_2O + Energy$$
$$CO + \tfrac{1}{2}O_2 \longrightarrow CO_2 + Energy$$
$$2S + 2H_2O + 3O_2 \longrightarrow 2H_2SO_4 + Energy$$
$$NaNO_2 + \tfrac{1}{2}O_2 \longrightarrow NaNO_3 + Energy$$

Oxidation can also occur in the total absence of oxygen. Electron transfer is involved in any increase in positive valence (i.e., loss of an electron), as when ferrous iron is oxidized to ferric iron: $Fe^{++} - (e^-) + (e^-$ acceptor$)$ $\longleftrightarrow Fe^{+++} + ($acceptor $\cdot e^-)$. This is an important type of reaction that occurs in the iron of iron-containing respiratory pigments, such as the cytochrome pigments of most aerobic bacteria (to be discussed).

### DEHYDROGENATION

In most cells oxidation of organic substrates is accomplished by the enzymic removal of hydrogen or *dehydrogenation.* The enzymes that catalyze dehydrogenations are called *dehydrogenases.* When hydrogen is thus removed from a substrate molecule an electron accompanies it; i.e., a hydrogen atom may be thought of as a hydrogen ion ($H^+$) with an electron ($e^-$) attached: $H^+ + e^- = H$ or ($H^+e^-$) or hydrogen-($e^-$). The $H^+$ may be considered to go into solution, the electron being taken into an enzymic electron-transfer system or "oxidative chain" that is described farther on. The enzyme systems, including the initial dehydrogenases, involved in hydrogen($e^-$) transfers are often called *electron-transfer systems.* An example of oxidation of an organic substrate by dehydrogenation is seen in the enzymic oxidation of alcohol to aldehyde, with free oxygen as hydrogen($e^-$) acceptor:

$$H_2=\overset{\underset{|}{CH_3}}{C}-OH \; - \; 2(H^+e^-) + \tfrac{1}{2} O_2 \longrightarrow$$

*ethyl alcohol*

$$H-\overset{\underset{|}{CH_3}}{C}=O + H_2O$$

*acetaldehyde*

Oxidation of an inorganic substrate by dehydrogenation is seen in the enzymic oxidation of hydrogen sulfide to sulfur:

$$H_2S - 2(H^+e^-) + \tfrac{1}{2}O_2 \longrightarrow S + H_2O$$

This reaction is found in several species of soil bacteria.

**Hydrogen Transport.** Dehydrogenases, like other enzymes, are highly specific for their respective substrates. Their coenzymes are less restricted; one coenzyme may act in turn with several different dehydrogenase apoenzymes or, conversely, several different dehydrogenase apoenzymes may use the same coenzyme. The molecular structure and functions of the dehydrogenase coenzymes are of particular interest.

NAD. Dehydrogenation in many cells is initiated first by the coenzyme *nicotinamide-adenine-dinucleotide* (NAD) or by *NAD phosphate* (NADP). These coenzymes were long known as diphospho-pyridine nucleotide (DPN) and triphosphopyridine nucleotide (TPN), respectively, and are found in all cells. These coenzymes act with many different apoenzymes that determine specificity of the enzyme for its substrate. The essential portion of NAD is in the nicotinamide group: the vitamin *"niacin"* (Fig. 9.1). The pyridine ring of this group accepts substrate hydrogen, being reduced to $NADH_2$. The $NADH_2$ yields the hydrogen to a second hydrogen acceptor, thus being reoxidized to NAD. Dehydrogenases that transfer substrate hydrogen by way of NAD or NADP are said to be *NAD* or *NADP-linked.* In aerobic cells NAD and NADP commonly transfer hydrogen($e^-$) to a second hydrogen($e^-$) carrier at a lower energy level, e.g., FAD.

FAD. FAD is a coenzyme common to several dehydrogenases. It is a yellow-colored nucleotide commonly called *flavin-adenine dinucleotide* (FAD). Dehydrogenases that transfer substrate hydrogen($e^-$) via FAD are said to be *flavin-linked.* As a point of interest it may be noted, as seen in Figure 9.2, that FAD contains the vita-

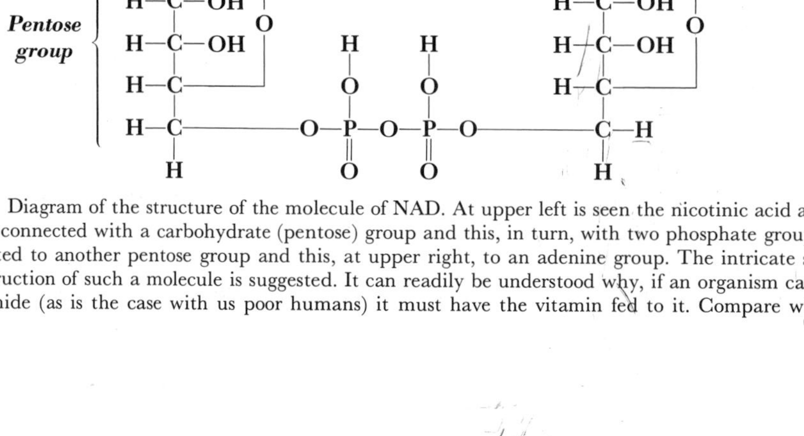

**Figure 9.1**    Diagram of the structure of the molecule of NAD. At upper left is seen the nicotinic acid amide ("niacin" vitamin). This is connected with a carbohydrate (pentose) group and this, in turn, with two phosphate groups. At the right these are connected to another pentose group and this, at upper right, to an adenine group. The intricate synthesis necessary to the construction of such a molecule is suggested. It can readily be understood why, if an organism cannot synthesize nicotinic acid amide (as is the case with us poor humans) it must have the vitamin fed to it. Compare with structure of DNA (Fig. 8.7).

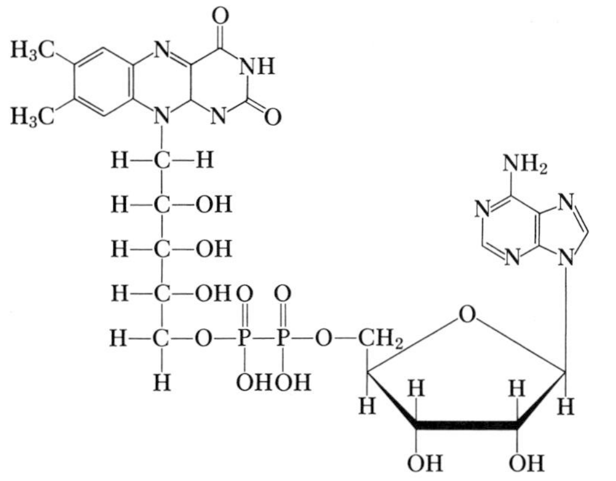

**Figure 9.2**  Flavin-adenine dinucleotide (FAD). The adenine group is shown at upper right (compare Figure 9.1) and a ribose group below it. The two are connected through a phosphate bond to the riboflavin 5'-phosphate group at the left.

min *riboflavin (vitamin B$_2$)*. So far as is known all vitamins are analogous parts of coenzymes.

When reduced by substrate hydrogen to FADH$_2$, the coenzyme may be reoxidized by enzymic transfer of the hydrogen(e$^-$) directly to oxygen, forming H$_2$O$_2$. Very commonly FADH$_2$ is reoxidized to FAD by transfer of the hydrogen(e$^-$) to an iron-bearing respiratory pigment of the *cytochrome system*.

## THE CYTOCHROME SYSTEM

The *cytochromes* (Gr. *cyto* = cell; *chroma* = color) are a group of yellow pigments (cyto-

chromes a, a$_3$, b, c, and others) commonly found in aerobic or facultative cells—cells that use free oxygen or an alternative substance as final hydrogen(e$^-$) acceptor, e.g., NaNO$_3$ + H$_2$ $\longrightarrow$ NaNO$_2$ + H$_2$O. Like the *heme* (red matter) in our blood corpuscles, cytochrome pigments contain iron in organic combination (*porphyrin;* Fig. 5.2). This iron can be readily reduced or oxidized by changing its valence as previously explained. The energy level of each successive cytochrome pigment in the series is progressively lower. Cytochromes occur only rarely in cells that cannot use free oxygen or an alternative as their final hydrogen(e$^-$) acceptor.

In the operation of the cytochrome system, substrate hydrogen is ionized, the H$^+$ going into solution, the electrons to the cytochrome system. The cytochromes mediate the transfer of e$^-$, not of H$^+$. The electrons descend the cytochrome "stairway," being transferred from one energy level to the next lower, yielding energy at each step. The final cytochrome of the series is relieved of its electrons by *cytochrome oxidase* (cytochrome a$_3$), the enzyme that catalyzes final combination of the hydrogen ion, the electron and free oxygen (or an alternative hydrogen(e$^-$) acceptor) such as NaNO$_3$, H$_2$SO$_4$ or CO$_2$ (Fig. 9.3).

## USE OF COMBINED OXYGEN

In biooxidation numerous species, among them bacteria and fungi, that preferentially utilize uncombined (free) oxygen as hydrogen acceptor by means of the cytochrome system nevertheless have the faculty, when free oxygen is scarce or entirely absent, to use oxygen in

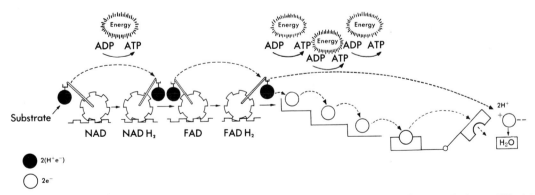

**Figure 9.3**  A typical hydrogen (e$^-$) transport chain or "physiological bucket brigade." Substrate hydrogen (H$^+$e$^-$) is transferred to the dehydrogenase coenzyme NAD which thus becomes NADH$_2$. NADH$_2$ yields its 2(H$^+$e$^-$) to the dehydrogenase coenzyme FAD, which thus becomes FADH$_2$, with the NADH$_2$ being thereby reoxidized to NAD. Energy is released and stored in ATP. The 2(H$^+$e$^-$) then go into solution and the 2e$^-$ are transferred to the cytochrome system, where further energy is released to ATP. Final combination of 2H$^+$, 2e$^-$, and oxygen of the air outside the cell is catalyzed by the enzyme cytochrome oxidase.

combined form as in $NaNO_3$ (see reaction on p. 105). Such organisms are said to be *facultative* with regard to oxygen. The process involves the activity of an inducible enzyme called *nitratase* that activates the combined oxygen. $Mo^{++}$ is an essential cofactor. The activated oxygen appears then to be passed to the cytochrome oxidase of the cytochrome system. Presence of free oxygen competitively interferes with nitrate reduction. Diagnostic tests for nitrate reduction should therefore be made under anaerobic conditions. Some organisms also reduce nitrates to nitrites via *nitritase* and then to nitrogen. Some cells use part of the nitrogen for synthesis of amino acids. The exact chemical pathways differ in species and remain to be fully clarified.

Several important bacteria can use combined oxygen in the form of sulfates or carbonates ($CO_2$). These organisms generally have little or no cytochrome system and are therefore restricted to anaerobic conditions of growth. They are said to be *strict anaerobes*. Sulfates may be reduced to $H_2S$; $CO_2$ to $CH_4$. The cells may also derive their S and C from such materials (see also Chapter 32).

### ENERGY-RICH BONDS

Energy released by biooxidation of a substrate is immediately taken up into a particular kind of hydrolyzable anhydride bond spoken of as a high energy or *energy-rich* (e-r) bond, for which $\sim$ is the conventional symbol. Actually, the bond itself is not solely concerned; the energy is distributed in the molecule itself. For present purposes, however, the concept of the bond is a convenient usage if its broader implication is kept in mind. A more precise term might be "compound with high energy level or potential." Several compounds in living cells have such e-r bonds: thioesters like

$$
\overset{\displaystyle O}{\underset{\displaystyle \|}{\phantom{.}}}
$$

acetyl$\sim$SCoA:   ($CH_3\overset{O}{\overset{\|}{C}}\sim SCoA$);   phosphates like phospho-enol pyruvic acid:

$$
\begin{array}{c}
COOH \\
| \\
H_2C{=}C{-}O{\sim}PO_3H_2.
\end{array}
$$

Functions of some of these will be discussed farther on.

Among the most important phosphates in energy transfer and storage for the present discussion (i.e., in bacteria) are those of *adenosine diphosphate* (ADP) and *adenosine triphosphate* (ATP). These, like NAD and FAD, are *nucleotide coenzymes* (Fig. 9.4). Unlike NAD and FAD, ADP and ATP accept and transfer phosphate groups instead of hydrogen($e^-$). Generation of e-r bonds, especially those of ATP, is one of

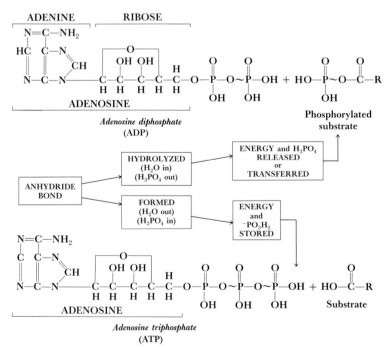

*Adenosine diphosphate*
(ADP)

*Adenosine triphosphate*
(ATP)

**Figure 9.4**   The ADP-ATP energy-transfer and storage system. The change from ADP to ATP, shown as reversible, can occur only when new energy for the phosphorylation is made available from biooxidation; i.e., it is an endergonic reaction. The change from ATP to ADP releases energy; it is an exergonic reaction.

the most important immediate results of biooxidation.

In nonphotosynthetic cells, the formation of
e-r phosphate bonds of ATP may occur at
several stages, or energy levels, of the stepwise
process of oxidation of an organic substrate
such as glucose. Glucose is a source of energy
for almost all living cells.

## PHOSPHORYLATION

**The Embden-Meyerhof Schema; Substrate
Phosphorylation.** For example, in the dissimilation of glucose via the series of steps called
the *Embden-Meyerhof pathway* or *glycolytic pathway*
(Table 9.1), one derivative of the glucose molecule, i.e., 3-phospho-glyceraldehyde, is dehydrogenated via NAD and concurrently combined
with inorganic phosphate (iP) to form $NADH_2$
and 1,3-diphosphoglyceric acid. The added
phosphate of the 1,3-diphosphoglyceric acid,
with energy derived from the simultaneous
dehydrogenation, is taken over by ADP, forming
e-r ATP. The 3-phosphoglyceric acid residue
then undergoes a molecular rearrangement to
form 2-phosphoglyceric acid. This is dehydrated, providing an e-r bond in the resulting
phospho-enol pyruvic acid. This e-r phosphate
is then transferred to ADP to form more ATP,
leaving pyruvic acid as a final residue at this
stage in the dissimilation of the glucose molecule. The formation of new e-r phosphate bonds
in derived portions of the substrate itself is generally called *substrate-level phosphorylation,* and
is best exemplified in the Embden-Meyerhof
pathway after the formation of the trioses (step
4, Table 9.1).

**Oxidative-Chain Phosphorylation.** In the
presence of available oxygen, when the cytochrome system is involved in substrate oxidations, at least three additional phosphorylations
occur during the progress of the substrate electrons from FAD, down the "steps" of the oxidative chain, to lower and lower energy levels in
the electron-transporting cytochrome system.
At each "descent" the electrons give up some
of their energy. In the presence of iP, ADP
and several enzymes, more e-r ATP is formed.
These *oxidative-chain* or *oxidative phosphorylations,*
as they are called, yield much additional energy.
(Fig. 9.4.) As previously mentioned, the use of
free oxygen as a final hydrogen(e⁻) acceptor
is often called respiration. If, in the absence of
free oxygen, an alternative *inorganic* hydrogen-
(e⁻) acceptor is used, e.g., $NaNO_3$, the biooxidation is sometimes called *anaerobic respiration.*

PHOTOPHOSPHORYLATION. In addition to
the phosphorylations just described, a third type
of phosphorylation, termed *photophosphorylation,*
occurs in photosynthetic species of cells. The
process derives its energy from the effect of light
on electrons in chlorophyll. The net result is
the same as in substrate-level or oxidative-
chain phosphorylations: i.e., generation of ATP.
However, the reaction is light dependent. It is
discussed more fully in Chapter 38.

**Phosphate-Bond Energy.** The energy of
the phosphate bonds in ATP formed during
all biooxidations, including photosynthesis, is
released when the phosphate bonds are hydrolyzed. ATP is thereby degraded to ADP; the
energy released is used in synthesis (Chapter 8)
and other vital functions of the cell. The ADP
is then available to accept a new e-r phosphate
group. Thus ADP and ATP act together as an
energy transfer and storage system; this is one of
the most important mechanisms in biooxidation (Fig. 9.4).

The energy of the phosphate bonds may
also be readily transferred into some other types
of e-r bonds (e.g., thioesters) at about the same
energy level, and vice versa. In some reactions
both of the phosphate bonds of ATP are hydrolyzed, forming ADP and AMP successively.
In other reactions pyrophosphate is split off from
ATP, leaving AMP. AMP is restored to ATP
by successive phosphorylations or by combination of AMP with pyrophosphate. Similar nucleotides of other nucleosides, e.g., guanidine,
uridine and cytidine, carry on similar functions
in other energy-yielding reactions and energy-
transfer systems (see Krebs cycle, protein synthesis, etc.) in various cells.

## COMPLETE AND INCOMPLETE
## BIOOXIDATIONS

**Biooxidation in the Presence of Available
Oxygen.** In most aerobic and some facultative bacteria, biooxidation of a substrate is
complete. If the substrate is an organic compound such as glucose the end products are
$CO_2$ and $H_2O$. This is illustrated by the aerobic utilization of glucose by bakers' yeast (*Saccharomyces cerevisiae*):

$$C_6H_{12}O_6 + 6O_2 \longrightarrow$$
$$6CO_2 + 6H_2O + 688,500 \text{ cal.}$$

If the substrate is inorganic the oxidation
may be equally complete, even though the end
products differ, as in the oxidation of sulfur to
sulfuric acid (see page 542). Such oxidations

**TABLE 9.1   THE EMBDEN-MEYERHOF SCHEME FOR GLUCOSE DISSIMILATION (THE GLYCOLYTIC PATHWAY)**

| Step No. | Substrate | Enzyme | Products | Result of Reaction |
|---|---|---|---|---|
| 1. | $C_6H_{12}O_6 + AT \simeq P$ <br> Glucose | Hexokinase $\longrightarrow$ | $C_6H_{11}O_6 \cdot PO_3H_2 + AD \sim P$ <br> Glucose-6-phosphate | *Energy* is yielded by breaking one energy-rich phosphate bond ($\sim$) of $AT \simeq P$, leaving $AD \sim P$. |
| 2. | Glucose-6-phosphate | Phosphohexose isomerase $\longrightarrow$ | $C_6H_{11}O_6 \cdot PO_3H_2$ <br> Fructose-6-phosphate | Molecule is rearranged; no yield of energy. |
| 3. | Fructose-6-phosphate $+ AT \simeq P$ | Phosphohexokinase $\longrightarrow$ | $C_6H_{10}O_6 \cdot (PO_3H_2)_2 + AD \sim P$ <br> Fructose-1,6-diphosphate | Molecule takes phosphate from $AT \simeq P$, yielding *energy* and leaving $AD \sim P$. |
| 4. | Fructose-1:6 diphosphate | Zymohexase (aldolase) $\longrightarrow$ | $C_3H_4O_2 \cdot OH \cdot PO_3H_2 + CHO \cdot CHOH \cdot CH_2O \cdot PO_3H_2$ <br> Dihydroxyacetone $\longrightarrow$ Glyceraldehyde-3-phosphate <br> phosphate (a form of triose) <br> (a form of triose) | Molecule is split into two interchangeable triose molecules. No yield of energy. |
| 5. | Glyceraldehyde-3-phosphate $+ Pi + NAD$ | Phosphoglyceraldehyde dehydrogenase $\longrightarrow$ | $C_3H_4O_4 \cdot (PO_3H_2)_2 + NADH_2$ <br> 1-3-diphosphoglyceric acid | Triose molecule takes up phosphate. $H_2$ is yielded to NAD, forming $NADH_2$, and yielding *energy* to be stored (see step 6). |
| 6. | 1-3-diphosphoglyceric acid $+ AD \sim P$ | Diphosphoglyceric dephosphorylase $\longrightarrow$ | $C_3H_5O_4 \cdot PO_3H_2 + AT \simeq P$ <br> 3-phosphoglyceric acid | Energy yielded in step 5 is stored as $\sim$ by changing $AD \sim P$ to $AT \simeq P$. Molecule loses phosphate. |
| 7. | 3-phosphoglyceric acid | Phosphoglyceromutase (triose mutase) $\longrightarrow$ | $C_3H_5O_4 \cdot PO_3H_2$ <br> 2-phosphoglyceric acid | Molecular rearrangement. No yield of energy. |
| 8. | 2-phosphoglyceric acid | Enolase $\longrightarrow$ | $C_3H_3O_3 \cdot PO_3H_2$ <br> Phospho-enol-pyruvic acid | 2-phosphoglyceric acid yields H and OH. *Energy* is stored in step 9. |
| 9. | Phospho-enol-pyruvic acid $+ AD \sim P$ | Phosphopyruvate dephosphorylase $\longrightarrow$ | $C_3H_4O_3 \left\{ \begin{matrix} CH_3 \\ C{=}O \\ COOH \end{matrix} \right\} + AT \simeq P$ <br> Pyruvic acid | Molecule is decomposed to pyruvic acid; phosphate and $\sim$ being transferred to $AD \sim P$ which thus becomes $AT \simeq P$. |

theoretically release all the energy available from the substrate. They are characteristic of aerobic metabolism. Actually, parts of the substrate are usually utilized in cell synthesis.

However, even in the presence of free oxygen, biooxidation may be incomplete. Much depends on the species, the enzymic equipment of the cell and the availability of an alternate hydrogen($e^-$) acceptor. An example of aerobic but incomplete oxidation is the formation of vinegar (acetic acid) from wine (alcohol) by *Acetobacter*. These aerobic bacteria, long familiar as "mother of vinegar," grow as a scum on the surface of wine and convert it to vinegar:

$$C_2H_5OH + O_2 \longrightarrow$$
$$CH_3COOH + H_2O + 118 \text{ kcalories}$$

Much of the available energy of the alcohol is left in the acetic acid. Many aerobic fungi can utilize this energy by oxidizing the acetic acid to $H_2O$ and $CO_2$:

$$CH_3COOH + 2O_2 \longrightarrow 2CO_2 + 2H_2O.$$

**Biooxidation in the Absence of Available Oxygen.** Biooxidations may occur in the total absence of available oxygen; in several genera of strict anaerobes, biooxidations can occur *only* in the total absence of free oxygen. Biooxidations in the total absence of free available oxygen, when the hydrogen($e^-$) acceptor is an *organic* substance, are called *fermentations*.

## FERMENTATION

Elsewhere (Chapters 5 and 32) we have indicated that some organisms, called *strict aerobes*, are enzymically equipped to use only free oxygen as final hydrogen($e^-$) acceptor; that others, called *facultative aerobes*, are equipped to use, as final hydrogen($e^-$) acceptor, either free oxygen or some alternative, reducible, *inorganic* substrate, commonly a nitrate. Here we shall consider biooxidations that occur in the absence of available inorganic oxygen and in which both hydrogen donors and acceptors are organic substances. Typically, donor and acceptor are different parts of the same organic substrate molecule. Such biooxidations are classed as *fermentations;* the substrates are commonly, but not necessarily, carbohydrates. In fermentations usually only NAD or NADP functions as hydrogen($e^-$) carrier. FAD and the cytochrome system are not required since the final hydrogen($e^-$) acceptor is not oxygen but an organic substance, commonly pyruvic acid.

The term fermentation is sometimes erroneously used for certain strictly aerobic processes, especially industrial processes, e.g., the aerobic oxidation of alcohol to acetic acid by *Acetobacter* sp., in "vinegar fermentation."

Fermentation may be caused by facultative organisms under anaerobic conditions, e.g., brewer's yeast (*Saccharomyces cerevisiae*); by *strictly anaerobic* organisms, e.g., bacteria of the Genus *Clostridium;* or even in the presence of free oxygen by "indifferent" organisms that do not ordinarily utilize free oxygen, e.g., species of *Lactobacillus*.

**Products of Fermentation.** Depending on the conditions of growth, the substrate and the organisms involved, the end products of fermentations vary greatly. *Clostridium* species commonly ferment glucose to yield butyl and other alcohols and certain acids; *Lactobacillus lactis* yields almost entirely lactic acid, while *L. brevis* yields lactic and acetic acids, ethyl alcohol and carbon dioxide. Other microorganisms produce numerous other valuable end products of fermentation (Fig. 9.5 and Chapter 47).

**Pyruvic Acid (Pyruvate).** Pyruvate is physiologically the most important first intermediate product in most biooxidations of glucose, aerobic or anaerobic. It is commonly produced from glucose by stages as shown in Table 9.1. However, several other analogous series of reactions occur in many bacteria and other microorganisms, e.g., the Entner-Doudoroff cycle in bacteria of the large and important Genus *Pseudomonas*. In this cycle the pathway to pyruvate progresses via glucose-6-phosphate, 6-phosphogluconic acid, 2-keto-3-deoxy-6-phosphogluconic acid, to pyruvate plus 3-phosphoglyceraldehyde.

Pyruvate may also be reached via the metabolism of sugars other than glucose, and by pathways other than those cited via the metabolism of fatty acids and of amino acids. The monosaccharides, fatty acids and amino acids are, of course, derived mainly from the preliminary digestive hydrolysis of starch, glycogen, cellulose, fats, poly-beta-hydroxybutyric acid, chitin or proteins depending on the species of organism. Thus, many kinds of organic nutrient may contribute to the pyruvate content of the cell.

Now, pyruvate is a sort of chemical "Grand Central Station" in that it is the point of arrival and departure for a wide variety of metabolic substrates and products (Fig. 9.5). Pyruvate serves as the electron acceptor in most fermentations, being reduced in many types of cell to lactic acid. It may also be decarboxylated and the product reduced to ethyl alcohol. Conversely, it may serve as a *source* of amino acids, fatty acids, aldehydes or other important cell-building materials.

For example, a series of reactions by which many amino acids are changed to pyruvate is summarized in the oxidative deamination of alanine:

$$
\begin{array}{c}
CH_3 \\
| \\
H-C-NH_2 - NH_3 + \tfrac{1}{2} O_2 \longrightarrow \\
| \\
O=C-OH
\end{array}
$$

*alanine*

$$
\begin{array}{c}
CH_3 \\
| \\
C=O \quad + NH_3^- \\
| \\
O=C-OH
\end{array}
$$

*pyruvate*

Long-chain fatty acids undergo somewhat more complex changes, but the residues of the changes often become pyruvate. For example, propionic acid may be oxidized to pyruvate:

$$
\begin{array}{c}
CH_3 \\
| \\
C=H_2 - H_2 + O_2 \longrightarrow \\
| \\
O=C-OH
\end{array}
$$

*propionate*

$$
\begin{array}{c}
CH_3 \\
| \\
C=O \quad + H_2O \\
| \\
O=C-OH
\end{array}
$$

*pyruvate*

A common source of pyruvate, especially in fermentations, is lactic acid:

$$
\begin{array}{c}
CH_3 \\
| \\
H-C-OH - H_2 + \tfrac{1}{2} O_2 \longrightarrow \\
| \\
O=C-OH
\end{array}
$$

*lactate*

$$
\begin{array}{c}
CH_3 \\
| \\
C=O + H_2O \\
| \\
O=C-OH
\end{array}
$$

*pyruvate*

If a substance, e.g., acetic acid, $CH_3COOH$, lacks a carbon atom to form pyruvate, it can be changed (via a series of enzymic reactions, with energy from CoA~S) to a three-carbon acid by addition of $CO^{--}$; if it has too many carbon atoms, it may be split enzymically; pyruvate is the biochemical procrustean bed which many molecules are made to fit.

A wide variety of end products of incomplete decomposition of glucose may be derived under a common condition of growth (e.g., in a test tube of glucose-infusion broth which is partly aerobic and partly anaerobic). For example, from a common saprophyte, the gram-negative, facultative bacillus *Klebsiella aerogenes,* the following end products have been shown to occur: hydrogen, carbon dioxide, ethyl alcohol, acetic acid, acetyl-methyl-carbinol, 2-3-butylene glycol, lactic acid, glycerol, succinic acid. There are undoubtedly others in minute amounts (Fig. 9.5).

Some of the end products of metabolism, e.g., acetyl-methyl-carbinol, $H_2$ and $CO_2$, are easily tested for in a culture tube and are often distinctive of certain species. Distinctive products of metabolism of various substances, glucose among others, are extremely useful in identifying certain organisms. Also, as already indicated, some of these products, e.g., lactic acid and butyl alcohol, are of great industrial value (Chapter 47).

## THE CITRIC ACID (TRICARBOXYLIC ACID OR KREBS) CYCLE

From a physiological standpoint one of the most important derivatives of pyruvate is *oxalacetic acid* (*oxalacetate*). This is a "stepping-stone" into the cyclical series of reactions that are involved in the terminal oxidation process in many aerobic biooxidations, i.e., the *citric acid* or *Krebs cycle*.

As brilliantly elucidated by Krebs (Nobel Prize winner), in the presence of available inorganic oxygen and in cells of aerobes and facultative anaerobes with necessary enzymes pyruvate undergoes complete oxidation to $CO_2$ and $H_2O$ through a cyclical series of interdependent reactions. The pyruvate is first dehydrogenated by pyruvic dehydrogenase, with liberation of energy that is taken up in ATP. In this reaction, as in many other enzymic catalyses, various ions, e.g., $Mg^{++}$, $NH_3^+$, $K^+$, are essential as cofactors. The pyruvate is also decarboxylated by the keto-acid-decarboxylating coenzyme called *cocarboxylase* or *thiamine pyrophosphate* (Fig.

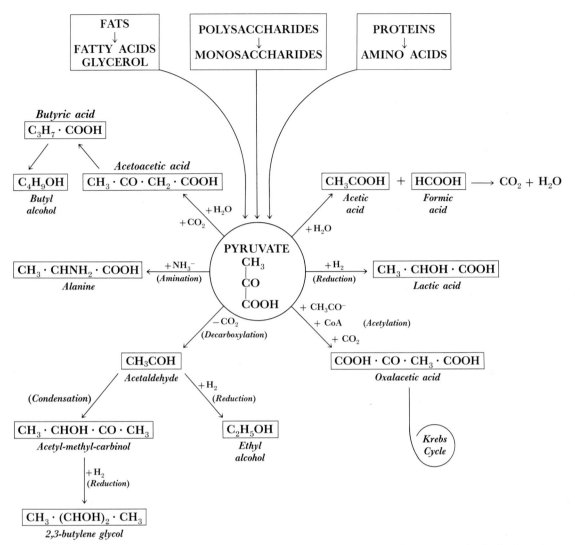

**Figure 9.5** Some of the products of aerobic-anaerobic dissimilation of pyruvate by a common facultative bacterium, *Klebsiella aerogenes*. Note that fats, carbohydrates and proteins can undergo preliminary digestive hydrolysis to yield products that may yield pyruvate. The derivatives of pyruvate shown here are only a few of the many possibilities.

9.6). Note the presence in this coenzyme of the antiberiberi vitamin, *thiamine* or *vitamin $B_1$*. The acetyl residue ($CH_3CO^-$) is transferred to the acetyl-transferring coenzyme, coenzyme A (CoA) carrying an e-r S-bond ($CH_3CO \cdot S{\sim}CoA$; Fig. 9.7):

$$\begin{array}{c} CH_3 \\ | \\ CO \\ | \\ COOH \end{array} \quad + \quad \xrightarrow[(-CO_2)]{S{\sim}CoA} \quad \begin{array}{c} CH_3 \\ | \\ C{=}O \\ | \\ S{\sim}CoA \end{array} \quad + \quad CO_2$$

Note the presence, in CoA, of the *B-vitamin, pantothenic acid.*

At the same time, oxalacetate is derived from pyruvate by carboxylation (combination with $CO_2$) through a series of steps, the overall reaction being:

$$\begin{array}{c} CH_3 \\ | \\ CO \\ | \\ COOH \end{array} \quad + \quad CO_2 \quad \xrightarrow{(+ H_2O)} \quad \begin{array}{c} COOH \\ | \\ CO \\ | \\ CH_2 \\ | \\ COOH \end{array}$$

*pyruvate*          *oxalacetate*

**Figure 9.6** Thiamine pyrophosphate (cocarboxylase).

The $CH_3 \cdot CO \cdot S{\sim}CoA$ then combines with oxalacetate to form citric acid (citrate) by means of a condensing enzyme, liberating $HS \cdot CoA$:

$$\begin{array}{l} COOH \\ | \\ CO \\ | \\ CH_2 \\ | \\ COOH \end{array} + CH_3 \cdot CO \cdot S{\sim}CoA \xrightarrow{\ (+H_2O)\ }$$

*oxalacetate*

Citrate then undergoes the series of changes called the *citric acid, tricarboxylic,* or *Krebs cycle* (Table 9.2; Fig. 9.8). The overall reaction shows

$$\begin{array}{l} COOH \\ | \\ CH_2 \\ | \\ HOC \cdot COOH + HS \cdot CoA \\ | \\ CH_2 \\ | \\ COOH \end{array}$$

*citrate*

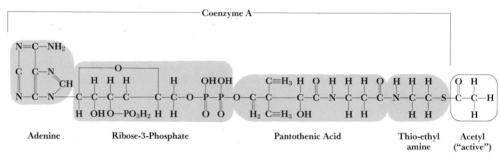

**Figure 9.7**   Structure of acetyl coenzyme A. Note the "active" acetyl group. Compare with structure of DNA (Fig. 8.7), noting the presence in coenzyme A (CoA) of various groups found in DNA and in other coenzymes.

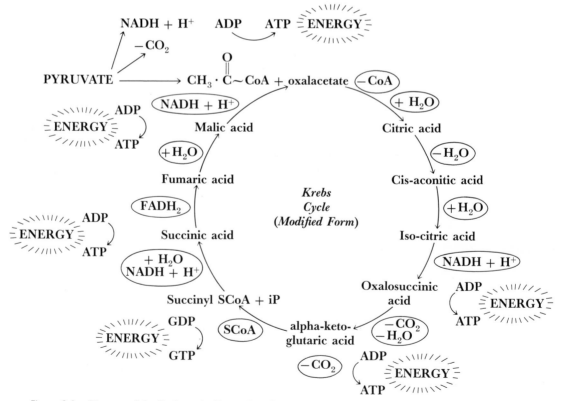

**Figure 9.8**   Diagram of the Krebs cycle. For explanation see text and Table 9.2. All the changes shown are reversible except the condensation between CoA and oxaloacetate resulting in the formation of citrate. Hydrogen taken up by NAD and FAD is transferred to the cytochrome system and so to oxygen.

**TABLE 9.2 THE KREBS (OR CITRIC ACID OR TRICARBOXYLIC ACID) CYCLE. (SEE ALSO FIG. 9.8.)**

| Step No. | Substrate | Enzyme | Products of the Reaction | Nature of the Reaction |
|---|---|---|---|---|
| 1. | $CH_3$ / $C{=}O$ Pyruvic + (CoA) / $COOH$ acid $+ NAD + AD \sim P + Pi*$ | Pyruvic dehydrogenase / Pyruvic decarboxylase $\longrightarrow$ | Acetyl CoA (see Fig. 9.7). $+ CO_2 + NADH + AT \approx P$ | Pyruvic acid is decarboxylated, the acetyl portion ($CH_3 \cdot CO$) combining with CoA to form acetyl CoA. H is transferred to NAD, forming NADH and yielding *energy* to $AT \approx P$. |
| 2. | Acetyl SCoA ("Active acetyl"). | Condensation $\longrightarrow$ | $C_6H_8O_7$ / Citric acid + SCoA / (a tricarboxylic acid) | "Active acetyl" combines with oxalacetic acid to form citric acid. SCoA is liberated to combine with more $CH_3 \cdot CO{-}$. No $AT \approx P$ is formed. |
| 3. | Citric acid | Aconitase $\longrightarrow$ | $C_6H_6O_6$ / Cis-aconitic acid + $H_2O$ | Citric acid is dehydrated to form cis-aconitic acid. No $AT \approx P$ is formed. |
| 4. | Cis-aconitic acid + $H_2O$ | Aconitase $\longrightarrow$ | $C_6H_8O_7$ / Iso-citric acid | Cis-aconitic acid is rehydrated to form iso-citric acid. No $AT \approx P$ is formed. |
| 5. | Iso-citric acid + NADP + $AD \sim P + Pi$ | Iso-citric dehydrogenase decarboxylase $\longrightarrow$ | $C_6H_6O_7 + H_2O + NADPH_2 + AT \approx P$ / Oxalosuccinic acid | Iso-citric acid is dehydrogenated to form oxalosuccinic acid. H is transferred to NADP, forming $NADPH_2$ and yielding *energy* to form $AT \approx P$. $CO_2$ is lost. |
| 6. | Oxalosuccinic acid | Oxalosuccinic decarboxylase $\longrightarrow$ | $C_5H_6O_5 + CO_2 + H_2O$ / α ketoglutaric acid | Oxalosuccinic acid is decarboxylated to yield alpha-keto-glutaric acid and $CO_2$. No $AT \approx P$ is formed. |
| 7. | α keto-glutaric acid + NAD + $AD \sim P$ + Pi + $H_2O$ + SCoA | α keto-glutaric dehydrogenase decarboxylase $\longrightarrow$ | Succinyl SCoA $+ CO_2 + NADH_2 + H_2O + AT \approx P$ | Alpha-keto-glutaric acid is decarboxylated and dehydrogenated. Hydrogen is transferred to NAD, yielding $NADH_2$. The *energy*, with phosphate, is transferred to $AD \sim P$, forming $AT \approx P$. |
| 8. | Succinyl SCoA + $H_2O + AD \sim P$ + Pi | Succinyl thiokinase $\longrightarrow$ | Succinic acid $+ AT \approx P$ + SCoA | The succinyl group of alpha-keto-glutaric acid combines with SCoA. This is converted to succinic acid, yielding SCoA and energy to form $AT \approx P$. |
| 9. | Succinic acid + FAD + Pi + $AD \sim P$ | Succinic dehydrogenase $\longrightarrow$ | $C_4H_4O_4 + FADH_2 + H_2O$ / Fumaric acid $+ AT \approx P$ | Succinic acid is dehydrogenated to fumaric acid, $H_2$ being transferred to FAD to form $FADH_2$ and yielding *energy* to $AT \approx P$. |
| 10. | Fumaric acid + $H_2O$ | Fumarase $\longrightarrow$ | $C_4H_6O_5$ / Malic acid | Fumaric acid is hydrated to form malic acid. No energy is released. |
| 11. | Malic acid + NAD + Pi + $AD \sim P$ | Malic dehydrogenase $\longrightarrow$ | Oxalacetic acid + $H_2O + NADH_2 + AT \approx P$ | Malic acid is dehydrogenated to form oxalacetic acid. This returns to step 2 to combine with active acetyl and continue the cycle. Hydrogen from malic acid is transferred to NAD, forming $NADH_2$ and yielding *energy* to $AT \approx P$. |

*Inorganic phosphate.

(a) Organic Substrate $2(H^+e^-) \longrightarrow$ NAD $\longrightarrow$ (FAD) $\longrightarrow$ Cytochrome system $+ O_2 \longrightarrow H_2O_2$ ⎫
⎬ Obligate aerobes

(b) Inorganic Substrate $\begin{cases} CO \\ S \\ NH_3 \\ H_2 \end{cases} + n/O_2 \xrightarrow{\text{Oxidases}} \begin{cases} CO_2 \\ SO_4^= \\ NO_3^- \\ H_2O \end{cases}$

(c) Organic Substrate $2(H^+e^-) \longrightarrow$ NAD $\longrightarrow$ organic $(H^+e^-)$ acceptor; e.g., pyruvate (fermentation)   Obligate anaerobes

(d) Organic Substrate $2(H^+e^-) \longrightarrow$ NAD $\longrightarrow$

→ Pyruvate $\longrightarrow$ lactic acid, etc. (fermentation)

$\begin{cases} NO_3^- \longrightarrow N_2 \\ SO_4^= \longrightarrow H_2S \\ CO_3^= \longrightarrow CH_4 \end{cases}$ anaerobic

→ Pyruvate $+$ oxalacetate $\longrightarrow$ Krebs cycle $\longrightarrow CO_2 + H_2O$ (aerobic)

⎫
⎬ Facultative species
⎭

**Figure 9.9**   Some representative types of mechanisms of biooxidation. Shown are mechanisms of oxidation of (a) organic and (b) inorganic substrates by strict aerobes; (c) oxidation of organic substrates by strict anaerobes using organic $H(e^-)$ acceptors (fermentation); (d) the anaerobic use of *either organic* $H(e^-)$ acceptors e.g., lactic acid (fermentation) *or inorganic* $H(e^-)$ acceptors (depending on species) or terminal oxidation via the Krebs cycle, by facultative species.

the complete oxidation of pyruvate to $CO_2$ and $H_2O$:

$$\begin{array}{l} CH_3 \\ | \\ CO \\ | \\ COOH \end{array} + 2\tfrac{1}{2}\ O \longrightarrow 3\ CO_2 + 2\ H_2O$$

*pyruvate*

Several mechanisms of biooxidation are shown in Figure 9.9.

## SUPPLEMENTARY READING

Cantarow, A., and Schepartz, B.: Biochemistry, 4th ed. W. B. Saunders Co., Philadelphia. 1967.

Gray, C. T., and Gest, H.: Biological formation of molecular hydrogen. Science, *148*:186, 1965.

Green, D. E.: Biological oxidation. Sci. Amer., *199*:56, 1958.

Greenberg, D. M.: Metabolic Pathways. 2 vols. Academic Press, Inc., New York. 1960, 1961.

Gunsalus, I. C., and Stanier, R. Y., editors: The Bacteria: A Treatise on Structure and Function. 2 vols. Academic Press, Inc., New York. 1960, 1961.

Harrow, B., and Mazur, A.: Textbook of Biochemistry, 9th ed. W. B. Saunders Co., Philadelphia. 1966.

Kaplan, N. O., and Kennedy, E. P., editors: Current Aspects of Biochemical Energetics. Academic Press, New York. 1966.

Lascelles, J.: Comparative aspects of structures associated with electron transport. Fifteenth Symposium, Function and Structure in Micro-organisms, page 32. Soc. Gen. Microbiol., London. 1965.

Lees, H.: Energy metabolism in chemolithotrophic bacteria. Ann. Rev. Microbiol., *14*:83, 1960.

Lehninger, A. L.: Energy transformation in the cell. Sci. Amer., *202*:102, 1960.

Lehninger, A. L., Wadkins, C. L., Cooper, C., Devlin, T. M., and Gamble, Jr., J. L.: Oxidative phosphorylation. Science, *128*:450, 1958.

Lieberman, M., and Baker, J. E.: Respiratory electron transport. Ann. Rev. Plant Physiol., *16*:343, 1965.

McMurray, W. C.: Report on meeting concerning bioenergetics. Science, *147*:413, 1965.

Oginsky, E. L., and Umbreit, W. W.: An Introduction to Bacterial Physiology, 2nd ed. W. H. Freeman, San Francisco. 1959.

Thimann, K. V.: The Life of Bacteria, 2nd ed. The Macmillan Company, New York. 1963.

Wagner, A. F., and Folkers, K.: Vitamins and Coenzymes. Interscience Publishers, New York. 1964.

# 2

---

## *The Protista:*
## *Eucaryotic and*
## *Procaryotic;*
## *The Viruses*

This section of "Fundamentals of Microbiology" presents a general description of the Protista and differentiates between the three major groups of Protists: the eucaryons, the procaryons and the viruses. The student is first introduced, or reintroduced, to several representative types of eucaryotic Protista. Only two chapters are devoted to this large subject, on the assumption that the student of microbiology has already made the acquaintance of these primitive plants and animals in elementary courses of Biology. On this basis, then, he needs only to renew acquaintance with these eucaryotic friends. After a reading of these two chapters both he and the beginner in Biology, even though the latter has not previously encountered the eucaryotic Protista, can appreciate fully the differences between the eucaryons and the strange new friends, the procaryons, the major subject of this book, as described in succeeding sections.

The discussions of procaryotic genetic phenomena and mutation, involving as they do detailed discussions of DNA and RNA and genetic recombination in the absence of sex, lead easily into the discussions of viruses, those strange wanderers in the microbiological cosmos that are neither cells nor alive, neither eucaryon nor procaryon. The viruses exhibit anatomical, physiological and genetic phenomena that are as suggestive of, yet as foreign to, the cellular protists as little green men from Mars are to us. Nevertheless the viruses are of fundamental importance in Microbiology and at least a reading knowledge of them is essential to an understanding of almost all the discussions of procaryons that follow.

**115**

# Chapter 10

# PROTISTA: EUCARYON AND PROCARYON

Robert Hooke, mentioned in Chapter 1 as a pioneer English microscopist, was also an inventor, artist, physician, philosopher and enthusiastic investigator of almost everything with the microscope. In 1665 he applied the term *cell* (L. *cella* = a small enclosure) to the microscopic "boxes" or spaces that are readily seen with the microscope in the honeycomb-like structure of dried cork. Hooke, however, had no knowledge of the living organisms that the cork "cells" had once contained. To him a cell in cork was a hollow shell composed of cork substance (cellulose). Likewise, although living microorganisms were first described by Leeuwenhoek in 1674, the Dutch microscopist had no knowledge of the true nature and structure of microscopic organisms.

## 10.1 CELLS AND PROTOPLASM

Accurate knowledge of the sizes, forms, habitats, functions and anatomy of microorganisms (including the tissue cells of higher plants and animals) accumulated slowly until about 1820, when microscopes were perfected that yielded magnifications as high as 600×. In 1824 Dutrochet, a French scientist, called attention to the fact that all organized tissues were aggregations of billions of microscopic units which he called cells, though their true nature was still far from fully realized. The fact that the internal substance of such cells was not entirely homogeneous was revealed in 1831, when Robert Brown described an often-seen though unidentified intracellular body now recognized as a nucleus. Its structure and function were not fully clarified for many years

after Brown's description and, in some respects, are still enigmatic.

Microbiologists of the eighteenth and early nineteenth centuries thought of the entire contents (except obviously inert inner granules of substances such as starch or fat) of microorganisms as a homogeneous, clear, viscous, colorless substance that had the unique and mysterious property of being alive. In 1839 the physiologist Purkinje gave this substance the name *protoplasm* (Gr. *protos* = original or primitive; *plasma* = fluid substance). Protoplasm was recognized as *living substance*. Max Schultz, in Germany about 1860, called it the substance of life and Thomas H. Huxley, in England in 1865, called it "the physical basis of life." Because we now know it to be a complex mixture of many chemically different substances, and to contain many distinct parts with a variety of structures and physiological functions, the term protoplasm is no longer used to refer to a single substance. The word is still sometimes used, however, as a convenient synonym for "*total living cell contents*," and the term will occasionally be so used here.

The first formulation of the modern cell theory in 1838 is generally ascribed to two German scientists: Schleiden, a botanist, and Schwann, a zoologist. Today the cell in biology is defined as the smallest living unit capable of autonomous growth and reproduction using food substances chemically different from itself. This definition of a cell excludes: (a) inorganic crystals that grow only by accretion of the same substance as themselves and (b) viruses. Viruses, as will be explained later, are not cellular in structure, according to the currently accepted definition of a cell, and do not have autonomous metabolism or, indeed, any life we know it. Viruses are "alive" only when inside other living cells and while being replicated at their expense. Otherwise viruses are inert.

## 10.2   PLANTAE AND ANIMALIA

Before the general use of the high-powered microscope, biologists had relatively little difficulty in classifying the various forms of life visible to their unaided eyes as animals (the Animal Kingdom; *Animalia*) or as plants (the Plant Kingdom; *Plantae*). No other kingdom was known. Differentiation was based mainly on such readily visible characteristics as motility, green color and the presence of leaves, flowers and stems as contrasted with eyes, teeth and legs. Plants were regarded as typically not motile and relatively simple; animals as typically mobile and obviously more complex. Similarly, early microscopists readily differentiated between the unicellular or microscopic *green* (chlorophyll-containing) algae on the one hand and the *colorless* (nonchlorophyll-containing) unicellular animals and fungi (yeasts, protozoa, molds and bacteria) on the other. All of the microscopic algae, fungi and bacteria were assigned to the Plant Kingdom because of their immobility, their supposedly simple, plantlike structure and their inability to catch and eat solid foods like animals. On the other hand, protozoa were readily classed as animals because of their more complex structure, their conspicuous motility and their ability to catch and eat solid foods such as other protozoa, bacteria and cell fragments.

As generally happens, this comfortable arrangement soon encountered difficulties. With advances in knowledge and improvements in scientific techniques, including microscopy, it became evident that, among the small, more primitive ("lower" or less highly evolved) organisms, and especially among microorganisms, classification as plant or animal was becoming difficult and often impossible. Many puzzling overlappings and inconsistencies were discovered. For example, it was found that plant cells generally have cell walls of cellulose (the basic material of all wood, stems and leaves), and that animal cells do not have any true cell wall at all, but instead thin, limp and fragile cell membranes. In some animal cells, this membrane, condensed and thickened, serves as a protective and retaining integument. Many species of animal cell synthesize supporting structures of chitin: a characteristically animal substance (insect and crustacean skeletal ma

terial). Yet many fungi have cell walls of chitin, whereas certain primitive animals, the group of chordates called sea squirts (tunicates), have some cell walls of cellulose.

Plants (except the fungi) contain the conspicuous green pigment, chlorophyll, that enables them to use sunlight as a source of energy. Typical animal cells and fungi do not contain chlorophyll, and cannot use radiations as a source of energy. They must obtain their energy from oxidations of their foodstuffs. Yet one group of flagellated protozoa, *Euglena*, of the Order Euglenoidina (botanists classify them as Euglenophyta) contain chlorophyll arranged in chloroplasts like those of higher plants and can use sunlight as a source of energy.

By contrast, some species of *Euglena* not only lack chlorophyll, in this resembling fungal and animal cells, but are nonmotile (in this resembling typical plant cells). Puzzlingly, several species of nonmotile protozoa are known, and some bacteria, classed as fungi (plants) partly because of their lack of chlorophyll, are actively motile like protozoa. Contrariwise, some of the bacteria (fungi) contain photosynthetic pigments like chlorophyll. Some algae (obviously [?] plants) produce motile, flagellate, protozoa-like reproductive cells. Some plants are structurally like blue-green algae but have no chlorophyll and so are classed as bacteria. There are numerous other illustrations of confusing combinations and overlappings of properties of organisms that were once classified in supposedly distinct and mutually exclusive groups.

## 10.3   KINGDOM PROTISTA

To avoid the confusion arising from growing knowledge of microorganisms, a third kingdom, the *Protista* (Gr. *protistos* = primitive or first), was proposed for *all microorganisms* in 1866 by Ernst Haeckel, one of Darwin's students. In Haeckel's time microscopes still lacked the high resolving power of modern instruments, and many species of microorganisms, including the rickettsias, the viruses and several other curious types that will be mentioned later, were then unknown. These have since been included in the Kingdom of Protista.* Except for the noncellular viruses, all members of the Protista Kingdom (*protists*) are distinguished from all members of the Plant and Animal Kingdoms by the single fact that protists exist only as

---

*Some authorities prefer not to recognize the Kingdom Protista.

autonomously synthetic, *unicellular* organisms. Some protists, as unicellular blue-green algae and true bacteria (Order Eubacteriales), are obviously plants; others, as protozoa, are obviously animals. Many others are intermediate: neither one nor the other. Viruses, being non-cellular, may (or may not!) be included as protists "by courtesy"; the exact position and status of viruses in the living world is still debatable. The Kingdom Protista is now more widely referred to than formerly in biological classifications, on an equal basis with the Plant and Animal Kingdoms. The term protist is commonly used to mean unicellular micro-organism as previously defined and will be frequently so used here.

The Kingdom Protista may for convenience be divided into six main groups, as follows:

1. Protozoa (Gr. *protos* = primitive or original; *zoion* = animal): unicellular animals;

2. Algae (L. *alga* = seaweed): unicellular, photosynthetic plants;

3. Eumycetes or true fungi (Gr. *eu* = true; *mykes* = fungus): yeasts and molds;

4. Schizomycetes or fission fungi (Gr. *schiza* = fission or separation): bacteria;

   (a) Rickettsiales, an order of bacteria-like microorganisms named for one of their famous investigators, Howard Taylor Ricketts;

   (b) *Mycoplasma* (from Greek meaning *formed like fungi*), a genus of microorganisms in many respects resembling bacteria and probably closely related to or even possibly(?) derived from them or vice versa; commonly designated as pleuropneumonia-like organisms or PPLO;

   (c) Psittacosis-lymphogranuloma-trachoma organisms, causes of the named diseases and formerly regarded as "large" viruses but now thought to be modified bacteria; commonly designated as the *PLT group* or Chlamydiaceae;

5. Virales (L. *virus* = noxious, slimy fluid): the order of viruses;

6. The cells of complex, *multicellular* plants and animals including humans, especially when, as is now done in laboratories of microbiology all over the world, these cells are induced to grow through many generations as separate, free-living, independent, unicellular micro-organisms *in vitro*.

Each of these six groups will be discussed in greater detail in the chapters that follow.

## 10.4  EUCARYOTIC AND PROCARYOTIC CELLS

As indicated, not all protists are by any measure alike. All available evidence strongly suggests that the protists of today were derived from still simpler cellular forms of life during eons of time billions of years ago by evolutionary processes. These simpler cells had in turn presumably developed during still more remote ages from complex but not actually living organic molecules, formed spontaneously in the dark ooze of primeval tropical seas by a process now called *chemical evolution,* as outlined in Chapter 1. See also the list of Supplementary Reading at the end of this chapter.

**Eucaryons.**   At some time during the untold millennia of the early development of cellular forms there seem to have occurred in some of the earlier protists (but not in others) hereditary changes (mutations) and natural selections (evolutionary processes) that resulted in greatly increased complexity of structure and function. The protists that underwent these presumed evolutionary upgradings and became animal-like are probably represented today by the protozoa. Their modern, presumed evolutionary derivatives include all of the "higher" (more highly evolved) animals including man: the Animal Kingdom.

The "improved model" protists that became plantlike are probably represented today by the higher fungi, molds and yeasts and the unicellular green (*not* blue-green) algae. Their modern, presumed evolutionary derivatives (or collaterals) include all of the higher plants: the Plant Kingdom. (There are various other ideas on evolutionary relationships, hence the use of words such as "presumed" and "apparently.")

Whatever their evolutionary history may be, the cells of all of these "upgraded" or higher plant and animal forms, including the higher protists (protozoa, molds, yeasts and higher fungi and green algae) are said to be *eucaryotic* (Gr. *eu* = true; *karyon* = nucleus) because the nucleus of each cell is enclosed within a well-defined *nuclear membrane* and thus segregated from the cytoplasm; it is a *true nucleus*. In addition, with a few exceptions among the simplest forms of molds, typical eucaryons exhibit well-defined sexual or mating phenomena and often well-differentiated sexual cells (gametes).

By the late 1950's, students of cytology had shown that all higher plant and animal cells typically* consist of several morphologically and physiologically distinct parts: (1) a definite *nucleus* (L. *nucis* = kernel) enclosed within a

---

*The use of the words "typically" and "typical" here and elsewhere implies that there are, or may be, "atypical" specimens that do not conform to the general description.

readily demonstrable *nuclear membrane* and containing a complex of deeply staining (*chromatinic*) fibrillar material, the basis of the genetic structures called *chromosomes*. (2) Surrounding the nucleus they observed a mass of clear, semifluid matter, the *cytoplasm*, having a colloidal (continuous phase + discontinuous phase) structure. The cytoplasm was seen to contain several kinds of definite, *membrane-enclosed*, subcellular bodies called plastids or organelles: *mitochondria* (the seat of energy-yielding enzymic activities); *chloroplasts* (the seat of photosynthesis in green

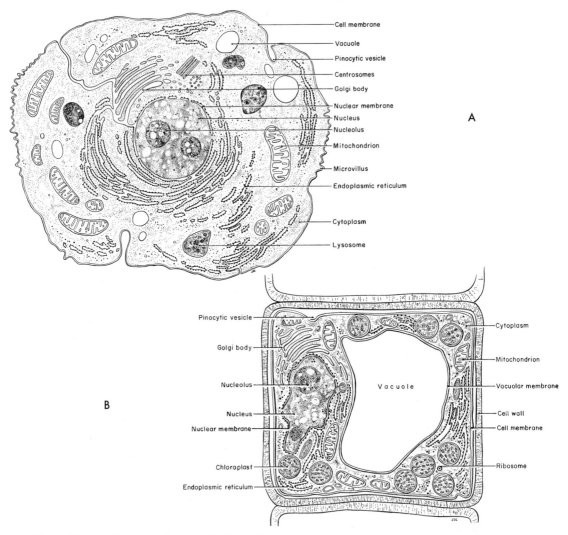

**Figure 10.1**   *A*, Composite diagram of a "typical" animal cell based on various cytological studies and use of the electron microscope. The *nucleus* controls hereditary properties and all other vital activities of the cell. Both nucleus and *nucleolus* have functions in the synthesis of cell material. The well-defined *nuclear membrane* appears to have pores or openings for communication with the cytoplasmic structures and direction of their synthetic and energy-yielding activities. The *cytoplasm* contains immense numbers of granules called *ribosomes,* concentrated especially along the periphery of a cell-wide labyrinth of connected, narrow sacs called the *endoplasmic reticulum.* These granules are involved in the continuous enzymic reactions which synthesize cell materials under direction from the nucleus. The *mitochondria* are involved in another set of enzymic reactions called *biological oxidation* (Chapter 9) which yield the energy for all the cell activities. *Lysosomes* appear to liberate the enzymes which digest part of the food of the cell. The gullet-like *pinocytic mouth* or invagination is a means of ingesting fluids or extremely minute food particles (see Chapter 3). The *centrosomes* are especially active in mitosis during reproduction of the cell by fission. The function of Golgi bodies is still under examination. There are other structures whose nature and function await elucidation by future cytological studies. Compare this complex cell with pictures of bacterial cells shown in this chapter. *B*, Diagram of a typical plant cell. Note the thick cell wall. (*A*, from the Living Cell, by Jean Bachet. Copyright © 1961 by Scientific American, Inc. All rights reserved.) *B*, from Villee: Biology, 5th ed. W. B. Saunders Co., 1967.)

plants); also granules (*blepharoplasts*), associated with motility; *centrosomes* (involved in mitosis); *Golgi apparatus* (function not yet clear); *kineto-plasts* or *kinetonuclei* and basal bodies, associated with motion and flagella or cilia; a *centriole* (in certain plants and animals only; important in fission); *nucleoli;* other organelles whose function and structure were then obscure. (3) Surrounding the cytoplasm a thin, pliable and relatively fragile *cell* (or *cytoplasmic*) *membrane* was demonstrable. It was seen to function as an enclosing and retaining sac for the whole cell, segregating the cell contents from the outer world (Fig. 10.1,*A*).

Typical eucaryotic plant cells (*not* typical animal cells) were seen to have a relatively thick, strong, rigid, retaining and protective *cell wall* outside the cell membrane. In the higher plants this consists generally of cellulose (the principal component of paper and wood) (Fig. 10.1,*B*). In many eucaryotic fungi, the cell wall contains chitin, which is the skeletal substance of insects and crustacea. The electron microscope reveals all the above details (Fig. 10.2) and others as well.

**Procaryons.** It is supposed that those protists that did not participate in the evolutionary upgrading that produced the eucaryotic form of cell, as described before, continued with their primitive nuclear structure. They are with us today as the blue-green algae and the bacteria: "living fossils." Their nucleus is not enclosed in a nuclear membrane and is not sharply segregated from the cytoplasm, though most of their fibrillar, chromatinic nuclear material is commonly aggregated into an irregular mass called a *nucleoid.* Hence this type of cell is said to be procaryotic (Gr. *protos* = primitive; *karyon* = nucleus).

There are numerous other differences: (1) The procaryotic nucleus exhibits none of the complex phenomena of mitosis and meiosis that are distinctive of typical eucaryotic cells. (2) In their manner of reproduction, procaryons are also more primitive than eucaryons, being without typical gametes and exhibiting, though only in some species, a primitive form of incomplete conjugation. (3) Procaryotic cells contain none of the complex, membranous, membrane-enclosed and other organelles which occur in typical eucaryotic cells. (4) The cell walls of eucaryotic plant cells (animal cells do not have cell walls) differ markedly in chemical composition from those of procaryons. The cell walls of eucaryotic green plants are of cellulose, those of eucaryotic fungi are principally of chitin. Not all procaryons have cell walls but in those that do the cell walls are composed of a polysaccharide amino-acid heteropolymer called *mucocomplex, mucopolysaccharide* or *muco-peptide.* In gram-negative bacteria this is combined in various configurations with lipids and lipo-proteins. However, the procaryotic cell wall serves the same protective and retaining purpose as the eucaryotic cell wall (Fig. 10.3). (5)

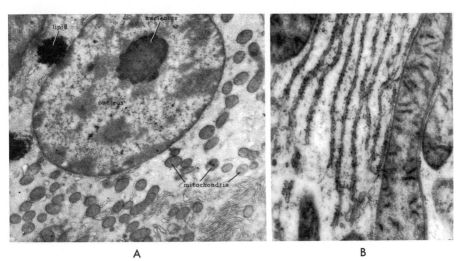

A                              B

**Figure 10.2**   *A,* Electron micrograph of the nucleus and surrounding cytoplasm of a frog liver cell. The spaghetti-like strands of endoplasmic reticulum are visible in the lower right corner (× 16,500). *B,* High power electron micrograph of a rat liver cell. Granules of ribonucleoprotein are seen on the strands of endoplasmic reticulum, and structures with double membranes are evident within the mitochondria in the upper left corner and on the right (× 65,000). (Electron micrographs courtesy of Dr. Don Fawcett in Villee: Biology, 5th ed. W. B. Saunders Co., 1967.)

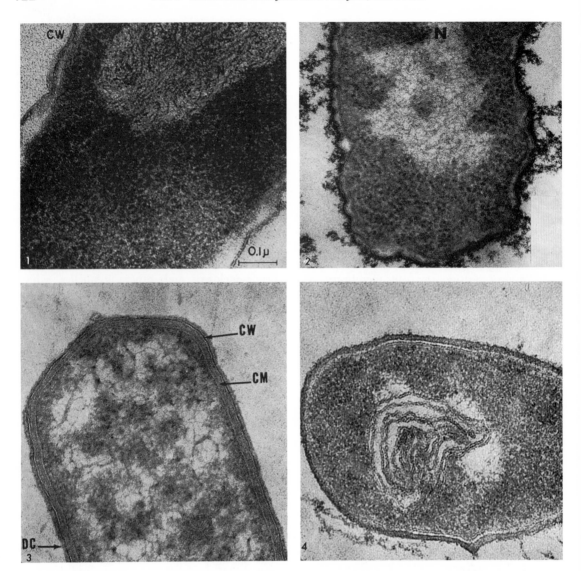

**Figure 10.3**   Electron micrographs of procaryotic cells. Note that in procaryotic cells the numerous organelles typical of eucaryotic cells are almost entirely absent. Only enclosing walls and membranes, ribosomes and nucleoids are regularly seen. Mesosomes may or may not be present. (1) *Escherichia coli.* Cell wall (CW) reveals the triplex structure characteristic of gram-negative bacteria; the "primitive nucleus" or nucleoid (N) exhibits typical, irregular fibrillar mass and a lack of nuclear membrane. (From Cota-Robles and Coffman: J. Bact., *86*:266, 1963.) (2) *E. coli* (× 80,000). DNA filaments form a network in the central nucleoid. (From Franklin and Granboulan: J. Bact., *91*:836, 1966.) (3) Unidentified strain of *Bacteroides* (× 114,000). Note three-layered structure of cell wall (CW), dense crust (DC) and definite cellular membrane (CM). (From Bladen and Waters: J. Bact., *86*:1339, 1963.) (4) *Bacillis subtilis.* Vesicular organelle (mesosome or chondrioid) is a whorl of membranes, exhibiting irregularity typical of procaryotic cell organization. (From Van Iterson: Bact. Rev., *29*:299, 1965.)

Another striking difference between eucaryons and procaryons is the fact that the cytoplasm of typical eucaryons constantly exhibits active streaming movements. This results, among other effects, in motility of many protists, e.g., amebas. The cytoplasm of procaryotic cells, on the contrary, exhibits no streaming. Some species of both types of cells, however, show *gliding mo-*

*tility* in contact with solid objects, which is not yet fully understood.

So different are procaryons from eucaryons that some classifiers would reasonably establish a fourth kingdom, *Monera,* for procaryotic organisms, to include Cyanophyceae, Schizomycetes and related microorganisms. The Kingdom Protista would be reserved for eucaryotic microorganisms alone. In this book we shall include all microorganisms in the Kingdom Protista.

## 10.5   MAJOR GROUPS OF PROCARYONS

In one taxonomic system ("Bergey's Manual," 1957), now obsolescent in view of recent intensive research but still widely used as a point of reference, the procaryons are grouped in the Division Protophyta, or primitive, typically microscopic plants, each of which consists of a single, undifferentiated cell or of unorganized groups of such cells. The Division Protophyta is divided into three main classes. The first comprises the photosynthetic blue-green algae (*Cyanophyceae*). All other algae are eucaryons.

**Blue-Green Algae.** The Cyanophyceae typically multiply by transverse, binary, cell fission; therefore they are also called *Schizophyceae*. In the Cyanophyceae true sexes and gametes are unknown. These algae commonly form long, multicellular chains, filaments or *trichomes*. Many grow singly or in masses of *slime* (like frogs' eggs), hence the group is often called *Myxophyceae* (Gr. *myxa* = slime). Like all higher plants but unlike all bacteria, the blue-green algae contain the green, photosynthetic pigment: chlorophyll *a*. Cyanophyceae require sunlight or another source of radiant energy for growth and give off oxygen during photosynthesis. The Cyanophyceae have morphologically and functionally distinct, rigid, cell walls. Like bacteria but unlike all eucaryotic protists, plant or animal, the supportive fibers of the cell walls of typical Cyanophyceae consist not of cellulose but largely of a complex heteropolymer, a mucocomplex that is described in Chapter 13 under The Cell Wall.

The cells of blue-green algae are unique in containing the blue-green pigment *phycocyanin,* which gives to typical species their distinctive blue-green color. In some species the blue-green color may be masked by red or brown pigments. Cells of most Cyanophyceae, while generally smaller than eucaryotic cells, are nevertheless large enough to be readily visible with optical microscopes. Many species of Cyanophyceae are readily cultivable on artificial media. Although Cyanophyceae exhibit neither flagella nor cytoplasmic streaming, they do exhibit slow gliding and oscillatory movements, the mechanisms of which remain obscure.

**The Bacteria.** The second of the three

Divisions of Protophyta consists of the bacteria, Class Schizomycetes (fission fungi), coordinate with the Schizophyceae. Like the Schizophyceae, the bacteria typically multiply only by transverse binary fission, and there are no true sexual phenomena or morphologically* differentiated gametes as seen in eucaryotic protists. With the exception of one small group, bacteria resemble all other fungi and all animals† in not containing any photosynthetic pigments.

Although generally much smaller than cells of blue-green algae, all bacterial cells are visible with optical microscopes and most are cultivable on inanimate media. Motility, when present, is generally by means of flagella. However, certain species of bacteria exhibit alga-like gliding and oscillatory movements, the mechanisms of which are obscure since, as previously pointed out, procaryons exhibit no cytoplasmic streaming.

**Rickettsias and Chlamydiaceae.** A third group of Protophyta, coordinate with Schizophyceae and Schizomycetes in the 1957 "Bergey's Manual," is called *Microtatobiotes* (smallest of living things). As organized in 1957, this group included two orders called Rickettsiales and Virales. The Order Rickettsiales included the true rickettsias (Family Rickettsiaceae) that cause typhus and Rocky Mountain and related fevers and also the organisms formerly called large or mantle viruses (Family Chlamydiaceae) that cause psittacosis, lymphogranuloma venereum, trachoma and inclusion blenorrhea: the so-called P-L-T group. Most of the Order Rickettsiales have since been generally recognized as modified bacteria and are now commonly described as such. They are very much smaller than Schizomycetes, although just within the range of vision of the best optical microscopes. Wholly unlike any of the Schizophyceae or other Schizomycetes, none of the Rickettsiales is cultivable on inanimate media. They may be propagated inside living organisms such as fertile hens' eggs since they are obligate intracellular parasites.

The Order Virales comprises the true or small viruses. Except for one group (poxviruses such as smallpox) that are just within the extreme range of resolution of the highest-powered optical microscopes, the true viruses are wholly invisible with optical microscopes and are visible only with electron microscopes. Like the Rickettsiales, they are not cultivable on inanimate

*Type F fimbriae? See Chapter 13.
†Except euglenoids.

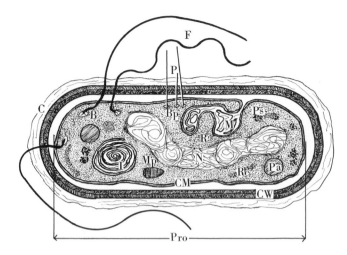

**Figure 10.4** Diagram of a typical bacterial (procaryotic) cell showing all recognized structures. F, flagella; P, pili; CW, cell wall; CM, cell membrane; R, ribosomes; N, nucleoid; B, basal granules of flagella; Bp, basal granules of pili; M, mesosome; Ps, polyribosomes; Rc, ribosomal concentration; I, intracytoplasmic membraneous structure; Mp, metaphosphate (volutin) granule; Pa, poly-beta-hydroxybutyric acid granule; C, capsule. The space (theoretical) between cell membrane and cell wall is exaggerated to show the extent of the protoplast (Pro).

media but are readily cultivable as obligate intracellular parasites in living animal or plant cells. The true viruses are not cellular as cells are currently defined and, in fact, are not actually alive as life is presently understood, although they are viable; hence they exhibit a curious and unique state of existence in the never-never land between the animate and inanimate. Because the viruses are not cellular, and neither eucaryotic nor procaryotic, alive or not-alive, they are discussed as a distinctive group in Chapters 16, 17 and 18.

## FORMS OF MICROORGANISMS

The drawings and reports by Leeuwenhoek gave humanity their first ideas of the true forms of microorganisms. Unlike the fantastic horned, scaly and dragonlike monsters sometimes depicted by the uninstructed as "germs," unicellular organisms are now known to have only two basic forms: (a) simple spheres, spheroids and ovoids, and (b) cylinders. Various simple modifications of the cylindrical forms are common: spindle (fusiform), club (coryneform) or spiral (spirillum, spirochete). Molds and some species of bacteria often grow as branching, elongated cylinders or filaments. Some common protozoa (amebas) are spheroid when inactive, highly irregular when active. Some highly specialized tissue cells have very irregular shapes when in contact with solid surfaces or other cells in various tissues: they may be spindle-shaped in muscles, dendroid or rhizoid or stellate in neural tissues, and so on. When cultivated as separate, individual cells, suspended in special fluid culture media (Chapter 16), many of them appear as spheroids.

## SIZES OF MICROORGANISMS

Leeuwenhoek had no exact means of measuring his animalcules. He described their size by comparing them with grains of sand and other small, familiar objects. When optical micrometers and other means of determining the dimensions of microscopic objects in terms of microns were perfected, many years after Leeuwenhoek's time, it was found that even the largest of the microorganisms listed on page 119 are almost inconceivably small.

Bacteria were found to measure commonly about 2 $\mu$ in diameter, ranging in a few species up to 4 or 5 $\mu$. The length of cylindrical or filamentous types of bacteria may range from about 5 to as much as 500 $\mu$. It has been estimated that a cubic inch could contain 9 trillion ($9 \times 10^{12}$ or 9,000,000,000,000) closely packed cells of a medium-size bacillus species (*Salmonella typhi*, the cause of typhoid fever). Certain common spherical bacteria (*Micrococcus*) 2 $\mu$ in diameter, magnified 1000$\times$, appear a little larger than a period on this page. The cells of rickettsias, much like bacteria, are about one-tenth the size of common bacteria, being of the order of 0.2 $\mu$ in diameter and perhaps as much as 2 $\mu$ in length (except occasional filamentous forms). The size of rickettsias is therefore close to the extreme limit of vision with the best optical microscopes. The smallest reproductive forms or "elementary bodies" of *Mycoplasma* species range around 0.135 $\mu$ in diameter. These are regarded as the smallest units capable of independent life. (Viruses are much smaller but are incapable of independent life.)

As for the other microorganisms mentioned

in the list on page 119, the size of microscopic cells of blue-green algae varies considerably with species, but many spheroid or ovoid species range from 5 to 15 $\mu$ in diameter; some are considerably larger. The cells of yeasts, protozoa and the tissue cells of higher plants and animals, as is perhaps consistent with their more elaborate internal structures, are generally larger than the cells of most blue-green algae, bacteria, rickettsias or *Mycoplasma.* Plant and animal tissue cells commonly have diameters of from 20 to 50 $\mu$ or even more.

Because of differences in shape, sizes of microorganisms are perhaps best compared on the basis of relative volumes. In terms of cubic microns ($\mu^3$), some approximate representative values would be: protozoa, 30,000; human and plant tissue cells, 10,000; yeasts and some blue-green algae, 25–35; bacteria, 3.0; rickettsias, 0.02; some viruses, 0.005.

FORM, SIZE AND FISSION. The size and shape of individual microbial cells bear important relationships to the nutrition and reproduction of each cell. This is because the volume of any cell increases more rapidly than its surface area. Thus, the area of a sphere ($4\pi r^2$) increases as the square of its radius; its volume ($d^3 0.5236$), as the cube of its diameter. The area of a cylinder ($d\pi h + 2\pi r^2$) increases as its diameter or length; its volume ($\pi r^2 h$), as its length or the square of its radius.

All foods, water, gases, ions and molecules necessary for the nourishment and growth of living cells must pass from the exterior into the cell contents through the cell membrane (which also lines pinocytic sacs [Chapter 13] and the mouthlike organelle of protozoa). Regardless of its means of taking in food, or excreting wastes, the cell increases in volume. All wastes also pass through the cell membrane, or the membrane of a contractile vacuole or an anal pore when present.

As the *spherical* or ovoid cell grows there arrives a critical point in the ratio of volume (which must be fed) to surface (which supplies food and removes wastes). The volume exceeds ability of the surface (cell membrane) to provide food and remove wastes. At this point the favorable, initial relationship between surface and content must be renewed. This (among other important physiological functions) is accomplished by fission into two small daughter cells. These grow and divide, and so the process continues. When fission proceeds much more rapidly than cell growth, the volume of each individual cell and the ratio of volume to surface diminishes to a fixed, optimal minimum

as the numbers of cells increase. Young, rapidly growing cells therefore tend to be smaller than old or dormant cells, or than young cells just before fission.

The evolution of *cylindrical* or *filamentous* cells with minimum *diameters* may be regarded as a step toward overcoming the difficulties imposed by the volume-surface relationship of spheroid cells. For example, in a cylindrical bacterium or mold filament, the axial center is never much more than a micron from the cell surface (i.e., from the source of food supply and the means of waste disposal). Length and branching can extend indefinitely, with no increased difficulty in feeding the cell contents or in removing wastes.

Whether, in filamentous cells, cell fission is initiated by *volume:surface ratio,* or whether (as seems more likely) wastes, nutritive requirements, reproductive cycle or other factors initiate cell fission is not fully known. Probably all of these factors play a combined role. Replication of the nuclear material (Chapter 8) and initiation of growth of new cell membrane appear to be closely connected.

Eucaryotic cells overcome the volume-surface difficulty to a large extent by the formation of extensively branched and ramifying invaginations of the cell membrane deep into the cell substance, the whole branched system constituting the *endoplasmic reticulum* (Fig. 10.1). Procaryotic cells have no obvious endoplasmic reticulum, though there are sometimes fairly extensive invaginations called *mesosomes* (Fig. 10.3). The nature and role of mesosomes are discussed in Chapter 13.

## SUPPLEMENTARY READING

Barghoorn, E. S., and Schopf, J. W.: Microorganisms from the late Precambrian of Central Australia. Science, *150*:337, 1965.

Brachet, J.: The Living Cell. W. H. Freeman & Co., San Francisco. 1966.

Calvin, M.: Chemical Evolution. *In:* Evolutionary Biology, *1*, Dobzhansky, T., Hecht, M. K., and Steere, W. G., editors. Appleton-Century-Crofts, New York. 1967.

Dixon, J. S., and Li, C. H.: Cyanoacetylene in prebiotic synthesis. Science, *154*:784, 1966.

Eglinton, G., and Calvin, M.: Chemical Fossils. Sci. Amer., *216*:32, 1967.

Jevons, E. R.: The Biochemical Approach to Life. Basic Books, New York. 1964.

Leete, E.: Biosynthesis of alkaloids. Science, *147*:1000, 1965.

Marshall, C. G. A., May, J. W., and Perret, C. J.: Fossil microorganisms: possible presence in Precambrian Shield of Western Australia. Science, *144*:290, 1964.

Oparin, A. I. (Tr. from Russian by Ann Synge): The Chemical Origin of Life. Charles C Thomas, Springfield, Illinois. 1964.

Oro, J., and Tornabene, T.: Bacterial contamination of some carbonaceous meteorites. Science, *150*:1046, 1965.

Ponnamperuma, C., and Mack, R.: Nucleotide synthesis under possible primitive earth conditions. Science, *148*:1221, 1965.

Schimpl, A., Lemmon, R. M., and Calvin, M.: Cyanamide formation under primitive earth conditions. Science, *147*:149, 1965.

Schopf, J. W., Barghoorn, E. S., Maser, M. D., and Gordon, R. O.: Electron microscopy of fossil bacteria two billion years old. Science, *149*:1365, 1965.

Stolp, H., and Starr, M. P.: Bacteriolysis. Ann. Rev. Microbiol., *19*:79, 1965.

# Chapter 11

## THE EUCARYOTIC PROTISTS

## Fungi

There are three major groups of protists that have eucaryotic cell structure: (1) Algae (higher algae, not Cyanophyceae); (2) the Protozoa; (3) the true (higher) fungi (Eumycetes). Differentiation between typical (i.e., most familiar) species of the three major groups of eucaryotic protists is easy; for example, a green, nonmotile alga like *Chlorella* is obviously unlike a colorless, actively motile and complexly structured ciliate like *Paramecium* or the large, cottony mycelium of a mold like *Rhizopus* (bread mold). However, on closer examination it is found that numerous other, less typical species in each group have important properties in common and that lines of demarkation are not always so clear. It seems certain that some species in each group are merely evolved forms (i.e., selected mutants) of species in other groups—a reasonable, but not necessarily correct, inference being that all may have originated from a common source billions of years ago. The origins of many are obscure: lost in the mists of antiquity.

The origin of the Animal Kingdom is as obscure as that of the Plant Kingdom. In view of their eucaryotic structure, absence of photosynthetic pigments and cell walls, animals might have developed as *loss mutants** from a eucaryotic type of plant cell; no procaryotic animal cells are known. Or could animal cells have evolved, before the appearance of sunlight and photosynthesis, from a cell-wall-less, non-

photosynthetic, procaryotic, heterotrophic progenitor like the mycoplasmas? On the other hand, as will be explained, many protozoa probably evolved from flagellate algae. Animals that contain chitin may be related, "far back," to the fungi whose cell walls also contain chitin. Family trees among the Protista are frustratingly delusory!

### 11.1  THE EUCARYOTIC FUNGI

The Greek word *mykes* (anglicized as *myces*) means fungus, and in current usage includes all of the nonphotosynthetic members of the Subkingdom Thallophyta: plants that (a) do not form embryos (as in seeds); (b) are without physiologically differentiated or functional roots, stems, leaves or flowers; (c) may consist of only one cell or of characteristic aggregations of many undifferentiated (or very slightly differentiated) cells. The group of fungi is commonly divided into two phyla of the Subkingdom Thallophyta: (1) the true fungi or *Eumycetes* (*Eumycophyta*), all of which are eucaryotic in structure, and (2) the fission fungi, *Schizomycetes* (*Schizomycophyta*) or bacteria, all of which are procaryotic. In this chapter we shall use the term fungi to mean Eumycetes.

Except for some Phycomycetes, as explained farther on, most fungi can grow with little free water, thriving on such as may be absorbed from damp atmospheres. They can take water from materials that have very high osmotic pressures, e.g., jams, jellies, syrups, pickling brines, wood and bread. Fungi are typically

---

*Mutants that result from *loss* of a functional genetic unit such as ability to synthesize cell walls. (See Chapter 15.)

aerobic. As a result of their various distinctive properties many species of fungi are found in damp, dark places where organic matter and oxygen occur. Like many bacteria, fungi can utilize solid food materials by secreting extracellular hydrolytic enzymes. Many species of fungi are adapted to marine and fresh-water habitats.

Typical Eumycetes differ from all other eucaryotic plants in having chitinous instead of cellulosic cell walls and, excepting yeasts and torulas, in the characteristically filamentous form of their basic structural units. Fungi resemble animal cells in that all are chemoorganotrophic. Fungi differ from typical animal cells in: (a) having a chemically and morphologically differentiated, rigid cell wall and (b) exhibiting a vegetative manner of growth (i.e., continuous, without regard to size).

## Activities of Fungi

Most fungi are saprophytes and active producers of various hydrolytic enzymes. Consequently they are of great value as scavengers and as promoters of soil fertility.

Many fungi decompose cellulose and lignin, and therefore ruin paper and wood products not protected from them. Some filamentous fungi grow in and under paint on walls and cause flaking and deterioration of the paint. Some can grow on the surfaces of lenses in binoculars in the tropics, diminishing clarity of vision. Some fungi grow well on rubber, including rubber tires and insulation, which ruins it. They also grow on the surface of electrical insulators, causing them to transmit electricity. Fungi, especially molds, are merry jokers of the microscopic world! Several species cause diseases, often serious, of man, lower animals and valuable crop plants.

The sea also has a most interesting indigenous flora of fungi. Marine fungi participate in the destruction of ropes and timbers exposed at water level. Some molds have done enormous damage by infecting and killing commercially valuable fish and shellfish, and animal and fish foods such as eel grass upon which many edible marine forms live.

On the other hand, a number of species of fungi, especially yeasts and molds, are of great commercial value in the production of various organic compounds which are used as foods, flavors or drugs. From carbohydrates various species of fungi produce hundreds of valuable substances that cannot easily be made by artificial processes. Among these products are penicillin, acetone, butanol, sorbitol and takadiastase. Yeasts are the familiar servants of brewers and bakers.

## Structure

Eucaryotic fungi typically exhibit two phases of growth: an asexually growing vegetative or thallus-plant phase and a "fruiting" or sexually reproducing phase.

During the vegetative phase virtually all filamentous fungi are seen to consist of tubular, widely branching filaments called *hyphae,* with rather uniform diameters of 10 to 50 $\mu$ in different species. An entire thallus consisting of such filaments is called a *mycelium.* A new mycelium may be formed by fragmentation of a mycelial segment or by outgrowth from a sexually or asexually produced *spore.*

Not all fungi are of the woolly, hairy or cobwebby sort popularly called *molds.* Mushrooms, puffballs, brain fungi, shelf fungi and the like are not filamentous as viewed with the naked eye. On microscopic examination, however, the fleshy portions are seen to consist of compact masses of the branching mycelial filaments that are characteristic of Eumycetes in general. On the other hand, some species of fungi, the yeasts and torulas, exist primarily as single, spheroid or ovoid cells or small aggregations of such cells. Some fungi, especially certain pathogenic species, may grow in either the yeastlike form or the filamentous form; they are said to be *biphasic.*

Four major groups of Eumycetes are differentiated on the basis of sexual reproductive mechanisms. Further subdivisions are based on structure of the mycelial filaments and on forms of asexual reproductive bodies. A convenient arrangement is as follows:

    I. Sexual spores are *free zygotes:* Phycomycetes

        Asexual spores are endogenous, i.e., enclosed in *sporangium;* mycelium is nonseptate (*coenocytic*) except at reproductive sites.

    II. Sexual spores are enclosed in sacs or *asci:* Ascomycetes

        Asexual spores are exogenous, i.e., formed at ends of special hyphae; mycelium is septate.

    III. Sexual spores are borne on *basidia:* Basidiomycetes

Asexual spore production very rare; mycelium is septate.

IV. Sexual stages not seen: Fungi Imperfecti (Deuteromycetes)

Asexual spores and mycelia mainly like Ascomycetes, though some are like Phycomycetes and Basidiomycetes.

Many authorities include as fungi a fifth group, the so-called slime fungi or Myxomycetes. The vegetative (or trophozoite) stages of these species are not filamentous but naked, multinucleated, ameba-like animals that form slimy masses of protoplasm, each called a *plasmodium*. These organisms are also claimed by the zoologists as *Myxameba* or *Mycetozoa*. They must not be confused with the procaryotic slime-bacteria, the Myxobacteriales, which they superficially resemble. The total number of species of Eumycetes is not known, but there are probably at least 80,000. Here we shall confine our discussion to a survey of a few representative species of the four major groups.

## THE PHYCOMYCETES

The Phycomycetes are probably the most primitive of the Eumycetes. Although the name refers to an algal habitat (Gr. *phyco* = seaweed; *myces* = fungi), not all species are aquatic, many being terrestrial and familiar in the household as bread mold and similar nuisances. Unlike all other fungi (but like some algae) the aquatic species produce motile, flagellate, asexual spores, *zoospores* or swarm spores, that can thus disseminate themselves in fluid media.

The most primitive forms of Phycomycetes are the aquatic Chytridiales or chytrids. Their life cycle is simple. An anteriorly uniflagellate, ameboid, unicellular zoospore attaches itself to a site favorable for growth, loses its flagellum and initiates the growth of a rootlike (*rhizoid*) mycelium into the substrate. The zoospore enlarges to form a sac, which by repeated divisions of the nucleus becomes a sporangium filled with motile zoospores, nourishment being drawn from the substrate via the rhizoids. Rupture of the sporangium wall liberates the zoospores. Zoospores may become gametes and conjugate, forming dormant, thick-walled, free zygospores. Some species of chytrids are pathogenic for plants of agricultural value.

The more definitely mycelial moldlike type of aquatic Phycomycetes is exemplified by the order Saprolegniales or water molds. They are common in ponds and pools, growing on dead organic matter. The mycelia of water molds are often extensive. The *asexual zoospores* are biflagellate, and the zoosporangia form on the tips of special hyphae and are commonly cylindrical or pyriform. The sporangium is separated from the supporting hypha by a septum. Rupture of the sporangium liberates the zoospores.

**Sexual Reproduction of Saprolegnia.** When conditions no longer favor asexual reproduction the saprolegnias can also reproduce sexually. The sex structures are morphologically distinct (compare chytrids), being an *antheridium* (♂) and an *oogonium* (♀). The sexual process is said to be *heterogamous* since the gametes are morphologically distinct. In species in which morphologically indistinguishable gametes are involved, the process is said to be *homogamous*. Both male and female gametes may occur on one mycelium or thallus; such species are said to be *homothallic*. Species in which the male and female elements are on separate mycelia are said to be *heterothallic*.

In *Saprolegnia* the oogonium is a bulbous outgrowth from a hyphal wall; within it many nuclear fissions occur. Most of the nuclei thus formed degenerate, but several grow into uninucleate *oospheres* (egg cells) ready for fertilization. The antheridia are formed at the tips of hyphae and penetrate into the eggs, with resulting fusion of male and female nuclei. The mature, fertile oospore forms a thick wall and becomes dormant for some months. Meiosis occurs and the oospore sends out a short hypha that forms an asexual zoosporangium at its tip.

Some species of *Saprolegnia*, e.g., *S. parasitica*, are familiar to those who work in fish hatcheries or aquaria as white, cottony growths on fish, sometimes on "domestic" goldfish.

**Terrestrial Phycomycetes (Order Mucorales).** This group is well exemplified by the familiar genera *Rhizopus* and *Mucor*. *Rhizopus nigricans* is the common, black, bread mold familiar to all who have seen bread after it has stood in a humid place for some days during the summer. Species of *Rhizopus* spread rapidly because they produce enormous numbers of asexual conidiospores and because they send out *stolons* or "runners" like Bermuda grass or strawberry plants. These runners take hold of the substrate by means of rhizoids or "holdfasts." At each such holdfast several erect, unbranched sporangiophores* (short hyphae) are

---

*The suffix *phore* is from the Greek word *phorein*, meaning carrier or bearer. Do not confuse sporangio*phore* with sporangio*spore;* similarly, conidio*phore* with conidio*spore* (Gr. *conidio* = dust).

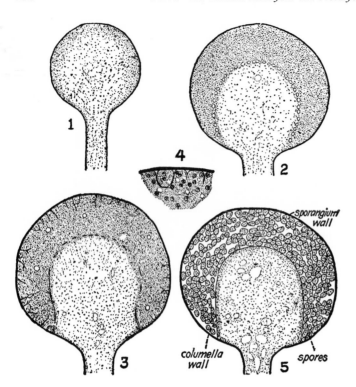

**Figure 11.1** One of the Mucorales. Stages in formation of a sporangium filled with spores. *1*, Sporangiophore and columella. *2*, Multiplication of spores from nuclei of the columella and formation of the retaining membrane. *3*, Completion of sporangium formation. *4*, Beginning of segregation of multiplied nuclei to form the individual spores or conidia. *5*, Final structure of the sporangium showing the thickened retaining membrane, the free conidia ready for dispersion on rupture of the membrane and the now inert, rounded columella which will be left behind. (From Swingle: Plant Life. Van Nostrand Co., Inc.)

produced. On the tip of each an enlarged cell called a *columella* is formed. This varies in form according to species. The sporangiospores are formed in a mass about the columella by many nuclear divisions inside the *sporangial membrane* (Fig. 11.1). The spores are liberated by rupture of the sporangial membrane. Not all Mucorales send out stolons like *Rhizopus* species. Zygospores are formed much as in *Saprolegnia* (Fig. 11.2).

Molds of the order Mucorales, like *Rhizopus* and *Mucor* species, are important commodity and food destroyers as well as valuable scavengers. Occasionally certain species of *Rhizopus* and *Mucor* may cause serious infection in man, especially if large numbers of the conidiospores are inhaled.

## THE ASCOMYCETES

The Ascomycetes as a whole may be considered either as one large group, the Endomycetales, or as two groups: (a) Euascomycetes, typically filamentous molds that form *ascocarps,* and (b) Hemiascomycetes, typically nonfilamentous yeasts that form their asci in separate cells or small clusters of such cells not enclosed in an ascocarp. (An ascocarp is a complete fruiting body including ascospores and surrounding, supporting structures.)

## FILAMENTOUS ASCOMYCETES (EUASCOMYCETES) ("MOLDS")

There are about 30,000 species of the filamentous Ascomycetes alone. They exhibit a bewildering variety of forms and mechanisms of sexual and asexual reproduction, habitat and activities. The unifying character of all, both filamentous molds and yeasts, is the formation of sexual spores inside sacs (*ascospores*).

**Asexual Reproduction.** In addition to the sexual spores there are various types of asexual spores. Some species of filamentous Ascomycetes form, in the mycelium, a number of closely spaced divisions, which develop into a number of short, more or less ovoid cells. These cells are sometimes called *oidia* (Gr. *oion* = egg; i.e., an ovoid body) or *arthrospores*. They tend to leave the parent filament by *fragmentation*. They then continue *vegetative* growth, each starting a new plant.

Some filamentous Ascomycetes also form yeastlike buds or *blastospores* as outgrowths along the hyphae. Blastospores develop much as do yeasts. Some fungi grow readily in either yeast or filamentous form, or both simultaneously (e.g., *Candida*), the form of growth depending on such factors as presence of oxygen and temperature.

During maturation of many protists, including Ascomycetes, one or more cells may

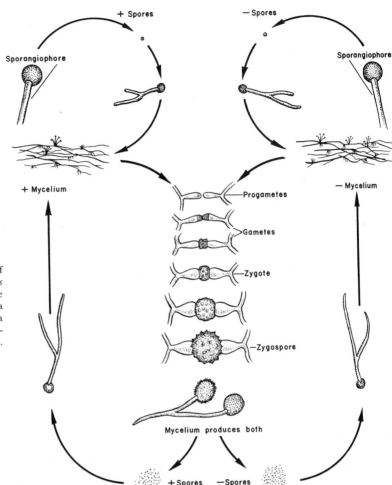

**Figure 11.2** The life cycle of the black bread mold, *Rhizopus nigricans*. The upper circles indicate the asexual production of mycelia from spores. In the center is a series of stages in sexual reproduction. (From Villee: Biology, 5th ed. W. B. Saunders Co., 1967.)

acquire thick walls and become dehydrated and filled with granular reserve material. In this form they can remain dormant and resist drying and sunlight for long periods. They are called *chlamydospores.*

CONIDIOSPORES, OR CONIDIA. Conidiospores are formed by filamentous Ascomycetes and by many Fungi Imperfecti at the free ends of elaborately branching special hyphae called *conidiophores.*

Each conidiophore arises as a branch of a cell in the mycelium called a *foot cell*. Each develops as a stem consisting of several cells end-to-end. From these, in various distinctive types of arrangements, numerous short stems or *sterigmata* arise. The conidial chains are produced at the tips of the sterigmata. Instead of being enclosed in sporangia, as are conidiospores of all Phycomycetes, the conidia of Ascomycetes are free, sometimes being produced in long chains like strings of beads. Since they are not

formed inside an enclosing structure, they are said to be *exogenous.* The size, form and arrangement of the branched conidiophores, the form of the chains and the color of the conidia are distinctive of the different genera and species (Fig. 11.3).

**Sexual Reproduction.** In the formation of sexual spores (ascospores) by filamentous Ascomycetes, the ends of certain fertile hyphae become multinucleate, reproductive structures of + and − "sexes." They meet and the cell walls dissolve at the points of contact. The nucleus of each + hypha passes into a − hypha. Pairs of + and − nuclei then fuse, forming *diploid zygotes.* Meiosis then occurs, followed by mitotic divisions, forming four or more *haploid nuclei.* In the process, each nucleus acquires some of the cytoplasm of the original fertilized − hypha, surrounds itself with a thick wall, and becomes dormant; i.e., it becomes an *endogenous spore*—in this case an ascospore since all

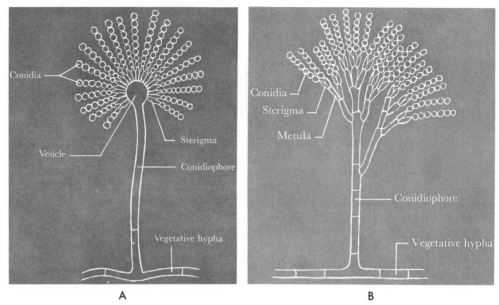

**Figure 11.3**   Distinctive types of conidiophore and of arrangement of conidia. *A, Aspergillus.* At intervals in the vegetative filaments a cell puts forth a branch upon which a conidiophore develops which later produces conidia in a radial arrangement. *B, Penicillium.* The conidiophore is produced as in *Aspergillus* but it afterward branches in a distinctive manner. The parallel chains of conidia are produced in an arrangement suggestive of a round paint brush. (From Carpenter: Microbiology. W. B. Saunders Co., 1967.)

of the spores are enclosed in the same sac or ascus. The ascospores are then liberated by rupture of the sac wall. Commonly, asci are formed in clusters within a protective and enclosing, distinctively shaped (bowl-like or cup-shaped) mass of hyphal cells. The whole "fruiting" structure is called an *ascocarp*. Depending on arrangement, the surrounding structure is sometimes called a *perithecium,* an *apothecium* or a *cleistothecium.*

Among the more familiar filamentous Ascomycetes are the common genera, *Aspergillus* and *Penicillium.*

GENUS *Aspergillus.* The fruiting hyphae of aspergilli have enlarged globular tips (*vesicles*). From the surface of these, numerous *sterigmata* radiate in all directions. On the tips of these the conidiospores are borne in long chains (Fig. 11.3, *A*).

There are some pathogenic species of *Aspergillus.* For example, a pulmonary infection of birds due to *Aspergillus fumigatus* is not uncommon, and infection of man by aspergilli (aspergillosis) is not rare. Infection generally occurs by inhalation of large numbers (clouds) of conidiospores.

*Aspergillus flavus,* a common saprophyte, is now known to produce several dangerous poisons (toxins), among them a group called *aflatoxins,* when growing in certain foods, notably stock feeds like ground peanuts. Aflatoxins, when eaten, cause illness and sometimes death. Their role in human disease remains to be determined. Aflatoxin appears to inhibit enzymes involved in the synthesis of DNA and hence in the synthesis of RNA and proteins in certain cells of susceptible animals and also in some bacteria.

GENUS *Penicillium.* The penicillia are widely distributed and contribute to the spoilage of various objects and materials composed of organic matter, especially ripe fruits. The conidiophores are composed of hyphae which branch at the tip into finger-like clusters of sterigmata, the whole roughly suggestive of the bone structure of the hand. The spores extend in chains from the ends of the sterigmata. This arrangement gives the whole conidiophore, with its chains of conidiospores, a form suggestive of a tiny paint brush, from which the generic name is derived (L. *penicillus* = paint brush or pencil) (Fig. 11.3, *B*). As in other groups of molds, the color and form of the fruiting body are of value in classification.

Some species of *Penicillium* are differentiated chiefly by their habitat. The blue-green molds found in Roquefort cheese (*P. roqueforti*), Camembert cheese (*P. camemberti*) and other cheeses of the same nature are distinguished chiefly by their occurrence there. The molds grow in or on the cheese (which must be perforated to admit air since the molds are aerobic), producing various enzymatic changes in the fat, carbohydrate and protein of the cheese, which result in characteristic aromas, flavors and textures. (See Chapter 45.)

There are many other species of penicillia. They are frequently seen on old bread, cheese, lemons and other fruits. They may usually be recognized as members of the genus by their sky-blue or green color. *Penicillium notatum* and *P. chrysogenum,* very similar species, have come into great prominence as sources of penicillin.

### NONFILAMENTOUS ASCOMYCETES (HEMIASCOMYCETES) ("YEASTS")

The term yeast, like the term mold, is one of convenience only; the term as commonly used, and as used here, refers to those Ascomycetes that are typically not filamentous but unicellular, ovoid or spheroid. However, some species of Basidiomycetes and Fungi Imperfecti are also yeastlike in form.

In size, yeasts average somewhat larger than bacterial cells, about 5 $\mu$ in diameter by 8 $\mu$ in length. Some oval yeast cells have a volume hundreds of times that of *Staphylococcus* cells. The yeast cell wall consists of two or probably three layers and contains chitin, like other eucaryotic fungi. Within the cytoplasm are a well-differentiated nucleus, numerous vacuoles containing food or waste substances and granules of glycogen and of *volutin* (polymerized phosphates). Yeast cells sometimes contain large quantities of fat, which may be used commercially.

#### Asexual Reproduction

BUDDING. Budding is the commonest and most distinctive method of asexual reproduction in yeasts (Fig. 11.4). In budding, large, mature cells divide, each giving rise to one or more daughter cells or *buds* that are at first much smaller than the mother cell and that characteristically cling to the parent cell, often even after the daughter cell has divided. A cell may form several buds at different sites simultaneously. Clumps and chains of cells, sometimes called *rudimentary filaments,* or *pseudomycelia,* are thus formed. The manner of forming buds is used to differentiate between species of yeasts.

FISSION. Some species of yeast, in the Genus *Schizosaccharomyces,* divide by equal, binary fission much as do the bacteria.

#### Sexual Reproduction

ASCOSPORES. The ascospores of yeasts are

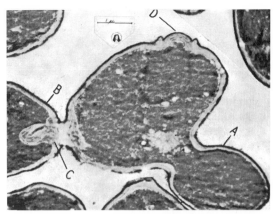

**Figure 11.4** Electron micrograph of a longitudinal section through a budding yeast cell (*Saccharomyces cerevisiae*). *A,* A young bud with its cytoplasm still continuous with that of the mother cell. *B,* A mature bud with the developing cross wall between mother and daughter cell. *C,* The extension of newly formed cell wall material into the cytoplasm, a phenomenon which appears to be characteristic of the later stages of the budding process. *D,* A bud scar, the surface of which is always convex. Degree of magnification indicated by the scale line showing 1 $\mu$; top, center. (From the collection of the Society of American Bacteriologists. Agar and Douglas: J. Bact., vol. 70.)

dormant, thick-walled and resistant to heat, drought and other unfavorable environmental conditions. They are not so thermoresistant as bacterial spores, being killed by a temperature of 60° C. in a short time. Since ascospores of yeasts are generally produced in groups of four or more per cell, they represent a process of multiplication as well as preservation, thus differing from bacterial endospores, of which, as a rule, only one is produced by each cell.

In some species ascospores are formed following *sexual fusion* of two vegetative, haploid yeast cells. In this process the cell walls between two adjoining haploid cells disappear at the point of contact, and the nuclei unite. The diploid nucleus thus formed then usually undergoes meiosis and two or more divisions, resulting in four or eight haploid *ascospores* within the original cell wall, which is now an *ascus* (Fig. 11.5). These ascospores grow out into asexually budding, haploid yeasts as before.

Ascospores may also be formed without preliminary fusion. The nucleus of a cell undergoes meiosis and then two or more divisions occur within the cell wall. Each portion of each haploid nucleus receives some of the cytoplasm of the parent cell and develops a new cell wall, becoming an ascospore. These spores fuse sexually, each pair forming a diploid *zygote* which goes on reproducing asexually by budding as before. Thus, some yeasts exist most of the time

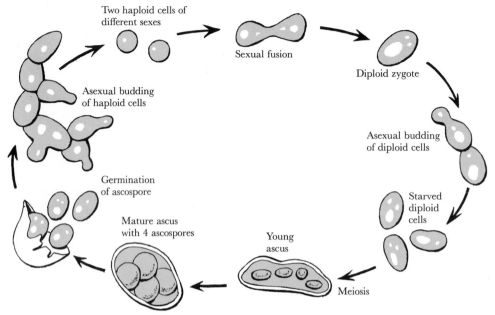

**Figure 11.5**   The life cycle of a yeast. Starved diploid cells (lower right) undergo meiosis, producing an ascus with four haploid ascospores which eventually mature, germinate, and leave the ascus (lower left). These haploid cells may multiply for a time by asexual budding of the haploid cells (upper left). Sooner or later sexually different haploid cells conjugate (upper center) and form a diploid zygote (upper right) which multiplies for a time in the diploid state (right). (From Carpenter: Microbiology, 2nd ed. W. B. Saunders Co., 1967.)

in the diploid state, and some in the haploid state. Ascospores are usually of a very distinctive form that is used in identification of species.

**The Torulas.**   These constitute a large group, Torulopsidaceae, containing several genera. These organisms resemble the yeasts but sexual stages have not been observed; i.e., they are Fungi Imperfecti.

## HABITAT AND ACTIVITIES OF YEASTS

Yeasts are widely distributed in nature. They commonly occur on grapes and on other fruits and vegetables. The spores pass the winter in the soil. The kind of wine made from grapes depends to some extent on the varieties of yeasts occurring upon them naturally. Yeasts, molds and torulas may also be found in dust, dung, soil, water and milk, and are not infrequently observed in cultures made with swabbings from the normal throat. Many species are found as contaminants in brewers' and picklers' vats, and many appear to live on the human skin and in the nectar of flowers.

The common bakers' and brewers' yeasts (species of *Saccharomyces,* chiefly varieties of *S. cerevisiae*) are facultative with respect to oxygen, producing alcohol and carbon dioxide by *fer-*

*mentation* of sugar under *anaerobic* conditions of growth. Their alcohol-forming power is used in the manufacture of wine, beer and industrial alcohol.

The ability of fermenting yeasts to form carbon dioxide is important in beer and wine making. It is also important in baking because the carbon dioxide produced by the yeast cells growing in newly made dough causes it to rise. This gives the finished bread its light, porous texture. Yeasts synthesize proteins and also several vitamins, especially those of the B complex, and therefore have great nutritive value. For this reason they are sometimes cultivated *aerobically* in vats. There they produce carbon dioxide and water instead of alcohol. They use all of the nutrient substrate to produce masses of nutritive yeast substance that can be fed to livestock (Chapter 47).

Yeasts are also important as nuisances. Various kinds of yeasts, and also torulas, cause "diseases," or off flavors, unpleasant odors and sliminess of various foods. Torulas, like most fungi, are common in soil, water and dust.

One group of torulas, called Rhodotorulaceae, produces reddish pigments. These torulas cause various reddish discolorations and spoilage of fresh foods in such places as butcher shops and sea-food establishments. They are not pathogenic. Most torulas have little fermentative ability and consequently are of little commercial value.

## THE BASIDIOMYCETES

These are familiar to everyone as mushrooms, toadstools, rusts, smuts, shelf or bracket fungi. The distinctive structure of all Basidiomycetes is the *basidium,* a swollen, clublike, sexually reproductive cell somewhat like the multinucleate reproductive structures (asci) of Ascomycetes. The basidium is produced by a binucleate cell at a hyphal tip. The two nuclei of this cell fuse, forming a diploid zygote that, as in Ascomycetes, divides meiotically to form four haploid nuclei. Unlike spores of the Ascomycetes, these haploid nuclei are not held inside any structure like an ascus but are extruded to the tips of four tiny projections, each called a *sterigma,* at the surface of one end of the basidium. In the process each haploid nucleus acquires cytoplasm and forms a thick spore wall, thus becoming a *basidiospore.*

The mycelial structure of most Basidiomycetes is commonly hidden underground or in a porous substrate like a rotting log, and is often many feet in extent. The large, fleshy parts of these fungi (e.g., mushrooms) are the fruiting bodies. The basidia and basidiospores are formed along the undersides of the "gills" of these plants. The spores are disseminated in wind and rain. In a suitable environment each germinates and produces a new thallophyte or mycelium.

Asexual spores of Basidiomycetes are rare.

## LICHENS (EUMYCOPHYTA)

These lowly plants are striking examples of highly successful "togetherness" (conjunctive symbiosis or mutualism). (See also symbiotic nitrogen fixation, Chapter 43.) Each lichen plant (there are over 12,000 species) consists of a fungus and an alga. The fungus is generally an Ascomycete or Basidiomycete that has become adapted to intimate life with an alga that may be eucaryotic or procaryotic. The alga, being photosynthetic, provides organic nutrients for the fungus which, in turn, provides mechanical support and protection as well as minerals for the alga. Each plant can, however, multiply independently. Lichens are familiar as flat, leafy, crusty or flaky growths, or mosslike plants on such inhospitable and barren places as rocks and the bark of trees as well as on rot-

ting wood and the soil, from pole to pole. They have a variety of commercial uses and are important sources of food for a variety of animals, e.g., "reindeer moss."

## FUNGI IMPERFECTI (DEUTEROMYCETES)

This group is entirely artificial and is heterogeneous. It contains species of fungi that cannot be assigned to any other group because no sexual process, the primary basis of classification of fungi, has been observed. This is because many of the filamentous fungi are heterothallous, and in many of these only one of the "sexes" has been discovered. When the two are observed to combine sexually then the species are removed from the Fungi Imperfecti to their proper group: usually the Ascomycetes. It is possible that some of the fungi may exist only in the form of one of the combining types. There are about 20,000 species. A threadbare comment about Fungi Imperfecti is that the imperfection usually lies not in the fungi but in our knowledge of them.

**Carnivorous Fungi.** Some of the Fungi Imperfecti are among the most useful and interesting plants because of their carnivorous habits. They are found in fertile, moist soils. They entrap and digest microscopic animals of the soil such as amebae, crustaceans, rotifers and also the much larger (though still microscopic) nematodes (round worms, or eel worms).

An interesting example of these soil-dwelling fungi is *Dactylaria gracilis.* Under some conditions, such as the abundance of certain crops (turnips, for instance), enormous numbers of root-eating nematodes appear and cause many dollars' worth of damage. The fungus sends out short hyphae that are extremely sticky, and the nematodes are caught in the adhesive. Each hypha is tipped with a doughnut-shaped loop of three cells. When a nematode, struggling in the sticky secretion, thrusts its head or tail inside the loop, the cells of the loop instantly swell up, obliterating the opening in the loop and constricting powerfully on the nematode (Fig. 11.6). They hold it in an inexorable grip in which it soon dies despite its struggles. The cells of the loop of fungus then send vegetative hyphae into the body of the worm; these excrete enzymes, so the worm is digested and absorbed by the fungus. Even if the worm tears the loop from the mycelium the ring still holds on and sends in its fatal vegetative hyphae. It grows and forms a new mycelium at the expense of the luckless nematode.

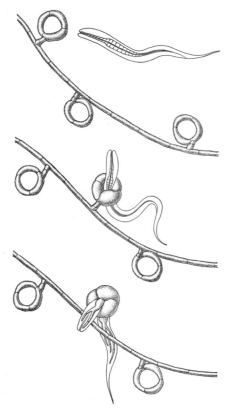

**Figure 11.6** Fate of a nematode trapped by a carnivorous fungus. At the top the worm nears the living snare which is part of a filament of the fungus. Once inside the ring the worm is immediately caught by expansion of the cells of the ring. As seen at the bottom, these cells quickly send out hyphae which penetrate the worm and secrete enzymes which digest it and adsorb the nourishment thus produced. (From Predatory Fungi, by Joseph J. Maio. Copyright © 1958 by Scientific American, Inc. All rights reserved.)

An interesting aspect of this phenomenon is that the ring constricts only when the worm touches the inner surface of the loop. No constriction occurs if the outer surface is touched. The sensitivity and exceedingly rapid action of these cells suggest some sort of nervous and muscular activity, yet none of this can be seen.

Other species of similar molds kill worms which infect sheep. Practical use of these molds has been made by inoculating sheep pens with them; the worms soon disappear.

## PATHOGENIC FUNGI IMPERFECTI

The pathogenic Fungi Imperfecti are of two general types: (a) those causing generalized or systemic infections of deep tissues, often fatal, and (b) those affecting only superficial tissues:

i.e., skin, nails and hair, and causing annoying but not dangerous diseases. The fungi of group (b) are collectively called *dermatophytes*, i.e., skin fungi. Infections by any fungi are collectively called *mycoses*.

FUNGI CAUSING SYSTEMIC MYCOSES. Nearly all of these fungi normally live as saprophytes in the soil. Infection of man usually occurs only accidentally through contamination of cuts and abrasions by soil, or by inhalation of dust containing spores or conidia. These diseases are rarely transmitted from person to person.

*Candida albicans.* This organism is commonly found on the oral or vaginal mucous membranes or in feces of normal individuals, and rarely on the skin. Unlike most of the systemic fungi it rarely occurs normally in the soil. Growth on Sabouraud's agar (widely useful in mycology) is best at 37° C. The colonies are creamy and have a yeasty odor. The growth consists mainly of small (2 to 4 $\mu$), yeastlike cells. Mycelial elements may occur, with blastospores. The ability of this fungus to form clusters of budding cells and distinctive, round chlamydospores on cornmeal agar or other suitable agar is useful in identification.

*Candida albicans* can cause a number of serious infections (*candidiasis*) in man and animals, especially of mucous membranes (thrush and vulvovaginitis), the skin (cutaneous candidiasis) and lungs (pulmonary candidiasis). Microscopic examination of scrapings from lesions usually reveals the organisms, but diagnosis should be made only by a skilled mycologist.

*Coccidioides immitis.* C. immitis is the cause of a disease called coccidioidomycosis, recognized originally in the San Joaquin Valley in California and known to occur in arid regions elsewhere. In nature the organisms live in the soil and their resistant cells (arthrospores) are blown about with dust and inhaled. Many of these infections pass unnoticed or result in a febrile disease in association with bronchitis, rheumatism or pneumonia. The disease is often confused with tuberculosis in x-ray and clinical examinations.

*C. immitis* is diphasic. When cultivated in dilute media, pH 6.0 to 8.0, in the dark, at 37° C. at reduced surface and oxygen tensions, or when invading the tissues of the body, it forms yeastlike cells, but they never form buds. On the contrary, the contents of these yeastlike cells divide into many smaller cells within the cell wall, forming a *spherule* or sporangium-like body. The sporangium or spherule wall ruptures, liberating a large number of small cells. These are then distributed by the blood throughout the body and repeat the cycle. When the fungus is grown aerobically on agar media or in the soil, the mycelial filaments are generally formed. Thus it is a dimorphic (or diphasic) fungus.

*Histoplasma capsulatum.* This organism resembles *Coccidioides immitis* in several respects. The spores are airborne and may be derived from soil, especially if polluted with dung of birds or animals. It causes infections (*histoplasmosis*) in man which may pass unnoticed in certain individuals, yet cause fatal generalized infections in others.

*H. capsulatum,* like *C. immitis,* is dimorphic. It may be cultivated on 10 per cent blood infusion agar at 37° C. Under such conditions the cells are yeastlike. In infected tissues, as in tissue cultures, only the yeastlike form is seen.

When cultivated at room temperatures on such media as Sabouraud's or glucose agar, a cottony, white, filamentous growth appears.

THE DERMATOPHYTES. Mycotic (fungal) infections of the skin (generally called *dermal mycoses*) are common; in fact, the dermal mycoses such as ring worm (*tinea*), *athlete's foot,* and various other forms of dermal mycosis of the hands and feet are among the commonest of infectious diseases.

Species of Fungi Imperfecti commonly involved are: *Microsporum audouini* (causing *ring worm* of the scalp, or *tinea capitis*); *Trichophyton rubrum* (causing various forms of *tinea* and *kerion*); *Epidermophyton floccosum* (causing various forms of tinea and athlete's foot).

## SUPPLEMENTARY READING

Ainsworth, G. C., and Sussman, A. S. (editors): The Fungi: An Advanced Treatise (Three Vols.) Academic Press, New York. 1965, 1966, 1967.

Ajello, L.: Comparative ecology of respiratory mycotic disease agents. Bact. Rev., *31*:6, 1967.

Al-Doory, Y., and Gordon, M. A.: Application of fluorescent-antibody procedures to the study of pathogenic dematiaceous fungi. J. Bact., *86*:332, 1963.

Aronson, J. M., Cooper, B. A., and Fuller, M. S.: Glucans of Oomycete cell walls. Science, *155*:332, 1967.

Bartnicki-Garcia, S.: Chemistry of hyphal walls of *Phytophthora.* J. Gen. Microbiol., *42*:57, 1966.

Beneke, E. S.: Medical Mycology. Lab. Manual, 2nd ed. Burgess Publishing Co., Minneapolis. 1966.

Conti, S. F., and Brock, T. D.: Electron microscopy of cell fusion in conjugating *Hansenula wingei.* J. Bact., *90*:524, 1965.

Cooney, D. G., and Emerson, R.: Thermophilic Fungi. W. H. Freeman & Co., San Francisco. 1965.

Duncan, C. G., and Deverall, F. J.: Degradation of wood preservatives by fungi. Appl. Microbiol., *12*:57, 1964.

Edwards, M. R., Gordon, M. A., Lapa, E. W., and Gihorse, W. C.: Micromorphology of *Cryptococcus neoformans.* J. Bact., *94*:766, 1967.

Emmons, C. W., Binford, C. H., and Utz, J. P.: Medical Mycology. Lea and Febiger, Philadelphia. 1963.

Gilardi, G. L.: Nutrition of systemic and subcutaneous pathogenic fungi. Bact. Rev., *29*:406, 1965.

Hawker, L. E., and Abbott, P. McV.: Fine structure of vegetative hyphae of *Rhizopus.* J. Gen. Microbiol., *30*:401, 1963.

Hesseltine, C. W., Shotwell, O. L., Ellis, J. J., and Stubblefield, R. D.: Aflatoxin formation by *Aspergillus flavus.* Bact. Rev., *30*:795, 1966.

Higgins, M. L., and Pramer, D.: Fungal morphogenesis: ring formation and closure by *Arthrobotrys dactyloides.* Science, *155*:345, 1967.

Kajihiro, E. S.: Occurrence of dermatophytes in fresh bat guano. Appl. Microbiol., *13*:720, 1965.

Klein, H. P.: Synthesis of fatty acids by yeast particles. J. Bact., *92*:130, 1966.

Lillehoj, E. B., and Ciegler, A.: Inhibition of deoxyribonucleic acid synthesis in *Flavobacterium aurantiacum* by aflatoxin B. J. Bact., *94*:787, 1967.

Maclean, N.: Electron microscopy of a fission yeast, *Schizosaccharomyces pombe.* J. Bact., *88*:1459, 1964.

Mahadevan, P. R., and Tatum, E. L.: Relationship of the major constituents of the *Neurospora crassa* cell wall to wild-type and colonial morphology. J. Bact., *90*:1073, 1965.

Mortimer, R. K., and Hawthorne, D. C.: Yeast genetics. Ann. Rev. Microbiol., *20*:151, 1966.

Northey, W. T., and Brooks, L. D.: Studies on *Coccidioides immitis:* I. A simple medium for in vitro spherulation. J. Bact., *84*:742, 1962.

Pisano, M. A.: Activities of the cephalosporia. Tr. N. Y. Acad. Sci., Ser. II, *25*:716, 1963.

Raper, K. B., and Fennell, D. I.: The genus *Aspergillus.* The Williams and Wilkins Co., Baltimore. 1965.

Schneierson, S. S., and Shore, B.: Adaptation of the Cooper recessed-top polystyrene culture dish to identification and investigation of *Candida* and other yeastlike fungi. Appl. Microbiol., *13*:286, 1965.

Shields, A. B., and Ajello, L.: Medium for selective isolation of *Cryptococcus neoformans.* Science, *151*:208, 1966.

Skinner, C. E.: A review of the genus *Candida.* Bact. Rev., *24*:397, 1960.

Various Authors: Symposium on biochemical bases of morphogenesis in fungi. Bact. Rev., *27*:305, 1963.

Walter, J. E., and Atchison, R. W.: Epidemiological and immunological studies of *Cryptococcus neoformans.* J. Bact., *92*:82, 1966.

Werner, H. J., Wright, P., and Baker, R. D.: Electron microscope observations of *Rhizopus rhizopodiformis.* J. Gen. Microbiol., *37*:205, 1964.

Wickerham, L. J., and Burton, K. A.: Phylogeny and biochemistry of the genus *Hansenula.* Bact. Rev., *26*:382, 1962.

Wilson, B. J.: Toxins other than aflatoxins produced by *Aspergillus flavus.* Bact. Rev., *30*:478, 1966.

Wogan, G. N.: Chemical nature and biological effects of the aflatoxins. Bact. Rev., *30*:460, 1966.

# Chapter 12

## THE EUCARYOTIC PROTISTS

## Algae and Protozoa

The eucaryotic algae are typical, photosynthetic, thallus plants (Gr. *thallos* = plant growth). They may be multicellular, "leafy," branching and attached to solid objects by rootlike holdfasts. They are, nevertheless, without vascular or differentiated tissues, flowers, seeds, physiologically differentiated true roots, stems or leaves. The cells are entirely undifferentiated; i.e., any single cell could asexually reconstitute the entire structure. There are scores of thousands of species of algae. Some (e.g., Phaeophyceae or brown algae) form very large plants (seaweeds), such as the kelps of the Pacific coast. These are often hundreds of feet in length and may weigh many tons. They contain *fucoxanthin,* a brown pigment that masks the green chlorophylls. The red algae (Rhodophyceae) are also multicellular, branching seaweeds containing red *phycoerythrin* (absorbs violet light) in addition to chlorophyll. They grow at depths of several hundred feet where other algae cannot grow. Several red algae are edible, e.g., *Irish moss* and *dulse.* Some, as *Gelidium* species, furnish the jelly-forming polysaccharide, agar, that is well known to the microbiologist, the pharmacist and the housewife. There are also numerous multicellular species of green algae (Chlorophyceae), e.g., sea lettuce.

### 12.1 ALGAL PROTISTS

There are many species of algal protists. The *desmids,* fresh-water green algae, are distinguished by their elaborate forms and delicate, symmetrical beauty (Fig. 12.1). One large group of the class Chrysophyceae (golden-brown algae) comprises the *diatoms* (Fig. 12.2). Like the kelps, these contain fucoxanthin. They are widely distributed as marine and fresh-water plankton.* Of special interest are their formation of silica-containing cell walls (compare Radiolaria among the Protozoa) that consist of two symmetrically formed and "decorated" parts, like a cut-glass Petri dish and its cover. They exhibit a sedate, gliding motion. They are also distinguished by intracellular storage of food as oil instead of as starch, a supposed origin of at least some petroleum deposits. Like the protozoan Radiolaria, diatoms, through eons of time, have formed enormously thick deposits of their silica shells on the sea bottom. When raised above the sea by geologic movements, these deposits are available as *diatomaceous earth,* which has many industrial uses as an abrasive and in filtration.

Many algal protists are nonmotile, ovoid cells like the familiar green *Chlorella:* the guinea pig of the space and submarine scientists because it grows well under simple laboratory conditions and can be cultivated in spaceships and undersea colonies with ultraviolet lamps. It serves man in such situations by using organic waste materials as nutrients, removing carbon dioxide from the air, and providing a constant source of oxygen by its photosynthetic activities. It synthesizes proteins and starch and can therefore also provide food, though it has not, by any-

---

*Plankton (Gr. *planktos* = wandering) includes minute plants and animals and also Protista that spend their lives floating passively in the sea or fresh water.

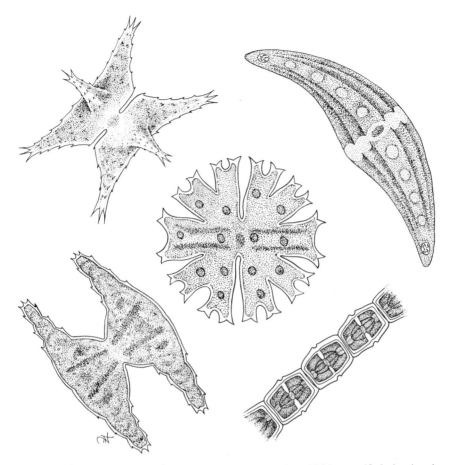

**Figure 12.1**   Several different species of desmids, unicellular green algae, highly magnified, showing the symmetry of the cells. (From Villee: Biology, 5th ed. W. B. Saunders Co., 1967.)

one's account, achieved the status of a gourmet dish.

*Chlamydomonas,* another green algal protist, is of special interest because it typifies unicellular plants that are animal-like in being actively motile by means of flagella. Although *Chlamydomonas* resembles flagellate protozoa, it differs in having a large chloroplast and a thick cellulose cell wall. The ovoid cell can reproduce asexually by intramural nuclear fissions, forming two to eight biflagellate *zoospores*. These are liberated by rupture of the cell wall, and then repeat the process. It may also produce morphologically indistinguishable male and female, biflagellate, haploid *gametes*. Fusion of a pair of the gametes produces a quadriflagellate, diploid zygote that becomes an unflagellated, dormant cyst or zygospore. On germination of

**Figure 12.2**   A side view (*A*) and a top view (*B*) of a typical diatom, highly magnified. Note the characteristic fine lines on the shells and the way the upper and lower shells fit together. (From Villee: Biology, 5th ed. W. B. Saunders Co., 1967.)

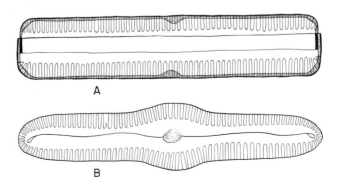

A

B

the zygospore meiosis occurs and the resulting four progeny are biflagellate, haploid, potential gametes.

## 12.2    FLAGELLATE ALGAE

The group of photosynthetic algal flagellates includes the biologically important dinoflagellates. The cells of most dinoflagellates have two unequal flagella and a complex outer wall or shell (armor) of cellulose. The armor is made up of segments or interlocking plates, arranged with transverse grooves or channels that give the cells a very distinctive appearance (Fig. 12.3). Commonly, one flagellum lies in the transverse channel. Multiplication may be by asexual cell fission or, depending on species, by intracellular division of the nucleus and the formation of zoospores analogous to *Chlamydomonas*. Sexual reproduction has also been described in some species; it is analogous to reproduction of *Chlamydomonas* though differing in details. A curious feature of dinoflagellates is their ingestion of solid food particles, e.g., other algae, bacteria and protozoa, by phagocytosis; a distinctly protozoan-like (holozoic) process.

Most dinoflagellates live as marine plankton in enormous numbers, their total weight and capacity for photosynthesis far exceeding those of all the terrestrial forests. Sometimes, under conditions especially favorable to their multiplication, certain dinoflagellates become so numerous as to impart a distinct color to the sea. Some, e.g., *Peridinium* and *Gymnodinium,* produce the dreaded "red tide" that kills tons of fish. Others are taken into mussels as food and are very poisonous to any human eating those mussels.

Thus we see, in the protozoan-like dinoflagellates, actively motile plants, some species of which exhibit phagocytosis.

Another group of photosynthetic flagellates, the euglenoids, is claimed by the botanists as plants (Phylum Euglenophyta) and by the zoologists as animals (Order Euglenoidina). Of the euglenoids *Euglena gracilis* is a widely studied curiosity, consisting of free-living cells with one or more chloroplasts with typical eucaryotic plant chlorophylls, accessory light-trapping pigments and alga-like *pyrenoids* that function in starch synthesis. Nutrition may be holophytic or holozoic but, if holozoic, is not by phagocytosis as in the dinoflagellates. *Euglena* is furnished with a mouthlike *cytostome* and *gullet* like the protozoan, *Paramecium,* described farther on. *Euglena* cells contain contractile vacuoles: a distinctly protozoan feature (see Protozoa). Other intracellular structures suggest a protozoan-like development and differentiation of organelles (Fig. 12.4).

The cells of *Euglena* are protozoan-like also in having no rigid or differentiated cell wall of cellulose or mucopolysaccharide but instead, like protozoan cells in general, a thickened and

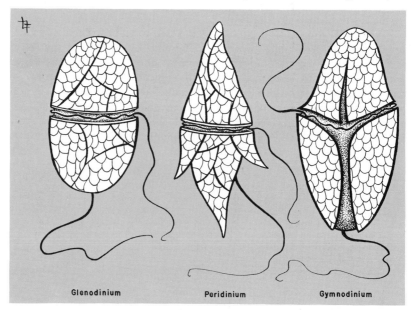

**Figure 12.3**    Three species of dinoflagellates. Note the plates which encase the single-celled body and the characteristic two flagella, one of which is located in a transverse groove. (From Villee: Biology, 5th ed. W. B. Saunders Co., 1967.)

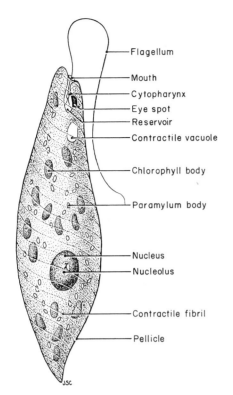

- Flagellum
- Mouth
- Cytopharynx
- Eye spot
- Reservoir
- Contractile vacuole
- Chlorophyll body
- Paramylum body
- Nucleus
- Nucleolus
- Contractile fibril
- Pellicle

**Figure 12.4**   *Euglena;* a photosynthetic, flagellate animal. (From Villee: Biology, 5th ed. W. B. Saunders Co., 1967.)

more or less plastic *periplast* or *plasmalemma*. A red-pigmented "eye spot" occurs in *Euglena* and other flagellate algae such as *Chlamydomonas*. This is light sensitive and serves to orient the flagellate to the light source. The red pigment is rare and, outside of flagellates, occurs only in an animal group, the Crustacea.

In some protists the ability to synthesize chloroplast or chromatophore appears to be an unstable property, subject to complete loss. When the chloroplast is lost by a eucaryotic, flagellate, green alga, e.g., *Euglena*, the result is, to all appearances, a flagellate protozoan; it becomes a "naturalized" member of the animal kingdom. When the chromatophore is lost by a procaryotic, filamentous blue-green alga like *Oscillatoria* it automatically becomes a procaryotic, filamentous bacterium like *Beggiatoa*. Loss of the photosynthetic system in either type of organism apparently can occur as a result of spontaneous mutation. In the case of the flagellate, *Euglena*, it can also be brought about in the laboratory by exposure to ultraviolet light and by other mutagenic methods. Thus we can

experimentally change a plant into an animal. Data appear to be lacking on the experimental transformability of blue-green algae into morphologically similar nonphotosynthetic bacteria, though it doubtless can be done.

In this connection it is interesting to note that many algae possess dual energy systems. As photolithotrophs they can utilize radiant energy by virtue of their photosynthetic systems; as chemoorganotrophs they can grow very well in the dark like fungi and protozoa. The interesting point at present is that, at the protist level, the demarcations between major groups often become very hazy or disappear. Many modern protozoa are not so obviously like the algae, having undoubtedly become altered in the course of millions of years of evolution. On close comparative study, however, their origin from algae can hardly be doubted.

The group of procaryotic algae, the blue-green algae or Cyanophyceae, the most bacteria-like of algae, are discussed in the next chapter.

## 12.3   THE PROTOZOA

Like other major divisions of protists, the Phylum Protozoa is a very heterogeneous group. There are probably well over 30,000 species of protozoa. One or two examples of each major type may be described to show some of the characteristics common to most protozoa. In general, protozoa are the most highly specialized, and their cell structures and modes of life and reproduction the most complex, of all the Protista. Unless one includes the flagellate algae, protozoa are the only animal group in the entire Kingdom Protista.

Examine with a microscope at a magnification of between 400 × and 1000 × a drop of sewage or of water in which a bit of dried grass has been allowed to soak at room temperature for two or three days. Not only are many kinds of bacteria seen, but also many fantastic and elegant creatures that resemble bacteria in some respects but that can, as a rule, be readily differentiated by their relatively huge though microscopic size, their elliptical or ovoid form, complex internal structure and other distinctive features. These are protozoa—microscopic animals, each consisting of a single cell.

One or more species of protozoa may be found in almost every habitable situation on earth: stagnant water, pond mud, surface waters, feces, the soil, dust, the ocean. They live in part upon other minute living things, including other protozoa and bacteria. All of the protozoa seem to have evolved in the direction of complexity of physiological function without differentiation of specialized organs such as heart, liver or brain.

**Classification.**  A complete classification of the protozoa is beyond the scope of this book. All are motile during at least one stage of their existence. The means of motility differ in each group and are used as a basis of classification. There are four principal groups of protozoa, as follows:

CLASS I. Sarcodina: move with pseudopods, some species also have flagella. (Includes *Ameba*, Radiolaria, Foraminifera.)

CLASS II. Ciliata: move with cilia.

CLASS III. Mastigophora: move with flagella.

CLASS IV. Sporozoa: move with pseudopods only in immature stages; the male gamete is flagellate.

Some authors include a fifth class, Suctoria, in which young stages are ciliated while adult stages are sessile and provided with tentacles.

**Structure.**  Protozoa vary greatly in size according to species and physiological state. Most of them are hundreds of times as large as most bacteria but some are not much larger. A commonly studied type, *Paramecium,* is roughly elliptical in shape and has dimensions of about 200 $\mu$ by 40 $\mu$ (Fig. 12.6).

As previously noted (Chapter 10), eucaryotic plant cells typically have a chemically and morphologically differentiated cell wall of cellulose or, in many fungi, chitin. In contrast, animal cells, such as protozoa and cells of the human body, have a typically eucaryotic structure but no cell wall. Their outer covering consists only of the cell membrane. In some groups such as the amebas, this is a thin, limp membrane that permits ameboid movement and phagocytosis, both motivated by intracellular *cytoplasmic streaming.* In some free-living protozoa the peripheral layer of cytoplasm is condensed into a protective layer called an *ectoplasm.* In other types, especially the large and active, flagellated and ciliated species, a thick and more or less flexible outer *integument, periplast, plasmalemma* or *cortex* is formed from the peripheral layers of cytoplasm. This often contains chitin. As will be seen, the cortex itself, especially of ciliates, may contain numerous organelles, such as *cilia, trichocysts,* mouth or *cytostome,* gullet or *cytophage,* anal pore or *cytopyge* or *cytoproct,* and contractile fibers called *myonemes.*

*Contractile vacuoles* are conspicuous in species of protozoa that live in fresh water. The vacuoles appear to be regulators of intracellular water and hence of intracellular osmotic pressure. Because of the low osmotic tension of fresh water and the much higher osmotic tension of intracellular fluids, cells in fresh water tend to take in water. Like bacterial protoplasts or PPLO, the cells would burst unless the excess water taken in could be excreted. This function is exercised by the contractile vacuoles, which act as macromolecular kidneys and sweat glands! (Marine protozoa rarely exhibit contractile vacuoles. Why?)

**Flagella and Cilia.**  As is true of flagella of motile green algae, protozoan flagella act as swimming appendages. Cilia are much like flagella in structure and function but are shorter and, unlike flagella, tend to move in a coordinated and rhythmical fashion—much like macromolecular fins! Coordination of movement of cilia is thought to be maintained by a neuromotor mechanism in the cortex suggestive of a macromolecular nervous system. As will be shown in Chapter 13, eucaryotic flagella and cilia have a complex, inner, multifibrillar structure not seen in procaryons.

**Reproduction.**  As in most protists, asexual reproduction by cell fission is the most efficient and commonly seen means of increasing numbers of cells or new protozoan individuals. In many species, no other kind of reproductive process is known. In other species genetic recombination and multiplication, usually resulting in rejuvenation of the asexual processes, is commonly brought about by *conjugation.* In some species this may be a quite complicated process as will be explained farther on.

**Encystment.**  During the life cycle of many protozoa some cells may produce a thick cell wall, lose water and become dormant. During this stage metabolism is reduced to a minimum or ceases entirely, and the dormant cell resists unfavorable environmental conditions such as prolonged drought, summer heat, increased salinity or unfavorable pH. Such a stage may be formed by mature, growing cells during asexual cycles of development or just after conjugation of gametes during sexual reproductive cycles. In protozoa these cells are commonly called *cysts.* Cells going into the cyst stage are said to be *encysting.*

After a physiologically and genetically determined period or, depending on species and type of cyst, when growth conditions again become favorable, the cell inside the cyst wall takes in water, resumes activity, bursts the cell wall and emerges in the actively growing or, in protozoa, *trophozoite* stage. The encysted cell is said to have *excysted*.

**Nutrition of Protozoa.**   Although some types of protozoa, especially certain blood parasites, exhibit holophytic-type nutrition, protozoa typically differ from plant cells in being able to take *solid* food particles into the cell. All protozoa are chemoorganotrophic. Ingestion of solid foods by protozoa is accomplished by three methods: by *phagocytosis,* by means of *cytostome* and by *pinocytosis.* In phagocytosis, typical of amebas and leukocytes of the blood, two or more pseudopodia are extruded like fingers around the food particle. The fingers merge into one, with the particle trapped within. The particle is passed through the cell membrane into the cytoplasm, where it is enclosed in a digestive or food vacuole—a macromolecular stomach. In other protozoa, most typically ciliates, food particles are wafted by cilia into a deep pouch or invagination of the cell coating called a *cytophage* or *gullet.* The food particle passes through the cell coating at the inner end of the gullet into a cytoplasmic digestive food vacuole. Pinocytosis is a somewhat similar process, though not dependent on cilia; the pinocytic gullets are numerous and very tiny (see Chapter 3). Protozoa commonly eat bacteria, each other and other minute organisms.

**Responsiveness of Protozoa.**   These little animals appear to have a certain intelligence, possibly of the type referred to by Immanuel Kant as "transcendental knowledge"; i.e., inherited or inherent. Protozoa accept or reject food particles with discrimination and have quite a delicate sense of touch (*tactile sense*), so that they recoil on contact with hard objects, turning aside quite as though they were highly sensate and responsive creatures. Some (e.g., *Euglena*) have eye spots and can distinguish light of different wave lengths. Although no such complex structures as nose, eyes or nerves are found in protozoa, many are nevertheless quite sensitive and responsive to such stimuli as heat, chemicals, gravity and electricity.

## 12.4   SOME REPRESENTATIVE PROTOZOA

### CLASS SARCODINA (THE AMEBAS)

There are many species of amebas, most of them harmless saprozoa. They are common in pools and ponds in which there are bacteria

and other minutely particulate matter and dissolved substances on which they can feed.

**Form.**   Amebas differ from most other protozoa in that while alive they have no particular form. They continually change from round or oval to very irregular shapes with temporary protrusions and finger-like processes sticking out from, or being retracted into, various portions (Fig. 12.5). They move by means of these finger- or footlike processes called *pseudopodia* (Gr. *pseudo* = false; *pod* = foot). The ameba thrusts out a pseudopodium and moves by flowing into the projected portion. This sort of motility is called *ameboid movement.* The cell wall is very thin and flexible, although the exterior portion of the cytoplasm is somewhat condensed and thickened, forming an *ectoplasm.* As in all typical eucaryotic cells the protoplasm maintains a constant intracellular streaming motion (*cytoplasmic streaming*), thus performing the function of a circulatory system. Waste products are excreted through the integument, which serves the purpose of a kidney, intestines and sweat glands. Ameboid movement appears to be dependent on protoplasmic streaming. Such movement cannot occur in species with rigid cell walls.

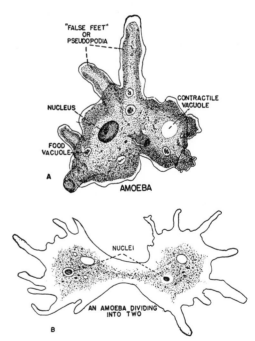

**Figure 12.5**   A species of harmless ameba from stagnant water (trophozoite forms). Note the numerous pseudopodia, the nucleus and the vacuoles inside the cell. This organism, itself microscopic in size, feeds upon bacteria and is thousands of times larger than them. (From MacDougall and Hegner: Biology. McGraw-Hill Book Co.)

The cells of some genera of the Class Sarcodina, unlike the naked genus *Ameba,* surround themselves with a protective and supporting shell or skeletal structure. In *Difflugia* the cells secrete a gummy cement substance that binds together a coating of sand grains. *Arcella* secretes a covering of chitin. The group called Foraminifera, a common and numerous marine type, characteristically form rather complex, chambered shells of calcium carbonate. The white cliffs of Dover are the accumulations of the shells of Foraminifera (chalk) deposited on the ocean floor during millions of years and later raised above the sea. A related marine group called Radiolaria secrete skeletons of silica ($SiO_2$), some of which are exquisitely delicate and radially symmetrical. Accumulated on the ocean floors and compressed during millions of years, these have become flint or flintlike. In all of the species just mentioned the cell itself is ameba-like; it thrusts its pseudopodia through openings in the shell or skeletal structure.

**Reproduction.**   Amebas, like all other protists, possess the primitive power of *asexual* or *vegetative* multiplication. In this process the cell divides itself into two cells, a phenomenon called *cell fission.* Cell fission is said to be binary when the cell divides into two equal parts, each part having (theoretically) all of the physiological and genetic potential of the parent cell. During binary fission amebas divide by a constriction somewhere near the physiological middle of the cell, i.e., by *transverse fission.* The nucleus undergoes mitosis, typical of eucaryons.

### SOME PATHOGENIC AMEBAS

**Amebiasis.**   Infection by any species of ameba is properly spoken of as *amebiasis.* The most harmful and best known of the species pathogenic for man bears the name *Entamoeba histolytica. E. histolytica* attacks the walls of the intestine. These amebas feed, characteristically but not exclusively, upon red blood corpuscles. They penetrate the intestinal lining and cause intense inflammation and ulcers (*amebic dysentery*). By means of proteolytic enzymes they can burrow through the lining and penetrate deep into the intestinal wall so that, occasionally, rupture of the intestine occurs. The patient may then die of peritonitis caused by escape of the bacteria of the feces into the abdominal cavity.

*Entamoeba histolytica* may also get into the lymph and blood vessels and then be carried to the liver, lungs, brain and other organs where they become localized and cause the formation of large abscesses.

TRANSMISSION OF AMEBIASIS. *Entamoeba histolytica* is passed in the feces, most commonly in the dormant, thick-walled, encysted form. Amebiasis is often chronic and may be present with little definite symptomatology for a long time. Thus amebic infection, especially of the intestine, like many other infections is often unknowingly disseminated widely by mild cases or *carriers.* Carriers who handle food may transmit cysts to food via their soiled hands. These cysts, after being swallowed, rapidly excyst in the intestine. Feces-soiled hands and flies appear to be major vectors of most intestinal pathogens: protozoan, bacterial and viral.

Anything recently contaminated with feces from a chronic case or carrier of amebiasis may transmit the cysts. Transmission on fruits and vegetables can occur when human sewage and feces are used for fertilizer. Under such circumstances fresh vegetables (lettuce and celery, for instance) may have viable *E. histolytica* cysts upon them when eaten.

Amebiasis is common in all regions in which sanitation of sewage is neglected or absent. Some serious outbreaks of amebic dysentery in the United States have been caused by sewage-polluted water supplies.

## CLASS CILIATA (THE CILIATES)

This class of protozoa takes its name from the cilia that are distributed over the surfaces of the cells. Ciliates are commonly ovoid or pear-shaped (pyriform). A much studied species, *Paramecium caudatum,* is sometimes called the *slipper animalcule* because of the slipper-like outline (Fig. 12.6). *P. caudatum* is commonly found in pond water. It is a representative of the most complex of the unicellular microorganisms. It maintains its form by means of a flexible but tough external pellicle that is covered with symmetrically arranged rows of fine hairs (*cilia*). The cilia move rhythmically like oars and by their means the animal swims in a spiral manner as gracefully as a seal. Near one end an *oral groove* or *cytostome* leads into a funnel-shaped *gullet* or *cytopharynx* into which food (bacteria, smaller protozoa) is wafted by cilia around the oral groove. The food is taken into the cell in a *food vacuole,* as in amebas. Digestion and absorption occur, and indigestible material is extruded through a posterior *anal opening.* Contractile vacuoles in the cytoplasm collect waste fluid (e.g., urine) and excrete it.

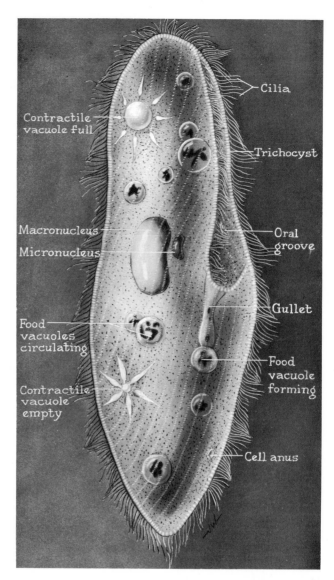

**Figure 12.6** *Paramecium* sp., showing complex structure of a unicellular animal without differentiated organs or tissues. (From Villee, Walker and Smith: General Zoology. W. B. Saunders Co., 1963.)

*Paramecium* can defend itself or catch food by means of *trichocysts*. These are small cysts beneath the pellicle or cortex. When the animal is disturbed, the trichocysts secrete a substance which (outside the pellicle) forms long, sticky filaments that entangle and immobilize other microorganisms.

*Paramecium* multiplies asexually by binary fission and sexually by conjugation. The process of conjugation in ciliates is well exemplified by *Tetrahymena pyriformis*, a related species of ciliate.

**Reproduction.**   In most vegetative cells of ciliates such as *Tetrahymena* there are two differing nuclei: a large *macronucleus* or "vegetative," polyploid nucleus and a minute, diploid *micronucleus*. Some cells contain only the macronucleus; these cells can multiply only vegetatively, i.e.,

by binary fission. Only cells containing micronuclei can conjugate. (Compare F$^+$ bacteria, Chapter 14.) Conjugating cells are morphologically indistinguishable as to sex.

The cells fuse and each diploid micronucleus undergoes meiotic divisions, producing four haploid nuclei in each cell. Of these, three degenerate; one divides mitotically. Thus there are two haploid (gamete-like) nuclei. One haploid nucleus from each cell of the conjugal pair is exchanged with the counterpart in the other cell. The residual and the exchange haploid nuclei in each cell then combine, thus forming a diploid nucleus and achieving genetic recombination.

In each cell the new nucleus, now a diploid zygote, twice divides by mitosis, yielding four diploid nuclei, two of which become macronuclei, the other two micronuclei. The old macronucleus disintegrates. The conjugants now separate, each with two macro- and two micronuclei. In each cell one of the micronuclei disintegrates; the remaining one divides by mitosis. Each of the conjugants now again has two of each kind of nucleus. Each of these *tetranucleate* cells divides by binary fission. Each daughter cell normally has one macronucleus and one micronucleus. In some instances a micronucleus may be "lost in the shuffle"; that cell has lost its sex factor and multiplies only asexually.

## Class Mastigophora (The Flagellates)

There are numerous species of the Class Mastigophora with ovoid, spindle-like or pear-shaped cells that resemble *Paramecium*, but that move actively about by means of one or more flagella commonly attached at one end of the animal. Many varied types can be found in sewage or infusions of hay. Some species contain chlorophyll and are regarded by many workers as flagellate algae, as previously described. Some species inhabit the human body and are pathogenic. Representative species are shown in Figures 12.7 and 12.8.

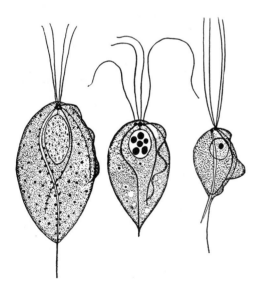

**Figure 12.7**   Three species of *Trichomonas* found in humans: (left to right) *T. vaginalis, T. buccalis* (or *T. tenax?*), *T. hominis.* The size differences shown are not very constant. *T. buccalis* is not known to be pathogenic but its continuous presence in the mouth in considerable numbers indicates bad oral hygiene. (× 2000.) (Powell.)

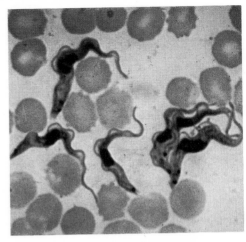

**Figure 12.8**   *Trypanosoma gambiense* in a droplet of blood (the large, round objects are erythrocytes). This is one of the species of trypanosomes causing African trypanosomiasis (African "sleeping sickness"). Note the prominent flagellum along the edge of the wavy, keel-like membrane on each trypanosome. (× 1525.) (Courtesy of Dr. A. Packchanian, The Medical School, University of Texas.)

## Class Sporozoa

The most important (to us!) representatives of the Class Sporozoa are parasites. Among these, probably the best known and most deadly are the malaria parasites. Since every advanced nation is now cooperating with the World Health Organization in a huge effort to eliminate these deadly animals from the entire earth, and since they are one of the worst enemies of soldiers in countries such as Vietnam, we will consider them in some detail.

### MALARIA

Malaria is one of the most important of the arthropod-borne diseases (Gr. *arthron* = joint; *pod* = foot). An arthropod is an animal with jointed feet or legs. Arthropods are represented by insects, bugs and Crustacea (scorpions, lobsters, crabs, shrimp).

In the United States, malaria as an epidemic or endemic disease has been eliminated (Fig. 12.9). Persons entering the country from malarious areas occasionally reintroduce it, but because of constant surveillance and control measures, it does not spread. However, it still remains a widespread and death-dealing scourge in many areas outside the United States, especially in tropical and subtropical zones. Hundreds of thousands of persons die annually from this

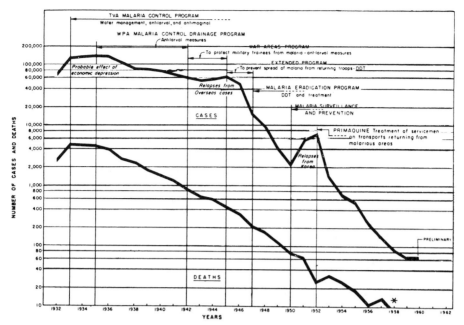

**Figure 12.9**   Reported malaria morbidity and mortality in the United States, 1932–1960.    *In succeeding years starting with 1958, the total reported deaths were as follows: 1958—0; 1959—1; 1960—0. (From Andrews and Langmuir: Am. J. Pub. H., *53*:1, 1963.)

disease and millions are made chronically ill by it.

**The Malarial Parasite.**   Malaria is caused by a protozoan parasite of the Class Sporozoa; Genus *Plasmodium.* Its life history involves two stages of development: one, asexual, passed in the human body; the other, sexual, passed in the female of various species of mosquitoes of the Genus *Anopheles.*

LIFE IN MAN.   The mosquito introduces the parasites into the blood of its victim with its saliva when it bites (Fig. 12.10). The female mosquito bites only to obtain blood proteins for egg production. The males live inoffensively on plant juices. The parasites undergo a short period of multiplication in certain tissue cells, particularly in the liver. This is called the *exo-erythrocytic* (or *pre-erythrocytic*) cycle. Very soon their asexual progeny enter red corpuscles and grow within them. This stage of the parasite is the *trophozoite* stage. The parasite multiplies asexually within the red cells, forming a number of small bodies or segments. Finally the affected corpuscle breaks up, and the segments escape into the circulating blood. Each segment is a new, active parasite called a *merozoite.* It no sooner gets out of one red cell than it attacks another red corpuscle and in turn multiplies. In this way the blood is soon teeming with the parasites and the infection becomes

clinically manifest; the *intrinsic incubation period* (bite to first symptom) is completed. The patient becomes anemic and weakened by the loss of so many red cells, and possibly also suffers from poisonous products formed by the parasites.

The parasites appear in the blood in successive generations, all the individuals of which divide and burst out of the corpuscles at about the same time. Each such process causes the chills and fever so characteristic of malaria. A chill indicates that a fresh crop of parasites has matured and entered the circulation.

After passing through several cycles of asexual development as just described, round, distinctive gametocytes begin to appear in the blood of the patient. These are larger than the asexual forms and are easily recognized by trained persons in the smears of the patient's blood examined under the microscope. Gametocytes undergo no further development in human erythrocytes. They die if not taken up by a mosquito.

LIFE IN THE MOSQUITO.   When an *Anopheles* mosquito bites a person who has mature malarial gametocytes in his blood, the sexual stage of the parasite begins.

After fertilization of the female by the male gamete in the stomach of the mosquito, the motile *zygotes* invade the cells lining the mosquito's stomach and multiply there, forming

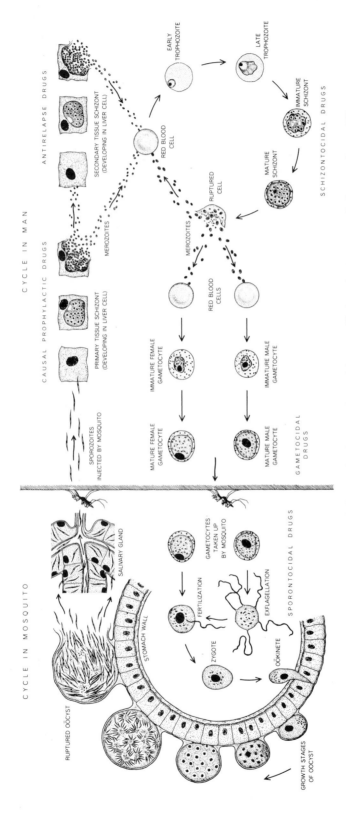

**Figure 12.10** Life cycle of *Plasmodium*, the malaria parasite, in mosquito and in man. Various drugs can attack the parasite at different stages as indicated. (From Malaria, by Carlos A. Alvardo and L. J. Bruce-Chwatt. Copyright © 1962 by Scientific American, Inc. All rights reserved.)

148

a sac wherein the parasites undergo further development by fission. The sac ruptures, liberating numerous new young parasites. After moving about for some days inside the mosquito, these reach the mosquito's salivary glands and from there are injected into man when the insect bites. The life cycle is thus complete. Because of the necessary period of sexual reproduction of the parasite, a mosquito that has bitten a malaria patient cannot transmit the disease to another person until the end of about 12 days—the *extrinsic incubation period.* A mosquito, once infected, remains so for the rest of its life, which may be two months or more.

**Species.**   There are four species of the human malarial parasite. One of the most widely distributed in temperate zones is called *Plasmodium vivax* (from the *vivacious* activity of its trophozoite stage). It requires about 48 hours to complete its development within the red cells. The chills, therefore, commonly occur at intervals of 48 hours or every third day, although there is considerable variation. This type of malaria is called *tertian (third) fever.* A second species, called *Plasmodium malariae,* requires about 72 hours for development, and groups of parasites mature approximately every fourth day. This species causes *quartan (fourth) fever.* A third form, *Plasmodium falciparum* (the word *falciparum* is derived from the curved or sickle-shaped— *falciform*—gametes) requires from 24 to 48 hours or more for development. This type of malaria is called *estivo-autumnal fever* because in temperate climates it typically occurs in the late summer and autumn. It is most prevalent in tropical zones. It is more severe than the other forms of malaria and is less easily controlled by antimalarial drugs. *Plasmodium ovale,* a fourth species, resembling *P. vivax,* causes a disease much like tertian malaria, but milder.

Mosquitoes, like most other two-winged insects (*Diptera*), pass through four stages of development: the *egg,* the *larva* (wiggler), the *pupa* and the fully developed insect (*imago*). The first three stages develop in water.

The female *Anopheles* mosquito may be recognized by her stance as she bites: a "head-on" position, with hind legs in the air. She usually has spots of silver or gray on her wings and often gray bands on her legs. The nonmalaria-bearing varieties are usually brownish or brown-gray and bite with body nearly parallel to the skin.

**Diagnosis of Malaria.**   The laboratory diagnosis of malaria is commonly made by spreading a small drop of the patient's blood on a slide and either examining it in the fresh state or staining it with any special stain used for blood smears. The parasites can be seen in or upon the blood cells and may have various appearances, depending on the species and the stage of their development in the red cells.

**Control of Malaria.**   As in other arthropod-borne diseases, control is directed primarily against the vector arthropod. Aircraft from areas where any foreign arthropod-borne diseases exist are generally sprayed with aerosols before landing. The control of mosquitoes in swamps and airplanes is an engineering problem. Mosquitoes may be kept out of homes and away from sleepers by screens and insect repellents. The repeated use of DDT, dieldrin or other residual sprays has been most effective since it kills the infected mosquitoes in the house. Unfortunately, insecticide-resistant mutants soon appear in numbers. Another very important measure is to eliminate the parasites in infected persons by treating them with antimalarial drugs like chloroquine and amodiaquin. Also unfortunately, drug-resistant mutants soon predominate. Drugs are suppressive, but do not always cure. Quinine, known as a valuable febrifuge extracted from bark of the Cinchona tree by pre-Colombian Peruvians, is less used than formerly. However, in those situations in which the malaria parasites are resistant to other drugs, the use of quinine is increasing.

Unfortunately, some species of *Plasmodium* formerly thought to be restricted to monkeys, e.g., *P. cynomolgi, P. brasilianum* and *P. knowlesi,* are also transmissible to man by *Anopheles* mosquitoes in the jungles under natural conditions. This discovery, by Eyles, Coatney and others, greatly complicates plans for control and complete elimination of malaria. The situation is somewhat similar to that which developed after the discovery of jungle yellow fever in various species of monkeys.

### SUPPLEMENTARY READING

Ahmadjian, V.: Lichens. Ann. Rev. Microbiol., *19*:1, 1965.

Algae in Water Supplies, U. S. Dept. of Health, Education, & Welfare, Pub. Health Serv., Washington, D. C., Government Printing Office. 1959.

Alexopoulos, C. J., and Bold, H. C.: Algae and Fungi. The Macmillan Co., New York. 1967.

Ammann, E. C. B., and Lynch, V. H.: Gas exchange of algae. I. Appl. Microbiol., *13*:546, 1965.

Chin, W., Contacos, P. G., Coatney, G. R., and Kimball, H. R.: A naturally acquired quotidian-type malaria in man transferable to monkeys. Science, *149*:865, 1965.

Corliss, J. O.: The Ciliated Protozoa. Pergamon Press, Inc., New York. 1961.

Droop, M. R.: Algae and invertebrates in symbiosis. Thirteenth Symposium, Symbiotic Associations, p. 171. Soc. Gen. Microbiol., London. 1963.

Faust, E. C., Beaver, P. C., and Jung, R. C.: Animal Agents and Vectors of Human Disease. Lea and Febiger, Philadelphia. 1962.

Fay, P.: Heterotrophy and nitrogen fixation in *Chlorogloea fritschii.* J. Gen. Microbiol., *39*:11, 1965.

Fitzgerald, G. P., and Faust, S. L.: Factors affecting the algicidal and algistatic properties of copper. Appl. Microbiol., *11*:345, 1963.

Grimstone, A. V.: Structure and function in protozoa. Ann. Rev. Microbiol., *20*:131, 1966.

Hunter, G. W., Frye, W. W., and Swartzwelder, J. C.: A Manual of Tropical Medicine, 4th ed. W. B. Saunders Co., Philadelphia. 1966.

Hutner, S. H.: The environment and growth: Protozoan origins of metazoan responsiveness. Eleventh Symposium, Microbial Reaction to Environment, p. 1. Soc. Gen. Microbiol., London. 1961.

Jackson, D. F. (editor): Algae and Man. Plenum Press, New York. 1963.

Massey, R. L., and Mattoni, R. H. T.: New technique for mass assays of physiological characteristics of unicellular algae. Appl. Microbiol., *13*:798, 1965.

Palmer, C. M.: Key for the identification of algae. *In:* Standard Methods for the Examination of Water and Wastewater, 12th ed. Amer. Pub. Health Assn., New York. 1965.

Pitelka, D. R.: Electron-microscopic Structure of Protozoa. The Macmillan Co., New York. 1963.

Seaman, G. R., and Reifel, R. M.: Chemical composition and metabolism of protozoa. Ann. Rev. Microbiol., *17*:451, 1963.

Smith, G. M.: The Fresh Water Algae of the United States. McGraw-Hill Book Co., New York. 1950.

Vela, G. R., and Guerra, C. N.: On the nature of mixed cultures of *Chlorella pyrenoidosa* TX 71105 and various bacteria. J. Gen. Microbiol., *42*:123, 1966.

Villee, C. A.: Biology. 5th ed. W. B. Saunders Co., Philadelphia. 1967.

Wolpert, L.: Cytoplasmic streaming and amoeboid movement. Fifteenth Symposium, Function and Structure in Micro-organisms, p. 270. Soc. Gen. Microbiol., London. 1965.

# Chapter 13

## PROCARYOTIC CELL STRUCTURE

Among the procaryons certain species of bacteria have been more thoroughly studied than others, and for this reason we shall use them to exemplify procaryotic cell structure in general. It must be borne in mind, however, that in biology, as in many other fields, one always treads on thin ice when he attempts to extrapolate data concerning one species, individual, or single cell, to others; what is true of one or two is not necessarily true of all.

The principal anatomic features of the bacteria that have been investigated are, proceeding from the outermost inward: flagella; pili or fimbriae; capsule or envelope; cell wall; cytoplasmic (or protoplast or cell) membrane; cytoplasm containing ribosomes, mesosomes, chromatophores in photosynthetic species, granules of stored nutritive substances (e.g., starch); nuclear material; and spore. Not all these structures are present in all species; some have been investigated in only a few species. Spores are discussed in Chapter 31.

### 13.1 MOTILITY AND FLAGELLA

In the Kingdom Protista at least four types of translatory motility may be distinguished: ameboid; gliding; progress caused by the rotatory motion of a helically coiled cell (see Spirochaetales); and motion caused by the oar-like or sculling action of flagella or cilia.

**Ameboid Movement.** Ameboid movement is distinctive of the protozoan class Sarcodina, which includes the amebas. Details of the motion are given elsewhere (page 143). The formation of pseudopodia in these organisms is dependent on protoplasmic streaming which, with the possible exception of gliding Cyanophyta and certain alga-like bacteria, is not found in procaryotic cells. Even if protoplasmic streaming occurred in procaryotic cells they could not exhibit ameboid motion because, with a few exceptions (PPLO), all have thick or rigid cell walls.

**Gliding Motion.** This form of motion is found in numerous species of Cyanophyceae, in some alga-like bacteria (Order Beggiatoales and Suborder Rhodobacteriineae) and in the protozoan-like (or alga-like?) slime bacteria, Order Myxobacteriales. The motion consists of a slow, steady, to-and-fro or steadily progressive, gliding of the cell in contact with a solid surface. The mechanism remains obscure.

**Rotatory Movement.** The rotatory movement of the helically coiled cells of spirochetes is apparently caused by contractions of fibers of a contractile protein that resembles myosin (muscle-fiber protein) in general properties. The rotation propels the organism through a fluid medium as the screw of a ship moves it forward or backward.

**Flagella.** Flagella (and cilia) are common in the Plant, Animal and Protista Kingdoms. Among eucaryotic protists, two large subphyla of protozoa (Mastigophora or Flagellata and Ciliphora or Ciliata) are classified on the possession of flagella or cilia, respectively. Among the procaryons the Cyanophyceae are typically without flagella (*aflagellate*). On the other hand, many species of bacteria move actively by means of flagella. The flagellum has proved to be a very useful swimming appendage in both Plant and Animal Kingdoms, in eucaryons and procaryons. When we examine the ultrafine structure of flagella, however, we find one of the most marked differences between procaryons and eucaryons.

The ultrafine structures of the flagella (and cilia) of all *eucaryotic* cells are remarkably alike. They are also astonishingly complex in view of their extremely small diameters of 0.1 to 0.05 $\mu$ —well beyond the resolving power of the optical microscope. Flagella may be as long as 200 $\mu$.

The typical *eucaryotic flagellum* (see Figure 13.1) is enclosed in an outer membrane that is continuous with the cell membrane. The structures of the flagellum penetrate entirely through the cell wall, and the capsule when one is present. Inside the membrane of the flagellum is a symmetrical arrangement of 10 pairs of longitudinal fibers, one axial pair and nine peripheral pairs that are evenly spaced in a circle around the central pair. Just within the cell membrane all of the fibrils of a flagellum are connected together in a distinct granule, the *kinetoplast* (or *parabasal body*). The central pair of fibrils arise in the kinetoplast. The peripheral pairs seem to go beyond the kinetoplast and to be rooted deep inside the cell, apparently very near to or in contact with a centriole, or a polar cap in plant cells without centrioles. The whole structure—

flagellum with kinetoplast and "roots"—acts as a type of autonomous, self-replicating plastid, coordinate with mitochondria and chloroplasts. Plastid replication is generally independent of nuclear fission. Some authorities count 11 fibrils: 9 peripheral (doublets), two central (singles).

The exact mechanism of motion of eucaryotic flagella is not yet entirely clarified, but it appears to result from rhythmical, coordinated contractions of the peripheral fibers. These consist of coiled elastic strands of a protein called *flagellin* that resembles the elastic protein, *myosin*, of muscles. Flagella might be termed macromolecular muscles. It is of interest to note in passing that the basic structure of eucaryotic flagella is used in various adaptations wholly unconnected with motion: e.g., in the olfactory hairs in the nose of mammals (rabbits) and in the rods and cones in the retina of the human eye.

The *procaryotic flagellum* (Fig. 13.2), unlike eucaryotic flagella, has no definite membrane. It consists of a bundle of three or more parallel or intertwined longitudinal fibers of flagellin-type protein. Each fibril is a polypeptide chain

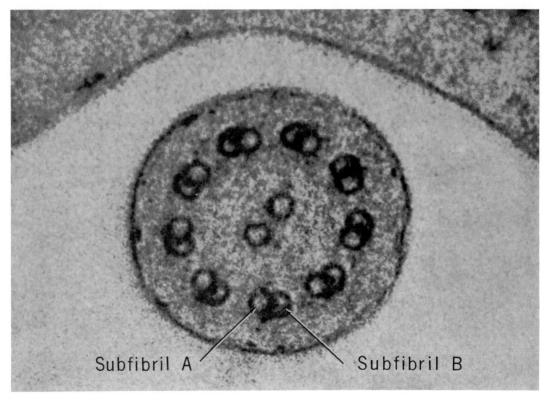

Subfibril A              Subfibril B

**Figure 13.1**   Cross section of flagellum of *Giardia muris* ($\times$ 300,000). Phosphate buffered osmium fixation; lead citrate staining. Clearly evident is symmetric arrangement of 10 pairs of longitudinal fibers. The nine outer pairs differ from the central pair in being doublets composed of subfibrils (A and B). (Micrographs courtesy of Dr. Daniel Friend.) (From Fawcett: An Atlas of Fine Structure: The Cell. W. B. Saunders Co., 1966.)

**Figure 13.2**   Electron micrograph showing flagella attached to portions of "ghost" cell (× 36,000). Also shown are terminal hooks and small spherical structures from which flagella originate (arrows). (From Abram, Koffler and Vatter: J. Bact., *90*:1337, 1965.)

in alpha-helix form, and the motion of the flagella, like that of eucaryotic flagella, depends on rhythmical contractions of the elastic fibers. Procaryotic flagella, like eucaryotic flagella, originate in a basal granule or *blepharoplast* just inside the cell membrane. However, there are no deeper roots as in eucaryotic flagella. Procaryotic flagella pierce the cell membrane and the wall and capsule when these are present. Removal of wall or capsule does not interfere with the flagella except that, when the wall is absent (see protoplasts) motility is diminished, probably because the wall serves as a fulcrum or "oarlock." Flagella may be broken off without injury to the cell and be regenerated. In several species of bacteria the flagella are bent sharply, close to the basal granules, and are said to be "hooked." This may serve to give leverage.

Although all procaryotic flagella proteins belong to the same general chemical class of flagellins, the structure of the flagellin of each species is sufficiently different from those of other species to confer *immunological specificity*

on the flagella of each bacterial species, subspecies or type. This is of importance in methods of identifying various species, as in medical diagnosis. (See flagellar antigens, Chapter 24.)

The speed of flagellar motility is sometimes very great when measured according to size. Some bacteria can cover a distance equal to scores of times their length in a second. An automobile would have to travel hundreds of miles an hour to accomplish the same thing. Some microorganisms move very slowly and sedately.

**Demonstration of Motility.**   Although bacterial flagella are not ordinarily visible with optical microscopes unless specially stained (see page 154), motility caused by movement of cilia or flagella is easily seen by direct microscopic observation of motile organisms in a droplet (*hanging drop*) of the fluid in which they are living. In any culture of bacteria, especially old cultures, motile cells may be difficult to find among thousands of dead or senescent cells. Young cultures should always be used. In cultures acidified, as by fermentation, bacteria lose their motility; strict anaerobes lose motility on contact with air.

If a drop of broth culture of motile bacteria is placed on a slide under a cover slip (a wet mount) and observed with a microscope, strict aerobes will be seen to migrate to the periphery of the slip, near the air. Strict anaerobes migrate to the center, and microaerophils to an intermediate position. This phenomenon is called *aerotaxis* (Gr. *aer* = air; *taktikos* = ordered arrangement).

Another method of detecting motile bacterial cells is to thrust a wire, previously dipped into a culture of the bacteria to be tested, deep into a column of semisolid (0.5 per cent, "mushy") agar. After 12 hours to six days of incubation motile organisms are seen to have migrated away from the line of initial stab for several millimeters, into the agar, forming a peripheral cloud of growth.

BROWNIAN MOVEMENT.   It is necessary to distinguish carefully between true motility and brownian movement. Truly motile bacteria progress definitely and continuously in a given direction. Brownian movement is a purposeless, undirected oscillation of any minute particles suspended in aqueous fluid, within a very limited area.

Among bacteria the power to move by means of flagella appears to have evolved mainly with elongation of form. Very few (if any) spherical bacteria have flagella.

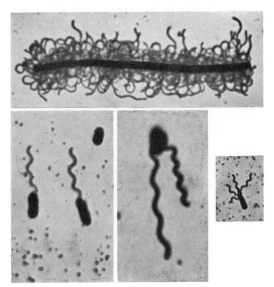

**Figure 13.3**   Bacterial flagella stained by Leifson's method. Note that in the bacillus with two flagella the wave length in one flagellum is twice that in the other. In two bacilli the wave forms are identical. Knowledge of the arrangements and wave lengths of flagella is an important factor in identification of bacterial species. (About × 3000.) (Courtesy of Dr. Einar Leifson, Strich School of Medicine, Loyola University.)

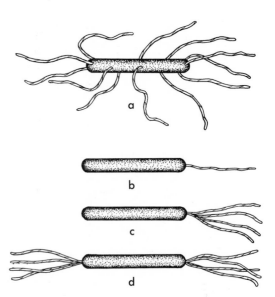

**Figure 13.4**   Types of flagellation: *a*, peritrichate; *b*, monotrichate; *c*, lophotrichate; *d*, amphitrichate.

**Demonstration of Flagella.**  In order to make bacterial flagella visible with the optical microscope it is necessary to increase their apparent diameter by first coating them with a mordant (a substance like tannic acid, which will adhere to them and hold a dye) and then applying a dye. A very good method is that of Leifson, given below.*

**Forms and Arrangements of Flagella.** There are several forms of bacterial flagella: coiled, curly, normal or wavy. Several forms may occur on one cell and even on one flagel-

---

* **Leifson's method for staining flagella**

Solution:
  I. NaCl . . . . . . . . . . . . . . . 1.5% in distilled $H_2O$
 II. Tannic acid . . . . . . . . . . . 3% in distilled $H_2O$
III. Pararosaniline acetate . . . . . . 0.9 gm.
     Pararosaniline
        hydrochloride . . . . . . . . . 0.3 gm.
        (or 1.2 gm. certified basic fuchsin)
     Ethyl alcohol . . . . . . . . . . . 100 ml.

Mix I, II and III in equal proportions and hold in tightly stoppered bottle at about 4° C.

On smear prepared as noted above quickly place 1 ml. of stain. Leave at room temperature for 7 to 15 minutes. (Try several smears; various intervals.) Rinse generously but gently with tap water—do not pour off stain first. Counterstaining with diluted methylene blue will often improve the results.

lum. The wave lengths and amplitudes of these coils (or curves or waves) appear to be fairly constant and to bear some significant relationship to each other and possibly to species. For example, the wave length of a curly flagellum may be one half the wave length of a wavy or normal flagellum on the same cell. This may be distinctive of the species (see Fig. 13.3).

Flagella may be arranged in various ways on bacterial cells. If protruding from all portions of the bacterial surface the flagella are said to be *peritrichous;* the bacteria, peritrichate. In polar flagellation, if only one flagellum is at one pole the cell is said to be *monotrichate.* If several flagella are at one pole the cell is said to be *lophotrichate.* If at least one flagellum is at each end the cell is said to be *amphitrichate* (see Fig. 13.4). It is worth remembering that all flagellate species of one large group of bacteria, the Order Pseudomonadales, are typically *polar* flagellate; in contrast, flagellate species of the Order Eubacteriales are peritrichate.

## 13.2  PILI (FIMBRIAE)

Pili are extremely fine, filamentous appendages extending outward from the surfaces of bacteria. They have so far been observed only on gram-negative rods. Their diameters are about 70Å (0.007 $\mu$), thus they are visible only with electron microscopes (Fig. 13.5).

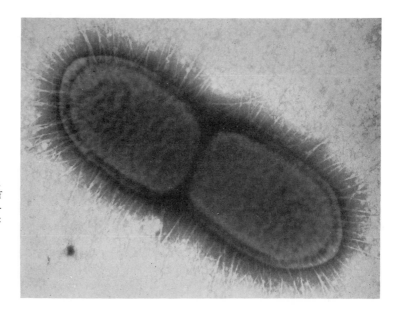

**Figure 13.5** *Proteus mirabilis.* Electron micrograph of a pair of coccobacilli. Fine, filament-like structure of pili is evident. (From Hoeniger: J. Gen. Microbiol., *40*:29, 1965.)

There are both thick (85 Å) and thin (30 Å) forms of pili. Their lengths are variable, ranging from 0.5 $\mu$ (probably stumps) to 20 $\mu$ or more. They are peritrichously arranged, about 150 to a cell. Like flagella, pili appear to originate in the cytoplasm and to pierce cell membrane, wall and capsule. They are straight or nearly so, and apparently rigid and immobile. Like flagella and capsules, they can be removed mechanically without affecting growth or viability of the cell.

Chemical studies show that pili are composed entirely of a protein, *pilin*, a heteropolymer of about 18 amino acids variously arranged in long, macromolecular helices. Since they are protein and vary in structure, they confer antigenic specificity on the cell in the same manner as flagella (see Flagellar [H] antigens). The presence or absence of pili is genetically controlled by structural and regulatory genes, and is therefore subject to mutation. Like R and S mutations (Chapter 15), mutation rates for pili at ordinary temperatures are high—around 1:100. Thus piliate and apiliate cells of the same species are common. Environmental conditions such as pH, temperature and oxygen tension strongly affect the presence or absence of pili.

Piliate bacteria strongly tend to adhere to, and cause *agglutination* (clumping together) of, themselves and various other microscopic particles such as plant or animal cells, yeast cells, red blood cells (*erythrocytes*) (Gr. *erythros* = red; *kytos* = cell), especially erythrocytes of sheep. In broth cultures of piliate bacteria the ag-

glutinative tendency is manifested by the formation of thin films or pellicles of adherent cells on the surface of the broth culture. The agglutination of erythrocytes (*hemagglutination*) by piliate bacteria appears to be caused by surface electrical charges or by a substance called *adhesin* that is firmly attached to the surfaces of the pili. Adhesion is interfered with in some species by the presence of D-mannose; this property is called mannose-sensitivity (MS). Species not so affected are said to be mannose-resistant (MR).

At least six types of pili (Types I through V, and Type F) have been described. The previous description given is based mainly on Type I. Type F pili are about 85 Å (0.0085 $\mu$) in diameter and up to 20 $\mu$ in length. Current studies indicate that, unlike Type I pili, the presence or absence of F pili is entirely controlled by the presence or absence of the F (fertility) factor of bacteria, such as that in *Escherichia coli* K12 and that F pili act as *conjugation tubes.* (See Chapter 14.)

### 13.3   CAPSULES

The composition of the outer surfaces of all cells, especially cells of protists, is of great importance, because it is here that the organism is in contact with all of the influences of the environment. The outermost structure of most procaryotic cells, notably blue-green algae and bacteria, is the capsule: a slimy, gummy or mucilaginous coating presumably synthesized by the cell membrane (cell walls have no known enzymatic activity) and extruded to the exterior surface through the meshes of the cell wall (Fig. 13.6). Bacterial capsules vary in thickness from a fraction of a micron (see Microcapsules) to 10 $\mu$ or more. Distinction between cell wall and capsule is not always clear. Sometimes wall and capsule appear to merge into each other. Generally, however, capsule and wall are distinct and separate structures. In most species the outer boundaries of capsules are sharply defined; in others the outer limits are vague and hazy as though the outer portion were dissolving in the surrounding fluid.

Capsules are not essential to the life of a cell. They may be removed artificially (by enzyme action or washing) or naturally (by mutation) without affecting the *viability* (ability to live and grow) of the cells.

The presence or absence of capsules is genetically controlled. Encapsulated and non-encapsulated mutants of many species of bacteria occur frequently. As will be discussed in Chapter 15, encapsulated mutants generally produce smooth (S) colonies and are immunologically S-type cells. Absence of capsules is associated with rough (R) colonies and immunologically R-type cells. Encapsulated mutants are also associated with virulence of pathogenic species, usually the S-type mutants. The capsules protect these bacteria from the defensive mechanisms of infected animals, including ingestion by the ameba-like white blood corpuscles of animals.

Since capsular material consists of about 98 per cent water, capsules probably also serve as defensive buffers against too rapid influx of water into the cell and also against dehydration, i.e., as osmotic barriers.

Development, or enhancement of size of capsules or amount of capsule-like materials, is genetically controlled but is also subject to environmental modification (see *Modifications*, Chapter 15). In many species large, easily seen capsules are evoked by special conditions of nutrition. For example, some species of spherical bacteria (*Leuconostoc dextranicus*, Chapter 34) form large, gummy masses consisting of billions of the cocci surrounded by *glucan* (dextran) or *fructan* (levan) gums. *Leuconostoc* is a nuisance bacterium when it grows in sugar-refining vats or dairies, since in both these locations appropriate carbohydrate is available from which to synthesize their capsules. *Streptococcus salivarius*, a species common in the normal human mouth, forms large, viscous (mucoid or M), colonies on agar containing about 5 per cent sucrose.

Because of their distinct and individual molecular structures, most capsular substances have the property of *immunological specificity* (see *Haptens*). This permits experimental distinction between closely similar species of bacteria that could not otherwise be differentiated, an important point in identification of unknown species for medical diagnosis, industrial processes and other purposes. Even with a given species, immunological *subspecies* or *types* may often be distinguished because of slight differences in the composition of their capsular substance. For example, there are about 75 distinct immunological types of the single species *Diplococcus pneumoniae* (a cause of pneumonia). The capsule of Type III, for example, is largely a polymer of 4-$\beta$-glucuronosido-glucose units: Type VI capsule is composed of galactose, rhamnose, glucose and ribitol-5-phosphate. The immunological mechanisms and methodology are described in Chapter 24.

**Composition of Capsules.** Capsules are generally made up of polymers of various subunits, the compositions varying with species.

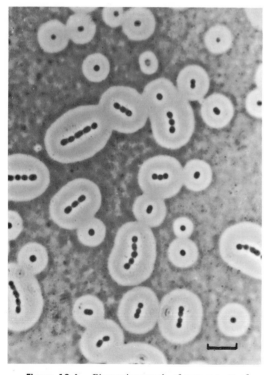

**Figure 13.6**   Photomicrograph of wet mount of an encapsulated bacterium in India ink. The scale line shows the size of 10 $\mu$ at this magnification. (From Taylor and Juni: J. Bact., *81*:688, 1961.)

In the Cyanophyceae, capsules or slimy matrices are gummy in nature and consist of *pectin* (a homopolymer of D-galacturonic acid) or of various pectin-like (i.e., gummy) polymers of glucose (glucans).

Among the simplest of the bacteria (the Eubacteriales) there are striking differences in capsular substance between species. For example, a common species, *Acetobacter xylinum*, familiar as a thick surface growth in vinegar ("mother of vinegar") produces a crudely tangled matwork of long fibers of cellulose (unique among bacteria) as an outermost secretion. It can hardly be said to be sufficiently organized to form a capsule. Capsules of many other bacteria consist of polymers of glucose or other sugars; some also contain amino (nitrogen-containing) sugars and sugar acids. Some capsules consist of polypeptides. Capsular substances generally combine with water to form viscous, gelatinous slimes.

In the animal body viscous polymers of amino sugars are found in synovial (joint) fluids, mucus, and as a "cement" (*hyaluronic acid*) between tissue cells. Curiously, among bacteria the dangerous streptococci (*Streptococcus pyogenes*) that cause "blood poisoning" and scarlet fever have capsules of hyaluronic acid. Some dysentery bacilli have very thin capsules (see *Microcapsules*) made up of polysaccharide, phospholipid and polypeptide; capsules of some *Bacillus* species (Chapter 31) are polypeptides of D-glutamic acid units.

**Demonstration of Capsules.** Most capsules do not have a marked affinity for the dyes commonly used to stain bacteria. While unstained capsules are often large enough to be dimly visible with optical microscopes, they are commonly colorless and have low refractive indices. Special means are therefore generally used to demonstrate them. Methods differ with capsules of different compositions. A method for staining many types of capsule is given below.* Also, in Figure 13.6 is shown a method (negative staining) employing India ink that has the advantage that the bacteria may be

examined in a moist, living state. The capsule is not stained in negative staining but is visible because of the space it occupies around the bacterial cell.

**Microcapsules.** Some organisms on which a definite capsule is not microscopically demonstrable may nevertheless possess a similar or analogous, though very thin, layer of distinctive molecular structure on the cell surface. These very thin layers have been called *microcapsules, sheaths* or *envelopes*. They determine the physicochemical and immunological reactivity of the cell to various surface-acting agents in much the same manner as a capsule. Like that of capsules, the physicochemical composition of microcapsules is distinctive for each species.

## 13.4  THE CELL WALL

Chemically and structurally distinct cell walls are typically lacking in the animal kingdom. Some of the protozoa, like *Paramecium* and some flagellates, have a relatively thick, tough, protective outer integument that performs several functions of a cell wall, including that of maintaining the form of the protozoan. Other protozoa (Radiolaria, Foraminifera) secrete protective exoskeletons of silica or calcium carbonate. Except for these and possibly a few other primitive or specialized and parasitic forms, animal cells are typically limp and readily deformed sacs.

In the plant kingdom, on the contrary, nearly all species are characterized by the synthesis of chemically and structurally distinct cell walls. Cell walls of cellulose in cork were first accurately drawn and described by Hooke in 1665 (Chapter 2). Cell walls may be flexible or rigid; all are relatively tough. They are not ruptured readily by osmotic pressure from within: i.e., they are osmotically protective. With a few rare exceptions, the cell walls of photosynthetic eucaryotic plants are made wholly or mainly of cellulose. The cell walls of eucaryotic fungi derive their rigidity and tensile strength from fibers of *chitin,* the glucosamine polymer of which the tough exoskeletons of Crustaceae are composed.

Among the procaryons the cell walls of blue-green algae appear to contain some cellulose fibers, but other compounds, common to both the Cyanophyceae and bacteria, are also probably present in greater amount. The cell walls of Cyanophyceae await further study.

In typical bacteria, and probably in all other procaryons (except viruses and PPLO,

---

* **Capsule Stain** (Tyler's method):

    Crystal violet         0.18 gm.
    Acetic acid (glacial)   0.25 ml.
    $H_2O$ (dist.)         100.0 ml.

1. Prepare thin smear and dry.
2. Apply stain about six minutes.
3. Gently but quickly flood with $CuSO_4 \cdot 5\ H_2O$ (20% aq.).
4. Blot dry without rinsing.

Capsules are blue-violet zones around dark blue bacteria.

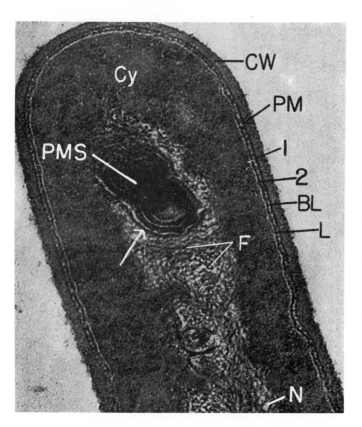

**Figure 13.7** *Listeria monocytogenes.* Cell in preparation for division (× 200,000). Section stained with chromyl chloride. The cell wall (CW) is in contact with the plasma membrane (PM). In this specimen the plasma membrane shows two dark lines (1 and 2), probably the protein layers, with a light layer, probably lipid, between. The protein layers are connected in places by bridges across the lipid layer (BL). An inner, unbridged, light layer (L) is also seen as part of the plasma membrane in this specimen. The cytoplasm (Cy) lies between the plasma membrane and the nucleoplasm (N). In the nucleoplasm are seen dense fibrils (F). A plasmalemmasome (PMS) is shown, apparently associated with the nuclear apparatus. (From Edwards and Stevens: J. Bact., *86*:414, 1963.)

which have no cell walls), the rigidity and strength of cell walls are due mainly to strong fibers composed of heteropolymers of the chemical class of *mucopolysaccharides, mucopeptides,* or *mucocomplex* (Figs. 13.7 and 13.8). These fibers form a relatively coarse (at the molecular level), reticular and tough meshwork or net rather than a solid structure. Such a net offers no obstacle to the inward passage of water, food substances such as minerals, glucose, amino acids and even larger organic molecules. All wastes of the cell can pass outward unobstructed.

In bacteria, rickettsias and chlamydias the mucocomplex macromolecules commonly consist principally of regularly spaced units of n-acetyl-glucosamine and n-acetyl-muramic acid linked by covalent, glycosidic bonds. Variations in composition and arrangement of these units occur in different species (e.g., in rickettsias). Short polypeptides are commonly attached to the muramic acid units. These peptides are commonly made up of the amino acids D-glutamic acid, D-alanine, L-glycine and *either* L-lysine *or* diaminopimelic acid (DAP), never both.

Muramic acid, DAP and several D-amino acids are found *only** in association with the procaryons: Cyanophyceae and Schizomycetes, including rickettsias and chlamydias; a strong indication of evolutionary relationships. D-amino acids also occur in some antibiotics produced by bacteria (Chapter 22).

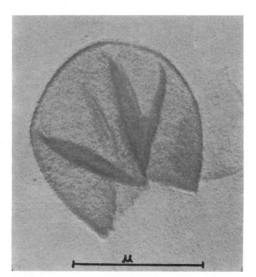

**Figure 13.8** Electron micrograph of empty and collapsed cell wall of a spheroidal bacterium (*Myxococcus xanthus*). (From Adye and Powelson: J. Bact., *81*:780, 1961.)

---

*There may be some rare exceptions elsewhere in the living cosmos.

While mucocomplex, so far as is known, is the principal supporting substance in bacterial cell walls (and apparently also in other procaryotic cells), important differences exist between types. This is illustrated by differences between gram-positive and gram-negative species of bacteria. For example, the walls of several species of gram-positive bacteria contain, in addition to mucocomplex, *teichoic acids.* These are complex polymers of ribitol phosphate, amino acids, glucose and n-acetyl-glucosamine. They add strength and density to the cell walls. Gram-negative species do not contain teichoic acids. On the other hand, although the cell walls of gram-negative bacteria have much less mucocomplex, they have one or two overlying layers of lipids, intricately connected with the mucocomplex network. These lipid-polysaccharide conjugates are called *lipopolysaccharides.* These lipopolysaccharides are especially important to the poisonous and pathogenic properties of many gram-negative bacteria (see *endotoxins*).

**Protoplasts and Spheroplasts.** Some microorganisms, both eucaryotic and procaryotic (e.g., yeasts, molds, .bacteria and some higher plants), that normally have a functionally and chemically distinct cell wall can at times exist without a cell wall, in what might be called a wall-less state. The cell membrane and its intact contents are then called a *protoplast.* Unless the solute concentration of the suspending fluid is *osmotically protective,* i.e., high enough (e.g., 3 to 20 per cent glucose; 2 to 5 per cent sodium chloride; 10 to 20 per cent serum) to balance the intracellular osmotic pressure, protoplasts, no longer retained by their thick, strong, cell walls, usually burst or undergo *plasmoptysis.* Protoplasts are therefore said to be *osmotically fragile.*

**Protoplasts and Penicillin.** An important property of bacterial cell walls is sensitivity to the antibiotic penicillin. Penicillin acts by inhibiting the synthesis of the mucocomplex of cell walls. This synthesis occurs only in actively growing cells. Young, actively growing, gram-positive bacteria are, therefore, typically susceptible to penicillin. Without their strong, retaining cell walls they are protoplasts and therefore osmotically fragile. They promptly burst unless the surrounding fluid is osmotically protective. Most gram-negative bacteria, on the contrary, are usually partly or wholly unsusceptible to penicillin because, with little mucocomplex in their cell walls, they are not wholly dependent on the mucopolymer for their cellular integrity. Other components of their cell walls prevent rupture. Penicillin susceptibility is thus

in great part a function of mucocomplex content and not of staining properties, although gram-positiveness and penicillin-sensitivity are commonly parallel. Animal cells, including human cells, are unsusceptible to penicillin. (Why?)

The lipocomplexes of gram-negative bacteria, besides making them less susceptible to the effects of penicillin, also protect them to a great extent from the action of a group of enzymes typified by *lysozyme,* an enzyme discovered by Fleming, discoverer of penicillin. Lysozyme is found in egg white, secretions of skin and mucous membranes, tears and elsewhere. It has the property of attacking specifically the glycosidic bonds in the structure of mucocomplex of bacterial cell walls. When lysozyme is applied to many species of gram-positive bacteria, the organisms are rapidly denuded of their cell walls and become naked protoplasts. In contrast, although the cell walls of gram-negative bacteria contain some mucocomplex, these fibers are protected or supplemented to a great extent by the outer layers of lipocomplexes. To make gram-negative bacteria vulnerable to lysozyme it is necessary first to remove the cell wall lipids with lipid solvents such as NaOH or ethylene-diaminotetraacetate (EDTA). The wall is not completely removed; cells only partially denuded are called *spheroplasts* (Fig. 13.9).

In osmotically protective media, protoplasts are able to carry on all of the essential functions of the intact cell including growth and fission. However, in the absence of the rigid wall, protoplasts often assume bizarre ring-

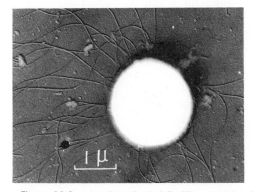

**Figure 13.9** A spheroplast of *Bacillus megaterium* in a medium made osmotically protective with 15 per cent sucrose. Ordinarily rigid and distinctly rod shaped, it is now a limp spherical sac devoid of supporting cell wall. Note that the flagella are retained, being rooted inside of the spheroplast membrane. (From Kawata, Asaki and Takagi: J. Bact., *81*:160, 1961.)

forms or ameboid forms with pseudopodium-like (though nonmotile) protuberances, or long, branching filaments containing many granular structures, like strings of beads. Protoplasts may undergo subdivisions by a process superficially resembling budding. Some of the bud-like extensions may be extremely minute, yet capable of multiplying and reverting to the forms of the cell from which they originated. Some of these forms are the smallest cells capable of independent growth. (Most viruses are smaller, but are neither cells nor capable of independent growth.)

Some bacterium-like organisms (PPLO or *Mycoplasma;* Chapter 41) exist normally in a wall-less state resembling protoplasts. Also, many bacteria and some other microorganisms may assume the protoplast form spontaneously as by mutation, or they may be made to assume the protoplast form experimentally. Bacteria temporarily in the protoplast form are referred to as *L-forms.* The relationships are complex. Protoplasts, L-forms, *Mycoplasma* and PPLO are discussed further in Chapter 41.

The physical nature of the protoplast membrane and the protective role of the cell wall are seen when protoplasts are derived from long, cylindrical bacilli or from branching mold filaments. These protoplasts promptly assume a spherical but easily distorted shape. It is evident that the cell wall is a rigid, retaining structure, whereas the protoplast membrane is limp and easily ruptured.

## 13.5 THE CELL MEMBRANE

In animal cells the cytoplasm is not clearly differentiated from the outer integument (which substitutes for a cell wall) and often cannot readily be sharply separated from it. The cytoplasmic membrane of procaryotic cells, on the contrary, is a distinct and separable structure. By gentle enzymic removal of the bacterial cell wall, followed by osmotic rupture of the resulting protoplast in a hypotonic solution, the contents of the cytoplasmic membrane can be removed and the resulting sac, sometimes called a "ghost," cleaned by gentle washing and centrifugation. Cell membranes can also be readily seen in cross sections of intact bacterial cells properly prepared and stained for observation under the electron microscope.

Studies of such materials show that bacterial cell membranes typically consist of three (in some species more than three) distinct layers (Figs. 13.7, 13.10). The two outer layers are

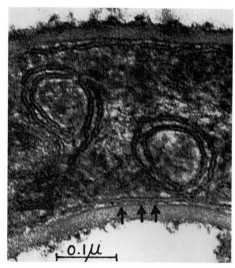

**Figure 13.10** *Actinomyces bovis.* Concentric rings of intracytoplasmic membranes are clearly visible. The two dark parallel lines are characteristic of the plasma membrane. Attachments between the outer dark line of plasma membrane and the innermost layer of the cell wall indicate adherence of the plasma membrane to the cell wall. (From Edwards and Gordon: *In* Proceedings of Fifth International Congress for Electron Microscopy. Academic Press, New York, 1962.)

electron dense (i.e., opaque to electrons) and are each about 25 Å thick. The middle layer, about 50 Å thick, is much less electron dense and appears to consist of a bimolecular layer of lipid oriented so that hydrophilic poles are outermost, hydrophobic groups opposed within. The chemical composition of the outer layers covering the inner bilayer of lipid remains to be fully clarified, but it appears that these layers contain some polysaccharide and a considerable amount of protein, but without the D-amino acids that characterize cell-wall material. There is no mucocomplex, since the cytoplasmic membrane is not dissolved by lysozyme. Most of the proteins are probably associated with the numerous enzymes that have been demonstrated to occur in cytoplasmic membranes. About 15 per cent of the dry weight of the membrane consists of RNA, probably as nucleoproteins associated with synthesis of enzymes or other proteins (such as pili?). The three-layered membrane just described is a general form found in all bacteria and probably other procaryotic cells. The same or a similar type of membrane, with various modifications, appears to be widely distributed in all cell types, not only as cytoplasmic membrane but in intracellular membranes as well. It is often called a *unit membrane.*

A number of authorities describe the unit membrane as two-layered; each half of the central, bimolecular, lipid layer, with its attached protein being considered as one layer.

Many of the enzymic activities of the procaryotic cell, especially those concerned with the energy-yielding (respiratory) biochemistry of the cell, undoubtedly take place in the cell membrane.

An extremely important function of the cell membrane is maintenance of a favorable, intracellular, osmotic pressure. As previously mentioned, the cell membrane is often called the *osmotic barrier* of the cell. It must admit the proper kind and amount of molecules, atoms, ions and water. Conversely, it must retain the soluble materials of the fluid matrix, nutrients and salts, and at the same time facilitate the egress of the proper amount of water, organic and inorganic wastes, some digestive enzymes, and so on. The cell membrane, aided by permease enzyme systems, thus exerts during life a truly remarkable degree of selective permeability, distinctive for each species, upon which the life of the cell depends. Functionally, the cytoplasmic membrane of the procaryotic protist acts as gastrointestinal tract, urinary system (genital system if F pili are correctly evaluated), lungs and skin. In addition, many of the important energy-yielding reactions of biooxidation occur in or on the cytoplasmic membrane.

## 13.6  CYTOPLASM

The term cytoplasm (Gr. *kytos* = cell; *plasma* = a substance), like the term protoplasm, is an inclusive one; i.e., cytoplasm is not a homogeneous substance. Except for the nuclear material, the cytoplasm comprises all of the different substances and structures inside the cell membrane: a variety of microsomes (Gr. *mikro* = microscopic; *soma* = body) or subcellular particles that are mainly proteins and nucleoproteins, with some lipoproteins and other materials. All of the particulate matter in the cytoplasm is surrounded by, and suspended in, an aqueous fluid or semifluid *"ground substance"* or *matrix*. The matrix is a complex mixture containing in solution a variety of ions ($H^+$, $PO_4^{+++}$, $Na^+$, $^-Cl$) amino acids, some proteins, lipocomplexes, peptides, purines, pyrimidines, glucose, ribose, vitamins, nucleotides, coenzymes, disaccharides and so on. Functionally these are: (a) precursors ("prefabricated" molecules) and other building materials to be used in cell synthesis; (b) sources of energy (e.g., glucose or other oxidizable material); (c) waste products of the cell to be excreted to the exterior. The matrix may also contain tRNA and complete, active enzymes in solution. Also present within the cytoplasmic substance are granules or globules of inert stored food substances, the composition of which depends on the species of cell and the nutritive conditions surrounding it: starch and similar polysaccharides, lipids, poly-beta-hydroxybutyric acid, sulfur.

### CYTOPLASMIC ULTRASTRUCTURES

**Ribosomes.** The minutely granular appearance of the major portion of the cytoplasm in all cells, eucaryotic and procaryotic, seen in electron micrographs is due to the presence of enormous numbers of minute, diffusely scattered particles varying considerably in size and specific densities. They are called *ribosomes* (Fig. 13.11). Because of their differing size and densities, they are found in different layers (density gradients) in differential centrifugation, and are designated according to their sedimentation coefficients (S*) as 70S, 80S, 16S and so on.

Each ribosome consists of a small (about 30S) subunit and a larger (about 50S) subunit. Ribosomes tend to form aggregates of varying sizes. These are called *polyribosomes* or *polysomes.* Some polysomes appear to consist of chains of ribosomes strung along a thread of connecting substance which may be messenger RNA. Indeed, ribosomes consist largely of ribosomal RNA (rRNA) with some protein (ribonucleoprotein). At least part of the RNA of ribosomes is messenger RNA (mRNA). Ribosomes are thus responsible for the synthesis of *specific* proteins, including the proteins of all enzymes.

**Intracytoplasmic Membranes.** In eucaryons ribosomes are concentrated at, and probably connected to, the inner surfaces of the cell membrane and along the surfaces of a very complex and all-pervasive membranous structure called the *endoplasmic reticulum*. This is formed by extensive, branching invaginations of the cytoplasmic membrane. The dendritic ramifications of these membranous invaginations in eucaryons form tubules and

---

*S = ratio of sedimentation velocity to gravitational force (G) under given conditions of viscosity.

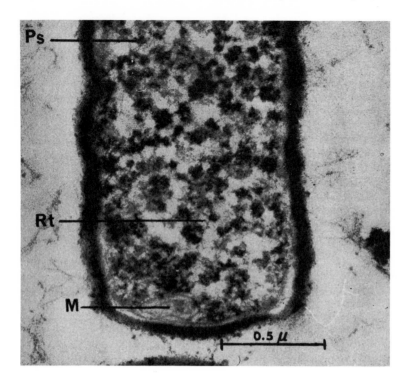

**Figure 13.11**   Thin section of *Bacillus cereus*. Alternate freezing and thawing of bacterium induced cell-wall breakage and thereby reduced cytoplasmic density. Clusters of polyribosomes (Ps) are visible with an interlacing reticulum-like (Rt) network. Note mesosome (M) in close association with the cytoplasmic membrane. (From Pfister and Lundgren: J. Bact., *88*:1119, 1964.)

channels everywhere deep in the cytoplasm: a sort of molecular vascular system. The endoplasmic reticulum brings both interior and exterior surfaces of the cell membrane close to all of the innermost reaches of the cytoplasm —an obvious advantage since the life of the entire cell is dependent on its communications with the outer world via the cell membrane.

Procaryons have no obvious endoplasmic reticulum. Their ribosomes appear to have no obvious arrangement or organization on, or in, membranes, beyond a tendency to accumulate close to the cell membrane. However, ribosomes in some procaryons appear to be clustered together in polysomes like those described for eucaryotic cells. Attachment of ribosomes to some sort of netlike (not membranous) structure has also been described in some species of bacteria.

In certain bacteria, invaginations of the cell membrane called *mesosomes** (Fig. 13.10) constitute a procaryotic, surface-extending organelle suggestive of the more extensive eucaryotic *endoplasmic reticulum*. The exact role of mesosomes in procaryons has not yet been fully clarified. Species of procaryons appear to vary considerably in the extent and form of these intracytoplasmic invaginations of the cell mem-

brane. These variations may represent evolutionary stages between very primitive and minute cells with no inward extensions of the cell membrane, to the endoplasmic reticulum and self-replicating *mitochondria* of larger eucaryotic cells familiar to students of elementary biology.

Attempts to demonstrate distinct and typical membranous mitochondria as such in procaryotic cells have yielded inconclusive results. In differential centrifuge sediments obtained from ruptured cells, particles that are possibly parts of mitochondria, and having mitochondrial enzymic properties, have been found and studied by a number of investigators. Whether these particles exist as distinct functional units in the procaryotic cell, or are parts of the cell membrane shattered by manipulation, or bits of some structure derived from the cell membrane, like a primitive endoplasmic reticulum or mesosomes, is not yet fully clarified.

### PHOTOSYNTHETIC ORGANELLES

Eucaryotic cells are more "advanced" than procaryotic cells in respect to photosynthetic mechanisms.

**Chloroplasts.**   These organelles, familiar to all students of elementary biology, contain the green chlorophyll pigments that are the

---

*The same or similar structures have been variously called *peripheral bodies, chondrioids, bacterial mitochondria*.

basis of the utilization of radiant energy, e.g., ultraviolet or sunlight, for photosynthesis by all eucaryotic green plants. Like mitochondria, chloroplasts are self-duplicating.

The intimate structures of chloroplasts are complex. Each chloroplast is discrete and is enclosed within a unit-type membrane. Within the membrane are elaborately and systematically ordered lamellar cross membranes or layered disks. These structures are so arranged as to provide maximum surfaces, with many reactive molecular points, at which the biochemical activities of the chloroplast can occur to the fullest extent. The layered disks and membranes also expose a maximum surface to the light.

**Chromatophores and Chromoplasts.** In the procaryons, chloroplasts are lacking. Nevertheless, all of the blue-green algae and some alga-like species of bacteria characteristically exhibit active photosynthesis. Unlike eucaryons, however, the photosynthetic functions of procaryotic cells are centered in pigment-bearing granules called, in bacteria, *chromatophores* and, in blue-green algae, *chromoplasts*. These bodies are not membrane-bounded, self-duplicating organelles like chloroplasts, but they are larger and heavier than ribosomes. The chromoplasts of blue-green algae have a finely layered or laminated structure, but they typically lack the elaborate internal, membranous structure of the chloroplasts of eucaryotic plants. The chromatophores of photosynthetic bacteria are more fully discussed in Chapter 38.

**Inert Cytoplasmic Inclusions.** Many species of microorganisms, procaryotic and eucaryotic, store up reserve food substances in intracellular granules or globules. When appropriate extracellular food is abundant they may be very conspicuous and occupy a considerable portion of the intracellular space, only to diminish or disappear when food is scarce. The chemical nature of most of these inclusions is well known because of their distinctive staining or other properties.

LIPIDS.  Many blue-green algae, bacteria, probably some rickettsias, and many eucaryons like yeasts, higher fungi and human tissue cells accumulate intracellular globules of fat. These are readily recognized because they are (a) easily extractable with organic solvents; (b) readily stained by fat-soluble lipid stains: blue by naphthol blue, black by Sudan black*; (c) microscopically structureless.

In bacteria, many of the inclusions formerly regarded as fat are actually a highly polymer-

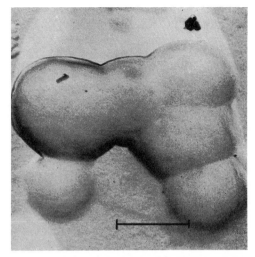

**Figure 13.12** Poly-beta-hydroxybutyric acid granules isolated from *Bacillus megaterium* ($\times$ 22,000). The smooth surface appearance and the coalescence of the granules are prominent features. (From Merrick, Lundgren and Pfister: J. Bact., *89*:234, 1965.)

ized form of a fatty acid, beta-hydroxybutyric acid (bha). Butyric acid is one of the constituent molecules of many fats, a familiar one being butter. The beta-hydroxybutyric acid units of poly-beta-hydroxybutyric acid (pbha) are joined by ester bonds linking the basic hydroxyl group of one molecule of butyric acid with the acidic carboxyl group of another with elimination of water (anhydrosynthesis).

Poly-beta-hydroxybutyric acid granules or globules are stained by fat-soluble dyes in the same way as fats (Fig. 13.12). When needed by the cell, the pbha is hydrolyzed to soluble, oxidizable bha or bha dimers, depending on species.

---

**\* Fat stain** (Burdon)

1. Prepare the film, dry and fix by gentle heating as for the Gram stain.
2. Flood the entire slide with Sudan Black (0.3 per cent dry dye in 70 per cent $C_2H_5OH$) and leave the slide for 5 to 15 minutes. Drying of the dye will not harm the preparation. Use of a Coplin jar is less satisfactory.
3. Drain off excess dye and blot dry.
4. Clear in xylol for about one minute, dipping in and out.
5. Counterstain with 0.1 per cent aqueous safranin for 10 seconds. Overstaining with counterstain will mask the fat stain. It may even be omitted.

The fat appears as dark, blue-black masses; the rest of the cell is pink.

The stock of solution of Sudan Black keeps well in a clean, stoppered bottle. It should be shaken occasionally and allowed to settle overnight before use. Sudan III and Scharlach R are *much less* satisfactory.

POLYSACCHARIDES. Many species of cells, both eucaryotic and procaryotic, synthesize and store up excess soluble carbohydrate food substances in the form of insoluble polysaccharides. These are commonly polymers of glucose, though polymers of other monosaccharides or oligosaccharides are not uncommon. In green plants these food reserves usually appear as *starch*, and in animal cells, as *glycogen* (so-called *animal starch*). In Cyanophyceae they are called *cyanophycean starch*. When cells containing them are treated with iodine, starch granules become conspicuously blue while glycogen granules may be brown or purple. In some species of the bacterial Genus *Clostridium*, granules staining blue with iodine are a starch-like material called *granulose*.

VOLUTIN. This substance was originally described in a bacterium called *Spirillum volutans* and was named for that species. It has since been observed in a wide variety of bacteria and blue-green algae and in some eucaryotic species. Volutin is especially rich in organic phosphates. It consists largely of polymerized metaphosphates (*polymetaphosphates*) in insoluble form associated with nucleic acids and lipids in various linkages and proportions. These differ in various species (Fig. 13.13).

Volutin is characteristically *chromophilic;* i.e., it has a marked affinity for basic dyes. It is also *metachromatic;* i.e., it often appears to be of a color different from that of the applied dye. For example, stained with methylene or toluidine blue, volutin granules often appear ruby red, probably due to red impurities in the dye. Volutin therefore often appears in large, conspicuous granules called *metachromatic granules,* and is usually abundant under conditions of good nutrition and slowed metabolism, especially in media containing glycerol or carbohydrates. It appears to accumulate when phosphates are not being used by the cell in its energy metabolism. Because of their marked affinity for basic dyes, volutin granules were formerly often confused with bacterial nuclei, which also are basophilic (*chromatinic*).

OTHER STORED SUBSTANCES. In some species of aquatic and soil-inhabiting bacteria, globules of pure, elemental sulfur accumulate in the cell as unused food. This sulfur is often derived from the intracellular dehydrogenation (oxidation) of hydrogen sulfide or other inorganic reduced forms of sulfur. The elemental sulfur in the globules can be extracted from the cells with carbon disulfide from which the sulfur is deposited as distinctive crystals.

FOOD STORAGE. The accumulation of food substances in the cell as polymers such as pbha, starch, glycogen and volutin has at least three advantages for the cell: (a) polymers are a sort of molecular *multum in parvo* in that many molecules, with accompanying energy, are condensed into a small space; (b) the substance and energy in the insoluble polymers are quickly made available for use by the cell by the simple process of hydrolysis into the soluble units; (c) being insoluble, the polymers do not affect the intracellular osmotic pressure and other colligative properties* of the cell contents as would an equivalent amount of the unpolymerized materials in soluble form.

## 13.7   THE NUCLEUS

As mentioned elsewhere the procaryotic nuclear apparatus (nucleoid or chromatinic

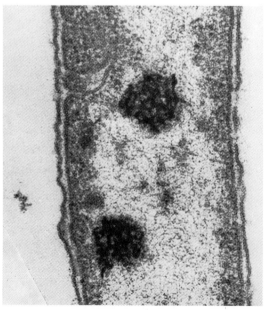

**Figure 13.13** Polymetaphosphate granules (volutin) in *Myxococcus xanthus* (× 110,000). Note also the distinct cell wall, the unit-type cell membrane with intracytoplasmic extensions, the ribosomes and the extensive fibrillar nucleoid. Electron micrograph by H. G. Voelz (unpublished data). (From Harold: Bact. Rev., *30*:772, 1966.)

*Colligative properties of a fluid are those that are affected only by the *number* of particles in suspension or solution, not their chemical nature. For example, 1 gm. of sodium chloride dissolved in 500 ml. of water will yield billions of tiny ions in the solution, and is easily shown to have a marked effect on all of the colligative properties. Osmotic pressure, vapor pressure, and boiling points are raised; freezing points are lowered. One gram of sugar or protein or bacteria (or buckshot!), all of which introduce relatively few, comparatively large, molecules (or objects) into the solution or suspension, have lesser effects in the order named.

body) differs most obviously from the eucaryotic nucleus in that the latter is enclosed within a definite nuclear membrane and exhibits mitotic cycles and, in forming gametes, meiosis. The procaryotic nucleoid is not membrane-bounded and exhibits no mitotic or meiotic phenomena. There are other, less obvious, differences. Structurally, the procaryotic nucleoid, as seen in ultrathin cross sections of blue-green algae, bacteria, rickettsias, *Mycoplasma* (PPLO) and organisms of the P-L-T group (formerly called "large" viruses), appears as an amorphous, rounded and lobular mass of fibrillar, intensely chromatinic material. It exhibits less electron density than ribosomes, cell wall and several other parts of the cell. It occupies from one half to two thirds of the intracellular space. Chromosomes, such as those seen during prophase and metaphase in mitosis of eucaryotic cells, are never seen. The procaryotic nuclear material appears to remain in a state resembling the interphase of the eucaryotic chromosomal matter (Figs. 10.3, 10.4, 13.7).

The fibrils seen in bacterial nucleoids with the electron microscope appear to represent at least one long (about 1400 $\mu$), thin (about 30 Å), flexible, circular (i.e., no free ends) filament of DNA. The arrangement of this structure in the cell may be visualized as being like a 6- to 10-foot-long filament of thin, two-stranded, twisted cotton thread, ends fastened together, the whole collected into an irregular, tightly packed bundle in the hand. Sometimes in actively multiplying cells several such strands, identical replicas of each other (see Chapter 14), are present in one cell because of chromosome replications that precede cell division. The circular filament of DNA just described is generally spoken of as the *bacterial chromosome*. Since it is an autonomously replicating unit, it is also called a *chromosomal replicon*. These fragile, ringlike DNA structures are in contrast with the relatively short, relatively thick, rigid and rodlike eucaryotic chromosomes. Procaryotic nuclei, when sought for by means of ordinary nuclear (basic) dyes, are generally masked because of the affinity of surrounding masses of ribosomes, rich in RNA, for the same dyes that color DNA. Only after removing the masking RNA by acid hydrolysis or by exposure to the enzyme *ribonuclease,* specific for RNA, can the DNA of the nucleoid be seen clearly. Since staining provides only indirect evidence of the nucleoid, the electron microscope method of direct observation of thin sections is preferable.

In bacteria (and in other procaryons?) chromosome-like structures similar to but smaller than the chromosomal replicon occur independently and apart from the main replicon. They, also, are autonomously self-replicating units. They have been variously called *factors, extrachromosomal conjugons* and *episomes.* (See Chapter 14.)

## 13.8   THE PROCARYOTIC ALGAE

Of all the procaryons the blue-green algae (Cyanophyceae,* Myxophyceae† or Schizophyceae) are the largest and most plantlike. About 2000 species are known, some of which live, like bacteria, as individual cells of microscopic size. The Cyanophyceae, like bacteria and many fungi, inhabit a wide range of environments from pole to pole, in arctic and antarctic seas and in thermal springs as well as in soils and fresh waters. Most are harmless and some, in mass growth, give bright colors to seas and lakes; many provide food for plankton and, collected in mass, fertilizer for land crops. Their food requirements are of the simplest and they are often found as the first forms of life on cooled outflows of new lava.

Most blue-green algae resemble bacteria in several respects but are much larger, although still microscopic. With a few exceptions the Cyanophyceae contain three pigments: the green pigment, photosynthetic *chlorophyll a;* a blue pigment, *phycocyanin,* formed in no other plants; and other pigments, e.g., *phycoerythrin, carotene* and *xanthophyll.* The blue-green algae are the smallest and most bacteria-like of the sunlight-dependent plants. Examples are *Oscillatoria, Nostoc, Coccochloris* and *Spirulina* (Fig. 13.14).

Some eucaryotic algae possess flagella and move actively like protozoa of the Class Mastigophora. The blue-green algae, however, are nonflagellate and not actively motile, although some species, like certain bacteria, can bend and creep. Nutritionally, typical blue-green algae are photolithotrophs and aerobic.

The Cyanophyceae, like bacteria, multiply by binary fission and have no distinct sexual cycle as do some protozoa. The nucleus of Cyanophyceae, unlike that of protozoa, is typically without nuclear membrane—i.e., it is procaryotic in structure. This is also a bacterium-like character. The chlorophyll of blue-green algae is lamellar but not confined to chloroplasts

---

*Gr. *cyano* = blue; *phyceae* = a group of algae.

†Gr. *myxo* = slime. Many Cyanophyceae form a slimy *capsule* or outer coating formed of pectin-like material.

**TABLE 13.1**   DISTINCTIVE PROPERTIES OF EUCARYOTIC AND PROCARYOTIC PROTISTS AND VIRUSES*

| Properties | Eucaryons | Procaryons | Viruses |
|---|---|---|---|
| *Nucleus* | | | |
| Membrane | Distinct; unit type (not all species) | None | None |
| Nucleolus | Distinct | None | None |
| Nucleic acids | DNA and RNA | DNA and RNA | NA core is RNA or DNA; not both |
| Mitosis | Distinct | None | None |
| Chromosomes | Typically more than one; rods in mitosis | One (+ episomes**); circular, never rod shaped | One circular replicon |
| *Cytoplasm* | | | |
| Centrioles | Distinct† | None | None |
| Streaming | Distinct (not all species) | None seen | None |
| Ameboid movement | Distinct in *Amoeba* | None seen | None |
| Ribosomes | Polysome groupings; membrane-oriented | Arrangement not clear; polysomes?; membrane-orientation probable in some | None |
| Endoplasmic reticulum | Extensive throughout cytoplasm | Suggestive membranous structures in some | None |
| Mesosomes | Not evident as such; (pinocytic invaginations?) | Saclike invaginations of cell membrane in numerous species; function? | None |
| Autonomous metabolic enzyme systems | Complex; active exergonic and synthetic | Complex; active exergonic and synthetic | None |
| Mitochondria | Numerous; distinct | None | None |
| Chloroplasts | Distinct in green plants | None | None |
| Chromatophores | None | In Cyanophyceae and some bacteria | None |
| Chlorophyll *a* | Present in chloroplasts | In Cyanophyceae only | Absent |
| Lysosomes | Numerous; distinct | None | None |
| Microtubules, microfilaments | Distinct | Seen in some species | None |
| *Flagella*** | Sheath containing 11 fibrils | Single naked fibril of flagellin | None |
| *Cell Membrane* | "Unit type" (protein-bimolecular lipid leaflet-protein [trilaminate] structure) | Unit membrane | None |
| *Cell Wall* (Principal strengthening material) | Fungi: chitin†† Green plants: cellulose†† Animals: none morphologically or chemically differentiated; plasmalemma. | Mucopolysaccharide or mucopeptide complex; morphologically and chemically differentiated except in Chlamydiaceae; absent in *Mycoplasma* | Protein coating (capsid); envelope of host origin containing lipopolysaccharides in some animal viruses |
| *Cell Size* ($\mu^3$) | Generally > 20 | Generally < 5.0 | < 0.02 |
| *Sexuality* | | | |
| Gametes | Distinct (not all species) | Not morphologically differentiated; obscure | None |
| Recombination | Generally only by conjugation in which entire genomes are combined; true, diploid zygotes are formed | Transformation; transduction; conjugation in which variable segments of (rarely complete) genomes are transferred, sometimes with episomes; episomes may be transferred independently of genome; merozygotes are formed§ | Can occur in vegetative state; mingling of NA strands by "copy choice" may occur in multiple infection of cells |

**TABLE 13.1**   DISTINCTIVE PROPERTIES OF EUCARYOTIC AND PROCARYOTIC PROTISTS AND VIRUSES*

(Continued)

| Properties | Eucaryons | Procaryons | Viruses |
|---|---|---|---|
| *Multiplication*<br>In inanimate media | Common | Common; absent in Chlamydiaceae and Rickettsia | None |
| Basic mechanism | Self-synthesis of entire cell followed by conjugation, fission, budding, etc. | As in eucaryons except in Chlamydiaceae and *Mycoplasma* (conjugation not common; see recombination above). | Synthesized largely by host enzyme systems, host-derived materials; no processes of fission, budding or independent growth. |

 *In all groups there are some species for which data are lacking or incomplete or which are exceptions or variations from the "typical," the "usual," or "selected examples."

 †Animal cells only; in many plants replaced by polar caps.

 **When present.

 ††Morphologically and chemically differentiated.

 §Established only in some species of bacteria; data on Cyanophyceae, Rickettsieae and Chlamydiaceae incomplete or absent.

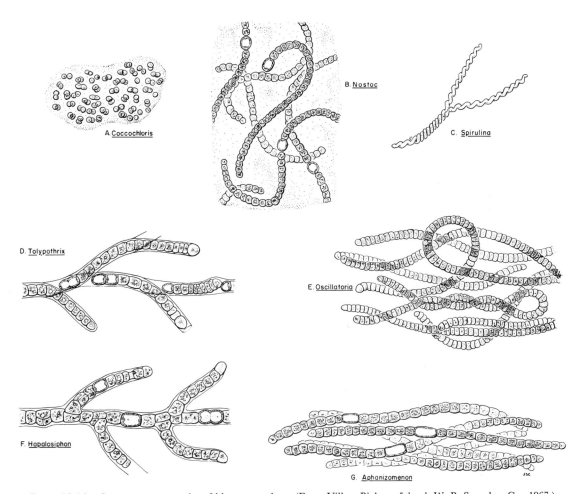

**Figure 13.14** Some common species of blue-green algae. (From Villee: Biology, 5th ed. W. B. Saunders Co., 1967.)

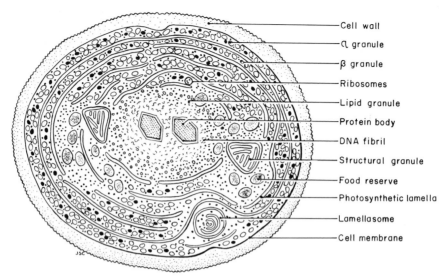

Cell wall
α granule
β granule
Ribosomes
Lipid granule
Protein body
DNA fibril
Structural granule
Food reserve
Photosynthetic lamella
Lamellasome
Cell membrane

**Figure 13.15**   Diagram of the structure of the cell of a blue-green alga revealed by electron microscopy. Note the lack of highly specialized structures found in eucaryons. (From Villee: Biology, 5th ed. W. B. Saunders Co., 1967.)

as it is in eucaryotic plants. In general, the structure of cells of blue-green algae is obviously bacteria-like (Fig. 13.15).

## SUPPLEMENTARY READING

Bladen, H. A., Nylen, M. U., and Fitzgerald, R. J.: Internal structures of a *Eubacterium* sp. demonstrated by the negative staining technique. J. Bact., *88*:763, 1964.

Brinton, Jr., C. C.: The structure, function, synthesis and genetic control of bacterial pili and a molecular model for DNA and RNA transport in gram-negative bacteria. Tr. N. Y. Acad. Sci., Ser. II, *27*:1003, 1965.

Burge, R. E., and Holwill, M. E. J.: Hydrodynamic aspects of microbial movement. Fifteenth Symposium, Function and Structure in Micro-organisms, p. 250. Soc. Gen. Microbiol., London. 1965.

Cho, K. Y., Doy, C. H., and Mercer, E. H.: Ultrastructure of the obligate halophilic bacterium *Halobacterium halobium.* J. Bact., *94*:196, 1967.

Cohen-Bazire, G., Kunisawa, R., and Poindexter, J. S.: The internal membranes of *Caulobacter crescentus.* J. Gen. Microbiol., *42*:301, 1966.

Echlin, P.: The fine structure of unicellular blue-green algae from the genus *Merismopedia.* Proc. Soc. Gen. Microbiol., London. 1965.

Fawcett, D. W.: An Atlas of Fine Structure: The Cell. W. B. Saunders Co., Philadelphia. 1966.

Fitz-James, P. C.: A consideration of bacterial membrane as the agent of differentiation. Fifteenth Symposium, Function and Structure in Micro-organisms. Soc. Gen. Microbiol., London. 1965.

Gibor, A., and Granick, S.: Plastids and Mitochondria: Inheritable systems. Science, *145*:890, 1964.

Graham, R. K., and May, J. W.: Composition of cell walls of some gram-negative cocci. J. Gen. Microbiol., *41*:243, 1965.

Hagen, P. O., Goldfine, H., and Williams, P. J. le B.: Phospholipids of bacteria with extensive intracytoplasmic membranes. Science, *151*:1543, 1966.

Harold, F. M., and Harold, R. L.: Degradation of inorganic polyphosphate in mutants of *Aerobacter aerogenes.* J. Bact., *89*:1262, 1965.

Hayes, W.: The structure and function of the bacterial chromosome. Fifteenth Symposium, Function and Structure in Micro-organisms, p. 294. Soc. Gen. Microbiol., London. 1965.

Horecker, B. L.: The biosynthesis of bacterial polysaccharides. Ann. Rev. Microbiol., *20*:253, 1966.

Imaeda, T., and Ogura, M.: Formation of intracytoplasmic membrane system of mycobacteria related to cell division. J. Bact., *85*:150, 1963.

Keeler, R. F., Ritchie, A. E., Bryner, J. H., and Elmore, J.: The preparation and characterization of cell walls and the preparation of flagella of *Vibrio fetus.* J. Gen. Microbiol., *43*:439, 1966.

Kerridge, D.: The effect of environment on the formation of bacterial flagella. Eleventh Symposium, Microbial Reaction to Environment, p. 41. Soc. Gen. Microbiol., London. 1961.

Loewenstein, W. R. (editor): Biological Membranes: Recent Progress. Ann. N. Y. Acad. Sci., *137*(Art. 2):403, 1966.

Martin, H. H.: Biochemistry of bacterial cell walls. Ann. Rev. Biochem., *35*:457, 1966.

Martinez, R. J., and Gordee, E. Z.: Formation of bacterial flagella. J. Bact., *91*:870, 1966.

Merrick, J. M.: Effect of polymyxin B, Tyrocidine, gramicidin D, and other antibiotics on the enzymatic hydrolysis of poly-p-hydroxybutyrate. J. Bact., *90*:965, 1965.

Nermut, M. V., and Murray, R. G. E.: Ultrastructure of the cell walls of *Bacillus polymyxa.* J. Bact., *93*:1949, 1967.

Newton, B. A., and Kerridge, D.: Flagellar and ciliary movement in microorganisms. Fifteenth Symposium, Function and Structure in Micro-organisms, p. 220. Soc. Gen. Microbiol., London. 1965.

Perkins, H. R.: Chemical structure and biosynthesis of bacterial cell walls. Bact. Rev., *27*:18, 1963.

Remsen, C. C., and Lundgren, D. G.: Multiple septation in variants of *Bacillus cereus.* J. Bact., *90*:1426, 1965.

Rhodes, M. E.: Flagellation as a criterion for the classification of bacteria. Bact. Rev., *29:*442, 1965.

Rhodin, J. A. G.: An Atlas of Ultrastructure. W. B. Saunders Co., Philadelphia. 1963.

Rich, A.: Polyribosomes. *In:* The Living Cell. W. H. Freeman and Co., San Francisco. 1965.

Robertson, J. D.: The membrane of the living cell. *In:* The Living Cell, W. H. Freeman and Co., San Francisco. 1965.

Rogers, H. J.: The outer layers of bacteria: the biosynthesis of structure. Fifteenth Symposium, Function and Structure in Micro-organisms, p. 186. Soc. Gen. Microbiol., London. 1965.

Schlessinger, D., Marchesi, V. T., and Kwan, B. C. K.: Binding of ribosomes to cytoplasmic reticulum of *Bacillus megaterium.* J. Bact., *90:*456, 1965.

Schnaitman, C., and Greenwalt, J. W.: Intracytoplasmic membranes in *Escherichia coli.* J. Bact., *92:*780, 1966.

el-Shazly, K., and Hungate, R. E.: Method for measuring diaminopimelic acid in total rumen contents and its application to the estimation of bacterial growth. Appl. Microbiol., *14:*27, 1966.

van Iterson, W., Hoeniger, J. F. M., and van Zanten, E. N.: Basal bodies of the flagella and particular microtubules in swarmers of *Proteus mirabilis.* Ant. Leeuw., *33:*221, 1967.

# Chapter 14

## RECOMBINATION IN PROCARYONS

As all students of biology are aware, genetic recombination is the transfer of genes (i.e., genetic units of heredity) from one cell genome to another. In typical, diecious, eucaryotic organisms this is accomplished by the joining of haploid male and female gametes and mingling of the maternal and paternal genes, with the formation of a diploid zygote. In procaryons genetic recombination is quite a different process. It can be accomplished by several different mechanisms without the aid of sex as previously described. Before discussing genetic recombination among procaryons we may review some ideas concerning genes themselves.

**The Gene.** The term gene, attributed to Johanssen in 1911, is derived from the classical science of heredity founded about 1870 by the Austrian monk Gregor Mendel (1822–1884). By 1940, through the work of Morgan, Muller, Sutton (Nobel Prize winners) and many others, the gene had been recognized as the genetic unit: the basis of mutation, recombination, the transmission of hereditary traits and the phenomenon of dominance and recessiveness. However, the true chemical and physical structures of the gene were clarified only within the current decade by Watson, Crick (Nobel Prize winners), Benzer and many others.

The term gene is now recognized as any genetically functional segment of a DNA filament. A gene is characterized by its ability to transmit heritable characteristics. It is subject to various kinds of alterations that cause progeny to have heritable characteristics different from their ancestral cells, i.e., to be *mutants* (Chapter 15). A gene may consist of from one nucleotide pair to thousands of pairs linked together, and is often made up of several distinct and separable segments of the DNA filament. An entire, double-helix DNA macromolecule with its genes constitutes a *chromosome,* a cytological unit familiar to all students of elementary biology. The gene includes numerous subunits called recons, cistrons, operons, etc.

**The Recon.** A *recon* may be defined as the *minimal genetic unit* that is capable of being transferred, intact, from one chromosome to another (i.e., recombination) and undergoing mutation. A recon may be a single nucleotide but probably usually consists of many nucleotides or pairs of complementary nucleotides, depending on the actual mechanism of recombination. (See also muton, page 177.)

**The Cistron.** During intensive studies of the location of genes on chromosomes (see chromosome mapping), it was discovered by Benzer and others about 1957 that if two similar genes, each having suffered different minor deletions due to some agent like x-irradiation, were on chromosomes of mating cells, one defective gene of each chromosome could, by recombinational crossing over or equivalent means, compensate, within the limits of that gene, for the defect in the other. For example, imagine a gene having a nucleotide sequence (No. 1) l, m, n, o, p, q, r, made defective in that it lacks o: l, m, n, . . . , p, q, r. Imagine the sequence on the corresponding gene of the mating chromosome (No. 2) to lack q: l, m, n, o, p, . . . , r. If the two sequences overlap, i.e., are both on the same side of a given point (in the "cis" [= this side] position), they can complement each other. *Complementation* is said to have occurred. If they are on opposite sides of the point at which they overlap (in the "trans" [= other side] position), then they do not complement each other. The limits of a nucleotide sequence can thus be established. The gene whose nucleotide sequence is thus established by complementation as a functional unit in its relation to a complementary gene is termed a *cistron*, from "cis-trans." A cistron, simple or complex, is the genetic unit of function: a gene, as currently understood. A cistron usually consists of hundreds or thousands of recons.

**The Operon.** Not all genes or cistrons are responsible solely for polypeptide synthesis. Those that are involved in the synthesis and specific structure of proteins, as previously described, are called *structural genes*. Other genes or cistrons are part of the "stop-go" mechanisms (Enzyme Control, Chapter 5). They are called *regulatory genes*.

Regulatory genes may be thought of as a sort of on-off switch. For example, the enzyme beta-galactosidase is inducible in several species of bacteria (Chapter 5). Inducibility consists in the fact that there is a genetic mechanism for beta-galactosidase production that is repressed by a removable repressor. The inducing agent (lactose, for example) in contact with the cell removes the repressor, allowing the beta-galactosidase mechanism to become functional. Beta-galactosidase is the enzyme involved in fermentation of lactose.

The genetic mechanism for beta-galactosidase formation consists of several factors: (1) two structural genes for synthesis of beta-galactosidase and another for synthesis of the permease enzyme to allow entrance of the substrate or inducer into the cell; (2) a regulatory gene that produces the repressor substance; and (3) a receptor site or unit called an *operator* that is affected by the repressor and inhibits production of the messenger RNA that is necessary to synthesis of the structural genes. The whole mechanism, including several cooperating structural genes, and several ancillary initiatory units (e.g., a promotor) influenced by one operator, is called an *operon* (Fig. 14.1). Several operons may be interconnected and influence each other. Some genes are said to be *modifiers* because they increase or diminish the activity of other genes. Complete details may be found in books and articles on genetics. (See list of Supplementary Reading at the end of this chapter.)

It is clear that genes are far from being autonomous agents, and that all are closely interadjusted and interdependent and tuned to the activities of each other and of the cell as a whole. As an analogy to the complex interrelationships of all of the many component parts of any living cell, one may think of a bowl

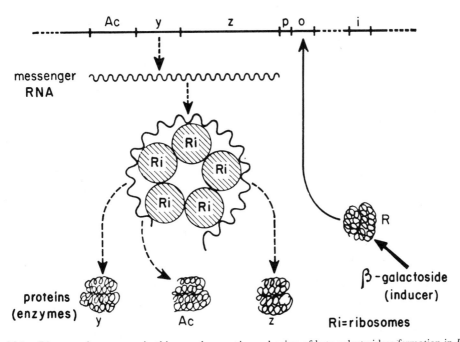

**Figure 14.1** Diagram of an operon, in this case the genetic mechanism of beta-galactosidase formation in *Escherichia coli*. At top an enlargement of the lactose region is shown. i, Regulatory gene; o, operator; p, promotor; z, structural gene for beta-galactosidase; y, structural gene for beta-galactosidase permease enzyme; Ac, structural gene for beta-galactosidase transacetylene; Ri, ribosome. See text for discussion. (From Jacob: Science, *152*:1470, 1966.)

of soapy water at rest, the surface covered by a thick layer of foam. The slightest motion, change or destruction of even the smallest bubble affects in some degree every other bubble in the entire layer of foam.

## 14.1   GENETIC RECOMBINATION IN PROCARYONS

In all cells, during the nondividing or resting stage (*interphase* in eucaryons) that exists prior to the beginning of cell *fission*, each chromosome, whether single as in procaryons, or multiple as in eucaryons, *replicates* itself from end to end by the process described in Chapter 13. Each chromosome thus forms two, usually identical, double-helix chains of nucleotides (called *chromatids* in eucaryons). The two identical chromosomes are so closely approximated that they appear to be one. During the interphase the chromosome threads seem to be in the form of amorphous granular material or of tangled masses of long fibrils of chromatinic material. When the cell undergoes fission one of each pair of identical DNA chains goes to each of the two progeny. Each daughter cell therefore receives an entire haploid set of all of the genetic determinants (a *genome*) of the parent cell, whether a single chromosome or many.

It is at this point, i.e., the manner of distribution of chromosomes to progeny, that one of the major differences between eucaryotic and procaryotic cells becomes manifest: eucaryotic cells exhibit the phenomena of mitosis and meiosis; procaryotic cells do not. It is assumed that the student has already made the acquaintance of mitosis and meiosis as they occur in eucaryotic cells in elementary biology. Therefore, we may turn our attention to heredity mechanisms of procaryons as represented by bacteria.

When the procaryotic cell undergoes fission, the genetic material shows no evidence of systematic organization into chromosomes of the eucaryotic type or any of the phenomena associated with mitosis or meiosis. The procaryotic analogy of mitosis appears to be a gathering together of the interphasic tangle of DNA strands, i.e., the *nucleoid,* into an amorphous skein, which then appears to divide merely by a constriction near the middle, like dividing a hank of yarn into two equal parts.

Although processes of nuclear fission in procaryons may seem haphazard, the replication and division of the DNA in procaryotic cells is as exact and as effective a heredity mechanism as in eucaryons. The great lack in the procaryotic system is the limited and variable opportunity for genetic recombination. Except for the primitive and "unreliable" form of conjugation seen in certain families of bacteria (Eubacteriaceae, Pseudomonadaceae, Streptomycetaceae and probably others), with its uncertain and irregular transfers of varying numbers of genes from one cell to another, true *sexuality,* in the eucaryotic sense, is absent from procaryotic life.

### RECOMBINATION MECHANISMS IN PROCARYONS

Although lacking the evolutionary advantages of sex as it occurs in eucaryons, genetic recombination among procaryons is brought about by several odd and interesting means. At least four mechanisms of gene recombination are seen in procaryons: *transformation, conjugation, sexduction* and *transduction.* A sort of pseudorecombination may also be seen in *viral conversion.* This occurs not between bacterial cells but between bacteria and viruses. It is possible that some, especially the last named, may also occur in some eucaryons.

Although viruses are noncellular and exhibit no sexual phenomena whatever, not even of the primitive type seen in some bacteria, each virus particle has its chromosome of DNA (or RNA) that is entirely similar to the chromosomes of bacteria. Viruses also exhibit phenomena of genetic recombination, as will be explained. In this chapter we shall describe transformation, conjugation and sexduction. Transduction and viral conversion, since they involve viruses, will be discussed after we describe the viruses themselves.

**Transformation.**   Before 1930 it had been observed that if one species of bacterium were cultivated in the presence of a different but closely related species the one would acquire distinctive properties of the other. Apparently something carrying an inheritable character passed from one to the other. This was called *entrainement* by Burnet in 1925. Later, a species of harmless streptococci from cream cheese was shown by Frobisher and Brown to acquire the property of forming scarlet fever toxin when grown in contact with scarlet fever streptococci. It was suspected at that time that a "scarlet fever virus" passed from one species of cell to the other; an idea subsequently abandoned. The mechanism of these alterations was not known at that time, nor is it now.

In later studies by Griffith and others it was shown that cell-free extracts of *dead,* encapsulated pneumococci of type III (see immunological specificity of capsular substance, page 156) would cause cells of live, nonencapsulated (and therefore not type-specific) pneumococci derived from type II, to produce type III capsular substance. By similar methods a variety of genetic changes have been produced in bacteria of several other species. Genetic changes induced in this way are called *transformations.*

THE TRANSFORMING SUBSTANCE. Subsequent studies by Avery, McCleod and McCarty and many others revealed that the substance in the extracts of encapsulated type III pneumococci responsible for the change of nonencapsulated type II pneumococci to encapsulated type III was type III DNA. In all other cases of transformation the transforming principle has likewise been found to be DNA. Transforming DNA is derived from supernumerary replications of DNA in the nucleus. In some species it accumulates on the outside of the cell in a capsule or slime layer. It may be obtained from such cells by washing them. It can also be obtained by rupture of the cell and its nucleus.

The chromosomal fibril of DNA is fragile. Consequently, when DNA is removed from a donor cell by washing or by rupture the DNA macromolecule (bacteria have only one true chromosome) can be broken into segments. Some, perhaps 10 per cent, of the fragments may consist of only one, less commonly two or three, closely linked complete genes. Some may be large (entire?) segments of chromosome. In any case, if they can pass through the recipient cell wall and membrane, one or more new genes may thus be integrated into the chromosome of the recipient cell. However, the DNA segments, large or small, before they enter the new cell are likely first to be destroyed by DNA-ase, an extracellular enzyme produced by many cells, or the DNA segments may be destroyed by other unfavorable factors such as pH or salinity. The recipient cell must also be in a state of *competence.*

COMPETENCE. Cells are "competent" for transformation if they do not secrete DNA-ase, do not have thick, interfering capsules and have other, still obscure, qualifications. Into a small (5–10?) percentage of these cells the donor DNA will quickly (in about 10 seconds) penetrate. Having once penetrated into the recipient, several genes of the DNA segment may or may not be integrated ("incorporated" or "fixed") into the chromosome of the recipient cell by recombination. When and if this occurs it may take from 10 minutes to many hours or generations. Once integrated, the transforming DNA is a permanent part of the recipient genome and is replicated as such. The appearance of the effects of transformation in the progeny (*transformant* cells) or *phenotypes,* awaits transcription of the new genetic message into mRNA, synthesis by the ribosomes of the necessary new enzymes and one or two fissions. The donor DNA that is integrated by recombination with recipient DNA appears to replace recipient DNA. Replaced recipient DNA, and donor DNA not integrated into the recipient genome, do not replicate and are eliminated.

CROSS TRANSFORMATION. Cross transformations between different genera, or *distantly* related species, are extremely rare. For successful transformations the respective DNA's must have similar base compositions, i.e., similar ratios of total number of G—C pairs to A—T pairs in their DNA. Even with similar base compositions, transformations between even quite closely related species may fail because of total dissimilarity between nucleotide sequences or because of slight chemical differences in DNA (e.g., attachment of a methyl group.) Such slight chemical differences between otherwise identical DNA's may be at least part of the basis of the obscure differences between "self" and "nonself" that are responsible for homograft rejections and other reactions referred to in the chapters on immunology. As to whether transformation occurs in nature there are experimental data indicating that it can occur.

Since we now know how to transform bacteria artificially, may we ever transfer DNA between cells of higher plants and animals, or add artificially synthesized DNA to nucleotide sequences of appropriately prepared gametes for the production of "better" animals? It would seem not much more difficult than a trip to the moon (and much less expensive!). Shall we, in the future, genetically manufacture men with specially coded characteristics, perhaps especially suited to weightlessness, prolonged space travel and life on distant planets? Stranger things have happened.

**Conjugation.** The term conjugation as applied to bacteria means physical contact between two genetically different cells of the same (or closely related) species and the establishment of a "conjugation tube" between them. This is usually followed by passage of genetic material from one ("male") to the other ("female"); there is no *exchange* of material between the conjugants.

As is true of transformation, conjugation in procaryons is a variable and uncertain means of gene transference. As previously mentioned, procaryons, as represented by bacteria, have only a single chromosome. Bacteria are therefore normally in a *haploid* state. As a self-replicating unit the bacterial chromosome is often called a *chromosomal replicon*. Presumably replication of the donor or "male" chromosome occurs before (or during?) the time of conjugation. Problems concerned with sources of energy for conjugation are being studied.

**Episomes.**    In several species of bacteria (possibly also in other procaryons) there are, in addition to a chromosomal replicon, smaller, self-replicating DNA units sometimes called *extrachromosomal replicons, plasmids, episomes* or, for convenience, *factors*. They are small, closed circles of DNA and may be thought of as little chromosomes entirely independent of the major chromosome. However, they multiply synchronously with the chromosome. Commonly they are in the cytoplasm (extranuclear); at times, as will be explained, they become integrated with the chromosomal replicon. They are subject to the same agencies that affect the chromosome itself. Episomes could be viewed, speculatively, as multiple chromosomes, e.g., as primitive forerunners of the multiple chromosomes of eucaryons. Their presence confers on the bacterial cell containing them "maleness" or the ability to *conjugate*. They are therefore sometimes called *conjugons*. Conjugation implies certain alterations in the cell wall, to be discussed. At least three types of conjugons are known: the F or fertility factor, the Cf or colicinogenic factor and the RTF (or RT) or resistance transfer factor.

THE F FACTOR.    Male cells normally have one F factor for each chromosome in the cell. Cells with at least one F replicon are designated F$^+$. The F factor may fail to replicate or it may be destroyed through the action of various agents, among them a dye called acridine orange. The F factor never *appears* spontaneously; it is acquired by a female (F$^-$) cell only by conjugation with an F$^+$ cell. The F factor is about one tenth of the size of the chromosomal replicon. Once the F factor is transferred to an F$^-$ cell the F$^-$ cell becomes F$^+$ and the F factor is rapidly replicated in both cells. The F factor confers on F$^+$ cells the genetic property of syn-

thesizing a distinctive polysaccharide at the cell surface that is necessary for conjugation. F$^-$ cells do not synthesize this surface material and cannot initiate conjugation. The surface of the F$^+$ cell is altered *antigenically* (Chapter 24) and in other ways.

In conjugation between bacteria an F$^+$ cell by chance contacts an F$^-$ cell and a conjugation tube opens between them. The F factor is readily transferred to the F$^-$ cell but the chromosome of the F$^+$ cell rarely enters the F$^-$ cell. The result is that although "maleness' (F factor) is spread rapidly by conjugation in a population of F$^-$ cells, genetic recombination (integration of chromosomal material) rarely occurs in such matings. F pili serve as conjugation tubes.

HFR CELLS.    In some F$^+$ cells the F factor becomes attached to the chromosomal replicon. Both circles break open, and one end of the F factor attaches to one end of the chromosome. The F factor is then a part of the chromosome and the two replicate as one.

Association of the F factor with the chromosome facilitates transfer of the chromosome during conjugation. As a result of mating between such cells and F$^-$ cells *recombination* occurs with high frequency; hence such F$^+$ cells (F factor associated with chromosome) are designated as *high frequency* (Hfr) cells. The word "frequency" refers not to frequency of mating but to frequency of transfer of chromosomal DNA, i.e., to frequency of genetic recombination.

In Hfr $\times$ F$^-$ matings, recombination is frequent but transmission of the complete chromosome is not. The recipient cell is rarely in a fully diploid state; it is not a complete zygote. It is referred to as a *merozygote* (Gr. *meros* = partial).

Curiously, the merozygotes produced by the Hfr $\times$ F$^-$ matings are usually F$^-$ (unlike F$^+$ $\times$ F$^-$ merozygotes, which are commonly F$^+$). This is explained by experimental data indicating that in Hfr cells the F factor, or a major part of it, attaches to the "rear" end of the chromosome, i.e., farthest from the end of the chromosome that first enters the F$^-$ cell. All (or part of?) the F factor may be thought of as a locomotive at the rear end of a train of cars, i.e., pushing the chromosome ahead of it. Because of the fragility of the DNA thread, the filament of DNA usually breaks before the termination of the transfer process, leaving part of the chromosome and usually all of the F factor in the donor cell. As in transformation, unintegrated donor material is eliminated from the recipient and the recipient is soon restored to the haploid state.

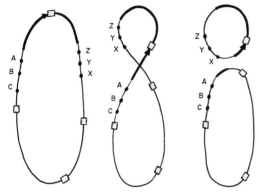

**Figure 14.2**   Formation of an F-genote by imperfect relooping of the F-chromosome-integrated replicon. Heavy lines denote F DNA; light lines chromosomal DNA. (From Adelberg and Pittard: Bact. Rev., *29*:161, 1965.)

F-DUCTION.   In Hfr cells the F replicon may become disassociated from the chromosomal replicon, re-establishing the F⁺ state. The point of break between the two replicons may occur slightly to one side or the other of the true junction. One replicon thus acquires a small portion of the other by exchange (or donation or crossing over). The exact mechanism remains to be fully clarified, though plausible hypotheses doubtless closely approximate the truth (Fig. 14.2). F⁺ cells in which the F factor thus carries some of the chromosomal material are said to be F′. The F factor, plus its bit of chromosome, is called an F-genote. F′ cells act like F⁺ but transfer their acquired chromosomal material to F⁻ cells as a unit along with the F factor. This transfer of chromosomal material from one cell to another with the sex (F) factor is spoken of as F-duction or sexduction.

THE RT (RESISTANCE TRANSFER) FACTOR. This factor is, in all essential respects, similar to the F factor but transfers, in addition to fertility, markers* of resistance to several antibiotics. These transfers occur mainly between gram-negative bacteria closely related to the enteric species: *Escherichia coli, S. typhi,* the cause of typhoid fever, and *S. dysenteriae,* the cause of epidemic bacterial dysentery. Antibiotic resistance, probably caused in large part by the spread of the RT factor among bacteria, is becoming increasingly prevalent in several epidemic areas and presents a grave problem in the treatment and control of enteric bacterial diseases. As mentioned in another chapter, antibiotic resistance may also develop as a result of *point mutations.*

---

*Genetic characters.

THE COLICIN FACTOR (CF).   This is an extrachromosomal replicon similar to the F and the RT replicons. It transfers the property of producing *colicins.* These are antibiotic-like substances lethal for closely related strains or species of the bacteria producing them. They were first observed in *E. coli,* hence their name. Similar substances are produced by other species of bacteria and are given the more general name of *bacteriocins.* Since all of these substances are suggestively similar to bacterial viruses (prophages), they are discussed more fully in Chapter 18.

**Chromosome Mapping.**   In Hfr cells the F element has a regular point of attachment to the chromosome. It is at this point that the chromosome ring appears commonly to open for transference to the F⁻ cell during the conjugation. In any given cell type, the genes on the chromosome thread therefore usually enter the recipient in a fixed and predictable order, like knots on a string being pulled through a hole in a door separating two rooms: the F element, or its major portion, last. As shown by many workers, led by Jacob, Lwoff, Monod (Nobel Prize winners) and Wollman in the early 1960's, it is possible to determine the exact *locus* (location in the chromosome) of any gene, and the order of loci of all genes on the chromosomal thread, by the order in which they are transferred from the Hfr cell to the F⁻ cell during mating. This location of genes on the chromosome is spoken of as *chromosome mapping.* For example, a culture of Hfr cells having certain genetic markers (e.g., various auxotrophies, enzymic characters or resistance to various antibiotics) is mixed under suitable conditions in a culture vessel with F⁻ cells. A sample of the mixture taken about eight minutes after mixing shows no cells with recombination of characters (markers). Two or three minutes later, and at each of several short intervals thereafter, a sample is taken and violently shaken in a Waring blendor. It is known that this is sufficient to break all DNA filaments and therefore to separate all conjugating cells. The shaken samples are immediately plated on agar media that are selective for the various markers to be identified. By observing (in thousands of experiments!) which markers appear in recombinants removed from the conjugation culture after each successive interval, it is possible to determine that certain markers always appear first, followed by the others in their regular and predictable order at predictable intervals. Having established the order of arrangement of markers on a chromosome, it

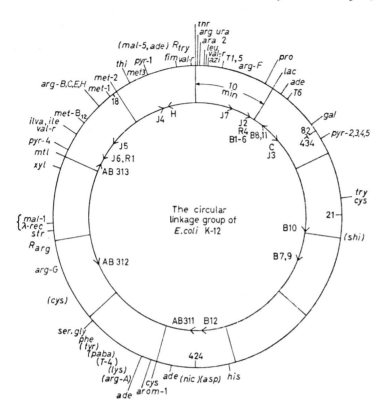

**Figure 14.3** Circular genetic linkage map of *E. coli* K-12. The double circle is divided into 11 sections, each representing a 10 minute transfer interval as determined from interrupted mating experiments. Around the outer circle are located various genetic markers: e.g., *gal* = galactose fermentation; *str* = streptomycin resistance. Prophage loci are indicated inside the outer circle. The various Hfr substrains of *E. coli* K-12 are shown inside the inner circle at the arrowheads (*J4, H, J7,* etc.), which mark the leading end and direction of the transfer of markers. (Prophages are discussed in Chapter 17.) (From Hayes: The Genetics of Bacteria and Their Viruses. John Wiley & Sons, Inc., 1964.)

became possible to draw up circular *linkage maps* of the bacterial chromosome (Fig. 14.3).

When, as rarely happens, the entire Hfr chromosome, including the F factor at the final tip of the chromosome, is transferred to the F⁻ cell, then, and only then, the recipient becomes an HfrF⁺ cell. The point of breakage, and consequently the point of attachment of the F factor to the opened chromosome, may differ in different species or in particular cultures (strains) of the same species. Thus, while the same sequence of genes may characterize all of the cells, the first markers to be transferred may differ. For example, we may have a circular

linkage l-m-n-o-p-q-r. In one strain of this species, breakage and attachment of the F factor may occur between l and r, the l and r being adjacent in the circle. The order of transfer then is l-m-n-o-p-q-r-F; markers l and m enter the F⁻ cell first, F last. If, in another strain, breakage occurs between markers n and o, then the first marker to enter the F⁻ cell may be n or o, depending on whether F is associated with n or o.

## SUPPLEMENTARY READING

(See list at end of Chapter 15.)

# Chapter 15

## MUTATION AND MODIFICATION

### 15.1 MUTATION

Although mechanisms of gene recombination differ in eucaryons and procaryons, the genetic material itself, DNA, is the same in all types of cells, differing only in type, quantity and arrangement of the various nucleotides. The hereditary traits transferred from generation to generation—feathers of a certain color, a Hapsburg jaw or red pigment in a certain bacterial type—are remarkably stable. A bluejay, for example, is always blue; he is seldom seen to have red wings. The stability of genetic traits in any species depends on the template type of replication of DNA and on the resulting, normally unchanging, sequence of nucleotides that make up the DNA of that particular species. If the nature, number or sequence of nucleotides in any genetic DNA is altered so that one or more heritable characters is lost, gained or altered, a genetic change or *mutation* is said to have occurred. A mutation may therefore be defined as a sudden change in heritable characters that is not a result of transfer, segregation or recombination of normal genes but of an alteration of the numbers, molecular structure or sequence of nucleotides that constitute the genes themselves.

Mutations in either eucaryons or procaryons under familiar conditions of life are rare events. Commonly, only one cell in many thousands or many millions may be a *mutant*. Most mutations are ineffective or trifling and have no significant effect on the cell one way or another. Others are occult; i.e., they are present in the genome but not manifest in the phenotype. They remain unrecognized or become evident only under special, selective, environmental conditions (see auxotrophs).

Many mutations are lethal or so detrimental that the cell dies or fails to reproduce.

**The Muton.** Although a mutation commonly involves more than one pair (perhaps thousands) of nucleotides, the *minimal genetic unit* capable of mutation is a single nucleotide: a *muton*.

Any change, however slight, in even one of a single pair of complementary nucleotides in any recon will produce a changed or misspelled nucleotide word that results in no enzyme or in a faulty enzyme. The error is automatically repeated in subsequent DNA replications, just as the error of a misspelled or omitted word on a printing press will be endlessly repeated until corrected.

In *multicellular, sexually reproducing* organisms a mutation in one of the body (somatic) cells is inherited only by the progeny of that cell. The cell may immediately die, the mutation may pass unnoticed, it may express itself as an overgrowth of the tissues locally (a benign tumor), or it may become manifest as a malignant cancer. The somatic cell mutation is not transmitted to the progeny of the multicellular individual. Only when a mutation occurs in the gamete is it transmitted to the progeny of the plant or animal in which the gamete mutation occurs. In protists that multiply both sexually and asexually, mutation in either the haploid (equivalent to gamete) or diploid (equivalent to somatic) cell may produce mutant progeny since the single cell is the entire individual.

CHROMOSOMAL MUTATIONS. These generally result from: *deletions* or loss, or failure to replicate of a segment of a chromosome consisting of numerous recons, mutons or cistrons; *addition* or duplication of chromosome segments; *translocation* or transfer of one chromosome seg-

**177**

ment to a nonhomologous chromosome in a new position; *inversion* or end-for-end reversal of a segment of a chromosome; and in eucaryons, *nondisjunction* or failure of chromosomes to separate at the second meiotic division so that one daughter cell lacks a chromosome while the other has it in duplicate. Many of these changes involve breakage of chromosomes.

POINT MUTATIONS. These involve smaller groups of genetic units than chromosomal mutations; often only a single muton. They may result from: chemical change in one or more mutons; deletion or gain of one or more mutons; or change in sequence in one or more pairs of nucleotides by reversal of nucleotide pairs (e.g., A—T to T—A), or inversion of a segment of the DNA chain involving one or many contiguous nucleotides.

MUTATION RATES. Under natural conditions mutations occur spontaneously—i.e., the cause of the mutation is not known. However, most recognized mutations occur as a result of exposure of growing cells to recognized mutagenic agents such as cosmic rays, sunlight or certain substances in smoke. Probably many "spontaneous" mutations result from familiar causes. Some probably cause some types of cancer.

Spontaneous mutation occurs among microorganisms at widely varying rates. For example, consider mutation to phage-resistance.* In an actively growing culture of a phage-*sensitive* bacterium, a mutant cell *resistant* to that particular phage may occur as rarely as one cell in $10^5$. This is a fairly high mutation rate. In another culture only one mutant (resistant) cell may be found among $10^{10}$ cells or more. On the other hand, one culture was reported in which 1.3 to 15 per cent of all live cells were mutants. Spontaneous mutation rates of various characteristics are commonly about 1 in $10^8$ cells. Further, the rate of mutation in a given

---

*Resistance to infection by viruses called *bacteriophage* (phage) that attack bacteria (Chapter 17).

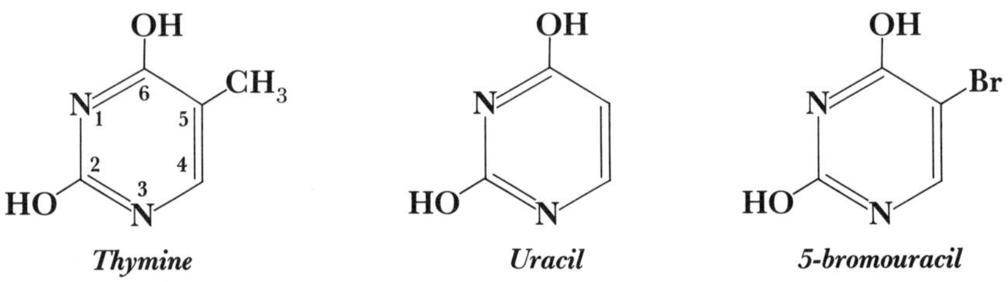

property may vary greatly. One reason for this is that in any given cistron a mutation in any one of the mutons in that cistron may produce the same effect; also, different mutons may vary greatly in their degree of mutability.

It is evident that unless very large numbers of individuals, human or bacterial, are examined, mutants are not likely to be found. In a small culture of bacteria (5 ml.), the billions of cells (e.g., $5 \times 10^9$) that could be present might contain only 500 mutant cells of a given type. The detection and isolation of one of these 500 mutant cells among five billion are not easy without special techniques. These are described on page 186 et seq.

**Mutagenic Agents.** A mutagenic agent may be defined as any substance (e.g., certain chemicals) or any physical influence (e.g., ultraviolet irradiation) that causes a change in the number, kind, sequence or structure of nucleotides (i.e., mutons) in the genetic materials in a cell such that alteration in heritable characteristics of that cell results.

By exposing microorganisms to mutagenic agents, the mutation rate is greatly increased; detection and isolation of mutants is thus facilitated. The changes thus caused are called *induced mutations*.

CHEMICAL MUTAGENS. Among the most interesting chemical mutagens are the *base analogues* (*cf.* metabolite analogues). These are substances that closely resemble in molecular structure (i.e., are *analogous* to) the purine or pyrimidine bases in DNA. Because of the similarity in structure these analogues can preempt positions of the correct bases in the nucleotides of the DNA and by so doing interfere with, or modify or destroy, the action of the nucleotide of which they become a part. They may alter the nucleotide sequence of the entire succeeding DNA chain. Very complex effects may result.

A simple example is seen in the effect of 5-bromouracil (BU), analogue of the pyrimidine base thymine. A glance at Figure 15.1 will show

*Thymine*          *Uracil*          *5-bromouracil*

**Figure 15.1**

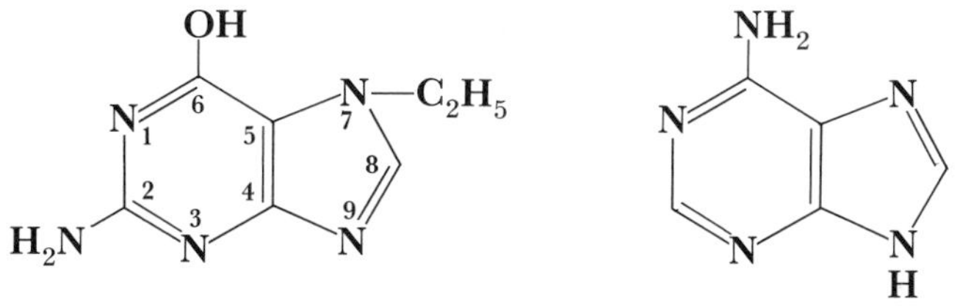

*7-ethyl-guanine*                    *Adenine*

**Figure 15.2**

the similarity between bromouracil, uracil (U) and thymine (T). BU can occupy the place of T in a strand of DNA. In the next replication process each BU may attract guanine (G) instead of adenine (A), as the displaced T would normally do. Thus a BU—G pair appears in place of each normal T—A pair. Since G has been drawn into the positions usually occupied by A, at the next replication each G attracts C. Thus in two DNA replications one or more A—T pairs have been replaced by a number of G—C pairs. This type of mutation by base analogues and many other substances that can usurp a variety of key positions in DNA has, as may be supposed, been the subject of a great deal of research in molecular genetics.

Among other substances that can cause point mutations are ethyl methane sulfonate (EMS) and ethyl ethane sulfonate. EMS acts by ethylating the 7 position of guanine (Fig. 15.2) or adenine. The bond between the purine and the deoxyribose in the nucleotide is hydrolyzed and the purine base is lost, leaving an unoccupied space; a *deletion mutation.* On replication of the DNA, if the purine base is replaced by the correct base no mutation occurs. But the purine may be replaced by other bases, resulting in a change in base sequence. The order of triplets in the DNA is thus changed. This can result in a meaningless or nonsense sequence; a mutation or a complete failure to reproduce is the result. Other chemical mutagens include nitrous acid, hydroxylamine, amino purines, proflavine, the nitrogen and sulfur mustards, formaldehyde, manganese chloride, methylcholanthrene, arsenic, chromium, urethane, creosote, tars and organic peroxides (see also ionizing radiations). Not all these mutagens act in the same manner; the effects of some are not fully elucidated. Some mutagens, both physical and chemical, act directly by combinations and changes in the nucleotides of the DNA. Others act indirectly by affecting the mechanisms (e.g., synthetases) or materials (e.g., purine and pyrimidine bases in solution) involved in DNA synthesis. The bases themselves may change by tautomeric alterations. In addition, various faults of nutrition, such as starvation of the necessary purine or pyrimidine bases, can result in the omission of nucleotide pairs or the incorporation of spurious substitutes for correct nucleotides or their constituent residues.

Physical Mutagens. DNA is susceptible to several physical agents. For example, temperatures above 80° C. may cause denaturation by "melting" (breaking H-bonds). Slightly lower temperatures cause lesser changes, notably liberation of purine bases from DNA, with resulting deletions of nucleotide pairs or replacement by "wrong" bases in the next replication. Data on melting points of DNA are used in classification (Chapter 30). DNA may also be destroyed or mutations may be induced by various forms of radiant energy. One effect of ultraviolet radiation (absorbed especially by bases of nucleic acids) is to cause a junction between adjacent thymine groups in DNA, with the formation of thymine dimers. This distorts the double helix and can be lethal.

## 15.2   RADIANT ENERGY

Radiant energy is energy which travels through space as a wave motion. Electromagnetic activity liberates radiant energy in the form of rapidly vibrating waves—the electromagnetic spectrum.

**The Electromagnetic Spectrum.** As seen in Figure 19.7, electromagnetic radiations may be arranged according to wave length in a spectrum which includes radio waves, x-rays, ultraviolet and the visible solar spectrum (red to violet), the latter being only a small part of the whole system of electromagnetic waves. The physiological effects of these various radiations differ greatly, ranging from warmth and vision to mutations and death. The study of effects of radiant energy on cells is often called *radiobiology.*

Radiobiology. The longest waves having

known physiological effect are (1) the infra-red or invisible "heating waves." Next are (2) the visible red rays, which affect the retina of the eye and bacteriochlorophyll.* Then come (3), successively, yellow, blue and violet, which affect the retina and have photodynamic (see page 181) and possibly other biophysical actions. Then come (4) the invisible ultraviolet rays, which have marked physiological and biochemical activities (page 181). Shorter waves are (5) x-rays (relatively long x-rays, called "soft," and shorter x-rays, called "hard"); (6) alpha, beta and gamma rays, and finally (7) the little-understood cosmic waves coming to the earth from outer space.

## BIOLOGICAL EFFECTS OF IRRADIATIONS

In radiobiology we consider two types of radiations: (1) long waves, specifically ultraviolet radiations (wave lengths 2000 to 2950 Å), which are much used in radiobiology (these waves have little power of penetration and do not cause ionization); and (2) short waves, especially x-rays (wave lengths 0.06 to 1000 Å) and gamma rays (wave lengths of 0.01 to 1.4 Å) have high energy content and great powers of penetration and cause ionization. Both types of waves can kill living cells. The lethal effect is of great value in disinfection and treatment of cancer. Nonlethal changes, however, are in many ways more important and useful.

**Ionization.** When short-wave radiant energy (e.g., x-rays) is passed through a cell, certain atoms absorb a quantum (unit amount) of energy. This removes an electron from each affected atom, which becomes a *positively* charged ion. The free electron immediately attaches to a neutral atom, which becomes *negatively* charged. Thus an *ion pair* is formed. Since changing the electron structure of atoms changes chemical bonds, molecular structures of cells containing those atoms undergo alterations. If the dosage of radiant energy is sufficient, the effect is lethal. If not lethal, then other changes are produced, most conspicuously in the *genetic* mechanisms of the cell. These changes are of tremendous importance to man, his offspring, his industries, his diseases and indeed his whole way of life. Some examples will be mentioned later. Atomic bombs and radioactive fallout produce a considerable amount of ionizing radiation and radioactive substances.

TARGET VS. FREE RADICAL. Two theories

concerning the effects of *ionizing radiations* are as follows:

*The Target-Hit Theory.* This theory holds that the effect is due to a direct hit of a quantum of radiant energy (photon) upon a *target* (e.g., an enzyme molecule, a gene molecule, nucleotide or muton). Undoubtedly, many such targets exist in a cell, and the greater the dosage of energy the more that are hit; a linear relationship exists between dosage and effect. While explaining many of the observed phenomena, this theory does not explain all of the biological effects of ionizing radiation.

*The Free-Radical Theory.* This theory is not the whole explanation either. It is based on the idea that water or some other nonspecific and generalized material in the cell (as contrasted with specific materials such as genes and enzymes) is broken down, liberating various *free radicals,* such as $HO_2$. Liberated throughout the cell in a very active condition, many free radicals form organic peroxides (in themselves mutagenic). These set up chains of destructive oxidation-reduction reactions. It is of great interest, in relation to these oxidative effects, that the presence of reducing agents or absence of oxygen tends to offset them. Catalase, a peroxide-destroying enzyme, has a similar effect. Probably both target-hits and free radicals are involved in the effects of ionizing radiations; undoubtedly other as yet unknown actions also play a role.

SOME GENETIC EFFECTS OF IONIZING RADIATIONS. The nuclear structures, especially nucleic acids (DNA, RNA), appear to be most sensitive to ionizing radiations, although cytoplasmic structures (e.g., enzymes) are also affected. Ionizing radiation greatly slows the process of mitosis. Division of most cells, regardless of species, is usually much retarded. Chromosomes are often broken and may be partly or wholly destroyed. Genetic mutations usually result. These mutations are characteristically manifested only in later generations of cells because the alterations in DNA in the parent cell are not effective until the next one or two replications of the DNA. A *mutational lag* is observed. The genetic effects are usually permanent and irreversible.

EFFECTS OF ENVIRONMENTAL CONDITIONS. Several factors, such as temperature, pH and concentration of oxygen, affect the action of ionizing radiations. It is of interest, in view of the danger from radioactive fallout, to find agents to offset the effects of ionizing radiations. Although this extremely important subject is beyond the scope of the present discussion, it

---

*Photosynthetic pigment of bacteria (Chapter 38).

might be said that since the presence of oxygen increases the effects of ionizing radiations, and since oxidations appear to be involved in their destructive effects, certain chemicals which take up oxygen (cysteine, glutathione) seem to offer promise in attempts to eliminate or ameliorate the effects of radiations. Other defensive reactions involving sulfur compounds and heat are also under investigation.

**Ultraviolet (Nonionizing) Irradiation.** Ultraviolet irradiation, though not possessing the penetrating and ionizing properties of x-rays, is able to penetrate into exposed cells and to set up—*not* ion pairs or free radicals—but *excitations* or *activations,* which have a variety of effects. Most of these effects are similar to those of ionizing radiations, although probably caused by a different mechanism. Sunlight contains much ultraviolet light.

As a rule, actively multiplying cells are most susceptible to irradiation, both ionizing and ultraviolet. In these cells DNA is in an actively replicating condition. Such are usually the cells most susceptible to other deleterious agents also: phage, antibiotics, various bacteriostatic agents and heat. Bacteria in a dormant condition or in a mature, slow-growing stage are markedly resistant compared with cells in an actively multiplying phase of growth. The relationship between dosage and effect of ultraviolet irradiation is generally exponential, suggesting that as irradiation proceeds multiple side effects develop.

REACTIVATION. In contrast to the irreversible injury caused by ionizing radiations, injury resulting from ultraviolet radiation may in large part be cured or reversed if not too extensive. This is done in one way by *postirradiation* exposure to waves longer than the ultraviolet waves. This is often called *photoreversal* or *photoreactivation.* Generally, visible light (wave lengths 4200 to 5400 Å) is used in photoreactivation. Exposure to the reactivating waves must be within 30 minutes after the inactivating irradiation. Curiously, among the various microorganisms, bacteria often fail to be reactivated. Some types of injury caused by ultraviolet rays may be prevented by *pre-irradiation* exposure to visible light.

Ultraviolet-irradiated cells may be reactivated in one way by incubation of the irradiated cells in a favorable growth medium at temperatures 5 to 30° C. lower than optimal. Another method is treatment of the cells with various chemical agents: indoacetate, pyruvate and a long list of others. These phenomena are not yet fully explained but much interesting and valuable research is being done in this field, especially in relation to radioactive fallout and nuclear warfare. In dealing with bacteria many variables affect reactivation: pH, temperature, age and composition of the culture.

**Photodynamic Sensitization.** Certain substances, combining with vital target portions of microorganisms, although not necessarily harmful *per se,* can render the cells very sensitive to visible light. This is usually spoken of as *photosensitization* or *photodynamic* action. For example, many bacteria can grow well in contact with low concentrations of certain dyes such as eosin and fuchsin provided no light reaches them. The combined effect of light and dye for only a few minutes usually kills the organisms. Photodynamic sensitization may also induce mutations. For example, methylene blue, in the light of an ordinary electric lamp, rapidly kills certain gram-positive bacteria that withstand much higher concentrations of the dye in the dark. Gram-negative bacteria are not so affected. One might infer that such differences are mediated by composition of the cell wall. Other organisms, such as viruses, and enzymes and proteins, are also affected. The exact mechanism of photodynamic sensitization is not clear, but may represent weakening of bonds by the dye and their rupture by the radiant energy in light. It has been shown that oxygen is essential to photodynamic action, since the effects are not observed if the microorganisms are placed in a vacuum or in atmospheres devoid of oxygen. (Compare with relation of oxygen to the effect of x-rays, page 180.) The action increases in acid media and in undiluted media.

## 15.3  SOME TYPES OF MUTANTS

**Auxotrophic Mutants.** Mutations often result in the production of *auxotrophs* (Gr. *auxein* = to add to, *trophe* = food), which require additional food substances. Auxotrophic mutants are caused by changes in, or destruction of, one or more mutons (which may be base pairs, cistrons or operons) that are responsible directly or indirectly for the synthesis of certain substances that are essential for cell growth and multiplication. In the auxotrophs these essential nutrients (growth factors)* fail to be

---

*Because the term metabolite is used sometimes to mean a waste substance and sometimes to mean a necessary nutrient, we here use growth factor to mean a specific, pure substance: e.g., a vitamin or an amino acid that is a necessary nutrient, and metabolite to mean a specific waste substance (e.g., antibiotics).

produced by the cell. Such mutants absolutely require that the missing growth factor(s) be supplied preformed in their diet.

As a single example, a common species of intestinal bacteria (*Escherichia coli*), in its normal state, is able to thrive and to synthesize all its cell components in a solution containing several minerals and glucose as a source of energy and carbon. While these bacteria can grow in a much more complex medium, this simple solution amply supplies all of their minimal requirements; such a medium is called a *minimal medium.** If a single ingredient is omitted, they cannot grow. After contact of the bacteria with a mutagenic agent, say UV radiation, mutant progeny may appear that have lost the ability of the ancestral *prototroph* (Gr. *protos* = original or primitive) to synthesize the amino acid tryptophan, a substance that is absolutely essential to their growth and reproduction. To these mutants tryptophan has become a growth factor. It must be added preformed, as such, to the minimal medium to make the medium (for them) a *complete medium*. As an additional example, humans are nutritional auxotrophs in respect to many substances, notably, vitamin C (ascorbic acid) and "niacin" (nicotinic acid). They cannot synthesize these substances for themselves. Ample vitamins are present in any normal, balanced diet. Humans share their auxotrophism in respect to vitamin C with guinea pigs.

Auxotrophic bacterial mutants are commonly designated by the name or a symbol of the growth factor that they cannot synthesize, e.g., "tryptophanless" (or t⁻) mutants. Other bacterial mutants may fail to produce certain enzymes that ferment a sugar, say lactose. They are designated lac⁻, and their prototype ancestors, lac⁺. Auxotrophic mutants are particularly common after irradiation with ultraviolet light or x-rays but they also not uncommonly appear spontaneously. Some mutagens appear to affect particular mutons: e.g., particular nucleotide bases or cistrons. They are said to be specific for that muton.

**Back Mutations.** Any given mutation, especially point mutations, may be "repaired," i.e., either reversed or suppressed, resulting in a reversion to the parent type of cells. For example, a certain species of bacteria (*Proteus mirabilis*) that is normally susceptible to the

antibiotic drug streptomycin (ss) produced mutants that, instead of being susceptible to streptomycin, could not grow and reproduce without it; i.e., they were *streptomycin-dependent* (sd). Mutations to dependence on various drugs and other substances are not at all rare. The sd mutants in this example produced other mutants that were no longer sd but had reverted to the prototype that was ss. Such repaired mutants are sometimes called *revertants.*

In a second type of reversion from the mutant sd cells back to the prototype, not only was the prototype ss state restored but the back-mutating cells had mutated to dependence on the amino acid valine (dv). In this case, two mutations could have occurred simultaneously: from sd "back" to ss; or "forward" to dv. It was also thought that the mutation to the dv state could have suppressed the effect of the sd muton. Experimental studies showed that the effect of the sd muton had indeed been suppressed by the dv muton.

These examples suffice to show that very complex genetic interactions and problems can arise in such situations. It is not always possible to be sure that an apparent back-mutation is not a suppression or some other effect. An apparent revertant may superficially resemble the prototype but carry new, occult mutant genes. A phenotype may represent the net result of several interacting simultaneous mutations.

Some mutations rarely revert, others apparently alternate rapidly between the prototype and the mutant type. For example, the well-known R⇌S types of cells and colonies in many bacteria and higher fungi are apparently oscillating mutations of this type. They seem to result from mutations that affect cell surface structures. Such mutations may be of the type referred to as occult.

**Mutations that Affect Cell Surfaces.** Not all mutations result in readily visible changes such as presence or absence of pigments or spores. A mutation that results in a change in the molecular structure of a certain part of the cell that is not visibly expressed may be called *occult* in that the change in molecules is not in itself visible but is made manifest only indirectly. Some examples of occult mutants among bacteria are auxotrophic mutants, drug or amino acid–dependent mutants and mutants with different enzymic activities or inducible enzyme potentialities. These are often called *biochemical mutants.*

Another type of occult mutation is seen in changes that affect the cell surface structure. In

---

*Minimal media may vary in composition according to the minimal nutritional requirements of the species under investigation.

bacteria the nature of the cell surface is closely related to a variety of important properties, four of which are: *ability to conjugate* (in the presence of F factor); *virulence* (if the species of bacterium is pathogenic for plants or animals); *immunological and antigenic properties* that, in turn, reflect specific molecular composition of proteins, enzymes and polysaccharides of the cell; and *colony form.* All these properties are subject to mutational change. Conjugation, virulence, immunology and antigenicity are discussed elsewhere. Mutations that result in changes in colony type are relatively frequent and appear to undergo back-mutation or progressive mutation quite often. Here we may briefly describe some of the colony forms that are often associated with immunological and pathogenic (virulence) properties.

SMOOTH AND ROUGH COLONIES. Many microorganisms, among them yeasts, molds and bacteria, produce several different forms of colonies. Common among these are the smooth (S) and rough (R) colony types (Fig. 15.3).

*S Colonies.*   These colonies on nutrient agar media are commonly about 2 to 4 mm. in diameter, circular, with regular margins, convex, translucent, homogeneous, smooth, moist and glistening. In broth media S type cells produce an even turbidity; i.e., a cloudy or milky suspension of individual cells. S type cells are frequently encapsulated. The presence of capsular material markedly affects their surface properties: electrical charge, susceptibility to various unfavorable influences, motility, agglutinability by metallic ions and serum proteins (antibodies). Frequently S forms of cells seem to represent a defensive reaction to unfavorable environmental influences. For example, contact with disinfectants and certain salts may stimulate the appearance of S forms, though sometimes these appearances are modifications (see p. 184), not mutations.

Among bacteria capable of infecting animal tissues, the mutational changes necessary to produce the S type of cell and its subsequent rapid multiplication are furnished by contact with the tissues of the infected host which tend to resist the infection. Virulence is thus commonly associated with the S form and this, in turn, is associated with the formation of a capsule or other protective surface modification. For example, capsulated cells more easily escape the phagocytic white blood corpuscles as well as antibodies of the infected animal.

Surface modifications of any sort usually affect the colloidal properties of cells and hence their immunologic and antigenic properties, since these are largely surface phenomena (Chapter 24). Whole systems of results, e.g., identification of species, medical diagnosis and value of vaccines, may depend on whether S or R forms of organisms are being used.

When S forms of bacteria are cultivated on artificial media in pure culture, under wholly uniform, benign and favorable conditions, removed from competition with other species of microorganisms that commonly occur in natural environments such as soil, feces or throat, R mutants are often selected and the populations tend to lose their virulence and their capsules or other protective surface properties.

*R Colonies.*   The R type of colony on nutrient agar is not glistening, like S, but is dull, granular or matte, opaque or less translucent than S colonies, and has rough or wrinkled surfaces and crenated or irregular edges. It is dry and crumbly (friable) in consistency. On the surface of solid media, rod-forms of bacteria (bacilli) in rough colonies commonly form long, tangled filaments of cells as contrasted with cells in S colonies which tend to occur singly. The long filaments of rough-type cells suggest a delayed or absent formation of septa or, if septa are formed, some alteration in the ends of the cells that cause them to cling together in strands instead of separating as in S cells. R cells are generally not encapsulated. In broth the R type growth is usually granular or flaky and irregular,

**Figure 15.3**   *A*, Rough (R) colonies of the bacillus of diphtheria (about three times actual size). *B*, Smooth (S) colonies of the bacillus of diphtheria (about three times actual size).

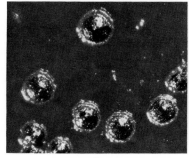

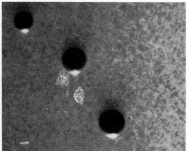

A                                    B

commonly forming a thick scum or pellicle on the surface or settling in flakes or lumps to the bottom.

*Mucoid Colonies.* Many species of bacteria produce what are called mucoid (M) colonies (Fig. 15.4). These are large, slimy and viscous, often almost watery. The mucoid material is like an exaggerated capsule or slime layer. Like the slime coating on a garden slug or the mucous secretions of the respiratory tract, and possibly the capsule of S cells, bacterial mucoid material has protective properties. In some species of bacteria the slime contains excess genetic DNA (see Chapter 14).

*Dwarf Colonies.* These are very minute, often just at the limit of unaided vision. Cultures derived from dwarf (D) colonies often have properties such as virulence and certain metabolic characters that differ markedly from corresponding properties of cultures from R, S, M or other type colonies. As is true of other colonial types, D mutants tend to change to M, R or S or others. Cells in D colonies often consist of smaller-than-normal cells and cells with certain metabolic deficiencies or peculiarities.

It is to be remembered that R, S, M, D and other colonial types are not mutations in themselves. Colony type is only one evidence of profound enzymic and other mutational changes within the cell. These mutations, while often associated, are not necessarily linked. Like many genetic characters, they can change independently. Thus, although R, S, M and D forms are described as if they are distinct types, hundreds of intermediate overlapping forms occur. A wide range of various combinations of properties can occur. For example, a cell may have some surface properties that cause the formation of a rough colony yet have some of the virulence or immunological properties of S type cells.

So important are the antigenic and virulence characters of cells that the letters R, S, etc., are sometimes used to designate the antigenic types commonly but not necessarily associated with those colonial types. The words rough, smooth, etc., are reserved for the gross, visible forms of colonies regardless of their antigenic and other occult properties. Change in gross colony form, although seemingly great, may in itself represent a very small change in composition of the cell wall of cells that are basically of another type.

*Acriflavine Test.* That surface structure of cells reflects more accurately their fundamental antigenic (enzymic, protein, polysaccharide) composition than does gross colony form is shown by studies of the reaction of various cells to the orange, fluorescent dye acriflavine. Cells from a given colony are suspended in a 0.1 per cent solution of the dye in 0.85 per cent saline. Cells that are unaffected by the dye are found to behave antigenically like S cells, even though they may have come from a rough or other type colony. Cells that are antigenically R, in contact with acriflavine gather together in floccules or clumps though they may be S in colony form. Cells that are antigenically M-type form slimy curds in the presence of the dye.

**Modifications.** Some seeming mutations are merely temporary effects of factors in the environment. They do not involve alterations in genes. Such nongenetic changes are spoken of as *modifications* or fluctuations. Typically,

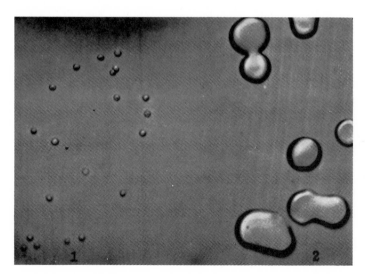

**Figure 15.4**   *1*, Colonies of R variant of Pneumococcus type II plated on blood agar from a culture grown in serum broth in the *absence* of the transforming substance (× 3.5). *2*, Colonies of the same cells after transformation during growth in the *presence* of active transforming principle isolated from type III pneumococci. The smooth, glistening, mucoid colonies shown are characteristic of Pneumococcus type III. (From Avery, MacLeod, Colin and McCarty: J. Exper. Med., vol. 79; photograph by J. B. Haulenbeck.)

modifications cease when the environmental stimulus that evoked them is withdrawn. Sometimes the reasons for modifications, like some causes of spontaneous mutations, are quite obscure.

Many different properties of organisms may undergo modification. For example, certain bacteria when cultivated on ordinary nutrient agar produce markedly rough-type colonies. If the same organisms are transferred to a new plate of the same agar, modified by the addition of a little phenol or other irritating substance, the growing cells produce slimy or mucoid-type colonies. On transferring the mucoid growth again to plain (phenol-free) medium the rough-type growth is produced promptly. The sudden and temporary nature of modifications, their dependence on an environmental influence and the generalized effect of the influence on all of the cells at once tend to distinguish modifications from mutations.

Modifications often produce changes, visible or occult, that closely resemble mutations. For example, induced enzyme production is a result of, and dependent on, an *environmental* stimulus, e.g., a specific substrate or substrate analogue (Chapter 5). The enzyme induction is not a genetic change but merely an evoked expression of an existing, but repressed, genetic property.

Some very complex situations can arise when mutation accompanies or follows modification. For example, the cells in the phenol-treated population described above produce apparently identical mucoid cells on phenol agar yet, on calcium chloride agar, both mucoid and smooth colonies may be formed. Obviously there are cells of two genotypes: on phenol agar the two phenotypes are seemingly identical; on calcium chloride agar their differences become manifest.

**Mutations and Population Changes.** Growth of a microbial population in a tube of culture medium generally changes environmental conditions. For example, all available essential growth factors or hydrogen acceptors (Chapter 6) may be used up, or acids, alcohols or other noxious waste substances may be produced. If, as is nearly always the case, there are mutant cells in the population that are favored by the new conditions, those mutants may grow and eventually partly or entirely replace and supersede the prototype. For example, in aging cultures of *Brucella* (cause of undulant fever) that were originated with S-type cells, some agent or condition (or both)

develops that is inimical to S cells of *Brucella.* The S cells cease growth. However, R-type *Brucella* cells are not injured by these changed conditions and may be favored by them. The R form eventually replaces the S form.

Factors responsible for such replacement of one mutant form by another of the same species vary. In the case of *Brucella* cultures the change in population may occur partly because of the accumulation in the broth culture of the specific waste product or metabolite, D- or DL-alanine, which suppresses the S form. Other organisms are affected by other metabolites. Oligodeoxynucleotides from DNA digestion, added to cultures of various bacteria, cause increased growth of S cells and suppression of R cells. Equally important for various species may be merely the depletion of oxygen and other hydrogen acceptors in the culture. Probably still other factors alter populations in other ways. An increase in acidity, for example, a common result of growth, could result in selection of an aciduric mutant and thus change the population from an acid-sensitive one to an aciduric one. Very complex interrelationships can occur, involving, for example, multiple mutations and changing environmental factors.

Whatever the mechanisms, the important biological fact is illustrated that the activities of a population, microbial or human, may so alter their environment as to replace the original type with a new type capable of coping with the new order of things. On the other hand, the environment may change independently of the population (reduction in temperature or decrease in water). Then only those capable of reproduction under the new conditions will survive (natural selection).

**Mutations in Colonies.** On a solid agar surface a bacterial colony grows radially. The oldest (and senescent) growth is at the center. The newest (and most active) growth is around the periphery. In the development of a colony the single cell initiating the colony may produce billions of progeny. If a visible type of mutation (for example, production of a bright red pigment) occurs in a single cell during the radial growth of the colony, a roughly triangular and visible sector of red cells appears. Typically the apex of the triangle is toward the center of the colony and is the point at which mutation occurred. The base of the sector is at the periphery of the colony (Fig. 15.5). Another visible type of sector in a colony is produced by loss (or gain) of the property of spore formation. If, in a colony of cells producing spores as they

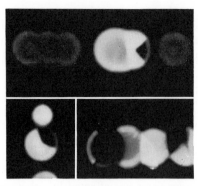

**Figure 15.5** Colonies of one species of bacterium growing on the same agar plate, originating from the same inoculum. Variation between white pigmentation (light) and nonpigmentation or transparent (dark) is clearly evident. Clearly shown also is the appearance of mutants during the development of each type of colony, with resulting pigmented (or nonpigmented), triangular sector in the colony. (From Barber: J. Gen. Microbiol., vol. 13.)

grow, sporeless mutation occurs, the progeny are sporeless and they appear as a translucent sector in the colony.

SECONDARY COLONIES. The formation of small excrescences, papillae or outgrowths from ordinary colonies of many species of bacteria after the first growth is mature and begins to age is a common phenomenon. The outgrowths are called secondary colonies, or *daughter colonies* (Fig. 15.6). They may appear on the surface, develop from within, or grow out from the edges. They vary in size, form, numbers and appearance. The cells in secondary colonies differ genetically from the original in many properties, both morphological and physiological, and are able to grow under the conditions of the *aged* colony.

## DETECTION AND ISOLATION OF MUTANTS

Detection of obvious mutants such as sporeforming or nonsporeforming, or production of different colors, in cultures of molds, yeasts and bacteria, is simple. For example, anyone who knows about culture methods and the resistance of spores to heat can devise a simple procedure to detect the presence of sporeforming mutants in a culture. Also, detection of mutants resistant to various unfavorable factors is obviously possible by submitting a culture containing a billion or so actively growing cells to graded concentrations of the unfavorable factor, such as heat, an antibiotic or a disinfectant. Survivors at each level of concentration obviously must be resistant to that concentration. An adaptation of this principle, especially for detection and isolation of mutants of graded resistance to antibiotics or other substances, consists of the gradient plate.

**The Gradient Plate.** In this method one pours a shallow layer of nutrient agar (10 ml.) into a Petri plate and allows it to solidify in a sloping position (Fig. 15.7). When solid, a second 10 ml. of agar containing an appropriate concentration of the test substance, e.g., an antibiotic, is poured over the first layer and the plate is held horizontal until the agar is solid. Owing to the reciprocating gradations in the thickness of the layers of agar, the concentrations of antibiotic on the top surface will be graded from high at one side of the plate to low at the other.

A culture is introduced at the area of low concentration and spread thinly toward the area of high concentration. Of the cells that are deposited on the areas of higher concentra-

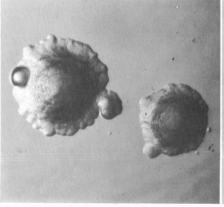

**Figure 15.6** Colonies of a single species of bacterium (*Acetobacter rancens*) showing various forms of colony, daughter colonies and mutant outgrowths. Do these outgrowths suggest neoplasms (malignant growths or cancers)? (From Shimwell and Carr: Ant. Leeuw., *26*:169, 1960.)

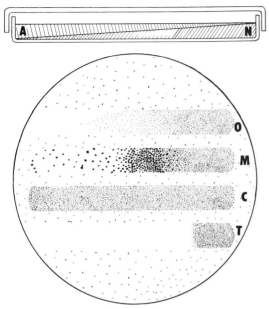

**Figure 15.7**   Use of the gradient plate to detect drug-resistant mutants and to measure their degree of resistance. In the Petri plate above, the bottom layer (N) consists of ordinary nutrient agar allowed to solidify in a slanting position. The upper layer (A), poured and allowed to solidify with the plate in a level position, consists of the same sort of agar but with a drug (say, Aureomycin or chlortetracycline) added in measured concentration. The antibiotic diffuses from the upper into the lower layer, leaving a gradient of concentrations of the drug at the surface; greatest at the left of the plate shown above, least at the right. Broth cultures of four different species of bacteria are streaked across the plate, with a sterile brush, parallel with the slope of the agar (in this case, left to right). After incubation it is seen that all organisms grow well at the very lowest concentrations of the drug but react differently in the increasingly greater concentrations. Organism *O* shows moderate resistance of most colonies; a few more than others, but none thriving much more than the majority. Species *M* shows some resistance by most cells but contains some that are wholly resistant and even appear to be stimulated by the drug. Organism *C* shows complete indifference to the drug. Species *T* contains many slightly resistant cells, but all are completely inhibited by exactly the same concentration of the drug. (Adapted from Szybalski: Science, vol. 116.)

tion, only those of higher resistance will grow and form colonies. They are thus revealed as resistant mutants. Their degree of resistance is indicated by their position on the gradient plate. They are transferred to other media for further study in pure culture.

**Replica Plating.**   This is a clever adaptation of the printer's art to bacteriological purposes by J. Lederberg (Nobel Prize winner) and E. M. Lederberg. One prepares a wooden disk with a flat surface, in diameter about 9 cm. (1 cm. less than that of a common Petri plate). A piece

of velvet about 12 cm. square is placed smoothly over the surface of the disk, drawn firmly down over the sides and fastened in place with a band. A handle, like that of a rubber stamp, is fastened firmly on the back of the disk (Fig. 15.8). Many modifications of the velvet disk have been devised. The whole is sterilized.

Let us now select a Petri plate containing nutrient agar, on the surface of which are several hundred colonies. How do we determine which colony consists of (a) streptomycin-resistant mutants and which of (b) "threonine-less" *auxotrophs?* Their appearance in no wise distingushes them. We could pick a portion of each of the several hundred colonies on the plate with a needle and transfer it to (a) a medium containing streptomycin, (b) a medium containing threonine and (c) one without threonine. If inoculum from any colony grows on the streptomycin-containing medium it is obviously streptomycin-resistant. If it grows on the medium with threonine and not on the same medium minus threonine, it is a threonine-deficient auxotroph. But this entails at least 300 (usually thousands) of inoculations (requiring 28 hours of work per day!) in order to find the one or two mutant colonies which may (or may not!) be among the hundreds of colonies on the plate.

Time and labor are saved if we press the sterile velvet disk gently down on the agar plate. Each colony leaves a small spot of cells where it touches the velvet. If, now, we press the velvet gently on the surfaces of three sterile plates successively, we have in three motions "printed" all of the colonies on the original plate in three *replica plates:* (a) one plate containing medium with streptomycin, (b) a plate with agar containing threonine and (c) a plate containing agar without threonine. The three replica plates are then incubated and colonies develop. Each colony is in its own, readily determined location on the surface of each of the selective replica plates (a, b and c). Only the colony of streptomycin-resistant mutants will grow on the streptomycin-containing plate (a); the threonine-deficient mutant will grow on threonine plate (b), but cannot grow on the plate without threonine (c). The mutant colonies are thus easily identified by their growth and locations on the replica plates.

**Isolation by Penicillin.**   This method, devised by Lederberg and also by Davis, depends on the fact, as previously explained, that organisms in the logarithmic (most actively multiplying) phase of growth are most susceptible to

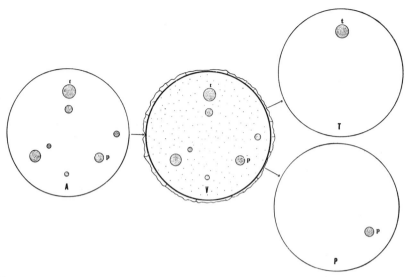

**Figure 15.8**   Use of the replica plate for detection of colonies of mutants. Plate *A* contains agar complete in all essential nutrients and free of penicillin. It was inoculated with a culture of a certain species of bacillus. It was then incubated. It is desired to determine which of the colonies (if any) consists (1) of mutants able to grow in the absence of the amino acid, threonine, and (2) of mutants resistant to penicillin. Plate *A* is inverted over, and lightly pressed down upon, the sterile velvet disk *V* and then removed, leaving spots of live organisms in positions corresponding to the positions of the colonies on plate *A*. Immediately thereafter, plate *T*, containing sterile agar like that in plate *A* but *devoid of threonine*, is pressed upon the velvet disk, removed and incubated. Plate *P*, containing agar in all respects like that in plate *A* but *with penicillin added* in measured concentration, is likewise inoculated by pressing it upon the velvet disk. After incubation, plate *T* has only one colony (t) obviously consisting of mutants able to synthesize their own threonine (or able to grow without it). Plate *P* has a colony (p) resistant to penicillin in the concentration, at least, in which it exists in plate *P*; perhaps wholly resistant.

numerous deleterious influences, including the action of penicillin.

Keeping this in mind let us irradiate a culture of bacteria with ultraviolet light. Suppose purineless auxotrophs are to be looked for. They are not immediately apparent. At least two generations of growth must be allowed before the mutational lag is overcome. After the proper, postirradiation incubation, all the cells are removed from the culture medium by sedimentation (centrifugation). They are then resuspended in an inert saline solution in which they will go into a resting state. To separate the auxotrophs from the prototrophs, penicillin is added to the suspension along with just enough *purine-free* medium to permit the purine-synthesizing prototrophs to grow but not the purine-less auxotrophic mutants.

As soon as the prototrophs start to grow the penicillin kills them. The still dormant auxotrophs are not affected. They are now removed to a penicillin-free, purine-containing (complete) medium where they grow vigorously.

A little scientific joke is sometimes played by the prototrophs in the final stage of the foregoing procedure, when the unsuspecting prototrophs are being done to death by en-

couraging them to grow in the presence of penicillin. As they start to grow they may synthesize just enough purine to start the auxotrophs growing also, and so the auxotrophs, too, are killed by the penicillin. Nevertheless the penicillin method is a very useful one. A number of very ingenious modifications have been devised. In one the culture is irradiated on a microscopically porous membrane filter (Chapter 36) that is lying on moist agar containing a minimal medium. The membrane is then transferred to minimal agar with penicillin. The prototrophs grow and are killed by the penicillin. The filter is transferred then to plain minimal agar to absorb and remove the penicillin. Then it is placed on agar with complete medium, i.e., in this case containing threonine. These penicillin methods obviously cannot be used with organisms that are resistant to penicillin.

## SUPPLEMENTARY READING

Baron, L. S.: Transfer of episomes between bacterial genera. Tr. N. Y. Acad. Sci., Ser. II, *27*:999, 1965.
Bautz, E. K. F., and Reilly, E.: Gene-specific messenger RNA: Isolation by the deletion method. Science, *151*:328, 1966.

Bernfield, M. R., and Nirenberg, M. W.: RNA codewords and protein synthesis. Science, *147*:479, 1965.

Boyes, B. C.: The impact of Mendel. Bioscience, *16*:85, 1966.

Braun, W.: Bacterial Genetics, 2nd ed. W. B. Saunders Co., Philadelphia. 1965.

Carlson, E. A.: The Gene. W. B. Saunders Co., Philadelphia. 1966.

Catlin, B. W., and others. Three studies on transformation. J. Gen. Microbiol., *37*:341, 353 and 369, 1964.

Conant, J. E., and Sawyer, W. D.: Transformation during mixed pneumococcal infection in mice. J. Bact., *93*:1869, 1967.

Crick, F. H. C.: The genetic code: III. Sci. Amer., *215*:55, 1966.

Crick, F. H. C., and others: The Genetic Code. Cold Spring Harbor Symposia on Quantitative Biology, 31, 1966.

Dubnau, D. A., and Pollock, M. R.: The genetics of *Bacillus licheniformis* penicillinase analysis from studies on mutation and inter-strain and intra-strain transformations. J. Gen. Microbiol., *41*:7, 1965.

Dunn, L. C.: A Short History of Genetics. McGraw-Hill Book Co., New York. 1966.

Gimlin, D. M., Hardman, S. D., Kelly, B. N., Butler, G. C., and Leach, F. R.: Effect of bromouracil-containing DNA on *Bacillus subtilis.* J. Bact., *92*:366, 1966.

Gross, J. D., and Caro, L.: Genetic transfer in bacterial mating. Science, *150*:1679, 1965.

Hanawalt, P. C., and Haynes, R. H.: The repair of DNA. Sci. Amer., *216*:36, 1967.

Hashimoto, H., and Hirota, Y.: Gene recombination and segregation of resistance factor R in *Escherichia coli.* J. Bact., *91*:51, 1966.

Hayes, W.: The Genetics of Bacteria and Their Viruses. John Wiley & Sons, Inc., New York. 1964.

Hirokawa, H., and Ikeda, Y.: Genetic recombination of transforming deoxyribonucleic acid molecules with the recipient genome and among themselves in protoplasts of *Bacillus subtilis.* J. Bact., *92*:455, 1966.

Hirota, Y., Fujii, T., and Nishimura, Y.: Loss and repair of conjugal fertility and infectivity of the resistance factor and sex factor in *Escherichia coli.* J. Bact., *91*: 1298, 1966.

Holly, R. W.: The nucleotide sequence of a nucleic acid. Sci. Amer. *214*:30, 1966.

Hutchison, D. J. (Moderator): Program of papers on interaction of mammalian cells with DNA. Tr. N. Y. Acad. Sci., Ser. II, *28*:713, 1966.

Jacob, F., and Wollman, E. L.: Viruses and genes. *In:* The Living Cell, W. H. Freeman and Co., San Francisco. 1965.

Kleczkowska, J.: Mutations in symbiotic effectiveness in *Rhizobium trifolii* caused by transforming DNA and other agents. J. Gen. Microbiol., *40*:377, 1965.

Lancaster, J. H., Goldschmidt, E. P., and Wyss, O.: Characterization of conjugation factors in *Escherichia coli* cell walls. J. Bact., *89*:1478, 1965.

Lark, K. G.: Regulation of chromosome replication and segregation in bacteria. Bact. Rev., *30*:3, 1966.

Mazia, D.: The partitioning of genomes. Fifteenth Symposium, Function and Structure in Micro-organisms, page 379. Soc. Gen. Microbiol., London. 1965.

Nirenberg, M. W.: The genetic code: II. *In:* The Living Cell, W. H. Freeman and Co., San Francisco. 1965.

Ørskov, I., and Ørskov, F.: Episome-carried surface antigen K88 of *Escherichia coli.* J. Bact., *91*:69, 1966.

Polsinelli, M., and Beretta, M.: Genetic recombination in crosses between *Streptomyces aureofaciens* and *Streptomyces rimosus.* J. Bact., *91*:63, 1966.

Richmond, M. H.: Dominance of the inducible state in strains of *Staphylococcus aureus* containing two distinct penicillinase plasmids. J. Bact., *90*:370, 1965.

Sager, R.: On non-chromosomal heredity in microorganisms. Fifteenth Symposium, Function and Structure in Micro-organisms, page 324. Soc. Gen. Microbiol., London. 1965.

Sen, M., and Sen, S. P.: Interspecific transformation in *Azotobacter.* J. Gen. Microbiol., *41*:1, 1965.

Spizizen, J., Reilly, B. E., and Evans, A. H.: Microbial transformation and transfection. Ann. Rev. Microbiol., *20*:371, 1966.

Stern, C., and Sherwood, E. R., editors: The Origin of Genetics. A Mendel Source Book. W. H. Freeman and Co., San Francisco. 1966.

Strauss, N.: Further evidence concerning the configuration of transforming DNA during entry into *Bacillus subtilis.* J. Bact., *91*:702, 1966.

Yanofsky, C.: Gene structure and protein structure. Sci. Amer., *216*:80, 1967.

# Chapter 16

## THE VIRUSES

## Discovery and Propagation

In 1891, bacteria were viewed as the boundary between the living and the inanimate. Investigators of that time felt that they had probed the depths of the mystery of life and had discovered its extreme limit with respect to minuteness of size and simplicity of structure. Yet many clear, colorless and seemingly sterile fluids that they examined with their most powerful optical microscopes teemed with billions of complex, often deadly "living" particles that escaped their vision and their knowledge.

The first viral disease of plants was discovered in 1892, when Iwanowski demonstrated that a common disease of the tobacco plant called *tobacco mosaic* could be transmitted to healthy plants in the sap from diseased plants, even though the sap had been passed through filters fine enough to remove all bacteria. Furthermore, the disease could be transmitted with sap filtrates from plant to plant in indefinite series. Yet no living thing capable of producing tobacco mosaic grew from the filtered sap of diseased plants on any culture medium in the laboratory, and nothing could be seen in the crystal-clear fluid with any microscope then available. Beijerinck, a famous microbiologist of the time, found that the filtrable, invisible and noncultivable infectious principle would diffuse through an agar gel like a fluid. He thought the fluid itself alive, and called it *contagium vivum fluidum*—a living infectious fluid! This concept is embodied in the very word *virus,* which is derived from a Latin root meaning a slimy, noxious liquid, a sort of living snake venom!

We now know that the sap from the diseased tobacco plant contained billions of particles of the virus of tobacco mosaic, the first known virus. Iwanowski had opened the door to the world of the ultramicroscopic, much as Hooke and Leeuwenhoek had opened the door to the world of the microscopic. In 1935 Stanley showed that the tobacco mosaic virus (TMV) can be crystallized but that the virus crystals, instead of being inorganic matter, were aggregations of thousands of submicroscopic nucleoprotein complexes; i.e., infective units (*virions*) of tobacco mosaic virus. Scores of viral diseases of other plants are now known.

Viral diseases of vertebrates were well known by 1892, since Pasteur had been studying canine rabies for some time. He spoke of the causative agent as a virus, although during his early studies he was apparently not aware of its true nature. The term virus was then commonly used for a variety of infectious agents, including bacteria. In 1898, the foot-and-mouth disease of cattle was shown by Loeffler and Frosch to be caused by an agent that, like TMV, passed through bacteria-retaining filters, and was neither visible with the microscope nor cultivable on inanimate media. These three properties were, at that time, the basic identifying properties of a virus. Foot-and-mouth disease was the first known viral disease of lower vertebrates. In 1900 Walter Reed and his associates discovered the virus of yellow fever, the first known viral disease of man. Today many viral diseases of vertebrates are well known.

Viral diseases of insects were studied by Pasteur during his investigations of diseases of commercial silkworms. The infectious agents of those diseases were first recognized as viruses by B. Wahl, by von Prowazek and by Escherich. Since then many viral diseases of arthropods have been recognized, important among them being sacbrood of honey bees and a viral disease of value in the control of destructive cabbage-looper worms.

Viruses that attack bacteria were first described in 1915 by the British scientist, Twort, and were independently observed and more fully studied about 1917 by the French investigator, d'Herelle, who named these viruses bacteriophage (Gr. *phagein* = to eat). The bacteriophage was originally (and erroneously) thought of as eating the bacteria from within. The shorter term, *phage,* is commonly used for bacteriophage and will be so used here.

Subsequent studies of many animals, bacteria and higher plants revealed the existence of hundreds of other viruses, and new ones are being discovered almost daily as techniques for their detection and identification are improved.

It is now clear that the three properties once thought to be unique and absolutely distinctive of viruses are no longer valid. Originally described as ultramicroscopic or invisible (with optical microscopes), viruses and their intimate structural details are now readily made visible by means of high-power electron microscopes (Chapter 17). For many years described as *filtrable* because they passed through unglazed porcelain, diatomaceous-earth (kieselguhr) and similar bacteria-retaining filters, they are now easily retainable (i.e., *nonfiltrable*) on specially prepared molecular filters made of very fine pore collodion or plastic materials (Chapter 17). For decades thought to be *noncultivable* (i.e., on inanimate media), they are now easily propagated in *living culture media,* as will be explained.

## 16.1  CULTIVATION OF VIRUSES

Viruses, chlamydias and rickettsias are often propagated for experimental purposes *in vivo,* i.e., in their natural living hosts by induced infection. In the laboratory we can imitate nature by transmitting infectious material (blood, serum, pus, tissue, sap of plants) from one animal or plant to another by such methods as injections, scratches, punctures or insect bites. This *in vivo* propagation is frequently necessary for research, but it is laborious, expensive and sometimes dangerous to laboratory personnel unless they can be vaccinated against the organism with which they are working.

### LIVING CULTURE MEDIA

#### TISSUE CULTURES

*In vitro* (tissue-culture) propagation of viruses eliminates the use of living animals or plants but it does not eliminate the necessity for living cells of animals or plants. It therefore makes necessary the cultivation of living tissue cells of plants or animals *in vitro.* A culture of tissue cells *in vitro* is called a *tissue culture.* A brief outline of methods used in cultivating tissue cells of vertebrates will illustrate the various techniques. For invertebrate and plant tissue cells appropriate modifications are made in details, such as nutrients supplied and temperature of incubation. Bacterial viruses (phage) require cultures of bacterial cells instead of tissue cells.

All tissue-culture work requires care and skill to keep out contaminating bacteria, molds, yeasts and mycoplasmas or PPLO (Chapter 41). Antibiotics, such as kanamycin, often are used to suppress PPLO. (Why is penicillin of little use in eliminating PPLO?)

A subtle and unfortunately common source of error is the unsuspected presence of extraneous viruses which are already infecting the supposedly sterile tissues when they are removed from the animal. Several viruses commonly remain latent in animal tissues for long periods. When penicillin is used in tissue cultures, bacterial contaminants accidentally introduced can become L-forms or protoplasts and have been mistaken for mycoplasmas, which have no cell walls.

**Infection of Tissue Cultures.**  Once vigorous, uncontaminated cultures of tissue cells are obtained they may be infected (or inoculated) with any desired microorganism. Bacteria and molds grow well in tissue cultures, but it is not customary to cultivate them in such expensive media since most of them grow well in simple nutrient fluids. However, very interesting observations have been made on the effects of various bacteria and molds, and their toxins, on living tissue cells *in vitro* (Fig. 16.1).

When a tissue culture is inoculated with a virus, the virus grows inside the multiplying tissue cells. The infected cells commonly, but not always, disintegrate. If the virus is *virulent,* new virus particles are liberated into the surrounding fluid. Most virus-infected tissue cultures show visible evidence of cell damage caused by the virus. If cells in the culture are examined daily under the microscope, the progress of the infection, and disintegration if it occurs, can readily be followed. Viruses which thus damage tissue cells are said to be *cytopathogenic.* Their effects are referred to as *CPE* (cytopathogenic effects). CPE are sometimes so distinctive in appearance as to be diagnostic (Figs. 16.11, 16.12).

**Plasma Cultures.**  Tissue cells may be

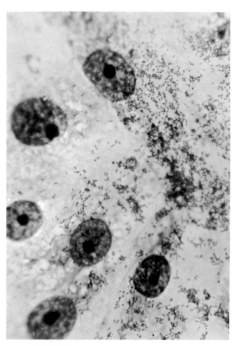

**Figure 16.1** Monkey kidney tissue-cell culture infected with *Bordetella pertussis* (the bacteria that cause whooping cough). The large, dark, rounded objects are the nuclei of the tissue cells. The lighter cytoplasms, filling most of the picture, are crowded with myriads of the tiny bacilli. Note the ragged and vacuolated appearance of the infected and damaged cytoplasms. Many bacteria grow in the culture fluid only. (About × 1400.) (From Crawford and Fishel: J. Bact., vol. 77.)

cultivated in plasma clots. These were among the earliest forms of tissue culture, developed by Carrel (Nobel Prize winner) and others, and are still sometimes used, although newer methods are better for most purposes. Briefly, a drop of sterile, fluid plasma is mixed with a nutrient fluid. A minute fragment of the freshly cut tissue to be cultivated is then placed in the center of the plasma drop on a glass slide. Clotting occurs almost immediately. The drop is then placed in a tightly sealed glass container with atmosphere rich in carbon dioxide and held at 35° C. Growth of the tissue may be observed on the slide with the microscope.

Such cultures are invaluable for some purposes, but their minute size makes them unsuitable for many applications. Also, being derived from whole tissue, they consist of cells of different types, e.g., muscle cells, fibroblasts, fat cells, etc., i.e., they are not pure cultures in a bacteriological sense.

**Roller Tubes.** In a modification of the plasma culture method called *roller-tube cultures,*

devised by Gey, tubes or bottles of any desired shape and size are wetted inside with plasma. Fragments of live tissue are then placed in the plasma. After clotting has occurred, nutrient fluid is placed in the vessels, which are then sealed. They are next placed in a nearly horizontal position and rotated in a drum-shaped roller at the rate of 7 to 10 r.p.m. in an incubator at 35° C. (Fig. 16.2). The tissues are thus bathed in the nutrient fluid each time the bottles or tubes rotate. These cultures can be maintained indefinitely since the nutrient fluid can easily be replaced every two or three days. Although microscopic observation is difficult, relatively large amounts of tissue and of virus are thus obtained, and prolonged experiments are possible.

**Primary Cultures.** Plasma-clot and roller-tube cultures made directly from live tissues are types of *primary tissue cultures.* As indicated, they have the disadvantage that, in addition to being mixtures of different kinds of cells (e.g., muscle, blood vessel and fibroblasts, present in the tissue), they are limited in size. However, primary cultures in larger volume are now feasible for bulk cultures, used in the commercial preparation of large amounts of vaccines such as polio vaccine, and for other purposes. Although they are initiated from the tissues of animals immediately after they are killed, the tissue cells may be contaminated with microorganisms that were infecting the living animal. However, these difficulties have been recognized and are being overcome to a great extent. A full and detailed description of the procedures is beyond the scope of the present discussion. A condensed outline of the principal steps in a representative procedure for preparing a primary culture follows. There are many modifications of this procedure, especially in regard to the growth medium used. New improvements are constantly being made. The first step, after preparation of the desired tissue fragments, is *dispersion* of the cells from the tissue. This is commonly done by digesting the intercellular cement substance with trypsin. Other dispersing agents are collagenase and Versene or ethylene-diamine-tetraacetic acid (EDTA).

TRYPSINIZATION. Suppose that a primary culture is to be made of rabbit kidney. The animal is killed by mechanical means or by administration of a barbiturate. The kidneys are immediately aseptically removed, stripped of their capsule and the cortex is then minced and washed repeatedly with a sterile saline solution such as Hanks's balanced salt solution

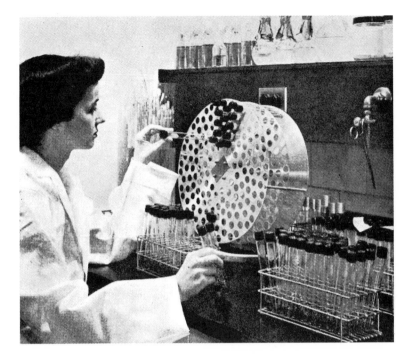

**Figure 16.2** Roller-tube technique of tissue culture. Poliomyelitis virus used in the preparation of vaccine is being tested in tissue cultures, which the virologist is placing in the roller-tube apparatus prior to incubation. (Courtesy of Parke, Davis Co.)

(BSS).* The minced, washed tissue is then placed in a flask with sterile trypsin solution at 4° C. and held in an agitator for six to eight hours. The mixture is then centrifuged and fresh trypsin solution is added. The *trypsinization* continues at 4° C. for 18 hours. Trypsin, a proteolytic enzyme, digests the material that binds the cells together, and they are thus dispersed in the fluid as individual cells; i.e., each cell is now an independent microorganism!

Enzyme solutions should be free of $Ca^{++}$ and $Mg^{++}$. These ions tend to interfere with the desired dispersion of the cells by making the intracellular "cement substance" or matrix more resistant to the dispersing agent.

WASHING. The cell suspension is then passed through a wire screen filter to remove coarse particles and to provide a smooth suspension of separated cells. By repeatedly centrifuging, and removing the supernatant fluid

---

*Hanks's balanced salt solution (10-fold concentration):

| *Mixture 1:* | *g./l. of $H_2O$* |
|---|---|
| NaCl | 80.00 |
| KCl | 4.00 |
| $CaCl_2$ | 1.40 |
| $MgSO_4 \cdot 7H_2O$ | 2.00 |
| *Mixture 2:* | |
| $Na_2HPO_4 \cdot 12H_2O$ | 1.52 |
| $KH_2PO_4$ | 0.60 |
| Glucose | 10.00 |
| Phenol red (1 per cent) | 16.00 |

Combine mixtures 1 and 2 slowly. Sterilize by filtration.

and replacing it with BSS, the cells are washed free of trypsin.

CULTIVATION. After appropriate adjustment of the number of cells per unit of volume, the cells are suspended in *growth medium* and dispensed in tubes or flat-sided flasks in 2- to 10-ml. amounts. A typical medium recommended for outgrowth is as follows:

| | *ml.* |
|---|---|
| Selected bovine serum | 5 |
| Lactalbumin hydrolysate (5 per cent) | 10 |
| Hanks's BSS | 82 |
| $NaHCO_3$ buffer and source of carbonate (2.8 per cent) | 2 |
| Antibiotic mixture | 1 |

The cultures are incubated undisturbed at 36° C. for about 72 hours.

**Monolayers.** When plasma-clot methods were first used for tissue culture it was thought that tissue cells require a solid support, such as the fibrin threads in a clot, on which to grow. It was found, however, that when prepared as just described and freely suspended in a glass vessel, tissue cells quickly settle out of suspension and attach themselves firmly to the bottom. If undisturbed for five to seven days at 36° C., they grow and spread over the glass surface in a sheet of one-cell thickness called a *monolayer* (Fig. 16.3). After renewal of the growth medium, this monolayer culture may be inoculated with viruses for a variety of purposes. Cell monolayers in numerous variations are

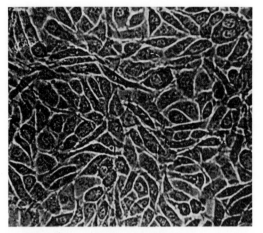

**Figure 16.3**  Monolayer of L (tissue) cells. These are normal cells. Note the distinctive, relatively uniformly polygonal, sharply angular appearance of the cells, all of which are joined together by intercellular cement substance into a *flat* layer. Cells that have been transformed to malignancy (page 233) often pile up in heaps in uninhibited growth. (From Trent and Scott: J. Bact., *88*:702, 1964.)

now widely used in studies of individual cell types, of effects of drugs, bacterial, viral and other infections, of growth of cancer cells and in tests of therapeutic agents.

**"Synthetic" Tissue-Culture Media.**   Several so-called synthetic* media have been devised for tissue cultures and, although complex, are widely used. Some are commercially available. For example, a much-used medium devised by Morgan, Morton and Parker, known as *solution 199,* contains eight *units:* unit 1, a balanced salt solution (BSS) containing seven salts; unit 2, glucose; unit 3, five growth accessory substances plus a surface-tension-reducing agent; unit 4, 13 vitamins; unit 5, seven purines and related substances; unit 6, 22 amino acids; unit 7, a pH indicator; unit 8, sodium bicarbonate. Each unit must be prepared separately with special precautions. Another medium, Eagle's, contains only 22 ingredients plus Hanks's BSS. For growth all of these media must be supplemented with serum or embryo extract (or for some cells with a substitute such as skim milk). Methyl cellulose has served as a substitute for serum in some cultures.

MAINTENANCE MEDIA.   Cells may often be kept alive without significant multiplication (for purposes of transportation and storage) in

a simplified solution such as solution 199 but without serum or embryo extract. Such solutions are called *maintenance media.*

**Secondary Cultures.**   For commercial and other purposes requiring large volumes, secondary cultures can be made from primary monolayers. The growth or maintenance medium is removed and the monolayer is washed with saline solution devoid of calcium and magnesium ions. The cells are then dispersed by adding 10 ml. of 1/3000 Versene (ethylene diamine tetra-acetate or EDTA) to *chelate* the calcium and magnesium ions in the intracellular matrix that holds the cells together and to the glass surface. After 15 to 30 minutes at 36° C., the loosened cells are shaken to separate them and resuspended in growth medium. The suspension is dispensed in large culture flasks and may be kept from forming sheets by constant agitation.

**Established Cell Lines.**   A tissue culture derived directly from an animal (or plant) which is not transferred or subcultured is referred to as a *primary culture* and usually consists of several different kinds of cells: muscle, fibroblasts and possibly parenchymal cells of liver or kidney (or various plant cells). Subcultures from the primary culture are called *diploid cell strains.* These cell strains cannot be immediately differentiated from the primary culture, and both may contain more than one kind of cell. However, repeated serial subculturing of a cell strain may result in final dominance of the fastest-growing cell type in the original culture, in mutations suggesting malignancy or in other undesirable changes in the cells. More important, they can become contaminated with extraneous, possibly oncogenic, viruses that can remain occult for long periods.

**Clonal Cell Lines.**   Although primary tissue cultures and diploid cell strains may contain several different kinds of tissue cells, it is possible to isolate single cells from these cultures. Each cell then forms a separate colony, much as bacteria do (Fig. 16.5). They can then be propagated separately as pure cultures, thus establishing *clones.* A clone is a population in which all individual cells are descendants of a *single cell.* Techniques for cloning are ingenious and varied.

CLONING.   In one type of procedure diluted suspensions of cells in growth fluid are allowed to settle on the bottoms of Petri dishes or similar vessels, or on small, thin slips of glass, or on glass beads immersed in growth medium (Fig. 16.4). The bottom of the culture vessel, or each

---

*That is, composed entirely of pure ingredients of which the composition is exactly known and reproducible. The exact composition of serum or tissue extracts is neither known nor reproducible.

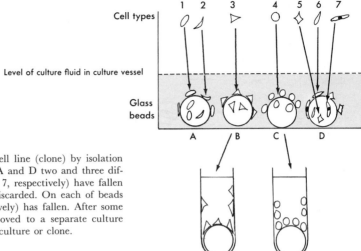

**Figure 16.4** Preparation of pure cell line (clone) by isolation of single cells on glass beads. On beads A and D two and three different cell types (1 and 2, and 5, 6 and 7, respectively) have fallen and started mixed growths. These are discarded. On each of beads B and C a single cell (3 and 4, respectively) has fallen. After some growth has developed each bead is removed to a separate culture vessel (B′ and C′) to grow out as a pure culture or clone.

slip of glass or glass bead, is examined with a microscope. A note is made of each spot or bead or glass slip having a single, isolated cell on it. After the cells have become attached, any desired single cell may be segregated by means of a small glass cylinder stood on end over the bead or glass to which it is attached, or the glass slips or beads may be removed to another separate, cell-free culture vessel. The cells may be left *in situ* to develop colonies, like bacteria.

Many established clonal cell lines (lung, kidney, various cancers such as HeLa and L strains) are available commercially.

A new "Registry of Animal Cell Lines Certified by the Cell Culture Collection Committee" of the U. S. Department of Health, Education and Welfare gives the complete life history and description of cell lines useful in vaccine preparation and research.

Tissue Cultures on Agar. Tissue cultures may also be transferred with platinum loops to agar slants or to agar in Petri plates or to strips of filter paper saturated with nutrient fluid, where they form colonies in the same manner as bacteria (Fig. 16.5).

*Necessity of Carbon Dioxide.* In all tissue-cell cultures the atmosphere must contain about 5 per cent carbon dioxide, similar to requirements of some bacteria (autotrophs, *Brucella* and *Neisseria*). Special buffer systems or special incubators may be used to maintain carbon dioxide-rich atmospheres. A simple but effective expedient for small projects is to place the cul-

ture vessels in a large jar or metal container. A lighted candle is placed in the container, which is immediately tightly covered. In a few minutes the carbon dioxide reaches a concentration of about 5 per cent and the candle ceases to burn (Fig. 16.6).

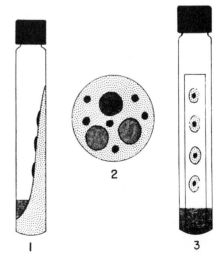

**Figure 16.5** Colonies of animal-tissue cell clones growing on: (1) agar slants supplied with nutrient solution which diffuses upward from the reservoir at the bottom of the slant; (2) agar in a Petri dish through which nutrient diffuses from fluid in the three large "cups," "wells," or depressions in the agar; (3) agar-impregnated filter paper strips carrying four colonies supplied with nutrient solution from the reservoir at the bottom of the tube. (About one half actual size.) (From Wallace and Hanks: Science, vol. 128.)

**Figure 16.6** "Candle-jar" method of providing an atmosphere with approximately 5 per cent $CO_2$ for microorganisms in cultures. The jar is closed and the burning candle will soon expire for lack of sufficient oxygen. (Courtesy of Communicable Disease Center, U. S. Public Health Service, Atlanta, Ga.)

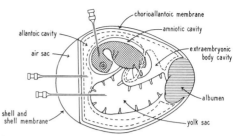

**Figure 16.7** Diagrammatic representation in sagittal section of the embryonated hen's egg 10 to 12 days old. The hypodermic needles show the routes of inoculation of the yolk sac, allantoic cavity, and embryo (head). The chorioallantoic membrane is inoculated after it has been dropped by removing the air from the air sac as explained in the text. (From Burrows: Textbook of Microbiology. 18th ed.)

## 16.2  CULTIVATION IN CHICK EMBRYOS

Chick embryos are live animals. For microbiological purposes they have as good a scientific standing as monkeys, rabbits or mice, and many obvious advantages. For example, they are so conveniently packaged in their shells that they seem almost like *in vitro* cultures of tissue cells. They are especially useful for propagating viruses and rickettsias. In order that they may contain growing cells in which viruses and rickettsias can multiply they must be fertile. They are incubated as for hatching until the embryo is well developed (from ten to fourteen days).

One procedure for introducing microorganisms is to inoculate the chorioallantoic membrane (one of the vascular membranes surrounding the embryo). (See Fig. 16.7.) Holding the egg against a small, bright window in a dark room (*candling* the egg), determine the location of the air sac at the large end. Pierce the shell over the air sac. The shell is then cut by means of a dentist's fine carborundum disk on a flexible shaft, rotated by a dental motor (Fig. 16.8). The square of cut shell is then gently

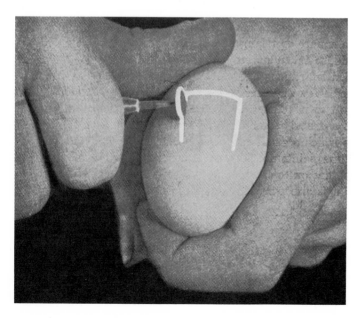

**Figure 16.8** Cutting window in shell with rotating carborundum disk. (From Goodpasture and Buddingh: Am. J. Hyg., vol. 21.)

lifted off with a sterile forceps, exposing the shell membrane immediately underneath. The shell membrane is pierced, the chorioallantois drops away from it (especially if a drop of sterile saline solution is allowed to spread between the two membranes) and gentle suction is applied at the opening of the air sac. The shell membrane may now be torn off like paper against the cut edge of the shell, leaving the vascular embryonic membranes exposed for inoculation.

This is done simply by applying the inoculum with a loop, a dropper or other gentle means. The hole in the shell is surrounded by sterile melted petrolatum or paraffin and immediately covered with a sterile cover slip of glass. Cellophane or gummed transparent plastic strip may also be used. The egg may then be incubated as for hatching.

Modifications of this method include injection through small, appropriately located cuts in the shell by a needle directly into the amniotic and chorionic cavities, yolk sac and embryonic tissue (Fig. 16.7).

Many saprophytic microorganisms, especially yeasts, molds and bacteria, which may enter as contaminants, are able to multiply as well in the fluids of the chick embryo as in a culture tube. The embryo is usually killed and destroyed by such contaminants. Extraneous contamination with such organisms from the air, from shell dust, implements, or from contaminated inocula such as feces or saliva is therefore an ever-present source of error in the use of chick embryos for the study of viruses and rickettsias. As in handling tissue cultures, rigid precautions against such contaminations and considerable technical skill are required (Fig. 16.9). Antimicrobial drugs that are known not to affect viruses (e.g., antibiotics), are usually mixed with materials such as feces or saliva before using them as inocula.

## 16.3   ENUMERATION OF VIRUSES

The simplest method of enumeration is by direct visual count. In the case of viruses this method involves the use of the electron microscope. By this means virus particles in a suspension may be counted, after first spreading a measured amount of the suspension evenly on a smooth, transparent surface such as cellophane. Usually a known number of minute, opaque particles of polystyrene are included in the suspension in order to compare the unknown number of virus particles (*virions*) with a known concentration. If the diameter of the opaque plastic particles is known, the size of the virions may be measured at the same time. Another method of enumeration is by plaque assay.

**Plaque Assay.** The plaque assay procedure consists in distributing a suspension of the virions to be counted, in contact with young, actively growing and susceptible host cells, in (or on) a medium appropriate for the host cells, over a flat surface such as a Petri dish or flat-sided flask. Each virulent virion infects a single susceptible cell. During the ensuing incubation period each virion, with its progeny, manifests itself by forming, in the immediately surrounding area, a typically clear, transparent, readily visible circular area of lysed cells called a *plaque* (Fig. 16.10). The number of virulent virions or *plaque-forming units* in the original suspension is determined by counting the plaques and applying appropriate arithmetic.

The procedures differ somewhat, depending on the type of virus dealt with. If phage virions are being assayed, the suspension of virus may be mixed with the suspension of bacteria immediately before distributing it over the agar, or the virions may be applied in a measured amount to the agar surface shortly after applying the bacterial suspension.

If it is necessary to assay an animal virus, young, actively growing, susceptible host cells from a tissue culture are allowed to form a

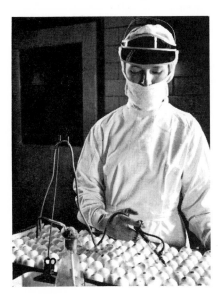

**Figure 16.9** Carefully dressed technician using a pressure-fed syringe to inoculate fertile eggs with suspension of living rickettsiae. The eggs, after suitable incubation, will be used in the preparation of vaccines or of antigens for diagnostic purposes. (Photo courtesy of E. R. Squibb & Sons.)

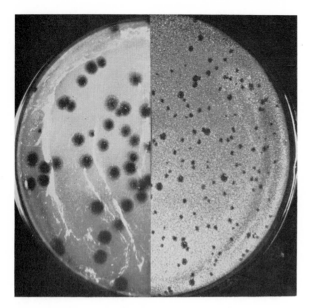

**Figure 16.10** Bacteriophage plaques. On the surface of agar of appropriate composition was spread a culture of tubercle bacilli (*Mycobacterium tuberculosis*) mixed with bacteriophage specific for this organism. After incubation, the generalized growth of tubercle bacilli is seen as a whitish film. (Such growth of any bacteria on agar is often called a "lawn.") The plaques of phage are seen as dark, circular holes in the "lawn." Each plaque is, in effect, a colony of phage that has grown at the expense of the tubercle bacilli. Two different races or types of phage are shown here: a large-plaque and a small-plaque race. Different races of phages specific for other organisms show these and other colonial peculiarities. (From Froman, Will, and Bogen: Am. J. Pub. Health. vol. 44.)

monolayer in a suitable growth medium in a Petri dish or flat-sided flask. A measured volume, say 0.2 ml., of a suspension of virions is then spread over the monolayer of host cells. The infected monolayer is then covered with a thin layer of nutrient agar (the *agar overlay*) to hold the cells and virions in place.

In either procedure, incubation is at a temperature suitable for the host cells and continues until cell growth ceases, usually within about 24 hours for bacteria, 48 to 72 hours or more for animal cells. Each plaque contains the progeny of the originating virion, and these may be "fished," like bacteria in a colony, to a new tissue culture as a (theoretically) pure culture of the virus.

In order to avoid confluence of neighboring plaques and resultant complete lysis of the entire *lawn, sheet* or *carpet* of bacteria, or the entire monolayer of tissue cells, by an overwhelmingly high ratio of virions to cells (i.e., *multiplicity* of virions), the original suspension of virulent virions is diluted. Usually the multiplicity of virions can be approximately 1:300; less if the plaques are very large. The required dilution may be determined beforehand if necessary. If the number of plaques per Petri dish (or equivalent area) is much less than 50 or much over 350 the count becomes accordingly less accurate.

In one modification, virions in a known volume of suspension are sedimented by centrifugation onto a monolayer tissue culture of susceptible cells on cover slips. After allowing time for adsorption and some growth of virus

(16 to 20 hours) the cover slip culture is stained with fluorescent antibodies (Chapter 24) which, in ultraviolet light, permits the number of infected cells (i.e., number of virions) to be visually determined (Fig. 16.11).

Technical details of virus assay by plaque count and other methods are not as simple as the basic principles involved. The interested student is referred to the literature cited at the end of this chapter for details of procedures, precautions and pitfalls.

PLAQUE REDUCTION.   By adding various noxious or stimulating agents (drugs, poisons, antibodies, vitamins) to a suspension of virus, the concentration or effect of the agents on the virus may be evaluated by noting the extent of reduction (or increase) in number of plaques, or alterations in the character of the plaques. The method opens wide possibilities for investigation of viral physiology and cell-virus relationships by the ingenious student—a rich field for the virological prospector!

**Titration by Dilution.**   Like bacteria, viruses may be enumerated by preparing serial dilutions and determining the highest dilution capable of initiating infection, and interference with growth, of tissue cells in culture medium. Inhibition of cell growth, i.e., multiplication of viruses may be determined in several ways.

THE METABOLIC INHIBITION TEST.   This method is based on the fact that healthy tissue cells growing in cultures acidify the medium by their metabolic activities. The change from the initial alkalinity of the culture medium to the acidity which is produced by the growing cells

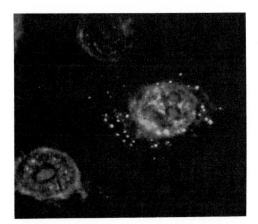

**Figure 16.11**   HeLa (ERK) cultures two hours after infection with rabbitpox virus $10^8$ p.f.u./ml.; stained with fluorescein-conjugated antiserum. The cytoplasm of one cell contains about 30 minute foci of antigen. (From Appleyard and Westwood: J. Gen. Microbiol., *37*:391, 1964.)

is readily observed by adding to the culture an indicator such as phenol red. If all the cells in the culture are killed by virus they obviously cannot produce the customary acidity; the lifeless culture remains alkaline. For enumeration based on these facts, dilutions of a virus suspension are prepared from an initial sample: $10^{-2}$, $10^{-3}$, and so on to $10^{-8}$. Of each dilution 0.1 ml. is transferred to a fresh, new, vigorous tissue culture tube in which the medium contains enough phenol red to indicate a change from the initial pH 7.8. The series of inoculated culture tubes is incubated and observed daily for alteration in pH.

Let us suppose that the contents of tubes 1 through 3 (dilutions $10^{-2}$ through $10^{-4}$) show viral growth (remain at pH 7.8), and the cultures in tubes 4 through 7 (dilutions $10^{-5}$ through $10^{-8}$) become acid, indicating that no active virions were introduced into those tubes. (The presence or absence of viral growth can also be checked by microscopic examinations for cytopathogenic effects [Fig. 16.12].) Theoretically, the undiluted sample contained at least $10^4$ infective virions but less than $10^5$ infective virions per ml. Such a number, expressed as the reciprocal of the highest dilution giving a positive result, is generally called an indicated number; in this case the indicated number of virions would theoretically be $10^4$ per 0.1 ml., a result that is useful for some purposes though far from precise. Greater accuracy can be obtained by setting up the series of dilutions in duplicate, triplicate or even pentuplicate and combining the results. Tables are available that show calculated numbers for various combinations (Chapter 42). Such a result is called a *"most probable number"* (MPN)—somewhat nearer the actual number but not the actual number. Theoretically, each tube in our series contains a known fraction of the number of virions in the undiluted suspension. For example, if there are 1000 virions per ml. in an undiluted suspension, then in 1 ml. of a 1:500 dilution there would be (ideally) two virions; one virion in a

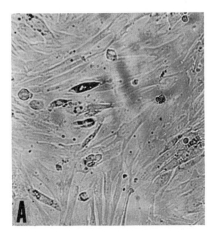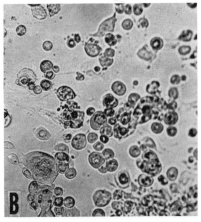

**Figure 16.12**   The cytopathogenic effect of a virus on human chorion cells in tissue culture. (The chorion is one of the membranes protecting the embryo in the uterus.) *A*, Normal cells: tissue culture five days old showing a fairly regular, organized network of uniformly elongated, spindle-shaped tissue cells of rather distinctive appearance. *B*, The same sort of cells 72 hours after being inoculated with the virus of herpes simplex ("fever blister"). The cells are largely destroyed. Those remaining have lost their distinctive form and arrangement and have become mere shapeless, disconnected, disorganized blobs of dead protoplasm ($\times$ 1500.) (Lerner, Takemoto and Shelokov: Proc. Soc. Exp. Biol. & Med., vol. 95. Copied by permission of Society for Experimental Biology and Medicine.)

1:1000 dilution (the theoretical *100 per cent end point*); and none in a 1:1001 dilution if it were prepared.

However, it is well known that, by the laws governing chance variations of distribution, any given dilution tube might contain many more or less organisms than the theoretical or "ideal" number. In the foregoing example the 1:500 tube might contain none or 78, the 1001 dilution might contain several, and so on. Such variations vitiate the accuracy of such titrations. Accuracy of titrations can be increased in several ways, one of which is the 50 per cent end-point method.

THE 50 PER CENT END-POINT METHOD. This procedure yields a much closer approach to the true number of virions in a solution than the MPN method just described. In the 50 per cent end-point process we prepare several tubes of each dilution, say five of each. We select the dilution (A) that infected *more* than 50 per cent (but less than 100 per cent) of the tissue cultures inoculated with that dilution and (B) the next higher dilution. We then mathematically interpolate between these two dilutions a dilution that should give an *exact* number of virions. Such a number is the reciprocal of the highest dilution between the two that produces death of the cells (persistent alkalinity) in exactly 50 per cent of the inoculated cultures. This number is called the *tissue-culture-dose*$_{50}$ (TCD$_{50}$) of the undiluted suspension.

For example, suppose that our virus suspension, diluted $10^{-4}$, killed the tissue cells in 75 per cent (instead of exactly 50 per cent) of the tubes of tissue culture inoculated with that dilution, while the $10^{-5}$ dilution produced cell death in 27 per cent of the tubes inoculated with that dilution. What dilution would have killed the tissue cells in exactly 50 per cent (the *50 per cent end point*) of the culture tubes? Obviously a dilution between $10^{-4}$ and $10^{-5}$. This dilution can be calculated by means of a formula devised by Reed and Munch in 1938:

$$\frac{A - 50}{A - B} = C$$

in which:

A = per cent of tubes remaining alkaline (i.e., cells killed) at the dilution (in this case $10^{-4}$) next *lower* than that which should kill all cells in 50 per cent of the tubes (*over* 50 per cent of the tubes are infected by the $10^{-4}$ dilution)

B = per cent of tubes remaining alkaline at dilution (in this case $10^{-5}$) next

higher than that which should kill all cells in 50 per cent of the tubes (*less* than 50 per cent of the tubes are infected by the $10^{-5}$ dilution)

C = the negative log of the difference between $10^{-4}$ and the dilution that should give the 50 per cent point.

In the example given:

$$\frac{75 - 50}{75 - 27} = \frac{25}{48} = 0.52.$$

C ($-0.52$) is added to the log ($-4$) of the lower dilution ($10^{-4}$) to give the exponent of the dilution required to give the 50 per cent end point: i.e., $-4 + -0.52 = -4.52$. Thus the required dilution is $10^{-4.52}$.

If the series of dilutions is not tenfold (dilution factor = 10; log = 1) but some other, say fourfold, then the amount to be added to the negative exponent of the lower dilution (in this case $-0.52$) is multiplied, not by the log of the tenfold factor, but by the log of the fourfold dilution factor, e.g., $-0.52 \times$ log 4 (0.6); or $0.6 \times -0.52 = -0.312$.

It may be noted incidentally that, by using other indicators, other 50 per cent doses or end points may be determined: e.g., half of the number of animals inoculated with a particular substance may die—the LD$_{50}$ (Lethal Dose$_{50}$) of that substance; exactly half of the chicks inoculated with a virus dilution may become infected—the CID$_{50}$ (Chick Infective Dose$_{50}$), and so on.

The 50 per cent end point is based on statistical considerations and is widely used in measuring dilutions of poisons, drugs, organisms and in many other biological applications.

## SUPPLEMENTARY READING

Bryant, J. C.: Mammalian cells in chemically defined media in suspension cultures. Ann. N. Y. Acad. Sci., *139*(Art. 1):143, 1966.

Cell Culture Collection Committee: Animal Cell Strains. Science, *146*:241, 1964.

Clark, P. F.: Pioneer Microbiologists of America. University of Wisconsin Press, Madison. 1961.

Committee on Tissue Culture Viruses and Vaccines: Continuously cultured tissue cells and viral vaccines. Science, *139*:15, 1963.

Ellison, D., Rigg, J., McConnell, S. J., Alexander, A. D., and Yager, R. H.: Use of antibiotics in the preparation of canine kidney tissue culture vaccines to eliminate leptospiral infection hazards. Appl. Microbiol., *13*:595, 1965.

Fraenkel-Conrat, H.: Design and Function at the Threshold of Life. Academic Press, Inc., New York. 1962.

Gibbs, J. L., and Dougall, D. K.: Growth of single plant cells. Science, *141*:1059, 1963.

Green, H., and Todaro, G. J.: The mammalian cell as differentiated microorganism. Ann. Rev. Microbiol., *21*:573, 1967.

Hahon, N.: Assay of variola virus by the fluorescent cell-counting technique. Appl. Microbiol., *13*:865, 1965.

Hayflick, L., Moorhead, P. S., Pomerat, C. M., and Hsu, T. C.: Choice of a cell system for vaccine production. Science, *140*:766, 1963.

Horne, R. W.: The structure of viruses. Sci. Amer., *208*:48, 1963.

Miller, R. E., Miller, N. G., and White, R.: Growth of *Leptospira pomona* and its effect on various tissue culture systems. J. Bact., *92*:502, 1966.

Notkins, A. L.: Lactic dehydrogenase virus. Bact. Rev., *29*:143, 1965.

Parker, R. C.: Methods of Tissue Culture. 3rd ed. Paul B. Hoeber, Inc., New York. 1962.

Perkins, F. T., and Hayflick, L.: Cell cultures. Science, *155*:723, 1967.

Philips, C. A., Melnick, J. L., and Grim, C. A.: Human aorta cells for isolation and propagation of rhinoviruses. Proc. Soc. Exp. Biol. Med., *119*:843, 1965.

Rosenthal, M. S.: Contamination of rhinovirus seed pools revealed in HEp2 cell suspension cultures. J. Gen. Microbiol., *38*:409, 1965.

Schmidt, N. J.: Tissue culture methods and procedures for diagnostic virology. *In:* Diagnostic Procedures and Reagents for Viral and Rickettsial Diseases. Lennette, E. H., and Schmidt, N. J. (editors): 3rd ed. Amer. Pub. Health. Assn., New York. 1964.

Schneider, L. E.: A simple all-glass device for isolating clones of mammalian cells and of viruses. Appl. Microbiol., *15*:959, 1967.

Schubert, J. H., Wiggins, G. L., and Taylor, G. C.: Tissue culture method for the titration of diphtheria antitoxin in human sera. Health Lab. Sci., *4*:181, 1967.

Somerson, N. L., and Cook, M. K.: Suppression of Rous sarcoma virus growth in tissue cultures by *Mycoplasma orale.* J. Bact., *90*:534, 1965.

Stanley, W. M., and Valens, E. G., et al.: Viruses and the Nature of Life. E. P. Dutton & Co., Inc. New York. 1961.

Steinhart, C. E.: Tissue cultures of a cactus. Science, *137*:545, 1962.

Trager, W.: Cultivation of insect tissues in vitro and their application to the study of arthropod-borne viruses. Am. J. Trop. Med. & Hyg., *12*:820, 1963.

Vasil, V., and Hildebrandt, A. C.: Growth and tissue formation from single, isolated tobacco cells in microculture. Science, *147*:1454, 1965.

White, P. R.: The Cultivation of Animal and Plant Cells. 2nd ed. The Ronald Press Co., New York. 1963.

Yasumura, Y., Tashjian, A. H., Jr., and Sato, G. H.: Establishment of four functional clonal strains of animal cells in culture. Science, *154*:1186, 1966.

Young, F. B., Sharon, W. S., and Long, R. B.: Preparation and use of dry powder tissue culture media. Ann. N. Y. Acad. Sci., *139*(Art. 2):108, 1966.

# Chapter 17

---

# THE VIRUSES

## Structure, Lytic Cycle, Properties, Classification

### 17.1  STRUCTURE AND MORPHOLOGY

As stated previously, viruses are not cellular in structure. They have no true nucleus, cytoplasm, cell membrane or cell wall. They multiply only within living cells. Outside living cells viruses are totally inert. Each virus particle or *virion* consists of only two major parts. One is a single linear molecule of either DNA or RNA. This constitutes the *core* or *nucleoid* of the virus. It is the active, disease-specific, host-specific, genetic, infective part of the virus. It should be noted that each virion contains only one kind of NA—DNA or RNA—never both. This distinguishes all true viruses from all cellular forms, eucaryotic or procaryotic, because all cellular organisms contain *both* DNA and RNA. Thus, all viruses are divided primarily into two groups: those containing DNA (sometimes called *deoxyviruses*) and those containing RNA (sometimes called *riboviruses*).

The NA in a given kind of virus may be single or double stranded. The two kinds of NA may be differentiated by chemical analysis in the following ways: (1) DNA is decomposed only by the specific enzyme DNA-ase; RNA is enzymically decomposed only by the specific enzyme RNA-ase; (2) when NA is fixed with an alcoholic fluid (e.g., Carnoy's), stained at pH 4.0 with acridine orange and examined in ultraviolet light, it usually fluoresces flame red if single stranded and yellow-green if double stranded. This method is not entirely error-free.

Surrounding the NA core is the second major portion of the virion: a protein shell or coating called a *capsid.* Since it is a protein, it has antigenic specificity (Chapter 24). The capsid is made up of many identical structural units called *capsomeres* (Gr. *meros* = part); their composition, numbers and forms vary with the kinds of viruses (Fig. 17.1). The capsid is physiologically inert and is believed to serve only as a protective shell. The core, with its capsid, is called the *nucleocapsid* of the virus. Many mammalian viruses also have, outside the capsid, an *envelope* or *limiting membrane* or mantle. As will be

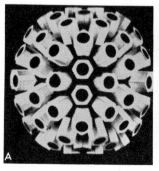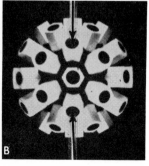

**Figure 17.1**  Models showing capsomere arrangements. *A,* model of a reovirus virion showing arrangement of hollow protein capsomeres on the outer surface of the nucleocapsid. Note that some of the capsomeres are pentagonally faced, others hexagonally faced; 92 capsomeres. *B,* model of an SV 40 (simian virus 40) virion; 42 capsomeres. The arrows show the axis of a two-fold symmetry. The shapes of the capsomeres are partly diagrammatic. (From Mayor, D. H., and Melnick, J. L.: Science, *137*:613, 1962.)

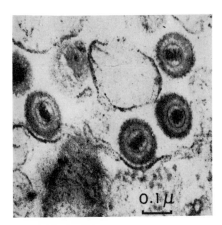

**Figure 17.2**    Canine herpes virions after release from an infected cell. Note the bar-shaped helix at the core, surrounded by a thin, dark membrane and a thicker outer mantle or envelope; also the spike-like projections from the outer surface (compare Figure 17.4). This preparation was not stained to show the 162 capsomeres demonstrable by negative staining. (From Strandberg and Carmichael: J. Bact., *90*:1790, 1965.)

explained farther on, this appears to be derived largely or wholly (depending on kind of virus and cell) from the nuclear or cytoplasmic membrane of the infected cell (Fig. 17.2). It is made up of structural units called *peplomers* (Gr. *meros* =

part), and often contains lipids or lipoproteins. These lipid components confer on the viruses that have them the distinctive property of sensitivity to lipid solvents such as ether and chloroform, or to emulsifying agents such as bile salts and detergents. Such viruses are sometimes called *lipoviruses.* Many viruses have no envelope; they are naked virions.

In outward form virions differ widely. They may be elongate, like a piece of insulated electric cable (Fig. 17.3), or rounded, polyhedral or cuboidal. Several appear to be pleomorphic. In elongate forms the NA strand of the core is usually coiled like a helical spring. The capsid is closely coiled about it or is arranged as a succession of rings. Such a virion is said to have *helical symmetry.* In some helical viruses the whole nucleocapsid is sufficiently flexible to be secondarily coiled on itself into a spheroidal form. Helical viruses of mammals generally have a lipid-containing envelope. Many are covered externally by thin, radially projecting spikes or rods suggestive of bacterial fimbriae (Chapter 10) (Fig. 17.4).

A common viral form is based on *cubic symmetry.* Such viruses may be polyhedral or roughly cuboidal. The cores of such viruses are surrounded by well-defined capsomeres usually

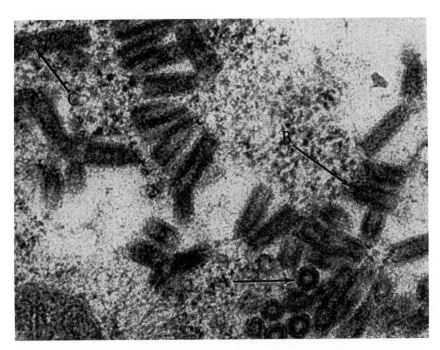

**Figure 17.3**    Details of rabies virus morphology seen in an infected cell. In transverse sections (A), the virus consists of an inner core surrounded by a dense membrane with surface projections. Longitudinal sections reveal bullet-shaped particles (B) or long rods flat at both ends (C). Thin section (× 80,000). (From Hummeler, Koprowski and Wiktor: J. Virol., *1*:152, 1967.)

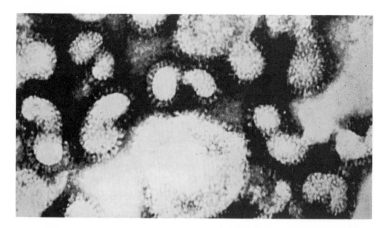

**Figure 17.4** Influenza virus PR8 after one hour incubation at 37° C. Projecting spikes or rods resemble bacterial fimbriae. (From Reginster: J. Gen. Microbiol., *42*:323, 1966.)

arranged in *icosahedral** *symmetry* (Fig. 17.5). Some viruses at times are bullet shaped (Fig. 17.3).

The numbers of capsomeres of virions that

---

*An icosahedron is a polyhedron with 20 identical triangular facets (Fig. 17.6). A distinguishing character of an icosahedron is that it may present any of several different symmetrical appearances depending on which of three axes it rotates about. Thus, when rotated about axis *a* it presents five identical appearances, about axis *b* it presents three appearances and about axis *c*, two appearances; there are 10 appearances in all. It is said to have 5-3-2 (icosahedral) symmetry. It is to be remembered that some other polyhedrons, e.g., a dodecahedron, may also exhibit 5-3-2 symmetry. Thus a virus with 5-3-2 symmetry may or may not be truly icosahedral in form.

show icosahedral symmetry are determinable and are distinctive of certain virus types. Capsomere numbers vary from about 12 to 812 or more. The symmetry and form of numerous viruses, especially the large poxviruses with lipo-complex peploses (smallpox, *myxoviruses*), are complex and often vague or indeterminable. Capsomeres of some helical viruses with envelopes are not sufficiently distinct to be accurately counted. Instead, the diameter of the helical nucleocapsid inside the envelope is measured as a distinguishing character.

**Disjunction of Viral Structures.** An interesting aspect of viral structure is that the NA of several representative viruses is easily separated from the protein coat (Fig. 17.7). The

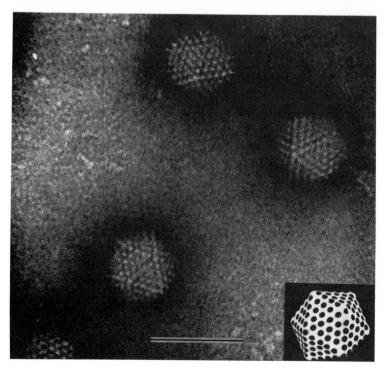

**Figure 17.5** Purified adenovirus type 2 particles (the bar equals 100 mμ). The model in the right corner shows the icosahedral form of the virions. (From Smith, Gehle and Trousdale: J. Bact., *90*:254, 1965.)

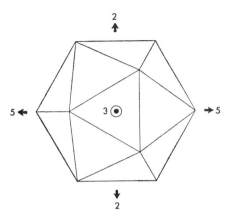

**Figure 17.6** Diagram of an icosahedron showing axes of rotation that reveal 2-, 3- and 5-face symmetry. (From Mayor and Melnick: Science, vol. 137.)

protein may be removed by treatment and extraction with sodium lauryl sulfate, a cationic detergent (Chapter 21), or with phenol. Whereas some viruses are very unstable in this condition and vulnerable to NA-digesting enzymes (RNA-ase and DNA-ase), the naked NA retains for some time the specific genetic and reproductive properties of the intact virus, although some of its infectivity is lost. Equally interesting is the fact that the naked NA may be recoated with the protein and assume its original form and properties.

## 17.2   SIZES OF VIRUSES

**Size and Visibility.** Except for certain "large" viruses (e.g., smallpox, vaccinia), a major distinguishing property of viruses is their invisibility under even the best optical microscopes (magnifications up to 2000×). However, electron microscopes, which can give clear resolutions at magnifications of several hundred thousand times, make even the smallest viruses and their innermost structures readily visible.

An idea of the degree of magnification implied by 200,000× may be gained by imagining the letter O on this page to be so magnified. Approximately 2.5 mm. in diameter, the letter would appear as an oval 200,000 × 2.5 = 500,000 mm. = 500 meters or nearly one half mile in diameter: a large race track! Magnified 2000× by an optical microscope the O would appear only about 16 feet in diameter.

**Size and Filtrability.** Iwanowski, Walter Reed and, later, many others demonstrated what was thought, until about 1930, to be a uniquely distinctive property of viruses: the ability when suspended in fluids to pass through porcelain filters of such fine porosity as to retain all known bacteria. However, it is now known that under some experimental conditions bacteria can readily be made to pass through the same porcelain filters by special means, since size is not the only factor that determines filtrability through silicious filters. Surface electrical charge, which can be altered experimentally, is also very important. The "filtrable" viruses, however, cannot pass through filters made from collodion or cellulose acetate (called *membrane filters*) if the filters are made with sufficiently fine pores. Thus the term filtrable, once widely used to distinguish viruses, is no longer applicable without appropriate qualifications.

Certain details of structure as well as sizes of viruses are often inferred from the results of indirect methods. Graded ultrafiltration is sometimes used. It consists of passage of an aqueous suspension of virus particles through successive collodion or plastic membranes of known, graded, decreasing pore sizes, the effect

**Figure 17.7** Electron micrographs of tobacco mosaic virus (TMV). *A*, The virus as usually seen (× 78,000). These rods appear to consist of hollow, round or hexagonal tubes of protein (94%) containing a thin core of ribonucleic acid (RNA) (6%). The RNA is the vital, specific, heredity-bearing part of the virus structure. *B*, The TMV particles after treatment with a surface tension reducer which removed part of the protein coat from many of the rods, revealing the RNA core (× 60,000). (From Hart: Proc. Nat. Acad. Sci., vol. 41.)

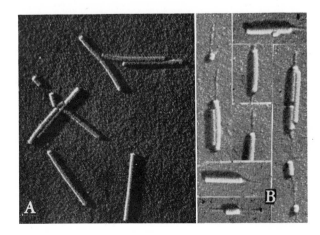

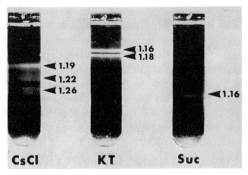

**Figure 17.8** Cesium chloride, potassium tartrate and sucrose density gradients of vesicular stomatitis virus (centrifuged 3½ hours at 99,972 × g) and the buoyant density of the bodies obtained. (From McCombs, Benyesh-Melnick and Brunschwig: J. Bact., *91*:803, 1965.)

being like that of a gravel sorter. An important source of error is electrostatic adsorption of the virions to opposite charges on the membrane surfaces. Measurement by direct observation of virus particles with electron microscopes is valuable but subject to error resulting from dehydration of the specimen and distortion by the electron beam. Sedimentation rates and buoyant densities as determined in ultracentrifuges under carefully controlled conditions of specific gravity (e.g., density gradients in cesium chloride solutions), viscosity or temperature furnish useful data if expertly determined (Fig. 17.8).

Virion size determinations are usefully accurate and are important in primary differ-

entiations of virus types and classifications of viruses.

There is a considerable range in size of viruses (Fig. 17.9). Some, such as those of yellow fever, foot-and-mouth disease and poliomyelitis, are "small," with diameters about 25 m$\mu$ (m$\mu$ = millimicron, or one millionth of a millimeter). Others, like the virus of smallpox (vaccinia), are "large," about 250 m$\mu$ (0.25 $\mu$) in size. These are just within the range of resolution by the best optical microscopes. There are many intermediate sizes.

## 17.3   MULTIPLICATION OF VIRUSES

### THE LYTIC CYCLE

Because viruses multiply only intracellularly and because the *in vitro* cultivation of cells of animals and eucaryotic plant tissues is time-consuming and expensive, many virologists have turned to bacterial cells and bacterial viruses (bacteriophages) for the study of viruses. Bacterial viruses are therefore commonly used as the model for viruses in general and will be so used here. It must be remembered, however, that we deal here with a procaryotic cell-virus system and that data obtained with such a system are not completely or necessarily applicable to eucaryotic cell-virus systems such as the multiplication of measles virus in human embryonic tissue cells. Nevertheless, the two types of system have been shown to be remarkably

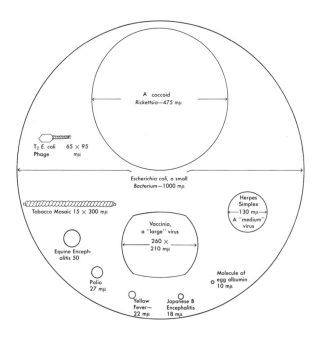

**Figure 17.9** Diagrammatic comparison of sizes of viruses and related structures. The largest circle, enclosing the whole, represents the diameter of *Escherichia coli*, a small cylindrical bacterium about 1 $\mu$ (1000 m$\mu$) in diameter. The other objects are drawn to approximately the same scale. (Sketch and sizes based on Rivers and Horsfall: Viral and Rickettsial Infections of Man. J. B. Lippincott Co., 1959.)

parallel in most fundamental respects. Many types of phage are known, each capable of parasitizing one or more different species of bacteria. A bacterium much used for virological studies is called *Escherichia* (for a German scientist, Escherich) *coli* (because the organism commonly occurs only in the colon). *E. coli* is a gram-negative, harmless (usually!), nonspore-forming, facultative, motile, rod-shaped bacillus of the Order Eubacteriales (Chapter 36). It grows vigorously and rapidly in simple nutrient solutions such as 1 per cent peptone, or in saline solutions like Hanks's or Earle's with a little glucose. Under optimal growth conditions new generations (fissions) of *E. coli* occur every 20 to 30 minutes.

**Isolation and Demonstration of Phage.** Various types of phage are commonly present in sewage or in the intestines of coprophagous insects, or in other situations in which they find bacteria on which to feed. Bacteriophages may easily be isolated and their bacteriolytic action demonstrated as follows. Pass about 30 ml. of raw sewage, or of 1 per cent peptone solution in which a dozen flies or cockroaches have been thoroughly macerated, through a sterile Seitz or Berkefeld-N-type of bacteria-retaining and virus-passing filter. Add 1 or 2 ml. of the bacteria-free, phage-containing filtrate to about 10 ml. of a young broth culture of bacteria (e.g., *Escherichia coli* or *Shigella sonnei*) that is just beginning to become turbid in its early, logarithmic phase of growth. Incubate the culture at 37° C., observing it every two to three hours. Usually the culture will at first become more turbid and then, within two to three hours or less, much less turbid and sometimes crystal clear, because of lysis of the bacterial cells by the phage.

If the lysed broth culture is filtered new, lytic phage will appear in the filtrate and can be demonstrated by plaque formation as previously described and can be transferred in high dilutions to new broth cultures. The process can be repeated indefinitely without loss, and usually a gain, in lytic potency of the phage in the filtrates, showing that the phage multiplies.

"T" Phages. Several types of *Escherichia coli* phages (*coliphages*) are known, designated respectively as T1 (T for type), T2, T3, . . . T7. Phage lambda and some others are known also. The discussion here will deal mainly with the *E. coli*-T2 phage system, since this has been widely used as a model. The *T-even* (2, 4, 6) phages differ in several respects (e.g., form, size,

chemical composition) from the *T-uneven* or *T-odd* (3, 5, 7) phages.

Although there are some tail-less phages, most known types, including "T" phages, have a tadpole-like or spermlike form with a polyhedral head or nucleocapsid about 50 m$\mu$ in diameter and a narrow tail, whose length is two to six times the diameter of the head. They vary considerably in form (Fig. 17.10). The head contains all the active material of the phage virion, i.e., a single, linear molecule of NA arranged in a closed circle suggestive of an episome like the F factor of bacteria. In most known phages this is double-stranded DNA. The phage tail is a hollow tube of protein attached to the protein coating of the head. The tube is enclosed within a retractable sheath. A system of fibers and an enzyme at the tip of the tail play a critical role in attaching the virion to the cell and penetrating the cell wall. Bacteriophages commonly destroy (i.e., cause lysis of) the bacterial cell that they infect.

**Lysis of Bacteria by Phage.** Analysis of the process of bacteriolysis by phage has resolved it into several steps, as described in the following paragraphs. The information thus gained has been of inestimable value in studying the mechanisms by which other viruses attack and destroy plant and animal cells, in the study of genetics and in the elucidation of many other biological phenomena. It is important, therefore, to have a good understanding of the mechanisms of *phage lysis*.

Adsorption and Cell Receptors. The bacterial cell wall, as previously described, is made up of molecular aggregations having various functional groups ($^-$OH, $^-$COOH, $^-$NH$_2$) with definite physicochemical structures and distributions of electrical charges. These are sites with physicochemical *specificity,* and are called *receptor sites.* Let us suppose that a phage particle comes into contact with a certain kind of bacterial cell. If the physicochemical structures in the tip of the phage tail correspond exactly and reciprocally to a specific receptor site in the bacterial cell wall, the phage tail is irreversibly adsorbed to the bacterial receptor site. The tail fibers thus play a critical role in the adsorption process.

It is important to note that bacteriophages appear unique in their mode of attachment to, and entry into, the host cell via a tail. Other viruses without such obvious structures, e.g., animal viruses, exhibit the same degree of specificity and the phenomena of attachment of the virion and entrance of NA. However, the exact

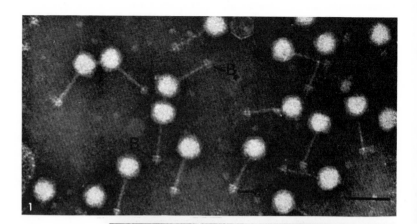

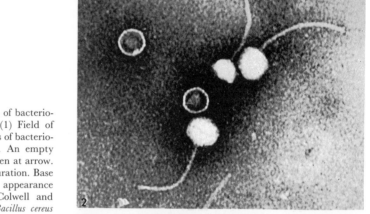

**Figure 17.10** Electron micrographs of bacteriophages. Phosphotungstate preparations. (1) Field of marine bacteriophages, showing properties of bacteriophages in general, i.e., heads and tails. An empty head displaying the hexagonal shape is seen at arrow. Base plates (A) reveal a triangular configuration. Base plates (B) present a rectangular appearance (× 150,000). (From Valentine, Chen, Colwell and Chapman: J. Bact., *91*:819, 1966.) (2) *Bacillus cereus* bacteriophage, phage B (× 120,000). (From Dawson, Smillie and Norris: J. Gen. Microbiol., *28*:517, 1962.) (3) Phage 66t⁻ (× 333,000) and (4) Model of phage T4 (× 300,000). (From Bradley: J. Gen. Microbiol., *31*:435, 1963.)

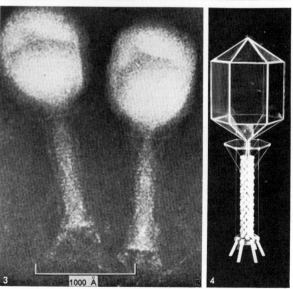

mechanisms are not yet fully clarified for all viruses. Some animal viruses appear to be taken into the cell by the process called pinocytosis (Chapter 3).

PENETRATION. Within a few seconds a lysozyme-like enzymic mechanism in the tip of the tail of the phage makes an opening through the bacterial cell wall. Through this opening the NA from inside the head of the phage is forced through the tail and into the bacterial cell (Fig. 17.11). The sheath around the tail is retracted at this time (Fig. 17.12). The protein coating of the head and tail of the phage, its mission accomplished, remains as an inert shell or "ghost" on the outside of the cell wall (Fig. 17.13).

ECLIPSE. Once inside the cell, the NA of the phage is no longer infective, since it has emerged from its means of entering a new cell. If the cell containing it is experimentally rup-

**Figure 17.11**   Fowlpox virus particle releasing DNA after exposure to sodium lauryl sulfate. Although this is an animal virus the DNA was frequently extruded in a configuration closely resembling a bacteriophage tail. Sample was dialyzed against phosphate buffer and prepared by the Kleinschmidt technique (× 85,000). Note that, except for one or two accidental breaks, the molecule of DNA is one continuous (circular) thread. (From Hyde and Randall: J. Bact., *91*:1363, 1966.)

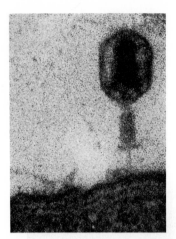

**Figure 17.12**   Bacteriophage T4r⁺ infecting *E. coli* (× 210,000). The retracted tail sheath, base plate and fibers are evident. (From Margaretten, Morgan, Rosenkranz and Rose: J. Bact., *91*:823, 1966.)

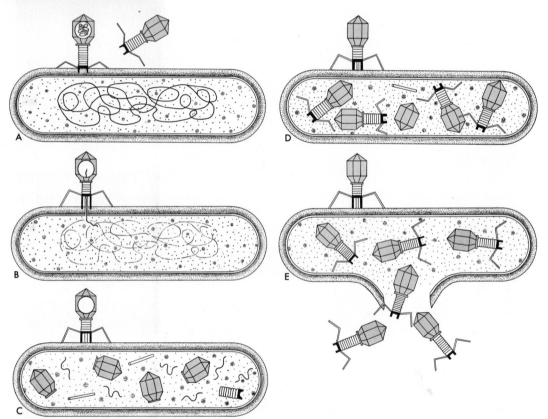

**Figure 17.13**   Development of a virulent phage in a susceptible bacterium. At *A* the polyhedral head of the phage (here shown in section to reveal the phage NA) is seen attached to the outer surface of the bacterium by its tail and tail fibrils. At *B*, within a few seconds or minutes the bacterial cell wall and membrane have been perforated by lytic enzymes in the tail and the NA of the phage has entered the bacillus through the phage tail. Note the retraction of the tail sheath. The opening through the cell wall is resealed. The inert protein coat of the phage remains on the outside of the cell. Disintegration of the cell DNA begins at once. The phage, as such, is no longer demonstrable. (What is this stage called?) During the next 12 minutes phage protein heads, tails and phage NA replicons are being synthesized, as seen at *C*. At *D*, about 12 minutes later, following a brief period of *maturation* during which some of the heads, tails and NA have been assembled, virulent phage virions are first demonstrable by artificial rupture of the cell. (This is the end of what period?) At *E*, about 12 minutes later, the assembly of parts into phage virions is complete and the now "eviscerated" cell, an inert sac, ruptures by enzymic lysis of the cell wall, liberating many new phage particles. Their number is characteristic of the *burst size* of the particular phage involved; in this case, six. The whole process, from *A* to *E*, occupies about 30 to 40 minutes in this particular virus-cell system. Note that in this diagram the phage virions have been drawn about 3 times as large proportionately in order to show more clearly certain structural details.

tured at this point, no infectious phage can be demonstrated. The phage is said to be in *eclipse*.

FORMATION OF NEW PHAGE. The immediate effects of entry of the viral NA are: *immunity*, i.e., formation of a specific enzyme repressor that prevents multiplication of any other phage of that type (but not of other types); and *suppression* of all further synthesis of messenger RNA (mRNA) and of ribosomal RNA (rRNA) by the cell and, consequently, suppression of synthesis of cell enzymes. Existing mRNA of the cell ceases to function. However, cell enzymes and rRNA already present at the moment of infection are not destroyed, but are made to serve the purposes of the phage, as will be outlined.

A third important effect of entry of the phage NA is formation by the phage, from the amino acid "pool" of the cell matrix, of new enzymes foreign to the cell. These enzymes are sometimes called *early proteins*. These do not become part of the phage but (1) seal the orifice of entry of the viral NA, (2) *depolymerize* the cell DNA, and (3) synthesize the *viral* NA from some of the nucleotides thus freed from the cell DNA, and from newly synthesized nucleotides. The exact mechanism of (3) is not

clear, but it appears that the two strands of the viral NA double helix unwind, and then rearrange, according to the viral genetic code, the newly synthesized nucleotides derived from degradation of the cell DNA. Thus the viral genome is replicated many times. It directs synthesis of new mRNA bearing the code of the virus. Using the cell rRNA and tRNA, the viral mRNA then directs synthesis of the protein portions of the phage virion—head or tail, according to the code of the virus. These first appear early in the eclipse period as separate, "prefabricated" parts. They are then assembled, with the already formed phage chromosomes, during a brief period of *maturation*. The result is dozens or hundreds of new, complete, mature, *infective* virions. Excess, unused, unassembled heads, tails or NA fragments often appear as surplus "incomplete" or "defective" units (Fig. 17.14). If the cell is ruptured at this time, the new infective units can be demonstrated, also the phage fragments and the incomplete or defective units.

The formation of mature, infective virion inside the cell signalizes the end of the eclipse period. The *eclipse period* is thus the interval between injection of viral NA through the cell

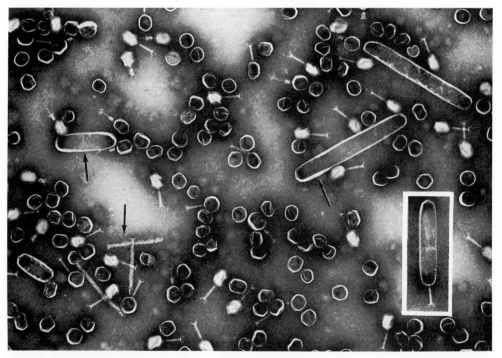

**Figure 17.14**   Abnormal forms and faulty maturation of T-even bacteriophage as induced by various substances; in this case by an amino acid analogue, L-canavanine. Note the numerous long ovals which are several connected heads (polyheads), some with tails attached (insert), tail-less heads, headless tails, empty heads, polytail sheaths, polytail tubes and small heads. (From Cummings, Chapman, deLong and Mondale: J. Virol., *1*:193, 1967.)

wall and first appearance of infective virions *inside* the cell. This is often called the *vegetative phase* of the life cycle of a virus. The duration of the eclipse period in the *E. coli*-T2 phage system is about 12 minutes under optimal conditions of growth. It varies for other virus-cell systems. For example, the eclipse period of the influenza virus in tissue-culture cells is about seven hours.

THE LATENT PERIOD. The assembly of new virions from the prefabricated parts continues inside the cell for some time after the end of the eclipse period. In the *E. coli*-T2 phage system the cell wall ruptures about 18 minutes after the end of the eclipse period, and the new phage units are then set free to begin the cycle anew. The cell is said to have undergone *lysis from within.* This signalizes the end of the *latent period.* The latent period is the time from adsorption up to, but not including, cell rupture. It includes the eclipse period. Do not confuse latent period of viral growth with *latency* (see farther on).

THE LYTIC CYCLE. The period from adsorption to cell lysis comprises one *lytic cycle* of phage activity (Fig. 17.15). As will be described, there are other cycles of viral activity.

BURST SIZE. The average number of ma-

ture virions released per cell by rupture of the cell wall at the end of the latent period is more or less constant in any given cell-virus system. It may range from about 20 to 200 or more. This number is referred to as the *burst size* of the cell at the end of the latent period. In the *E. coli*-T2 phage system just described the burst size is about 200.

CAUSE OF CELL LYSIS. Cell lysis is apparently not caused by expansive pressure from within. Under the influence of the phage the cell appears to form, or to cease to inhibit, enzymic agents capable of destroying the cell wall. This causes *lysis from within.* Similar lytic agents have been found in *phage lysates* (suspensions of cells lysed by phage) of numerous bacterial species. In some respects these lytic agents resemble an enzyme called *lysozyme* that hydrolyzes the mucocomplex of cell walls (Chapter 13). Some of the enzymes found in phage lysates can depolymerize capsular polysaccharides; others digest mucopeptides of cell walls and cause *lysis from without.* Whether such lytic agents are involved in lysis of virus-infected cells of animals or higher plants is not yet clear.

Animal cells, of course, have no cell walls. This affects the mechanisms of attachment of

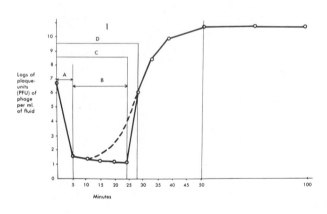

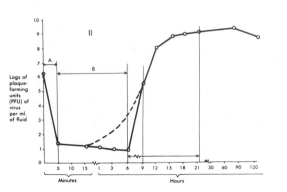

**Figure 17.15** Representative curves of growth of virus in cell cultures: (I) bacteriophage; (II) animal virus such as poliovirus. Each culture of young, actively growing cells was inoculated with a suspension containing from $10^6$ to $10^7$ virus particles, each capable of infecting a cell. Within a few minutes (the period of *adsorption* and *penetration; A*), most of the virus particles were adsorbed onto, and had penetrated into, the susceptible cells. Virus particles virtually disappeared from the suspending fluid. However, a few remained unadsorbed, demonstrable in low and declining numbers as plaque-forming units (PFU) in the suspending fluid during the *eclipse period* (B). During this time the virus particles that had penetrated were replicating intracellularly (broken line; exact form hypothetical). At the end of the *latent period* (C) (25 to 27 minutes in I; 6 to 9 hours in II) complete, mature virus particles (PFU) were demonstrable intracellularly by cell rupture. A short time later the cell walls and membranes ruptured by lysis from within and new virions were released in large numbers almost simultaneously from virtually all the cells in the cultures, producing a precipitate rise in numbers of free virions, each a PFU. This completed one *lytic cycle* (D). This continued for a period of about 22 minutes in I; 12 hours in II.

In different cell-virus systems the time relationships and numbers of PFU may vary considerably from those noted here, but in general the forms of the curves are basically alike. Compare with Figure 4.15.

viruses and penetration of animal cells by animal viruses. As will be explained, certain types of animal viruses do not cause lysis from within, but virions continue to be matured slowly on or in the cell membrane during a period of days or weeks. In passing out of the cell, each viral nucleoid acquires a part of the nuclear or cell membrane as its outer envelope (Fig. 17.16). Poliovirus is one of the group of viruses that have no host-derived envelope. They cause lysis from within, like phage.

The growth of phage during the latent period has been cleverly investigated. As shown by providing nutrients containing radiophosphorus ($P^{32}$) and radioisotopes of sulfur, carbon and nitrogen, the virus seems to derive some of its phosphorus and nitrogen from compounds in the medium in which the host cell is growing, but about one fifth of each of these elements in the virus is derived from molecules of the host cell itself. Improperly nourished cells may fail completely to support multiplication of a virus to which they are ordinarily fully susceptible.

**Host Specificity.**   An important factor in multiplication of viruses is *host specificity*. In the case of phages, host specificity, as mentioned previously, depends on the presence of reciprocally adaptive adsorption sites on cell wall and phage tail. In the case of viruses of animal cells and cells of higher plants, the phenomenon of host specificity is evident to the same degree but its exact mechanism is not so clear.

Under natural (as distinguished from ex-

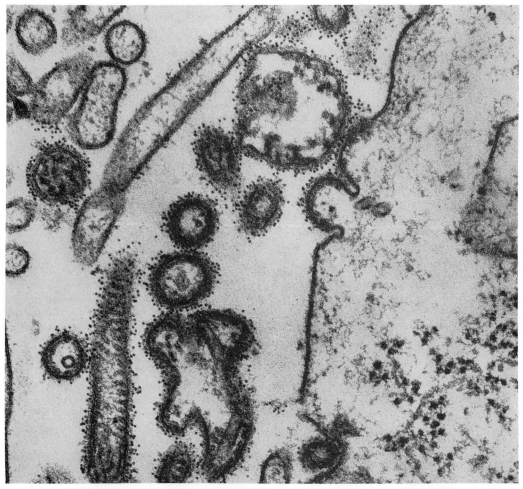

**Figure 17.16**   Maturation of parainfluenza virions at the surface of a human tissue cell. The proteins (antigens) of the virions have combined with ferritin-labeled antibody (Chapter 24) and are seen as numerous minute black specks surrounding the virions, some of which are rounded (left, center), some apparently misshapen. The release of two new virions is exemplified by the rounded, budlike bodies (right, center) at the cell margin ($\times$ 70,000). (From Howe, Morgan, St. Cyr, deVaux, Hsu, and Rose: J. Virol., *1*:215, 1967.)

perimental) conditions, all viruses, including phages, are more or less restricted as to host. For example, plant and fish viruses cannot directly infect mammalian cells (so far as we know at this moment!). However, plant viruses commonly infect their insect vectors (e.g., leafhoppers) and some animal viruses infect the insects (e.g., mosquitoes) that transmit them. Smallpox, measles and polioviruses normally infect only humans. On the other hand, rabies virus will infect virtually any mammal but not any plant or insect. Yellow fever virus in nature is restricted to man, certain monkeys and a few lower animals; however, under experimental conditions it will infect avian embryos, mice and guinea pigs' brains if introduced with a hypodermic syringe. Among bacterial viruses a given phage is usually restricted to a single species of bacteria or even to a single special type (called a *phage* type) of that species. Some animal viruses will infect only cells from certain specific tissues of certain specific animals; others can infect cells of a wide range of species.

**Intracellular Inclusions.** Within many types of cells infected by a virus, various abnormal granules are visible with optical microscopes. These abnormalities are called *intracellular inclusions*. They may occur in the nucleus (*intranuclear inclusions*) or cytoplasm (*cytoplasmic inclusions*) or both (Fig. 17.17). Some appear to be dead and altered cellular debris, and others may be aggregations of virus particles.

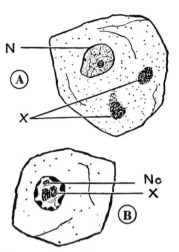

**Figure 17.17** *A,* One type of cytoplasmic viral inclusion bodies is shown at *X.* The nucleus is shown at *N. B,* Intranuclear inclusions in liver cell of victim of yellow fever. *Nc,* nucleolus; *X,* inclusion bodies. These are eosinophilic da Rocha–Lima bodies and probably of the A type mentioned in the text. Note the characteristic basophilic lobulations at the nuclear membrane resembling inclusions of the B type. (Redrawn from Cowdry and Kitchen.)

Depending on location and staining properties, intranuclear inclusions have been tentatively classified as Type A (a single, *eosinophilic* particle filling most of the central nuclear area) and Type B (variable numbers and sizes of *basophilic* intranuclear granules). The location and type of intracellular inclusions are highly distinctive of certain viruses.

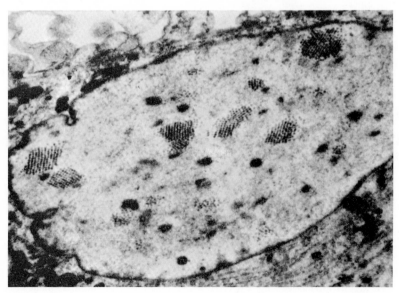

**Figure 17.18** Electron micrograph of an ultrathin cross section of an animal cell 48 hours after infection with a virus (adenovirus type 4). Single virus particles and close packed arrays ("crystals") of virus particles are distributed throughout the nucleus (large, light area filling most of the picture). (From Tousimis and Hilleman: Virology, vol. 4.)

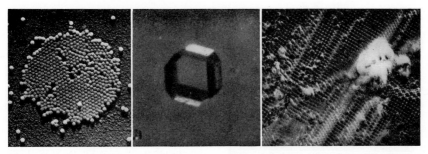

**Figure 17.19**   Polio virus particles in a flat array (left) and in a three-dimensional crystal (center). A cut surface of a crystal (right) shows it to consist of virus particles in orderly arrays. (From Burrows, after Schwerdt.)

VIRUS CRYSTALS.   These are aggregations of virus particles that arrange themselves in infected cells as orderly arrays. If the viruses are spherical or polyhedral, they often appear in electron micrographs like many marbles or buckshot placed as close together as possible in ordered rows (Fig. 17.18). These arrangements are typically three-dimensional. In this arrangement they constitute *crystals* of viruses (Fig. 17.19). The crystal form is characteristic of the virus-cell system involved.

**Resistance and Interference.**   In preceding paragraphs viral infection of a susceptible cell was described as resulting in lysis of the cell or a lytic cycle of the virus. A virus that, on entering a cell, promptly becomes vegetative in the cell and destroys it, liberating many new mature, infective virions, is said to be *virulent*. As indicated, cell lysis is not the only or inevitable result of contact between a cell and a virus particle. The phenomena of *resistance* and *interference* may be exhibited or, as detailed in the next chapter, *lysogeny* may result.

A cell may be wholly *resistant* to a virus because adsorption cannot occur. Failure of adsorption may be caused by the absence of specific receptor sites for that specific kind of virus on the cell surface because of species peculiarities of that cell. A cell species, ordinarily susceptible, may undergo a genetic mutation altering its receptors for a specific virus. Further, receptor sites present on a cell may be destroyed or altered by some nongenetic environmental factor such as heat, pH, enzymes from other cells or viruses, or presence or absence of certain metallic ions.

In *interference,* adsorption of an active virion by a fully susceptible cell may fail because all the specific receptors of the cell have been preempted or saturated by the same sort of specific virions which have been previously inactivated by heat, ultraviolet light or other agents. Adsorption is said to be *interfered with*. Receptors may also be blocked by defective or incomplete virions. Some fully active viruses can interfere with secondary infection by a closely related active virus, presumably by prior pre-emption of receptors specific to both forms of virus. For example, if monkeys are infected with a neurotropic (i.e., adapted specifically to nerve tissue) variant of yellow fever virus they are immediately resistant to the normal or viscerotropic (i.e., adapted to the viscera) yellow fever virus; if rabbits are infected with fibromavirus (which causes a disease of rabbits) they are immediately wholly resistant to the closely related myxomavirus. Irradiated virus of influenza or Newcastle disease of chickens will interfere with infection by an active virus of the same type. The immunizing effect of the Sabin oral polio vaccine, an active virus that immunizes by initiating a mild intestinal infection, may be interfered with by prior presence of several related common intestinal viruses (enteroviruses). (See Classification of Viruses, this chapter.) Interference of the types just described must not be confused with the action of a protein called *interferon,* which is synthesized by tissue cells after they become infected, and which prevents replication of viruses in other cells of the same type and species (Chapter 23).

## PHAGE TYPING OF BACTERIA

The host specificity of viruses has already been discussed. If we continuously propagate a virus in a single type of cell, the virus often becomes highly adapted to that single type of cell and will not infect cells of any other type. In a practical application of this fact, adaptation of phage may be carried to such a degree that a given *strain** of phage becomes so selec-

---

*Any designated specimen or culture, or progeny of same. (See Chapter 30.)

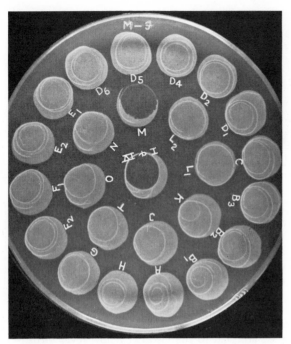

**Figure 17.20**   Use of highly specific bacteriophages to type typhoid bacilli. Separate drops of a culture of *Salmonella typhi* of unknown type have each been mixed with a different type of *Salmonella typhi* bacteriophage (indicated by letters) on the plate. Lysis (circular dark area in the white growth) occurs only where phage type and bacillus type correspond—in this case, type M. The lysis in the center of the plate is a control test. Closely parallel processes are used in the phage typing of staphylococci, *Shigella,* and other bacteria. (Photo courtesy of U. S. Public Health Service, Communicable Disease Center, Atlanta, Ga.)

tive with respect to a single species of bacterium, or even to a certain type or subdivision of that species, that it will not infect any other. Thus, it will distinguish, by its lytic effect, between apparently identical bacteria that are indistinguishable by any other means.

For example, when we propagate a given phage on a certain selected strain of *Salmonella typhi* (typhoid bacillus), the phage becomes so specific for that particular strain of *Sal. typhi* that when appropriately diluted* it will not act on any other strain of the same species. The first highly specific typhoid phage of this sort was designated as *typhoid phage A* and the corresponding susceptible strain of typhoid bacilli as *phage-type A* of *S. typhi*. By a similar process several other phage types of *S. typhi* were discovered and designated by the letters A, B, C, D, E and so forth. Similar bacteriophage typing systems have been developed for several other species of bacteria, notably *Staphylococcus* (see Chapter 33). Phage typing is widely used in medical diagnosis and industry (Fig. 17.20).

## STABILITY OF VIRUSES

Phage and plant viruses such as TMV are in general much more stable chemically and

physically than viruses of warm-blooded vertebrates. Many animal viruses tend to become inactivated on exposure outside the animal or cell in which they multiply. There are wide variations, however; TMV will last for years in infected dried plant tissues, and poliovirus can survive for days or weeks in sewage. Yellow fever virus and many similar viruses, on the contrary, are inactivated merely by storage overnight in blood in a refrigerator, or in a few minutes by dilution of infectious blood in saline solution.

In general, mammalian viruses are inactivated in a few minutes by temperatures like that for pasteurization (63° C. for 30 minutes) (Chapter 45); some phages are inactivated in 10 minutes at temperatures as low as 56° C. There are exceptions, however, an important one being the virus of homologous-serum jaundice, which can withstand boiling for some minutes.

Most viruses are highly resistant to intense cold and will remain infective at −76° C. for a year or longer. They are commonly stored in carbon dioxide ice. They are well preserved by rapid desiccation *in vacuo* (Chapter 19) after rapid freezing (freeze-drying, or *Lyophilization*). Ordinary bactericidal strengths of disinfectants such as phenol, cresol, beta-propiolactone, formaldehyde and halogens are not always effective in dealing with viruses. Certain disinfectants may inactivate some viruses but not all. Surface-active agents, such as soap, some detergents

---

*If not diluted, the selective specificity is masked by an overwhelming action on nearly all forms of typhoid bacilli. The highly specific dilution used for typing is called the *critical dilution*.

**TABLE 17.1   A GROUPING OF SOME MAMMALIAN VIRUSES***

| Virus Groups and Subgroups | Size (mμ) | Symmetry‡ | Capsomeres; Envelope or Mantle | Core† (NA) | Inclusions (intra-) | CPE | Resists: Ether | pH 3.0 | 50° to 60° C. | M/1§ MgCl$_2$ |
|---|---|---|---|---|---|---|---|---|---|---|
| Poxviruses Variola, etc. | 200–250 | helical 100A | Mantle | DNA | cytoplasmic | ... | − | − | + | ... |
| Herpesvirus (herpes simplex) *Herpesvirus hominis* | 180–250 | cuboidal | 162; mantle | DNA | nuclear | Syncytial | − | − | − | − |
| Adenoviruses | 60–85 | cuboidal | 252 | DNA | nuclear d-d†† | d-d lysis | + | + | − | + (−) |
| Papovaviruses Rabbit papilloma Polyoma Human warts | 40–50 | cuboidal | 72 | DNA | ... | ball;‖ vacuo§§ | + | + | | |
| Reoviruses | 70–85 | cuboidal | 92 | RNA | cytoplasmic d-d | | + | + | + | + |
| Myxoviruses | 80–350 | helical 90A | Mantle | RNA | cytoplasmic d-d | Syncytial | − | − | − | − |
| Influenza viruses Paramyxo(influenza)virus | 80–120 | | | | cytoplasmic d-d | | | | | |
| Mumps and Newcastle disease Measles, rinderpest and canine distemper viruses | 70–350 | | | | nuclear and cytoplasmic d-d | | | | | |
| Respiratory syncytial (RS) virus | 90–130 | | | | cytoplasmic d-d | | − | − | ... | ... |
| Rabiesvirus | | | | | | | − | − | ... | ... |
| Arboviruses Serogroup A# Serogroup B Serogroup C Bunyamwera and others | 15–120 | cuboidal | Mantle | RNA | various | various | − | − | − | − |
| Picornaviruses Enteroviruses | 15–30 | cuboidal | 32 | RNA | cytoplasmic nuclear | rapid lysis of cells | + | + | − | + |
| Polioviruses Coxsackie viruses Echoviruses Rhinoviruses | | | | | cytoplasmic | | + | − | ... | ... |

*As in any group of organisms there are always exceptions; the descriptions given are for "typical" or "most" strains.

†DNA viruses in tissue cultures are inhibited by 5-fluoro-2-deoxyuridine; RNA viruses are not so inhibited.

‡Diameters of helical viruses are given in Å.

§Stabilized to heat by divalent cations, e.g., M/1 MgCl$_2$ (cationic thermostabilization)

††d-d = diagnostically distinctive

‖ ball = "ballooning" of cells

§§ Vacuo = vacuolation of cells

# Serogroup A resist proteases; Serogroup B do not.

and bile salts (Chapter 21), can inactivate some viruses readily *in vitro,* especially those having lipids in the envelope (Table 17.1). Ultraviolet light is rapidly destructive to all viruses, since nucleic acids are very sensitive to irradiation. (See Mutagenic Agents; Environment.) Differences in resistance to pH, heat and lipid solvents have been used as bases for classification secondary to type of NA.

## 17.4   CLASSIFICATION OF VIRUSES

Beginning with the discovery of tobacco mosaic virus (*Protovirus tabaci*) by Iwanowski in 1892, continuing discovery of large numbers of viruses and virus-like organisms with one or more obvious characteristics in common has demanded, in the face of chaos, some system of classification. An ordered arrangement (classification) into groups or *taxa* of similar viruses and a ruled system of descriptive nomenclature of the groups and species (*taxonomy*) has gradually evolved. The history of the classification and taxonomy of viruses is similar to that of bacteria, enzymes and other biological groups: one of trials, casual classifications and names, rearrangements and successive improvements with increasing knowledge. Some of these casual classifications and names, based on host, vector or diseases, are outlined in the following paragraphs.

For convenience, viruses may be subdivided primarily on the basis of the hosts* in which they multiply in nature. One or more representatives of most (all?) major divisions of both the animal and plant kingdoms are subject to invasion by one or more viruses; a few examples follow.

Viruses that infect:
  I. *Plants only*
   a. Green plants: tobacco mosaic virus and many others
   b. Blue-green algae
   c. Fungi
     1. Bacteria: bacteriophages
     2. Yeasts: zymophage
     3. Other fungi: e.g., edible mushrooms

---

*In microbiology a host is a plant or animal or single cell that is parasitized by another creature, generally smaller. For example, certain beetles are infected by bacteria; the bacteria are, in turn, infected by virus (bacteriophage). The beetle is host to the bacteria; the bacterium is host to the virus.

  II. *Arthropods only*
   a. Insects: numerous "polyhedral" diseases such as cabbage-looper (*Trichoplusia ni* Hbn) disease; a viral disease of fruit flies (*Drosophila melanogaster*)
  III. *Dual-host viruses*
   a. Arthropods and plants: virus of aster yellows borne by, and also multiplying in, the aster leafhopper (*Macrosteles fascifrons*)
   b. Arthropods and warm-blooded vertebrates: viruses causing diseases in birds and mammals transmitted by and multiplying in arthropods, e.g., Eastern and Western Equine Encephalitis (EEE and WEE) occurring in man, equines and birds and transmitted by mosquitoes (*Culiseta melanura* and others)
  IV. *Warm-blooded vertebrates only:* measles, influenza, fowlpox, chicken sarcoma, rabies, foot-and-mouth disease and many others
  V. *Cold-blooded vertebrates:* pancreatic necrosis of brook trout and others

A convenient classification of the viruses of animal disease may also be based on the types of tissues or organs principally affected. Another sort of classification could be based on mode of transmission and another on type of disease caused. A suggestive list may be constructed as shown in Table 17.2.

Classifications such as those just discussed, although convenient for purposes of discussion, are arbitrary and incomplete and cannot take into consideration the fact that viruses often become modified and cause atypical or entirely different types of disease. Further, the tissue affinities of some viruses can change completely. Also, one is at a loss where to place some viruses, such as that of mumps and fowl plague, in Table 17.1. These groupings were useful when little was known of viruses except that they caused disease.

In the sixth (1948) edition of "Bergey's Manual of Determinative Bacteriology," viruses were listed as the Order Virales with three suborders: Phagineae, Phytophagineae and Zoophagineae (bacterial viruses, plant viruses and animal viruses). The viruses were named according to the binomial Linnean system. However, agreement on final classification and nomenclature of viruses is still far from complete, and those currently in use (based on newer information) differ completely from those given in the 1948 edition of Bergey's Manual. (See

**TABLE 17.2**  A CRUDE CLASSIFICATION OF SOME ANIMAL VIRUSES

| Group | Tissue Principally and Visibly Affected* | Types of Disease Caused | Mode of Transmission* |
|---|---|---|---|
| Dermotropic | Skin; mucous membranes of nose and mouth | Various pox-like diseases (smallpox, fowl pox), herpes, warts, measles | Close contact, probably sputum; fomites |
| Neurotropic | Nervous tissues | Poliomyelitis<br>Rabies<br>Various encephalitides | Feces, sputum<br>Bites of animals<br>Mosquitoes and other arthropods |
| Pneumotropic | Respiratory tract | Influenza, "colds," etc.<br>Pneumonitis | Nasal and oral discharges |
| Viscerotropic | Various internal organs | Yellow fever<br>Dengue<br>Louping ill<br>Rift Valley fever | Mosquitoes<br>Mosquitoes<br>Ticks<br>Mosquitoes |
| Neoplastic | Various | Fowl sarcoma<br>Fibroma of rabbits<br>Myxoma of rabbits<br>Fowl leukemia | Unknown<br>Unknown<br>Dust, fur, contact<br>Unknown |
| Enteric | Gastrointestinal tract | Epidemic diarrhea, nausea and vomiting, polio<br>Polio-like diseases | Probably by hands, foods and objects contaminated with feces |

* Under natural conditions.

discussion of this problem in the seventh edition of Bergey, page 985.)

**Modern Classification.** Current methods of classifying viruses are based to only a minor extent on type of disease caused (e.g., polioviruses, poxviruses, herpesviruses). Recent groupings depend largely on detailed and accurate knowledge of physical and chemical properties of viruses. These data have accumulated only during the last decade and continue to accumulate daily.

The entire group of viruses, plant and animal, is currently divided primarily into two types on the basis of the kind of NA in the core: DNA or RNA. Each of these two groups is then subdivided on the basis of other characteristics.

In one system the viruses of vertebrates are dichotomously arranged on the basis of NA and several physical characters (Fig. 17.21).

One semiofficial system currently in use is based on: type of NA; symmetry of nucleo-

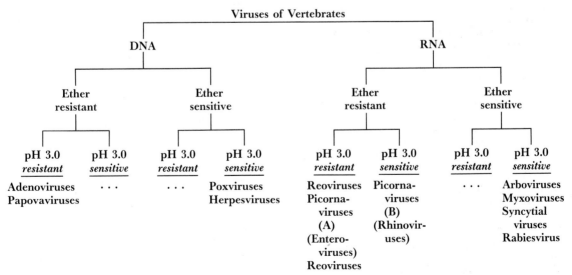

**Figure 17.21**  Dichotomous arrangement of some animal viruses on the basis of type of NA, ether sensitivity (lipoid envelope) and resistance to pH 3.

capsid; presence or absence of envelope; and number of capsomeres. The nomenclature in this system, though now well established by usage, is not wholly consistent with rules of nomenclature and is, to some extent, arbitrary. A partial list of mammalian viruses based upon it is shown in Table 17.1. In a more recent system all of the viruses, bacterial, plant and animal, are grouped in the Phylum Vira. This is divided into subphyla, classes, orders, suborders and families on the basis of four major features called "essential integrants."

1. Type of NA: DNA or RNA.
2. Symmetry: helical, cuboidal or binal (binal refers to possession of head and tail by viruses like bacteriophage).
3. Presence or absence of envelope around the nucleocapsid.
4. Diameter of helical nucleocapsids; number of capsomeres in cuboidal viruses.

The families established on these four integrants are named according to rules adapted to viruses by a single, generally recognized authority, The Provisional Committee on Nomenclature of Viruses (P.C.N.V.) established by the executive committee of the International Association of Microbiological Societies. The P.C.N.V., headed by Sir Christopher Andrews, provisionally adopted in slightly modified form a system drawn up by Lwoff, Horne and Tournier. Neither perfection nor immutability is claimed for the system but, as the first of its kind, it marks a milestone in the science of virology. An abbreviated version follows.

Phylum Vira
   Subphylum Deoxyvira (DNA viruses)
     Class Deoxyhelica (helical symmetry)
       Order Chitovirales (Gr. *chiton* = tunic or envelope)
         Family Poxviridae 100 Å* (poxviruses) ("large viruses")
     Class Deoxycubica (cubical symmetry)
       Order Haplovirales (Gr. *haploos* = simple: i.e., without envelope)

| | | |
|---|---|---|
| Family Microviridae | 12 caps† | (phage φX174) |
| Parvoviridae | 32 | (a rat virus) |
| Papilloviridae | 72 | (papovaviruses) |
| Adenoviridae | 252 | (adenoviruses) |
| Iridoviridae | 812 | (plant viruses) |
| Inoviridae | ? | (fd phage) |

       Order Peplovirales (mantle viruses)
         Family Herpesviridae 162 caps. (Herpesviruses)
     Class Deoxybinala (viruses with head and tail)

---

*Å = Angstrom units (0.1 mμ) in diameter (helical viruses).

†Caps or numbers refer to numbers of capsomeres (cuboidal viruses).

       Order Urovirales
         Family Phagoviridae (bacteriophages)*
   Subphylum Ribovira (RNA viruses)
     Class Ribohelica (helical symmetry)
       (Order Rhabdovirales (Gr. *rhabdos* = rodlike)
        Suborder Rigidovirales

| | | |
|---|---|---|
| Family Dolichoviridae | 120–130 Å | } Plant |
| Protoviridae | 150 Å | } viruses |
| Pachyviridae | 200 Å | |

        Suborder Flexiviridales

| | | |
|---|---|---|
| Family Leptoviridae | 100–110 Å | } Plant |
| Mesoviridae | 120–130 Å | } viruses |
| Adroviridae | 150 Å | |

       Order Sagovirales (L. *sagum* = mantle)

| | |
|---|---|
| Family Myxoviridae | 90 Å |
| Paramyxoviridae | 180 Å |
| Stomatoviridae | . . . |

     Class Ribocubica (cuboidal symmetry)
       Order Gymnovirales

| | | |
|---|---|---|
| Family Napoviridae | 32 caps. | A. Plant viruses; B. Picornaviruses |
| Reoviridae | 92 | (Reoviruses) |

       Order Togavirales (L. *toga* = Roman mantle)
         Family Arboviridae . . . (Arboviruses)

Properties that determine genera within families include (for example):

1. NA: base sequence, relative numbers of bases, number of nucleotides.
2. Capsomeres: structure, antigenic properties, molecular weight.
3. Capsid: number of capsomeres, antigenic properties, reaction to heat, pH, other physical and chemical agents.

Additional features for generic and specific differentiations include data on envelope or mantle, enzymes, mode of development, sensitivity to interferon, specificity for host, virulence, clinical effect.

Examples of some viruses in two or three terminologies are:

| | |
|---|---|
| Poxviruses: | |
|   Variola (smallpox) | *Poxvirus variolae* |
|   Sheep pox | *Pustulovirus ovis* |
| Papovaviruses: | |
|   Rabbit myxoma | *Fibromavirus myxomatosis* |
|   Shope papilloma | *Papillomavirus sylvilagi* |
|   Polyomavirus | *Polyomavirus neoformans* |
| Adenoviruses: Adenovirus 5 | *Adenovirus (hominis) quintus* |
| *Herpes simplex:* Herpesvirus | *Herpesvirus hominis* |
| Phage T2: | *Phagovirus (coli) T secundus* |
| Tobacco mosaic: | *Protovirus tabaci* |
| Reovirus: | *Reovirus (mammalis) primus* |
| Myxo- or syncytial: | |
|   Influenzavirus A | *Myxovirus (influenzae) A* |
|   Rabiesvirus | *Rabiesvirus canis* |
|   Parainfluenzae | *Paramyxovirus (parainfluenzae) primus* |
|   Respiratory syncytial (RS) virus | *Bronchovirus syncytialis* |

---

*There are also phages with RNA.

Arboviruses: Arbovirus WEE    *Arbovirus occidentalis*
Picornaviruses:
   Poliomyelitis type I      *Poliovirus primus*
   Coxsackievirus type A I    *Coxsackievirus (A) primus*
   Echovirus I      *Echovirus (hominis) primus*
   Rhinovirus I      *Rhinovirus (hominis) primus*

Each species name in the right-hand column is that of the type species of that genus. It is seen that many familiar names have been retained as *nomina conservanda*. Names in parentheses are of subgenera.

## PARASITIC STATUS OF VIRUSES

Most bacteria can live independently of higher plants and animals and can thrive in the outer world. They can synthesize their cell substance from simple minerals alone or from inert organic foods from the outer environment. However, some parasitic species of bacteria appear to have lost some of their ability to adapt to the outer world, through long generations of life in a sheltered environment such as the animal body, in which much of their food is synthesized for them. They tend to become sensitive and dependent. Such parasitic bacteria must receive from their host, in an already synthesized state, complex nutrient materials from the blood, or very complex substances such as polypeptides and vitamins. Their demands on the host depend on the degree of parasitism (or dependence on host) to which they have evolved. However, with one or two possible exceptions, they are not absolutely restricted, as are the viruses, to life inside host cells. Parasitic bacteria are mainly and typically extracellular.

Advancing a step further, we may imagine that certain bacteria have undergone such mutations in size and metabolism toward auxotrophy that they can actually enter the host cell and become an *obligate intracellular parasite*. As such they are capable of living only there at the expense of the proteins and other essential constituents of the cell, having lost many of their own synthetic and other physiological powers. Indeed, just such visible but extremely minute, intracellular, bacterium-like parasites are well known, and constitute the Family Rickettsiaceae (in Bergey's Manual) and the PLT group or Family Chlamydiaceae.

As the few remaining synthetic powers are lost through genetic mutations (as seen in rickettsias and chlamydias) size decreases until nothing remains but a bit of substance which has the properties of the viruses—that is, it is capable of "life" only if furnished with the enzymic

mechanisms, nutritive resources and sources of energy of some particular animal or plant to which it has become adapted. It would, "as it were, live a borrowed life, truly the supreme summit of parasitism."* Such a parasite would possess, as its sole, essential part, only the NA core capable of transmitting the specific properties of the virus.

Thus it is hypothesized that viruses have originated through the development of parasitism to its ultimate perfection—an evolutionary process of a highly successful sort, if we regard first-rate parasites as the goal of nature. On the other hand, viruses may represent an involutionary or degenerative trend, if we regard the independent, self-supporting creature as the universal ideal. The latter, carried to its logical, nonparasitic extreme, could be either the completely autotrophic† type or the heterotrophic‡ type, if the evidence for chemical evolution of organic substances is correctly interpreted.

---

*Laidlaw, "Virus Diseases and Viruses," 1939. By permission of The Macmillan Company.

†Capable of living on exclusively inorganic matter, including carbon dioxide as a source of carbon. Many such organisms are known.

‡Dependent on an organic source of carbon such as glucose.

## SUPPLEMENTARY READING

Akai, H., Gateff, E., Davis, L. E., and Schneiderman, H. A.: Virus-like particles in normal and tumorous tissues of *Drosophila.* Science, *157*:810, 1967.

Andrews, Sir Christopher: Viruses of Vertebrates. 2nd Ed. The Williams and Wilkins Co., Baltimore. 1967.

Arber, W.: Bacteriophage lysogeny. Thirteenth Symposium, Symbiotic Associations, Soc. Gen. Microbiol., London. 1963.

Arber, W.: Host-controlled modification of bacteriophage. Ann. Rev. Microbiol., *19*:365, 1965.

Bradley, D. E., and Dewar, C. A.: Intracellular changes in cells of *Escherichia coli* infected with a filamentous bacteriophage. J. Gen. Virol., *1*:179, 1967.

Cairns, J., Stent, G. S., and Watson, J. D., editors: Phage and the Origins of Molecular Biology. Cold Spring Harbor Laboratory, Cold Spring Harbor, N. Y. 1967.

Colter, J. S., and Paranchych, W., editors: The Molecular Biology of Viruses. Academic Press, New York. 1967.

Coyette, J., and Calberg-Bacq, C.-M.: Morphological characteristics of three new actinophages. J. Gen. Virol., *1*:13, 1967.

Cummings, D. J., Chapman, V. A., De Long, S. S., and Mondale, L.: Induced structural defects in T-even bacteriophage. J. Virol., *1*:193, 1967.

Easterbrook, K. B.: Morphology of deoxyribonucleic acid extracted from cores of vaccinia virus. J. Virol., *1*:643, 1967.

Fraser, F.: Viruses and Molecular Biology. The Macmillan Co., New York. 1967.

Herold, F., and Munz, K.: Morphological studies of maize mosaic virus I. J. Gen. Virol., *1*:227, 1967.

Horiuchi, K., and Adelberg, E. A.: Growth of male-specific bacteriophage in *Proteus mirabilis* harboring F-genotes derived from *Escherichia coli.* J. Bact., *89*:1231, 1965.

Levintow, L.: The biochemistry of virus replication. Ann. Rev. Biochem., *34*:487, 1965.

Lodish, H. F., and Zinder, N. D.: Replication of the RNA bacteriophage f2. Science, *152*:372, 1966.

Luria, S. E.: General Virology. John Wiley and Sons, Inc., New York. 1967.

Lwoff, A., and Tournier, P.: The classification of viruses. Ann. Rev. Microbiol., *20*:45, 1966.

Maramorosch, K., and Koprowski, H., editors: Methods in Virology. Academic Press, Inc., New York. 1967 et seq.

Nagai, K., and Hammon, W. McD.: Plaque studies with certain Group B arboviruses I. Proc. Soc. Exp. Biol. Med., *117*:154, 1964.

Safferman, R. S., and Morris, M. E.: Observations on the occurrence, distribution and seasonal incidence of blue-green algal viruses. Appl. Microbiol., *15*:1219, 1967.

Schade, S. Z., and Adler, J.: Purification and chemistry of bacteriophage x. J. Virol., *1*:591, 1967.

Simon, E.: Recombination in bacteriophage T4: a mechanism. Science, *150*:760, 1965.

Smith, K. M., Brown, R. M., Walne, P. L., and Goldstein, D. A.: Electron microscopy of the infection process of the blue-green alga virus. Virology. *30*:182, 1966.

Spiegelman, S.: An *in vitro* analysis of a replicating molecule. Am. Sci., *55*:221, 1967.

Welker, N. E.: Purification and properties of a thermophilic bacteriophage lytic enzyme. J. Virol., *1*:617, 1967.

Wilner, B. I.: A Classification of the Major Groups of Human and Other Animal Viruses. 3rd ed. Burgess Publishing Co., Minneapolis. 1965.

Wittman, H. G., and Scholtissek, C.: Biochemistry of viruses. Ann. Rev. Biochem., *35*:299, 1966.

Yarus, M. J., and Sinsheimer, R. L.: The process of infection with bacteriophage $\phi$X174. XIII. Evidence for an essential bacterial "site." J. Virol., *1*:135, 1967.

Zinder, N. D.: RNA phages. Ann. Rev. Microbiol., *19*:455, 1965.

# Chapter 18

## THE VIRUSES

## Genetic Phenomena, Lysogeny, Transduction

### RECAPITULATION

At this point it may be helpful to recapitulate what has been said of the lytic phase of phage reproduction as exemplified by $T_2$ phage. Infection (specific adsorption and penetration; beginning of the eclipse period) by phage causes the immediate cessation of synthesis of nearly all bacterial enzymes and mRNA and institutes a total immunity to superinfection by the same type of phage. Cell DNA is then enzymically degraded to its component nucleotides by means of "early" (phage-induced) enzymes and possibly by some cell enzymes. The phage-induced enzymes commandeer the amino acid pool that would have been used to synthesize cell proteins. With these the phage DNA, using cell ribosomes and cell tRNA, induces the formation of new enzymes, notably a *DNA polymerase system* that synthesizes new phage DNA and complete genomes from the segments of the degraded cell DNA, combined with newly synthesized nucleotides and certain molecules from the environment. Phage-coded mRNA is then synthesized instead of cell-coded mRNA. The new mRNA guides synthesis, by the cell ribosomes and cell tRNA, of the protein capsids of the virions. The process of phage maturation (assembly of genomes and protein coverings into complete virions) then commences. The *eclipse period* ends with completion of the first, new, infective virion intracellularly. After some minutes cell *lysis* liberates all of the newly formed virions, terminating the *latent phase*.

## 18.1 LYSOGENY

A virus may contact a susceptible cell and the viral NA may enter that cell without causing immediate lysis. In a phage infection, lysis may fail to occur or be delayed because the phage is not fully *virulent* for that cell; i.e., the virus NA is not able to initiate the immediate, unrestricted, vegetative replication of phage that is necessary to the lytic cycle. The phage is said to have undergone a change (*reduction*) to what is designated as the *temperate* state. When the phage becomes temperate it becomes closely associated with, or actually a segment of, the single, circular, bacterial chromosome or *replicon*.* Just what determines the change to the temperate state is not clear. A phage may be invariably highly virulent in one type of cell under one set of growth conditions, yet temperate in the same type of cell under other conditions or in another type of cell. Note that the terms virulent and temperate are applicable *only* to phage.

Unlike the rapid and unrestrained replications of the virulent virus, the temperate viral genome is restricted to replication synchronously with, seemingly as part of, the cell genome. In this state viral proteins are not synthesized and no separate or complete virions appear. Because

---

*A *replicon* is any unit of DNA that replicates. The term includes chromosomes and certain chromosome-like bodies called *episomes* that replicate like separate chromosomes.

the temperate virus is not itself a complete virus but, as will appear, can suddenly become one, it is spoken of as a *prophage*. The phenomenon has been described fully only for the bacterium-phage system. The prophage may remain in, or closely attached to, the cell genome and be distributed to the cell progeny as part of the cell genome for millions of generations. Unless some peculiar influence is brought to bear, the presence of the viral NA in the cell may never be suspected. One clue to its presence is the immunity of the cell to superinfection by that specific virus. Another clue is its inducibility.

**Induction.**   If a cell containing a temperate virus is subjected to certain influences such as ultraviolet radiation or agents such as hydrogen peroxide, the prophage is immediately activated. It becomes vegetative and at once begins a lytic cycle as previously described. It is said to have been *induced*. Induction often occurs spontaneously.

A bacterium containing an inducible prophage may thus be lysed at any time and, because virions are liberated, contribute to the lysis of other cells. Such bacteria are said to be *lysogenic;* the phenomenon of reduction of a phage to temperance and association of its replicon with the bacterial genome is called *lysogeny* (Fig. 18.1). The term lysogeny is applicable

only to phages. Similar states, e.g., latency (see farther on), appear to exist in some animal cell-virus systems but differ in some respects from true lysogeny.

**Lysogenic Immunity.**   A cell containing a prophage (a lysogenic cell) is immune to super-infection by any other virion of that specific kind of virus even though an infective virion may be adsorbed and penetrate into the cell. Immunity thus conferred on a cell by viral infection appears to be caused in part by the immediate synthesis, not of lytic enzymes as in the lytic cycle, but of a *repressor substance* that represses vegetative replication of any secondarily entering genome of the same specific kind of virus. It appears also that any given, specific phage replicon has its own definite place or *locus* of attachment to (or in?) the cell replicon. If, for a given virus, this locus is already occupied by a viral replicon, it cannot serve for the attachment of an additional replicon of that identical viral type. However, one or more viruses of some other type(s) may enter the cell and either destroy it at once or be severally reduced to the temperate state if there are specific, unoccupied loci in the cell replicon for their attachment.

The immunity of lysogenic cells is called *lysogenic immunity*. Lysogenic immunity to a

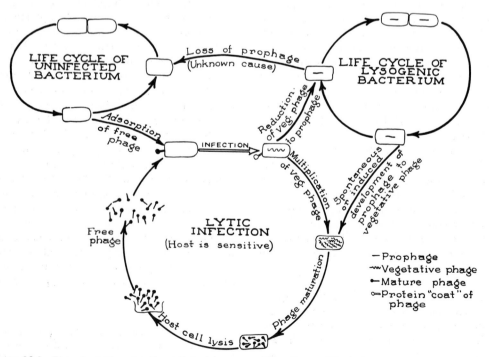

**Figure 18.1**   Phage-host life cycles. For explanation see text. (From Jawetz, Melnick and Adelberg: Review of Medical Microbiology, 6th ed., Lange Medical Publications, 1964.)

given virus persists only so long as that provirus is present in the cell. If, as sometimes happens, the cell is "cured" of its lysogenicity; i.e., if the prophage is inactivated or for unknown reasons fails to be transmitted to a daughter cell, lysogenic immunity of that cell and of its progeny to that type of virus disappears. Note that lysogenic *immunity* and *resistance* of a cell to viral infection are two distinct phenomena dependent on totally different mechanisms. (Explain.) Compare also with interferon.

Many strains of lysogenic bacteria are well known and are widely used in virological investigations. They are designated by adding to their specific name, parenthetically, as a suffix, the designation of the prophage that they carry; thus the lambda (λ) phage in the lysogenic strain of *Escherichia coli* known as K12 is indicated as *E. coli* K12 (λ).

## 18.2  COLICINS, C-FACTOR AND PROPHAGE

Colicins are proteins or polypeptides released into the surrounding medium by certain strains of *Escherichia coli.* Colicins are extremely lethal to other strains of bacteria of the same species or to closely related species. A single molecule of colicin, once adsorbed to a susceptible cell, kills that cell. Colicins are often compared with antibiotics but colicins are proteins and thus differ markedly from the substances (e.g., penicillin; Chapter 22) commonly thought of as antibiotics. Colicins are specific as to the strains for which they are lethal; i.e., they will adsorb only to certain strains (Fig. 18.2). Adsorption of colicin appears to occur, like adsorption of phage, at specific receptor sites on the outer cell surface. It is notable that some of these receptors serve also for the adsorption of certain bacteriophages. The exact mode of action and the biological significance of colicins remain to be fully elucidated.

Various colicins are lettered and numbered primarily according to the letter-number (if any) of the producing strain. Some strains of *E. coli* may produce more than one type of colicin; these are often given letters such as H, K or E. For example, a colicin produced by a strain of *E. coli* designated as R450 might be identified as colicin R450-K. Classification and nomenclature of colicins have not been fully systematized.

The ability to produce colicin constitutes the property of *colicinogenicity.* Colicinogenicity

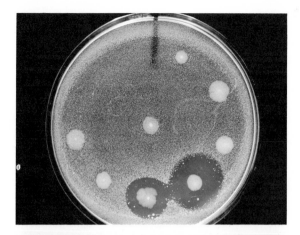

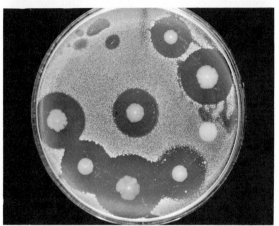

**Figure 18.2** Action of colicins (bacteriocins). The two Petri plates contain nutrient agar, the entire surface of which was inoculated with two different types of dysentery bacilli (*Shigella boydii* 2). Growth of these bacteria is seen as smooth, grey, overall pebbling. Colicin-producing bacteria were "spot" inoculated at center and several points around the periphery corresponding in the two plates. Action of colicin is seen as inhibition of growth in dark circular zones around "spot" colonies of the colicin producers. The two types of *S. boydii* 2 (both plates) differed in their susceptibility to the various colicins. (Courtesy Drs. Ikari, Robbins, and Parr: Proc. Soc. Exp. Biol. & Med., vol. 98.)

appears to be a transferable property of bacteria dependent on the presence of an episome like the F factor. The episome of colicinogenicity is called the *C-factor,* or *Cf.* Unlike F, Cf does not appear to integrate with the cell chromosome. It is transferred by conjugation (cell contact) but not in association with the cell chromosome or F. It may also be transferred by transduction. Presence of Cf confers immunity to the colicin produced, though the colicin may be adsorbed on the producing cell. This immunity to colicin suggests the immunity to superinfection conferred on a cell by the presence of a prophage, though the mechanisms of the immunity would seem to differ.

The presence of Cf does not necessarily result in production of colicin. However, like prophage, Cf can be *induced* by ultraviolet light and other agents; it then becomes active and causes colicin production. Thus, there are similarities (Table 18.1) between prophage, F and Cf, though they are clearly not identical. There is evidence that imperfect or defective phages are associated with the presence of Cf. Whether Cf is, or is influenced by, incomplete phage is currently under investigation. Cf's, or Cols, and the colicins they induce, differ considerably among themselves in physiological and morphological characters.

In the foregoing paragraphs colicins have been used as a model to describe what has been found to be a whole class of these curious microbicidal agents. Similar lethal agents are produced by numerous other species of bacteria. The more inclusive term *bacteriocins* is commonly used to include the entire group. Some bacteriocins are named according to the species that produce them, e.g., pesticins and staphylococcins. Perhaps the symbol for the episome group should be Bf (bacteriocin factor) instead of Cf.

## 18.3   INAPPARENT INFECTION

Any infection, viral or otherwise, in which the infectious agent multiplies in the host without producing visible or sensible (*clinical*) evidence of disease is said to be *inapparent* or *subclinical*. Animals or plants that have such inapparent infections often can transmit the infectious agent to other organisms. They are said to be *carriers* of the infectious agent. The carrier state is very common at all phylogenetic levels throughout the living world. In healthy animal carriers of bacterial or viral pathogens, the bacteria or viruses are usually readily seen or cultivated in body fluids and tissues or tissue cultures.

**The Carrier Tissue Culture.** In viral infections of animal cells there are several states of inapparent infection in which the cell and the virus seem to have arrived at some sort of still obscure "peaceful coexistence" or lysogeny-like equilibrium. In some cases a virus cannot be demonstrated by culture or C.P.E., though there may be strong indirect evidence of its presence; the virus is said to be "*occult.*" In other situations a demonstrable virus may be present and multiplying vegetatively in the cells,

**TABLE 18.1   PROPERTIES AND EFFECTS OF EPISOMES**

| Factor | Effect of Induction | Attachment to chromosome | Replication | Mode of Transfer | Distinctive Effect of Presence |
|---|---|---|---|---|---|
| F | . . . | Attaches to chromosome at any site; may remain unattached | Replicates synchronously with chromosome whether attached or not | Transferred by conjugation | Confers mating ability (F⁺); sometimes Hfr state |
| Cf or Col | Induces colicin production | Rarely if ever attaches to chromosome or F | Replicates synchronously with chromosome | Transferred by conjugation and by transduction | Confers ability to synthesize colicin (bacteriocin) |
| Prophage | Induces separation of prophage from chromosome and replication as virulent phage | Attaches at a specific site of chromosome | Replicates synchronously with chromosome only when attached (integrated); very rapidly when free | Transferred as part of cell chromosome when attached; otherwise independent as mature, free phage | Confers new genetic properties (phage conversion) and property of lysogenicity |

but fail to kill them. In such situations infective virions may mature slowly and be liberated continuously from the cells over a considerable period, before death of the cell occurs or other evidence of infection is detectable.

In infected tissue-cell cultures of this nature a virus may persist in many successive subcultures. The tissue cells multiply fast enough to more than replace all cells destroyed by the virus. Only a few cells are infected at a time, because the ratio of number of active virions present at any one time to the number of susceptible cells (the *multiplicity* of the virus) is low, possibly only 1:1000. Such a culture, constantly carrying and releasing small numbers of fully virulent virus particles, is said to be a *carrier culture.* The carrier state is sometimes called a *chronic infection.* Eventually, only resistant mutant cells may survive, with ultimate disappearance of the virus, or the virus may suddenly gain the ascendancy and kill all of the cells. Much depends on how favorable the conditions are for growth of the cells and for multiplication of the virus inside the cells.

**Latency.** Latency is well exemplified by infection with the virus of *herpes simplex* ("fever blister"). An initial infection, common during childhood, can be quite severe, sometimes fatal. Survival and recovery appears to involve a persistence of the virus, throughout life, in a latent state. In this state the virus is present but not multiplying. The virus appears to be made manifest (activated? induced?) readily enough by such influences as sunburn (ultraviolet irradiation) and increase in body temperature (fever) due to other infection (hence, *"fever blisters"*). There are numerous other viruses that appear to exist in the same latent state.

In any comparison between bacterial lysogeny and the carrier state or latency in viral infections of eucaryotic plants or animal cells, the following structural details must be remembered. Bacteria are procaryons with a single "miniature," chromosome-like genome not secluded within a nuclear membrane, and most bacteria have a thick cell wall. In animal cells there are usually several different chromosomes; the nucleus is surrounded by a nuclear membrane, endoplasmic reticulum and other cytoplasmic organelles; and there is no cell wall. Mechanisms of infection differ. Entry of at least some animal viruses, e.g., poxviruses, into animal cells appears to depend on passage of the complete virion through the plasmalemma (Gr. *lemma* = husk or rind) by a pinocytosis-like process followed by intracellular, enzymic "un-

coating" (removal of envelope, capsid and accessory materials) that must precede liberation of the naked core NA inside the cell. Further studies of viral mechanisms in animal cells will doubtless reveal many other variations from the familiar *E. coli*-phage system.

## 18.4   SOME GENETIC PHENOMENA IN VIRUSES

**Lysogenic Conversion.** The establishment of a prophage in the genome of a bacterial cell results in the addition of new genetic units. This commonly alters the heritable characters of the cell, often so profoundly that the bacterium becomes essentially a new species, except for the fact that the prophage is apt to leave at any time, taking its genetic characters with it. A genetic change caused by addition of genetic characters by infection with a virus is sometimes called *infective heredity.* It is also known as *lysogenic conversion* or, in the case of phage, *phage conversion.* For example, *Corynebacterium diphtheriae* is the bacillus which causes diphtheria (see Chapter 35). The principal effects of diphtheria on the patient are those caused by diphtheria *toxin,* a poisonous protein waste product which the toxigenic bacteria secrete whenever they grow in a suitable medium in a laboratory, or in a patient's throat. Strains of *C. diphtheriae* are often found which are *atoxigenic* although typical in all other respects; that is, they appear never to have had (or to have lost?) the power to produce toxin. In 1951 it was first observed by Freeman that a certain strain of temperate bacteriophage from toxigenic *Corynebacterium diphtheriae,* when propagated in completely nontoxigenic strains of *C. diphtheriae,* caused lysogenic conversion to toxigenicity in the formerly nontoxigenic strains. The newly altered strains remained toxigenic only as long as the prophage was present. Cells that lost the phage lost their toxigenicity. The toxigenicity of some other bacteria may likewise be based on lysogenic conversion.

DEFECTIVE PHAGES. A phage not only contributes new genetic properties to a lysogenized cell but is itself subject to genetic mutation, as is any genetic material. For example, mutation in a prophage may destroy its power to mature. Even though it may confer immunity to superinfection on induction, as by ultraviolet irradiation, it reveals its defective state by failing to develop into a vegetative virus. Although the infected cell may die, no mature, infective virus particles are released. The provirus is said to be *defective*. It produces *incomplete* or defective virus particles, perhaps minus their protein coating or unassembled fragments of virions. Some may have multiple tails or no tails. Sometimes these incomplete virus particles may actually cause the cell to lyse, but the incomplete virus particles thus released cannot infect other cells (Fig. 17.13). Such defective prophages may act as bacteriocinigenic factors, as previously mentioned.

**Complementation.** Some viruses are defective in such a way that they cannot multiply normally or at all. However, they may be helped to multiply if their defect can be compensated for by a second helper virus which may also be defective in another locus. The two *complement* each other. Neither alone can cause cytolysis but together they can do so. This relationship is suggestive of syntrophism or satellitism as observed among bacteria, though the mechanisms are apparently quite different. The phenomenon of complementation and helper viruses is of interest in studies of viruses as a cause of malignant growths (page 233).

**Phenotypic Mixing.** Although infection of a bacterial cell by phage precludes superinfection with an identical phage, mixed, simultaneous infections by two or even three related, but not identical, phages can occur, presumably since each has a different locus of attachment to the bacterial replicon. In such mixed infections one or more phages may mature at the same time. In the process of assembly, interchange can occur with some of the "prefabricated" parts such as heads, tails, DNA or proteins. The resulting mature phages (*phenotypes*) exhibit mixtures of the characters of the various phages involved. The process is spoken of as *phenotypic mixing*. Note that the molecular structures of the respective genomes have not changed; i.e., neither genetic mutation nor genetic recombination has occurred. The change is not heritable. On later reproduction the proper capsid protein is produced.

**Copy Choice.** If two different kinds of phage simultaneously infect a single cell, each virus synthesizes its own DNA. However, the combining strands of one helix can combine, to varying extents and in various segments, with strand segments of the other: a sort of "crossing over" process of genetic recombination called *copy choice*. When different phages thus mix and lysis occurs, recombinant phage progeny are found that exhibit heritable properties of both parent phages. If, as can happen,

three different phages infect a single cell, repeated partial pairings between one and another of the strands of DNA from three virions can occur, and progeny can be found to exhibit some properties of all three—they have three parents! Thus, viruses appear to be especially favored in the evolutionary struggle for existence as compared with cells that reproduce only asexually.

**Transduction.** As we have seen in previous sections (Chapter 14) genetic material may be transferred from one cell to another by conjugation and transformation. *Transduction,* another mechanism of genetic transfer, is the transmission of a portion of the chromosome of one bacterial cell (*a*), into another bacterial cell (*b*), by a matured, lytic bacteriophage that becomes temperate on entering bacterial cell *b*. The phenomenon of transduction was first observed by Zinder and Lederberg (Nobel Prize winner with Beadle and Tatum) in 1952.

The phage NA, initially an integrated part of the genome of bacterium *a*, has been induced or activated and has separated from the cell chromosome. In so doing it has exchanged a bit of itself for a bit of the genome of bacterium *a*. This is an abnormal and faulty separation and occurs relatively rarely. The phage now infects cell *b*. The bit of bacterial *a* genome (sometimes called an *exogenote*) carried into bacterium *b* is said to have been *transduced* from *a* to *b* by the phage. The genome of the recipient cell *b* is called an *endogenote*. The genome of *b* (endogenote), after the addition and integration of the exogenote, is called a *heterogenote* (Fig. 18.3). Since both the phage NA *and* the *a* exogenote can add new genetic characters to a recipient cell, it is evident that both viral conversion and transduction can occur simultaneously.

If the exogenote fails to be integrated into the endogenote, it may manifest its phenotypic character in that single generation, but it is not replicated and disappears from the cell. *Abortive transduction* is said to have occurred. It is the most common event in transduction.

Some phages can transduce any of a variety of genetic units of the donor cell. This is spoken of as general or *nonspecific transduction*. For example, in the Genus *Salmonella*,* some phages have transduced various special nutrient requirements (auxotrophies), enzymic functions,

---

*The genus of gram-negative rods containing the bacillus of typhoid and paratyphoid fevers and named for the American bacteriologist, Salmon.

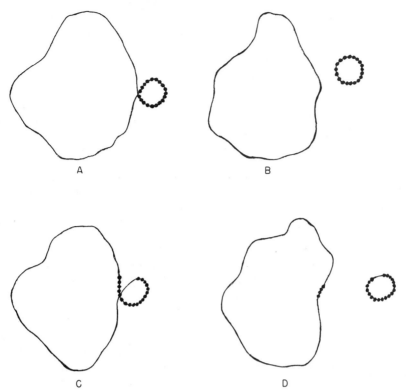

**Figure 18.3**   A and B: normal separation of prophage DNA from its association with the chromosomal replicon; C and D: aberrant separation resulting in the incorporation of a piece of chromosomal DNA into the phage DNA, and vice versa. (From Braun: Bacterial Genetics, 2nd ed. W. B. Saunders Co., 1965.)

resistance or susceptibility to various antibiotics, motility, and the chemical makeup of the flagella. Some phages carry only the specific genetic unit to which they are most closely linked in the genome of the donor cell.

It is worth noting here some points of differentiation between the types of genetic transfer among bacteria. In *transformation* the transforming NA exists in a free, soluble, naked condition and is completely vulnerable to the action of pH, electrolytes or specific enzymes (DNA-ase or RNA-ase). This is not true in *conjugation* or *transduction*. In these the transferred NA either remains intracellular or is inside a virion and so is not accessible to any extracellular enzymes or other deleterious influences.

*Viral conversion* is differentiated from transduction by the fact that in viral conversion the altered characters of the cell are caused by the *viral* NA and, as in lysogenic immunity, depend on the continued presence of prophage in the converted cell. The characters leave when prophage leaves (or is lost by failure to be transmitted to a daughter cell). In transduction, on the contrary, the altered characters of the trans-

ductant are due to bacterial (not viral) NA. The exogenote remains as part of the heterogenote whether the prophage stays or leaves; i.e., a permanent genetic mutation has occurred.

## 18.5   SOME ANTIVIRAL SUBSTANCES

### CHEMOTHERAPY

*Chemotherapy* is the treatment of infections with specific chemical substances. These may be antibiotics, sulfonamides or, in preantibiotic days, empirical treatments such as malaria with quinine and syphilis with mercury compounds or arsenicals (salvarsan or 606 of Paul Ehrlich; Nobel Prize winner). Typical modern chemotherapeutic agents are effective in amounts that are harmless to the infected host but that inhibit or destroy the infecting agent. Typically, the inhibition or destruction of the parasite is achieved through chemical combination of the chemotherapeutic agent with a specific enzyme, coenzyme, vitamin, or other essential metabolic mechanism of the parasite. In their highly specific action, chemotherapeutic agents differ markedly from the wholesale, generalized, destructive action of disinfectants like the cresols, bichloride of mercury and the halogens. These, in effective amounts inside the body, would be fatal to the host as well as to the parasite.

The sulfonamide drugs and the antibiotics derived from bacteria and molds, e.g., streptomycin and penicillin, in general act on cellular parasites such as bacteria or protozoa by interference with certain specific enzyme systems, most of which are not present in viruses. Viruses are not vulnerable to most such enzyme-inhibiting chemotherapeutic agents. However, viral NA must be synthesized if viruses are to multiply. An agent that interferes with synthesis of viral NA, or that causes the formation of faulty or distorted viral NA, could be an antiviral chemotherapeutic agent if not toxic for the host cells in the amounts needed to inhibit the virus. A number of substances have been found that are more or less effective *experimental* antiviral agents though, so far, only a very few have practical clinical usefulness. The field is under active investigation, however, and more will certainly appear. (See Mutagenic Agents and Metabolite Analogues.)

**Analogues in Chemotherapy.** Antiviral action may be brought about by chemical analogues of the purine or pyrimidine bases that occur naturally in NA. Analogues of normal nucleosides of NA can be prepared by halogenation of the bases and coupling them to ribose or deoxyribose. These altered or "ersatz" nucleosides can occupy the place of the normal substances but cannot perform the normal functions. They are chemical "imposters." Some of them, e.g., 5-fluoro-2′-deoxyuridine, inhibit the enzyme system, thymidylate synthetase, that synthesizes the nucleoside deoxythymidine, essential to the synthesis of viral DNA. Others, e.g., 5-bromo-2′-deoxyuridine, are built into the viral DNA. The resulting "erroneous" DNA containing the analogue cannot form perfect virions. In other examples, 5-iodo-2′-deoxyuridine (IUD or IUDR) and isatin-beta-thiosemicarbazone (IBT) and its methyl derivative (MIBT) (Fig. 18.4) appear to act by preventing final maturation of some DNA viruses; synthesis of DNA and other parts of the virion occurs but they remain unassembled. These drugs have preventive or curative value in certain cases of herpes simplex and smallpox; both are caused by DNA viruses.

RNA viruses (e.g., several picornaviruses) are selectively inhibited by 2-(α-hydroxybenzyl) benzimidazole (HBB) and guanidine. These drugs appear to inhibit formation of virus-induced RNA polymerase. As a result viral RNA and, secondarily, capsid proteins are not produced. The drugs have little or no effect on host cells or on DNA viruses. Most of these mechanisms are still under investigation.

In another example of analogue effectiveness 5-fluorouracil "fed" to infected cells can be taken into virus-coded mRNA in place of normal uracil. It prevents replication of the viral DNA though not necessarily of other parts of virions. Thus, in herpesvirus so treated, the "virions" that are so produced have no DNA cores.

As will be seen in Chapter 21, chemical analogues of many sorts, and their stoppage or distortion of various enzymic functions, are basic factors in antimicrobial chemotherapy.

**Interferon.** Unlike artificial inhibitors of viral replication, interferon is a natural substance produced by cells infected by a virus. Actually, several interferons exist.

The nucleic acid of many animal viruses, on entering a mature (not embryonic) animal cell, induces the cell to produce a new type of protein that prevents replication of the infecting virus and also of many others. The first such protein was described by Isaacs and Lindenmann in 1957. Because it was found to *interfere* with *intracellular* viral multiplication, it was called *interferon*. The inhibitory effect of any interferon appears to be exerted early in the eclipse phase of the viral growth. Probably the interferon inhibits the viral NA synthetase system, although its exact mode of action, and the mode of its induction, are still under intensive investigation. It does not interfere with normal cell metabolism. Its action is entirely intracellular; it does not act in any way upon the intact virion outside the cell—i.e., it does not prevent infection. Interferon production may be induced in cells growing in tissue culture (*in vitro*) as well as in cells in living animals (*in vivo*). It is now known that there are several proteins of slightly different chemical and physical properties that have the characteristics of interferon, i.e., there are several different forms of interferons. All are produced only by cells, not by viruses.

An interferon is liberated by an infected cell into the surrounding fluid. If taken into adjacent cells of the same species, it interferes with intracellular viral replication in them also. Interferons are thus probably important factors in recovery from (not prevention of) many viral infections. Their value as therapeutic agents is still under investigation.

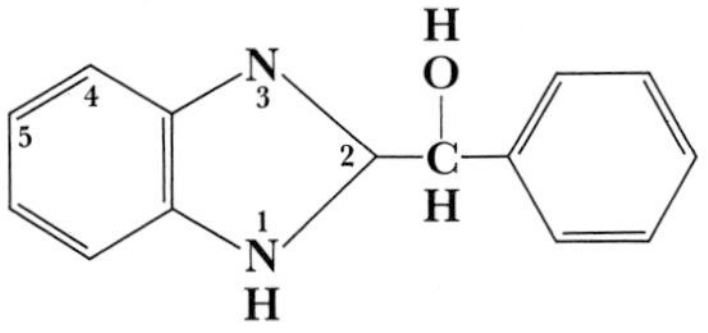

HBB 2-(α-hydroxybenzyl)-benzimidazole

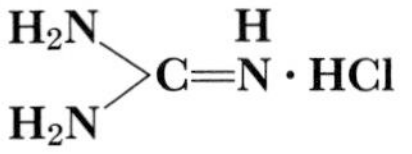

Guanidine HCl

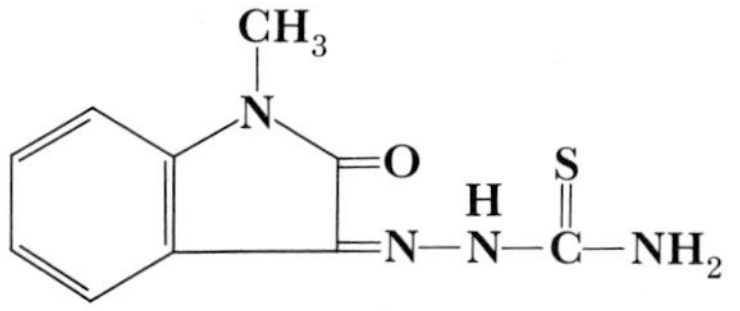

Methylisatin beta-thiosemicarbazone
(MIBT)

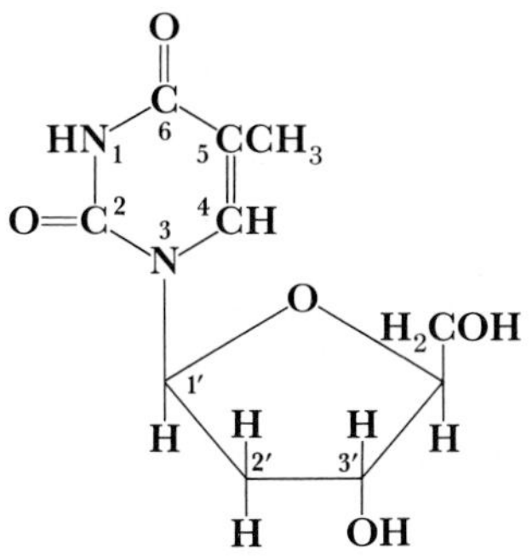

Thymidine

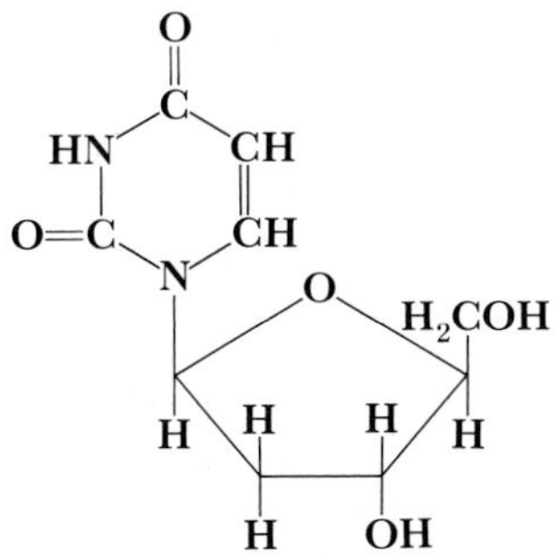

2'-deoxyuridine

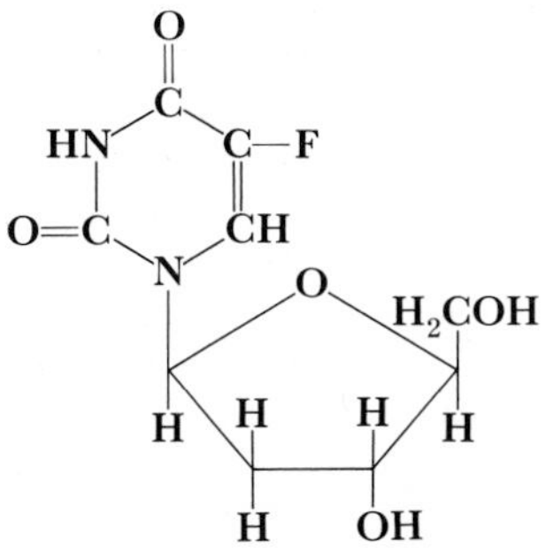

5'-fluoro-2'-deoxyuridine
(FUDR)

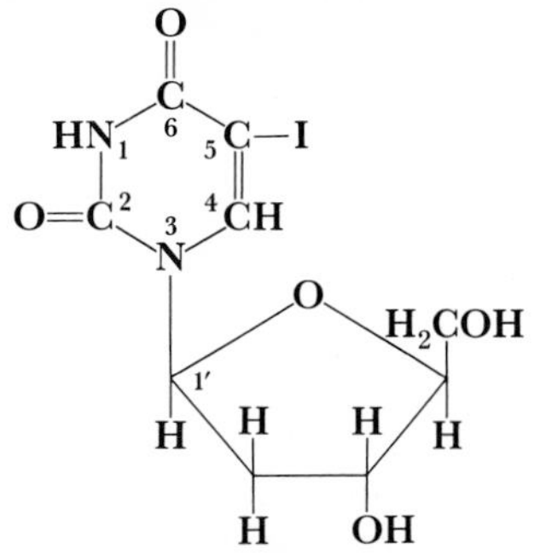

5-iodo-2'-deoxyuridine
(IUDR)

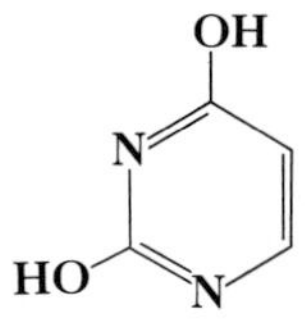

Uracil

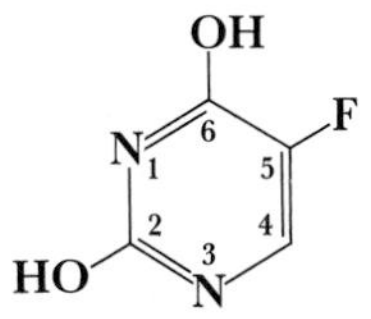

5-fluorouracil

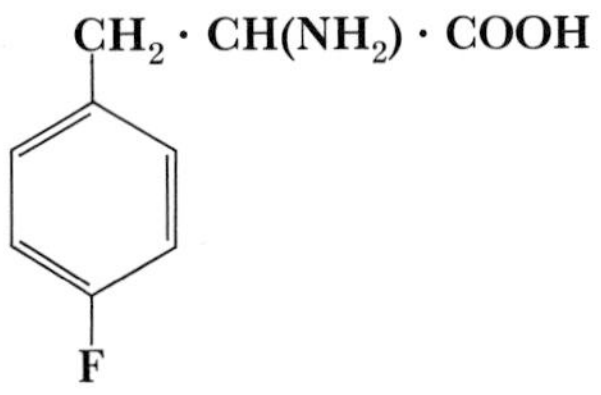

$CH_2 \cdot CH(NH_2) \cdot COOH$

p. fluorophenylalanine

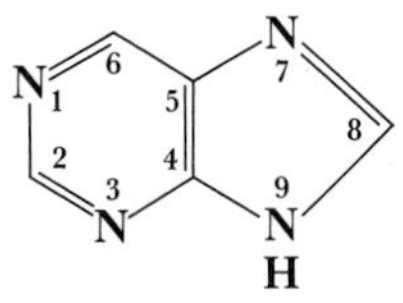

Purine

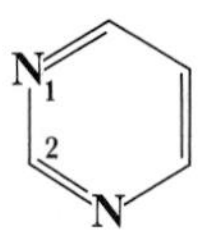

Pyrimidine

**Figure 18.4** Formulas of purine, pyrimidine and of halogenated derivatives and nucleosides and some other antiviral drugs. Note similarities between normal and derived substances (analogues).

A practical difficulty in therapeutic use of interferons is production in sufficient quantities. However, interferons may also be induced in cells in the absence of viral infection by various bacteria, bacterial cell walls (i.e., endotoxins; Chapters 27 and 36), animal nucleic acids, yeasts, etc. Thus, therapeutic quantities of interferons may become available without the necessity of infecting cells with viruses.

Interferons taken into cells appear to act indirectly against viruses by inducing the cell to synthesize (or removing a repressor substance that prevents synthesis?) of a substance that is the actual antiviral agent. The exact nature of this substance is not yet clear. The cell must be genetically capable of such synthesis. The antiviral agent appears to act by inhibiting synthesis of viral mRNA and hence of viral NA.

In physicochemical properties interferons are neither enzymes, coenzymes nor antibodies as defined in Chapter 23. Interferons have no immunological relationship to the viruses that induce them. Interferons are relatively small, yet nondialyzable protein molecules ranging in molecular weight from about 20,000 to 100,000, depending on source and inducer. They are readily hydrolyzed by proteolytic enzymes, e.g., trypsin. Unlike enzymes, they are relatively stable to heat (60° C. for 1 hour) and remarkably stable to a wide range of pH (2.0 to 10.0). An exact definition of interferon(s) in terms of physicochemical properties remains to be formulated.

A striking property of any interferon is its relative species specificity. Although it can interfere with replication of many different kinds of viruses, it does so only in cells of the species that produced it or in phylogenetically closely related species. For example, interferon produced by chick cells will not interfere with virus replication in cells of mice, and vice versa. However, the species specificity of interferons is not absolute, since it may extend, in a limited degree of effectiveness, across boundaries between closely related species. Thus, monkey interferon will have a small but definite effect in human cells, and mouse interferon will show some effect in cells of related rodents such as rats and hamsters. Specificity sometimes extends also to particular types of cells in animal species.

There are a number of substances that resemble interferons in physicochemical and biological properties. These substances occur inside cells and in association with them, but their source and nature are not yet understood. They are collectively called "interfering substances."

Some may actually be interferon normally present in cells, and some may be mixtures of other antiviral substances. Some are found free in blood and in other biological substances in the absence of viral infection. Most may be differentiated from true interferon(s) on the basis that they are normal, preformed components of cells in which they occur and not newly synthesized proteins like interferon. The antibiotic, Actinomycin D, which blocks synthesis of DNA-dependent mRNA, also prevents synthesis of true interferons but not of the "interferon-like" substances.

## 18.6   VIRUSES IN INDUSTRY

There are several important industrial aspects of viruses. For example, the preparation of viral vaccines, both inactivated and active but weakened or *attenuated* in virulence, is a multimillion-dollar industry. Some viruses are cultivated on a very large scale in enormous tissue-cell culture vats for the preparation of inactivated vaccines such as the Salk polio vaccine, as well as the active Sabin oral vaccine. Some viruses, such as that of rabies, are propagated on a large scale in living avian embryos. Various factory-sized means of cultivation and propagation are used to prepare other viral vaccines of veterinary importance. Some mass-produced viruses of insects are used to combat arthropods of medical and economic importance.

A contrary role of viruses in industry is their destructive activity. For example, a bacterial virus called *actinophage* is virulent for the moldlike bacterium, *Streptomyces griseus,* from which the antibiotic streptomycin is obtained. Unless carefully excluded from the culture vats, the actinophage can be an expensive nuisance.

Another industrially important phage is one active against *Streptococcus lactis* and related species of bacteria that are used to cause souring of milk, i.e., to produce lactic acid and "buttery" flavor in the milk and cream used for dairy products. These phage particles are widely distributed, and when such a phage gets into the creamery vats, whole batches of valuable culture-soured dairy products are spoiled. The control of such phages is an important industrial problem (see Chapter 45). One method of control consists in selecting strains of milk-souring streptococci that are genetically resistant to the phage.

Many bacteriophages have been found, each active against a specific bacterium. Bacteria for which phages have been found include tubercle bacilli, diphtheria bacilli and certain very valuable nitrogen-fixing bacteria (*Azotobacter*) of the soil. The latter phages can constitute a serious problem to agriculture. Other phages infect sporeforming bacilli of the Genus *Bacillus;* and bacilli of the Genus *Brucella* (brucellaphage), active against the cause of brucellosis (undulant fever).

There is also a virus called *zymophage,* which infects yeast cells of the genus *Saccharomyces.* Species of *Saccharomyces,* as pointed out elsewhere, are of enormous importance in the manufacture of bread, industrial alcohol and alcoholic beverages. Zymophage attacking any of these yeasts while they are at work is a serious matter for the stockholders as well as for the resident microbiologist.

A virus active against the blue-green algae, *Plectonema boryanum,* was discovered in 1963. Others have been found since then. These viruses resemble bacteriophages. Algal viruses are significant because blue-green algae are important agents in sewage disposal (Chapter 42) and their destruction by viruses constitutes a problem of some magnitude.

## 18.7   VIRUSES AND TUMORS

A tumor is a swelling (L. *tumere* = to swell). In pathology, plant or animal, the word tumor generally means a mass of abnormal, independently growing tissue that is without physiological function or that exhibits abnormal activity. A mass of such new growth is also called a *neoplasm* (Gr. *neos* = new; *plasm* = formation or substance).

Neoplasms may be *benign,* i.e., they may grow slowly, apparently under at least some physiological restraint, remain *in situ* and neither vigorously invade adjacent normal tissue nor give off numerous rapidly growing tumor cells that migrate and localize elsewhere in the body. In contrast, some neoplasms consist of cells that are markedly different from normal cells. They grow rapidly and are unimpeded by contact with other cells. They tend to damage and invade neighboring tissues and give off many cells that, distributed in body fluids (e.g., lymph), localize elsewhere (*metastasize*) in the body and rapidly extend the process. Such tumors are said to be *malignant.* Depending on the type of cell of origin (in animals), malignant neoplasms may be *carcinomas* (Gr. *karkinos* = crab) or *epitheliomas,* both of which are epithelial in origin or *sarcomas* (originate from connective and supporting tissues or striated muscle) or *leukemias* (involve cells of the lymphatic system). The term *cancer* (the Latin word for *crab,* from the fancied resemblance of the shape of some skin cancers to crabs) is widely used to mean any or all malignant neoplasms in general. Neoplasms, especially if malignant, do damage by absorbing nutrients necessary to the host, by swelling and blockage of body channels, by pressures, and possibly by the effects of toxic waste products of their abnormal metabolism. Neoplasms are not inheritable, although a tendency to develop certain types of neoplasm seems to be associated with certain families.

A basic cause of malignant neoplasms appears to be a genetic mutation in a body-tissue cell (a *somatic* mutation). As is true of other cells, mutations in body-tissue cells may be caused by a variety of agents: ionizing radiations, ultraviolet light, various chemical substances such as methylcholanthrene, substances in smoke from wood, coal and vegetable leaves and in automobile exhaust fumes, cresols and mechanical irritants. These agents, physical and chemical, are collectively called *mutagens.* Any mutagen is a potential producer of neoplasms or tumors. Tumor-producing agents are often said to be *oncogenic* (Gr. *onkos* = mass or swelling). Virus-induced changes in normal cells that result in malignancy are called *malignant transformations* (do not confuse with transformation of bacteria by *free* DNA).

Numerous malignant tumors of lower animals are well known to be caused by viruses. One of the first-discovered viral causes of malignant tumors was the virus of chicken sarcoma (P. Rous, 1911; Nobel Prize winner, 1966); the "Rous sarcoma." An oncogenic virus that causes a wartlike disease (papilloma) of rabbits was discovered by Shope in 1933; a leukemia virus of mice was discovered in 1951. A virus of mice producing a wide variety of malignancies in mice, rats and hamsters and called *polyoma virus* was discovered in 1957. Certain viruses of monkeys (*simian virus* 40 or SV 40) and some other animals were found to cause large vacuoles in infected cells and were called *vacuolating viruses.* A commonly used name of the group that includes all neoplasm-producing or oncogenic viruses is derived from the first two letters of the names of various types of lesion: *pa*pilloma, *po*lyoma, *va*cuolation = *papovaviruses.* Some distinctive properties of papovaviruses are shown in Table 17.1. The naked DNA of several papovaviruses is as oncogenic as the naked NA of a number of other viruses. The DNA of at least one papovavirus is also very heat-resistant, in this resembling hepatitis viruses.

It is notable that only one neoplastic disease of humans (warts) is mentioned in Table 17.1. With a few possible exceptions (e.g., leukemias and the Burkitt tumor of Africa), warts have been the only one of the dozens of neoplastic diseases of humans in which a papovavirus, or indeed any virus, has been demonstrated. That at least some of the many other human neoplasms are also caused by viruses seems highly probable, though numerous devices to demonstrate viruses in human cancers have been tried without success. In some malignant tumors very suggestive, virus-like bodies have been seen in electron micrographs but final proof of their identity is lacking.

Some "common cold" viruses (e.g., adenovirus 7) cause malignancies when injected into newborn mice and hamsters. The simian virus (SV 40) can likewise induce cancer-like transformations in monkey tissue cells in tissue cultures. Yet in none of the cells thus transformed by either adenovirus or SV 40 can any ordinary type of virus be demonstrated. However, the malignancies that these viruses cause continue to grow!

The tumor cells contain a new, virus-controlled protein: a specific, *tumor* (T) *antigen* (Chapter 24). This antigen continues to appear in the progeny of the transformed cells, indicating that viral genes that cause antigen production and malignancy have become incorporated into the genomes of the transformed cells—a phenomenon suggestive of permanent viral conversion or infective heredity. By means of this antigen, the seemingly virus-free tumor cells confer immunity to superinfection by the inducing virus. Thus though complete viruses themselves cannot be demonstrated in the malignant cells, it is evident that they were present in at least one original cell, since the antigen that only they can cause the cells to synthesize continues to be produced by the malignant progeny. The status of the virus in virus-free(?) growing tumor cells is under intensive investigation.

**Hybrid Viruses.** It has been found that adenovirus and SV 40, when jointly present in tissue cultures of monkey cells, can "hybridize"; i.e., the adenovirus capsid is spontaneously transferred to SV 40 nucleoids or DNA, a phenomenon called *transcapsidation*. The resulting adeno-SV 40 is called a hybrid virus. Actual recombination does not occur.

Now, adenovirus type 7 multiplies in human cells but not in monkey cells. However, aided by the hybrid virus the adenovirus can replicate in monkey cells. The hybrid is designated PARA for "Particle Aiding Replication of Adenoviruses." PARA cannot replicate in either monkey cell or human cell unless the adenovirus is present. Thus, the harmless adenovirus, aided by PARA, becomes oncogenic in monkey cells (Fig. 18.5). PARA, the helper virus, supplies the oncogenic DNA of SV 40 and enables the adenovirus to replicate, and the adenovirus supplies the capsid that carries the SV 40 DNA. The tumor cells carry the SV 40 tumor antigen but not adenovirus tumor antigen.

Thus, difficulty in demonstrating viruses in human neoplasms may result, at least in part, from the fact that oncogenicity may depend, not on the presence of an entire, demonstrable

| | ● ADENOVIRUS | Ⓓ PARA | Ⓓ ● PARA-ADENO | ◎ SV 40 VIRUS |
|---|---|---|---|---|
| INDUCTION OF SV 40 TUMOR ANTIGEN | | | YES | YES |
| INDUCTION OF SV 40 VIRUS ANTIGEN | | | | YES |
| INDUCTION OF ADENO 7 TUMOR ANTIGEN | YES | | YES | |
| INDUCTION OF ADENO 7 VIRUS ANTIGEN | YES | | YES | |
| REPLICATION IN MONKEY KIDNEY CELLS | | | YES | YES |
| REPLICATION IN HUMAN KIDNEY CELLS | YES | | YES | SLIGHTLY |

**Figure 18.5** For discussion see text. (From The Footprints of Tumor Viruses, by Fred Rapp and Joseph L. Melnick. Copyright © 1966 by Scientific American, Inc. All rights reserved.)

virus, but on the presence of only a few of its genes or on the presence of two interdependent viruses, neither of which can be separately demonstrated or, alone, cause neoplastic growth.

## SUPPLEMENTARY READING

Acton, J. D., and Myrvik, Q. N.: Production of interferon by alveolar macrophages. J. Bact., *91*:2300, 1966.

Baron, S., and Levy, H. B.: Interferon. Ann. Rev. Microbiol., *20*:291, 1966.

Bawden, F. C.: Plant Viruses and Virus Diseases. 4th ed. The Ronald Press Co., New York. 1964.

Bradley, D. E., and Dewar, C. A.: The structure of phage-like objects associated with non-induced bacteriocinogenic bacteria. J. Gen. Microbiol., *45*:399, 1966.

Buckler, C. E., and Baron, S.: Antiviral action of mouse interferon in heterologous cells. J. Bact., *91*:231, 1966.

Burke, D. C., Skehel, J. J., and Low, M.: Interferon production and viral ribonucleic acid synthesis in chick embryo cells. J. Gen. Microbiol., *1*:235, 1967.

Butel, J. S., and Rapp, F.: Replication in simian cells of defective viruses in an SV40-adenovirus "hybrid" population. J. Bact., *91*:278, 1966.

Carver, D. H., and Rosen, F. S.: Studies on viral inhibitors of biological origin. II. A viral inhibitory factor obtained from *E. coli* O111 and inhibition of viral replication by nucleic acid derivatives. Proc. Soc. Exp. Biol. Med., *116*:575, 1964.

Cunningham, C. H.: A Laboratory Guide in Virology. 5th ed. Burgess Pub. Co., Minneapolis. 1964.

Dulbecco, R.: The induction of cancer by viruses. Sci. Amer., *216*:28, 1967.

Finter, N. B., editor: Interferons. *In:* Frontiers of Biology, Vol. 2, W. B. Saunders Co., Philadelphia. 1966.

Fraser, D.: Viruses and Molecular Biology. The Macmillan Co., New York. 1967.

Girardi, A. J., Larson, V. M., Hilleman, M. R., and Zwickey, R. E.: Search for viruses in human malignancies. 4. Proc. Soc. Exp. Biol. Med., *121*:428, 1966.

Glasgow, L. A.: Leukocytes and interferon in the host response to viral infections. II. Enhanced interferon response of leukocytes from immune animals. J. Bact., *91*:2185, 1966.

Hampar, B.: Persistent cyclic herpes simplex virus infection in vitro. IV. J. Bact., *92*:1741, 1966.

Herschman, H. R., and Helinski, D. R.: Comparative study of the events associated with colicin induction. J. Bact., *94*:691, 1967.

Ho, M.: Identification and "induction" of interferon. Bact. Rev., *28*:367, 1964.

Holland, J. J.: Viruses in animals and in cell culture. Fourteenth Symposium, Microbial Behaviour 'in Vivo' and 'in Vitro', page 257. Soc. Gen. Microbiol., London. 1964.

Howe, C., Morgan, C., St. Cyr, C. de V., Hsu, K. C., and Rose, H. M.: Morphogenesis of type 2 parainfluenza virus examined by light and electron microscopy. J. Virol., *1*:215, 1967.

Hsiung, G. D.: Diagnostic Virology. Yale University Press, New Haven, Conn. 1964.

Kim, K. S. W., and Boatman, E. S.: Electron microscopy of monkey kidney cell cultures infected with rubella virus. J. Virol., *1*:205, 1967.

Klein, G.: Tumor Antigens. Ann. Rev. Microbiol., *20*:223, 1960.

Lee, S. H. S., and Ozere, R. L.: Production of interferon by human mononuclear leukocytes. Proc. Soc. Exp. Biol. Med., *118*:190, 1965.

Luria, S. E., and Darnell, J. E., Jr.: General Virology. John Wiley & Sons, Inc., New York. 1967.

Matumoto, M.: Multiplication of measles virus in cell culture. Bact. Rev., *30*:152, 1966.

Nomura, M.: Colicins and related bacteriocins. Ann. Rev. Microbiol., *21*:257, 1967.

Pollard, M.: Perspectives in Virology, Vol. 5. Academic Press, Inc., New York. 1967.

Rabson, A. S., Malmgren, R. A., and Kirchstein, R. L.: Induction of neoplasia in vitro in hamster kidney tissue by adenovirus 7–SV40 "hybrid" strain (LLE46). Proc. Soc. Exp. Biol. Med., *121*:486, 1966.

RNA replication, Symposium on: Bact. Rev., *30*:267, 1966.

Rous, P.: The challenge to man of the neoplastic cell. Science, *157*:24, 1967.

Rustigian, R.: Persistent infection of cells in culture by measles virus. II. J. Bact., *92*:1805, 1966.

Smith, K. M.: Insect Virology. Academic Press, New York. 1967.

Sonnabend, J. A., Martin, E. M., Mécs, E., and Fantes, K. H.: The effect of interferon on the synthesis and activity of an RNA polymerase isolated from chick cells infected with Semliki Forest virus. J. Gen. Virol., *1*:41, 1967.

Thomas, M., and le Bouvier, G.: Transformation of bovine cell cultures by preparations of polyoma virus. J. Gen. Virol., *1*:125, 1967.

Whipple, H. E., editor: Antiviral Substances. Ann. N. Y. Acad. Sci., *130*(Art. 1):1, 1965.

World Health Organization: Viruses and Cancer. WHO Technical Report Series No. 295, 1965 (IQB/1965).

Zabriskie, J. B.: Viral-induced bacterial toxin. Ann. Rev. Med., *17*:337, 1966.

# 3

## Microbiology, the Patchwork Quilt

As mentioned in the introduction to Part 1 of this book, the invention and evolution of high-resolution microscopes and improvements in technical microscopy were the making of the science of Microbiology. It has been mentioned also that other sciences have contributed, and daily continue to contribute greatly to every aspect of Microbiology. Indeed, Microbiology is a sort of conglomerate or patchwork quilt science.

This section of "Fundamentals of Microbiology" therefore presents, from various other fields, information that is inextricably intermingled with, and absolutely essential to, the study and understanding of the science of Microbiology and its many applications in other fields. Included are data on the effects of various physical and chemical factors of the environment on living cells and viruses and the application of our knowledge thereof to the fields of microbial control through sterilization, disinfection and microbistasis. From an adjoining field there is presented information on the origin and nature of antibiotics and some other antimicrobial agents and their uses in selective microbiology, industry, chemotherapy, agriculture and so on; all separate themes that are closely interwoven in the intricate, overall pattern of the patchwork quilt that is Microbiology.

The wondrously complex system called Immunology, another patchwork motif in the quilt, and its intricate and exceedingly important part in the general picture of Microbiology are then presented. A knowledge of Immunology is basic to the later discussions of the role of microorganisms in disease, systematic microbiology, and nearly all other important phases of the subject.

# Chapter 19

# MICROORGANISMS AND THEIR ENVIRONMENT

We can only guess at the environmental conditions under which the most primitive microorganisms made their first appearance on this planet. At present their descendants live all over the earth under a wide variety of environmental conditions. Since some of their present habitats, such as the living tissues of mammals and plants, presumably did not exist in Proterozoic ages, it may be assumed that evolution selected many microorganisms capable of adapting to conditions vastly different from those which they first encountered. Microorganisms exist today that are capable of utilizing what seem to us the most indigestible of foods (pure sulfur, kerosene, naphthalene, carbolic acid) and of thriving in the most remote, dismal and uninhabitable places, such as the depths of ocean ooze, subterranean slimes, petroleum wells, hot sulfur springs and arctic seas, as well as inside other living cells. So complete and highly specialized are some adaptations that many forms of microorganisms perish when transferred suddenly to other environments. In this chapter we shall discuss some of the environmental factors governing microbial life.

## 19.1  TEMPERATURE

**Temperature and Growth.**  Temperature is one of the most important factors influencing all forms of life. The relation of temperature to growth of microorganisms is somewhat complex. In the following discussion of temperature effects it is to be understood that the organisms are suspended in an aqueous fluid medium unless otherwise noted.

MESOPHILES.  Many species indigenous to the soil, waters and the vertebrate body can grow at temperatures from 10° to 45° C. (hu-man body temperature is 37° C.; Figs. 19.1 and 19.2). Their *optimum* growth temperatures are about 25° to 39° C. and vary with species. Species growing best at such temperatures are called *mesophilic* (Gr. *meso* = middle or medium; *philic* = prefer).

PSYCHROPHILES.  Psychrophiles are commonly defined as microorganisms capable of growth at 0° C. Other microorganisms that are adapted to life in the sea or soil grow best at temperatures below or near the freezing point (10° to −2° C.). These also are referred to as *psychrophilic* (Gr. *psychros* = cold). Many psychrophiles will also grow well at temperatures in the lower mesophilic range. They might be called *facultative psychrophiles*. On the other hand, certain marine bacteria, adapted to life at about 4° C., the temperature at profound depths, die if held at about 30° C. for more than a few minutes. These could be called *obligate psychrophiles*, since they are limited to low temperature as a condition of life. Psychrophilic microorganisms occur all over the earth.

The importance of psychrophilic microorganisms is easily realized when we consider the enormous volumes of organic matter to be decomposed continually in the oceans and soil. However, psychrophilic molds, yeasts and bacteria can cause spoilage of foods and many other materials that are stored at refrigeration temperatures. They are thus important in the huge frozen food industry. Few species of psychrophilic microorganisms are pathogenic; most are aerobic or facultative.

THERMOPHILES.  There are species of microorganisms that thrive only at high temperatures (50° to 72° C.). Such species are called *obligate thermophiles*. Obligate thermophilic bacteria and algae are commonly found in hot

**239**

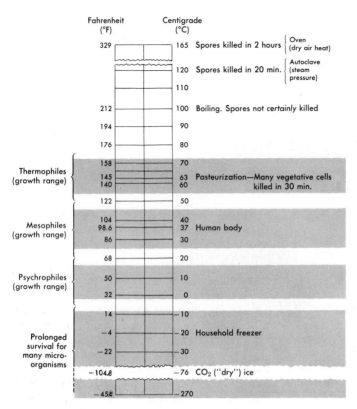

**Figure 19.1** Some temperatures of significance in microbiology. Note the slow killing action of dry air heat and the relatively rapid killing action of steam (moist heat) at lower temperature. Boiling kills some but not all spores. Note overlapping growth ranges of thermophilic, mesophilic and other forms.

sulfur springs and similar habitats. They are not rare in arctic and antarctic seas. Some occur in milk, soil, manure and related situations. No organisms are known that grow at temperatures above 73° C.

ENDURANCE COMPARED WITH GROWTH. A distinction should be made in all cases between ability to *endure* a given temperature and ability to *grow* well under the same conditions. Many microorganisms, including fungi, mammalian tissue cells, most bacteria and viruses, can live for months or years frozen in "dry ice" (carbon dioxide ice at −76° C. or liquid nitrogen, −195° C.) yet they do not grow at all. They might be called *psychroduric*. Thermoduric (heat-enduring) organisms survive well at temperatures above 50° C., but only *thermophilic* species grow well under such conditions. Some microbiologists would draw the line between mesophiles and thermophiles at somewhere between 44° and 52° C.

It is worth noting that the optimal temperatures for growth of nearly all microorganisms are near the upper maximal limits of their range and that lethal temperatures are only a little above optimal. Most microorganisms have a wide tolerance to temperatures far below optimal.

GROWTH TEMPERATURES AND ENZYMES. The optimal and limiting growing temperatures for microorganisms and, indeed, for all living cells are in general the optimal and limiting temperatures of their enzymes. As pointed out in Chapter 5, enzymes have minimal, optimal and maximal reaction temperatures.

At temperatures well below the optimum, most enzymes function more slowly or not at all. This is in part because low temperatures generally decrease chemical reaction rates and cause increases in viscosity of fluids and hardening of lipids. Growth is retarded or inhibited, but low temperatures are not highly destructive as are high temperatures. High temperatures cause rupture of H-bonds in proteins and in DNA, resulting in denaturation of proteins and "melting" (separation of strands) of DNA.

THERMAL RESISTANCE. Most microorganisms in an actively growing (vegetative) state are killed by exposures to temperatures of about 70° C. for one to five minutes. Some are killed in 10 minutes at temperatures as low as 54° C. Commercial *pasteurization* of milk (63° C. for 30 minutes or 72° C. for 15 seconds) kills all vegetative *pathogens* (disease producers) in milk, including tubercle bacilli (*Mycobacterium tuberculosis*). However, numerous thermoduric *sapro-*

| Cent. | Fahr. | Cent. | Fahr. | Cent. | Fahr. |
|---|---|---|---|---|---|
| Deg. | Deg. | Deg. | Deg. | Deg. | Deg. |
| −40 | −40.0 | 9 | 48.2 | 57 | 134.6 |
| −39 | −38.2 | 10 | 50.0 | 58 | 136.4 |
| −38 | −36.4 | 11 | 51.8 | 59 | 138.2 |
| −37 | −34.6 | 12 | 53.6 | 60 | 140.0 |
| −36 | −32.8 | 13 | 55.4 | 61 | 141.8 |
| −35 | −31.0 | 14 | 57.2 | 62 | 143.6 |
| −34 | −29.2 | 15 | 59.0 | 63 | 145.4 |
| −33 | −27.4 | 16 | 60.8 | 64 | 147.2 |
| −32 | −25.6 | 17 | 62.6 | 65 | 149.0 |
| −31 | −23.8 | 18 | 64.4 | 66 | 150.8 |
| −30 | −22.0 | 19 | 66.2 | 67 | 152.6 |
| −29 | −20.2 | 20 | 68.0 | 68 | 154.4 |
| −28 | −18.4 | 21 | 69.8 | 69 | 156.2 |
| −27 | −16.6 | 22 | 71.6 | 70 | 158.0 |
| −26 | −14.8 | 23 | 73.4 | 71 | 159.8 |
| −25 | −13.0 | 24 | 75.2 | 72 | 161.6 |
| −24 | −11.2 | 25 | 77.0 | 73 | 163.4 |
| −23 | −9.4 | 26 | 78.8 | 74 | 165.2 |
| −22 | −7.6 | 27 | 80.6 | 75 | 167.0 |
| −21 | −5.8 | 28 | 82.4 | 76 | 168.8 |
| −20 | −4.0 | 29 | 84.2 | 77 | 170.6 |
| −19 | −2.2 | 30 | 86.0 | 78 | 172.4 |
| −18 | −0.4 | 31 | 87.8 | 79 | 174.2 |
| −17 | +1.4 | 32 | 89.6 | 80 | 176.0 |
| −16 | 3.2 | 33 | 91.4 | 81 | 177.8 |
| −15 | 5.0 | 34 | 93.2 | 82 | 179.6 |
| −14 | 6.8 | 35 | 95.0 | 83 | 181.4 |
| −13 | 8.6 | 36 | 96.8 | 84 | 183.2 |
| −12 | 10.4 | 37 | 98.6 | 85 | 185.0 |
| −11 | 12.2 | 38 | 100.4 | 86 | 186.8 |
| −10 | 14.0 | 39 | 102.2 | 87 | 188.6 |
| −9 | 15.8 | 40 | 104.0 | 88 | 190.4 |
| −8 | 17.6 | 41 | 105.8 | 89 | 192.2 |
| −7 | 19.4 | 42 | 107.6 | 90 | 194.0 |
| −6 | 21.2 | 43 | 109.4 | 91 | 195.8 |
| −5 | 23.0 | 44 | 111.2 | 92 | 197.6 |
| −4 | 24.8 | 45 | 113.0 | 93 | 199.4 |
| −3 | 26.6 | 46 | 114.8 | 94 | 201.2 |
| −2 | 28.4 | 47 | 116.6 | 95 | 203.0 |
| −1 | 30.2 | 48 | 118.4 | 96 | 204.8 |
| 0 | 32.0 | 49 | 120.2 | 97 | 206.6 |
| +1 | 33.8 | 50 | 122.0 | 98 | 208.4 |
| 2 | 35.6 | 51 | 123.8 | 99 | 210.2 |
| 3 | 37.4 | 52 | 125.6 | 100 | 212.0 |
| 4 | 39.2 | 53 | 127.4 | 101 | 213.8 |
| 5 | 41.0 | 54 | 129.2 | 102 | 215.6 |
| 6 | 42.8 | 55 | 131.0 | 103 | 217.4 |
| 7 | 44.6 | 56 | 132.8 | 104 | 219.2 |
| 8 | 46.4 | | | | |

**Figure 19.2**  Table of equivalents of centigrade and Fahrenheit thermometric scales. (To convert F° to C°, subtract 32 from F° and take 5/9 of the remainder. To convert C° to F°, take 9/5 of the C° and add 32.)

*phytes** in milk survive pasteurization, thus pasteurized milk is safe but not sterile.

Thermophiles are quite resistant. Some vegetative thermophilic cells can survive 80° to 90° C. for as long as 10 minutes. These obviously can survive pasteurization temperatures and hence certain species are great nuisances in dairies. Boiling (212° F. or 100° C.) kills all vegetative microorganisms (certain viruses excepted) within 10 minutes.

Endospores of bacteria of the Family Bacillaceae are the most heat resistant of all living things. Some of these spores can survive boiling or higher temperatures for many hours. (Killing of spores is more fully discussed in Chapters

---

*Gr. *sapros* = decay. Saprophytes, involved in decay of dead organic matter, are generally nonpathogenic though there are some notable exceptions (Chapters 27 and 32).

20 and 21 on disinfection.) Spores of eucaryotic fungi and of some moldlike bacteria (Family Streptomycetaceae) are resistant to drought, unfavorable pH and salinity, but have only slightly greater thermal resistance than their vegetative cells.

THERMAL DEATH POINT. The lowest temperature at which all the bacteria of a given species in a given culture are killed within 10 minutes is called the *thermal death point* of that species. This is an inexact expression because at a given temperature, say 70° C., the bacteria in a given culture or situation do not all die simultaneously and suddenly just as the clock registers the expiration of 10 minutes. Some are more heat resistant than others, as are humans. Unless the temperature is catastrophic, as when a culture is dropped into a furnace, thermal death point merely tells us when the last survivor of all has expired. Furthermore, the thermal death point is influenced greatly by the numbers of bacteria originally present, their age, the acidity of the suspending fluid, its osmotic pressure and so forth. The term *thermal death point,* therefore, can be correctly used only if the exact conditions of an experiment are known. When the exact conditions are carefully controlled, information on thermal death points can be of some limited use, in canning and in the commercial preservation of milk and other products.

THERMAL DEATH TIME. The time required to kill all the bacteria of a certain species in a given substance at a stated temperature is called the *thermal death time.* The thermal death time of various species of microorganisms is influenced by the same factors that affect thermal death point, but under known conditions knowledge of thermal death time is of practical use, especially in the canning industry.

RATE OF DEATH (THERMAL DEATH RATE). As we have noted, death of all the bacteria of any given species in a given material does not occur simultaneously, but in a definite relationship to time, the rate being determined by factors such as number, age and kind of cells, temperature, moisture and acidity.

Mature (not senescent) cells are more resistant than young ones. Moisture and acidity greatly increase the vulnerability of cells to heat. Cells inside solid material such as mucus or canned meats may escape heat or the action of disinfectants longer than the same cells suspended naked in distilled water or broth, because the heat or disinfectant does not penetrate immediately into the center of solid masses.

If we know the number of cells initially

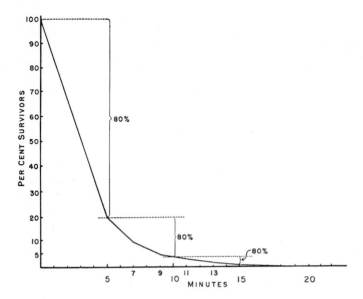

**Figure 19.3** Ideal arithmetic death curve. Relation between time and per cent survivors in a situation in which the lethal agent acts at a constant rate under uniform conditions.

present, we can determine the number and percentage of survivors of organisms present in a disinfection or heat-resistance test. If these are determined at various intervals and plotted against time, regular curves are formed (Fig. 19.3). If the logarithms of the numbers are similarly plotted, a straight line is formed (Fig. 19.4). Under certain influences such as pH, presence or absence of certain cations ($Mg^{++}$, $Ca^{++}$) or osmotic conditions, these theoretical straight lines may be much distorted: rapid at first, slow toward the end, and vice versa (see Chapter 20).

## 19.2   DESICCATION

Many species of microorganisms can survive complete drying or *desiccation* for long periods, although they do not grow under such conditions. Many substances, such as hay, fruits, fish and meat, "preserved" by drying, contain large numbers of living microorganisms that are dormant but that soon grow and cause spoilage if the dried product becomes moist. On the other hand, some microorganisms, especially marine and aquatic species and delicate pathogenic species, are quickly killed by dry-

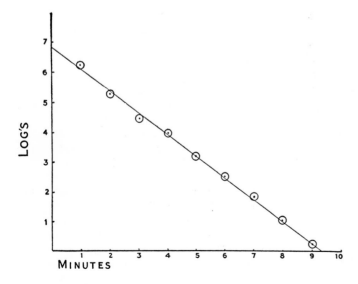

**Figure 19.4** Ideal logarithmic death curve. Relation between logarithms of numbers of surviving organisms and time in a one per cent aqueous solution of phenol at fixed temperature and pH. The straight line is characteristic of the relation between time and survivors under fixed adverse conditions when no growth occurs.

ing. Spores, conidia, arthrospores, chlamydospores and cysts of protozoa, of course, are dormant cells specially adapted to withstand drying for long periods.

**Desiccation and Vacuum.** Not only do many kinds of microorganisms in a vegetative state withstand desiccation, but they may be simultaneously subjected to the highest possible vacuum without harm. In fact, some organisms appear to be more thermoduric in high vacua and therefore possibly capable of travel through space on the outside of space ships. The possibility of transporting terrestrial microorganisms to the moon and other celestial bodies is a major problem with space scientists.

As a practical procedure in the laboratory, organisms to be preserved by desiccation *in vacuo* are suspended in a harmless or protective fluid like broth or blood. About $\frac{1}{4}$ ml. of this suspension is placed on absorbent material like bits of filter paper or sand previously sterilized in a small, cotton-plugged vial. Many such vials may be placed in a single jar that contains a desiccant such as calcium sulfate and that can be evacuated rapidly and sealed while evacuated. Water in the suspending fluid and in the microorganisms is rapidly transferred to the desiccant. Desiccation must be rapid (hence the vacuum) to avoid prolonged exposure of the cells to deleterious osmotic and other effects of slowly increasing concentrations of solutes in the suspending fluid. To reactivate the organisms it is only necessary to transfer them to a suitable fluid medium and then incubate. Survival of microorganisms under these conditions has both practical and philosophical implications.

PRACTICAL IMPLICATIONS.   The survival of bacteria when desiccated in a vacuum is of great practical importance. Once preserved by desiccation *in vacuo,* a large number of cultures may be stored in a small space, and many bacteria will survive for decades. When cultures are maintained in this state, contamination and mutation are avoided, and both time and money are saved as compared with frequent renewal of active cultures. These considerations are of great importance in science and industry.

Species of pathogenic streptococci, for example, have survived unharmed for 25 years, while diphtheria bacilli have survived for 15 years and tubercle bacilli for 17 years. Many can survive much longer under these conditions. However, though many species of bacteria resist freezing, vacuum and drying, this is not true of all. Some sensitive species will be discussed farther on.

PHILOSOPHICAL IMPLICATIONS.   In a cell in a state of virtually complete desiccation and in a high vacuum, there must be an unimaginably small vital activity. The metabolic processes must stop almost completely, since these depend on osmosis, diffusion, ionization and the colloidal state, all of which are dependent on hydration. How, then, can microorganisms exist desiccated in a vacuum? How can living beings survive in the entire absence of vital activity? The condition of microorganisms desiccated in a vacuum must be as near an approach to suspended animation as can be imagined.

If time (for human beings) be measured by successive events, such as heartbeats, train of thought, action of enzymes, or wars, then when these activities or their effects cease to be observed (i.e., in the absence of consciousness), time ceases for the individual involved. It begins again, for that individual, only when his *consciousness* again begins to pace exterior events or when vital activity produces the effects of age. A person deeply preoccupied by study,* pain, play or worry, or who is wholly unconscious or in an abnormal mental state (amnesia, delirium) in which consciousness of the course of events is temporarily lost, has a totally different idea of time from that of a normal, conscious person. An analogous situation exists for microorganisms dried in a vacuum. They have no consciousness of the passage of time and appear to undergo no physiological aging. When the air and moisture are withdrawn from their environment, time is withdrawn also. Time (for them) returns only when air and fluid are added. In the vacuum jar their chronological age may become great as measured by human standards, but they appear to remain physiologically young and unchanged even for many years of existence in vacuity.

It might be concluded that time, like space, has no real existence, but is only a concept that varies as does the state of mentality or consciousness.

The use of desiccation *in vacuo* to preserve microorganisms is one means of producing the condition called *microbistasis.* The organisms, though in a vegetative state to begin with, are reduced to a completely static condition. Other means of causing microbistasis are freezing and the use of chemicals that inhibit various enzymic activities (see Bacteriostasis; Chemotherapy).

---

*For example, serious students of microbiology!

## 19.3  EXTREME COLD

Many microorganisms are highly resistant to extremes of cold even when in the vegetative state. It is possible that certain species of organisms have survived glacial epochs of the earth's history because of this capacity. Some species can survive (not grow) while frozen in ice for weeks. The fragile syphilis spirochetes and numerous viruses are routinely maintained frozen in carbon dioxide ice at −76° C. (−104.8° F.) or liquid nitrogen (−198° C.) for years without loss of infectivity. Many species of bacteria and animal cells will grow, apparently unaffected, even after subjection to the temperatures of liquid hydrogen (−252° C. or −421° F.).

The microbistatic effect of freezing in some respects resembles that of desiccation. In both, water is made unavailable for physiological purposes: freezing immobilizes it; desiccation removes it.

**Uses of Extreme Cold.** The preservation of microorganisms by temperatures ranging from −76° C. to that of liquid nitrogen is of great importance in industry and medicine. For example, sperm of valuable breeding animals are kept for artificial insemination; living cells of various cancers and normal human and animal tissues are kept for preparation of vaccines, and for use in cancer research and in the diagnosis of disease; and strains of bacteria, molds and commercial yeasts are kept for industrial fermentations, antibiotic production and enzyme manufacture.

**Freeze-drying (Lyophilization).** This procedure depends on extreme cold and vacuum. The materials to be preserved are suspended in a suitable fluid and distributed in small glass ampules as for desiccation in a vacuum. The ampules are connected to a high-vacuum pump. The contents of the ampules are frozen almost instantaneously by immersion in a bath of carbon dioxide ice in methylcellosolve (−76° C.). The water is rapidly withdrawn from the ampules by the application of a high vacuum. The water passes directly from the solid to the vapor state without melting (*sublimation*). When all water vapor has been removed, the necks of the ampules are sealed with a needle of flame before disconnecting the pump. The product is a highly *lyophilic* (readily dissolving) powder, sealed *in vacuo*. The process is widely used in industry and medicine.

LETHAL MECHANISMS OF FREEZING. For practical reasons the factors favoring survival and those causing death during freezing are the subject of much study.

One cause of death of frozen cells is believed to be the formation of intracellular ice crystals with consequent mechanical destruction of the cells. Very rapid freezing (one to 10 seconds) has therefore been used as a means of preventing excessive intracellular crystallization and favoring *vitrefication* (formation of a solid, uncrystallized, glasslike mass of ice). Other researchers hold that slow freezing (20 to 30 minutes) is a preferable method, if the cells are suspended in a 5 to 50 per cent glycerol solution or in solutions that (a) withdraw water from the cell to avoid crystallization, (b) act as "antifreeze" inside the cell, or (c) allow time for osmotic and other adjustments between the interior of the cell and the environmental fluid, or a combination of these factors. Some regard *excessive* drying (above about 85 per cent) as harmful.

AUTOLYSIS. In the preservation of microorganisms by freezing, desiccation or similar means, the preserving agent must act quickly in order to prevent deleterious effects of autolysis.* Autolysis may occur if cells undergoing preservation are held at the threshold between active and inactive existence too long.

## 19.4  IONIC EFFECTS

**Hydrogen Ion Concentration.** A factor profoundly affecting all microorganisms, including each individual cell of all plant and animal tissues, is the acidity or alkalinity (*reaction*) of the fluid by which they are surrounded. The reaction is commonly expressed in terms of *hydrogen ion concentration* because the acidity of an aqueous fluid is determined entirely by the hydrogen ions ($H^+$) present in the fluid. (See Chapter 6.)

The approximate pH's of some familiar substances are shown in Figure 19.5.

It is important for the microbiologist to remember that, as a rule, increases in temperature increase dissociation of acids. Thus, a solution which is neutral or slightly alkaline, and therefore favorable to growth of most microorganisms at room temperature (about 22° C.), may become definitely acid and lethal if incubated at a commonly used incubator temperature (37° C.). If a nutrient solution is prepared

---

*Self-digestion by intracellular enzymes which are released or cease to be inhibited when the cell dies or becomes almost wholly inert (Chapter 46).

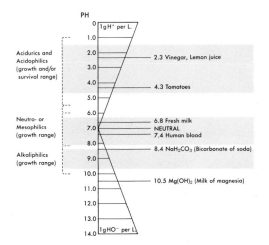

**Figure 19.5** Some pH's of significance in microbiology. The slanting lines starting at pH 7.0 indicate increasing concentration of H$^+$ or $^-$OH to the maximum of 1 gram per liter.

at a definite pH while near the boiling point, it will be more alkaline when cool.

Unfavorable influences of many sorts are enhanced in acid fluids. For example, coagulation of protein by heat occurs more readily in acid solutions. Thus, milk that is only very slightly sour (not sour as to odor or taste) may curdle on being warmed.

Enzymes are even more sensitive to alterations in pH than they are to temperature. They have definite minimal, optimal and maximal zones and limits in respect to pH just as they do to temperature. What is true of enzymes in these respects is consequently largely true of living cells. The reaction of microbiological culture media must, therefore, be very carefully adjusted with respect to pH. The pH to be selected depends upon the organisms to be cultivated. This is usually about pH 7.0, but commonly extends from pH 6.5 to pH 8.0 and, for some species, considerably beyond (Fig. 19.5). For example, the vibrio that causes Asiatic cholera is *alkaliphilic,* i.e., it prefers an alkaline reaction (about pH 9.0). Some soil bacteria (*Agrobacterium* sp.) grow well at about pH 12. Many yeasts and molds and certain bacteria prefer acid reactions of about pH 5.0. Still others grow at reactions about pH 2.0. These are said to be *acidophilic.*

**Buffers and Buffer Action.** It is often necessary in microbiology to change the pH of culture fluids (i.e., to "adjust the pH"). In attempting an adjustment of the pH of bacteriological media such as meat-infusion broth it is found that, unlike the titration of aqueous solutions of

acid or alkali, no sharp end point is reached at which a single drop of 0.1 N acid or alkali added to a liter of solution can change the pH 10-million-fold. In a fluid such as meat broth the change from an acid to an alkaline reaction or vice versa is very gradual, requiring the continuous addition of relatively large amounts (10 to 100 ml. per liter) of acid or alkali. In other words, even at or near the neutral point, the solution being titrated shows a marked tendency to resist any change in its reaction. This resistance is caused by the *buffer action* of certain constituents of the broth. Important among these constituents from a biological standpoint are amino acids and their polymers. These have both amino and carboxyl groups and will combine with either acid or alkali: they are said to be *amphoteric.* For example, the amino acid, glycine, combines with HCl or NaOH (Fig. 19.6). $^-$SH, imidazolium- and other groups that occur in proteins also serve as buffers.

A commonly used buffer in biological laboratories is a mixture of the monobasic and dibasic phosphates, $KH_2PO_4$ and $K_2HPO_4$. These dissociate relatively little in aqueous solution, i.e., they are neither strongly acid nor basic. When acid is added the dibasic salt absorbs H$^+$, changing into the monobasic and forming a potassium salt with the acid. When alkali is added, the monobasic salt releases H$^+$ to form $H_2O$ with the $^-$OH, and the incomplete salt combines with the cation of the alkali:

$$KH_2PO_4 + NaOH \rightleftharpoons KNaHPO_4 + H_2O$$
$$KNaHPO_4 + NaOH \rightleftharpoons KNa_2PO_4 + H_2O$$
$$K_2HPO_4 + HCl \rightleftharpoons KH_2PO_4 + KCl$$

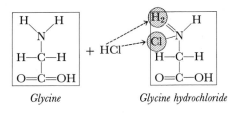

**Figure 19.6** Glycine as buffer.

Other important buffer constituents of organic media are carbonates and bicarbonates:

$$Na_2CO_3 + 2HCl \longrightarrow 2NaCl + H_2O + \overset{\overset{\text{gas}}{\uparrow}}{CO_2}$$

or

$$NaHCO_3 + NaOH \longrightarrow Na_2CO_3 + H_2O$$

Mixtures of acids and their salts also act as buffer systems. If hydrogen ions are added they suppress ionization of the acid and combine with anions of the salt. If hydroxyl ions are added they combine with the acid to form water and a salt. Buffer mixtures may be prepared at any desired pH. For example, in microbiological work a desired pH such as 7.2 is maintained by a mixture containing 0.1 M NaCl, 0.001 M ethylene-diamine-tetraacetate (EDTA) and 0.05 M tris (hydroxymethyl) amino methane, usually designated as *Tris.*

**Other Ions: Cations.**   Ions of heavy metals such as gold, silver, lead, copper and mercury, except in minimal amounts, are usually more toxic to microorganisms than are ions of light metals such as sodium, potassium and calcium. We may think of heavy metal ions as acting in at least three different ways, two inimical and one essential:

In relatively large concentrations (e.g., 1.0 per cent or more), they act by causing general coagulation of proteins (e.g., enzymes); this is as lethal to cells as a blow with a hammer is to a mosquito! Consequently, certain heavy metal salts such as copper sulfate and bichloride of mercury are often used as general disinfectants or antiseptics. Copper, zinc and iron compounds are commonly used in garden sprays to control fungal and bacterial diseases of plants. Silver nitrate is very effective in decontaminating burns.

Some metals (e.g., $Hg^{++}$, $Ag^+$, $Pb^{++}$ and $Zn^{++}$) are poisonous even in very low concentrations (of the order of 0.0001 per cent) because they combine with and inactivate certain essential functional groups in the cell. For example, $Hg^{++}$ combines with the $^-SH$ group of enzymes, inhibiting their action.

In minute, barely detectable (*trace*) amounts, several heavy metal ions, including some of those just mentioned, are essential for cell growth because these ions are parts of coenzyme molecules. Examples are the presence of iron in the red respiratory pigment, hemoglobin, in our own red blood corpuscles and in the cytochrome system of respiratory pigments of aerobic bacteria. Molybdenum is essential in nitrogen fixation by certain soil organisms (Chapter 43); others will be mentioned farther on.

Toxicity of metallic ions depends greatly on the species of microorganism being dealt with, the presence of chelating* agents and other substances that combine with the metal ions, and the pH of the surrounding medium. Some metals are poisonous for one species but not at all for others. As a rule, light metals such as sodium, potassium, lithium, strontium, magnesium, calcium and nonmetal ammonium (usually present as chlorides) are not only harmless but most are essential to bacteria as salts in concentrations of from 0.05 to about 1.5 per cent.

The less toxic metal ions act favorably in a great variety of ways, sometimes by effectively suppressing the ionization of unfavorable substances, or by reacting with these substances to prevent them from affecting bacteria unfavorably. For example, the relatively benign calcium chloride protects against noxious sodium oxalate by forming an insoluble precipitate of calcium oxalate, thus removing the toxic oxalate radicle from the solution.

**Ion Antagonisms.**   Some cations are biologically antagonistic to each other. For example, $Li^+$ and $Zn^{++}$ are definitely toxic to certain bacteria of importance in the dairy industry (*Lactobacillus* and *Leuconostoc*) and to others as well. These ions appear to drive $H^+$ from its normal position and to take its place in certain enzymes. This results in a stoppage of the action of the enzymes. The ions are said to *antagonize* the $H^+$. By increasing the concentration of $H^+$, i.e., lowering the pH, this toxicity of $Li^+$ and $Zn^{++}$ is reduced or eliminated. The antagonism is said to be *reversed*. Complex organic molecules can act to block and unblock enzymes in much the same way.

As will be seen later, knowledge of this sort of antagonism, its reversal, and competition between ions and molecules in living cells is of fundamental importance in the science of chemotherapy, as well as in cell physiology, industry, genetics, oncology, and other activities. It would be well to keep the basic idea of ionic and molecular antagonisms in mind.

ANIONS.   The physiological value of any ionizable compound for microorganisms is

---

*\*Chelating agents* are organic compounds which form a complex compound with a heavy metal, enclosing it in a ringlike molecular structure as though held in a claw (Gr. *chēlē* = claw). The position of iron in the molecule of heme, part of the respiratory pigment of our red blood corpuscles, is a typical example (Fig. 5.1).

determined in part by the anion. In order of favorable or nontoxic action with regard to bacteria we may list several anions (with sodium as the cation) as follows: sulfate, tartrate, chloride, nitrate, acetate, citrate, oxalate, iodide, benzoate, salicylate, sorbate, hydrogen sulfide, tellurite; sulfates the least toxic, tellurites the most unfavorable. Generalizations here are apt to mislead because organisms differ greatly. For example, *Corynebacterium diphtheriae* (cause of diphtheria) grows well in the presence of tellurite, whereas many other microorganisms are completely inhibited by tellurium compounds.

The toxicity of alkalies also varies but depends mainly on the anion, $^-$OH. However, the cation of alkaline substances also plays its role, as it does in the action of acids and salts. For example, barium hydroxide, a much weaker (less dissociated) alkali than sodium hydroxide, is nevertheless much more toxic at the same pOH. This is partly because the barium ion is more toxic (for the organisms studied) than the sodium ion, though the exact mechanism of the toxic action is not clear. It is important to remember that species vary greatly in respect to sensitivity toward various ions.

**Undissociated Molecules.** The biological activity of most ionizing compounds, inorganic as well as organic, depends not only on anion and cation but also on the undissociated molecule. For example, the toxic effects of benzoic, acetic and sorbic acids are much greater than would be expected from the pH of their solutions. Thus, hydrochloric acid and sulfuric acid, although "strong" acids, are much less poisonous to most bacteria at a given pH than benzoic, sorbic or acetic acid at the same pH. About 7.5 to 7.7 parts per million of hydrochloric or sulfuric acid are required to produce the same toxic effect as 0.1 and 1.2 parts per million, respectively, of benzoic or acetic acid. Benzoic and acetic acids, also sorbic acid, are common food preservatives because of the high toxicity of the undissociated molecules for microorganisms (and relatively low toxicity for you and me!).

## 19.5  ELECTRICITY

The passage of electric current, direct or alternating (110 v), through a suspension of microorganisms appears to have little effect by itself. If a current of great intensity is passed for a long time, however, electrolysis of some of the constituents of the medium will result. Some of these have deleterious effects. Heat, also, will be generated. Biological effects of intense magnetic fields on microorganisms is a special field just being explored.

**Electrophoresis.** The student familiar with *colloids* (very minute particles suspended in fluid) knows that all very minute particles, including molecules of protein and microorganisms, when suspended in aqueous solutions acquire an electric, usually negative, charge on their surfaces. Therefore, when an electric current is passed through a suspension of such particles, those with a negative charge travel toward the positive electrode (anode), while those with a positive charge travel toward the negative electrode (cathode). Those with a strong charge travel faster than those having a weaker charge. This migration is termed *electrophoresis.*

The electrophoretic migration of microorganisms may be observed directly with a microscope focused on a thin hollow cell with electrodes at each end. Electrophoretic migration may also be detected by testing for the presence of the migrating organisms in one or the other of the legs of a U-tube with electrodes at each leg, the particles being introduced at the middle of the U.

Gel Electrophoresis. In 1937 Tiselius (Nobel Prize winner) devised a means, called the "moving boundary" method, for observing electrophoresis in fluids. More recently refined methods have been developed that permit not only measurements of rate and direction of electrophoretic migration but accurate separation of many different proteins from complex mixtures such as serum.

In a representative procedure the material to be analyzed (say serum) is placed as a narrow, transverse stripe, usually near the cathode at an angle of 90 degrees to the long axis, on a ribbon of gel (e.g., starch, cellulose acetate, agar, acrylamide) about 1 by 8 inches in dimensions. The gel ribbon is kept saturated with cold (5° to 10° C.) buffer solution. The ribbon, kept perfectly horizontal at all times, is held by suitable clamps so that one end dips into a buffer bath in contact with an anode while the other end is in similar contact with a cathode. A high voltage current (110 to 500 volts or more) at low amperage (1 to 2 ma.) is passed from end to end of the buffer-saturated ribbon of gel for from 20 minutes to several hours.

The proteins in the cross-wise stripe of sample migrate along the length of the ribbon of gel, commonly toward the anode, *at different rates.* After stopping the current each different kind of protein may be identified by its position in the ribbon of gel; special staining methods are used to locate the different proteins. Each protein forms a transverse bar across the gel ribbon.

*Electrohydraulic Shock.* The passage of high-voltage discharges (8 to 15 kv.) through fluid results in what is called electrohydraulic shock; i.e., sudden, short waves at pressures of up to 75,000 pounds per square inch. The treatment is lethal to bacteria and bacteriophage suspended in the fluid. Lethal effects are ascribed in part to mechanical action, in part to chemical causes: oxidations, free radicals (see ionizing radiations, page 180), liberation of toxic metal ions from the electrodes and so on. (See also immunoelectrophoresis; Chapter 24.)

## 19.6   OSMOTIC PRESSURE

If living cells are immersed in fluids with abnormally high osmotic pressures, water will be drawn out of the cells until the cell collapses (*plasmolysis*). If cells are immersed in a fluid of abnormally low osmotic pressure, water will be drawn into the cells until they rupture (*plasmoptysis*). Ordinarily, osmotic pressure within the cell is sufficient to keep it slightly distended or in a *turgid* condition. When the osmotic pressure of the surrounding fluid is in equilibrium with that of the cell contents, the surrounding fluid is said to be *isotonic* with that of the cell. If the osmotic pressure of the surrounding fluid is less than that of the cell contents the fluid is *hypotonic* with respect to the cell. If the osmotic pressure of the surrounding fluid is greater than that of the cell contents, the surrounding fluid is *hypertonic* with respect to the cell. Extremely hypertonic solutions like pickling brines and concentrated sugar syrups have a "preservative" value because they withdraw water from cells, which has a microbistatic effect on many organisms. A method of preserving numerous species of bacteria in salt solutions has been described. The action of strongly hypertonic solutions is comparable with desiccation, which removes water entirely, and with freezing, which immobilizes water in the cell. Only organisms that can imbibe water from very hypertonic solutions, e.g., many molds and some bacteria, can grow under such conditions.

Probably because of their minute volume, relatively strong cell wall and thin cytoplasmic membrane which permits rapid adjustment of osmotic equilibria, most bacteria are not highly sensitive to variations in salt concentrations between about 0.5 and 3 per cent. Concentra-

tions much above this may adversely affect some of the more sensitive strains. Some marine bacteria adapted to the salinity of ocean water (about 3.5 per cent) are quite sensitive to lower or higher salinities and will not grow if the salinity is less than about 2 per cent or over about 15 per cent.

HALOPHILIC ORGANISMS. There are bacteria that have become adapted to the high salinity (about 29 per cent) of various salt waters such as the Dead Sea and the Great Salt Lake of Utah. These organisms cannot grow in lake water diluted to a salinity of less than about 13 per cent. Such organisms are spoken of as *halophilic* (salt-loving). There are halophilic and also *haloduric* bacteria that grow in commercial pickling brines with salt concentrations up to 30 per cent. Some are a cause of spoilage of various commodities preserved with salt, such as fish, meat, hides and pickle stock (Chapters 46 and 47).

**Alterations in Membrane Permeability.** Even though the favorable osmotic pressure of a given culture medium may continue unchanged, there often appear in it, as a result of aging and metabolic activities, substances that alter the permeability of the cell membrane so that excessive water diffuses inward and the cells become swollen and distorted. Such alterative substances may be various waste products (e.g., acids or alcohol) of cells that have grown in the culture. Such distorted forms of bacteria are often called *involution forms*. Cell lysis finally results.

## 19.7   RADIANT ENERGY

The nature of radiant energy and its effects on living cells, especially its genetic or mutagenic effects, are discussed in Chapter 15. We may here mention some practical uses made of lethal effects of radiations.

**Infrared Rays.** To be effective radiations must penetrate into the irradiated substance, and their energy must be liberated within it. They are ineffective if they are completely reflected from the surface of the substance, or if they pass completely through it. The energy content of each quantum of radiant energy is an inverse function of the wave length. Waves longer than about 10,000 to 12,000 Å (infrared) contain less energy than visible ultraviolet and x-rays and are reflected by smooth surfaces that are opaque to visible light. When absorbed by nonreflecting materials their relatively low energy is given off as heat ("heating rays"). Such

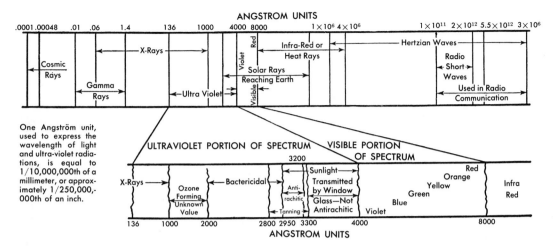

**Figure 19.7** Spectrum charts. (From The Westinghouse Sterilamp and the Rentschler-James Process of Sterilization, courtesy of the Westinghouse Electric & Manufacturing Company, Inc.)

long waves are neither ionizing nor "exciting," although their heat may be lethal. They are sometimes used in quick cooking.

**Ultraviolet Light.** Ultraviolet light is a component of sunlight and produces suntan and sunburn. It is also mutagenic and carcinogenic (Chapter 15). It also activates green-plant chlorophyll. Ultraviolet light has very slight powers of penetration. It is therefore effective mainly at surfaces or in thin films. It is *non-ionizing* but produces lethal photochemical changes in protoplasm if exposure is sufficient. Ultraviolet light, like visible light, consists of a spectrum of different wave lengths from about 4000 to about 136 Å (see Fig. 19.7). Those between 2800 and 2300 Å, especially 2537 Å, are most useful biologically, being strongly microbicidal yet readily produced and managed.

It is of interest to note that the microbicidal effects of ultraviolet radiation differ from those of heat, in that very thermostable endospores are easily killed with ultraviolet light. Ultraviolet light is as effective in the absence of oxygen as in its presence; ionizing radiations, on the contrary, are more effective in oxygen.

**X-rays.** Unlike ultraviolet and longer waves, x-rays have marked powers of penetration and are not much reflected. X-rays cause abnormal making and breaking of H-bonds of DNA and disturbance of secondary molecular structures. These are lethal, but the use of x-rays for routine sterilization is costly and dangerous.

**Sunlight.** The microbicidal or disinfectant ("purifying") action of sunlight has been known for centuries. We now know that it is caused mainly by the ultraviolet rays (4000 to 2950 Å)

in solar light. The heating and drying effects of sunlight also have a bactericidal effect.

**Photodynamic Sensitization.** See page 181.

## 19.8 HYDROSTATIC PRESSURES

If living microorganisms in aqueous fluid are placed in a steel cylinder and a piston is pressed down upon the suspension with great force, the organisms may or may not be affected, depending on the source and species of organism, the pH and salinity and other properties of the medium and the temperature. Some species of bacteria found in the deepest known valleys in the floor of the Pacific and Indian oceans obviously thrive under pressures of over 16,000 lb. per square inch. Deep-sea bacteria and others from deep oil wells appear to be favorably influenced by such pressures; they are said to be *barophilic* (Gr. *baros* = weight; *philic* = prefers). In the range above 9000 lb. per square inch, death of most familiar shallow-living species occurs within one hour.

Pressures much above 15,000 lb. per square inch denature ordinary proteins and inactivate ordinary enzymes. High pressures also increase rates of some chemical and enzymic reactions, and cause diminution in volume of organic colloids, enzymes and molecules, increases in viscosity of many fluids and increased electrolytic dissociation. Probably all of these changes are involved in the biological effects of high pressures, but exact details of the mechanisms are still under investigation.

**Pressure and Temperature.** In general there is a compensatory relation between pressure and temperature. Unduly high incubation temperatures may be thought of as causing deleterious *expansion* of enzymes (colloids), perhaps with weakening of H-bonds of primary and secondary structures. Increased pressures tend to prevent the expansion and so lessen this unfavorable effect of high temperatures. Cooling may be thought of as causing undue *contraction,* and hence diminution or loss of activity of enzyme colloids. High pressures enhance the retarding effect of low temperatures, while relief from pressure tends to overcome the contraction. For example, organisms normally growing best at 20 to 30° C. were completely inhibited at 20° C. by 4500 lb. per square inch pressure but they grew well at 40° C. under the same pressure. Experimental data may vary somewhat under different experimental conditions.

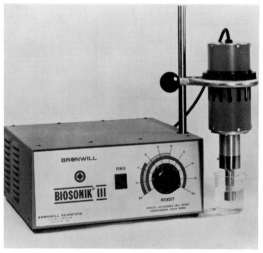

**Figure 19.9**   Ultrasonic probe. See text for discussion. (Courtesy of Bronwill Scientific, a division of Will Scientific, Inc.)

## 19.9   MECHANICAL IMPACT; VIBRATION

In order to investigate the inner substances of cells, liberation of the cell contents by mechanical rupture of the cell walls and membranes is often preferable to the use of chemical extractants, enzymes or solvents.

CRUSHING. Most unicellular microorganisms (not viruses) are easily crushed by the

**Figure 19.8**   In mechanical cell homogenizer, cell walls are broken down by collisions between thousands of tiny glass beads in the violently agitated cylinder. (Courtesy of Bronwill Scientific, a division of Will Scientific, Inc.)

impingement upon them of solid particles such as steel or glass balls. Violent shaking in a vessel half filled with minute glass beads or sand is often used for the mechanical disruption of bacteria (Fig. 19.8). They shatter especially readily if made brittle by freezing. Cells may also be ruptured by grinding them with fine abrasives or by repeated freezing and thawing.

RAPID VIBRATIONS. Bacteria, because of their small mass and their relatively tough cell walls, are not readily disrupted by slow vibrations. The high limit of audible tone has a vibration rate of around 10,000 per second; the lowest audible tone has a vibration rate of around 100 per second. This is the range of *sonic vibrations.* (In defining sonic limits much depends on the intensity and quality of the sound and the individual ear.) Sonic and supersonic, or ultrasonic, vibrations for microbiological purposes are generally produced in fluids by electrically vibrated disks or rods of nickel, stainless steel or quartz (Fig. 19.9).

Immersed in a fluid that is subjected to vibrations of appropriate rate and intensity, bacteria are torn, the protoplasm disrupted and the cells killed (Fig. 19.10). Much of the damage is believed to be caused by *cavitation:* the *intracellular* formation of a foam of minute bubbles of the gas that is ordinarily in solution in the protoplasm, or extracellularly in the fluids surrounding the cell. Bacteria differ greatly in their susceptibility to mechanical rupture by any means. Some are much tougher than others.

OSMOTIC SHOCK. Another method of disrupting cells without using chemicals is the im-

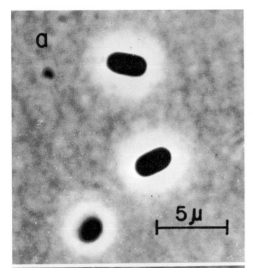

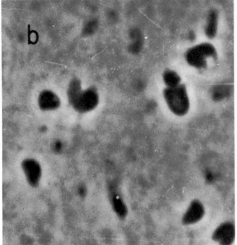

**Figure 19.10** Effect of intense sonic vibration on a common bacterium of the soil, *Azotobacter vinelandii*. (a), before vibration; (b), after vibration for one minute. Note the shattering effect on the bacilli. (From Marr and Cota-Robles: J. Bact., vol. 74.)

mersion of prepared protoplasts (see page 159) in distilled water (*osmotic shock*). They immediately burst.

## 19.10  SURFACE FORCES

For purposes of the present discussion a surface is the boundary between a solid and a fluid (L. *fluidum* = substance that flows; liquid or gas) or between two immiscible fluids. Commonly encountered interfaces are (1) between a cell and its surrounding medium; (2) between a colloidal particle such as an enzyme and the fluid matrix of the cell; (3) between a bubble of gas and the fluid surrounding it; (4) between

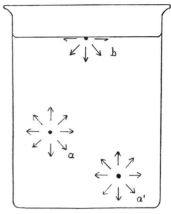

**Figure 19.11** Diagram showing how surface tension acts. The molecules *a* and *a′* are attracted equally from all directions and are in a state of equilibrium. Molecules at the surface, like *b*, are under a greater tension from below than above and the entire surface therefore tends to pull inward much as though the surface film were a rubber membrane.

a globule of oil and the aqueous fluid surrounding it, or, conversely, between a droplet of aqueous fluid and the oil in which it is suspended.

In any cell, most of the chemical and physical changes on which life depends take place at surfaces. Biologically effective surfaces are found at the outer surfaces of cells and at the surfaces of the intracellular colloidal particles, enzymes, lipids, membranes and ribosomes.

**Surface Tension.** One of the most important surface forces is called *surface tension*. Surface tension results from the universal attraction, or cohesive force, between molecules. As shown in Figure 19.11, molecules (a, a′) in the depths of a fluid are attracted equally from all sides. At the air-liquid interface the attraction between the liquid molecules (b) is along the interface and from below. These unbalanced attractions produce surface tension. The surface tension of any fluid is a physical constant under any stated condition and, for liquids, is expressed in terms of dynes per cm. of surface (a dyne is the force required to accelerate one gram a distance of one centimeter per second (per second). Increases in temperature usually lower surface tension. The lower the surface tension of a liquid, the more easily molecules escape from the surface, i.e., the more volatile it is.

Under the influence of surface tension, any fluid surface acts in some respects like an elastic membrane. If we take for an example the surface of water in a clean teaspoon or beaker we find that we can "stretch" this membrane by filling the spoon or beaker 2 or 3 mm.

**Figure 19.12**  *A*, Spoon super-filled with water (surface tension: 77 dynes per centimeter). Drawing shows the effect of surface tension of water in holding the surface film intact against the hydrostatic pressure of water above the actual rim of the spoon.

*B*, Spoon level-filled with alcohol (surface tension: 28 dynes per centimeter). The level of alcohol is exactly at the rim of the spoon; another drop of alcohol will cause it to overflow.

above the actual top edge of the vessel before it overflows (Fig. 19.12).

SURFACE TENSION REDUCERS. Many organic substances, such as alcohols, organic acids, polypeptides, bile and certain substances, e.g., soaps, classed as "detergents," can weaken this intermolecular pull and thus lower surface tension. Such substances are called *surface tension reducers* or, commonly, *surfactants*. In the presence of such agents the spoon or beaker previously referred to overflows almost exactly at the top edge. There are many such substances: alcohols, organic acids, bile, serum, peptone, some antibiotics, detergents and others to be discussed.

Three important phenomena associated with surface tension are *adsorption, wetness* and *detergency* which, in turn, is often dependent on *emulsification.*

**Adsorption.**    Surface tension reducers (except physical agents like heat) generally consist of polar molecules; i.e., the molecules of the reducer have one pole or group that is more strongly attracted to the fluid in which it is dissolved, e.g., water, than the remainder of the molecule. The group attracted by water (e.g., $Na^+$, $-SO_3^-$, etc.) is said to be hydrophilic. The other group may be a long chain alkyl group, less attracted by water; it is said to be hydrophobic. When surface tension reducer molecules are dissolved in water they tend to group themselves closely side by side at the interface of the fluid, with the hydrophilic groups toward the fluid, the hydrophobic groups toward the interface. The attraction between these molecules is lower than that between the molecules of water, thus the surface tension of the solution is lowered (see Figure 21.8).

Suppose that a substance (e.g., soap) that reduces surface tension is added to the water in the beaker shown in Figure 19.11. It must, according to physical laws (entropy or second law of thermodynamics), tend to release as much of the potential energy, i.e., the intramolecular pull or surface energy, as possible.

In this case it must carry the reduction of surface tension as far as possible. The surface tension reducer can lower the surface tension to the greatest extent only by accumulating at all of the surfaces of the fluid as just described. This accumulation is known as *adsorption.* Adsorption occurs at the air-fluid surface, at the surface in contact with the glass walls of the containing vessel and on the surfaces of any particles, such as microorganisms, suspended in the fluid. If the surface tension reducer can pass through cell membranes, it can accumulate (be adsorbed) on the surfaces of intracellular colloids and membranes also.

Of two surfactants at a given surface, the more potent will generally displace the weaker by *competitive adsorption.*

**Wetness and Surface Tension.**    The property of wetness of liquids is determined by their surface tension. Wetness increases with lowered surface tension. Fluids of low surface tension achieve more intimate and effective contact with solid surfaces than fluids of high surface tension. Mercury at room temperature, for example, has a very high surface tension (around 466 dynes per centemeter). As a result, as everyone who has held mercury in the palm of the hand knows from experience, mercury possesses the property of wetness in a negligible degree. The inward pull between molecules at the surface causes liquid mercury to draw inward into globules of itself in a very unsociable manner. It does not spread out and come into intimate contact. Water has only a *moderately* high surface tension (77 dynes per centimeter) and a moderate degree of wetness, while alcohol has a much lower surface tension (about 28 dynes per centimeter). Alcohol, therefore, wets or spreads when in contact with surfaces much better than does water and thus comes into more intimate contact with objects which it touches. It is wetter than water, physically, physiologically and politically!

Many important fluids—cell fluids, disinfectants, culture media, paints, fountain pen ink, cosmetics and drugs—are really *wetter* than water. The importance of wetness will be reemphasized in the discussion of disinfectants.

The presence of some surface tension reducers, such as soap or bile salts, in culture media is manifested by failure of some organisms to grow. Others may grow in media of abnormally low surface tension, but fission or septum formation is delayed so that large spheres of cocci and very long filaments of bacilli are formed. Spore formation may be delayed or abolished.

A difficulty in studies of the effect of low surface tension as a biological factor is the differentiation between the *physical* effects of a surface tension reducer and its effects as a *chemical* agent or lipid solvent. Careful comparative controls are necessary in such studies.

Many of the substances that nourish cells are potent surface tension reducers; so are some important disinfectants. For example, at the same surface tension, say about 40 dynes per centimeter, peptone will nourish but phenol will kill.*

## 19.11  GERM-FREE (AXENIC) LIFE; GNOTOBIOTICS

As we know, microorganisms are found almost everywhere in our environment as well as on all parts of the body surface, the entire alimentary canal, the upper respiratory system, the eyes, the ears and the genital openings. The newborn animal is contaminated at birth and remains an involuntary and often unknowing host to billions of various species of microscopic parasites or commensals throughout his life. Some of them help digest his food and furnish him with vitamins. Even the interior of the living cell is not immune from parasitic invasion by viruses and rickettsias. These relationships have existed since Archeozoic periods, and animal life is well adapted to existence in contact with most microbial life. Only a few species of microorganisms cause much disturbance in modern man; among them are pathogens like typhoid bacilli, hookworms, malaria parasites, viruses, certain fungi, pneumococci, gonococci and tubercle bacilli. It would be of great interest and extremely useful to know how this ages-long contact between host and parasite has affected the hereditary, physiologic, biochemical, anatomic and other properties of each of the participants in the relationship.

**Interrelations of Organisms.**  What effect does the enormous number of supposedly harmless bacteria in the intestine have on our nutrition? Do they synthesize vitamins for us? Do they produce antibiotics which are taken into our systems? Do they produce poisons which damage us subtly and shorten our lives, or do they exert favorable or even absolutely necessary influences? Do they immunize us to infection? What is the role of each of the species?

We begin to realize the importance of such interrelationships when it is found that suppression of certain groups of bacteria that normally inhabit the gastrointestinal tract (as sometimes occurs during presurgical antibiotic therapy) permits growth of other groups which are normally held in abeyance by the suppressed microorganisms. This often has evil and sometimes fatal results. Could we answer some of the above questions by producing an animal entirely free from microorganisms and then contaminating it with single species of microorganism at a time?

To do such a thing it would be necessary, by the use of fantastically rigorous aseptic technique, to separate an animal from all demonstrable microorganisms at the beginning of life, to maintain it for months or years free from any demonstrable live microorganisms, and then to observe how it fares in life without its usual living mates, the microorganisms. Such an animal might be said to represent "germfree" life, or *axenic* life (Gr. *a* = without; *xeno* = foreign material).

Experimental Approaches.  Pasteur realized the value of such investigations as early as 1885 and actually reared some germ-free or axenic chicks. Because of the great difficulties involved, only four workers prior to 1928, including Pasteur, had successfully reared any germ-free animals. In 1928 Reyniers started work on chickens and, with his coworkers, succeeded in raising numerous germ-free animals. Completely axenic insects, fish, chickens, rodents, dogs, pigs and monkeys have been born and held axenic for many generations.

The original apparatus for such work consisted of large steel cylinders that could be steam sterilized, with closed glass observation ports; hand holes fitted with airtight, arm-length, seamless rubber gloves; and airtight systems of outer chambers or locks through which sterilized food, water and equipment could be passed into the chamber while waste materials were passed out. Air was passed through sterilizing filters and conditioning apparatus. Such equipment and its operation necessitated solution of some difficult engineering problems. In the original apparatus, one chamber was big enough for an attendant to enter, dressed in a diving suit, through a deep tank of disinfectant.

As an improvement over these ponderous steel containers, vinyl-plastic, tentlike "flexible film isolaters" have been introduced. These can be quickly and easily sterilized by filling the interior with germicidal gas. They are made airtight and have the advantages of being completely transparent, flexible, easily portable,

---

*Microorganisms also vary. Some strict autotrophs are inhibited by peptone; others, common in soil, thrive on phenol as a source of energy and carbon! Thus, generalizations about microorganisms are hazardous.

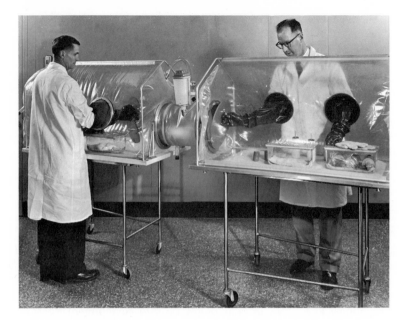

**Figure 19.13** One type of plastic film apparatus for rearing animals under germ-free (axenic or gnotobiotic) conditions. (Courtesy of American Sterilizer Co.)

relatively inexpensive and convenient. They come in a variety of sizes (Fig. 19.13).

Some of the technical difficulties are great, as for example, feeding young rats delivered aseptically inside the germ-free compartment at Cesarean section (to say nothing of doing a completely germ-free Cesarean section!). They require milk every hour, 24 hours a day, for weeks on end. It took much research to synthesize a satisfactory substitute for mother rats' milk!

Careful control is necessary at all times, and all animals, their feces and bodies, and the dust, feed and water in the germ-free compartments are examined bacteriologically at short intervals to detect any contamination. The first significant studies on germ-free life were carried on at the Laboratories of Bacteriology at the University of Notre Dame (Lobund). Within the last decade germ-free life has taken an important role in many aspects of biology. Axenic animals are reared in a number of places and shipped in special containers all over the world. Who will produce the first axenic human family, and *must* it be on the Moon?

Germ-free animals thrive. Axenic animals in general live longer and seem healthier than ordinary (conventional) animals. However, they are often susceptible to fatal infections with usually harmless bacteria. The living cells of axenic rats and chickens seem to remain "younger" than those of conventional animals. Is this because they are germ-free? If antibiotics

are fed to farm stock, this possibly reduces their bacterial burden. Young stock fed with antibiotics certainly grow much faster. If antibiotics are fed to *axenic* poultry there is no such improvement. This suggests that unless the birds are contaminated the antibiotic is without effect.

GNOTOBIOSIS AND ITS EFFECTS. The study of axenic animals that have been experimentally infected with *known* microorganisms is spoken of as gnotobiology (Gr. *gnos* = known; *bios* = life). The animals are said to be *gnotobiotic*. Studies of gnotobiotic animals have yielded interesting data.

An important observation was made when it was found that axenic guinea pigs did not develop dysentery or amebic abscesses when infected with the ameba, *Entamoeba histolytica,* which usually causes a particularly severe form of dysentery in guinea pigs. Now it is known that *E. histolytica* feeds on bacteria. In axenic guinea pigs there were no bacteria. The ameba-infected axenic guinea pig, free from disease, quickly developed dysentery (or amebic abscesses in the liver) and died when fed ordinary "harmless" intestinal bacteria! It is suggested that certain antibiotics are effective in curing amebic dysentery, not because they affect amebae, but because they deprive the amebae of their food, the bacteria. The problem requires further study.

Studies of the blood of axenic animals show that they have less defense against infection (less antibodies) than conventional animals.

Numerous other important differences between axenic and conventional organisms have been noted. A serious problem has arisen from the finding that apparently axenic animals harbor intracellular viruses (Chapters 39–41) in latent form and transmit them from generation to generation *in utero* or even *in ovum*.

## SUPPLEMENTARY READING

Anderson, D. L., and Bradley, S. G.: The action of ultrasonic vibrations on bacteriophages. J. Gen. Microbiol., *37*:67, 1964.

Barnothy, M. F., editor: Biological Effects of Magnetic Fields. Plenum Press, New York. 1964.

Bausum, H. T., and Matney, T. S.: Boundary between bacterial mesophilism and thermophilism. J. Bact., *90*:50, 1965.

Böck, A., and Neidhardt, F. C.: Isolation of a mutant of *Escherichia coli* with a temperature-sensitive fructose-1,6-diphosphate aldolase activity. J. Bact., *92*:464, 1966.

Borick, P. M., and Fogarty, M. G.: Effects of continuous and interrupted radiation on microorganisms. Appl. Microbiol., *15*:785, 1967.

Boyd, W. L., and Boyd, J. W.: Soil microorganisms of the McMurdo Sound Area, Antarctica. Appl. Microbiol., *63*:116, 1963.

Burns, V. W.: Reversible sonic inhibition of protein, purine, and pyrimidine biosynthesis in the living cell. Science, *146*:1056, 1964.

Chance, H. L.: Salt—a preservative for bacterial cultures. J. Bact., *85*:719, 1963.

Davis, N. S., Silverman, G. J., and Keller, W. H.: Combined effects of ultrahigh vacuum and temperature on the viability of some spores and soil organisms. Appl. Microbiol., *11*:202, 1963.

Dewald, R. R.: Preservation of *Serratia marcescens* by high-vacuum Lyophilization. Appl. Microbiol., *14*:561, 1966.

Duguid, J. P., and Wilkinson, J. F.: Environmentally induced changes in bacterial morphology. Eleventh Symposium, Microbial Reaction to Environment, page 69. Soc. Gen. Microbiol., London. 1961.

Evison, L. M., and Rose, A. H.: A comparative study on the biochemical bases of the maximum temperatures for growth of three pychrophilic microorganisms. J. Gen. Microbiol., *40*:349, 1965.

Fox, R. R., and Burdick, J. F.: Preservation of rabbit spermatozoa: ethylene glycol vs glycerol for frozen semen. Proc. Soc. Exp. Biol. Med., *113*:853, 1963.

Gilleland, S. E., and Speck, M. L.: Mechanism of the bactericidal action produced by electrohydraulic shock. Appl. Microbiol., *15*:1038, 1967.

Guda, H. E., Frajola, W. J., and Lessler, M. A.: Molecular changes in deoxyribonucleic acid induced by X-rays. Science, *137*:607, 1962.

Hungate, R. E.: The Rumen and its Microbes. Academic Press, New York. 1966.

Hwang, S. W.: Long term preservation of fungus cultures with liquid nitrogen refrigeration. Appl. Microbiol., *14*:784, 1966.

Ingram, M.: Micro-organisms resisting high concentrations of sugars or salts. Seventh Symposium, Microbial Ecology, page 90. Soc. Gen. Microbiol., London. 1957.

Johnson, F. H.: The action of pressure and temperature. Seventh Symposium, Microbial Ecology, page 134. Soc. Gen. Microbiol., London. 1957.

Kempner, E. S.: Upper temperature limit of life. Science, *142*:1318, 1963.

Landau, J. V.: Protein and nucleic acid synthesis in *Escherichia coli:* pressure and temperature effects. Science, *153*:1273, 1966.

Lev, M.: Studies on bacterial associations in germ-free animals and animals with defined floras. Thirteenth Symposium, Symbiotic Associations, page 325. Soc. Gen. Microbiol., London. 1963.

Luckey, T. D.: Germ-free Life & Gnotobiology. Academic Press, New York. 1963.

Meyer, R. C., Bohl, E. H., and Kohler, E. M.: Procurement and maintenance of germ-free swine for microbiological investigations. Appl. Microbiol., *12*:295, 1964.

Morita, R. Y., and Mathemeier, P. F.: Temperature-hydrostatic pressure studies on partially purified inorganic pyrophosphatase activity. J. Bact., *88*:1667, 1964.

Olson, G. B., and Wostman, B. S.: Electrophoretic and immunoelectrophoretic studies of the serum of germ-free and conventional guinea pigs. Proc. Soc. Exp. Biol. Med., *116*:914, 1964.

Phillips, B. P., and Gorstein, F.: Effects of different species of bacteria on the pathology of enteric amebiasis in monocontaminated guinea pigs. Amer. J. Trop. Med. Hyg., *15*:863, 1966.

Pollard, M.: Germfree animals and biological research. Science, *145*:247, 1964.

Ron, E. Z., Kohler, R. E., and Davis, B.: Polysomes extracted from *Escherichia coli* by freeze-thaw-lysozyme lysis. Science, *153*:1119, 1966.

de Serres, F. J.: Some aspects of the influence of environment on the radiosensitivity of micro-organisms. Eleventh Symposium, Microbial Reaction to Environment, page 196. Soc. Gen. Microbiol., London. 1961.

Shaw, M. K., and Ingraham, J. L.: Synthesis of macromolecules by *Escherichia coli* near the minimal temperature for growth. J. Bact., *94*:157, 1967.

Smith, H.: Microbial behaviour in natural and artificial environments. Fourteenth Symposium. Microbial Behaviour 'in vivo' and 'in vitro', page 1, Soc. Gen. Microbiol., London. 1964.

Stokes, J. L., and Redmond, M. L.: Quantitative ecology of psychrophilic microorganisms. Appl. Microbiol., *14*:74, 1966.

Subcommittee on Radiological Health: Ionizing Radiation. Amer. Pub. Health Assn., New York. 1966.

Tomita, Y., and Prince, A. M.: Photodynamic inactivation of arbor viruses by neutral red and visible light. Proc. Soc. Exp. Biol. Med., *112*:887, 1963.

Upadhyay, J., and Stokes, J. L.: Anaerobic growth of psychrophilic bacteria. J. Bact., *83*:270, 1962.

Wheeler, W. B., and Hollinshead, A. C.: Photosensitizing substance in human serum: effect on HeLa cells. Science, *141*:1279, 1963.

Whipple, H. E., editor: Gel Electrophoresis. Ann. N. Y. Acad. Sci., *121*(Art. 2):305, 1964.

Woods, D. D., and Foster, M. A.: Metabolic considerations relating to the life of bacteria in vivo. Fourteenth Symposium, Microbial Behaviour 'in vivo' and 'in vitro,' page 30. Soc. Gen. Microbiol., London. 1964.

Zobell, C. E., and Cobet, A. B.: Growth, reproduction, and death rates of *Escherichia coli* at increased hydrostatic pressures. J. Bact., *84*:1228, 1962.

*Chapter 20*

---

# STERILIZATION AND DISINFECTION
## Basic Principles

An important phase of microbiology is knowledge of methods for killing, for removing and for inhibiting (preventing growth of) microorganisms. Species of microorganisms vary in the ease with which they may be destroyed, removed or inhibited, and the situations in which they may occur differ greatly (e.g., blood, foods, water, sewage, soil). Therefore, no one or two methods are generally applicable. Each situation is a problem in itself, and the methods employed must depend on the knowledge, ingenuity and purposes of the operator. There are basic facts, however, which guide the procedure in any given situation.

There are four main reasons for killing, removing or inhibiting microorganisms. They are: (1) to prevent infection of man, his animals and plants; (2) to prevent spoilage of food and other commodities; (3) to prevent interference by contaminating microorganisms in various industrial processes that depend on pure cultures; (4) to prevent contamination of materials used in pure-culture work in laboratories (diagnosis, research, industry) so that studies of the growth of one kind of organism in a particular medium or infected animal may not be confused by the presence and growth of others at the same time. In this chapter we shall discuss some basic principles underlying common methods of killing or removing microorganisms.

## 20.1 DEFINITION OF TERMS

Several new terms used in this chapter may be explained as follows:

**Sterilization.** In microbiology sterilization means the freeing of any object or substance from all life of any kind. For microbiological purposes microorganisms may be killed *in situ* by: heat; gases such as formaldehyde, ethylene oxide or beta-propiolactone; solutions of various chemicals; ultraviolet or gamma irradiation. Organisms may be removed mechanically by very high speed centrifugation or by filtration (see farther on, this chapter).

**Disinfection.** Disinfection means the killing or removal of organisms capable of causing infection. Disinfection does not necessarily include sterilization, although some processes of disinfection accomplish sterilization. Disinfection is usually accomplished by chemicals such as carbolic acid (phenol), formaldehyde, chlorine, iodine or bichloride of mercury. In the case of milk, disinfection—but not sterilization—is brought about by *pasteurization*, a heating process described elsewhere. Disinfection is generally thought of as killing the more sensitive vegetative cells but not heat-resistant spores.

A *disinfectant* is an agent accomplishing disinfection. The term is often used synonymously with *antiseptic*. However, one ordinarily thinks of disinfection and disinfectants as applicable mainly to situations and objects not part of the body; floors, dishes, laundry and bedding. The terms *sanitizer* and *sanitization* are often used with this meaning.

ANTISEPTIC. Antiseptic is an ill-defined term, closely allied to disinfectant. A disinfectant is often used as an antiseptic and vice versa. Antiseptics are substances that kill or inhibit microorganisms, especially in contact with the body. Most disinfectants are too destructive of tissues to be useful as antiseptics.

BACTERICIDE. Any substance or agent that kills bacteria is a bactericide or bactericidal agent. The suffix, *-cide,* indicates *killer* and is used with germ (germ*icide*) and virus (viru*cide*).

SEPSIS. *Sepsis* is the growth of harmful microorganisms in contact with living tissue.

ASEPSIS. In a strict sense, *asepsis* is the absence of infectious microorganisms in living tissue, i.e., the absence of sepsis. However, the term is usually applied to any technique designed to keep all unwanted microorganisms out of any field of work or observation. Gnotobiotics is asepsis developed to its utmost extent. The work of microbiologists and surgeons involves aseptic technique. The surgeon and his assistants have sterile instruments, handle them with sterilized gloves, cover the patient with sterilized sheets and wear sterilized caps, gowns and masks to prevent infected hair, dust, droplets of saliva, perspiration or sputum from entering the sterile field and possibly infecting the patient. The patient's skin cannot be absolutely sterilized without injury because microorganisms live deep in sweat and sebaceous glands, but the site of the operation is disinfected as thoroughly as possible by applications of some suitable antiseptic or dilute disinfectant.

The microbiologist works in a "germ-free" cabinet or uses sterilized culture media and sterilized glassware kept sterile until the moment of use by coverings of paper and cotton plugs and by *aseptic technique* (i.e., avoidance of touching sterile materials with hands or unsterile objects and the exclusion of dust).

**Microbistasis.** *Stasis* is a Greek word meaning to stand still. *Microbistatic* (bacteriostatic, fungistatic) agents are substances or conditions that do not immediately kill microorganisms but that inhibit multiplication so that, after an initial decline in numbers, the microorganisms die after hours, days or many years without significant increase or decrease in number. Important microbistatic agents are desiccation, very low temperatures, antibiotics, sulfonamide drugs, extremely hypertonic solutions and certain dyes, such as crystal violet.

Microbistasis is more fully discussed in Chapter 21. Here it is necessary to note only that numerous disinfectants are chiefly microbistatic; i.e., they appear to kill microorganisms whereas actually the microorganisms are merely temporarily inhibited. Under certain conditions, such as introduction into the body, they are reactivated. For example, many valuable drugs (the sulfonamides and numerous antibiotics) are bacteriostatic in their action.

## MECHANISMS OF STERILIZATION AND DISINFECTION

Except for centrifugation and filtration, which are mainly mechanical in their action, sterilization and disinfection are generally accomplished by heat; chemicals such as chlorine or compounds of phenol (carbolic acid); and radiations, especially ultraviolet and gamma rays (Chapter 15).

## 20.2   TYPES OF CELL DAMAGE

**Denaturation and Coagulation.** When solutions of protein are heated at temperatures above 80° C., or when acids or certain divalent or trivalent cations are added to them, a white precipitate appears. The process by which this change from liquid to solid form occurs is termed *coagulation.* Coagulation is preceded by a partial dissolution or *denaturation* of the protein by breakage of hydrogen (or disulfide) bonds in the secondary and tertiary structures. The resulting separated and extended protein fibers become less soluble and the solution becomes more viscous. Functional properties such as enzymic activity are destroyed, and the protein is more readily hydrolyzed. The protein becomes flocculent and the floccules coalesce into the solid mass typical of coagulation (a hard-boiled egg). Some agents that cause the preliminary denaturation may or may not also cause coagulation. They may coagulate if in the presence of strong, colloid-precipitating agents such as $H^+$, heavy metal salts and especially heat.

Colloidal protein particles may be thrown out of suspension if their surface charges are neutralized. They are then said to be at their *iso-electric point.* For example, proteins are precipitated by certain cations: $H^+$, $Cu^{++}$, $Zn^{++}$, $Fe^{+++}$. Because of this, several heavy metals are commonly used as disinfectants: $CuSO_4$, $AgNO_3$, $HgCl_2$, $ZnO$. Of metallic ions it may be said that, in general, coagulating power is exponentially related to valency and also to atomic weight; e.g., $Fe^{+++}$ has much greater than one third more coagulating power than

Cu$^{++}$ or Zn$^{++}$. Hydrogen ions, however, are among the most active coagulants.

Certain organic substances are also important as denaturants or coagulants, among them alcohols, phenols, formaldehyde and many related and derived substances.

The general rule may be stated that any agent, physical or chemical, that induces denaturation or coagulation is lethal to living cells.

**Nonspecific Chemical Combinations.** Various chemically active substances will combine indiscriminately with any and all proteins and related and derived compounds. Chlorine is such a substance, iodine another; cresols, carbolic acid (phenol), and formaldehyde are others. Lye (strong alkali) and strong acids are destructive of nearly all organic matter. Such substances are entirely nonspecific in their action; that is, they will combine as readily with body tissues, casein, feces, mucus, blood, wood or leather, as with the protoplasm of microorganisms.

**Specific Chemical Combinations.** There are several classes of substances of low molecular weight that can enter certain cells and, even in very low concentrations, interfere with or completely stop the action of one or more *specific molecular groups* (e.g., coenzymes) in a particular enzyme or enzymes, ribosomes or mRNA in such cells. This may result promptly in death or, more commonly, it may produce microbistasis, depending on type of cell and agent. Substances of this nature are represented by sulfonamide drugs and antibiotics. Cyanide and carbon monoxide "poison" hemoglobin and cytochrome oxidase by combining with the enzyme to the exclusion of oxygen, and thus inhibit cell respiration. However, they are far too poisonous for common use. Sodium fluoride interferes with carbohydrate metabolism; arsenicals with respiration, but these, too, are very poisonous for humans and must be used cautiously if at all. These phenomena are discussed in Chapter 21.

**Action on Surfaces.** As we have seen in Chapter 19, surface tension reducers (*surfactants*) tend to accumulate on surfaces by adsorption. Disinfectants that are also surfactants would be expected to have added effectiveness, because they would tend to concentrate and form coatings on microbial and enzymic surfaces. Indeed, some surfactants appear to act largely by coating the microbial surfaces and the effective surfaces of enzymes. This interferes with contact between enzymes and their substrates,

**TABLE 20.1   SOME MICROBICIDAL AND MICROBISTATIC AGENTS**

| |
|---|
| I. *Destruction* by |
|    A. Heat (boilers, ovens) |
|    B. Chemical agents (disinfectants) |
|    C. Radiations (x-rays, ultraviolet) |
|    D. Mechanical agents (crushing, shattering) |
| II. *Removal* (especially bacteria) by |
|    A. Filtering |
|    B. High speed centrifugation |
| III. *Inhibition* by |
|    A. Low temperatures (refrigeration, "dry ice") |
|    B. Desiccation (drying processes) |
|    C. Combinations of A and B |
|    D. High osmotic pressures (syrups, brines) |
|    E. Microbistatic chemicals and drugs |
|       1. Certain dyes such as eosin and methylene blue, crystal violet; bile (desoxycholate) |
|       2. Chemotherapeutic drugs such as sulfonamides and antibiotics |

with permeability of the cell wall and also with permease and other enzyme systems, thus preventing entrance and utilization of food substances.

Many surfactants also appear to injure or destroy the cell wall, causing inimical alterations of permeability or immediate *lysis*. These effects are probably caused, at least in part, by the dissolving or emulsifying effects of several surfactants on lipids of cell membranes and cell walls. Some important antibiotics (e.g., polymyxin) are surfactants of this nature.

Many disinfectant substances probably act by more than one of the mechanisms just mentioned, and by others that are only partly understood. Some microbicidal and microbistatic agents are listed in Table 20.1.

## 20.3   FACTORS THAT AFFECT STERILIZATION AND DISINFECTION

**Hydration.** The role of *hydration* in denaturation or coagulation by heat is shown by experimental data listed in Table 20.2. Obviously, coagulation proceeds best when protein is well hydrated. The same principle holds true, within limits, in coagulation by chemicals. The resistance of bacterial *endospores* to heat is probably caused in part by their almost completely dehydrated condition. In this discussion, unless otherwise noted, all statements on disinfection refer to nonsporing cells in aqueous suspension.

**TABLE 20.2**   EFFECT OF HYDRATION AND HEAT
ON EGG ALBUMEN*

| Water Content (Per Cent) | Approx. Coagulation Temperature (° C.) |
|---|---|
| 50 | 56 |
| 25 | 76 |
| 15 | 96† |
| 5 | 149 |
| 0 | 165‡ |

*Albumen is one form of protein.
† Boiling water = 100° C.
‡ 165° C = Oven temperature.

An example of the resistance of dehydrated protein to coagulation is seen in the difficulty of making dried-egg powder coagulate. Heated in a test tube, it will turn brown or char, but it will not coagulate unless a considerable quantity of water has been added. Of course, mixing dry egg with dry chemical disinfectants such as powdered bichloride of mercury produces no coagulation at all until moisture is added.

Aside from purely coagulative effects, the chemical reactions necessary to the actions of a variety of disinfectants are facilitated by the presence of water. Solution or *ionization* is essential.

**Time.**   No disinfectant as ordinarily used acts instantly. Sufficient time for contact and for whatever chemical and physical reactions will occur must be allowed. The time required will depend on: nature of the disinfectant; concentration; pH; temperature; nature of the organisms and existence in the bacterial population of cells having varying susceptibilities to the disinfectant.

**Rate of Disinfectant Action.**   Under uniform conditions of temperature, concentration and pH, the *rate* at which death of organisms in a pure culture occurs in contact with a disinfectant (including heat) is theoretically a function of time only.

If all the cells in a given culture are absolutely equal in vulnerability to the lethal agent, the line obtained by plotting logs of numbers of surviving organisms against units of time should be *straight* and *vertical;* i.e., the cells should all die at the same instant. Experience shows, however, that such curves are rarely vertical but are instead *slanting,* indicating that some of the cells are more vulnerable than others and thus that some cells die early, others after various intervals (Fig. 20.1). If the slope is steep the death rate is high; if it slopes gently, the death rate is low. Further, the theoretically straight, sloping line is often a curve. The line may be concave (steep at first, less steep in the middle segment and almost level toward the end) indicating that a large proportion of the cells in the culture are more rapidly killed (more vulnerable) than those that survive to the end of the experiment. For example, in an old culture many cells may become almost dormant,

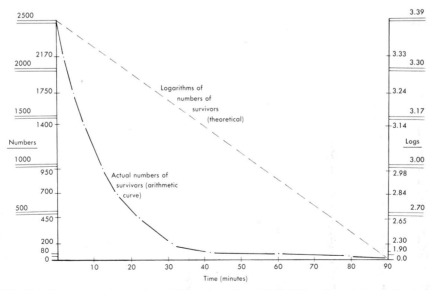

**Figure 20.1**   Relation between time and sporicidal action of heat (105° C.) in saline solution buffered at pH 7.0. Both logarithmic and arithmetic curves (idealized) are shown. Actual curves are not always so ideally symmetrical.

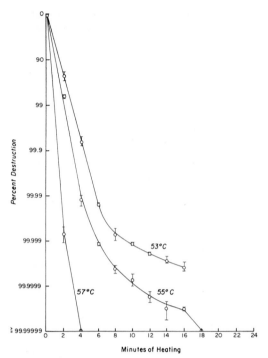

**Figure 20.2** Percentage destruction of *Staphylococcus aureus* strain B-120 in neutral phosphate buffer. (From Walker and Harmon: Appl. Microbiol., *14*:584, 1966.)

with their enzymic and reproductive functions slowed or stopped. Passage of microbicidal substances inward is diminished; cell walls are possibly thickened; some of the cells may even be encapsulated. Such matured cells would probably be less vulnerable to heat or chemical disinfectants than young cells. Thus, the proportion of old to young cells, as well as other factors such as species of organism and number of cells initially present, can affect both the slope of the death curve (rate of death) and its form (differences in vulnerability) (Figs. 20.2 and 20.3).

Of course, if very high concentrations of disinfectants or very high temperatures are applied, all of these gradual depopulations and measurable fluctuations are minimized (Fig. 20.2) or entirely masked and lost in one instantaneous, catastrophic stroke.

**Temperature.** With respect to microbicidal action of heat, temperature is inversely related to time. The lower the temperature, as a rule, the longer the time required to kill the organisms (Fig. 20.4).

In the case of chemical microbicides, as a rule, the warmer a disinfectant, the more effective it is. This is based partly on the principle that chemical reactions in general are speeded

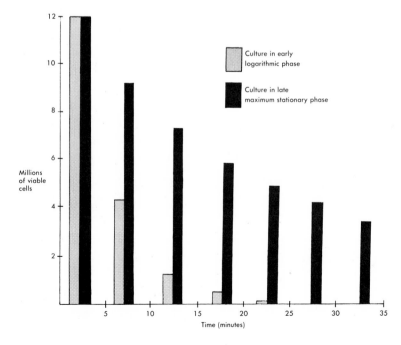

**Figure 20.3** Comparison between young and old cells as to susceptibility to a lethal agent. The young cells are all killed within 25 minutes, while a considerable part of the more resistant, older cells still survive.

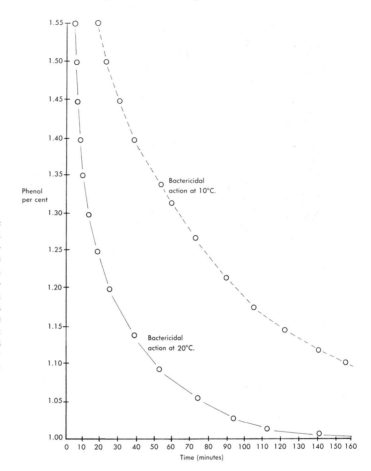

**Figure 20.4** Effect of temperature and of concentration of a disinfectant on killing time for a nonsporeforming bacterium in broth at pH 7.0. Note that: (1) at a given temperature a slight increase in concentration of phenol produces a relatively enormous increase in killing rate; (2) a 10° C. increase in temperature at a given concentration greatly enhances the rate of death. For example, a 1.1 per cent solution at 20° C. sterilizes in 50 minutes while at the same temperature a 1.29 per cent solution sterilizes in 14 minutes; in 64 minutes at 10° C.

up by raising the temperature. Usually, within the range of growing temperatures for microorganisms, a rise in temperature of 10° C. increases reaction rates two to eight times. However, since many disinfectant actions are partly physical in character, the laws governing chemical reactions do not apply exclusively. Higher temperatures generally lower surface tension, increase acidity, decrease viscosity and diminish adsorption. The first three increase and the last would diminish the effectiveness of a disinfectant.

**Concentrations.** Within narrow limits, the more concentrated a disinfectant, the more rapid and certain will be its action.

Effectiveness is generally related to concentration exponentially, not linearly. For example, doubling a 0.5 per cent concentration of phenol in aqueous solution does not merely double the killing rate for bacteria but may increase it by 500 or 900 per cent. Doubling the concentration again may increase the effect by only a negligible amount. There is clearly an optimal concentration of phenol at about

1 per cent. Thus, a concentration of a disinfectant beyond a certain point accomplishes increasingly less, and is wasteful (Fig. 20.4). Microorganisms vary considerably in their susceptibility to phenol. Some species use it as food!

When a disinfectant is in a colloidal state (*emulsion*), the material in each minute globule is highly concentrated. The bacterial cell in contact with these colloidal globules is, therefore, in contact with a high concentration of disinfectant. Many commercial preparations of cresols and chemically related substances are in the colloidal state.

**Oligodynamic Action.** Several substances that are toxic in relatively high concentrations stimulate growth at low concentrations. To illustrate, a bright piece of a heavy metal, such as copper, silver or gold, is placed on a plate of nutrient agar which has previously been heavily inoculated with an organism such as *Staphylococcus aureus* (a cause of boils). The plate is incubated. Small quantities of the metal diffuse into the agar and inhibit the growth of the organisms in a zone around the metal piece.

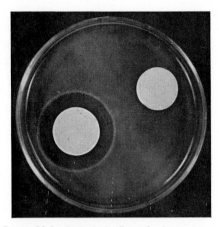

**Figure 20.5** Biological effect of minute amounts of certain metals (oligodynamic action). The agar medium was heavily inoculated with micrococci while warm, well mixed, and poured into the plate. When solid, the metal disks (coins) were placed on the agar surface and the plate was incubated. The bacteria grew where they could, producing a greyish granular appearance. Note that the silver disk (quarter) is surrounded by a clear zone where no growth occurred, while the nickel disk shows little or no zone of inhibition. Note also the increased density of the growth at the outer margin of the clear zone around the quarter. This may be due to: (a) less competition for food at the edge of the sterile area, (b) stimulation by a critically small concentration of the metallic ions or (c) both. The difference in action between nickel and silver is not necessarily a general one. With another species of test organism the situation could be reversed. Further, the coins are not pure silver or nickel. (Courtesy of Dr. W. C. Burkhart, Department of Bacteriology, University of Georgia, Athens, Ga.)

This phenomenon is ascribed to what is called *oligodynamic\* action* of the metal (Fig. 20.5).

At the periphery of this barren zone one might suppose that, as the concentration of metal ions diminishes with distance from the metal piece, growth would gradually increase and finally reach a density equal to normal in all areas beyond the zone where the metal ions had not yet migrated. On the contrary the sterile zone is sharply demarkated. At the periphery of the sterile zone, where concentration of the toxic metal ions is minimal, a narrow but distinct opaque ring of *extra dense* growth is often clearly evident. This may be caused by absence of competition for food in the nearby barren zone or to stimulation of growth by an optimal low concentration of metal ions. The same phenomenon is seen in similar experiments with many other antimicrobial substances.

---

\*Gr. *oligo* = little; *dynamis* = power; hence, acting in small amounts.

**pH.** As a general rule, the lethal or toxic action of harmful agents, both physical and chemical, is increased by increased concentrations of $H^+$ (or of $^-OH$). The synergistic relationship between heat and $H^+$ has already been discussed. Heat tends to increase acid effects in part by causing greater dissociation of acids. The close relation of pH and temperature in lethal processes is illustrated in Table 20.3. In this table it is seen that $^-OH$ also is an adjuvant of heat but to a lesser degree than $H^+$. Both acidity and alkalinity increase denaturation and coagulation by heat.

The increase in effectiveness of benzoates, sorbates and salts of several other organic acids in acid solution is an excellent example of one effect of $H^+$ on disinfectant action. In the case of these salts of weak organic acids, the *undissociated* molecules, and not the sorbate or benzoate anions *per se,* are the active agents. The effect of decreased pH (*increased* acidity) of their solutions is to suppress ionization of these weak acid salts, thus increasing the concentration of the toxic undissociated molecules.

**Extraneous Organic Matter.** Most common disinfectants such as compounds of phenol, bichloride of mercury, strong acids and the halogens are quite general in their affinity for protoplasm and many other organic materials, whether part of a living cell or not. The presence of considerable quantities of extraneous organic materials such as blood serum, plant or animal tissues, mucus or feces in any material being disinfected will therefore protect the organisms to a great extent, since any of these materials will combine with and inactivate the disinfectant before it reaches the organisms.

**Osmotic Pressure.** Fluids of high osmotic pressure (e.g., food-preserving syrups and brines) tend to dehydrate the cell contents and so increase resistance of microbial cells to heat and chemical disinfectants.

**Chemical Antagonisms.** Many antimicrobial agents are inactivated, or their action is

**TABLE 20.3  RELATION OF pH AND TEMPERATURE TO SURVIVAL OF TETANUS SPORES**

| pH | Survival (minutes) at | | | |
|---|---|---|---|---|
| | 105° C | 100° C | 95° C | 90° C |
| 1.2 | 4 | 5 | 6 | 6 |
| 4.1 | 6 | 11 | 14 | 23 |
| 6.1 | 9 | 14 | 38 | 54 |
| 7.2 | 11 | 29 | 53 | 65 |
| 10.2 | 5 | 11 | 21 | 24 |

reversed (*antagonized*), by certain specific substances. For example, bichloride of mercury exerts a *specific toxic* (not coagulative) effect in high dilutions (e.g., 1:100,000 or more). The *toxic* action of *dilute* bichloride of mercury is an effect of its combining specifically with the sulfhydryl ($^-$SH) group, which, as explained elsewhere, is a very important, functioning part of the glutathione or cysteine molecule of many proteins and enzymes (Fig. 20.6). When one enzyme is stopped or blocked by any agent, a whole series of dependent enzyme reactions may also stop, both above and below the blocked enzyme, as in an assembly line in a factory. Bichloride of mercury may thus be viewed as a poison of specific enzymes and proteins, as well as a coagulative agent. However, the toxic action of bichloride of mercury may be completely antagonized or reversed by putting $^-$SH compounds such as glutathione and cysteine into the suspending fluid. These combine with the bichloride of mercury, eliminating blockage of $^-$SH groups of enzymes so that they are enabled to function again. In another example, the lethal action of dilute phenol on micrococci and on *Salmonella typhi* may be stopped and the apparently dead organisms "revived" by removal of the phenol with activated charcoal or ferric chloride.

In Chapter 15, it is explained how microorganisms apparently killed by ultraviolet irradiation can be reactivated by visible light and some other agents. Everyone knows how men pronounced dead have been restored by cardiac massage. Thus, all is not dead that seems so. The terrible, dark and secret realms of death

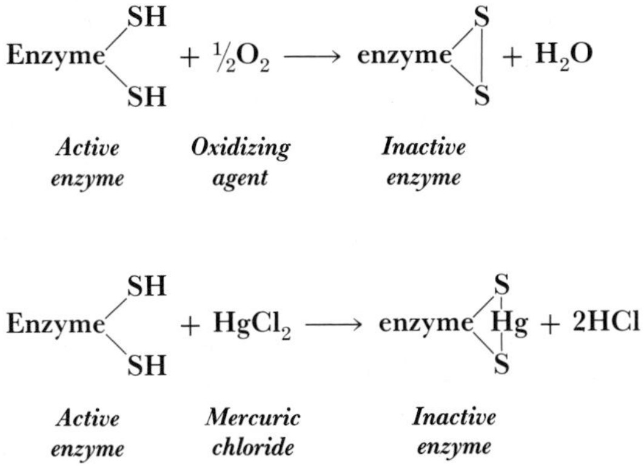

**Figure 20.6** Inactivation of an enzyme by combination of its sulfhydryl groups ($^-$SH) with an oxidizing agent (above) and with bichloride of mercury (below). The effect of HgCl$_2$ is bacteriostatic; i.e., it is reversible by H$_2$S, etc.

shrink daily before the onslaughts of scientific research!

**Surface Tension.** Surface tension is of basic importance in disinfection (see Chapter 19). In dealing with aqueous solutions of disinfectants, there are two aspects of this factor: *adsorption* of surface-tension-reducing disinfectants or interfering substances on the surfaces of cells, and the effect of surface tension reducers on the wetting and spreading properties of the solution. Both affect contact between disinfectant and microorganisms.

Adsorption.   For example, when phenol is added to an aqueous suspension of bacteria, contact between disinfectant and bacteria is immediate. The bacteria float naked, as it were, and are reached by the disinfectant in effective concentration without delay, partly because phenol lowers surface tension and is therefore *adsorbed* and consequently concentrated upon their surfaces. A nonsurfactant like bichloride of mercury is not concentrated in this way. Once the surface-active substance is in contact with the organism, further action depends on such factors as toxicity of the agent, its coagulative action, presence of interfering substances, pH, temperature, species of organism and whether or not the disinfectant penetrates readily inside the cell.

Wetness.   As explained in Chapter 19, surface tension reducers enhance the effectiveness of disinfectants by increasing their *wetness*.

Soap, although a relatively weak disinfectant in most situations, is a good surface-tension reducer; soapy, or *saponated*, solutions wet surfaces thoroughly. Phenol and related compounds such as cresols also lower surface tension and are powerful germicides besides. A combination of soap, with "carbolic acid" (crude phenol) or cresols, would therefore seem to have exceptional possibilities as a disinfectant. Indeed, mixtures containing these substances in effective proportions (see next paragraph) are widely used in hospitals and laboratories. Products of this type (for example, Lysol) are available on the market or can be made up as Liquor Cresolis Compositus from the U. S. Pharmacopeia. Solutions of iodine with low surface tension (i.e., *iodophors*, or surface tension reducers combined with iodine) are now available commercially (e.g., Wescodyne).

Competitive Adsorption.   An excess of soap, however, can interfere with the adsorption of some disinfectants. If more than minimal amounts of a bactericidally ineffective but very surface-active substance like soap are added to surfactant disinfectant solutions, the relatively inert soap is adsorbed on the bacterial surfaces to the exclusion of the disinfectant. Such displacement of one surfactant by another is called *competitive adsorption.*

If organisms are coated with waxy material, as is the case with tuberculosis bacilli, a disinfectant solution affects them with difficulty unless it contains a good surface tension reducer which allows it to wet the wax. Certain surfactant disinfectants (*quaternaries;* see page 278) are very effective against tubercle bacilli if dissolved in alcohol, since alcohol is both a wax solvent and a potent surface tension reducer.

## 20.4   EVALUATION OF DISINFECTANTS

Disinfectants or microbicidal agents are usually described as "strong," "weak" or "mild." These terms are inexact and convey different meanings to different people. To one the term "strong" may mean a disinfectant odor; to another, pain on application to a scratch; to still another, corrosive action; to another, a bright red or brown or other color. Rarely does the untrained person think of disinfectants in terms of *microbicidal* activity, or *toxicity* for human beings, plants or animals. Actually, the value of any substance as a disinfectant depends on a number of factors. The ideal disinfectant should be:

(1) highly effective against a wide variety of microorganisms in concentrations so low as to be economical to use and nontoxic for animals (or plants);

(2) noninjurious and nonstaining to materials like fabrics, furniture or metal wares, and nonoffensive to odor or taste;

(3) as specific as possible for microorganisms, i.e., not inactivated by extraneous materials;

(4) a good surface tension reducer (have good wetting and penetrating properties);

(5) stable in storage;

(6) readily available and not expensive;

(7) easily applied under household or other practical conditions of use;

(8) (and very important) completely microbicidal within a few minutes or an hour at most, and not induce a state of microbistasis leading to a false sense of security.

No single disinfectant has all of these ideal properties. Some properties may be ideal under some conditions but not under others; e.g., strong lye or cresol may be ideal for stable floors or sanitary plumbing but harmful in infants' eyes. Not all disinfectants are equally effective, and some of them are more effective against certain bacteria than against others. Some are effective in pure cultures in the test tube but not in contact with organic matter such as blood, feces or dead tissues; some are effective in the vapor phase but not as liquids.

The microbicidal effectiveness of disinfectants may be estimated by mixing them with cultures of whatever microorganisms are to be destroyed, and then measuring the time required for the substance to kill the organisms. If this is done under carefully standardized conditions (i.e., using a constant quantity of culture of a stated composition, a fixed temperature and a suspension of measured numbers of microorganisms of known and constant resistance) the results will be accurate and reproducible.

**The   Phenol   Coefficient   Determination.** The effectiveness of a water-soluble disinfectant that is chemically similar to phenol is tested by determining its *phenol coefficient.* The phenol coefficient is based on the effectiveness of the test disinfectant as compared with that of pure phenol under the carefully standardized conditions just noted.

In a commonly used and representative procedure, 5 ml. amounts of a series of dilutions of a disinfectant to be tested (here called X) are placed in a row of tubes of standard size. A similar series of dilutions of pure phenol (here called P) of 1:80, 1:90 and 1:100 is prepared. The temperature of all is brought to 20° C. in a water bath. To each tube is added 0.5 ml. of a standard, young, broth culture of a particular strain of *Salmonella typhi* ("typhoid bacillus"). At intervals of 5, 10 and 15 minutes, a standard loopful (4 mm. loop of No. 23 B and S wire) is transferred from each tube in succession to a corresponding tube containing 10 ml. of sterile broth of standard composition.

After 48 hours of incubation at 37° C., growth in the broth tubes is recorded. If all of the organisms in all of the disinfectant X tubes were killed, *no growth* should appear in any of the corresponding subcultures. The test must then be repeated with higher dilutions of the disinfectant X such that not all of the organisms are killed in at least some of the tubes and some of the corresponding broth subcultures show growth.

The phenol coefficient is then calculated as the ratio of the highest dilution of X not killing the organisms in five minutes (evidenced by growth in the corresponding broth tube), but killing in 10 minutes (evidenced by no

**TABLE 20.4** TYPICAL DATA FROM A PHENOL COEFFICIENT DETERMINATION

| Disinfectants | Dilutions | 5 Min. Sub-cultures | 10 Min. Sub-cultures | 15 Min. Sub-cultures |
|---|---|---|---|---|
| Phenol | 80 | −* | − | − |
| | 90 | +* | − | − |
| | 100 | + | + | + |
| | 350 | − | − | − |
| | 400 | + | − | − |
| | 450 | + | − | − |
| "Unknown" | 500 | + | + | − |
| | 550 | + | + | − |
| | 600 | + | + | + |
| | 650 | + | + | + |

*+ = growth; − = no growth.

growth in the broth), to the corresponding dilutions of P. The values obtained are shown in Table 20.4. In this experiment the 1:90 dilution of P failed to kill in five minutes but killed all the *S. typhi* cells in 10 minutes. This is compared with X which did the same in a dilution of 1:450. The ratio of X to P is $\frac{450}{90}$ or 5, the FDA* phenol coefficient of X. A slightly modified procedure is prescribed by the AOAC.† If desired, dilution plate counts of the numbers of organisms remaining alive in the disinfectant tubes after various intervals of time can be plotted on graph paper, thus establishing a "death curve."

The significance of a phenol coefficient has definite limitations. For example, a disinfectant dissolved in distilled water may have a phenol coefficient as high as 50. However, it may be wholly ineffective if applied in the presence of blood, or used in contact with organic matter such as pus, saliva, feces or milk, as these may combine with the disinfectant and remove it from the bacteria. Further, it may have a coefficient of only 2 or 3 when, as is commonly done, it is tested against some other organisms, such as *Staphylococcus aureus*. When a substance is said to have a certain phenol coefficient, the limitations of the method must be kept in mind.

**The Use-Dilution Test.** Once a phenol coefficient has been determined for a disinfectant, it has been customary to use the disinfectant in an arbitrary concentration 20 times

*United States Food and Drug Administration.
†Association of Official Agricultural Chemists. There are many modifications of the procedure, such as the Rideal-Walker and Chick-Martin methods.

the phenol coefficient (i.e., if the phenol coefficient is 5 the *use dilution* of the disinfectant is 1:100). The arbitrary use dilution has been found an often unreliable guide to disinfection. A *use-dilution test* (UDT) is therefore often applied as a check.

Small steel cylinders are wet with broth culture of one or more test organisms and dried. They are then placed for a standard interval in the disinfectant diluted for use. On removal to separate tubes of sterile broth no growth should occur in any tube if the recommended use dilution is to be certified as effective.

In another test, whole milk is added to the use dilution of a disinfectant to measure its effectiveness. This simulates the presence of extraneous proteins in actual use. Sometimes blood and serum are used in a similar way. A variety of test organisms often gives a still better idea of the effectiveness of a disinfectant under general conditions. Obviously, no one test method can give an accurate evaluation of all disinfectants under all conditions.

As a result, many different modifications have been suggested by various workers. For example, some workers with the UDT logically substitute, for the steel cylinders, bits of the actual materials on which the disinfectant is to be used, e.g., asphalt tile, linoleum or wood flooring, and use a large variety of test organisms. In testing effects of disinfectants on viruses, live chick embryos may be used instead of tubes of the bacteriological culture media for the testing of viability of the virus after contact with the disinfectant dilutions.

**Inactivation.** It is important to note that many disinfectant substances are also highly microbistatic. If, in the phenol coefficient or other test, a microbistatic substance clings to the test organisms on removal from the disinfectant-dilution tubes to the broth subcultures, no growth of the organisms occurs even though they are still alive. To eliminate this error it is sometimes sufficient merely to *dilute out* the microbistatic agent by making two or three successive transfers of test objects from tube to tube of broth, or to use large volumes of broth in the subcultures. However, some disinfectants, such as bichloride of mercury, sulfonamide drugs and quaternary ammonium compounds (see farther on), appear to be adsorbed upon or inside the cells and cannot be removed or stopped by dilution. A definite antagonist or inactivator is then added to the broth subculture tubes. For sulfonamides, para-aminobenzoic acid is used (see paragraphs on microbistasis). Bichloride of mercury is fully inactivated by sodium thioglycollate (an organic compound of sulfur) in the broth culture medium. For quaternaries, Luramin sodium combined with sorbitan mono-oleate (Tween-80) and Azolectin, and other substances acting as competitive adsorbents have been found useful.

**Gaseous Disinfectants.** Methods of testing disinfectants that are applied in the gaseous state, of which several are in fairly wide use (page 279), obviously cannot be based on procedures like the phenol coefficient determination. Final methods for the testing of germicidal gases are still to be perfected. One method recently under experimental trial is designed to catch a standardized number of microorganisms on a bacteria-retaining membrane filter. The filter is then placed in a specially designed exposure chamber to which carefully metered gas is admitted at fixed temperature and humidity for a measured time. The organisms are then washed from the filter membrane into broth and incubated. The measure of effectiveness is not complete killing, but *injury* and *percentage kill* as indicated by slowed rate of development of turbidity in the broth as compared with an untreated *control*. Other methods of testing are under investigation.

**Toxicity of Disinfectants.** One of the great problems in the selection of disinfectants or antiseptics to be used in contact with living tissues is excessive *toxic effects*. One may determine the toxic dose of a disinfectant in various ways —for example, by observing the smallest quantity necessary to stop completely the action of leukocytes (white blood corpuscles) in a test tube in a given time. Other methods measure the inhibitory or lethal effect of the tested substance on various tissues, while still others measure the respiratory quotient (i.e., the ratio of carbon dioxide given off to oxygen consumed) of tissue cells in contact with the germicides. One method is based on observing the survival time of chick embryos into which the tested substances are injected. A time-honored, simple and effective method for many substances is the direct trial on living animals. The results are sometimes expressed as *toxicity index* (i.e., ratio of minimal toxic dose to minimal germicidal dose).

Probably no single test gives a generally applicable result, and species of microorganisms as well as tissue cells vary greatly in their susceptibility to different substances. For any disinfectant, therefore, the toxicity index will vary for each type of tissue cell and microorganism.

## 20.5   REMOVAL OF MICROORGANISMS (STERILIZATION BY FILTRATION)

**Clay and Paper Filters.** A useful method of sterilizing fluids that cannot be sterilized by other means is that of filtration. Filters made of specially graded and purified clays and fine unglazed porcelain are commonly used. For certain filters, compressed paper or asbestos disks take the place of clay. In some filters the clays or porcelain are shaped into convenient, hollow cylindrical forms closed at one end and mounted on funnel-shaped stems. Filters for microbiological purposes are also made of masses of very finely porous Pyrex glass. These are called *fritted* or *sintered glass* filters. They have the ad-

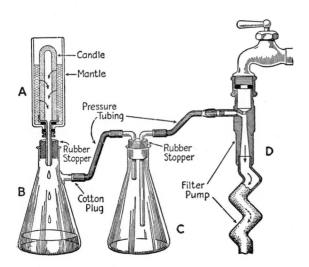

**Figure 20.7** Typical filtration apparatus for microbiology. The hollow "candle" of filtering clay, surrounded by the fluid to be filtered, enclosed in a glass cup or mantle, is seen at *A*. The fluid passes through the clay and is drawn into the flask (*B*) by suction developed by the pump (*D*). The flask (*C*) is to trap any fluid that might be sucked back from *D* or over from *B*. The cotton plug in the side arm of *B* is to prevent ingress of dust when *B* is disconnected from the tubing. (Belding and Marston: A Textbook of Medical Bacteriology. D. Appleton-Century Co.)

vantages of durability and cleanability with strong acids and heat. Clay, porcelain, glass and asbestos are siliceous materials; paper is cellulose.

Filters are sterilized by heat before use so that bacteria in the filter or glassware will not contaminate the *filtrate* (filtered product).

Various forms of bacteria-retaining filters are used in the laboratory, a common type being shown in Figure 20.7. A convenient filter using disks of compressed filter paper as the filtering agent is the Seitz type (Fig. 20.8). For industrial purposes the same basic principles are used, but the apparatuses are adapted to heavy and continuous work loads.

**Mechanisms of Filtration.** In the filters mentioned, the passages are wide enough for most microorganisms to pass, with room to spare. The filtering effect is achieved not by sieve action but largely by adsorption of the microorganisms to the surfaces of the filter tunnels. Most microorganisms in aqueous suspension possess surface electrical charges that are more negative than the charges of the tun-

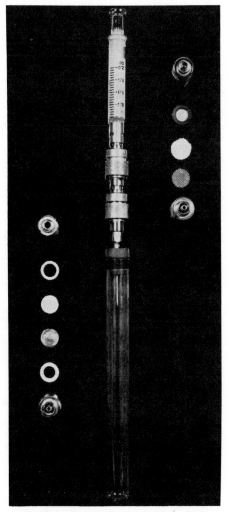

**Figure 20.9**  Filter set consists of a 2 ml. syringe, two Swinny adapters, a hypodermic needle and a vacutainer tube. The disassembled filter units show the adapter tips, screen support disks, filter disks and necessary rubber washers. (From Hsiung: Bact. Rev., *29*:477, 1965.)

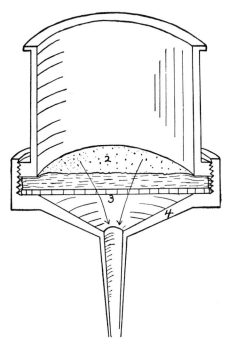

**Figure 20.8**  Seitz-type filter. The fluid to be filtered is poured into the cylindrical cup (1). The fluid passes through the bacteria-retaining disk of compressed paper or asbestos (2) which is supported on a wire screen (3). The stem of the funnel-shaped base (4) is inserted in a suction flask through a rubber stopper and the whole assembly sterilized before use. There are many variations of this principle. In some the filter disk is placed at the tip of a hypodermic syringe and the fluid to be filtered is forced through it. (See also Fig. 20.9.)

nel surfaces. The microorganisms therefore tend to be adsorbed electrically by the filter (Fig. 20.10, *A*).

The importance of the surface electrical characteristics of the tunnel surfaces in such filters is shown by the fact that when the linings of the filter tunnels are coated with oil or albumin, or saturated with dyes, or even with bacteria, or are made of electronegative materials like plaster of Paris, microorganisms pass through without difficulty. Thus, whereas the filter pores must be small enough to bring the microorganisms within the influence of the mural electrical charges, filtration by this class of filters is clearly not wholly dependent on fineness of the filter pores.

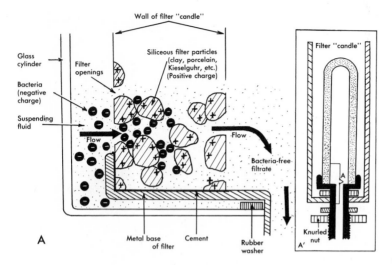

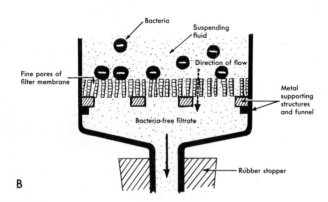

**Figure 20.10** Comparison of adsorption action of clay, porcelain or asbestos fiber filter (*A*) and sieve action of plastic membrane filter (*B*).

In *A* note the large size of the filter openings relative to the bacteria and the opposite charges of bacteria and filter particles. In *B* note that the filter openings are much smaller than the bacteria and the passages shorter. Note also the absence of charges on the filter. There is some evidence that membrane filters do actually carry some charge.

The inset (A′) shows the overall arrangement of a Mandler or Berkefeld-type filter (see also Fig. 20.7). The bracketed part of A′ is the portion shown enlarged at the left. The proportions are distorted to emphasize the principles involved. If the thickness of the filter wall in A were enlarged as much as the bacteria it would be over 275 feet thick! If the membrane filter in B were similarly enlarged it would be many inches thick; actually, such membranes are paper-thin.

**Membrane or Ultra-Filters.**   A particularly useful and versatile type of filter is the *membrane filter* made of collodion, cellulose acetate or similar substance. A common form is a paper-like disk about 50 mm. in diameter and 0.1 mm. in thickness (Fig. 4.4). It has myriads of very fine vertical tubular openings from upper to lower surface (Fig. 20.10, *B*). The diameter of these tubulations may be varied by the manufacturer from over $1.0\mu$ to less than $0.005\mu$, the last sufficiently fine to strain out even the smaller viruses from fluid passing through the filter membrane.

Membrane filters, unlike the siliceous and cellulose filters discussed, depend for their effectiveness to a greater extent on the sieve action of their perforate structure and on the fineness of the pores. Adsorption and Van der Waals forces play a lesser but still significant role.

A particular advantage of the membrane filter is that all of the microorganisms in a relatively large volume of fluid (water, milk, urine or diluted blood) may be collected on one small disk, where they may be observed directly or cultivated *in situ* (Fig. 4.5). There is no need to handle hundreds of tubes or flasks with large-volume cultures. Some special uses of these filters are mentioned in discussing the bacteriological examination of drinking water supplies (Chapter 42).

**SUPPLEMENTARY READING**

(References for this chapter will be found at the end of Chapter 21.)

# Chapter 21

## STERILIZATION AND DISINFECTION
## Practical Applications

### 21.1 STERILIZATION BY HEAT

Heat may be applied for sterilization in three ways: by steam or hot water (moist heat), by prolonged baking in the oven (dry heat), and by complete incineration. The last needs no comment beyond pointing out that common sense will direct what may be burned and that care must be taken to see that such material is completely burned.

#### MOIST HEAT

**Boiling in Water.** The role of moisture in the lethal effects of heat was described in the foregoing chapter. The use of boiling for preserving foods and for disinfection is very simple. It is necessary to remember only that bacterial endospores (Family Bacillaceae) may remain alive even after hours of boiling. For ordinary household purposes of *disinfection* (not *sterilization*), five minutes of boiling is usually sufficient, provided that the hot water actually comes into contact with the microorganisms and not merely with the outside of lumps of food or packets of instruments or other objects containing the microorganisms.

Boiling in water can never be depended on for sterilization, especially at high elevations above sea level, as shown by Table 21.1.

**Free-Flowing (Live) Steam.** *Live,* or free, steam is usually applied in a loosely covered container that will hold steam without pressure. Boiling water and free steam never reach a temperature above 100° C. (212° F.). In mountainous regions it is lower than 100° C. (Table 21.1). Free steam is sometimes used to accomplish *fractional sterilization,* or *tyndallization.*

TYNDALLIZATION. John Tyndall, a famous British scientist, noticed that a period of about 24 hours at ordinary room temperatures is usually sufficient to enable dormant and heat-resistant spores to germinate and grow into the vegetative state in which they are sensitive to heat. He devised a process of sterilization based on these observations. It consists in steaming for a few minutes at 100° C. on three or four successive occasions, separated by 24-hour intervals at a temperature favorable to spore germination. The intervals permit the dormant, resistant spores to become active, vulnerable vegetative cells, readily killed by 100° C. This process renders an infusion sterile, whereas one single continuous boiling for one hour may not, since many spores remain in their dormant and resistant state during this time. This intermittent process is sometimes put to practical

**TABLE 21.1 BOILING POINT AT VARIOUS ALTITUDES**

| Location | Altitude* | Boiling Point† |
|---|---|---|
| New York City | 0 | 100 |
| Chicago, Ill. | 589 | 98.9 |
| Denver, Col. | 5,280 | 94.3 |
| Fort Laramie, Wyo. | 7,380 | 92.2 |
| Tahoe, Nev. | 10,000 | 89.1 |

\* Feet above sea level.
† Degrees C.

269

use in the home canning of foods. A disadvantage of the method is the time required to achieve complete sterilization; an advantage is that it requires no special apparatus. In some fluids, such as water, spores may not grow out promptly. Also, if the material is freely exposed to air, anaerobic spores may not germinate and may survive the process. If not freely exposed to air, aerobic spores will not grow out freely.

**Compressed Steam: Autoclaving.**   Anyone familiar with the operation of a home pressure cooker is familiar with an *autoclave*, because the cooker is a simple form of autoclave. In the autoclave (Fig. 21.1), be it a small and simple home pressure cooker or an apparatus large enough to fill a room and fitted with various gauges, pipes, valves, clocks and wheels, the object of both is alike: to heat the articles to be sterilized by means of steam under considerable pressure.

Steam under pressure is hotter than boiling water or free-flowing steam such as is used in tyndallization. The higher the steam pressure, the higher the temperature will be.

The relation of steam pressure to temperature is shown in Figure 21.2.

It must be remembered that it is the compressed steam (moisture, hydration) that sterilizes and not compressed air (dry and usually not as hot as steam).

For example, pure steam at 15 pounds pressure has a temperature of 121° C. If the steam is mixed with an equal amount of air, at the same pressure the temperature is only 110° C., while if the mixture is two thirds air the temperature is only 109° C.

Steam *hydrates* and thus promotes coagulation; air does neither. Steam, being water vapor, also produces *hydrolysis* at autoclave temperatures. Dry air cannot do this at any pressure or temperature. In autoclaving, therefore, as in using a pressure cooker, a valve is left open for the escape of all air before the steam pressure is allowed to rise.

The actual amount of water present as steam in an autoclave is small, and articles soon dry off after removal, especially if removed from the autoclave while hot.

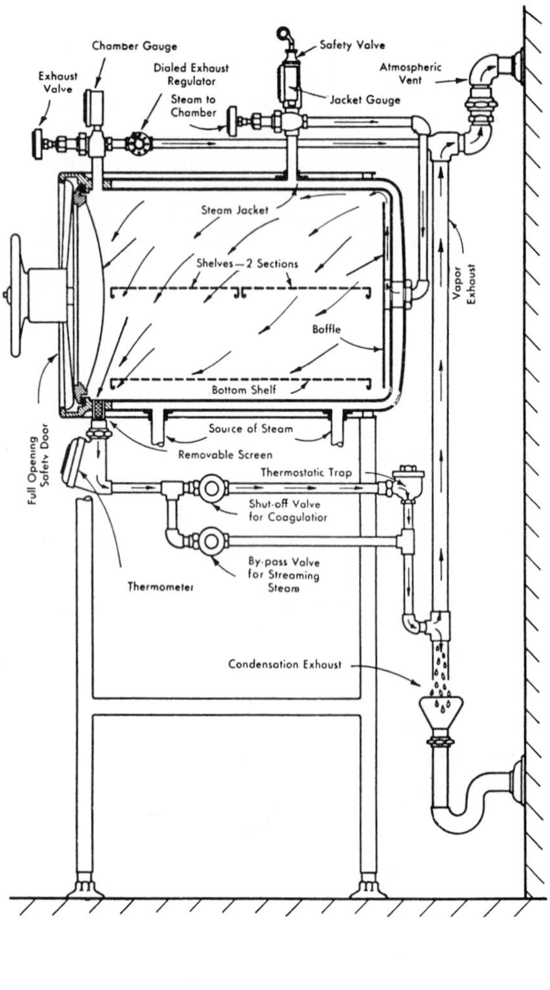

**Figure 21.1** Diagrammatic illustration of steam jacketed autoclave. Steam enters the *jacket*, a double-walled shell, at two places just beneath the cylinder. It passes out the top through a pipe to which are attached: a wheel valve admitting the steam to the inner *chamber*, a *safety valve*, a gauge showing *pressure in the jacket*. The steam enters the inner chamber at the right of the diagram, filling the upper portion. Its pressure registers on the *chamber gauge*. It may be allowed to escape rapidly by the *exhaust valve*. If this is closed, steam pushes the cooler air in the lower portion out at the bottom (left), where the *thermometer* registers proper temperature only when the air is gone and is followed by the hot steam. The escaping steam may be allowed to flow out without building up any pressure if the *by-pass valve* is fully opened. If the by-pass valve is closed and the *shut-off valve* is opened, steam passes through the *thermostatic trap* where the heat shuts off all but a pinhole opening. This causes pressure to build up in the chamber, yet prevents stagnation by permitting a constant minute flow of steam through the apparatus. (Courtesy of American Sterilizer Co.)

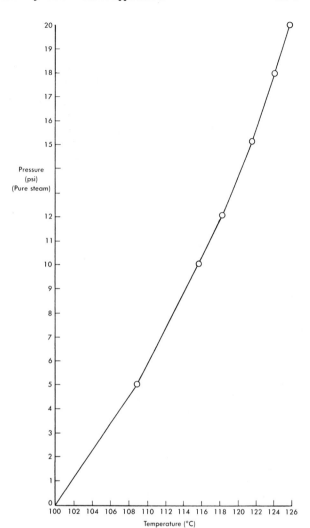

**Figure 21.2** Relation between temperature and pressure of pure steam.

The *thermometer* on the autoclave is the important guide to the process of autoclaving, not the pressure gauge. However, the latter, as well as a steam-escape or safety valve, is essential to safety.

The common practice in autoclaving fluids or freely exposed surfaces such as those of dishes and instruments is to apply 115° to 125° C. (10 to 20 pounds' pressure) for 20 minutes. The pressure must be allowed to subside *slowly* after the heating is over or *superheated* fluids in open (cotton-plugged) vessels will boil over. Any large, solid masses must be heated a longer time to allow for heat penetration. Packages must be spaced so as to allow free circulation of steam. Substances such as mineral oil or petrolatum, sand, or any dry objects in tight jars, or substances that are impervious to moisture, cannot be satisfactorily sterilized in the autoclave. The temperature may rise as high

as 125° C., but in the absence of moisture this is ineffective. Such materials are more effectively sterilized by dry heat in an oven.

Acid materials, such as canned tomatoes, acid fruits, pickles or sauerkraut (pH more acid than 4.5), require much shorter periods or lower temperatures for sterilization than low acid foods (pH 6.5 to 7) such as milk, corn and meats. This is because of the synergistic action between pH and temperature. (Chapter 20).

## DRY HEAT

Dry heat is used in oven sterilization (Fig. 21.3). It is necessary to bear in mind that significant coagulation does not occur when moisture is not present.

Articles in ovens are very dry and, therefore, in order to be freed of live spores, must

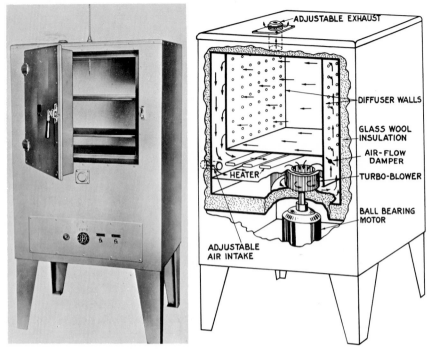

**Figure 21.3**  A type of sterilizing oven for microbiology. The motor at the bottom of the oven forces streams of hot dry air through the chamber of the oven, as indicated by the arrows. (From Perkins: Principles and Methods of Sterilization. Charles C Thomas, 1960.)

reach a very high temperature (165° to 170° C.; 329° to 338° F.). It is customary to apply 165° C. for a period of two hours. This accomplishes no coagulation but, what is more effective, slight charring.

A home oven can easily be used for sterilization. A "moderate" temperature (330° F.) is satisfactory, and the heating should be allowed to proceed for two hours *after* reaching that temperature. Paper wrappings should be slightly browned but not brittle; muslin or string should be faintly yellow due to the heat.

Only dry articles not injured by baking (glassware, bandages, instruments, mineral oils, petrolatum, talcum powder and the like) may be thus sterilized. Solutions containing water, alcohol or other volatile substances will, of course, boil away and be ruined.

## 21.2   TIME AND CONTROLS

**Thorough Heating Necessary.** In any process of disinfection or sterilization by heat it is absolutely essential that the object be heated through and that the center of the object be held at a killing temperature long enough to destroy the bacteria.

Thus, in home canning, a quart jar of spinach may be held in free steam (100° C.) for five to ten minutes and when grasped with the hand will feel very hot, yet the center may be well below a microbicidal temperature. Large masses of nonfluid materials like quart jars of canned vegetables and roast meat, in which the contents cannot circulate, require a long time (one and one-half to two hours), even in the autoclave, to be heated so thoroughly that the center reaches a sporicidal temperature. Pieces of meat or vegetables to be sterilized in jars by heating should be loosely packed, allowing space for circulation of the fluid in the jar. Air pockets in the jars should be carefully removed. Penetration of the heat is facilitated if the cans or jars or pieces of roasting meat are small and not packed too closely together, promoting free circulation of steam or hot air around and between them.

**Sterility Checks.** For many purposes—industrial, hospital, research—it is important to have some absolute means of determining after a heat sterilizing process that even the most heat-resistant spores have been killed. Two general types of check are commonly used. One consists of pieces of paper, gauze or thread to which are applied spots of some thermolabile

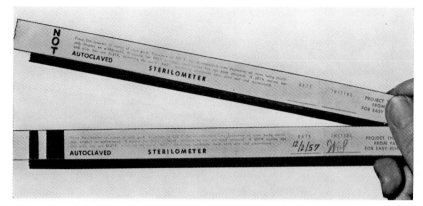

**Figure 21.4**   One type of device for indicating proper autoclaving. Before heating the word "NOT" appears clearly as on the upper indicator. After partial heating the leftmost black bar appears as seen on the lower indicator. Not until autoclaving is complete both as to time and temperature is the word "NOT" obliterated by a second dark bar on the lower indicator. (Courtesy of Sterilometer Laboratories, Inc., N. Hollywood, Calif.)

dye. Inserted in the materials being sterilized, the dye turns a distinctive color if the contents of the sterilizer have been subjected to a sterilizing temperature for a sufficient time (Fig. 21.4).

A more direct check (though more time-consuming) consists of strips of filter paper having on them the very heat-resistant spores of *Bacillus subtilis*. This is a harmless aerobic bacterium. The spore-impregnated strips are inserted (enclosed in sterile envelopes) inside materials being sterilized. Afterward the strips are removed to tubes of culture medium and incubated. If growth occurs in the tubes within

seven days then it is evident that the sterilization process in which they were involved was inadequate to kill the spores. In a modification of this process, sealed ampules (commercially available) containing culture medium with dormant spores of harmless *Bacillus stearothermophilus* already in it are inserted in the materials being sterilized. After sterilization the complete ampules are incubated at 55° C. (since *B. stearothermophilus* is a strict thermophile). If no growth occurs in seven days it is proof of effective sterilization, since spores of *B. stearothermophilus* are among the most heat-resistant of known living things (Fig. 21.5).

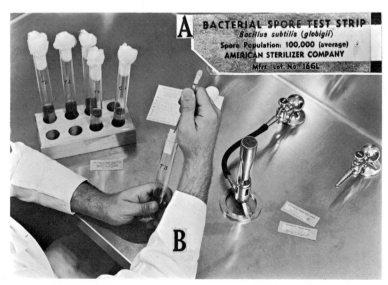

**Figure 21.5**   One method of checking effectiveness of heat sterilization is by testing the sterility of a strip of paper (*A*) containing 100,000 very heat-resistant bacterial spores (*Bacillus subtilis*). The strip of paper is placed inside the material being sterilized before the application of heat. After the heating process the strip of paper, with its spores, is placed by means of sterile forceps in a culture tube of sterile broth (*B*). If any of the spores grow during seven days of incubation, the heating process did not achieve complete sterilization. (Courtesy of American Sterilizer Co.)

## 21.3   SOME USEFUL DISINFECTANTS

There are hundreds of disinfectants on the market and it would obviously be impossible to discuss even a small part of them here. A few commonly used representatives of several classes will illustrate general principles and usages. For convenience we may group the disinfectants as follows: halogens and halogen compounds, compounds of heavy metals, phenol and its derivatives, alcohols, detergent disinfectants, microbicidal gases and radiations.

### HALOGENS AND HALOGEN COMPOUNDS

Iodine and chlorine are the most widely used of this group. Chlorine gas is used to disinfect filtered water at all municipal water-purification plants and many sewage-disposal plants. It is usually handled in tanks or tubes like oxygen. It is applied to drinking water in a final concentration of about 1.0 part per million.

A more convenient form of chlorine for the individual and household user is calcium or sodium hypochlorite. Solutions (5 per cent) of sodium hypochlorite are purchasable in all grocery stores under various names (e.g., Clorox). They have a multitude of household and sanitary uses. They depend for their effectiveness probably on their liberation of free chlorine.* Directions for use of these solutions are on each bottle. Four points need to be remembered in their use: the chlorine tends to evaporate from the solution; they give a bad odor to the hands; chlorine is poisonous; and it is readily inactivated by all organic matter.

**Chloride of Lime.**   Chloride of lime (0.5 to 5 per cent aqueous solution) is excellent for similar purposes and is inexpensive. The ordinary chloride of lime of commerce is unstable and soon loses most of its free chlorine. Many organic chlorine compounds which liberate their chlorine more slowly are very effective. *Azochloramid* is one of these; *dichloramine toluol* is another. The odor of chlorine may be objectionable.

In addition to the above substances, there are many new proprietary chlorine compounds on the market based on principles given above.

---

*Various theories ascribe the antimicrobial action of hypochlorites to HOCl, HCl, *nascent* oxygen and free chlorine. Thus: $2 CaOCl_2 + 2 HCl \longrightarrow 2 CaCl_2 + 2 HOCl$; $HOCl + HCl \longrightarrow H_2O + Cl_2$; or $2 HOCl \longrightarrow 2 HCl + O_2$; or $2 Cl + H_2O \longrightarrow 2 HCl + \frac{1}{2}O_2$; or $Cl_2 + H_2O \longrightarrow HCl + HOCl$.

**Iodine.**   The most actively antimicrobial of the halogens is iodine. However, it is not commonly used for the same large-scale purposes as chlorine because of its physical properties and its cost. Formerly used widely as a local antiseptic in a 7 per cent tincture (alcoholic solution), this strength is far too caustic and poisonous for local application and does more harm than good. The 2 per cent tincture is much better and is the most generally useful for small cuts and abrasions. If the alcohol causes too much pain, the tincture may be diluted with two to four volumes of water.

An aqueous solution containing approximately 1.85 per cent of iodine and 2.2 per cent of potassium iodide is excellent but has a high surface tension.

**Iodophors.**   Nonirritating, nonstaining, virtually odorless and very effective solutions of organic compounds of iodine in which the iodine is loosely combined with a surfactant organic *iodophor* (Gr. *phor* = bearer or carrier) are available commercially. The iodophor releases the iodine slowly and also lowers the surface tension of the solution. Some idea of the amount of iodine remaining in such solutions is readily gained by comparing the diminishing brown color with that of the original full-strength solution. This is not possible with colorless chlorine solutions. Examples of such iodine products are Wescodyne, Ioclide and Betadine. In such forms iodine may be used for a variety of purposes, from clinical uses to sanitization of dishes, with aqueous solutions containing 200 parts per million. Under certain conditions of concentration and temperature such solutions may be sporicidal. They appear to kill bacteria, molds and some viruses quickly. Iodine is a much more effective germicide than chlorine.

Iodine, like chlorine, combines indiscriminately with organic matter; its solutions are unstable and, like chlorine, it is poisonous.

### COMPOUNDS OF HEAVY METALS

The first scientifically designed, specifically acting drug was based on the heavy metal arsenic. Arsenic was compounded with an organic group to diminish its poisonous properties. Prior to 1907, Paul Ehrlich and his coworkers had synthesized and tried many such compounds in the treatment of spirochetal diseases, notably syphilis, without success. The 606th compound ("SOS" or "606" or Salvarsan or arsphenamine), discovered in 1907, was very effective and, with various modifications such as neoarsphenamine, was used for years in the treatment of syphilis and other spirochetoses. It fell into disuse after 1943 when it was found by Mahoney et al., in the U. S. Public Health Service, that penicillin is much more active against the same organisms and almost nontoxic.

Other metals in common use as microbicides today are iron and zinc, previously discussed, and mercury, silver and copper. All act mainly by coagulative action except in very low concentrations (e.g., 1:10,000 and lower) in which they appear to have specific molecular toxic effects (see *oligodynamic action* and *ionic effects*).

Mercury compounds were first used in the fifteenth century specifically to treat syphilis. More recently zinc in a chelated form called *Zinc Omadine* has been shown to have potent microbicidal properties, as well as the sodium salt of *Omadine*.

**Bichloride of Mercury.** Long used as a general disinfectant and as an antiseptic, bichloride of mercury (mercuric chloride) is now much less used than formerly. For general disinfection it may be prepared in dilutions of 1:1000 to 1:5000. However, it is very toxic to tissues, very poisonous internally and corrosive to materials, especially metals (hence its older name of *corrosive sublimate*). In many situations it fails because it forms a thick coating of coagulum on the outer surface particles of mucus, tissues and feces, and thus protects the microorganisms within. As described previously, in dilutions of 1:10,000 or more its action is more bacteriostatic than coagulative. This action may be reversed by sulfur compounds unless coagulation has occurred.

ORGANIC MERCURIALS. Attempts have been made, following Ehrlich's lead with arsenic, to decrease the toxic, corrosive and irritating qualities of mercuric disinfectants by incorporating mercury in complex organic molecules. This has yielded a number of products that are less toxic and irritating than bichloride of mercury, among them *Mercurochrome, Merthiolate* and *Metaphen*. In the presence of organic matter they are more effective than bichloride of mercury. Mercurochrome is often used for local, superficial application for disinfecting cuts, wounds and skin. Some of these organic mercury compounds are used as preservatives in biological materials. Other useful organic mercurials are *phenylmercuric nitrate,* very effective and of sufficiently low toxicity for external use, and *ammoniated mercury,* long used as a 10 per cent ointment for external wounds and fungal infections of the skin. These mercurials all mainly act microbistatically, and their action, like that of bichloride of mercury, is reversed by thioglycollate and hydrosulfuric acid. All mercury compounds are poisonous internally to some degree, and mercury is absorbed through the skin.

**Silver Nitrate.** Silver nitrate (1 per cent aqueous solution) is used principally for application to infants' eyes at birth to prevent infection. Silver is also used as a local disinfectant in the form of organic colloidal preparations such as Argyrol or Protargol, in which form it is nonirritating and may be used in adult eyes at 20 per cent concentration. It is not for use in infants' eyes in place of silver nitrate. The use of silver nitrate (1 per cent aqueous) or an equivalent, approved antibacterial in the eyes of infants at birth is required by law in most states as a safeguard against blindness of the newborn (*ophthalmia neonatorum*). However, antibiotic treatment may be satisfactory in some situations.

**Copper Sulfate.** Copper sulfate is used chiefly to control the growth of algae in open water reservoirs and as a fungicide in garden sprays (*Bordeaux mixture*). Organic compounds of iron are also used as fungicides in garden sprays.

## PHENOL AND ITS DERIVATIVES

Phenol ($C_6H_5OH$) (carbolic acid) in the pure state is not commonly used as a disinfectant because it is expensive and because there are more than a dozen derivatives that are not only less costly but more effective. All act similarly to phenol (i.e., mainly by coagulation, partly by little understood lytic and toxic effects). Unlike the halogens, which are indiscriminately effective against a wide range of microorganisms, susceptibility to phenolic disinfectants varies greatly. Some organisms use phenol as a food.

**Surface (Residual) Disinfection.** Phenol and, more especially, many of its derivatives are surface tension reducers and are commonly used in solutions containing additional surfactants to improve wetting properties. Since they are surfactants themselves, the phenolic disinfectants tend to be adsorbed in thin, and more or less durable, films on inert surfaces to which they are applied, resulting in what is termed *surface,* or *residual,* disinfection. As compared with the volatile halogens or alcohols their action is thus prolonged, often for many

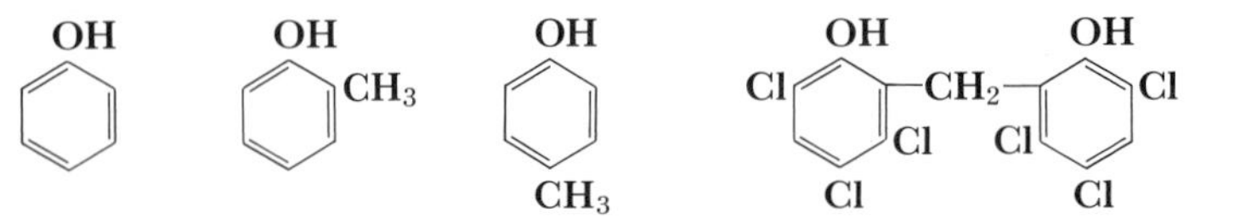

**Figure 21.6** Structures of phenol, representative cresols and one commonly used bisphenol (hexachlorophene).

*Phenol*        *o-Cresol*        *p-Cresol*        *Hexachlorophene, a bis-Phenol*

hours. This is an especial value of certain preparations of phenol derivatives for surgical and hospital hand washes.

**Types of Phenolic Disinfectants.** Phenolic disinfectants are of many types, common among which are: the *cresols,* the molecules of which are like phenol but have methyl groups attached; and the *bis-phenols,* the molecules of which consist of two phenolic groups joined directly or through some other radicle (Fig. 21.6).

CRUDE CRESOLS. Crude cresols form colloidal (milky) suspensions in water and are therefore especially effective as disinfectants, because each colloidal droplet consists of *concentrated* cresol. This is true of many colloidal disinfectants. There are many excellent cresol preparations on the market. Some have a clinging odor. Most of them contain a surface tension reducer in addition to the disinfectant. They are commonly used for disinfecting floors, furniture, barns and stables in from 1 to 5 per cent concentrations. Some may also be used in temporary contact with human tissues in 0.5 to 1.0 per cent strengths. Good examples are Lysol and saponated cresol solution, *U.S.P.* The preparation of such solutions is an important industry.

BIS-PHENOLS. Like the cresols, bis-phenols have surfactant properties. In order to increase their solubility in water they are commonly used in solutions with other surfactants or detergents.* In general they are less toxic than the cresols. Among well-known bis-phenols is one combined with chlorine (one of the class of *halogenated bis-phenols*), called Hexachlorophene (G 11). Because it is a surfactant it provides good residual surface disinfection of the skin, and it is not irritating if used properly. It is incorporated especially in surgical soaps and hand washes (Gamophen, pHisohex and Hex-O-San).

ORTHOPHENYLPHENOL. A similar compound, orthophenylphenol, is used in mixtures

such as *O-syl. Chlorothymol* and *Chlorohexidine* are other halogenated bis-phenols which are similar in general properties. All are broadly germicidal, and each has distinctive properties that adapt it to particular situations. Some can be used effectively as irrigations in surgical wounds in 1:1000 to 1:10,000 concentrations.

The activity of all phenolics is markedly depressed in the presence of extraneous organic matter, and they are highly microbistatic.

## ALCOHOLS

There are many substances that chemically are alcohols: many of these are effective microbicides. Like various organic disinfectants, their microbicidal activity is directly related to increased length of their carbon chain and molecular weight; beyond their critical point (different for each type) microbicidal activity decreases. The two alcohols most commonly used for disinfection or sanitization are ethyl ("grain") alcohol and isopropyl ("rubbing") alcohol. They are mild disinfectants and are nontoxic on external application. Methyl or "wood" alcohol and its vapor are extremely poisonous and should never be used in any bodily contact whatever.

Ethyl alcohol is a surface tension reducer, a lipid solvent and a coagulating agent, properties that should contribute to microbicidal potency. However, it is also a potent dehydrating agent, a property that interferes greatly with its coagulating power and probably also with its other antimicrobial properties. Because of its dehydrating power it is best used as a 70 per cent aqueous solution. Stronger concentrations (95 or 100 per cent "absolute") are much less effective. As a coagulating agent it tends to combine nonspecifically with extraneous organic matter and can produce a thick, protective coating of coagulum around microorganisms. As a lipid solvent it is useful as a *cleansing* agent ("disinfectant"?) for skin prior to hypodermic injections. It adversely affects viruses and cells with envelope lipids (Chapters 18 and 20). As a surface tension reducer it is a potent adjuvant of other disinfectants such as

---

*Detergency (L. *detergere* = to cleanse) does not necessarily confer disinfectant properties. Virtually all household detergents are strong surface-tension reducers but are not therefore necessarily good disinfectants.

phenolics and quaternaries. Similar considerations apply to isopropyl alcohol.

## DETERGENT DISINFECTANTS

As just mentioned, not all detergents are disinfectants. However, several compounds combine the properties of detergent, surface tension reducer and disinfectant.

**Soaps.**   Among these versatile compounds are the common soaps; potassium or sodium esters of higher fatty acids (stearic or glyceric). They are actively lethal for certain species of microorganisms: *Treponema pallidum,* the syphilis spirochete; *Diplococcus pneumoniae,* a cause of pneumonia; some streptococci; and a few other organisms. Unfortunately, with these few exceptions, soaps are relatively ineffective as general disinfectants. However, soaps are potent surface tension reducers and consequently are good emulsifying and foaming or "sudsing" agents. Foaming results from the fact that, since the surface tension is greatly weakened, the surface can be extended almost indefinitely as foam or as droplets in an emulsion; compare with mercury, page 252. When soapy water is applied to skin or instruments, microorganisms are carried into the emulsified grease droplets and removed by rinsing. Detergency is the chief virtue of neutral soaps. Soluble soaps are precipitated by acids, ions of heavy metals, and by $Ca^{++}$. Hand soap is often used as a carrier for phenolic disinfectants, as previously discussed.

**Synthetic Detergents.**   As generally understood, this term comprises a group of potent surface tension reducers that are not typical soaps. They are synthesized commercially and much used for household and commercial cleansing and laundry purposes. They are available in "large, economy" packages in all grocery stores. Most of them are long-chain, alkyl-benzyl-sulfonates (ABS; see Chapter 42). Few are markedly microbicidal. They are *anionic* compounds (see following paragraphs).

Another group of synthetic compounds, classed as detergents because they are strong surface tension reducers, are much more important as disinfectants and sanitizing agents. The first was discovered in 1936 by Domagk (Nobel Prize winner), who described the properties of dodecyl-dimethyl-benzyl-ammonium chloride, now familiar as *Roccal* or *Zephiran* (Fig. 21.7, *A*). This is a quaternary alkyl ammonium salt, and is representative of a number of similar compounds that have since been developed commercially as disinfectants or detergents. As a group they are commonly called *quaternaries* or "quats." Basically, they are ammonium halides (for example, ammonium chloride) in which the hydrogen atoms have

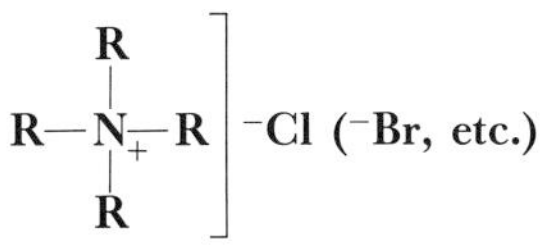

A. *General formula of alkyl ammonium halides*

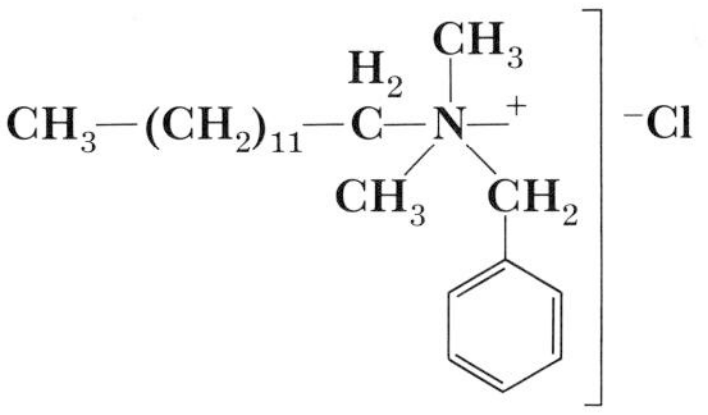

B. *Alkyl-dimethyl-benzyl-ammonium chloride; a cationic, microbicidal detergent*

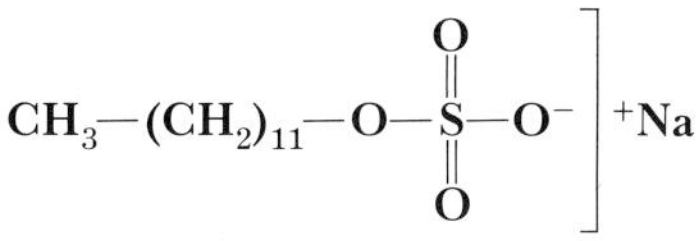

C. *Sodium lauryl sulfate; an anionic microbicidal detergent.*

**Figure 21.7**  Forms of microbicidal detergents.

been replaced by various alkyl groups (Fig. 21.7, *B*).

**Chemical Structure and Activity.** In general, the more effective of these detergent-disinfectant compounds are those in which at least one of the alkyl groups contains a chain of 12 to 16 carbon atoms, whereas the less effective are those of lower or higher molecular weight. This represents a common observation previously mentioned; i.e., the germicidal efficacy of many organic compounds is greatly affected by chemical structure, especially length of carbon chains.

**Cationics, Anionics and Nonionics.** There are three types of microbicidal detergents: (1) those in which the surfactant portion is the *cation* (e.g., quaternary alkyl ammonium halides (Fig. 21.7, *A*); (2) those in which the surfactant portion is the *anion* (e.g., complex soaps like sodium lauryl sulfate (Fig. 21.7, *C*); and (3) those that do not ionize. These compounds are classified as *cationic, anionic* and *nonionic* detergents, respectively. The cationic compounds appear to be the most generally effective as disinfectants and are what is generally meant by the term "quaternary." Soaps are anionic detergents. The nonionic compounds are relatively weak disinfectants. They are sometimes used with anionic compounds in household detergents as adjuvants.

**Mechanism of Action.** Since detergents like the quaternaries and sodium lauryl sulfate are generally alkyl compounds of chlorine or sodium, they are bipolar, i.e., they exhibit both fat-soluble (lipophilic) and water-soluble (hydrophilic) sides. When dissolved in aqueous culture media, the longer alkyl chains tend to be oriented toward, and to dissolve in, the cell lipids. The negatively charged residue (chlorine or sodium ion) is oriented away from the cell and is drawn toward the surrounding aqueous fluid. The surface tension reducer molecules are systematically arranged side by side at the cell–aqueous medium interface, as closely placed as possible (Fig. 21.8). Since the reducer molecules at any surface have a lower mutual attraction than the water molecules in which they are dissolved, the surface tension of their solution is lowered. Lipids upon which detergents in aqueous solution become oriented tend to become divided into smaller and smaller particles, each coated with the surface tension reducer (i.e., to be *emulsified*); detergents thus characteristically "cut" (remove) grease.

The lipophilic property of quaternaries and alkyl sulfates is thought to disrupt the lipids, and therefore the whole structures, of bacterial cell walls and membranes, especially of those rich in lipids like many gram-negative bacteria. Disruption of the cell walls and membranes would permit outward passage of vital intracellular components and passage inward of the surface tension reducer. Electron micrographs show the destruction of bacterial cell walls and inner structures by antimicrobial substances which reduce surface tension. Prob-

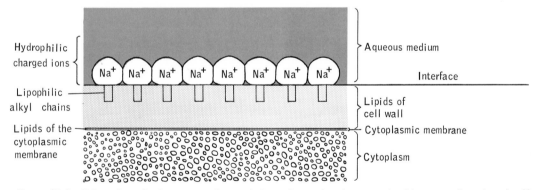

**Figure 21.8** Orientation of polar groups of an *anionic,* surface-active detergent, in this case sodium lauryl sulfate [$Na^+(C_{12}H_{25}OSO_3)^-$], in relation to the surrounding aqueous medium and a cell having lipids in its cell wall or cytoplasmic membrane. The hydrophilic group (here represented by $Na^+$) orients at the fluid-cell interface; the hydrophobic group (here represented by the lauryl sulfate group$^-$) is oriented in the lipids of the cell wall or membrane.

At the air-water interface the hydrophilic groups orient themselves within the surface water while the hydrophobic alkyl groups are at the air-water interface, weakening the intermolecular attraction between water molecules at the surface; i.e., *lowering the surface tension* of the water. Accumulation of molecules of a surface-active, polarized agent at any interface between solids and fluids or between immiscible fluids is called *adsorption*.

A very similar relationship would be that between a cell and a *cationic* detergent of the class of quaternary ammonium compounds; e.g., cetyl pyridinium chloride (Ceepryn): $\left[ \bigcirc N-C_{16}H_{33} \right]^+ Cl^-$.

ably these detergents also act in part by occluding the bacterial surfaces by being adsorbed there.

In use, soaps and other anionic compounds should not be mixed with cationic compounds, because the oppositely charged molecular complexes neutralize each other and the agents are precipitated or inactivated. For the same reasons hard, acid and iron-rich waters tend to inactivate them. Unlike many other disinfectants, quaternaries retain much of their activity in the presence of considerable organic matter. The quaternaries tend to be microbistatic or slowly lethal rather than to kill instantly.

When the effectiveness of quaternaries as disinfectants is being measured, their marked microbistatic action must be offset by the use of special inactivators to allow the microorganisms to grow in the subculture (see Section 20.4). *Tinctures** of quaternaries appear to be very effective indeed against tubercle bacilli, and some are effective against molds, but they are of limited value against certain viruses. Since they are emulsifying agents for lipids quaternaries should be effective against viruses that have lipid-rich components, e.g., envelopes, and there are data in support of this view. Opinions differ concerning other viruses. Picornaviruses are resistant. Quaternaries are not sporicidal. They are much used for disinfection of skin and for purposes of sanitization in restaurants and hospitals.

## MICROBICIDAL GASES

Attempts to cure and prevent disease with vapors and smokes date from the earliest human records, when "aromatics," smudges, perfumes and the like were endowed by popular supposition with almost miraculous, and generally quite factitious, powers to drive away evil spirits and "noxious humors."

More objective studies in the last few decades have yielded several exceedingly valuable results in the form of definitely sporicidal, and therefore *sterilizing,* gases: formaldehyde, ethylene oxide and beta-propiolactone. Chlorine and sulfur dioxide, formerly used, are too destructive and poisonous for general purposes. As sterilizing agents, gases have the advantages that destructive heat and aqueous solutions are not needed and that they can be applied in large volumes in buildings. On the other hand they affect only exposed surfaces, except

---

*Solutions in alcohol.

those made of porous or permeable materials, and they must be applied under conditions of controlled temperature and humidity. Such sterilizing agents are often referred to as *sterilants.*

**Formaldehyde.** This very irritating gas (formula: HCHO) is generated by heating paraformaldehyde or concentrated solutions of formaldehyde. Unless very carefully applied at raised temperatures, formaldehyde tends to polymerize as paraformaldehyde or *paraldehyde* in a thin white film over all surfaces, and hence has definite limitations to places not containing valuable furniture or equipment. Its action is to some extent microbistatic and reversible with sulfite ions. In some solutions it is definitely sporicidal and therefore sterilizing but, like bichloride of mercury, it tends to form protective coatings of coagulum around microorganisms if extraneous organic matter is present. For best results a relative humidity of about 70 per cent and a temperature of about 22° C. are requisite. Formaldehyde vapor has low penetrability into such materials as blankets. It is much less used now than formerly.

**Ethylene Oxide.** This substance (formula: $CH_2 \cdot O \cdot CH_2$) is liquid at temperatures below 10.8° C. (51.4° F.), its boiling point. It is relatively inexpensive and is handled in metal tubes or bottles like other compressed gases. In the pure state it is very toxic, irritating and explosive. For use it is mixed with other substances: ethylene oxide, 10 per cent and carbon dioxide, 90 per cent (sold as Carboxide); ethylene oxide, 20 per cent and carbon dioxide, 80 per cent (sold as Oxyfume); ethylene oxide, 11 per cent and halogenated petroleum, 89 per cent (sold as Cryoxcide). Each preparation has special advantages in certain situations.

The desired mixture is generally applied in autoclaves or other closed containers where humidity, temperature and pressure may be controlled. The concentration of the gas is generally expressed in milligrams of pure ethylene oxide per liter of space. A typical use situation is 500 mg. of gas per liter at about 58° C. (130° F.) and a relative humidity of 40 per cent for four hours. If one factor is varied the others must be varied accordingly. For example, if the concentration is doubled, the time may be halved. At a relative humidity of 30 per cent the action of the gas is about 10 times as fast as at 95 per cent relative humidity.

In using ethylene oxide in an autoclave, a typical procedure involves seven steps, all of which can be carried out by fully automatic equipment now available for the purpose (Fig. 21.9):

(1) Withdraw almost all air with a vacuum pump.

(2) Admit a controlled volume of steam or water vapor.

(3) Admit ethylene oxide in required concentration.

(4) Adjust the temperature as indicated and hold constant.

(5) After the required time turn off heat.

(6) Take out all gas with vacuum pump.

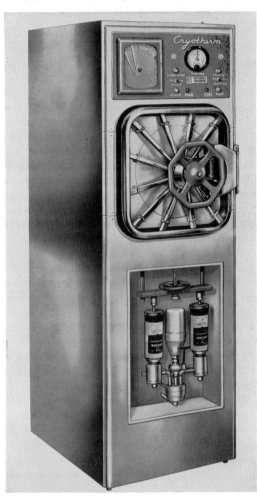

**Figure 21.9** Autoclave arranged for sterilization by sporicidal ethylene oxide gas (Cryoxcide). Below the steel door are seen the containers of gas and a water inlet so arranged that the vapors can be mixed and humidified (much as gasoline, air and water vapor are mixed in a modern automobile carburetor) before admission of the sterilizing vapor mixture to the chamber of the autoclave. Above the door are the dials controlling sterilizing temperature and time, vacuum pump, gas and humidity inlet and a maximum and minimum recording thermometer. Operation is almost completely automatic. (Courtesy of American Sterilizer Co.)

(7) Admit sterilized air to normal pressure.

Ethylene oxide is a very effective general microbicide and kills bacterial endospores. It is therefore a sterilizing agent. It acts by alkylation or introduction of an organic group in place of a hydrogen atom, in various compounds in protoplasm. It does not injure even delicate organic materials that are injured by heat and aqueous solutions. It penetrates well, does not condense on objects and soon dissipates from all materials.

It can also be used in the liquid state in 1 per cent concentration to sterilize unstable organic fluids, such as bacteriological culture media, by mixing fluid ethylene oxide with them at 10° C. After a few hours the ethylene oxide is driven off by a short incubation at 37° C.

**Beta-Propiolactone (BPL).** In pure form at 20° C. this is a liquid with a sweetish but very irritating odor [formula: $(CH_2)_2 \cdot CO$]. Unlike ethylene oxide, it is not explosive. It may be stored at 4° C., but is more stable in sealed glass containers at $-25°$ C. Its aqueous solutions are very unstable. It kills most microorganisms, including bacterial spores, and is therefore a sterilizing agent. It probably acts by alkylation, as does ethylene oxide. In fluid form it has been used to sterilize vaccines, tissues used for grafting and other delicate biological materials that could not be sterilized in any other way. Like ethylene oxide, it must be used in closed chambers where temperature and humidity can be accurately controlled. A relative humidity of 70 to 80 per cent and a temperature of about 25° C. are optimal, with a final concentration of beta-propiolactone of about 2 to 4 mg. per liter of air and a sterilizing time of 2 to 3 hours (Fig. 21.10).

When properly applied, beta-propiolactone is much more active than either formaldehyde (HCHO) or ethylene oxide. It is noncorrosive, and does not condense on surfaces as does formaldehyde. However, beta-propiolactone lacks the penetrating power of ethylene oxide and is more like formaldehyde in this respect. It also requires higher relative humidities. It is generally recommended to replace formaldehyde for use in buildings.

Since they are so effective, gaseous disinfectants such as ethylene oxide, formaldehyde, and beta-propiolactone have tremendous potential value in combating massive and widespread dissemination of infectious agents such as might be employed in biological warfare.

**Toxic and Destructive Properties.** Experience shows that prolonged and repeated ex-

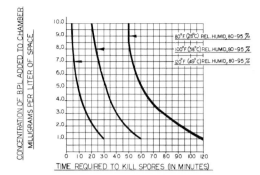

**Figure 21.10** Relation between concentration of beta-propiolactone and time required to kill spores of *Bacillus globigii* on filter paper strips. Curves are shown for three different temperatures at a relative humidity of 80 to 95 per cent. (Courtesy of Wilmot Castle Co., Rochester, N.Y.)

posure to any chemically active disinfectant, or any sterilant, may cause tissue irritation or destruction, and may damage articles containing certain unstable organic and inorganic substances such as magnesium (instrument housings) and some plastics. Users must always be alert to this possibility.

They must also be alert to toxic properties, especially dangerous potentialities of newly developed disinfectants. For example, with continued study of beta-propiolactone, data have appeared suggesting that it may be carcinogenic as well as irritating. The toxic or carcinogenic properties of a disinfectant do not necessarily militate against its use; otherwise, such substances as chlorine, formaldehyde, bichloride of mercury and phenol, and radiations such as ultraviolet, x-rays and gamma rays would be banned. However, proper precautions must be taken in handling such agents to prevent ingestion or undue contact.

## RADIATIONS

**Ultraviolet Light.** As described in Chapters 15 and 19, ultraviolet light is actively microbicidal when applied properly. It has very slight powers of penetration. Exposure must be direct, intense and sufficiently prolonged. Eyes must be protected, as they can be severely damaged. It is sometimes used in hospitals, especially in operating rooms, reportedly with good results, to kill microorganisms on instrument tables, in the air and on floors and walls. Ultraviolet light is used on a large scale to prevent growth of molds in meatpacking houses, bakeries and other commercial and industrial establishments. Another application is in the treatment of

biological fluids, such as blood plasma and vaccines, to kill contaminating viruses. The rays are directed on fluid that is made to flow in a micro-thin film that ultraviolet rays can penetrate. The wave length commonly used in disinfectant applications of ultraviolet light is 2537 Å, because it is most practical. Shorter waves, such as 1849 Å, are much more lethal but are difficult to handle and apply. Ultraviolet kills spores as readily as vegetative cells.

**Cathode Rays.** A recent development in radiation sterilization, cathode rays (electron beams) are expensive to apply, but are being developed on a commercial scale. They can be made to penetrate thin metal, paper or plastic sheets and have been used successfully to sterilize sealed packages for surgical use, packaged meats, vegetables and other foods. (See also Chapter 46.)

## 21.4   INHIBITION OF MICROORGANISMS (MICROBISTASIS)

As previously indicated, microbistasis denotes a condition of microorganisms in which, although they are alive (or *viable*), they do not multiply. Their enzymic or other vital functions are in a static condition.

In one sense the dormant ascospores of yeasts, conidia or molds, cysts of some protozoa and the endospores of bacteria represent microbistasis as a part of their normal life cycles. However, microbistasis is usually thought of as affecting vegetative cells and as being produced artificially. Microbistasis is exceedingly important in all aspects of microbiology. There is even published discussion of preserving important(?) people in "deep-freeze" ("Homostasis"?).

**Physical Methods.** As mentioned elsewhere, there are several physical methods of inducing microbistasis. Most of them are fundamentally methods of depriving the cell of liquid water: desiccation; immobilizing intracellular water by changing it into ice; drawing most of the water out of the cell by immersion in a fluid of high osmotic pressure; and combinations of these.

In addition, mild irradiations with ultraviolet light and x-rays are often microbistatic instead of lethal. Their microbistatic action is not clearly understood but it is not related to dehydration. Apparently, oxidations are among the most important reactions that occur (Chapter 19).

**Reversibility.**   The action of microbistatic agents is *characteristically reversible;* that is, the organisms can be reactivated if the inhibiting action has not been so prolonged that the cells have gradually died off. We have seen in foregoing chapters how the microbistatic effect of irradiations may be reversed by visible light and certain chemicals, and how bichloride of mercury poisoning may be "cured" by glutathione. Tubercle bacilli dried in a vacuum were found fully viable and virulent after 17 years; diphtheria bacilli and scarlet fever streptococci, after 25 years. Microbial spores (natural microbistasis) will survive for decades. Viruses are commonly held unaltered for months or years frozen in carbon dioxide ice at $-76°$ C. Cattle breeders and others preserve sperm by freezing. In all cases the totally inactive cells can be reactivated.

## MICROBISTASIS AND DISINFECTION

The distinction between chemical microbistasis and disinfection is interesting but entirely arbitrary; a matter of semantics. The differentiation depends on what one means by killing "quickly" (i.e., disinfection) and what one may mean by killing "slowly" (i.e., microbistasis). Even under the most effective conditions of microbistasis, some of the weaker cells die fairly soon; presumably the others are not actually immortal and die eventually, even though only after decades or centuries. As applied to bacteria, one could say that death within a time less than the maximal for one generation (i.e., one cell-fission) under optimal growth conditions might be regarded as more than mere prevention of multiplication and, therefore, true killing or disinfectant action. If death were delayed beyond one generation-time, one might say that multiplication had been delayed or that the organisms had been in a static condition for at least a short time. This last situation could represent true bacteriostasis. There are many obvious difficulties in making such a distinction. The term bacteriostasis (or microbistasis) is, however, widely used and usually means "long" delayed death (i.e., the cells die only after some hours, days or decades), rather than in, say, 10 to 30 minutes (Fig. 21.11).

### CHEMICAL MICROBISTASIS

We may note three general types of chemical microbistatic agents: certain aniline dyes; sulfonamide and similarly acting drugs; and antibiotics.

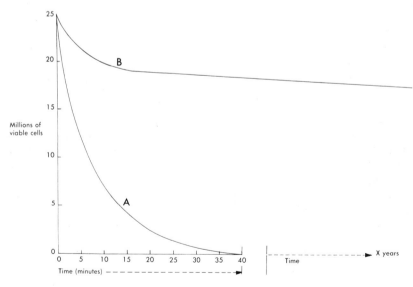

**Figure 21.11**   Comparison of disinfectant action with microbistasis. The microorganism concerned has a generation time of 40 minutes at 37° C. in broth at pH 7.2. Curve *A* shows complete sterilization within one generation time resulting from action of an applied microbicidal agent such as heat or disinfectant. Curve *B* shows initial rapid diminution of numbers caused merely by the action of the microbistatic agent such as freeze-drying. Bacteriostatic action is characterized by very slow decline in numbers.

**Aniline Dyes.**   We have already referred to selectively bacteriostatic culture media containing dyes (Chapter 4). A representative dye used in such media is crystal violet, commonly used in the Gram stain. Since it is a basic dye, it has a marked affinity for acidic constituents of the bacterial cell, notably nucleic acids. With these the dye forms unstable salts that (in the absence of iodine) soon dissociate, and are either disposed of by the cell or can be removed by washing the cell with a harmless solvent such as water. Cells stained in this way with crystal violet, especially gram-positive cells, are in a static condition. They will not grow in media containing such dyes. They can be quickly reactivated by washing.

On the other hand, gram-negative cells in contact with crystal violet are not stained and generally grow well on media containing such dyes as crystal violet, basic fuchsin or methylene blue–eosin. Such dye-containing media are therefore commonly used for *selective* bacteriostasis; especially to isolate gram-negative bacteria from materials contaminated with gram-positive bacteria.

**Sulfonamide Drugs.**   The sulfonamides are excellent examples of bacteriostatic agents. They were discovered by Domagk (Nobel Prize winner) about 1936. Sulfonamide drugs are derived from the same basic material (coal tar) as aniline dyes. All are derivatives of sulfanilamide (Fig. 21.12). Like basic dyes they are effective mainly (with a few notable exceptions: *Neisseria, Shigella, Proteus, Klebsiella* and *Escherichia*) against gram-positive bacteria.

Sulfonamide Drugs and Metabolite Antagonism.   The true sulfonamide drugs are those that readily release the sulfanilamide residue in the living cell. Sulfanilamide so closely resembles para-aminobenzoic acid (PABA) that it can displace PABA in the absolutely essential vitamin, folic acid (Fig. 21.13). This important vitamin is necessary to a coenzyme (CoA; Chapter 6) involved in synthesis of amino acids and hence of proteins. Such absolutely essential specific substances, necessary to the completion of a particular functional part of the cell, but not used as sources of energy or bulk, are sometimes called *essential metabolites* or *micronutrients*. In the present discussion PABA is considered to be an essential metabolite.

When we compare the diagrams of the molecules of sulfanilamide and PABA (Fig. 21.13), the resemblance between the major parts of the two is made clear. As shown in the diagram, the folic acid molecule consists of three functional groups: pterin, PABA and glutamic acid. If any form of a sulfonamide drug is present in a sufficient amount, part of it goes into the folic acid complex in place of PABA. It is said to be a *metabolite antagonist*. In this case it *antagonizes,* or is *competitive* with, the metabolite PABA. The sulfonamide is therefore often called a *competitive inhibitor*. Because the structure of the sulfonamide is analogous to that of PABA, the drug is also called a *metabolite analogue.*

But no form of sulfonamide is capable of carrying on the functions of PABA. The sulfonamide is, in effect, a molecular imposter. The enzymic functions of the microbial cell depending on folic acid are therefore promptly stopped by sulfonamides. Since all of the functions of the cell are closely interdependent, the whole cell mechanism stops also. The cell is then in a state of microbistasis. The production of microbistasis in this way by chemicals or drugs is the basis of modern *chemotherapy* (see page 286). There are many substances besides sulfonamides (e.g., amino acids, certain ions [see ion antagonism], organic acids and esters, purines, pyrimidines and sugar derivatives) that, because of similarity of structure, can act as metabolite analogues. They antagonize or displace ions or molecules of vital cell structures such as proteins, enzymes and coenzymes or nucleic acids. In the nucleic acids nucleotide analogues can produce mutations (Chapters 13 and 15).

**Reversal of Metabolite Antagonism.**   It is important to note that, like most other microbistatic reactions, the enzyme blockage produced by sulfonamide is not fatal and may be reversed in several ways—for example, by adding enough PABA to displace and exclude the sulfonamide; by supplying new folic acid ready-made in the medium; by supplying, in the culture medium, the product that would have been formed by the blocked enzyme (or any subsequent enzyme in the chain); or by supplying the finished product of the entire enzymic series, in this case certain amino acids.

## 21.5   DRUG RESISTANCE

The cell itself may be capable of bypassing or overcoming the effects of metabolite antagonists. For example, let us suppose that in a parallel series of enzyme reactions (series I and II, Fig. 21.14) enzyme D is blocked by some

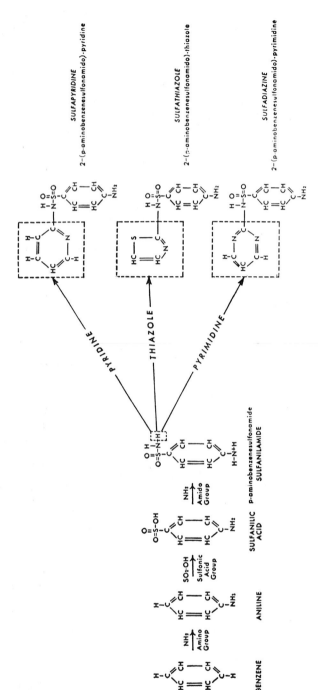

**Figure 21.12**   How the sulfonamide drugs are derived from benzene. First, an amino group is added, yielding aniline (a base from which dyes are synthesized). The addition of a sulfonic acid group to aniline yields sulfanilic acid. The addition of another amino group yields sulfanilamide. The addition to this, in place of one hydrogen atom, of various other chemical groups yields other sulfanilamide drugs, three of which are shown in the diagram.

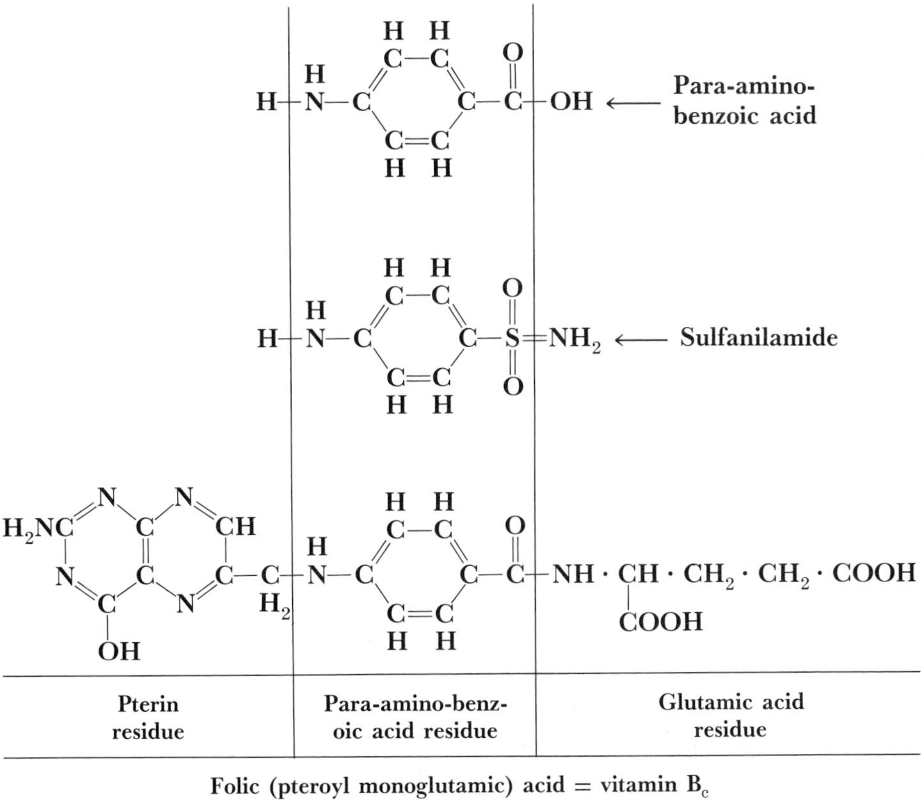

Folic (pteroyl monoglutamic) acid = vitamin $B_c$

**Figure 21.13**  Structural resemblance between molecules of para-aminobenzoic acid (PABA) and sulfanilamide (above), and the antagonism of PABA by sulfanilamide in the folic acid molecule (below).

microbistatic drug. However, let us assume that some of the substance usually made by the blocked enzyme D is produced as a side reaction or intermediate stage in the function of another enzyme, H. This product becomes available to E and thus the blockage at D is bypassed. Such a cell is more or less *drug-resistant,*

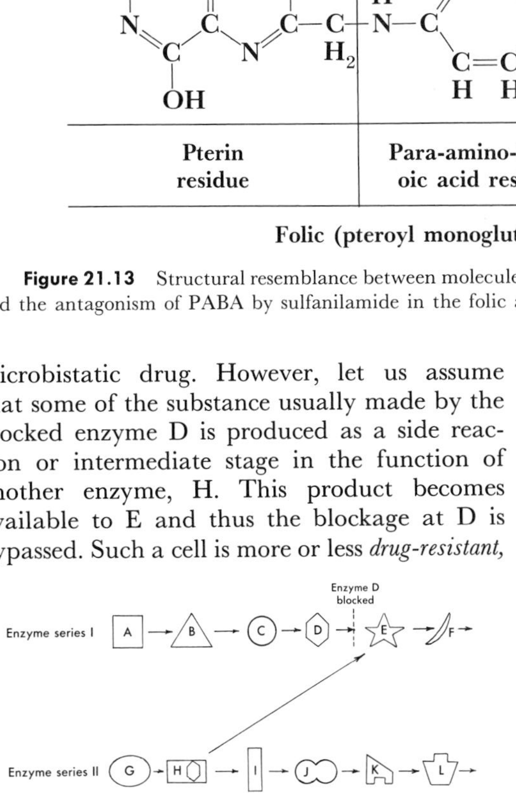

**Figure 21.14**  Two parallel series of enzymes carrying on different synthetic functions. If enzyme *D* in series I becomes blocked, as by an antimetabolite, the entire series of reactions in series I stops. However, enzyme *H* in series II may, because of similar structure of one of its parts, produce a small amount of the substance produced by *D* and required by *E* (or the substance required by *E* may be derived from some other source in the organism). In either case series I continues to function though possibly at a reduced rate. The different geometrical figures are intended merely to indicate different specificities of the different enzymes.

depending on how much of the product needed by E is available from H.

Such enzymic rearrangements and bypassings (*alternate metabolic pathways*) are quite common. From the clinical standpoint, sulfonamide resistance of an infecting organism means that the patient must receive some other drug.

**Resistant Mutants.**  In Chapter 15 it was shown that among any large number of microbial cells in a given pure culture, mutant forms may be found. Among the large numbers of bacterial cells of a given species infecting a patient there are, therefore, likely to be mutants with enzymic arrangements that will be unaffected by a microbistatic drug such as sulfonamide. In the presence of the drug these mutants will thrive, while all the other microbial cells are killed off. We thus have bred up a sulfonamide-resistant strain of the infecting organism which is dangerous to the patient and to those who contract the resistant organism from him.

In some microorganisms that are ordinarily susceptible to penicillin, notably *Staphylococcus,* penicillin-resistance depends on production of an extracellular enzyme (*penicillinase*) which destroys the drug. Mutants that produce such enzymes are able to grow unhampered in the presence of the drug, to the eventual exclusion of the nonenzyme-producing sensitive mutants.

**Induced Drug Resistance.** In addition to the occurrence of drug-destroying enzymes that appear as a result of mutation, such enzymes appear also as *induced* or *adaptive enzymes* resulting from contact of the cell with the drug. The whole problem of mechanisms of drug resistance, not only in microorganisms but in insect pests (e.g., resistance of mosquitoes and flies to insecticides), is a major problem in chemotherapy and pest control, and an excellent field for profitable research.

**Drug Dependence.** The appearance of strains that are not merely resistant to drugs but wholly *dependent* on them seems as strange as the emergence of resistant strains. The two are probably not related except that they are two manifestations of the phenomenon of mutation. Drug-dependent mutants obviously could not survive and develop significantly except in an environment containing the drug on which they are dependent. It is only because we have tried to cultivate microorganisms in contact with antimicrobial drugs that these curious mutant forms have been revealed.

## 21.6 CHEMOTHERAPY

Chemotherapy, broadly speaking, is therapy by means of chemicals. The term is generally restricted, however, to the use of drugs that act by metabolite antagonism or enzyme blockage. In order to be truly chemotherapeutic such drugs must act on the parasite in concentrations that have no effect (or at least no serious "side" effects) on the host. Some valuable chemotherapeutic drugs are toxic to the patient as well as to the parasite and so must be used with great care and under medical supervision.

**Chemotherapy and Cancer.** A very interesting aspect of chemotherapy concerns the possibility of selectively poisoning the cells of *neoplasms* (Gr. *neo* = new; *plasm* = form) (e.g., cancers). Neoplasms are thought to have metabolic mechanisms different from those of normal cells. The obvious possibility presents itself of finding some metabolite antagonist that will poison an enzymic mechanism peculiar to the neoplasm cell and not present in the normal cell. Thus, it is conceivable that we could cure cancer overnight by means of a few tablets or injections of some antibiotic-like drug.

This rosy dream may not be too far from reality. For example, the cells of certain cancers of mice differ from normal mouse cells by synthesizing cyanocobalamin (vitamin $B_{12}$), a cobalt-containing coenzyme. At least two types of antimetabolites that interfere with synthesis of $B_{12}$ produced cures of the cancer when fed to mice. The antimetabolites are 1,2-dimethyl-4(P-carboxyphenylazo)5-hydroxybenzene and 1,2-dichloro-4-benzenesulfonamide-5-nitrobenzene. Several other drugs have been found that, if not the whole answer, at least point definitely to the possibilities for chemotherapy in research on cancer metabolism. Honor, Fame and Fortune are to be won in this field!

## SUPPLEMENTARY READING

Armstrong, J. A., and Froelich, E. J.: Inactivation of viruses by benzalkonium chloride. Appl. Microbiol., *12*:132, 1964.

Brock, T. D., Mosser, J., and Peacher, B.: The inhibition by streptomycin of certain *Streptococcus* bacteriophages, using host bacteria resistant to the antibiotic. J. Gen. Microbiol., *33*:9, 1963.

Brown, B. L., and Fuerst, R.: Ethylene oxide sterilization of tissue culture media. Science, *142*:1654, 1963.

Cliver, D. O.: Factors in the membrane filtration of enteroviruses. Appl. Microbiol., *13*:417, 1965.

Cook, A. M.: The evaluation of disinfectants. Roy. Soc. Health Jour., *87*:199, 1967.

Cox, W. A.: Site of action of certain antibacterial heterocyclic quaternary ammonium compounds. Appl. Microbiol., *13*:956, 1965.

Ernst, R. R., and Shull, J. J.: Ethylene oxide gaseous sterilization: I. Concentration and temperature effects. Appl. Microbiol., *10*:337, 1962.

Farkas-Himsley, H.: Killing of chlorine-resistant bacteria by chlorine-bromine solutions. Appl. Microbiol., *12*:1, 1964.

Favero, M. S., and Drake, C. H.: Factors influencing the occurrence of high numbers of iodine-resistant bacteria in iodinated swimming pools. Appl. Microbiol., *14*:627, 1966.

Fellowes, O. N.: Some surface-active agents and their virucidal effect on foot-and-mouth disease virus. Appl. Microbiol., *13*:694, 1965.

Hazeu, W., and Hueck, H. J.: The use of β-propiolactone for the sterilization of heat-labile materials. Ant. Leeuw., *31*:295, 1965.

Himmelfarb, P., El-Bisi, H. M., Read, R. B., Jr., and Litsky, W.: Effect of relative humidity on the bactericidal activity of propylene oxide vapor. Appl. Microbiol., *10*:431, 1962.

Humphrey, A. E., and Nickerson, J. T. R.: Testing thermal death data for significant nonlogarithmic behavior. Appl. Microbiol., *9*:282, 1961.

Kelsey, J. C., Beeby, M. M., and Whitehouse, C. W.: A capacity use-dilution test for disinfectants. Monthly Bul., Min. Health, Pub. Health Lab. Service, *24*:152, 1965. *See also:* Dodd, A. H., and Kelsey, J. C.: Ibid., *25*:232, 1966.

Kruse, R. H., Green, T. D., Chambers, R. C., and Jones,

M. W.: Disinfection of aerosolized pathogenic fungi on laboratory surfaces. Appl. Microbiol., *11*:436, 1963.

Kundin, W. D., Robbins, M. L., and Smith, P. K.: Antiviral activity of 3,5 di-iodo-4-hydroxybenzenesulfonamide in chick embryo lung tissue culture. Proc. Soc. Exp. Biol. Med., *116*:425, 1964.

Lawrence, C. A., and Block, S. S.: Disinfection, Sterilization and Preservation. Lea & Febiger, Philadelphia. 1967.

Levine, S. I., Goulet, N. R., and Liu, O. C.: β-propiolactone decontamination of simian virus-40 as determined by a rapid fluorescent-antibody assay. Appl. Microbiol., *13*:70, 1965.

Lorenz, D. E., and Jann, G. J.: Use-dilution test and Newcastle disease virus. Appl. Microbiol., *12*:24, 1964.

Neely, W. B.: Action of formaldehyde on microorganisms. J. Bact., *86*:445, 1963.

Omadine, data on. Tech. Bull., Olin Chemicals, New York. 1967.

Ortenzio, L. F., Opalsky, C. D., and Stuart, L. S.: Factors affecting the activity of phenolic disinfectants. Appl. Microbiol., *9*:562, 1961.

Ostrander, W. E., and Griffith, L. J.: Evaluation of disinfectants for hospital housekeeping use. Appl. Microbiol., *12*:460, 1964.

Pan, Chao-Han, Gast, J. H., and Estes, F. L.: A comparative procedure for evaluating antimicrobial activity of gaseous agents. Appl. Microbiol., *9*:45, 1961.

Perkins, J. J.: Principles and Methods of Sterilization. Charles C Thomas, Springfield, Ill. 1956.

Pitsch, B. L., and Nakamura, M.: Replacement of nicotinic acid requirement of *Shigella sonnei* by pyridine-3-sulfonic acid. J. Bact., *86*:159, 1963.

Reddish, C. F., ed.: Antiseptics, Disinfectants, Fungicides and Sterilization. Lea & Febiger, Philadelphia. 1957.

Reich, M., and Mandel, H. G.: Dissociation of cellular functions in *Bacillus cereus* by 5-fluorouracil. J. Bact., *91*:517, 1966.

Richardson, L. T., and Monro, H. A. U.: Fumigation of jute bags with ethylene oxide and methyl bromide to eradicate potato ring rot bacteria. Appl. Microbiol., *10*:448, 1962.

Richmond, M. H.: The effect of amino acid analogues on growth and protein synthesis in microorganisms. Bact. Rev., *26*:398, 1962.

Rosenwald, A. J., Hodge, H. M., Metcalfe, Jr., S. N., and Hutton, R. S.: Use of the replica-plate technique in studies of toxicity of metals and plastics to bacteria. Appl. Microbiol., *10*:345, 1962.

Shaw, M. K.: Effect of aerosolized lactic acid on the survival of airborne microorganisms. Appl. Microbiol., *15*:948, 1967.

Stedman, R. L., Kravitz, E., and King, J. D.: Studies on cell-surface-germicide and enzyme-germicide reactions and their contribution to the lethal effect. J. Bact., *73*:655, 1957.

Stierli, H., Reed, L. L., and Billick, I. H.: Evaluation of sterilization by gaseous ethylene oxide. Pub. Health Monogr. No. 68. (Pub. Health Serv., Publication No. 903). U. S. Government Printing Office, Washington. 1962.

Sykes, G.: Disinfection and Sterilization. Chapman and Hall, Ltd., Publishers, London. 1965.

Various Authors: Biochemical Studies of Antimicrobial Drugs. Sixteenth Symposium, Soc. Gen. Microbiol., London. 1966.

Vesley, D., and Michaelsen, G. S.: Application of a surface sampling technic to the evaluation of bacteriological effectiveness of certain hospital housekeeping procedures. Health Lab. Sci., *1*:107, 1964.

Voss, J. G.: Effect of inorganic cations on bactericidal activity of anionic surfactants. J. Bact., *86*:207, 1963.

Wallis, C., and Melnick, J. L.: Concentration of enteroviruses on membrane filters. J. Virol., *1*:472, 1967.

Wang, D. I-C., Scharer, J., and Humphrey, A. E.: Kinetics of death of bacterial spores at elevated temperatures. Appl. Microbiol., *12*:451, 1964.

# Chapter 22

# ANTIBIOTICS

The term antibiotic was introduced by S. A. Waksman (Nobel Prize winner) in 1945, as the name of a class of substances of biological origin that are inimical to microorganisms. Strictly speaking, antibiotic means "against life." Since antibiotics, as commonly used, are inimical only to microorganisms they might logically be called "antimicrobiotics." Although substances of biological origin with antimicrobial properties were known before 1900, antibiotics as now defined first came into world-wide prominence about 1940. There followed a widespread search for new antibiotics. It was found that antibiotic substances are produced by a wide variety of living organisms, ranging from man to microbes. The most important and widely used antibiotics at present are derived from microorganisms—mainly from various bacteria of the genera *Bacillus* and *Streptomyces* and certain common species of mold (e.g., *Penicillium*).

Since the earliest studies with pure cultures, microbiologists had known that when certain airborne, saprophytic microorganisms contaminated their cultures they suppressed the growth of the desired species. The phenomenon was so commonplace and attention was so fixed on other problems that the antagonistic action of such contaminants was pushed aside as merely an inevitable nuisance. The true significance of the "nuisance" was largely overlooked until 1929, when Alexander Fleming (afterwards Sir Alexander Fleming, Nobel Prize winner with Florey and Chain) realized it, acted upon the basis of his idea, and discovered, named and described penicillin.

## 22.1 PENICILLIN

The antagonistic airborne saprophytic organism that first attracted Fleming's attention was a colony of the common mold, *Penicillium notatum*. When it contaminated one of his cultures in a Petri plate (Fig. 22.1), Fleming experimented with its antimicrobial action. He passed broth cultures of the mold through filters, removed the mold filaments and was thus able to study the activity of the soluble growth products alone as they occurred in the clear broth. He found that the clarified, sterile broth contained a highly potent antimicrobial principle, the activity of which was readily demonstrated in contact with sensitive microorganisms, especially gram-positive bacteria. He called this principle *penicillin*. In a much purified and refined form it is still one of the forms of penicillin used therapeutically today.

Fleming realized the practical possibility of his discovery and made use of it in his laboratory to eliminate gram-positive contaminants from cultures but was not, at that time, in a position to develop it more fully. For some years the value of such antibiotic phenomena remained relatively unknown.

Interest was reawakened when, realizing that many nonsporeforming pathogenic organisms in the soil are rapidly destroyed, presumably by antimicrobial substances produced by saprophytic microorganisms, Waksman suggested that the search for antibiotic-producing microorganisms be carried to the soil. In 1939 Dubos found, in bogs, organisms (*Bacillus brevis*) that produced two valuable antibacterial substances (*gramicidin* and *tyrocidin*). These antibiotics, while of enormous value therapeutically for surface application and of great interest scientifically, were too toxic for internal use. Dubos's discoveries stimulated new interest in Fleming's observations on *Penicillium notatum;* work on penicillin was begun in England on a large scale by Florey, Chain, Abraham and others (the Oxford Group) in 1940, just after

**Figure 22.1** Sir Alexander Fleming, penicillin discoverer and Nobel Prize winner, points with his inoculating needle to a giant colony of *Penicillium notatum,* the organism that produces penicillin, on agar in a Petri dish. (Courtesy of Pfizer *Spectrum.* In J.A.M.A.)

the outbreak of World War II. Because of the exigencies of the war, work on mass production methods was transferred largely to the United States.

Since that time penicillin has played a role in the greatest war in human history; in the most far-reaching piece of cooperative research ever organized prior to atomic research; in a great industrial development; in the most complete control over a variety of diseases ever achieved by man in a short time; and, because of its impact on venereal diseases, in a tremendous new social and moral trend, the possibilities of which are still only partly realized. The military importance of penicillin in World War II, then just beginning, can hardly be estimated. The development of American facilities for mass production of penicillin, not then available in Europe, was soon of great benefit to all concerned.

**Production.** Production of penicillin and other antibiotics is now a billion-dollar industry in the United States alone. In 1943 an ounce of penicillin cost around twenty thousand dollars. Now it costs about three dollars because of mass production methods.

Production of penicillin involves cultivation of *Penicillium notatum* under conditions most favorable to growth and penicillin production (i.e., at about 24° C. and at a pH between 7 and 8). As the mold is strictly aerobic, exposure to air is essential.

Commercially, a process using submerged growth in closed but vigorously aerated tanks holding thousands of gallons of medium (Fig. 22.2) is most widely used today.

In all methods, suitable medium is first inoculated with suspensions of the conidia of *Penicillium notatum* or the closely related *P. chrysogenum,* which also produces penicillin. The entire procedure is a *pure-culture* process and necessitates costly aseptic technique at all stages.

During the 7 to 14 days of incubation in the large vat of aerated fluid medium the mold excretes at least three waste substances that are of importance: the yellow pigment *chrysogenin,* which must be removed by adsorption with charcoal or similar means; *penicillin;* and *notatin,* or *penicillin B.* The last occurs especially if the acidity of the medium is too great. It is removed during the final purification process. Other substances are also produced, some of them related to penicillin. In general, if a microorganism produces one antibiotic it produces others of the same nature, some valuable, others of little significance.

MEDIUM.   Different formulas are doubtless in use by various manufacturers, but basically they are similar and are mainly modifications of the following:

| | | |
|---|---|---|
| Corn-steep liquor* | 40.0 | ml. |
| Lactose monohydrate | 27.5 | gm. |
| $NaNO_3$ | 3.0 | gm. |
| $MgSO_4 \cdot H_2O$ | 0.25 | gm. |
| $KH_2PO_4$ | 0.50 | gm. |
| $ZnSO_4 \cdot H_2O$ | 0.044 | gm. |
| $MnSO_4 \cdot H_2O$ | 0.020 | gm. |
| Glucose monohydrate | 3.0 | gm. |
| Water ad | 1000.0 | ml. |

After about seven days, growth is complete, pH rises to 8.0 or above, and penicillin production ceases.

When no more penicillin is being formed, the masses of mold growth are separated from the culture fluid by centrifugalization and filtration. The complex process of extracting the penicillin from the clear fluid then begins. The method involves various extractions with or-

---

*Corn-steep liquor is a by-product of the distilling industry, being the water used to soak (steep) corn prior to fermentation. It contains various growth factors (vitamins), proteins and carbohydrates, and is one of the best sources of nutrients for antibiotic production.

**Figure 22.2**  Like a steel igloo, the top of a 9000-gallon aerated-growth tank rises above the floor level of the penicillin plant at the Lederle Laboratories Division, American Cyanamid Company, Pearl River, N.Y. Like an iceberg, nine tenths of the huge fermentation tank is out of sight below the floor. The small tank at the right contains chemicals to prevent excessive foaming of the liquid containing the mold. (Peter Winkler, Lederle Laboratories, Inc.)

ganic solvents and recrystallizations. These are chemical engineering problems and do not concern us at present.

**Properties and Uses.** The material extracted from the culture medium is in reality a mixture of six chemically related penicillins called X, G, two forms of F, dihydro F and K. (These are discussed on page 291.) The most important is penicillin G (benzyl penicillin), which is usually meant when the term penicillin is used. Penicillin is readily soluble in water and alcohol, but the latter inactivates it. It is quickly destroyed by acid, so that in the unmodified form it is ineffective if taken orally. In the crystalline form it is quite stable, even for several days at 100° C. or for months refrigerated in the dark; however, in aqueous solution it is very unstable and quickly decomposes.

Penicillin acts mainly by inhibiting the enzymes concerned in the incorporation of muramic acid into the mucocomplex of the bacterial cell wall. Whether this action is of the nature of an antimetabolite is not known at present. Since synthesis of cell wall is carried on only by young, actively multiplying cells, the antibacterial action is manifested only during active growth. Because septum formation appears particularly vulnerable to penicillin, rod-shaped bacteria tend to form aseptate filamentous forms like mycelia in the presence of nonlethal concentrations of penicillin.

Among the most valuable properties of penicillin is its relatively low toxicity for man and animals, even in large doses, coupled with the fact that its antibacterial potency is such that a concentration of 0.000001 gm. per ml. will exert marked bactericidal effects. It may be administered subcutaneously, intravenously or locally. A particular disadvantage of penicillin is that it is a potent allergen in some persons and can cause fatal allergic reactions (Chapter 26).

**Chemistry of Penicillins.** The naturally occurring penicillins are compounds of the strong, monobasic acid, *penicillanic acid*. The penicillins usually occur as salts of sodium and potassium. The general chemical structure assigned to them is shown in Figure 22.3. They are unstable to heat and to strong acids and alkalis. Laboratory synthesis of penicillin was announced shortly after the formula was known. The substance artificially synthesized was penicillin G.

BIOSYNTHESIS OF PENICILLINS. It has been found possible to induce *Penicillium* cultures to

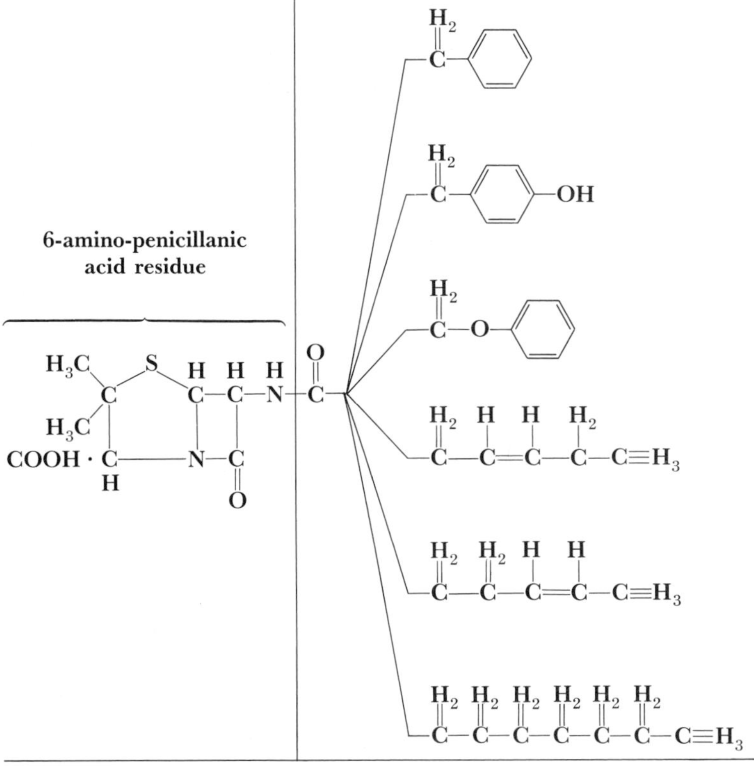

| Residue common to all penicillins | Various forms of R or acyl group (Natural Penicillins) | Common name. Penicillin: | Chemical designation (-penicillin) |
|---|---|---|---|
| 6-amino-penicillanic acid residue | (benzyl structure) | G or II | Benzyl |
| | (para-hydroxybenzyl structure —OH) | X or III | Para-hydroxybenzyl |
| | (phenoxymethyl structure C—O—phenyl) | V | Phenoxymethyl* |
| | (2-pentenyl structure) | F or I | 2-pentenyl |
| | (3-pentenyl structure) | F | 3-pentenyl |
| | (n-heptyl structure) | K or IV | *n*-heptyl |

*Produced only if phenoxyacetic acid is present in the medium as a precursor.

**Figure 22.3**   Various forms of penicillin. They differ only in the form of *R* in the general formula. The different forms of *R* are shown in the second column.

synthesize new forms of penicillin. The method consists of "feeding," to cultures of *Penicillium notatum*, synthetic substitutes for the normal "R's" (i.e., the distinctive side chains) of the penicillin molecule. These substitutes, "prefabricated" molecules, are referred to as *precursors* of the new "R." In the presence of such abnormal precursors, the mold unwittingly conjugates them "as is" with penicillanic acid, thus forming new and more valuable penicillins that have been synthesized partly by man, partly by the mold. An important product is *phenoxymethyl penicillin* (*penicillin V*), produced by feeding the precursor phenoxyacetic acid to the mold. Penicillin V is fairly stable to gastric acidity and is less quickly excreted from the blood than other penicillins. It is widely used for oral administration.

This same method (i.e., providing abnormal precursors) has been extended to other industrial processes in which a desired product is synthe-sized partly by man and partly by a living organism. The field of *biosynthesis* is clearly wide open for the ingenious, well-trained and energetic student.

PENICILLINASES. Several hydrolytic enzymes can attack and destroy penicillins. One, an inducible enzyme, is commonly called *penicillinase*. It is a type of penicillinacylase. This type of penicillinase is produced by a number of dangerous pathogenic bacteria, notably *Staphylococcus* and several species of gram-negative intestinal bacteria. By virtue of this enzyme these and other bacteria are penicillin-resistant and so defeat therapeutic uses of natural penicillins in many cases. These bacterial penicillinases attack the $\beta$-lactam bond of penicillins G, X and, to a lesser extent, V, and are often referred to as $\beta$-lactamases.

Another kind of penicillinase is produced by many common genera of fungi, including *Penicillium*, *Aspergillus* and *Mucor*. The penicillin-

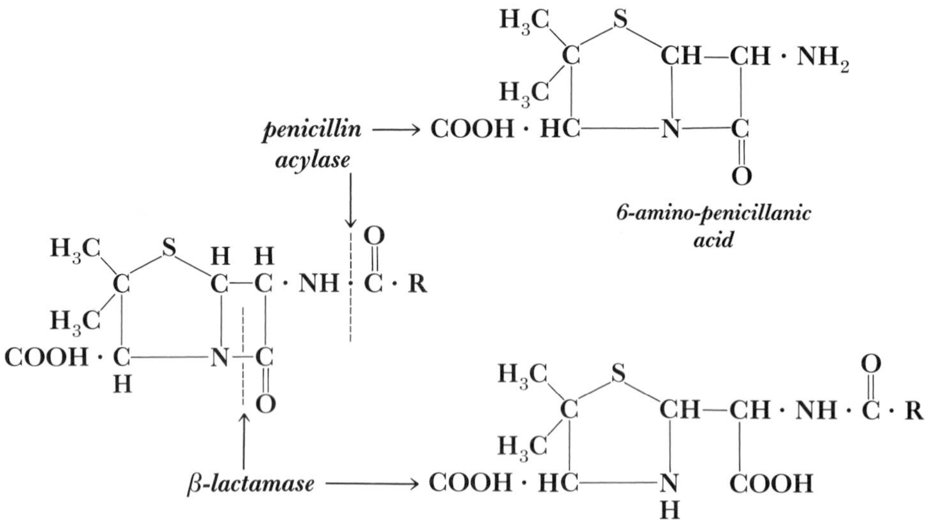

$$H_3C \quad S \quad CH-CH \cdot NH_2$$
$$H_3C \quad C$$
$$penicillin \longrightarrow COOH \cdot HC——N—C$$
$$acylase \qquad\qquad O$$

*6-amino-penicillanic acid*

$$H_3C \quad S \quad H \ H \quad O$$
$$C \quad C-C \cdot NH \ C \cdot R$$
$$H_3C$$
$$COOH \cdot C——N—C$$
$$H \qquad O$$

$$\beta\text{-lactamase} \longrightarrow COOH \cdot HC$$

$$H_3C \quad S \quad CH-CH \cdot NH \cdot C \cdot R$$
$$C \qquad\qquad\qquad O$$
$$H_3C$$
$$COOH \cdot HC——N \quad COOH$$
$$H$$

*benzyl penicillin, etc.*          *penicilloic acid*

**Figure 22.4**   Action of two major types of penicillinase: penicillinacylase (penicillin amidase) and β-lactamase (commonly called penicillinase). The dotted lines and arrows show which bonds are broken.

ases produced by these organisms differ from bacterial β-lactamase in that they attack the peptide bond between the 6-amino-penicillanic acid residue and the "R's". These enzymes are sometimes called *penicillin amidases*. They attack penicillins V and K most rapidly, G more slowly (Fig. 22.4).

SEMISYNTHETIC PENICILLINS.   When it was discovered, about 1958, that 6-amino-penicillanic acid, the "nucleus" of all penicillins, could be produced in commercial quantities, it became possible to attach various artificially synthesized acyl groups to 6-amino-penicillanic acid on a large scale. Hundreds of such semisynthetic penicillins have been made and tried. Some are extremely valuable, e.g., phenethycillin, which is quickly absorbed into the blood and is as effective as penicillin G; methicillin, cloxacillin and nafcillin, which are not readily destroyed by gastric acidity and which are resistant to β-lactamase; and ampicillin, which is more effective against a range of bacteria, both gram-positive and gram-negative, than other penicillins, and is effective in oral administration. The acyl groups of some of these are shown in Figure 22.5 for comparison with natural penicillins.

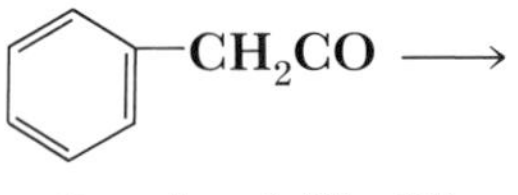

**Figure 22.5**   R groups of some representative biosynthetic penicillins compared with that of a natural penicillin, benzylpenicillin (G).

$$—CH_2CO \longrightarrow$$

*Benzyl penicillin (G)*

$$OCH_3$$
$$—CO \longrightarrow$$
$$OCH_3$$

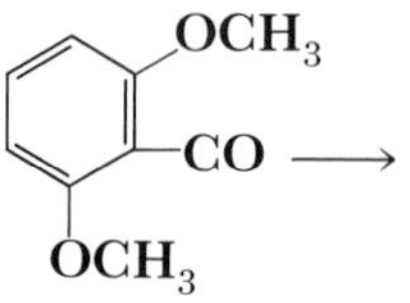

*Methicillin (Dimethoxyphenyl penicillin)*

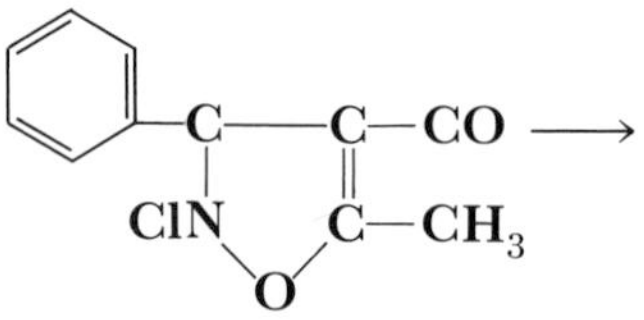

$$C—C—CO \longrightarrow$$
$$ClN \quad C—CH_3$$
$$O$$

*Cloxacillin (5-methyl-3-phenyl-4-isoxyzolyl penicillin)*

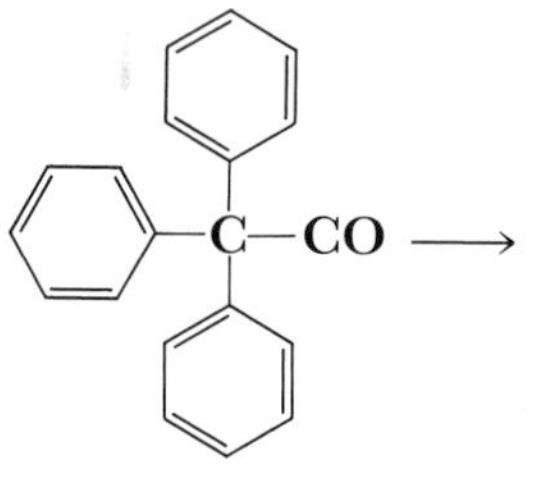

$$C—CO \longrightarrow$$

*Triphenyl methyl penicillin*

THE CEPHALOSPORINS.   These are a group of antibiotics, the first described type of which, cephalosporin C, is produced by the mold, *Cephalosporium acremonium.* Although a relatively ineffective antibiotic, cephalosporin C is of great interest because it has a formula very similar to that of penicillin (Fig. 22.6). Like penicillin, cephalosporin C lends itself to production of a large number of synthetic derivatives. Knowledge of these processes is based on the work of Woodward (Nobel Prize winner) and many other skillful chemists and biologists. The central residue of the cephalosporins is indicated in Figure 22.6. Various acyl groups may be attached to this residue, with the production of much more valuable cephalosporins than cephalosporin C; e.g., *cephalothin* (Fig. 22.6).

**Penicillin and L Bodies.**   Numerous species of bacteria cultivated in the presence of penicillin in a medium of increased osmotic pressure (see Protoplasts) grow but produce no cell wall, i.e., they produce protoplasts (L forms) or spheroplasts. In media of ordinary osmotic pressure these immediately burst because the strong, retaining cell wall is lacking. This is the basis of the lethal effect of penicillin; i.e., removal of the cell wall followed by osmotic rupture. Animal cells (e.g., our own body cells), viruses and the PPLO or *Mycoplasma* (Chapter 41) are completely resistant to penicillin because they do not synthesize cell walls. In general, the gram-positive bacteria are most susceptible to penicillin because their cell walls consist almost entirely of mucopolysaccharide.

**Adaptive   Penicillinase.**   Penicillinase (β-lactamase) production may appear in some bacteria as a result of induced enzyme formation. For example, strains of some kinds of bacteria are ordinarily sensitive to penicillin because they do not produce penicillinase. However, contact with nonlethal concentrations of penicillin appears to induce penicillinase production. They are then penicillin resistant.

**Various Strains of *Penicillium notatum.***   Fleming's strain of *P. notatum* for a time was thought to be unique. It was later found that some "wild" strains of this organism were better producers of penicillin and that other closely related organisms, especially *P. chrysogenum,* also produce penicillin. These findings led to a very extensive search for better strains of *P. notatum* and for penicillin-producing strains of other organisms. Many thousands of cultures were tested, and it was found that the penicillin-producing property is widely distributed in the *P. notatum-chrysogenum* group and that

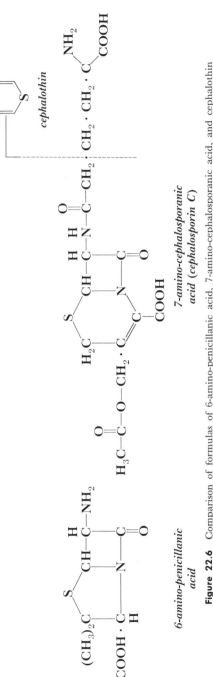

**Figure 22.6** Comparison of formulas of 6-amino-penicillanic acid, 7-amino-cephalosporanic acid, and cephalothin as a derivative of cephalosporin.

some strains are better than others, especially for the various methods of production (i.e., some were good in tanks, not so good on surfaces, and vice versa). Irradiation with ultraviolet light has furnished many thousands of mutant strains for testing, among them some very potent penicillin-producing mutants.

The same principle of hunting for new and more effective mutants for a variety of purposes can be applied in most fields of industrial microbiology, using yeasts, molds and bacteria.

DEVELOPMENT OF RESISTANCE (DRUG-FASTNESS) AND DEPENDENCE.   An undesirable aspect of the continued clinical use of antibiotics (as well as of sulfa drugs) is the emergence of mutants having *increased resistance* to the drugs (*drugfast* strains) or being wholly *dependent* on the drugs. Drug-fastness and drug dependence have been described in Chapter 21.

**Laboratory Uses of Penicillin.**  As mentioned, the value of penicillin as a selective bacteriostatic agent in laboratory bacteriology had been immediately recognized by Fleming and was adopted by others. It is a convenient aid to the isolation of penicillin-resistant organisms (such as the gram-negative whooping cough and influenza bacilli) from throat cultures, since it suppresses the growth of unwanted penicillin-sensitive (mainly gram-positive) organisms. It is also used for suppressing bacterial

growth in animal tissue cultures used in studies of viruses, since viruses and animal cells are wholly resistant to most antibiotics.

**Range of Activity.**  The clinical uses of penicillin are beyond the scope of this discussion, but some of the common infectious organisms against which natural penicillins are more or less effective are listed in Table 22.1.

Note that most of the susceptible species are gram-positive. Notable exceptions are *Treponema pallidum,* cause of syphilis, and gram-negative *Neisseria gonorrhoeae,* cause of gonorrhea; both very susceptible.

Natural penicillin is generally ineffective in infections caused by gram-negative bacilli, viruses, rickettsias or PPLO, and in infections with protozoa, yeasts and molds. As we have noted, several biosynthesized penicillins have much broader ranges of antimicrobial activity.

## 22.2  STANDARDIZATION OF ANTIBIOTICS

Standards of potency for all antibiotics are established by international agreement as to what shall constitute an *International Standard Sample* and an *International Unit.* Generally, the International Standard Sample of an antibiotic consists of a certain highly purified and tested lot of that antibiotic. For example, the 1960 International Standard Sample of the antibiotic tetracycline (see farther on) was a 500-gm. lot of highly purified tetracycline chloride furnished by an American manufacturer. The International Unit of tetracycline was defined as the antibiotic activity contained in 1.01 $\mu$g. of that particular standard sample; 1.01 $\mu$g. was equivalent in activity to 1 $\mu$g. of pure, crystalline tetracycline chloride.

### ASSAY AND SENSITIVITY TESTING

Several types of procedure are in use for assaying the potency of antibiotic preparations for therapeutic purposes. This is commonly done in manufacturers' control laboratories under the supervision of the U. S. Food and Drug Administration. These methods, conversely modified, are also used for measuring sensitivity (*sensitivity testing*) of "unknown" organisms to antibiotics. This is commonly done in hospital laboratories and is essential to rational chemotherapy, although not always feasible. There are sources of error in all of these methods, and so they must be used and interpreted by experts.

**TABLE 22.1**  PENICILLIN SENSITIVITY OF SOME COMMON PATHOGENS

| Gram Stain | Organisms* |
|---|---|
| | **Highly Susceptible** |
| + | *B. anthracis* |
| + | Various clostridia including *Cl. tetani* and *Cl. welchii* |
| + | *D. pneumoniae* |
| − | *Neisseria* spp., including gonococci and meningococci |
| + | Micrococci, *Staphylococcus aureus* |
| + | *Streptococcus pyogenes* |
| + | *C. diphtheriae* (in vitro) |
| ± | *Treponema pallidum* |
| | **Moderately Susceptible** |
| − | *Borrelia* of relapsing fever |
| + | Various alpha (viridans) type hemolytic streptococci |
| − | *Leptospira* spp. |
| | **Not Significantly Susceptible** |
| − | Enterobacteriaceae |
| − | *Pseudomonas* species |
| − | Brucellaceae |

*Except nonconforming mutants.

## ASSAY METHODS

**Serial Dilution in Broth.** Serial dilutions of the antibiotic being assayed are made in uniform amounts of standard broth in culture tubes. These are then inoculated with a uniform number of cells of the test organism, which is selected on the basis of its known degree of sensitivity. After incubation, turbidity (or its absence) is noted and may be measured by means of a photoelectric turbidimeter. The turbidities (amounts of growth) are compared with a dilution series made in the same way but with an antibiotic reference standard of carefully measured potency.

The method is time consuming and sometimes requires preliminary sterilization of the sample, which destroys some of its potency. However, the dilution method is an accurate procedure, and results can be stated in exact terms of units of antibiotic.

SENSITIVITY TESTING BY BROTH METHOD. The serial dilution procedure—reversed—is often used to measure the sensitivity to various antibiotics of an organism freshly isolated from an infected patient. Graded dilutions of an antibiotic of known strength are placed in series of tubes. Each tube is inoculated with a drop of the organism whose sensitivity is being tested. If growth occurs in all tubes, the organism is resistant; if no growth occurs, the organism is sensitive. Growth in some of the tubes permits a measure of the sensitivity of the organism (Fig. 22.7).

**Serial Dilution (Streak Assay) in Agar.** The streak assay method is rapid, convenient and much used for preliminary assays of crude material in the search for new antibiotics.

Graded dilutions of the substance to be tested (for example, a plant extract thought to have antibiotic properties) are placed in a series of Petri dishes. Into each of these is

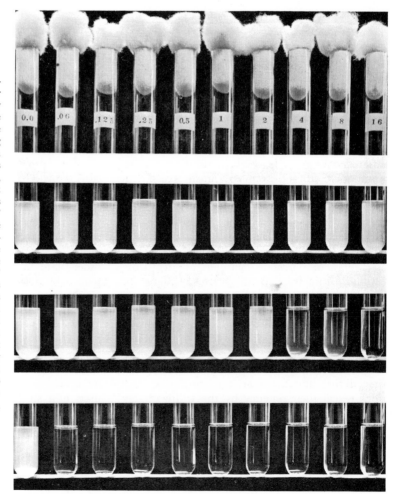

**Figure 22.7** Testing sensitivity of a bacterium to antibiotics or other chemotherapeutic agents by the "tube dilution" method. The top row of tubes of broth culture contain agent "A" in increasing amounts as shown by the figures on the tubes. The second row contains agent "B" in the same amounts, while the third row contains agent "C" in the same dilutions. All tubes were inoculated with organism "X" from the same culture at the same time and incubated together. Luxuriant growth, as shown by white turbidity, has occurred even in the highest concentration of agent "A," showing that organism "X" (perhaps from a patient very ill with this infection) is not in the least affected by this drug. The drug of choice will be agent "C" which prevents growth of organism "X" even in the smallest concentration. Agent "B" is slightly effective. The tube at the left of each row is a control tube containing no inhibitory agent. (Courtesy of the Abbott Laboratories, North Chicago, Ill.)

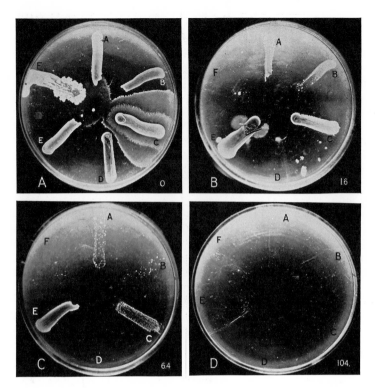

**Figure 22.8** Testing sensitivity of several species of bacteria to three different concentrations of streptomycin by the agar-dilution method. Plate A contains no antibiotic and is inoculated with (A) *Escherichia coli,* (B) *Salmonella typhi,* (C) *Proteus* sp., (D) *Klebsiella pneumoniae,* (E) *Pseudomonas aeruginosa,* (F) *Mycobacterium tuberculosis.* In Plate B, containing 1.6 mg. of streptomycin per ml. of agar, organisms D and F have been virtually eliminated. Larger amounts of the antibiotic, as shown in Plates C and D, successively eliminate all but a few *resistant* colonies of the other organisms. (What is the significance of these resistant colonies?) Note the great sensitivity of this strain of *M. tuberculosis* to streptomycin. (Courtesy of Merck & Co., Inc.)

poured about 10 ml. of melted and cooled (45° C.) agar, which is thoroughly mixed with the antibiotic dilution by tilting the plates back and forth. After the agar has hardened, the plates are marked into several sectors, each of which is streaked with a different test organism. After incubation, the highest dilution of the antibiotic that inhibits each organism is recorded (Fig. 22.8).

This method—reversed—also is often used for sensitivity testing by using *known* strengths of known antibiotics and *unknown* organisms.

**The Cylinder-Plate Method.** A series of steel, glass or porcelain cylinders about 10 by 6 mm. in dimensions with perfectly square-cut ends (like a drainage tile) are heated and then sealed to the upper surface of already inoculated agar in a Petri plate by placing them, end up, on the solid agar. Dilutions of the single antibiotic to be tested are placed in the cylinders (Fig. 22.9). The plate is then incubated. When they diffuse into the agar, the antibiotic dilutions reveal their potency by the width of the zone of inhibition of growth in the agar around each cylinder. The potency of *different* antibiotics cannot be compared on the basis of the width of their zones of inhibition, however, because a very potent antibiotic may not diffuse readily through the agar and will therefore

produce relatively narrow zones, while a weak antibiotic may diffuse very well and produce deceptively wide zones. In such measurements the test organism, agar density, time, temperature and pH must be very exactly standardized. This is true of all the methods described.

**The Disk or Tablet Method.** This is possibly a little less exact than the procedures just described but is reasonably accurate and is quick, convenient and economical. It is therefore a preferred and widely used method for many purposes not requiring high degrees of precision. The principle is the same in the cylinder-plate method, but the cylinders are replaced by disks or tablets.

Nutrient agar of appropriate composition is heavily inoculated with the desired organism all over the surface of the solidified agar or mixed with the agar while still fluid before pouring the plate. If an antibiotic solution of unknown potency is being assayed (e.g., manufacturer's sample, blood, urine) the organism used is a stock strain of known sensitivity to standard doses of that antibiotic.

Measured strengths of the antibiotic solution to be tested are applied to the inoculated agar in disks of sterile filter paper or in small tablets, which are placed on the surface of the agar plate before incubating. Several devices

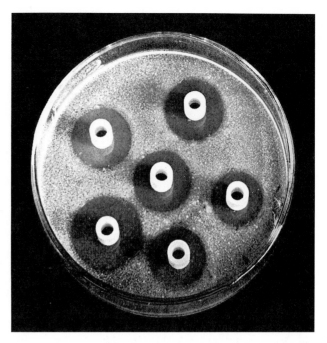

**Figure 22.9** Cylinder plate standardization of penicillin. The culture plate contains a very carefully standardized medium, uniformly and heavily seeded with staphylococci or spores of *B. subtilis.* In each cylinder was placed a measured quantity of penicillin-containing extract. Following incubation under standard conditions, growth of bacterial colonies gave the medium the pebbled, gray appearance seen everywhere except around the cylinders. Here, growth has been inhibited by penicillin. Measurement of these zones of inhibition permits standardization of penicillin in Oxford units by comparison with zones produced under identical conditions of test by standard solutions of known unit strength. The sensitivity of an unknown organism to any antibiotic is tested in exactly the same way; inoculation of the plate is made with the "unknown" in place of the staphylococci or *B. subtilis* routinely used. Known amounts of various antibiotics may be placed in the cylinders. (From Therapeutic Notes, Parke, Davis & Co.)

are available for application of the disks (Fig. 22.10). The antibiotic diffuses outward from each disk or tablet and inhibits growth in the agar around it (Fig. 22.11).

**Growth-Indicator Methods.** In these methods some early-perceptible indicator of

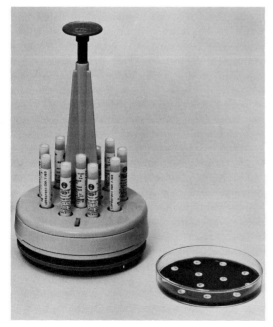

**Figure 22.10** Antibiotic solutions are released automatically onto an inoculated plate when plunger of Sensi-Disc dispenser is pushed. (Courtesy of Baltimore Biological Laboratory.)

growth is looked for rather than the often-delayed growth itself. In a representative procedure, sterile blood agar is poured into a Petri dish to a depth of about 3 mm. This is the base layer.

Similar fluid agar is heavily inoculated with the organism being tested. After this is thoroughly mixed, it is poured over the base layer to an equal depth (seed layer). When solid, antibiotic disks are placed on the surface, and the plate is placed in the incubator. The plate may be examined after two hours and then every hour thereafter. Diffuse growth of the organism, whether actual colonies are visible or not, produces a marked discoloration or hemolysis of the blood, except where inhibited under and around disks containing effective antibiotic concentrations. Here the blood remains unchanged.

Modifications of this method employ indicators of growth other than discolorations of hemoglobin; i.e., pH indicators such as phenol red, and oxidation-reduction indicators such as resazurin (see Reductase Test in Milk). In all of these methods the change in color of whatever indicator is used reflects growth of the organism hours before growth itself is apparent.

## 22.3   ANTIBIOTICS FROM *STREPTOMYCES*

*Streptomyces* (Chapter 37) is a genus of bacteria that has some of the physiological and

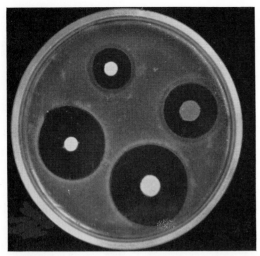

**Figure 22.11** Testing sensitivity of a bacterium to antibiotics or other chemotherapeutic agents by the "disk method." The entire surface of agar medium in a Petri plate is inoculated with the organism to be tested. Paper disks of uniform thickness containing graded amounts of the agent to be tested (or the same amount of different agents if a comparison is desired) are then placed on the surface of the agar. The agent diffuses into the agar and prevents growth of the bacterium in a zone around the disk. The width of the zone indicates, roughly, the sensitivity of the organism to the agent or agents being tested, though the *presence* or *absence* of a zone is of greater significance. (About ½ actual size.) (Courtesy of Drs. R. W. Fairbrother and A. Rao: Dept. of Clinical Pathology, Manchester Royal Infirmary, Manchester, England. In J. Clin. Path., vol. 7.)

gross morphological characteristics of molds like *Penicillium notatum*. *Streptomyces* species are, however, minute in size as compared with true molds and are entirely procaryotic in cellular structure.

A number of species of *Streptomyces* produce antibiotics of medical and commercial value. More are constantly being found. Some of the antibiotics produced by *Streptomyces* are said to be active against chlamydias (Chapter 41), others against certain viral neoplasms and some against certain protozoa. A description of *streptomycin* will exemplify all the *Streptomyces*-derived antibiotics, although each has its special properties and values (Table 22.2).

STREPTOMYCIN. The discovery of streptomycin dates from 1944, and followed naturally in a long series of researches by Waksman and his collaborators, Schatz and Bugie, into the numbers and kinds of antagonistic microorganisms in the soil. The source organism, *Streptomyces griseus,* produces moldlike conidia and aerial mycelia suggestive of some of the filamentous Ascomycetes (e.g., *Aspergillus*) but

is one species of the bacterial order of Actinomycetales.

The principles underlying the production, purification, assay and standardization of streptomycin are analogous to those of penicillin, differing mainly in respect to cultural details and technical procedures appropriate to the organism and antibiotic involved.

Aeration of the culture is essential for rapid streptomycin production, which is at its maximum in two to three days. Various strains of *Streptomyces griseus* are more or less active producers of the drug.

The molecular formula of streptomycin is $C_{21}H_{39}O_{12}N_7$. It is structurally much more complex than penicillin. Numerous salts and derivatives have been prepared, some of them of great therapeutic value. Dihydrostreptomycin, in which two hydrogen atoms are added, is of especial importance. Both streptomycin and dihydrostreptomycin are much more stable than penicillin, both in dry form and in solution. In the refrigerator the solutions retain potency for months; at 37° C. for about two weeks. Boiling for 10 minutes produces about 50 per cent loss of potency. Both drugs, *in vitro,* are bactericidal in commonly used concentrations.

*Scope of Action.* The therapeutic range of streptomycin is in some respects broader than that of penicillin; it is active against a variety of gram-negative and several gram-positive organisms, some of which are listed in Table 22.3. It has been used in tuberculosis with striking results and in many infections with species of gram-negative rods that are not susceptible to penicillin or sulfonamides. Streptomycin is not so rapidly destroyed in or excreted from the body as penicillin. Some toxic effects (vertigo, deafness) have been described. It must be used only under medical supervision.

*Mode of Action.* Although the method is not entirely clear, streptomycin undoubtedly acts by interfering with enzyme action, notably enzymes concerned in early stages of the synthesis of proteins. Streptomycin has other, little-understood actions. Dihydrostreptomycin acts similarly. Both streptomycin and dihydrostreptomycin are much less active anaerobically than aerobically; i.e., their action may therefore be related to aerobic oxidative metabolism that is dependent on the Krebs cycle. Like penicillin, both are mainly bactericidal rather than bacteriostatic in their action.

No streptomycin-destroying enzyme has been reported, but resistant organisms appear and, unfortunately, often occur in patients dur-

**TABLE 22.2**   PARTIAL LIST OF ANTIBIOTICS*

| Common Name | Trade Name | Characteristics† | Source |
|---|---|---|---|
| Penicillin‡ | | Gram-positive bacteria; Treponema; Neisseria | *Penicillium notatum* |
| Fumagillin | | Entamoeba histolytica | *Aspergillus fumigatus* |
| Paromomycin | Humatin | E. histolytica | *Streptomyces rimosus* |
| Streptomycin | | Myco. tuberculosis; Gram-negative bacteria | *Streptomyces griseus* |
| Dihydrostreptomycin | | Like streptomycin | Streptomycin; also some species of *Streptomyces* |
| Tetracycline | Achromycin | Broad-spectrum | Chlortetracycline |
| Oxytetracycline | Terramycin | Broad-spectrum | *Streptomyces rimosus* |
| Chlortetracycline | Aureomycin | Broad-spectrum | *Streptomyces aureofaciens* |
| Chloramphenicol | Chloromycetin | Broad-spectrum | *Streptomyces venezuelae* |
| Erythromycin | Ilotycin, Erythrocin | Broad-spectrum (not Enterobacteriaceae) | *Streptomyces erythreus* |
| Carbomycin | Magnamycin | Like erythromycin | *Streptomyces halstedii* |
| Oleandomycin | Matromycin | Broad-spectrum | *Streptomyces antibioticus* |
| Neomycin B‡ | Flavomycin | Mycobacteria | *Streptomyces fradiae* |
| Viomycin | Viocin | Like penicillin | *Str. floridae; Str. funiceus* |
| Oligomycin | | Fungi of plants | *Str. diastatochromogenes* |
| Amphotericin B | Fungizone | *Candida* sp. | *Streptomyces nodosus* |
| Kanamycin | Kantrex | Broad-spectrum | *Streptomyces kanamyceticus* |
| Nystatin | | Pathogenic fungi | *Streptomyces noursei* |
| Cycloheximide | Actidione | Saprophytic fungi | *Streptomyces griseus* |
| Griseofulvin | Grifulvin | Pathogenic fungi | *Streptomyces griseus* |
| Bacitracin | | Like penicillin | *Bacillus subtilis* |
| Polymyxin B‡ | | Gram-positive bacteria | *Bacillus polymyxa* |
| Pyocyanin§ | | Miscellaneous | *Pseudomonas aeruginosa* |

* Several not listed here are valuable commercially, agriculturally and horticulturally.
† Not necessarily the only activity.
‡ Several of these antibiotics are in reality mixtures consisting of related compounds such as the penicillins, polymyxin A, B, C, D, carbomycin A and B and so on.
§ Not used medicinally. One of the first known antibiotic substances.

**TABLE 22.3**   SOME BACTERIAL SPECIES SENSITIVE TO STREPTOMYCIN

**Gram-Positive**

*Mycobacterium tuberculosis*
*Staphylococcus aureus*
*Diplococcus pneumoniae*
*Streptococcus* species
*Bacillus subtilis* and related species

**Gram-Negative**

*Salmonella typhi*
*Pasteurella tularensis*
*Klebsiella* species
*Brucella abortus*
*Proteus vulgaris*
*Salmonella paratyphi B*
*Bordetella pertussis*
*Haemophilus influenzae*
*Pseudomonas aeruginosa*
*Escherichia* species

ing treatment. Strains of tubercle bacilli wholly dependent on streptomycin have also been found in treated patients.

CHLORAMPHENICOL. The organism producing chloramphenicol is much like other species of *Streptomyces*. It was found in 1947 by Paul R. Burkholder in soil collected near Caracas, Venezuela, and is called *S. venezuelae*. Like most other natural antibiotics, the drug is a by-product of growth. It may be produced in a manner analogous to the production of penicillin and streptomycin, but is now produced mainly synthetically.

It affects many species of both gram-positive and gram-negative bacteria in high dilutions and may be given either orally or intravenously. Unlike either penicillin or streptomycin, it is also effective against the chlamydias and rickettsias. It is the first antibiotic discovered to have definite rickettsicidal properties. It has proved of inestimable value in the treatment of many infectious diseases, including especially typhoid fever. Because of its wide range of activity, it is classed as a *broad-spectrum* antibiotic.

*Mode of Action.* As in the case of streptomycin, although chloramphenicol does not with certainty compete with any known metabolite, it appears to block several important enzymes, possibly by *noncompetitive combination* (i.e., at a site other than the functional center in the coenzyme). Whatever its mechanism or mechanisms, the most obvious effect is to stop synthesis of proteins. There is also interference with oxidations at higher concentrations. Chloramphenicol does not stop the synthesis of nucleic acids.

The therapeutic excellence of chloramphenicol led to intensive chemical studies, as in the case of penicillin. The formula was soon learned and the drug synthesized (*Chloromycetin*) in 1949 in the laboratories of Parke, Davis and Company (Fig. 22.12). It is the only antibiotic of major clinical importance that can be made synthetically on a profitable basis. It must be used only under medical supervision.

THE TETRACYCLINES. This group includes three antibiotics: tetracycline (*Achromycin*), chlortetracycline (*Aureomycin*) and oxytetracycline (*Terramycin*). Their similar molecular structures are seen in Figure 22.13. Chlortetracycline differs from tetracycline in having a chlorine atom attached to carbon atom No. 7 in place of hydrogen (encircled in Figure 22.13). It is produced by *Streptomyces aureofaciens*. Oxytetracycline has a hydroxyl group attached to carbon atom No. 5 in place of hydrogen (encircled). It is produced by *S. rimosus*. Tetracycline is an artificial derivative of chlortetracycline. All have similar antibiotic properties.

Unlike penicillin and streptomycin, tetracyclines are bacteriostatic in clinical concentrations. They are effective against many gram-negative and gram-positive species of bacteria, chlamydias and some rickettsias. For this reason, they are also classed as broad-spectrum antibiotics and have similar ranges of therapeutic activity. All are effective orally or hypodermically. However, in any given patient, any one of these drugs may at times show surprising irregularities and give unexpectedly brilliant results—or fail. They are not identical.

*Mode of Action.* These antibiotics disrupt ribosomes and thus interfere with protein synthesis, especially in actively growing cells. They may also interfere with functioning of the Krebs cycle. Other noxious actions in the bacterial cell have been demonstrated but not yet explained.

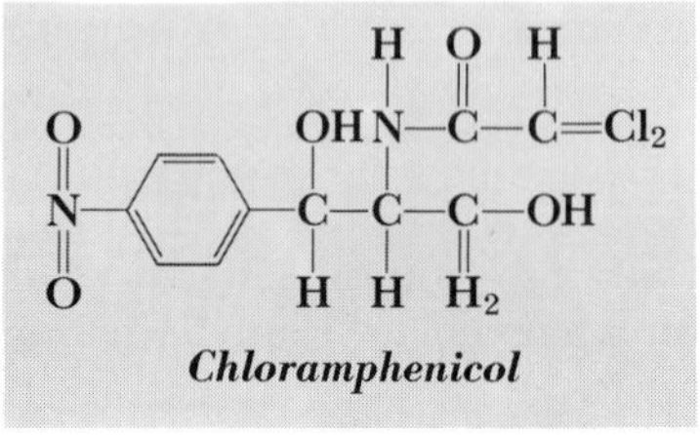

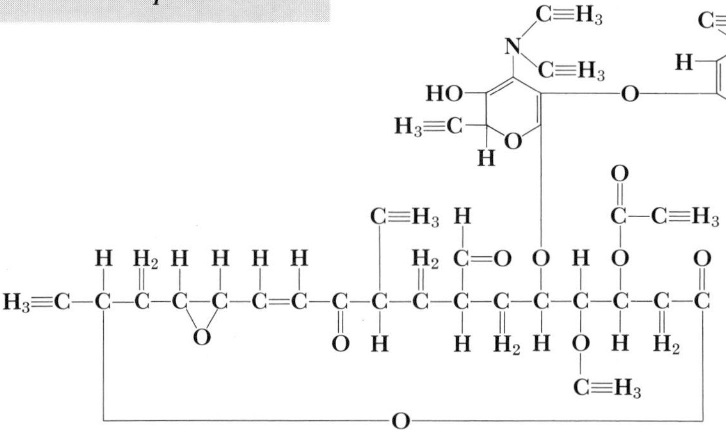

**Figure 22.12** Structural formula of carbomycin, a typical macrolide. Compare with formulas of penicillin, the tetracyclines and (above) chloramphenicol. (Adapted from Goldberg: Antibiotics; Their Chemistry and Non-Medical Uses. D. Van Nostrand Co., Inc., 1959.)

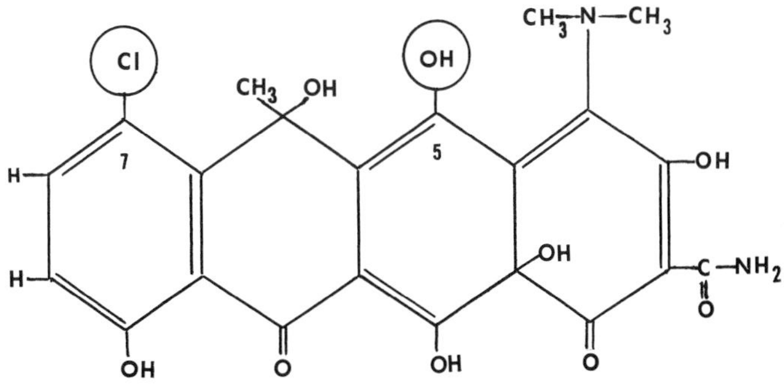

**Figure 22.13** Composite formula of the tetracycline group of antibiotics. In tetracycline each of the numbered carbon atoms (5 and 7) has an attached hydrogen atom. In chlortetracycline, chlorine (circled) replaces the hydrogen of the number 7 carbon atom; in oxytetracycline an OH group (circled) replaces the hydrogen of the number 5 carbon atom.

Also, since they are active chelating agents, they may deprive the cell of essential metal ions.

ERYTHROMYCIN. This antibiotic, one of a group including erythromycins A and B, is representative of several valuable and widely used antibiotics, including *carbomycin* and *oleandomycin.* All are substances of a basic nature derived from *Streptomyces* species and having relatively high molecular weights. Because of their large, complex molecules, the group name *macrolides* has been given to them (Fig. 22.13). They act principally against gram-positive bacteria, but also attack several species of gram-negative bacteria as well as other types of pathogens. They are therefore generally included with the broad-spectrum antibiotics. Their chief effect is to inhibit synthesis of proteins, possibly by blocking or destroying one or more types of RNA.

## 22.4  ANTIBIOTICS FROM *BACILLUS*

Several useful antibiotics have been derived from gram-positive, aerobic, sporeforming bacteria closely related to, or identical with, *Bacillus subtilis.* The first to be described, *tyrothricin* or *gramicidin,* from *B. brevis,* was discovered by Dubos, as previously mentioned. Another is *bacitracin,* discovered by F. L. Meleney.

BACITRACIN. Bacitracin was first described in 1945. The source organism is a particular strain of *Bacillus subtilis,* a common and usually harmless organism widely distributed in dust. It was found contaminating a wound in a patient named Tracy, hence baci*trac*in. Bacitracin is a yellowish powder readily soluble in water. Like penicillin it is active clinically mainly against infections due to gram-positive bacteria. However, it also affects the gram-negative meningococcus (*Neisseria meningitidis;* cause of meningitis), gonococcus (cause of gonorrhea) and *Haemophilus influenzae,* as well as *Treponema pallidum*

(cause of syphilis). Unlike penicillin, streptomycin, chloramphenicol and the tetracyclines, bacitracin is quite toxic if given internally and is therefore used only for topical applications.

OTHER POLYPEPTIDE ANTIBIOTICS. Bacitracin is representative of several *polypeptide* antibiotics with similar properties, derived from species of *Bacillus:* the polymyxins A, B, C, D, E (*B. polymyxa*); subtilin and bacitracin (*B. subtilis*); the gramicidins and tyrocidin (*B. brevis*); biocerin (*B. cereus*); and circulin (*B. circulans*). Commercial bacitracin, and probably these related polypeptides, are all mixtures of related substances.

These are curious chemically in that they contain rare types of peptide linkages and amino acids of the D-series which have not been found elsewhere in nature except in bacterial cell walls (Chapter 13). They are alike in being surface tension reducers, or surfactants.

*Mode of Action.* Antibiotics such as bacitracin resemble other surfactants, such as the quaternaries and soap, in quickly destroying susceptible bacteria by attacking the cell membrane, possibly by acting as an emulsifying agent on the lipids in the membranes. They affect many gram-negative species, cell walls of which are rich in lipids. They act so quickly as to suggest that, unlike most other antibiotics, interference with enzymes is not involved. Unlike penicillin, these antibiotics leave the cell wall intact.

Other polypeptide antibiotics (e.g., streptogramin, vernamycin and ostreogricin) produced by *Streptomyces* sp., act by inhibiting protein synthesis but not synthesis of nucleic acids or cell walls.

*Lysostaphin.* This antibiotic, discovered in 1964, is remarkably effective against coagulase-positive (pathogenic) *Staphylococcus aureus,* which is often resistant to other antibiotics. Instead of inhibiting synthesis of cell walls as does penicillin, lysostaphin destroys cell walls, regardless of penicillinase. (See also Chapter 33.)

## 22.5  NONMEDICAL USES OF ANTIBIOTICS

Many antibiotics are extremely effective as antimicrobials but are too toxic for medicinal use. The industrial, agricultural and other uses of such antibiotics have grown enormously. Over three million pounds of antibiotics are used for such purposes annually. They are used in such ways as preventing spoilage of various products; supplementing stock feeds, greatly increasing growth; and controlling bacterial diseases of plants. Further information on nonmedical uses is given in Chapters 39, 45 and 46.

## SUPPLEMENTARY READING

Au, W. Y. W.: Broad-spectrum antibiotics. Amer. J. Nursing, *64*:105, 1964.

Chang, T. W., and Weinstein, L.: Use of cephalinosporinase in blood cultures. J. Bact., *90*:830, 1965.

Cole, M.: Formation of 6-aminopenicillanic acid, penicillins and penicillin acylase by various fungi. Appl. Microbiol., *14*:98, 1966.

Day, L. E.: Tetracycline inhibition of cell-free protein synthesis. II. Effect of the binding of tetracycline to the components of the system. J. Bact., *92*:197, 1966.

Demain, A. L.: Biosynthesis of cephalosporin C and its relation to penicillin formation. Tr. N. Y. Acad. Sci., Ser. II, *25*:731, 1963.

Ennis, H. L.: Inhibition of protein synthesis by polypeptide antibiotics: I. in intact bacteria; II. in vitro. J. Bact., *90*:1102 and 1109, 1965.

Gladson, I., editor: The Impact of the Antibiotics on Medicine and Society. International Universities Press, Inc., New York. 1958.

Godzeski, C. W., Brier, G., and Pavey, D. E.: Cephalothin, a new cephalosporin with a broad antibacterial spectrum. Appl. Sci., *11*:122, 1963.

Goldberg, H. S., editor: Antibiotics: Their Chemistry and Non-medical uses. D. Van Nostrand Co., New York. 1959.

Gorini, L.: Antibiotics and the genetic code. Sci. Amer., *214*:102, 1966.

Hamilton-Miller, J. M. T.: Penicillinacylase. Bact. Rev., *30*:761, 1966.

Hobby, G. L., editor: Antimicrobial Agents and Chemotherapy. The American Soc. for Microbiol., Ann Arbor, Michigan. 1965, 1966, 1967, et seq.

Huff, E., and Silverman, C. S.: Lysis of *Staphylococcus* cell walls by a soluble staphylococcal enzyme. J. Bact., *95*:99, 1968.

Hurst, A.: Biosynthesis of the antibiotic nisin by whole *Streptococcus lactis* organisms. J. Gen. Microbiol., *44*:209, 1966.

Isenberg, H. D.: A comparison of nationwide microbial susceptibility testing using standardized discs. Health Lab. Sci., *1*:185, 1964.

Laszlo, J., Miller, D. S., McCarty, K. S., and Hochstein, P.: Actinomycin D: Inhibition of respiration and glycolysis. Science, *151*:1007, 1966.

Martí-Ibáñez, F.: Men, Molds, and History. M. D. Publications, Inc., New York. 1958.

Morgan, C., Rosenkranz, H. S., Carr, H. S., and Rose, H. M.: Electron microscopy of chloramphenicol-treated *Escherichia coli*. J. Bact., *93*:1987, 1967.

Newton, B. A.: Mechanisms of Antibiotic Action. Ann. Rev. Microbiol., *19*:209, 1965.

Newton, B. A., and Reynolds, P. E., editors: Biochemical Studies of Antimicrobial Drugs. Sixteenth Symposium. Soc. Gen. Microbiol., London. 1966.

Odum, E. P.: Fundamentals of Ecology. 2nd ed. W. B. Saunders Co., Philadelphia. 1959.

Old, D., and Gorini, L.: Amino acid changes provoked by streptomycin in a polypeptide synthesized in vitro. Science, *150*:1290, 1965.

Reusser, F., and Bhuyan, B. K.: Comparative studies with three antibiotics binding to deoxyribonucleic acid. J. Bact., *94*:576, 1967.

Slotnick, I. J., and Sells, B. H.: Actinomycin resistance in *Bacillus subtilis*. Science, *146*:407, 1964.

Snell, J. F., editor: Biosynthesis of Antibiotics, Vol. 1. Academic Press, New York. 1967.

Suzuki, H., and Kilgore, W. W.: Decomposition of ribosomal particles in *Escherichia coli* treated with mitomycin C. J. Bact., *94*:666, 1967.

Suzuki, Y., Okamoto, S., and Kono, M.: Basis of chloramphenicol resistance in naturally isolated resistant staphylococci. J. Bact., *92*:798, 1966.

Umezawa, H.: Index of Antibiotics from Actinomycetes. University Park Press, Baltimore, 1967.

Vazquez, D.: Studies on the mode of action of the streptogramin antibiotics. J. Gen. Microbiol., *42*:93, 1966.

Woodruff, H. B.: Antibiotic production as an expression of environment. Eleventh Symposium, Microbial Reaction to Environment, page 317. Soc. Gen. Microbiol., London. 1961.

Woodward, R. B.: Recent advances in the chemistry of natural products. Science, *153*:487, 1966.

Zygmunt, W. A., Browder, H. P., and Tavormina, P. A.: Influence of blood and serum on the antistaphylococcal activity of lysostaphin. J. Bact., *91*:725, 1966.

# Chapter 23

## IMMUNOLOGY

## Nonspecific Resistance to Infection

Immunology derives its name from the early concept that all reactions of animal tissue to certain extraneous substances and microorganisms were mechanisms of defense against, or *immunity* to, infectious disease, with little other use or significance. It is important for the student to realize that modern concepts of immunology embrace a much wider range of ideas, including many fundamental physical, chemical and physiological phenomena having nothing to do with infectious disease. A modern definition of immunology might state that it is the study of reactions of vertebrates, or certain cells of vertebrates, to proteins, protein complexes and certain polysaccharide complexes foreign to the reacting cells. Disease, and defense against it, is only one segment of modern immunology, though certainly a very considerable one. Modern methods and phenomena of immunology are widely used as laboratory tools in many fields of work such as biochemistry, diagnostic and preventive medicine, genetics, ethnology, microbiology and criminology. Here we will outline the basic principles and some of their applications and implications. One must understand them before a more detailed study can prove profitable.

### 23.1   BLOOD

It is advisable to review some facts about blood and its constituents, since blood plays a most important role in immunological reactions and investigations. For the purposes of this discussion blood may be considered to have seven important constituent parts: plasma,

fibrin components, platelets, serum, lymph, erythrocytes and leukocytes.

**Plasma.**   First, there is the *plasma*—the yellowish, transparent, fluid part of the unclotted, circulating blood. It consists of about 92 per cent water and 7 per cent proteins, and is a solution of salts, buffers (to maintain a constant reaction of pH 7.4) and other soluble substances including cell foods (such as amino acids and glucose) and cell wastes. The plasma also has in solution the components of *fibrin,* which are essential in the clotting of blood and also of plasma. Essentially, plasma is blood minus all of its cellular elements.

**Fibrin Components.**   Fibrin, as such, does not normally occur in circulating blood. Fibrin components ordinarily combine only after the blood leaves the blood vessels. Fibrin is a protein which forms an elastic network of microscopically fine fibrils. As a result of the formation of fibrin, blood clots. The elastic fibrin meshwork soon shrinks to about half the original volume of blood, squeezing out of its meshes the fluid part of the blood, which is now called *serum.* Serum is equivalent to plasma minus the fibrin components. Most of the blood cells (and bacteria if any are present) are caught and held in the fibrin clot (Fig. 23.1).

**Platelets.**   Associated with fibrin production are small bodies called *platelets,* or *thrombocytes* (Gr. *thrombus* = clot). These are deeply staining, amorphous or stellate particles, variable in size but smaller than red corpuscles (Fig. 23.2). They are fragments of marrow cells. There are normally about 350,000 platelets per cubic millimeter of blood. Their role in the coagulation of blood is important, though not

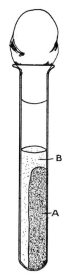

**Figure 23.1** Tube with clot (*A*) which has shrunken, enmeshing virtually all of the blood corpuscles and exuding clear serum (*B*).

entirely clear. Platelets appear to facilitate clotting by liberating one of the components of fibrin called *thromboplastin.* They also have other functions in the clotting process. The ability of blood to clot appears to be directly related to the number of platelets in the blood.

**Serum.**  Since fibrin usually enmeshes the blood corpuscles as it forms, serum is yellowish and transparent, like plasma. Serum contains most of the soluble substances, especially *gamma globulins (antibodies)*, in which the immunologist is interested. After blood has clotted, the serum

may be withdrawn in pipettes, centrifuged to remove stray red blood corpuscles and stored in the refrigerator. It must be handled with every aseptic precaution to keep it sterile, since microorganisms gaining access to it would soon cause it to decompose. Immunologists often add minute quantities of preservatives.

**Lymph.**  Lymph is very much like blood that has been deprived of red corpuscles by passing through the intercellular spaces in the thin walls of the smaller blood vessels as through a fine filter (i.e., lymph closely resembles plasma). The lymph thus seeping out of the vessels travels slowly in the fine spaces surrounding the blood vessels and between the tissue cells and various organs. It contains *leukocytes* or white blood corpuscles that are derived from lymphatic tissues. Like plasma, it can clot. Lymph is in contact with, or close to, all active tissue cells. Lymph is the nutrient fluid or "culture medium" in which tissue cells grow in the animal body. It also collects the cell wastes. It eventually collects from all parts of the body in large drainage vessels (the *lymphatic ducts*) and is returned to the blood. Wastes carried from cells by serum and lymph are excreted in the kidneys.

**Erythrocytes.**  In the plasma, before clotting, are suspended the red corpuscles or *erythrocytes* (Gr. *erythro* = red; *cyte* = cell). These are the non-nucleated* cells that give blood its opacity and red color and that carry oxygen from the lungs to the tissues and carbon dioxide from tissues to lungs. The color of erythrocytes is caused by the red, oxygen-carrying substance, *hemoglobin* (respiratory pigment), which they contain.

Erythrocytes are about 8 $\mu$ in diameter and number four to five million per cubic millimeter of blood. When they are ruptured by plasmoptysis or other means, the hemoglobin is released and the blood becomes transparent, like red ink. The released hemoglobin appears in the urine. The cells are said to have been "laked," or *hemolyzed.* Certain bacteria are very active in producing *hemolysis* by means of toxins. Some snake venoms are very hemolytic.

## 23.2   THE PHAGOCYTIC CELLS

**Leukocytes.**  In addition to erythrocytes, blood contains several kinds of colorless cells called, collectively, *leukocytes* (Gr. *leuko* = white). Leukocytes are relatively large, 10 to 20 $\mu$ in di-

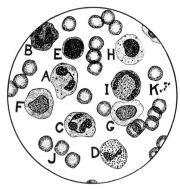

**Figure 23.2** Drawing of a smear of blood stained with Jenner's stain, showing common forms of blood cells. *A*, *B*, and *C*, Polymorphonuclear leukocytes with 2, 3, and 4-lobed nuclei, respectively. *D*, Eosinophil showing lobular nucleus and prominent, eosinophilic (red-staining) granules. *E*, Lymphocyte. *F*, *G*, and *H*, Various forms of monocytes ("large lymphocytes"). *I*, Lymphocyte with horseshoe-shaped nucleus ("transitional cell"). *J*, Erythrocytes (red blood corpuscles); note biconcave-disk shape, thin at center. *K*, Platelets. (Magnification about × 1000.)

---

*Mammalian erythrocytes are non-nucleated; erythrocytes of birds, amphibians and reptiles are nucleated.

ameter. Unlike mammalian erythrocytes, leukocytes have a definite nucleus. Normally there are seven to eight thousand leukocytes of all types per cubic millimeter of blood (Fig. 23.2). In many infectious processes, such as appendicitis, they increase greatly in numbers (up to 15,000 or more) and the patient is said to have a *leukocytosis*. In some infections they diminish in numbers to 3000 or less; a *leukopenia*.

The several kinds and sizes of leukocytes may be listed as follows:

I. Granulocytes or Myelocytes
    A. Polymorphonuclear leukocytes (12 to 14 μ)
        1. neutrophils
        2. basophils
        3. eosinophils
    B. Monocytes (16 to 22 μ)
II. Agranulocytes or Lymphocytes
        1. large (15 to 20 μ)
        2. small (10 to 14 μ)

The *polymorphonuclear leukocytes* are so called because their nuclei are divided into two to five distinct lobes connected by thin threads. They are classed as *granulocytes* because they contain numerous conspicuous granules. They originate in bone marrow where erythrocytes are formed (myeloid tissue), and are therefore classed as *myelocytes*. Three types are differentiated by the nature of their granules. Granules of the *neutrophilic* polymorphonuclear leukocytes have no particular affinity for either acidic or basic dyes. Granules of the *basophils* stain darkly with basic dyes like crystal violet, while granules of the *acidophilic* type ("eosinophils") stain bright red with acid dyes like eosin. The functions of the granules are not clear.

The *monocytes* are the largest of the leukocytes. They, like the polymorphonuclear leukocytes, are of myeloid origin. They have large, kidney-shaped or lobular nuclei. In many respects they resemble the polymorphs, to which they are closely related, but they are not granulocytes.

The *large and small lymphocytes* have few if any conspicuous granules and are classed as *agranulocytes*. They are produced mainly in the lymphatic tissues; i.e., germinal centers in the spleen, lymph nodes, adenoid tissues and, until the onset of puberty, in the thymus. Their nuclei are large and rounded. The lymphoid cells that are the sites of the continued production of small lymphocytes in spleen and adenoid tissues (outside the thymus) probably have their origin in the thymus in fetal and neonatal life.

A very important property of the polymorphonuclear neutrophilic granulocytes ("polymorphs") is that they can move about in the tissues and body fluids by means of pseudopodia, remarkably like amebas. Also like amebas, they can ingest small solid particles such as bacteria, cellular detritus and other foreign particulate matter (Figs. 23.3, 23.4). Thus they serve as scavengers and also as "policemen" in the blood. By means of intracellular enzymes they injure or kill most types of invading microorganisms that they ingest and then digest the organic particles. Because these cells can "eat" cells and other small particles they are called *phagocytes* (Gr. *phagein* = to eat). Because the neutrophils are the most numerous and active of the granulocytes, the term leukocyte is often used as though it were synonymous with polymorphonuclear neutrophilic leukocyte.

In normal blood the ratios (per cent or "differential count") of different types of leukocytes vary greatly but commonly are:

|  | Per Cent |
|---|---|
| Neutrophils | 60–70 |
| Basophils | 0–2 |
| Acidophils | 0–4 |
| Lymphocytes | 25–30 |
| Monocytes | 2–8 |

In acute infections the differential count shows a relative increase in neutrophils or lymphocytes.

The lymphocytes show little if any phagocytic activity but, as the source of *antibodies*,

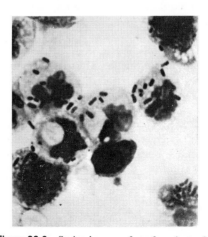

**Figure 23.3** Stained smear of pus from lung of mouse inoculated with a species of pathogenic bacilli. The bacilli are seen to have been engulfed by the leukocytes (phagocytized) in large numbers. This is an excellent illustration of one of the most important defensive measures. (From Smith and Wood: J. Exp. Med., vol. 86.)

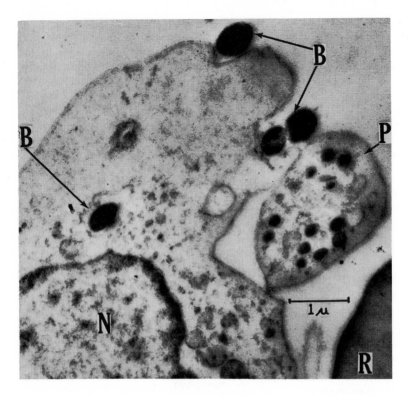

**Figure 23.4** Electron micrograph of an ultrathin (about 350Å) section of part of a human polymorphonuclear leukocyte showing phagocytosis of cells of virulent *Staphylococcus aureus*. *N* is part of one lobe of the nucleus of the leukocyte; note the well-defined nuclear membrane. *B* are cells of *S. aureus;* note that one bacterium is undergoing fission. The bacteria at the upper right are just being surrounded or grasped by the finger-like pseudopodia of the leukocyte. The bacteria will be "ingested" or drawn completely inside the leukocyte. They will be surrounded by a vacuole wall such as is seen to be forming around the bacterium at the left of center. Note the granular structure of the cytoplasm of the leukocyte and its differentiation from the nuclear plasm. *P* is a platelet; *R* is part of a red cell. Note the line indicating 1 micron. (× 27,500.) (Courtesy of Drs. J. R. Goodman and R. E. Moore, V. A. Hospital, Long Beach, Calif.)

play an extremely important role in the defensive mechanisms that are discussed farther on.

**Macrophages and Histiocytes.** The phagocytic cells we have described float freely in the blood and lymph or wander in the tissue spaces. They are sometimes called free or "wandering" phagocytes. There is another group of phagocytic cells called *fixed phagocytes* or, because they are relatively large, *macrophages* or, because they are fixed portions of tissues, *histiocytes* (Gr. *histion* = tissue). Fixed phagocytes are principally cells that occur in reticular connective tissue; some are special endothelial cells of sinuses of liver (Kupffer cells), spleen, lymphatic tissue and bone marrow. Some are monocytes that have become localized in tissues. The macrophages and histiocytes phagocytize foreign particles from the blood or lymph as it flows past them. Together they constitute what is called the *reticuloendothelial* system of phagocytes; it is one of the most important defensive mechanisms of the body.

### 23.3   CELLULAR VS. HUMORAL IMMUNITY

The relation of phagocytosis to defense against infection (immunity) was first pointed out by Elie Metchnikoff (Nobel Prize winner) about 1882 and was the origin of the doctrine

of *cellular immunity*. In 1890 certain proteins, now known to be *gamma globulins* and called *specific antibodies*, were discovered by von Behring (Nobel Prize winner), Buchner and others in the serum of persons and animals who had been vaccinated against, or who had recovered from, certain specific infectious diseases. These specific antibodies were found to be defensive only against the specific microorganisms, or their toxins, that evoked those particular antibodies. For example, diphtheria antibodies (*antitoxin*) "neutralize" diphtheria toxin, but not the toxin of tetanus or any other kind. Specific antibodies in the blood were therefore hailed as the real basis of immunity to disease and gave rise to the doctrine of *humoral* (fluid) *immunity*. A long, and often acrimonious, controversy arose between the two schools of thought.

**Antibodies and Phagocytes.** Long and intensive studies proved that both phagocytic cells and antibodies are important in immunity. Phagocytes can act without the aid of antibodies, but specific antibodies, with one or two possible exceptions, are important *adjuvants* to phagocytosis (see *opsonins*).

Phagocytes are like a standing army, ready at all times for immediate duty. They are a first line of defense. Specific antibodies, on the contrary, like interferon (see Chapter 18) are a biological response to a stimulus and appear only after the stimulus, e.g., an infection, has begun. Obviously they can be of only secondary (though usually critical) assistance. However, there are certain *nonspecific* enzyme-like and antibody-like factors, often called *normal antibodies* or *nonspecific antibodies,* that are constantly present in the blood and that give immediate aid to phagocytes and otherwise repel a variety of invaders. (See also properdin.)

**Opsonic Effect of Antibodies.**   Many pathogenic bacteria have slimy capsules that make it difficult for the leukocytes to grasp them with their pseudopodia preparatory to engulfing them. This is true especially if the microorganisms are floating freely in a fluid such as blood. One may visualize the situation by trying to grasp fresh watermelon seeds or bits of ice when they are floating in water.

Antibodies, specific and "normal," clump (*agglutinate*) organisms together or prepare the surfaces of the microorganisms so that they are less slimy and do not readily slip from the grasp of the phagocytes. This preparation of microorganisms to be eaten more readily by the phagocytes is often referred to as *opsonization* (Gr. *opsonin* = to prepare food for).

Surface Phagocytosis.   Regardless of opsonins, if the phagocytes can get the microorganisms against a surface from which the organisms cannot escape ("on the ropes," to use a prizefighter's term), the phagocytes can grasp the organisms much more effectively. The surfaces of adjacent tissue cells or of any uneven or rough surface, or strands of fibrin, serve the purpose very well. Phagocytosis is, therefore, not necessarily dependent on antibodies, nor even on surfaces.

**Nonspecific Defenses Against Infection.**   In addition to those cellular and humoral factors just enumerated that serve as defenses against infection, there are several rather general, *nonspecific* physiological and anatomical factors that determine susceptibility to infection. They may be grouped as follows:

I. Genetic factors
II. Physiological factors
   A. State of general health and age
   B. Mechanical and chemical factors
   C. Inflammatory response

Genetic Factors.   By this is meant *individual, racial* or *species* resistance to disease; that is, horses do not have measles, man does not contract fowl pox and pathogens of mammals do not infect plants. The facts are obvious, and sometimes the explanations are also evident. For example, "cold-blooded" (*poikilothermic*) animals (normal temperatures from 40° to 80° F.) and birds (normal temperatures around 104° F.) are not susceptible to microorganisms that grow only at mammalian temperatures (normal temperatures around 98° F.). However, as Pasteur proved in a dramatic demonstration, chickens will die of anthrax, to which they are ordinarily resistant because of their high body temperature, if they are infected and then cooled by partial immersion in ice water. In many instances complete explanations of species and racial resistance are lacking. Species resistance undoubtedly involves complex chemical factors in addition to differences in temperature. Tissue-cultured cells (Chapter 16) of an animal may be very susceptible to infections to which the intact animal is wholly resistant. For example, embryo chicks succumb to many infections that do not affect the adult bird.

Physiological Factors.

*State of General Health and Age.*   Persons weakened by overwork, starvation, exposure, alcoholism, drug-addiction, age and disease are known to become more susceptible to various infections such as tuberculosis and pneumonia. Children often suffer little from diseases that are fatal to older persons, and vice versa. The mechanisms are still obscure.

*Mechanical and Chemical Factors.*   The *outer skin,* especially of adults, is an obvious mechanical barrier to the entrance of many foreign agents. It is chemically aided against microorganisms by its oily secretion and by the acidity of perspiration. The acetic acid in perspiration is quite toxic to many bacteria. The skin may be bypassed, however, by hypodermic needles, wounds and by entrance of certain microorganisms into deeper tissues via hair follicles and sweat glands.

The *hairs in the ears and nose* mechanically entangle or enmesh particles of dust, insects and bacteria. Secretions of *mucus* cause all of the respiratory surfaces, such as those in eyes, nose and throat and others in contact with the exterior, to be sticky. Foreign bodies accumulate in the mucus. Removal from the respiratory tract to the exterior is then accomplished by sneezing, coughing, salivation and tears. The *deeper air passages* are lined with *ciliated epithelial cells.* The cilia maintain a constant upward-waving movement that pushes mucus (with entrapped bacteria and dust) up to the larynx and throat where the mucus is either coughed up or swallowed. Further, these mucous surfaces are always "policed" by small numbers of leukocytes.

In the *gastrointestinal tract, acidity* of the stomach (pH about 2.0) kills many organisms.

The *upper intestine* is freed of microorganisms to a great extent by the *bile* and other *digestive juices.* The lower small intestine and large bowel contain great numbers of bacteria, many of which are highly pathogenic if they gain entrance to the blood or body tissues. They are normally held in check by the thick mucous membranes lining the intestines and by phagocytic and other mechanisms. A ruptured intestine, stomach or appendix is a source of serious infection which, if untreated, is usually fatal.

The adult *genitourinary tract* is protected against most bacteria mainly by thick mucous membranes, leukocytes and the flow of *urine,* which is normally acid. A protective acidity is maintained on the mucous membranes of the vagina by growth of harmless, acid-producing bacteria of the Genus *Lactobacillus.*

*The Inflammatory Response.* Inflammation is a complex response of tissues to damage or irritating agents of any sort: chemicals, burns, excessive ultraviolet irradiation (sunburn), mechanical injury, bites and stings of insects and infections. Inflammation is characterized by five distinctive features: *calor* (heat), *rubor* (redness), *turgor* (swelling), *dolor* (pain) and *infiltration* by phagocytic cells. Inflamed areas feel hot because of local dilatation of blood vessels and increased blood supply; redness also is caused by dilatation of the capillary blood vessels locally. Swelling is caused by the extra blood in the dilated capillary vessels and by extravasation (seepage outward), under pressure, of lymph, plasma and serum into the local lymph and tissue spaces. This accumulation of fluid in tissues is called *edema.* Pressure on and irritation of local sensory nerve endings causes pain. Nonspecific substances called *pyrogens* (Gr. *pyr* = heat) emanate from the site of injury and circulate in the blood. If they occur in sufficient amount they cause *fever.*

Within a few minutes after plasma seeps into tissues, fibrin threads begin to form a meshwork in the edema fluid. This tends to contain and prevent the spread of the invading microorganisms. Less evident, but just as important, is the attraction of both phagocytic and antibody-producing leukocytes to the area. They start their journey by adhering to the linings of the local capillaries. Then, by their ameboid motility, the phagocytic leukocytes leave the capillary blood vessels, passing between the cells of the capillary walls by a process called *diapedesis,* somewhat as ghosts are said (by some) to pass through keyholes. The leukocytes congregate in tissues and blood wherever any injury

or infection exists. The cause of the attraction of the leukocytes is not fully known, but it appears to be a substance released by injured cells in the affected area. The attraction is called *chemotaxis* (Gr. *chemo* = chemical; *taxis* = orientation toward).

Often many phagocytic leukocytes are killed by the poisons of the bacteria or other noxious agents that they ingest, and by crowding, acidity and lack of oxygen in the region of concentration and activity.

The white, creamy material in a boil or other infected lesion, or around a festering splinter, is made up largely of dead and living white corpuscles, dead and living bacteria, tissue debris, lymph, serum and possibly fibrin. It is called *pus,* and the dead leukocytes in it are called *pus cells.*

On the other hand, leukocytes are sometimes unable to kill or suppress the growth of microorganisms that they ingest. Leukocytes containing live, virulent microorganisms may then be carried by the blood or lymph to other parts of the body, there to set up *secondary* or *metastatic* infections.

Infectious agents of any sort contain substances (*antigens*) that stimulate antibody-forming cells (mainly large lymphocytes) to produce specific antibodies. The antibodies evoked by the infecting agent begin to appear within a few minutes after infection. It is probably because of these and fibrin formation, the constant presence of pre-existing normal or nonspecific antibodies in the blood (see next section) and phagocytic cells that inflamed tissue tends to *localize* and hold the infective invaders. Firm combinations occur between the local tissue cells and organisms. Increased phagocytosis of antibody-covered (*opsonized*) microorganisms also occurs. If the inflammatory reaction in the local tissues, with its antibodies and phagocytes, can then hold and destroy the invader, the infection is suppressed. If not, then the victim may succumb.

During the inflammatory process, new tissue cells (*fibroblasts*) grow in and around the area, attempting to immure and contain the infection and to replace dead tissue with tough, new tissue, which eventually becomes *scar tissue.*

## 23.4   NORMAL, "NATURAL" OR NONSPECIFIC ANTIBODIES

In addition to phagocytic cells, there are constantly present in the normal blood, as defensive mechanisms, soluble, *nonspecific,* antimicrobial factors which are enzyme-like or antibody-like. Natural antibodies are those that occur in various body fluids in the absence of any known infection or vaccination. A controversy of long standing concerns the question whether such antimicrobial substances are the result of unknown, specific, antigenic stimulation (e.g., unnoticed infection) or whether they can occur in the absence of any antigenic stimulus. "Normal" serum has long been known to be actively bactericidal. The antibodies are especially active against gram-negative bacteria. Some act like specific agglutinins, some like bacteriolysins and some like antitoxins. The bacteriocidal or bacteriolytic natural antibodies, like specific antibodies (Chapter 24), require the presence of $Ca^{++}$ and $Mg^{++}$ and of another nonspecific serum component called *complement*.

**Complement.** Complement has little or no antimicrobial power by itself but it aids and *complements* (hence its name) the action of various antibodies, specific and natural. Complement is a complex of at least five distinct serum proteins called C′1, C′2, C′3a, C′3b, and C′4. It behaves as though it were a part of an enzyme though it is not a coenzyme. In combination with specific, and some nonspecific, antibodies at pH 7.0 to 7.6, at about 36° C., and in the necessary presence of $Mn^{++}$ and $Ca^{++}$, complement becomes actively cytolytic. Several of the specific antibodies and nonspecific antimicrobial factors cannot function without it. These cytolytic actions markedly affect the cell walls and internal structures.

Complement component C′3 is a complex of six proteins: C′3, C′5, C′6, C′7, C′8 and C′9. Some become modified into enzyme-like forms: C′1a, C′2a, etc. They interact with each other in complex systems but always in the same sequence. Not all occur in all antigen-antibody combinations: in opsonization, C′1a, C′4, C′2a, C′3; in cytolysis, C′1a, C′4, C′2a, C′3, C′5, C′6, C′7, C′8, C′9.

Complement is quite labile—all C′ components are inactivated by violent shaking or by temperatures of 56° C. for 30 minutes or room temperature for a few hours. Note especially that it is readily adsorbed upon the surface of colloidal materials such as any fine floc, powdered charcoal or chalk dust, and also by a substance called *zymosan,* extracted from yeast. The special significance of the ready adsorbability of complement is made clear farther on.

**The Properdin\* System.** A group of serum components that work together, the *properdin*

*system* apparently plays an important role in nonspecific resistance to infection. There are three components in the system: *properdin,* a serum protein; *magnesium* ions; and *complement.*

Properdin is perhaps more accurately designated as properdin *activity,* because properdin, originally thought of as a definite, enzyme-like protein, may be merely a special manifestation of the activity of complement component C′3 and other factors. The activity is closely related to, if not an actual part of, the complement complex.

The amount of properdin activity in the blood seems to be directly related to the degree of nonspecific resistance of an animal to numerous types of infection: bacterial, protozoal and viral. Injection of properdin-rich serum from animals having naturally high levels of properdin activity in their serum increases resistance to infection. Any agent (hemorrhage, shock, electromagnetic irradiations, cancer and infection) which lowers the properdin activity of the blood also lowers nonspecific resistance to infection. The injection of zymosan, or of certain lipopolysaccharides (*endotoxins*) found in the cell walls of many gram-negative bacteria, results in a rapid lowering of properdin activity. In order for properdin to affect microorganisms it is necessary for $Mg^{++}$ and $Ca^{++}$ to be present.

OTHER NONSPECIFIC FACTORS. In general, other nonspecific factors are not well defined. Their action is not clearly understood and has been demonstrated chiefly by *in vitro* experiments. It is suggested by some that these substances are released from tissue cells (including leukocytes) only after injury and rupture of those cells, and that they do not exist free in the blood until such injury occurs. However this may be, the fact has been amply demonstrated that, *in vitro,* the fresh blood or serum of most animals exerts actively microbicidal action against numerous species of microorganisms. It seems reasonable to suppose that such mechanisms observed *in vitro* also occur *in vivo.*

**Lysozyme.** A bacteriolytic enzyme, *lysozyme* is found in tears, saliva, white of egg, tissues and leukocytes. As previously stated, it was discovered in 1922 by Fleming, the discoverer of penicillin. It acts (at least *in vitro*) to destroy the cell wall of several species of gram-positive (rarely gram-negative) bacteria. It produces, as does penicillin, protoplasts (*L bodies*) in hypertonic media. Though theoretically an important nonspecific defensive agent, its true significance *in vivo* is still obscure.

BETA-LYSINS. The beta-lysins are a group

*(L. *perdo* = to destroy.)

of poorly defined lytic agents that occur in fresh serum and exert bactericidal action mainly against gram-positive bacteria. Their origin and the nature of their action are obscure.

Basic Polypeptides.    Basic polypeptide structure is known to characterize certain antibiotics (e.g., polymyxins, subtilin, bacitracin). Many of these are surface-tension reducers. As previously indicated, low surface tension is inimical to numerous species of microorganisms, destroying the cell walls. Like the polypeptide antibiotics, certain serum- and tissue-derived polypeptides are surface-tension reducers active mainly against gram-positive bacteria.

*Cell-derived Factors.* Several antimicrobial substances are liberated by the disintegration of phagocytes, one of which, *phagocytin,* is lethal for gram-negative bacteria. Others, leukins and plakins, derived from platelets, adversely affect gram-positive bacteria. More studies of these substances are needed.

Interferons, substances that interfere with replications of viruses, are released by virus-infected cells. (See Chapter 18.)

## SUPPLEMENTARY READING

Carpenter, P. L.: Immunology and Serology. 2nd ed. W. B. Saunders Co., Philadelphia. 1965.

Cohen, I. R., and Norins, C. N.: Natural human antibodies to gram-negative bacteria: Immunoglobulins G, A, and M. Science, *152*:1257, 1966.

Donaldson, D. M., Jensen, R. S., Jensen, B. M., and Matheson, A.: Serological relationships among $\beta$-lysin, plakin and leukin. J. Bact., *88*:1049, 1964.

Evans, R. T., and Mergenhagen, S. E.: Occurrence of natural antibody in human parotid fluid. Proc. Soc. Exp. Biol. Med., *119*:815, 1965.

Fitzpatrick, F. W., and DiCarlo, F. J.: Zymosan. Ann. N. Y. Acad. Sci., *118*(Art. 4):233, 1964.

Heimpel, A. M., and Harshbarger, J. C.: Symposium on microbial insecticides. V. Immunity in insects. Bact. Rev., *29*:397, 1965.

Hirsch, J. G.: Phagocytosis. Ann. Rev. Microbiol., *19*:339, 1965.

Johnson, R. C., and Muschel, L. H.: Antileptospiral activity of normal serum. J. Bact., *89*:1625, 1965.

Mackaness, G. B.: The behaviour of microbial parasites in relation to phagocytic cells in vitro and in vivo. Fourteenth Symposium, Microbial Behaviour 'in Vivo' and 'in Vitro,' page 213. Soc. Gen. Microbiol., London. 1964.

Spector, W. G., and Willoughby, D. A.: The inflammatory response. Bact. Rev., *27*:117, 1963.

Spector, W. G., editor: The Acute Inflammatory Response. Ann. N. Y. Acad. Sci., *116*(Art. 3):747, 1964.

Spitznagel, J. K.: Normal serum cytotoxicity for $P^{32}$-labeled smooth Enterobacteriaceae. III. Isolation of $\gamma$G normal antibody and characterization of other serum factors causing $P^{32}$ loss. J. Bact., *91*:401, 1966.

Weidanz, W. P., and Landy, M.: A simplified method for bactericidal assay of natural antibodies against gram-negative bacteria. Proc. Soc. Exp. Biol. Med., *113*:861, 1963.

# Chapter 24

# IMMUNOLOGY
# Antigens and
# Specific Antibodies

Specific resistance to infection, in contrast with nonspecific resistance, depends on the presence of *specific antibodies* in the blood or tissues. Specific antibodies are produced by certain body cells in response to the stimulus of *specific antigens.*

*Antigens* are complete proteins or protein complexes, usually foreign to the blood, that, on contact with certain cells (mainly small lymphocytes), stimulate those cells to produce proteins called *antibodies* that have reciprocally corresponding (*specific*) physicochemical or molecular structures. Some substances are strongly antigenic in some animals but not in others. Some animals react better than others to any given antigen or to antigens in general.

*Specific antibodies* are proteins (mainly gamma globulins) produced by lymphocytes of vertebrates in response to contact with antigens. Molecules of antibody tend to combine with those antigens by virtue of mutually reciprocal physicochemical structures of antigen and antibody molecules. The combination of antibody with antigen is commonly followed by destruction or removal of the antigen from the body. The bonds between antigen and antibody are not covalent: H bonds, ionic bonds, etc., and hence are not very strong.

The property of producing specific antibodies evolved relatively late in the history of life, appearing only in vertebrates above the chondricthyes (sharks, rays, etc.). Antibodies (immune gamma globulins) are of three electrophoretically separable and physiologically different major groups: $\gamma A$, $\gamma G$, and $\gamma M$. Others are $\gamma Y$ and $\gamma E$, the last important in allergy (Chapter 26). About 85 per cent of immune gamma globulins in humans are $\gamma G$.

Each molecule of gamma globulin consists of two pairs of polypeptide chains, linked parallel in "sheet" form by about 22 —S—S— bonds. In each pair, one chain is called L or light (about 22,000 mol. wt.); the other H or heavy (about 50,000 mol. wt.). The L chains of all are identical; the H chains immunologically different (specific). The two pairs of chains account for the bivalence of $\gamma G$ globulins. In humans the $\gamma G$ (but not the $\gamma A$ or $\gamma M$) pass to the fetus and give passive protection against many infectious agents for up to about 6 months of age. It is then customary to immunize infants against polio, tetanus, diphtheria, measles, etc. (Chapter 24). The maternal antibodies in the younger infants interfere with the antigenic effect of the "vaccines."

Substances that combine specifically with antibodies (antigens and haptens, page 318) and also the specific substrates of enzymes are sometimes collectively called ligands (specifically connected substances). Here, however, haptens and antigens are spoken of as such for clarity of discussion.

**Properties of Antigens.** Since they are proteins and protein complexes, antigens are substances of large molecular weight—of the order of 100,000 to several million. Antigens may be components of infectious agents or they may be usually harmless substances such as casein of milk or egg white. They may be viruses, whole cells, parts of cells or soluble products of cells or enzyme proteins. Antigens lose antigenicity on being denatured, digested or hydrolyzed to residues of small molecular weight. Consequently, to retain their antigenicity they must gain access to the antibody-producing cells by a route other than via the digestive system. They may be introduced by hypodermic injection (as vaccines), by absorption through the skin or mucous membranes of the respiratory tract, eyes or genitalia, or by infection. Such routes of entry, other than through the enteric or *enteral* tract, are said to be *parenteral*. In order to enter the body through the stomach and intestines, antigenic agents must be protected from the stomach acids and digestive enzymes by masses of food or by capsules.

**Source of Specific Antibodies.**  The ability to produce specific antibodies (*immunological competence*) is absent from, or very limited in, body cells in early embryonic life. Lymphocytes, on which specific antibody production largely depends, appear first in germinal (cell-proliferative) centers in the thymus after the second month. The thymus is a soft, fatty, cell-rich mass near the heart. It is miniscule in early fetal life but becomes large and active in late fetal and neonatal life, and then shrinks to insignificant size at puberty. During development and activity of the thymus, immature small and large lymphocytes leave the thymus and establish active germinal centers of lymphocyte production (lymphoid tissues or *lymph nodes*) in the spleen, adenoid tissues, tonsils and throughout the body. When infected, these lymph nodes become the familiar, sore, "swollen glands."

On contact with any antigenic substance, the small lymphocytes, and probably to a lesser extent the large ones, mature into antibody-producing *plasma cells*. The thymus itself does not produce antibodies under ordinary conditions; it seems to be sequestered from the blood and antigens. However, if antigens are artificially injected directly into the thymus its immature lymphocytes, thus stimulated, mature into plasma cells and produce antibody. If the thymus is absent or removed early in life, the immunological processes of the adult are absent or defective.

## 24.1  SELF AND NONSELF

We may think of responses of cells like lymphocytes, to antigens, as resulting from ability of the cell (*self*) to recognize and react against anything that is *nonself*. Anything that is not derived from that cell, or from genetically identical cells, is nonself; i.e., a "foreign substance,"

and is reacted against or *rejected* or "resented." For example, if we inject horse serum (e.g., diphtheria or tetanus antitoxin derived from blood of horses) into a man, the man's tissue cells instantly recognize the equine proteins as "not self," and they respond by producing antibodies to destroy and reject it.

## 24.2  ANTIGENS OF "SELF"

**Iso-antigens.**  In an attempt to avoid such a rejection reaction against proteins from a different species (in this case equine) we might use antitoxin-containing serum taken from another person. But even this human protein (unless the donor were an identical [*monozygotic*] twin) would be considered "nonself" by the antibody-forming tissues of the recipient person and be rejected likewise though, being more closely allied to the recipient than equine serum, the human protein is not rejected so rapidly or violently; it is said to be an *iso-antigen* (Gr. *isos* = the same). An iso-antigen is any substance from one individual that exhibits antigenic activity in another individual of the *same species*.

Important examples of human iso-antigens are the A, B, and Rh antigens of our erythrocytes that divide the human race into several immunological ("blood") groups: A, B, AB (AB = both iso-antigens present) or O (O = neither A nor B present), Rh⁺ (containing Rh antigen) or Rh⁻ (containing no Rh antigen) (Table 24.1; Fig. 24.1). There are many such iso-antigens among humans, and they occur in other species of related vertebrates.

THE HOMOGRAFT REACTION.  On the same basis, if we were "grafting" (transplanting) skin

**TABLE 24.1  ISOHEMAGGLUTINATION. INTERNATIONAL SYSTEM OF BLOOD GROUPS**

| Sera from Persons of Group: | Agglutinate the Erythrocytes of Persons of Group:* | | | |
|---|---|---|---|---|
| | AB | B | A | O |
| AB (neither anti-A nor anti-B) | − | − | − | − |
| B (anti-A) | + | − | + | − |
| A (anti-B) | + | + | − | − |
| O (anti-A and anti-B) | + | + | + | − |

\* + = agglutination occurs;  − = agglutination does not occur.

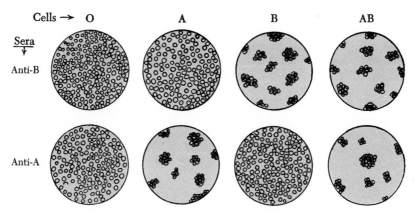

Cells →    O         A         B         AB

Sera ↓

Anti-B

Anti-A

**Figure 24.1**  Diagram of hemagglutination in blood grouping. Anti-B serum and anti-A serum have been mixed on glass slides with erythrocytes of groups O, A, B, and AB. Anti-B serum agglutinates erythrocytes of persons of groups B and AB; anti-A serum agglutinates erythrocytes of persons of groups A and AB.

to cover a burned area on a person, we would not use horse or pig skin but human skin. But, unless the donor were an identical twin, the recipient's body cells would reject even these human tissues as nonself, i.e., iso-antigens. Such a rejection is called a *homograft reaction*. Usually, skin grafts are successful only with the patient's own skin. Certain drugs have been found to suppress homograft reactions. Tolerance to "nonself," e.g., grafts, may also be induced as described below as *induced tolerance.*

**Auto-antigens.**  Certain tissues of an individual's own body (eye lens protein, certain connective and nervous tissues, and some others) that would ordinarily be thought of as "self" may be attacked as nonself, possibly because during embryonic and fetal development and early infancy the antibody-forming tissues have been too immature or sequestered from those particular tissues. On maturation, the antibody-forming tissues react to the lens, nerve or connective tissues as nonself. Substances that, though naturally part of an individual's own body, nevertheless exhibit antigenic activity in the *same body* are said to be *auto-antigens*. (How are they different from iso-antigens?) Some types of arthritis, multiple sclerosis and other "autoimmunization" diseases may have such reactions as a basic cause.

**Acquired or Induced Tolerance.**  One of the problems of the "self" and "nonself" relationship is why "self" (except for the few special tissues that are auto-antigens) is not antigenic in its body of origin. It appears that in embryonic, fetal and neonatal life the thymus-derived cells that react to antigens (i.e., that recognize foreign substances as "nonself") have not yet begun to function. The other tissues are not

equipped to recognize nonself; to them, everything is "self."

Therefore, if antigenic substances are injected into the embryo or fetus, or during neonatal life (the time varies in different animals and with different antigens), these antigenic substances are not recognized as nonself. The fully mature adult is therefore as tolerant to them as though they were self.* This type of early-life adaptation to antigenic substances is called *acquired* or *induced tolerance* or immunological paralysis. Practical use of such information is made in avoiding the use of immunizing "shots" for such diseases as polio, diphtheria or tetanus in very young infants whose antibody-producing tissues still fail to recognize microbial antigens as nonself, i.e., whose tissues may be said to be "immunologically naïve." Currently many studies are directed to means of avoiding homograft reactions, not only of bits of skin but of whole transplanted organs such as hearts and kidneys. In spite of newspaper publicity, such transfers have rarely succeeded.

The surgery and postoperational care in such transplantations are mechanically and technically magnificent. Unfortunately, human efforts are apt to be frustrated by the rejection reaction in the patient. The immunological rejection response may be held in abeyance by continuous immunologically suppressive measures such as heavy doses of radiations (e.g., x-rays; cobalt 60) which are said to be *lympholytic* since they destroy the proliferating antibody-forming lymphocytes. Large doses of analogs of purines, pyrimidines, etc., that inter-

_____

*The work of Sir MacFarlane Burnet, with Sir Peter Brian Medawar (Nobel Prize winners), led to this discovery.

fere with DNA formation in the multiplying lymphocytes also suppress antibody formation. The patient, however, in addition to sustaining various "side effects" of these treatments is totally deprived of all antibody defenses and becomes highly vulnerable to infection by many pathogenic microorganisms and to some that are ordinarily harmless.

Tolerance to homografts and other foreign substances can also be induced in adult animals. The injection of massive doses of any antigen has long been known to produce "immunological paralysis." Large doses of antigen appear to saturate and overwhelm the antibody-producing reticuloendothelial and lymphocytic cells so that they fail to function. The tolerance induced in fetal or neonatal animals by injection of large doses of antigen may likewise depend on saturation, overloading and "paralysis" of the embryonic or very immature antibody-producing systems.

## 24.3   SPECIFICITY

Specificity has been referred to as an attribute of antigens and antibodies that is a result of mutually corresponding physicochemical structures. The structural resemblance between molecules of an antigen and molecules of the corresponding antibody may be visualized as analogous to the relationship between a mold and its replica or casting. Each is *specific* for the other.

Specificity, either in enzyme-substrate relationship (Chapter 5) or in antigen-antibody relationships, is dependent on corresponding chemical and physical structures of the respective molecules. For example, a *synthetic* antigen (of which several have been prepared experimentally by combining protein with certain inorganic radicles) having a given chemical structure (e.g., $NH_2C_6H_4 \cdot AsO_3H_2$ + protein) will, upon injection into the body, engender antibodies in the serum that react only with that compound. Let us alter the antigen, for instance by substituting a $^-SO_3H$ group in place of the $^-AsO_3H_2$ group. Antibodies to the arsenilic antigen will not react significantly with this altered antigen. Almost any sort of chemical alteration in an antigen will alter its specificity. Too great an alteration will destroy its antigenicity.

Specificity of an antibody molecule relates fundamentally to a single functional or haptenic group or combining site at the surface of the

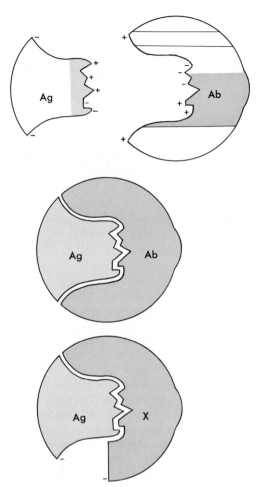

**Figure 24.2** Specificity in antigen-antibody reactions. At top are shown, diagrammatically, antigen (Ag) and antibody (Ab), each with an indented margin, each margin the mirror image of the other. In the middle, antigen and antibody are shown forming a large colloidal complex by virtue of the perfect "fit" between Ag and Ab. At bottom is shown a colloidal complex formed by Ag with an antibody (X) of similar but not perfectly corresponding form. A visible precipitate may or may not be formed by such a combination.

antigen molecule. If the antigen molecule is small and contains only one combining site (i.e., is *univalent*) then only one antibody molecule can combine with each such antigen molecule (though two antigen molecules may combine with each antibody molecule since antibody molecules are typically bivalent). Such antigen-antibody combinations are small and soluble.

The more complex the form of the antigen molecule the more combination sites there are for specific combination with antibody, and the larger, more stable and insoluble the combination is. For example, most protein antigens have up to about five different combining sites, each of which evokes an antibody molecule specific for that site. Thus, even though such a multi-valent antigenic protein is a pure substance, the "antibody" produced in response to it is really a mixture of antibody molecules, each specific for a different combining site on the antigen molecule. Saturation of all the combining sites with specific antibodies forms a large, stable, insoluble and *precipitable* colloidal complex. This is of basic importance and will be referred to again under *Precipitins* (next section) and *Lattice Formation* (page 321).

**Cross-Reactions.** A slight reaction with antibodies to the arsenilate may occur if, instead of substituting a ⁻SO₃H group, we introduce, say, a ⁻Cl atom in place of an H atom. The antibodies produced in response to the original arsenilic antigen are said to *cross-react* with the chlorinated antigen. Such cross-reactions occur between many closely related antigens (Fig. 24.2).

## 24.4   MECHANISMS OF ANTIGEN-ANTIBODY REACTIONS

Both antigen molecules and gamma globulins (antibodies) are substances of high molecular weight and are likewise colloidal in nature. Substances are in the colloidal state when they are in the form of ultramicroscopically minute particles stably suspended in a fluid (gas or liquid). For example, smoke is a colloidal

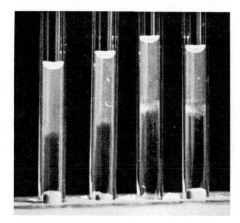

**Figure 24.3** Precipitin test in narrow-bore glass tubes. The antigen solution is the cloudy zone above; the antiserum is the clear zone below. At the interface between them, in the two right-hand tubes, a definite white floc or precipitate has formed, representing a reaction between specifically related antigen and antibody. The same antigen fails to react with a different (nonspecific) serum in the two left-hand tubes (× 5). (Preparation by Dr. Elaine L. Updyke. Photo courtesy of the Communicable Disease Center, U. S. Public Health Serivce, Atlanta, Ga.)

suspension of minute particles of carbon, tars and other substances in air; milk is a colloidal suspension of casein protein and fat globules in whey; enzymes are colloidal proteins.

Colloidal particles in aqueous suspensions generally have negative, mutually repellent, electric charges. These help to keep the particles suspended and prevent their coalescing and precipitating as floc, or from coagulating as in the souring of milk. Microorganisms, because of their minute size, generally have many of the properties of colloids.

**Precipitin Reactions.** Both antigens and antibodies, as complexes of amino acids, also have both positive and negative polar groups distributed over their surfaces in specific but reciprocal patterns. When antigen and corresponding antibody molecules are mixed, electrical attractions and repulsions, modified by van der Waals and ionic surface forces, result in an orientation of the corresponding antigen and antibody molecules with respect to their molecular forms and electrical charges, so that an absolute "fit" (mold and cast) is obtained. The compound colloidal particles formed as a result of the interaction are very large. In the presence of electrolytes that, presumably, neutralize exterior colloidal charges, the particles become unstable and are thrown out of suspension. In a test-tube reaction they become visible as a cloudy precipitate (Fig. 24.3). This sort of reaction is commonly seen when specific antibody reacts with a soluble protein or polysaccharide antigen. The reaction is called a *precipitin reaction.*

**Stages of Antigen-Antibody Reactions.** The first stage of antigen-antibody reaction is *adsorption* or complex physicochemical, sometimes reversible, combination between antibodies and antigens. This combination may proceed rapidly at temperatures near 37° C. The second stage is a *visible* (or indirectly demonstrable) *reaction* (precipitation, cell lysis or other effect; see Section 24.7). This stage often develops slowly and may be demonstrated best after 12 to 18 hours at 4 to 6° C. As mentioned before, the presence of electrolytes (magnesium chloride, sodium chloride) and certain enzyme-like components of serum (*complement*) are necessary for certain types of reaction in the second stage.

## 24.5   ANTIGENS OF CELLS

Reactions of antibodies with antigens that are parts of entire cells instead of being free colloids are basically the same. However, since entire cells instead of colloidal molecules are involved as antigen, the result of the antigen-antibody combination is somewhat more complex. Several cellular antigens are described in the following paragraphs.

In nature, antigens seldom occur in a pure state. This complicates the study of antigen-antibody reactions involving microorganisms. A bacterial cell, for example, may contain several antigens; e.g., the proteins of various enzymes, nucleoproteins, ribosomes, protein-polysaccharide complexes of the cell wall and capsule. The serum of a person or animal following infection by, or injection of such cells (as by vaccination) usually contains a mixture of antibodies specific for each separate antigen. Most of these antibodies are ineffective, however, since antibodies react mainly with antigens at the cell surface.

For illustrative purposes let us consider the surface antigens of a group of common rod-shaped, nonsporeforming bacteria, e.g., gram-negative eubacteria of the Family Enterobacteriaceae. These bacteria are more or less constant inhabitants of the intestinal tract of many animal species and are widely known and important bacteria. Some are pathogenic. Their antigenic structure is representative of that of many species of bacteria.

**Flagellar (H) Antigens.** Various forms of the protein, *flagellin,* are localized in the flagella of motile species of Enterobacteriaceae. Flagellar antigens are called *H antigens* (see also O antigens). H antigens are destroyed (denatured) by boiling, also by alcohol and dilute acids. In at least one genus, *Salmonella,** H antigens often exist in one of two different degrees of specificity, called *phases.* In the *specific phase* (phase I) they are specific for the species in which they occur. In the less specific or *group phase* (phase II) they resemble antigens in a group of closely related species or types (see heterogenetic antigens). They vary, often unpredictably, from one phase to the other for various reasons, some known, some unknown. This is spoken of as *phase variation.*

**Fimbrial Antigens.** Fimbriae occur on many species of enterobacteria. They are strongly antigenic. They differ from flagellar antigens in being somewhat more resistant to heat and in resisting the effects of alcohol. They are not related to any other antigens of the cell surface.

---

*Named for an American bacteriologist, Salmon.

**Capsular Antigens.** Among the Enterobacteriaceae, capsules are found in the group called *Klebsiella* (for German bacteriologist, Klebs). Most capsules are heteropolymers of various simple sugars with glucosamine and other sugar derivatives. As part of the cell they are conjugated with proteins. Some are polypeptides. The possible number of different combinations of subunits in such capsular heteropolymers (*antigens*) is very large. Capsular substance, when present, dominates the surface. Since antibodies act chiefly at cell surfaces, the physicochemical structure (i.e., specificity) of the capsular antigen thus determines antigenic specificity of the entire cell.

The property of *antigenic specificity* conferred by the capsular substance of *Klebsiella* is paralleled in the capsules of such organisms as pneumococci, influenza bacilli and streptococci, and is highly distinctive of each species or type. Stripped of this *specific* surface antigen, the exposed antigens of the naked cells often cross-react with antibodies produced against related or even unrelated species. For example, the antigens of the naked cell walls of most pneumococci are immunologically alike. Antibodies for one react equally well with others. But the heteropolysaccharide antigens of the capsules are not all alike. There are about 75 distinct types of pneumococcus capsular antigens. Each antigen determines a different antigenic or serological type of pneumococcus. Similar series of capsular types are found in *Klebsiella;* influenza bacilli (*Haemophilus influenzae,* types A, B, C, D, E); in meningococci (*Neisseria meningitidis,* types I, II, II alpha); and in numerous other species.

In addition to conferring antigenic specificity on the cell, capsules act as a protective coating against antibodies, phagocytes, drying and other unfavorable environmental influences.

Capsular substances, especially capsular polysaccharides, exemplify the class of "partial antigens" or *haptens.* (See Section 24.6.)

**K Antigens.** The K antigens resemble capsular antigens both in their location on the cell surface and in their specificity. Commonly they are not as readily demonstrable or as voluminous as most capsules. Their origin is not wholly clear; they may be derived by extrusion of material from inside the cell wall or by some modification of the exterior surface of the cell wall. Since they coat the surface, K antigens dominate the response of the cell to antibodies and confer antigenic specificity in the same manner as capsules. Like flagellar antigens (proteins), K antigens are denatured by boiling.

**O Antigens.** The designations "H" and "O" for certain antigens are derived from early studies, by Weil and Felix, of a genus of Enterobacteriaceae called *Proteus*. Like many other enterobacteria, *Proteus* species characteristically occur in two variant forms, motile and non-motile. It was observed that on moist agar medium the flagellate forms rapidly spread over the entire surface of the agar in a thin, grey film that was described by the German observers as *Hauch* (German for fog or "cough in very cold air"). The nonflagellate variant formed the usual, discrete, round colonies *"ohne Hauch"* (German for "absence of the foglike film"). The term Hauch (or *H*), associated with motility, soon became almost synonymous with the organs of motility, flagella (see flagellar or H antigens). The *ohne Hauch* or nonmotile form was correspondingly called the "Ohne" or "O" form; "O" came to be associated with the bodies of the bacilli without flagella. "O" is now used to designate the body antigens (also called *somatic antigens;* Gr. *soma* = body).

Further study of the Family Enterobacteriaceae (Chapter 36) and other gram-negative rods has shown that O antigens are components of the lipopolysaccharide portion of the cell walls of most gram-negative organisms, in loose combination with somatic proteins. Unlike the species and type-specific flagellar and capsular antigens, O antigens of the Enterobacteriaceae, while specific, are less restricted in distribution. A given O antigen may occur in several species in different groups of Enterobacteriaceae. For example, in the Genus *Salmonella,* the O antigens designated as 9 and 12 (see *Salmonella*) are common to some 75 species or sero-types that are included in the *Salmonella* Group D. Over 58 O antigens and dozens of groups are known in the Genus *Salmonella* alone. Other O antigens, in addition to 9 and 12, are also present in some species of Group D. In such groups the individual species may be differentiated by their H antigens. The H antigens are more highly type or species specific. Several O antigens may occur in each individual species, though in different combinations; see also common antigens of Enterobacteriaceae. The antigenic structure of the Enterobacteriaceae is discussed more fully in Chapter 36.

O antigens are heat stable (100° C.) and are not injured by alcohol or dilute acid.

As previously indicated, O antigens may be completely covered and masked by capsules or by K antigens, a fact of great importance to diagnostic microbiologists.

**Extracellular Antigens.** Some of the extracellular metabolic products (sometimes called *metabolites*) of living cells are potent antigens. For example, diphtheria and tetanus toxins are antigenic, poisonous proteins released to the exterior of the cell by secretion or by lysis of the cell or both. Extracellular antigens like diphtheria toxin are called *exotoxins*. Some other potent, extracellular, toxic antigens are the proteins of certain enzymes. More will be said of them in Chapter 27 on disease production. As protein antigens, all toxins, including enzyme proteins, stimulate the production of *antitoxins* or *antienzymes* (Fig. 24.4).

**Heterogenetic (Shared, Common or Group) Antigens.** As previously indicated, cells of two or more different species, whether closely or distantly related, may have certain antigens in common. (For example, pneumococci and chickens contain antigens like human blood-group A substances. Students of evolution may not be humiliated to learn that their blood contains antibodies related to proteins in certain fish. The relation of cow to whale by immunological methods is perhaps an unexpected revelation, but serology would seem superfluous in establishing the relation of horse to mule.) The antigens are said to be *heterogenetic*. *Antiserum* (serum containing antibodies) prepared by injecting cells of one species into an unrelated animal will react, to a greater or less extent, with other species of cells that contain the common antigen.

For example, three related species of dysentery bacilli (Genus *Shigella*) may each contain four antigens (Fig. 24.5). Upon injecting species I into a rabbit, antibodies a, b, c and d will be engendered, corresponding to antigens A, B, C and D. Upon injecting species II into another rabbit, antibodies c, d, e and f will be called

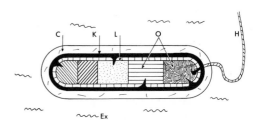

**Figure 24.4** Location of various bacterial antigens. *C,* Capsular antigens; generally polysaccharides. *K,* Sheath or envelope antigens derived from O antigens. *L,* Lipopolysaccharide antigens of the cell wall. *O,* Somatic antigens of the cell interior. *H,* Antigens of the flagella. *Ex,* Antigens excreted to the exterior like diphtheria toxin.

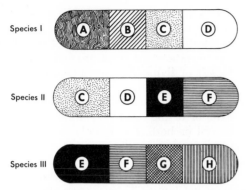

**Figure 24.5** Sharing of antigens by different species. For explanation see text.

forth. Likewise, species III will stimulate production of antibodies e, f, g and h. Now, the serum of rabbit I will react best of all with species I when these bacteria and serum of rabbit I are brought into contact. Serum II will similarly react best with species II, and serum III with species III. However, since serum I contains antibodies c and d, it will cross-react to some extent with cells of species II, since the latter have these antigenic compounds in common with species I. There will be no cross-reaction between serum I and antigen III, but serum II will cross-react with species III. Such cross-reactions are common.

ANTIBODY ADSORPTION. If a volume of serum I (say, 5 ml.) be mixed with a heavy suspension of cells of bacterial species II, then antibodies c and d and antigens C and D will combine, leaving antibodies a and b still free in the serum. By centrifuging the mixture, the bacteria of species II, with their attached antibodies c and d, can be removed, leaving serum I free from antibodies c and d and *specific* with regard to species I (i.e., the serum will no longer cross-react with species II; it will react only with bacteria containing antigens A and B). If we further adsorb antibody b by treatment of the serum with some species having only antigen B in common with species I, then we obtain a pure A serum (such a serum is said to be *monovalent*). Many such specific sera are thus prepared with a wide variety of both procaryotic and eucaryotic cells, and it has been possible to make extensive analyses of antigenic structures and to detect hitherto unsuspected antigenic and phylogenetic relationships.

## 24.6 HAPTENS

Haptens are substances that are not antigenic per se but that have antigen-like specificity of molecular structure. They can therefore form specific combinations with corresponding antibodies but cannot stimulate the formation of those antibodies. Haptens may be complex substances of high molecular weight, such as partial proteins or protein derivatives, capsular polysaccharides (*without protein* attached), or they may be relatively simple compounds of low molecular weight, such as the arsenilate previously referred to, or certain drugs, cosmetics and antibiotics.

The combination of *complex* haptens such as capsular polysaccharides with specific antibodies can result in the familiar, visible or demonstrable antigen-antibody reactions such as precipitation or flocculation previously described. Simple haptens of low molecular weight can combine with antibodies but they cannot cause any visible or demonstrable reaction such as precipitation. Combination of haptens with specific antibodies blocks combination of those antibodies with complete antigens. Haptens are therefore sometimes called *blocking antigens* or *partial, incomplete* or, because they occur as residues after partial destruction of cells or complete antigens, *residue antigens.*

Many haptens, both simple and complex, can become complete, specific, true antigens by combining with an appropriate protein. The relationship of a hapten to its appropriate protein may be thought of as analogous to the relation of a coenzyme to its protein apoenzyme: neither coenzyme nor hapten alone is effective in its sphere of activity, whereas the combination of each with its appropriate protein makes it fully effective. As a parallel to enzyme structure we might manufacture the terms "coantigen" for a hapten; "apoantigen" for its protein moiety; "holoantigen" for the complete antigen.

Complex haptens are well represented by the type-specific capsular polysaccharide ("SSS" or soluble specific substance) of Type II pneumococci. This (in some animals only) is not antigenic per se but, like complex haptens in general, precipitates readily with Type II antipneumococcus antibodies. When combined as a holoantigen with its appropriate Type II pneumococcus protein it becomes completely antigenic, and engenders specific Type II antibodies. Most naturally occurring antigens are complex hapten combinations.

Simple haptens, such as certain drugs, cosmetics and antibiotics, may at times form holoantigens by combination with body proteins. Thus many persons who come into contact with such drugs or cosmetics, internally or externally, can become "sensitized" to them (see Allergy) and then experience allergy-like reactions with rashes, blotches, itching or gastro-intestinal symptoms.

## 24.7   ANTIGEN-ANTIBODY REACTIONS

There are several manifestations of antigen-antibody reactions; some are visible in test tubes, some are demonstrable only by secondary tests. The different manifestations are spoken of as though many different antibodies were involved, but there are fewer types of antibodies than types of reaction. In fact, according to the *unitarian hypothesis,* there is only one kind of antibody. Regardless of type of reaction, all antibodies are one kind of protein, i.e., *gamma globulin.*

The kind of reaction seems to depend in great part on the kind and size of antigen and whether molecules or cells, the physical conditions of the suspending fluids, the presence of electrolytes and other factors. For convenience, we shall speak of "types of antibody," as meaning "types of antigen-antibody reactions." Among the best understood types of antibody are *antitoxins* and *precipitins, agglutinins, cytolysins, immobilizing antibodies,* and *protective* and *neutralizing antibodies.*

**Antitoxins and Precipitins.**   When bacteria gain a foothold in the body and liberate toxin into the blood, the toxin, a protein antigen, stimulates the production of antibody. As pre-viously described, this antibody combines specifically with the toxin and is therefore called *antitoxin.* The reaction may be thought of as a precipitin reaction in which the particles of precipitated toxin-antitoxin are too small to be seen. Under certain conditions in which the quantitative relations and electrolyte content are carefully adjusted, large, visible floccules are produced. The toxin-antitoxin reaction (sometimes called a "neutralization reaction") is basically a precipitin reaction.

QUANTITATIVE RELATIONS (THE FLOCCULATION REACTION).   Note carefully that it is only when certain *proportions* of toxin and antitoxin, regardless of amounts, are brought together in a test tube that a visible precipitate, or flocculation, occurs. This fact is of fundamental importance and is well illustrated by the following practical application for determining the concentrations or "strengths" of toxin or antitoxin. We set up a row of ten tubes. In the first we put serum containing a quantity of diphtheria (or any other) antitoxin, arbitrarily spoken of as two units.* In the next tube we place four

---

*A unit (approximately) of diphtheria antitoxin is the least amount necessary to protect standardized (250 to 300 gm.) guinea pigs against 100 minimal lethal doses (M.L.D.) of diphtheria toxin. An M.L.D. kills 50 per cent of such pigs in from four to five days (an $LD_{50}$ dose for guinea pigs). Week-old chicks are advantageously substituted for guinea pigs in such determinations. Units of other toxins are determined by modified but analogous procedures.

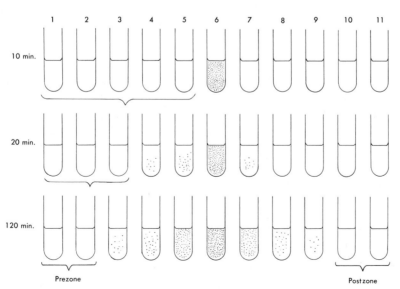

**Figure 24.6**   Prompt antigen-antibody reaction (10 min., tube 6) in the presence of *optimal proportions* of antigen and antibody. Later (20 min., tubes 4, 5, and 7) reactions occur in the presence of suboptimal proportions of antigen and antibody. Still later (120 min.), these reactions are extended to other tubes. In each series prezone and postzone are shown beyond the range of visible reactions.

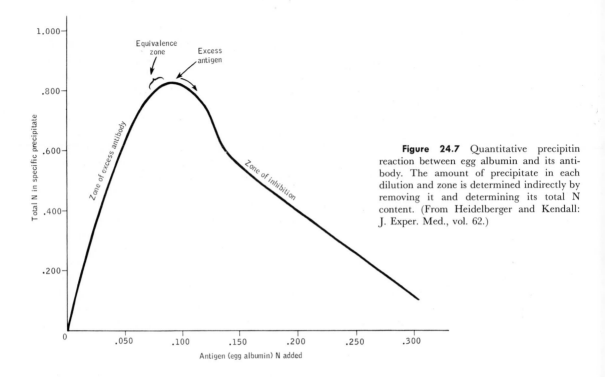

**Figure 24.7** Quantitative precipitin reaction between egg albumin and its antibody. The amount of precipitate in each dilution and zone is determined indirectly by removing it and determining its total N content. (From Heidelberger and Kendall: J. Exper. Med., vol. 62.)

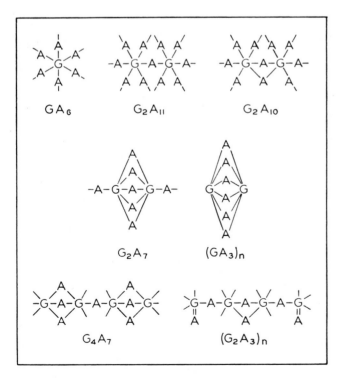

**Figure 24.8** Lattice-like structures postulated by Heidelberger for antigen-antibody complexes with various proportions of G and A as indicated by the formulas $G_2A_{11}$, etc. G = antibody; A = antigen. (Redrawn from Heidelberger: Bact. Rev., vol. 3.)

units, in the next six units, and so on. We then add to each tube a fixed amount, say 1 ml., of filtered broth culture of *Corynebacterium diphtheriae* that contains diphtheria toxin in unknown amount. After a short time flocculation appears in one of the tubes, let us say the sixth tube (Fig. 24.6). Since this contained 12 units of antitoxin, we have a measure of the *precipitating* potency of the toxin broth. We say that it contains 12 *flocculation units* ($12L_f$) of toxin per milliliter. This is an arbitrary unit of potency and is used for convenience to define diphtheria, tetanus and other toxins. It shows *haptenic* combining and flocculating potency but not necessarily toxicity. Partly deteriorated toxins (*toxoids*) (i.e., haptens) will give the same undiminished $L_f$ value though wholly devoid of *toxic power.*

Conversely, by using a series of tubes containing known, graded amounts of toxin (or toxoid), we may determine the number of $L_f$ *units* of antitoxin in a serum of unknown potency.

ZONE PHENOMENON. The reaction just described illustrates what is called a *zone phenomenon* or prezone and postzone of inhibitions.

In the experiment just performed (Fig. 24.6) flocculation failed to occur promptly in a zone of five tubes before the sixth tube (*prezone*) and in a zone of four tubes after the sixth (*postzone*). Smaller amounts of floc appeared in some of the tubes near the sixth tube on long standing. This resulted from the fact that for *maximal* amounts of visible precipitate (or flocculation or any other antigen-antibody reaction) to occur most rapidly and extensively, *optimal relative proportions* (not necessarily actual *quantities*) of antigen and antibody must be present. If there is too great an excess of either, less precipitate, or none at all, will appear. Many factors are involved, among which are type of animal serum used, nature of antigen and antibody, pH and electrolytes (Fig. 24.7).

LATTICE FORMATION. Zone phenomena are related to the formation or nonformation of lattices. In any given reaction, if the antigen and antibody molecules are *univalent*, i.e., if each has only one combining site, they can form only pairs—small colloids usually not visible in test tube reactions. If, as is usually the case, an antigen molecule has several different combining sites (i.e., is *polyvalent*), it may combine with several antibody molecules. If, as is also usual, the antibody molecules are bivalent, they can in turn combine with several antigen molecules.

A combination of polyvalent antigen with polyvalent antibody can thus form large complex masses or *lattices,* consisting of many antigen and antibody molecules joined together. The result is the precipitation of large, readily visible flocs as previously described (Fig. 24.8). This flocculation occurs, however, only if antigen and antibody molecules are present in approximately equal numbers or in *optimal relative* or *equivalent proportions.*

If excess antigen is present (relative to antibody), then all of the combining sites on the relatively few antibody molecules are saturated by antigen. Lattice (visible precipitate) formation is therefore minimal or absent. Conversely, if antibody is present in excess, antigen combining sites are saturated and lattice formation is likewise inhibited. The prezones and postzones previously described represent zones of antibody or antigen excess; the midzone (of precipitation) represents the presence of antigen and antibody in optimal or equivalent proportions.

Lattices may be formed by reactions between antibodies and antigens that are in solution, as in the toxin-antitoxin precipitation reaction, or between antibodies and antigens that are attached to the surfaces of cells. Antibody-cell lattices consist of large, visible flocs of bacteria (or other cells) held together by antibodies linking their surface antigens. The cells are said to be *agglutinated,* a traditional term expressing the idea that the bacteria are "glued" together by special "sticky" antibodies called *agglutinins.* The terms agglutinin and agglutination are still used, but the underlying mechanism is now better understood.

Zone phenomena are important factors in determining the antibody content of serum, or the amount of antigen in various materials, by serial dilution methods. The series of dilutions should be made fairly extensive and the intervals between dilution steps not too great, otherwise the zone of optimal proportions may either not be reached or may be passed over. Dilutions must be sufficient to eliminate partial, or blocking, antibodies as well as haptens. The same considerations hold for most other serological tests that involve antigen-antibody reactions.

OTHER APPLICATIONS OF THE PRECIPITIN REACTION. Because of the high degree of specificity that can be achieved by using adsorbed, monovalent sera in precipitin reactions, serological differentiation between soluble proteins of closely similar composition is easily made.

An interesting application is seen in the use of precipitin tests to determine the animal (*host*) from which a mosquito had its most recent blood meal. This illustrates the general method of using the precipitin test to identify "unknown" proteins.

In determining mosquito-host blood, the mosquito is crushed in 1 or 2 ml. of saline solution and the blood is thus extracted. This fluid constitutes the antigen to be tested. The sera with which to test it are previously prepared in rabbits by injecting the rabbits with blood from various animal species. One rabbit receives bovine blood, another equine blood, and so on. The serum of each rabbit contains precipitins against a certain species of animal. By mixing 0.25 ml. of the mosquito extract (antigen) with each of the rabbit sera (specific antibody) in turn, one serum will usually be found which causes a definite precipitation. If that serum is from a rabbit immunized with bovine serum, then we may say that the mosquito probably got its blood meal from one of the nearby cattle. This information is of use in the control of mosquito-borne diseases. It guides efforts toward eradication of the mosquitoes that bite man.

PRECIPITIN REACTIONS IN GELS; IMMUNO-DIFFUSION. An important method of demonstrating precipitin reactions makes use of gels of agar or starch. Precipitin reactions not demonstrable by other methods can readily be made visible by this method. For example, into a

Petri dish one pours a warm, clear 2 per cent solution of agar containing an 0.85 per cent solution of sodium chloride. When the agar has hardened, one places in the center a paper disk (or makes a depression or "cup") containing any desired specific antiserum. Several antigens to be tested are similarly applied at several spots at the periphery of the dish. Antigens and antibodies diffuse through the agar and encounter each other in series of diminishing concentrations of each. White lines of precipitate appear at the zones of optimal concentration between those antigens and antibodies having mutual reactivity (Fig. 24.9). This method and numerous variations (Fig. 24.10) are widely used in the study of many sorts of antigen-antibody relationships. The process is commonly called *immunodiffusion.*

IMMUNOELECTROPHORESIS. This is a related procedure for first separating and then detecting individual antigens in a mixture such as mouse serum (animal serum contains many antigenic proteins in addition to the proteins or gamma globulins that constitute antibodies). Separation of the antigenic components of the serum is first accomplished on the basis of their different electrophoretic mobilities (Chapter 19) in a gel that is traversed by an electric field. Because of their different rates of electrophoresis they are distributed in successive bands or zones in

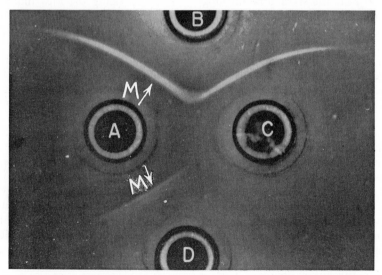

**Figure 24.9** Immunodiffusion. Precipitin reaction in an agar gel in a Petri plate (actual size). From a cup in the agar at *A* a soluble protein antigen (M) has diffused outward into the surrounding agar in all directions. Serum containing antibodies (precipitins) against antigen M similarly diffuses outward from *B*. Along the line where the two advancing reagents meet in the agar, a precipitin reaction occurs, as shown by the broad white line of precipitate between *A* and *B*. *C* contains antigens related to those in *A*, which likewise react to some extent with the antibodies from *B*, as shown by the white line between *B* and *C*. *D* is a serum which contains only a very small amount of precipitins against the M proteins in *A*, as shown by the faint line between *A* and *D*. (From Korngold: Ann. New York Acad. Sc., Art. 4, *69*:681, 1958.)

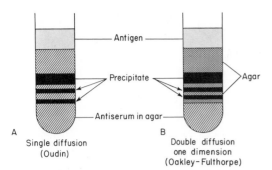

**Figure 24.10** Two examples of qualitative precipitin tests. *A*, Oudin's single-diffusion method. Antigen solution diffuses into agar containing an antibody. Formation of a band of precipitate indicates a positive reaction. *B*, Oakley-Fulthorpe double-diffusion method. Antiserum is suspended in agar at the bottom of the test tube and the antigen is poured on top of a layer of agar. Both reagents diffuse through agar until they meet. A precipitate forms if they are homologous.

the gel between anode and cathode. Detection of each individual band is then achieved by allowing anti-mouse antiserum (for example, anti-mouse serum prepared by injecting mouse serum into a rabbit) to diffuse (*immunodiffusion*) into the gel from a long trough at a right angle to the positive-negative axis of the electric field. The anti-mouse antibodies in the rabbit serum, and the corresponding antigens in the mouse serum that have been separated by electrophoresis, form precipitates in the gel at each zone (Fig. 24.11). Factors such as pH, temperature, electrolyte concentration, distance between antigen source and antibody source and time must be carefully controlled.

**Agglutinins.** In a foregoing discussion of lattice formation it was explained that polyvalent antibodies can link antigen molecules together whether the antigen molecules are proteins in solution or are components of intact cells. In the latter case the linkages result in a

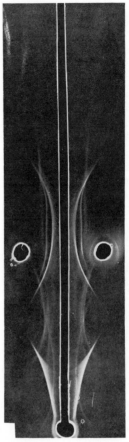

**Figure 24.11** Immunoelectrophoretic pattern of sera of germfree mice before (left well) and 21 days after (right well) influenza A infection reacting with rabbit anti-mouse serum in center trough. During passage of the current from end to end (lengthwise) of the slide, various proteins from the "before" and "after" sera migrated to different zones in the gel. Anti-mouse antibodies then diffused laterally from the central trough and formed white lines of precipitate with the various proteins in their distinctive positions in the gel. Differences between the two samples of serum ("before" and "after") are hardly perceptible in this preparation. (From Dolowy and Muldoon: Proc. Soc. Exp. Biol. Med., *116*:365, 1964.)

**Figure 24.12** Agglutinated bacteria as seen with the microscope by darkfield illumination. Two different types of agglutination are seen here: H (flagellar or flocculent) agglutination, left; O (somatic or granular) agglutination, right. (Carpenter: Immunology and Serology, 1956.) (After Adrianus Pijper.)

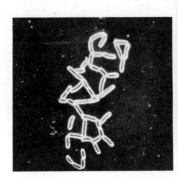

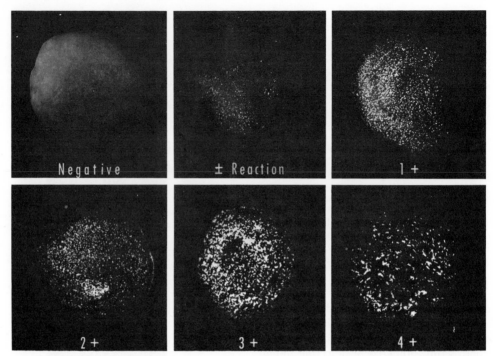

**Figure 24.13**  A slide agglutination test. Large drops (about 0.10 ml.) of serial dilutions of a sample of serum containing antibodies specific for the bacterium under examination were placed in all squares except the upper left square. The serum in this square, marked "negative," was a "normal" control containing none of the specific antibodies. To each drop of diluted serum was added one drop of a heavy suspension of the specific bacteria and each mixture was gently stirred. A ± reaction (slight but definite agglutination) occured in the highest ("weakest") dilution of serum, a 4+ reaction in the most concentrated serum. Intermediate reactions are indicated by 1+, 2+ and 3+. (Approximately actual size.) (Courtesy of Difco Laboratories, Inc., Detroit, Michigan.)

gathering or clumping together of the cells; a reaction called *agglutination*. The antibodies involved are said to be *agglutinins* because it was originally thought that they "glued" the cells together. Both living and dead cells can be agglutinated provided that their surface antigens have not been altered by agents such as heat or chemicals. If the agglutinated cells are erythrocytes, the phenomenon is called *hemagglutination*.

As a defense mechanism agglutination does not necessarily kill bacteria, but aids the leukocytes by gathering microorganisms into groups. A leukocyte or other phagocytic cell can engulf 50 agglutinated bacteria fifty times as easily as 50 separate ones, and in much less time (Figs. 24.12 and 24.13). Furthermore, the agglutinins appear to *opsonize* the surfaces of the bacteria so that the phagocytes can grasp and engulf them more readily.

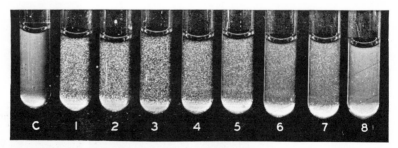

**Figure 24.14**  Macroscopic agglutination test. Control tube (*C*) contains bacterial suspension only. Numbered tubes contain bacterial suspension plus the following dilutions of serum: 1:100, 1:200, 1:500, 1:1000, 1:2000, 1:5000, 1:10,000 and 1:20,000. Agglutination is evident in dilutions 1:100 to 1:10,000 (tubes 1 through 7) but not in 1:20,000 (tube 8). The titer of the serum is therefore 1:10,000. (From Burrows: Textbook of Microbiology.)

DIAGNOSTIC USE OF AGGLUTININS. Agglutinins are widely used in the identification of bacteria and the diagnosis of disease. Let us assume that a patient has a febrile disease which has remained undiagnosed for a week or more. Presumably during this time demonstrable amounts of antibodies have accumulated in the blood. We draw a little blood from a vein and allow it to clot. We then remove the clear serum and mix it, suitably diluted (1:20; 1:40, 1:80; . . . 1:2560), in a series of test tubes with, for example, a suspension of typhoid bacilli (*Salmonella typhi*). Cultures of these bacteria are commonly maintained in diagnostic laboratories for this purpose. If the patient has typhoid fever his serum will contain typhoid agglutinins and the bacilli in the test tube will be found in flocs or clumps (Fig. 24.14). If no agglutination occurs, either the patient does not have typhoid fever or he has not yet had time to develop antibodies. Another test is generally made later.

This means of diagnosing typhoid fever is called the *Widal reaction* after Widal, who first published upon the subject. The term *Widal test* is sometimes (improperly) applied to *any* agglutination test.

IDENTIFICATION OF BACTERIA BY THE AGGLUTINATION REACTION. Conversely to the detection and identification of antibodies by means of the agglutination test just described, an unknown organism may be identified by using sera containing various *known* antibodies. The known sera are mixed with suspensions of the unknown bacterium, and agglutination is looked for. Suppose, for example, that we have a gramnegative rod that, by its cultural reactions, we know to belong to the typhoid-dysentery group. We may, as a preliminary test, set up two series of tubes: *A*, containing serial dilutions of serum of a typhoid-immune animal, and *B*, containing dilutions of serum of a dysentery-immune animal. A drop of our "unknown" bacterial suspension is added to each tube. If after several hours no change has occurred in the first series of tubes while the serum in the tubes of series *B* has caused the bacilli to agglutinate, we know that, since the serum in *B* contained only dysentery agglutinins, our unknown organism must be some species of *Shigella* (dysentery bacilli). Many other bacteria, saprophytic and parasitic, of agricultural, industrial and other special interests, may be identified in this way.

THE INDIRECT (PASSIVE) HEMAGGLUTINATION REACTION. This procedure, widely used in immunology, illustrates very nicely the fact that antigens at the *surface* of a cell determine its immunological specificity. Erythrocytes of a sheep or a cow are washed free from their serum. The surface of the cells is generally modified and the cells made more solid and stable in suspension by treating them with tannic acid or formaldehyde. The erythrocytes are again washed and then suspended in a saline solution containing any desired *soluble* antigen (viral or bacterial)—for example, an antigen extracted from tuberculosis bacilli. This antigen is adsorbed by the surfaces of the erythrocytes and covers them as a coating. The cells are removed from this suspension and excess antigen is removed.

A series of dilutions is now made with serum containing antibodies specific for the tuberculosis antigens with which the erythrocytes are coated. Into each serum dilution is introduced a drop of the suspension of antigen-coated erythrocytes. These behave as though they were

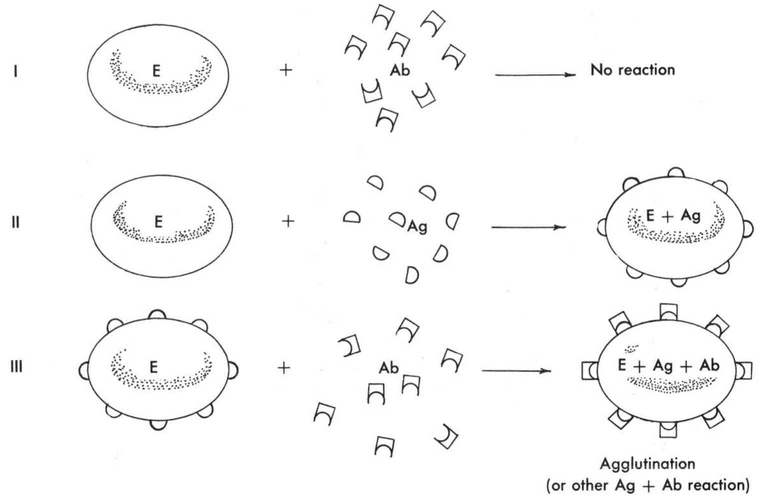

**Figure 24.15** Indirect hemagglutination. I, Erythrocytes (E) with surfaces prepared by formaldehyde or tannic acid treatment are mixed with antibodies (Ab). No reaction occurs because there are no specific receptors for Ab on the surfaces of the erythrocytes. II, In another tube similarly (formaldehyde) prepared erythrocytes are suspended in a solution of antigen (Ag) specific for Ab. Ag is adsorbed to the surfaces of the erythrocytes (E + Ag). III, Suspended in a solution of specific Ab the erythrocytes, now specifically coated with Ag, combine with Ab and are agglutinated.

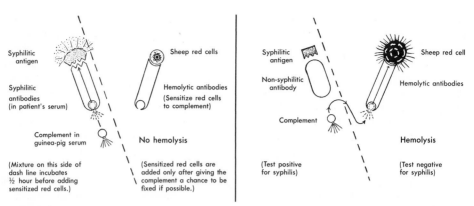

**Figure 24.16**   Diagram of the Wassermann test; a typical complement-fixation reaction. At far left is seen a reaction in a test tube between syphilis antigen and syphilis antibodies (sensitizer) in a sample of patient's serum. Complement combines with the sensitizer to destroy the antigen (shown "exploding"). When sheep cells (second from left) that are already sensitized with sheep-cell-hemolytic antibodies are added, they are not destroyed by the complement because complement has all been used up (fixed) in the syphilitic antigen-antibody reaction. Had there been no syphilitic antibody in the patient's serum (another, unrelated antibody is shown, third from left), no specific antigen-antibody combination could have occurred. Complement would not have been fixed and would have been left free to combine with and destroy (*hemolyze*) the sensitized sheep cells (shown exploding; far right).

tubercle bacilli. Within a short time the coated sheep erythrocytes are agglutinated. Tuberculosis antibodies have no visible effect on the normal, untreated erythrocytes of a sheep or the uncoated tannic-acid-treated erythrocytes (Fig. 24.15). It is interesting that totally inert particles of colloidal plastic, gum arabic, latex and the like can be similarly coated with antigen and agglutinated by specific antibodies. Conversely, antigens may be detected by coating the cells or particles with antibodies.

**Cytolysins and Complement.**   The somatic antigens of certain types of cells call forth antibodies that assist in the *lysis* of that cell. These antibodies are termed *cytolysins*. They are sometimes called *sensitizers* or, by an older term, *amboceptors*. The cytolytic antibody first combines with specific antigens on the surface of the foreign cell that called it into being. The cell may be a bacterium, an erythrocyte or a cell of other nature.* This simple combination is, however, not sufficient to destroy the cell. There is no visible reaction. A second substance, *complement* (previously described; see properdin, page 309), is necessary to complete the lytic action. Complement, too, combines with the cell, which in order for the complement to act must already have been sensitized (hence the term *sensitizer*) by the specific cytolytic antibody. Lysis then results (Fig. 24.16). The term *amboceptor* expresses the concept that the antibody

combines with the cell by one valence and with the complement by a different valence; i.e., the antibody is ambivalent.

Complement cannot by itself destroy foreign cells; it must act through the intermediation of the sensitizer. The sensitizer is a specific antibody, but complement is nonspecific; it helps any sensitizer to complete its work.

COMPLEMENT FIXATION.   After complement has combined with the sensitized cell, the complement is no longer active. It is said to be *fixed*. It is adsorbed onto the sensitized cells. The complement fixation reaction, discovered in 1901 by Bordet, a famous Belgian scientist and Nobel Prize winner, is the basis of several valuable tests used in microbiology, diagnosis and serology. As previously stated, complement is adsorbed (fixed) onto any finely divided material like chalk dust, clay or soot in aqueous suspension. It is also fixed by precipitates formed by antigen-antibody combinations, but it is not a *necessary* component of such reactions as it is in cytolysis. The fixation of complement in the cytolytic reaction is evidence that cytolysis involves a type of precipitin reaction on the cell surface.

The specificity of the complement fixation reaction enables an investigator to identify unknown antigens or antibodies. For example, if antibody, antigen and complement are mixed in a tube, we can determine whether antigen and antibody have combined by testing to see whether the complement has been fixed. If complement has been fixed, then we know that an

---

*Not all types of cells are equally subject to cytolysis in this manner.

immunologically specific antigen-antibody reaction (precipitation) has occurred. If we know the identity of one (antigen or antibody) we can identify the other. (But since complement is not visible, how can we know whether complement has been fixed? See Figure 24.16.)

**Immobilizing Antibodies.** The etiological (causative) agent of syphilis is a spirochete, *Treponema pallidum*. The organism is actively motile, rotating on its long axis and bending and flexing vigorously. In the serum of patients with syphilis *T. pallidum*–specific antibodies appear some days after initial infection. These antibodies *immobilize* and *kill* the spirochetes within a few hours when mixed with them in test tubes. This effect is readily seen by examining the mixture with a darkfield microscope. It is commonly spoken of as the TPI (*T. pallidum immobilization*) test. The immobilizing action does not take place unless complement is present. Curiously, little or no complement is *fixed* in this reaction. The role of antibody seems to be that of a sensitizer, but the action of the complement is not so obvious, as no lysis occurs.

The TPI test is one of the most important immunological developments in syphilology. It was the first *specific** serological test for the disease.

Immobilization by specific antibodies also occurs in other microorganisms. This is readily seen in *Entamoeba histolytica* (the cause of amebic dysentery) when the active trophozoites of this protozoan are treated with the serum of *E. histolytica*–immune animals. Similarly, there are specific immobilizing antibodies for the ciliated larval state (*miracidium*) of a pathogenic worm (the fluke, *Schistosoma mansoni*) and for motile bacteria other than *T. pallidum*.

In immobilization phenomena other than the TPI, complement is not always necessary, though it may be fixed, and death of the organisms does not necessarily follow immobilization. The organisms may, on the contrary, recover completely.

**Protective and Neutralizing Antibodies.** All the immune reactions so far mentioned are demonstrable by *in vitro* methods. It was mentioned that immunity does not necessarily result solely from the presence of such antibodies. Indeed, it seems that, as previously indicated, most of them act principally by aiding in the process of phagocytosis. Some are clearly lytic, some antitoxic, some immobilize.

The action of others is not demonstrable *in vitro*. The only reliable method of detecting and measuring such antibodies is to infect experimental animals (e.g., mice) and give them doses of the serum to be tested, before, after or simultaneously with the infection, to see whether they are thereby protected. This measures *protective* or *neutralizing power* directly, regardless of whether this power depends on agglutinins, cytolysins or some still-undiscovered antibody. Such a test is known as a *protection test* and is widely used to measure the antigenic virtues of antigens (by measuring the immunological response) and the protective power of sera.

In dealing with viruses the term *neutralization test* is generally used. Instead of using live animals in neutralization tests one may use animal-tissue cells growing in tissue cultures. The serum, if effective, will prevent virus from producing cytopathogenic effect or from forming plaques in monolayer cell cultures. (Chapters 16, 17, 18.)

## 24.8 FLUORESCENT* ANTIBODY STAINING

One of the most interesting and valuable advances in the field of microbiology is the fluorescent labeling of antibodies so that their combination with specific antigen can be detected visually and immediately. By means of this technique, microorganisms and their antigens, as well as antibodies, may be detected and identified within a few minutes, an improvement over the time-consuming and expensive methods of systematic study of cultures and antigenic tests previously described.

The fluorescent-antibody-staining procedure is technically complex, although the principle is relatively simple. A first step is separation and concentration of the specific antibody globulins from the bulk of the serum in which they occur. The concentrated antibody globulins are then combined (conjugated) with a fluorescent dye, commonly fluorescein isothiocyanate. The antibodies are then said to be *labeled*. When illuminated with ultraviolet light they give off a brilliant yellow glow. We may use such a

---

*The antigen used in the Wassermann and similar "standard" tests for syphilis is not specific but is a lipid derived from healthy cattle. False positive reactions sometimes occur. (See *T. pallidum*.)

*By fluorescence is meant the property of reflecting rays having a wave length (color) different from that of the incident rays. Fluorescent objects are particularly brilliant in ultraviolet light.

preparation of fluorescent-antibody-globulin to detect the corresponding specific antigen by four different methods: direct, indirect, inhibition and indirect-complement. Only the direct and indirect methods need be described here.

Let us suppose that our fluorescent globulin is specific for an antigen on the surface of typhoid bacilli (*Salmonella typhi*). Let us suppose also that a single bacillus of this species is suspected to be present in a large section of gram-stained spleen tissue from a typhoid victim. It is impossible to find the one tiny organism by ordinary microscopic means, even though gram-stained, because of the relatively enormous mass of surrounding tissue, which takes the same stain as the bacillus. The bacillus is lost like the proverbial needle in a haystack.

Let us prepare another section of the same tissue, unstained. We flood it with fluorescein-labeled antibody specific for *S. typhi*. The fluorescent antibody attaches itself to the corresponding antigen in the bacillus. Then we wash out all of the unattached antibody. When the tissue section is illuminated with ultraviolet light and examined with the microscope the hidden

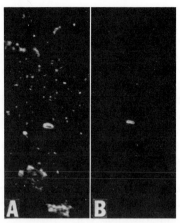

**Figure 24.17**  Use of fluorescent antibody to detect specific antigen in a mixture of materials. *A*, A sample of soil infected with *Malleomyces mallei,* a very dangerous pathogenic bacterium. This is a fluorescent-antibody-stained smear illuminated by ordinary light (darkfield preparation). It is impossible (without glancing at *B*) to distinguish the single cell of *M. mallei* from the many saprophytic soil bacteria and soil particles that are present in the sample. In *B*, illuminated by ultraviolet light, the single cell of *M. mallei* is brilliantly and exclusively evident. (From Thomason, Moody and Goldman: J. Bact., vol. 72.)

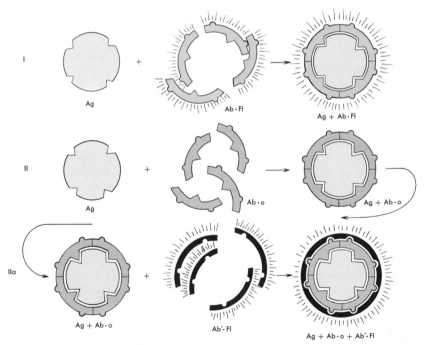

**Figure 24.18**  Direct and indirect fluorescent-antibody staining. In the direct method (I; top row) antigen (Ag) is allowed to react with its specific antibody which has previously been conjugated with a fluorescent dye (Ab · Fl). When viewed in the microscope with ultraviolet illumination the antigen-antibody combination (Ag + Ab · Fl) glows brilliantly.

In the indirect method (II; second row) the antigen is allowed to combine with ordinary (nonfluorescent) specific antibody (Ab · o) in the usual manner. Viewed with ultraviolet light no fluorescence is seen. The invisible Ag + Ab · o combination is now treated (IIa; third row) with fluorescent antibody specific for any gamma globulin (Ab′ · Fl). All antibody, including Ab · o, is gamma globulin. Ab′ · Fl therefore combines with the Ab · o on the surface of Ag, causing the particles of Ag + Ab · o to glow in ultraviolet light: (Ag + Ab · o + Ab′ · Fl).

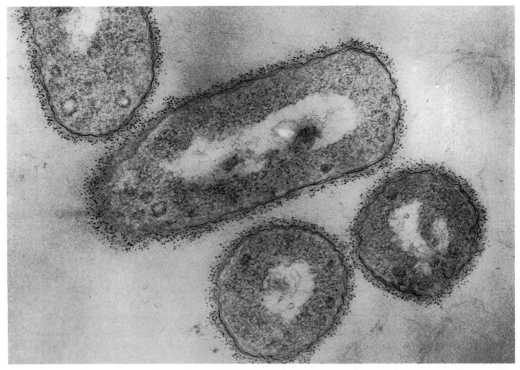

**Figure 24.19**   *Salmonella typhimurium* agglutinated by ferritin-conjugated antibody to somatic antigen. × 60,000. The antigen-antibody complexes, being electron-opaque due to ferritin, are revealed as myriads of black specks close around the bacterial cells. (From Shands: J. Bact., *90*:266, 1965.)

bacillus reveals itself by its brilliant yellow fluorescent light, like a full moon at midnight (Figs. 24.17; 24.18, I).

A serious difficulty with this method is the necessity of preparing dozens of different antibody globulins, each representing one of the dozens of different antigens which we might want to detect. The labeling procedure is difficult, time consuming and expensive. This difficulty is overcome in great part by using indirect methods, one of which is indicated in Figure 24.18, II, IIa. The fluorescent staining method in various modifications is used to locate viruses in cells and tissues, identify organisms and many other procedures.

**Ferritin Labeling.**   In an adaptation of the "labeling" principle of fluorescent-antibody staining, antibody may be made visible in electron micrographs by labeling it with ferritin. Ferritin is an organic complex of ferric hydroxide and ferric phosphate associated with apoferritin, a protein of the liver and spleen that serves as a storage place for iron. Ferritin is *opaque to electrons*. Ferritin-conjugated antibody combines with specific antibody as does fluorescein-conjugated antibody. To visualize the electron-

opaque ferritin-antibody, however, the electron microscope is used instead of ultraviolet light (Figs. 17.16 and 24.19).

## SUPPLEMENTARY READING

Billingham, R. E., and Silvers, W. K.: Sensitivity to homografts of normal tissues and cells. Ann. Rev. Microbiol., *17*:531, 1963.

Bloomfield, N., Gordon, M. A., and Elmendorf, Jr., D. F.: Detection of *Cryptococcus neoformans* antigen in body fluids by latex particle agglutination. Proc. Soc. Exp. Biol. Med., *114*:64, 1963.

Boziecevich, J., Scott, H. A., and Vincent, M. M.: The bentonite flocculation test for detection of plant viruses and titration of antibody. Proc. Soc. Exp. Biol. Med., *114*:794, 1963.

Burrell, R. G., and Mascoli, C. C.: Experimental Immunology. Burgess Pub. Co., Minneapolis. 1966.

Campbell, D. H., Garvey, J. S., Cremer, N. E., and Sussdorf, D. H.: Methods in Immunology. W. A. Benjamin, Inc., New York. 1963.

Cherry, W. B., and Moody, M. D.: Fluorescent-antibody techniques in diagnostic bacteriology. Bact. Rev., *29*:222, 1965.

Claflin, A. J., and Smithies, O.: Antibody-producing cells in division. Science, *154*:1561, 1967.

Cuadro, R. R., and Casals, J.: Differentiation of arboviruses by immunoelectrophoresis. J. Immunol., *98*:314, 1967.

Cunningham, J. C., Tinsley, T. W., and Walker, J. M.: Haemagglutination with plant and insect viruses. J. Gen. Microbiol., *42*:397, 1966.

Domingue, G. J., and Neter, E.: Opsonizing and bactericidal activity of antibodies against common antigen of Enterobacteriaceae. J. Bact., *91*:129, 1966.

Frederick, J. F. (Chairman): Gel electrophoresis. Ann. N. Y. Acad. Sci., *121*(Art. 2):305, 1964.

Freeman, B. A., Musteikis, G. M., and Burrows, W.: Protoplast formation as the mechanism for immune lysis of *Vibrio cholerae*. Proc. Soc. Exp. Biol. Med., *113*:675, 1963.

Eyal, Z., Warwick, W. J., Mayo, II, C. H., and Lillehei, R. C.: Homograft rabbit skin protection by phenothiazine derivatives. Science, *148*:1468, 1965.

Goto, S., Homma, J. Y., and Mudd, S.: Electron microscopy of the combination of antibodies with flagellar antigen and with a pyocine. J. Bact., *94*:751, 1967.

Heller, P., and Yakulis, V. J.: Autoantigenicity of connective tissue extracts. Proc. Soc. Exp. Biol. Med., *112*:1064, 1963.

Kelly, W. D., Smith, J. M., Martinez, C., and Good, R. A.: Induction of tolerance to skin grafts in mice with disrupted liver and kidney cells. Proc. Soc. Exp. Biol. Med., *115*:8, 1963.

Kimball, A. P., LePage, G. A., Bowman, B., and Herriot, S. J.: Suppression of the homograft response by purinethiol nucleosides. Proc. Soc. Exp. Biol. Med., *119*:248, 1965.

Lacey, B. W.: Non-genetic variation of surface antigens in *Bordetella* and other micro-organisms. Eleventh Symposium, Microbial Reaction to Environment, page 343. Soc. Gen., Microbiol, London. 1961.

Lefkowitz, S. S., Williams, J. A., Howard, B. E., and Sigel, M. M.: Adenovirus antibody measured by the passive hemagglutination test. J. Bact., *91*:205, 1966.

Lennox, E. S., and Cohn, M.: Immunoglobulins. Ann. Rev. Biochem., *36*:365, 1967.

Leskowitz, S.: Tolerance. Ann. Rev. Microbiol., *21*:157, 1967.

Luderitz, O., Staub, A. M., and Westphal, O.: Immunochemistry of O and R antigens of *Salmonella* and related Enterobacteriaceae. Bact. Rev., *30*:192, 1966.

Michelson, E. H.: Miricidia-immobilizing substances in extracts prepared from snails infected with *Schistosoma mansoni*. Amer. Jour. Trop. Med. Hyg., *13*:36, 1964.

Miller, J.: Immunological competence: Alteration by whole body X-irradiation and shielding of selected lymphoid tissues. Science, *151*:1395, 1966.

Miller, J. F. A. P.: The thymus and the development of immunologic responsiveness. Science, *144*:1544, 1964.

Moor-Jankowski, J., Wiener, A. S., Kratochvil, H., and Fineg, J.: Chimpanzee blood groups: Demonstrated with isoimmune and cross immune sera. Int. Arch. Allergy, *29*:397, 1966.

Muschel, L. H., Jackson, J. L., and Schmoker, K.: Effect of actinomycin D on immune antibody, normal antibody and complement. J. Bact., *91*:270, 1966.

Najarian, J. S., and Dixon, F. J.: Induction of tolerance to skin homografts in rabbits by alterations of placental permeability. Proc. Soc. Exp. Biol. Med., *112*:136, 1963.

Neter, E., Harris, A. H., and Drislane, A. M.: The detection of enterobacterial infection in institutionalized children by means of the hemagglutination test. Amer. J. Pub. Health, *55*:1164, 1965.

Pike, R. M.: Antibody heterogeneity and serological reactions. Bact. Rev., *31*:157, 1967.

Rosenberg, L. T.: Complement. Ann. Rev. Microbiol., *19*:285, 1965.

Saunders, G. C., and King, D. W.: Antibody synthesis initiated in vitro by paired explants of spleen and thymus. Science, *151*:1390, 1966.

Singer, S. J., and Doolittle, R. F.: Antibody active sites and immunoglobulin molecules. Science, *153*:13, 1966.

Springer, G. F., and Tritel, H.: Blood group active substances in embryonated chicken eggs and their relation to egg-grown virus. Science, *138*:687, 1962.

Stone, S. H.: Cellular commitments to immune responses. Ann. Rev. Microbiol., *21*:181, 1967.

Wiener, A. S.: Elements of blood group nomenclature with special reference to the Rh-Hr blood types. J.A.M.A., *199*:985, 1967.

Wiener, A. S., and Ward, F. A.: The serologic specificity (blood factor) **C** of the A-B-O blood groups. Amer. J. Clin. Pathol., *46*:27, 1966.

Wiener, A. S., and Wexler, I. B.: Immunogenetics. Certified Blood Donor Service, Inc., Woodbury, L. I., N. Y. 1966.

Wiener, L. M., and Neely, J. J.: The nature of the antigenic relationship between *Trichinella spiralis* and *Salmonella typhi*. J. Immunol., *92*:908, 1964.

Winkler, G. F., and Arnason, B. G.: Antiserum to immunoglobulin A: Inhibition of cell-mediated demyelination in tissue culture. Science, *153*:75, 1966.

Wolff, S. M., Ward, S. B., and Landy, M.: Serologic properties of bentonite particles coated with microbial polysaccharides. Proc. Soc. Exp. Biol. Med., *114*:530, 1963.

# Chapter 25

## IMMUNOLOGY
## Artificial Immunization

It has been observed from antiquity that persons become immune to certain infectious diseases by surviving natural attacks of those maladies. It is now known that the body develops specific antibodies as an *active* response to a *natural* antigenic stimulus. Since this type of resistance is actively acquired in the course of natural events it is often spoken of as *natural, active immunity*. In this chapter we shall speak of *purposefully induced* immunity, or *artificial* active immunity.

Natural infections are often very mild; they are said to be *inapparent*. Inapparent infections are those in which symptoms, if any, are so very slight that little or no attention is paid to them. They are also sometimes called *silent* or *subclinical* infections. The vast majority of infections are, fortunately, of this type. They produce immunity as effectively as though they were more serious. However, we cannot rely on nature for pleasant and painless immunization. Natural infections are all too frequently very severe; they may be disabling and disfiguring or fatal, even though antibodies are formed. It would be much better if we could become immune by some means that we can control. Furthermore, we should like to become safely immune to infectious disease early in life and not have to wait for accidental natural infection, occurring perhaps at a very inconvenient time in adult life. It is often desirable to be able to produce immunity to certain diseases at certain definite times. For example, Americans traveling outside the North American continent must have a valid certificate of vaccination against smallpox before they are allowed to re-enter the United States. A person desiring to do laboratory research with yellow fever virus would like to be able to immunize himself before starting the work, since infection with the virus might otherwise prove fatal. So also, physicians and nurses or others working in plague areas or with poliomyelitis, diphtheria or tuberculosis patients should be immunized safely and comfortably against these diseases in time to begin their work. All this, however, is too much to expect of natural processes.

In view of these needs, man has devised means of developing specific immunities artificially and safely. The methods involve natural processes, but are used under *modified*, carefully controlled conditions and are therefore called *artificial immunization*. Two types of immunization are used: *active* and *passive*.

### 25.1 ARTIFICIAL ACTIVE IMMUNITY

In artificial active immunity the patient's body is stimulated to develop resistance by being injected or infected with certain kinds of antigens (Chapter 21). These are of three general types: sterile, bacterial *exotoxins;* sterile, microbial antigens consisting of *dead* microorganisms; and *living* infectious microorganisms, the virulence of which has been reduced or attenuated by various procedures so that no serious infection results.

#### ANTIGENS USED IN ARTIFICIAL ACTIVE IMMUNIZATION

**Exotoxins.** A culture of exotoxin-producing bacteria, such as *Clostridium tetani*, cause of tetanus or "lockjaw" (Chapter 32) or *Coryne-*

*bacterium diphtheriae,* cause of diphtheria (Chapter 35), is made in broth. After sufficient growth of the bacteria, the culture is passed through very fine-pored filters which remove the organisms. The now-sterile *filtrate* (broth that has passed through the filter) contains the exotoxin liberated by the cells during their growth. This may be injected hypodermically (under the skin) into the persons to be immunized, in from one to five *very* minute doses, at weekly intervals. Eventually (usually after two to six weeks) their blood will be found to contain tetanus antitoxin (or diphtheria antitoxin) which protects them from tetanus toxin (or diphtheria toxin). There is danger from the toxin, however, and it is now *never* injected as such, even when mixed with antitoxin as "toxin-antitoxin" or T-A-T. Fatal accidents have occurred, caused by overdoses of toxin or by dissociation of toxin from the antitoxin in T-A-T.

TOXOIDS.  In Germany in 1890, von Behring (Nobel Prize winner), Fränkel and Kitasato discovered that diphtheria and tetanus toxins that had been heated for one hour at 70° C. were no longer poisonous but could stimulate antibody production. The possibilities for the safe and effective prevention of tetanus and diphtheria were immediately recognized and used. In France in 1924, Ramon found that formaldehyde detoxifies the toxins of diphtheria and tetanus as well as heat. Formaldehyde-detoxified—but antigenic—exotoxin was called *toxoid.* Formaldehyde-treated toxoids soon came into general use for active immunization against diphtheria and tetanus.

In 1933 in the United States, Havens and Wheeler found that, on the addition of alum to broth containing toxoid, the toxoid is adsorbed onto the particles of alum, which then *precipitates.* The alum-toxoid may then be collected by sedimentation, concentrated and purified. Alum-precipitated (AP) toxoids are highly effective. Two or three injections at intervals of about one month commonly stimulate production of sufficient antibodies.

ACTION OF ADSORBED (AP) TOXOIDS.  When fluid (*not* AP) toxoid is injected under the skin, the soluble material is eliminated within a few hours. The antigenic stimulus is transitory. If the toxoid could be held *in situ* for several days, as occurs naturally in actual infections, the antigenic stimulus would be prolonged and continuous.

ADJUVANTS.  The toxoid is kept from dissolving by means of the alum-toxoid. The toxoid is *adsorbed* on the surfaces of the alum precipitate. The alum precipitate remains undissolved where

injected, releasing its adsorbed toxoid slowly, thus giving the patient a prolonged and continuous antigenic action which is highly effective. Substances that thus enhance the effectiveness of antigens are called *adjuvants* and are of several sorts, such as mineral oil, peanut oil or bacterial lipids (see Chapter 26). The persistence in the body of any antigen, living or dead, maintains immunity by its continuous antigenic action.

This principle is not confined to diphtheria immunization but is of broad significance. For example, in a modified form it is used with antibiotics to maintain a high concentration of antibiotics in the blood over a long period without repeated injections.

The principle of adjuvants has also been adapted to bacterial vaccine against whooping cough. It is now common practice to mix diphtheria and tetanus toxoids as well as alum-precipitated bacterial antigens (especially whooping-cough bacilli). *Inactivated* polio virus (Salk vaccine) is often included though not in AP form. The combination of three or four antigens is even more effective with respect to each than any one of the antigens alone. In addition, the number of separate injections required for immunization is reduced.

## 25.2  PRIMARY AND SECONDARY STIMULUS

In the ordinary course of life in the United States one is constantly exposed to infectious organisms such as pneumococci, streptococci, tubercle bacilli and influenza virus and polioviruses from healthy carriers and from ambulatory, mild and inapparent cases of the diseases. In the nonimmunes after about four months of age, these exposures most commonly result in mild or unrecognized cases; much less commonly in perceptible or severe illness; least commonly in fatal illness. The survivors are actively, *naturally* immunized against the organism(s) that infected them. Renewed contact with each infectious agent has no outwardly perceptible effect, but inwardly and all unseen it restimulates the production of specific antibodies. Thus, these *repeated antigenic stimuli* serve to keep one's immunity in a good state.

The beneficial and protective effect of *repeated* antigenic stimuli is exploited in artificial processes also. For example, suppose that a child is given a single, initial dose (or 2 or 3 weekly doses) of any antigen, say diphtheria toxoid, or Salk polio vaccine. This initial dose or series of doses is called a *primary stimulus.* In about two weeks his blood, tested by appropriate methods, shows few if any antibodies. After four to six weeks, however, his blood is found to contain a satisfactory amount of diphtheria antitoxin, or polio antibodies. The development of detectable amounts of antibody has been relatively slow (Fig. 25.1). A year later the amounts (*titers*) of antibodies in his blood may be found to have declined to a very low level or to have disappeared entirely. This diminution of antibody titer from the serum is very common. However, *immunity* has not necessarily disappeared.

**"Booster" Doses; The Anamnestic Reaction.** Let us now give the child a second dose of diphtheria toxoid (or polio vaccine) and test his blood for diphtheria antitoxin (or polio antibodies) at short intervals. A surprisingly rapid and extensive response is now noted. After the first or *primary stimulus,* given a year before, response was slow. Response to this second dose (*secondary stimulus*) occurs at once. In a few *hours* or a day or two the child may be found to have one or more units of diphtheria antitoxin (or ample polio antibodies) per milliliter of blood. In practice, the secondary stimulus is often referred to as a *"booster" dose.* The underlying physiological response is called the *anamnestic* or *recall* reaction (Gr. *anamnesis* = to remember or recall; the reverse of Gr. *amnesia* = forgetfulness).

The body cells react as though, having once had an "antigenic experience," they are more alert and expert in forming antibodies of this particular sort, and do so with great facility whenever called upon. Ability to withstand disease largely depends upon this very rapid

reactivity. This explains in part why resistance to disease, on the one hand, and titer of specific antibodies in the serum, on the other hand, are not necessarily related.

CLONAL SELECTION HYPOTHESIS. A suggested explanation of the anamnestic reaction, and also of immunological specificity, is based on the *clonal selection hypothesis* of Burnet (Nobel Prize winner). This postulates that each of the millions of developing lymphocytes formed in early life undergoes a different mutation, so that the DNA in each and in its progeny is coded to produce a different form of gamma globulin (antibody protein). An antigen gaining access to the antibody-producing cells for the first time (the primary stimulus) is thus practically certain to encounter a cell having or producing gamma globulin of a corresponding specific molecular structure. The two combine and the cell is thus immediately stimulated to mature as a *plasma cell.* It is also stimulated to reproduce vigorously and to form more of the specific gamma globulin. Alone, it can form little gamma globulin. Under the stimulus of the antigen, however, and after several days or weeks have passed to permit time for the cells to mature and multiply, this type of cell becomes very numerous. Its billions of progeny (*selected clone*), acting together, finally produce large enough amounts of the specific antibody globulin to be detectable in the blood by appropriate tests (agglutination or precipitation).

After the subsidence of the infection, or removal of the antigen by other means, the antibodies tend to disappear from the circulating blood. However, the antigen-selected clone of billions of lymphocytes (or plasma cells) or their

**Figure 25.1** Quantities of antitoxin demonstrable in the blood following primary stimulus (light bars) and following secondary stimulus (dark bars). The rate of production by the stimulated cells is probably alike after both primary and secondary stimuli, but the *number of cells participating* is much greater after the secondary stimulus. These are representative data only, as individuals differ greatly in response to both primary and secondary stimuli.

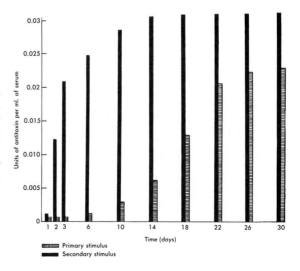

progeny remains largely intact. On renewed contact with the same antigen (*secondary stimulus*), even many years later, this ready-grown mass of cells again pours such large amounts of antibodies into the blood that the antibodies are detectable within a few minutes, hours or days; an *anamnestic reaction*. The clonal selection hypothesis agrees with several of the well-known phenomena of immunity but not with others; therefore it remains as a challenging point of departure for further experimentation; i.e., an engaging hypothesis.

**Dead or Inactivated Microorganisms.** Many microorganisms pathogenic for man do not produce convenient exotoxins for the preparation of toxoids. The pathogenic properties of many are caused by *endotoxins*. For immunization against a number of these organisms it is common practice to use suspensions of killed, intact organisms with their entire complements of antigens. Such suspensions of killed or inactivated microorganisms are frequently referred to as vaccines. If prepared from bacteria, they are correctly termed *bacterins*. The term *vaccine* is properly restricted to smallpox vaccine, since smallpox vaccine is derived primarily from cows (L. *vacca* = cow). However, the term *vaccine* is widely used for any immunizing agent and is so used here.

BACTERIA. Bacteria for the purpose of vaccination are usually cultivated on the surface of agar media, and the growth is removed with physiological (0.85 per cent) sodium chloride solution. The bacteria are *killed* by heating at 60 to 65° C. for 30 to 60 minutes. Such vaccines as typhoid, cholera and whooping cough are commonly prepared from gram-negative bacilli (see Chapter 36). Except whooping-cough vaccine they are less effective than many viral and rickettsial vaccines.

VIRUSES. Viruses (e.g., poliovirus) are cultivated for vaccines in tissue cultures. Following the discovery, in 1949, by Enders, Weller and Robbins (Nobel Prize winners), that polioviruses could be propagated in *in vitro* cultures of primate tissues, the Salk inactivated polio vaccine was developed. The tissue-culture virus is *inactivated* with formaldehyde and gentle heat. This is the basis of the Salk inactivated polio vaccine. Inactivated-virus vaccines are also available against measles and are in process of development against German measles (rubella) and mumps.

RICKETTSIAS. Rickettsias are cultivated for rickettsial vaccines in live, chick-embryo yolk sacs. Vaccines against Rocky Mountain spotted fever are made from this material. The tissue and other extraneous matter are removed by filtration or centrifugation. The rickettsias are killed with formaldehyde or other substances. Rigid tests are made to ensure that all of the microorganisms are dead. A minute amount (0.25 per cent) of phenol, tricresol or some other antimicrobic agent is often added to insure sterility.

The principle of the secondary stimulus is widely used in connection with killed vaccines as well as with toxoids.

**Attenuated, Living Infectious Agents.** A third method of artificial active immunization involves actual infection of the person or animal to be immunized. The immunizing organisms are so treated that their virulence is greatly *attenuated* or diminished.

There are at least four means of obtaining strains or clones of pathogenic organisms that can be safely used to induce artificial active immunity: passage of the organism in abnormal hosts or, virtually the equivalent, many successive passages of the pathogen in cultures of tissues from some animal other than the usual host of the pathogen; prolonged search, by repeated trials, for clones of low virulence; treatment of the pathogen with unfavorable agents such as desiccation; cultivation of the pathogen under unfavorable conditions such as low surface tension or high temperature.

PASSAGE IN ABNORMAL HOST. This is well illustrated by the development of a vaccine against fox distemper, a scourge to silver fox-fur farmers. The virus from a sick fox was injected into a ferret. Infectious fluid from the sick ferret was injected into another ferret. This ferret-to-ferret transfer (animal passage) was continued through a long series. The virus became adapted to, and enormously virulent for, ferrets. When fluid from the last ferret in a long series was tested in a fox, it had little or no virulence for the fox. However, the fox was afterward found to be completely immune to natural fox-distemper virus. The virus had become highly adapted to ferrets but *modified* or *attenuated* with respect to foxes. The method of animal passage, so valuable to fox farmers, has been much used with other viruses.

*Smallpox Vaccine.* The classic illustration of what was once thought to be the effect of animal passage on virulence is seen in the preparation of smallpox vaccine. It was originally thought that cows became infected with smallpox but that they developed only the relatively mild disease, *cowpox*. Contact with the cow (passage in an abnormal host) was supposed to have modified the virulence of the original small-pox virus. It was then called *vaccinia virus.*

The original supposition may be correct, but it may also be that the cowpox virus and smallpox virus are distinct "species" but so closely related that the one immunizes against the other. This sort of relationship is exemplified by the fact that one may immunize dogs to canine distemper by injecting them with tissue-culture measles virus. These viruses are related but not identical.

The value of immunization against small-pox was demonstrated in 1798 by Edward Jenner, then a country doctor but later a famous British scientist. Jenner observed that dairy workers associated with cows having cowpox, or *vaccinia,* did not succumb during epidemics of smallpox, which were then dreadful scourges. On the basis of this observation he later demonstrated experimentally that anyone could safely become immune to smallpox through infection with cowpox. The resistance to small-pox conferred by vaccination usually lasts at least three to seven years.

Vaccinia virus, as generally used today, is prepared by scratching the virus into the shaved and disinfected skin of a calf. When the pustules are fully developed the lymph is collected from them and put up in glass tubes ready for use (Fig. 25.2). Its potency and cleanliness are carefully controlled by the National Institutes of Health, in Bethesda, Maryland. Tissue culture virus preserved by lyophilization is also used, especially in tropical countries.

Revaccination should reveal either an al-lergic or an anamnestic response; both are commonly seen (Fig. 25.3).

Other examples of living vaccines prepared by the attenuation of virulence of viruses by animal-passage or tissue-culture passage are rabies vaccines cultivated in tissue cultures and in live avian embryos; also yellow fever, measles and canine hepatitis vaccines, cultivated in live animal cells in tissue cultures.

SELECTION OF MUTANT CLONES OF LOW VIR-ULENCE; "LIVE" POLIO VACCINE. Active (commonly called "live") tissue-cultured, attenuated polio vaccine has been available for public use since about 1958. It is administered orally and is called oral polio vaccine or Sabin vaccine. It has been administered to millions of persons of all age groups throughout the world. The immunizing effect against all three types of polio has been excellent, with antibodies appearing in one to two weeks. Attenuated polio-virus strains were developed only after years of devoted and grueling researches by many workers, notably Albert B. Sabin, Hilary Ko-prowski and Herald R. Cox, each working independently.

Many methods of obtaining attenuated poliovirus were tried: induced mutation and recombinations; trial of naturally occurring strains of low virulence; selection and trial of clones of mutant virus from plaques in mono-layer tissue cultures, and so on. The work was triply arduous since it had to be done with each of three types of poliovirus.

The clone of live polio-vaccine virus of each type finally selected is a tissue culture of an attenuated mutant of that type selected by

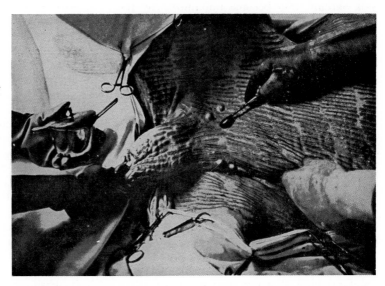

**Figure 25.2** The collection of cowpox lymph from the skin of a calf. The skin has been shaved, cleaned, disinfected and inoculated in long parallel scratches (clearly seen in the picture) with cowpox lymph. Typical pustules have developed along the scratches and the lymph from these is being collected with surgical cleanliness. (From Monteiro and Godinho.)

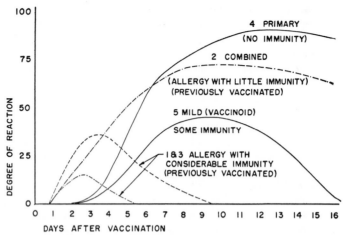

**Figure 25.3** Types of reaction to smallpox vaccination. Curves 1 and 3 represent rapid, superficial reactions beginning during the first 24 hours, sometimes showing small vesicle formation, but terminating rather quickly after a mild course, without scar formation. These occur *only in previously vaccinated persons* (or in those convalescent from smallpox), and the quick reaction of short duration and mild degree is characteristic of immunity *with allergy* to the smallpox virus, living or dead. Allergy may exist when immunity has all but lapsed, as shown in curve 2. This *begins* as an allergic reaction but goes on to a real "take" with papule, vesicle, pustule and eventual scar formation, much like the primary "take" in a wholly susceptible person without allergy, shown in curve 4. Curve 5 is a milder reaction in a person without allergy but with a considerable degree of immunity. This is a "vaccinoid" reaction, usually without scar formation. Note that the reactions in the absence of allergy (curves 4 and 5) do not *begin* until the second or third day. It is occasionally difficult to differentiate the types of reaction. (Adapted from Mitman: Monthly Bull. Min. Health, Vol. 2.)

pure colony (plaque) technique. (See Chapter 16.) Each of the attenuated strains is able to produce only a mild intestinal infection. After millions of tests none has caused any significant disease. Because oral vaccine produces an actual infection of the intestinal tract (see poliomyelitis), it is transmissible to other persons just as natural polio infection. This is a desirable result since these other persons, if they are not already immunized by natural means or by Salk vaccine, also become immunized by the attenuated strain spread by the vaccinated person.

The three types of virus are often administered separately, if feasible, since one may interfere with and exclude the others if all are given simultaneously. However, some preparations are *trivalent*, i.e., they contain all three types. Several booster doses are given over a period of years. In populations with low sanitary standards, other feces-transmitted viruses such as Coxsackie, Echo, "wild" (natural) polio, and adenoviruses may be so prevalent as to interfere with the vaccine strains. The same principles have been applied in preparation of live, attenuated measles vaccine and several others.

DESICCATION. Pasteur's name is immortalized in the term "Pasteur treatment" for *rabies* (mad-dog bite). Pasteur's process is not really a

curative treatment but rather a course of immunizing injections with the living, attenuated virus of rabies. In the modern Pasteur treatment of human beings, an inactivated virus cultivated in avian embryos is now widely used. A live, attenuated strain, the HEP Flury vaccine, is commonly used for *preventive* purposes in veterinary practice and may well become available for use in humans.

If the injections of Pasteur treatment are started soon enough after the bite of the infected animal, resistance or interference (?) develops from the injections before the virus from the infectious bite can cause disease.

For years Pasteur experimented with rabbits, dogs and guinea pigs (one of the many brilliant illustrations of the value of animal experimentation), until he felt certain that his method of attenuating rabies virus was safe and effective. It consisted in passing the virus from an infected dog to the brain of a rabbit and then from rabbit to rabbit (passage in different animal species) to establish attenuated virulence for man. Like the fox-distemper virus that became fatal for ferrets, the rabbit rabies virus acquired a maximum and fixed virulence for rabbits. Pasteur called this virus *virus fixé*. The potency of the virus for *man* was further reduced by *desiccation*. Desiccated virus fixé was injected in increasing doses.

Pasteur's first human immunization against rabies in a boy bitten by a rabid wolf, in 1885, was an extremely dramatic event and marked the beginning of an epoch in the war on disease. Indeed, Pasteur is referred to as "the Father of Immunology." His experiments on rabies have been movingly described by Vallery-Radot, his grandson. (See Suggested Reading.)

CULTIVATION IN SPECIAL MEDIA; IMMUNIZATION AGAINST TUBERCULOSIS. A method for immunization against tuberculosis with living, attenuated tubercle bacilli has been known and widely and successfully used for years. The procedure is known as the *Calmette-Guerin process* and the attenuated cultures as BCG (*Bacillus Calmette-Guerin;* Calmette and Guerin were the French scientists who developed the method). The process consists of the injection of *live* tubercle bacilli, the virulence of which has been reduced by cultivation of the organisms on certain media containing bile. This method of cultivation results in the development of a stable variant of the tubercle bacillus having low virulence. This is the only important use, at present, of immunization of human beings with living bacteria.

Large scale studies conducted in many countries for decades prove that BCG is a safe and valuable immunizing agent. In any procedure involving immunization of millions of human beings some unfortunate episodes are to be expected, and a few were reported in the days of pioneer use of BCG. Pioneering is often hazardous, but without the courage to undertake it there would be little progress. BCG is used especially for groups frequently exposed to the disease: nurses, doctors and inhabitants of areas where tuberculosis is highly prevalent. It is discussed further under Tuberculosis (Chapter 39). Vaccines of killed and disrupted BCG organisms are currently under investigation.

CULTIVATION AT UNFAVORABLE TEMPERATURES. Although this method is not much used at present, its discovery and demonstration by Pasteur constitute an episode of great dramatic interest in the history of bacteriology. The principle was first used with *Pasteurella avicida,* the bacterial cause of fowl cholera. It was later developed in connection with studies of anthrax which, in the nineteenth century, decimated the sheep flocks of France. Following numerous preliminary experiments by the tireless Pasteur on variants of *Bacillus anthracis,* cultures of the organisms were prepared by incubation at unfavorably high temperatures of 39 to 43° C. (optimum about 35° C.). This caused the bacilli to lose some of their virulence, and often their

power of spore formation. The method has since been shown to vary in result, so that neither loss of spores nor cultivation at 42° C. should be assumed to have deprived these organisms of their dangerous properties.

The first great public demonstration of the value of anthrax immunization gave the indomitable Pasteur some uncomfortable hours, because his ideas had been unfavorably regarded by many and his experiments were closely and skeptically watched. He publicly injected about 100 sheep with his culture of attenuated organisms. After a suitable period had been allowed for immunity to develop, these animals, as well as an equal number of normal, unprotected animals, were publicly inoculated with large doses of fully virulent anthrax bacilli. The test injections were made on May 31, 1881, at Pouilly le Fort.

A day or two later when Pasteur arrived at Pouilly le Fort after some sleepless nights,

the carcasses of 22 unvaccinated sheep were lying side by side; two others were breathing their last; the last survivors of the sacrificed lot showed all the characteristic symptoms of splenic fever (anthrax). All the vaccinated sheep were in perfect health.*

As a result of animal and human experimentation, poliomyelitis, smallpox, rabies, tuberculosis, measles, yellow fever, malaria and many other scourges of the human race and of many animals are at the vanishing point—banished by the flaming sword of scientific truth.

## 25.3   ARTIFICIAL PASSIVE IMMUNITY

In some cases it is necessary that a large supply of antibodies appear in the blood immediately in order to combat an overwhelming infection. This is especially well illustrated in such diseases as diphtheria and tetanus. The chief symptoms in these diseases are caused by the bacterial exotoxins in the body of the patient. The poisonous action is very rapid. When the patient is already ill there is no time to lose waiting for him to develop active immunity, natural *or* artificial; he must *passively* receive ready-made antibodies. Immunity resulting from injections of these ready-made antibodies is *immediate* and is called *passive immunity.*

It is now possible to purchase at all well-stocked pharmacies and health departments syringes or ampules already filled with *antitoxic*

---

*From "The Life of Pasteur," by René Vallery-Radot, reprinted with permission from Doubleday Company, Inc.

serum prepared for just such emergencies. Such antibody-containing serum is obtained from animals, usually horses, that have received, weeks or months previously, repeated injections of the special antigen against which antibodies are desired.

**Passive Immunity in the Prevention of Disease.** Passive immunity is also used in the prevention (*prophylaxis**) of disease. For example, if it is known or suspected that a person is likely to become exposed, or has very recently been exposed, to certain diseases, it is (under circumstances to be determined *only* by the physician) an excellent plan to inject a small quantity of serum, or some derivative of serum (e.g., purified gamma globulin) containing the appropriate antibodies, as a prophylactic measure.

As will be explained in the following chapter on allergy, a single injection of *foreign* (e.g., horse or rabbit) protein such as serum, whether or not it contains antibodies, can not only cause a serious, even fatal, allergic reaction but will usually make the recipient allergic for life. To avoid such effects gamma globulins of *human* origin are commonly used for preventive purposes; notably against German measles and infectious hepatitis. Diseases against which equine serum is occasionally used for prophylaxis are diphtheria and tetanus. Effective human sera are also available for rabies and pertussis.

**Passive Immunity and Serum Jaundice.** It is mentioned elsewhere that a considerable number of apparently normal and healthy persons carry in their tissues and blood the viruses of *hepatitis*. This is a good example of latent viral infection. Unless suitable precautions are taken, the viruses are readily transmitted in the blood of donors, in gamma globulin and in other blood derivatives. Serum hepatitis is easily transmitted by improperly sterilized syringes, needles, razors and other objects that can carry blood, serum or lymph from one person to another.

## NATURAL PASSIVE IMMUNITY

Most antibodies can pass from mother to infant through the placenta; consequently, they are commonly found in the blood of the infant at birth. They serve to protect the child for some months after birth. By three to six months after birth maternal antibodies have largely disappeared and the child becomes susceptible to

many infectious diseases. It is therefore advisable to begin active immunization of the child early (fourth to sixth month) by injections of combined antigens of diphtheria, tetanus, polio and pertussis. If injections are begun too early, the maternal antibodies still in the child may interfere with the antigenic effect, or the immature antibody-forming mechanisms may be ineffective. Data from an interesting study on the interference of antibodies with antigenic effect indicate that an $Rh^-$ mother can be protected from the antigenic action of erythrocytes of an $Rh^+$ baby by giving the mother antibodies to the Rh factor.

It is important to note that antibodies in the newborn infant imply immunity in the mother. The expectant mother who does not have good antibody titers to diphtheria, tetanus, polio, rubella (German measles), pertussis and possibly salmonellosis would do well to receive immunizing injections herself to confer passive immunity to these diseases on her child.

**Transitory Nature of Passive Immunity.** If antibody-containing serum used for passive immunization or treatment is of *other than human* origin, the antibodies disappear from the body in two to three weeks (i.e., they are rejected as nonself). During their presence infection may be entirely prevented or, if infection occurs, the resulting disease is usually very mild. Maternal antibodies persist in the infant for one to several months after birth because the antibodies are of maternal origin; i.e., self or nearly self.

## SUPPLEMENTARY READING

Aach, R. D., Elsea, W. R., Lyerly, J., and Henderson, D. A.: Efficacy of varied doses of gamma globulin during an epidemic of infectious hepatitis, Hoonah, Alaska, 1961. Amer. J. Pub. Health, *53*:1623, 1963.

Ager, E. A.: Current concepts in immunization. Amer. J. Nursing, *66*:2004, 1966.

Brown, G. C., and Kendrick, P. L.: Serologic response of infants to combined inactivated measles-poliomyelitis vaccine. Amer. J. Pub. Health, *55*:1813, 1965.

Budd, M. A., Scholtens, R. G., McGehee, Jr., R. F., and Gardner, P.: An evaluation of measles and smallpox vaccines administered simultaneously. Amer. J. Pub. Health, *57*:80, 1967.

Calafiore, D. C.: Eradication of measles in the United States. Am. J. Nursing, *67*:1871, 1967.

Cockburn, W. C.: Progress in international smallpox eradication. Amer. J. Pub. Health, *56*:1628, 1966.

Creighton, H., and Armington, Sister Catherine: The bite of a stray dog. Amer. J. Nursing, *64*:121, 1964.

Douglas, G. W.: Rubella in pregnancy. Amer. J. Nursing, *66*:2664, 1966.

Editorial Note: Blood for better rabies treatment. Amer. J. Pub. Health, *54*:1606, 1964.

---

* Gr. *prophylassein* = to guard against.

Edsall, G.: Principles of active immunization. Ann. Rev. Med., *17*:39, 1966.

Fenje, P., and Pinteric, L.: Potentiation of tissue culture rabies vaccine by adjuvants. Amer. J. Pub. Health, *56*:2106, 1966.

First International Conference on Vaccines Against Viral and Rickettsial Diseases in Man. Scientific Publication No. 147, Pan American Health Organization, W.H.O., Washington, D.C. 1967.

Freda, V. J., Gorman, J. G., and Pollack, W.: Rh factor: prevention of isoimmunization and clinical trial on mothers. Science, *151*:828, 1966.

Gelfand, H. M.: A critical examination of the Indian small-pox eradication program. Amer. J. Pub. Health, *56*:1634, 1966.

Gottlieb, S., McLaughlin, F. X., Levine, L., Latham, W. C., and Edsall, G.: Long-term immunity to tetanus—a statistical evaluation and its clinical applications. Amer. J. Pub. Health, *54*:961, 1964.

Laborde, H. F., and de Fajardo, C. L.: *Pseudomonas* vaccine. J. Bact., *90*:290, 1965.

Miller, G., Gale, J., Villarejos, V., James, W., Artega, C. G., Casey, H., and Henderson, D. A.: Edmondson B and a further attenuated measles vaccine—a placebo controlled double blind comparison. Am. J. Pub. Health, *54*:1333, 1967.

Morris, J. A., Hatano, M., Robinson, R. Q., Aulisio, C. G., and Smadel, J. E.: Antigenic relationship of 1961–1963 A2 influenza viruses to prototype A2 1957 strain. Proc. Soc. Exp. Biol. Med., *114*:406, 1963.

Ribi, E., Larson, C., Wicht, W., List, R., and Goode, G.: Effective nonliving vaccine against experimental tuberculosis in mice. J. Bact., *91*:975, 1966.

Schwarz, A. J. F.: Immunization against measles: Development and evaluation of a highly attenuated live measles vaccine. Annales Paediatrici, *202*:241, 1964.

Smith, D. W., Fregnan, G. B., de Laquerrier-Richardson, L., and Valdivia, E.: Induction of acquired resistance in guinea pigs with defatted *Mycobacterium tuberculosis* vaccines. J. Bact., *88*:87, 1964.

Soper, F. L.: Smallpox—World changes and implications for eradication. Amer. J. Pub. Health, *56*:1652, 1966.

Vallery-Radot, R.: The Life of Pasteur. Doubleday-Doran & Co., New York. 1926.

Waksman, S. A.: Brilliant and Tragic Life of W. M. W. Haffkine, Bacteriologist. Rutgers University Press. New Brunswick, N. J. 1964.

Woodhour, A. F., Metzgar, D. P., Stim, T. B., Tytell, A. A., and Hilleman, M. R.: New metabolizable immunologic adjuvant for human use. I. Development and animal immune response. Proc. Soc. Exp. Biol. Med., *116*:516, 1964.

Youmans, A. S., and Youmans, G. P.: Preparation of highly immunogenic ribosomal fractions of *Mycobacterium tuberculosis* by use of dodecyl sulfate. J. Bact., *91*:2139, 1966.

# Chapter 26

## IMMUNOLOGY
## Allergy

### 26.1  THE ALLERGIC STATE

When specific antibodies circulate in the blood, they apparently become adsorbed to cells in certain tissues of the body which seem to retain them for indefinite periods of time. It is conceivable also that those same tissues may have produced the antibodies in the first place and continue to do so unless, as supposed by the clonal selection hypothesis, antibodies are produced only by the lymphatic tissues. Regardless of the source of the antibodies, when the specific antigen that evoked those antibodies is again brought into contact with the antibody-containing (or antibody-coated) cells, the cells react in a very distinctive manner (the *allergic reaction*). The allergic reaction is a manifestation of an antigen-antibody reaction occurring *in* or *on* certain tissue cells. The reacting cells are said to be in a *hypersensitive* or *allergic* (Gr. *allos* = changed; *ergon* = activity) state. The initial dose of antigen is called a *sensitizing* or *inducing dose;* the second dose is called a *toxic* or *shocking* or *eliciting* dose. The particular tissues or organs involved in an allergic reaction are often called the *target* or *shock tissues* or *shock organs*. In the language of allergy, antigens are often called *allergens;* immunization is spoken of as *sensitization*. The cells of the shock tissues are damaged and may be killed by the allergic reaction.

THE INDUCTION PERIOD.  A period of one to several weeks must elapse between the *sensitizing stimulus* and the *toxic dose*. This *induction period* allows time for antibody formation.

However, an allergic response may also be induced immediately in previously unsensitized cells by injection of a mixture of antigen and antibody in which the antigen is present in excess (i.e., no precipitate present). Presumably excess antigen is removed by enzymes and phagocytes so that an antigen-antibody reaction (precipitation?) occurs on or in the previously unsensitized cells, causing an allergic response.

### 26.2  TYPES OF ALLERGIC REACTION

There are many different manifestations of allergy. The nature of an allergic reaction depends on many factors, such as the shock tissue, the nature of the antigen, the nature of the antibody, the anatomy of the animal involved (i.e., the location of the shock tissue), the dose of antigen and the degree of hypersensitiveness.

Allergic reactions are of two general types: the *immediate wheal*, or *anaphylactic type;* and the *delayed*, or *infection* or *tuberculin*, type. In general, the immediate type of allergy is produced by soluble-protein antigens such as undenatured egg white or serum, while delayed allergy is evoked by cellular antigens, such as bacterial cells. The types of allergy are not always easily differentiated. Sometimes both appear to be present together, and apparently the same antigen may at times produce one type of reaction and at other times another.

Immediate-type reactions appear to result from adsorption of circulating antibodies such as precipitins by various tissue cells. Delayed-type reactions are related to lymphocytes or macrophages that have been affected by allergens (sensitized?) so that they react by means of special antibody-like receptors that are closely bound to, or inside of, these cells and do not circulate freely as do the antibodies involved in immediate-type allergy. Unlike immediate-type allergy, delayed-type allergy can be transferred to other animals only with the cells to which they are attached, not by means of serum.

## 26.3 IMMEDIATE-TYPE ALLERGY

General characteristics of immediate-type allergic reactions may be tabulated as follows:

*a.* A demonstrable, often visible, reaction of hypersensitive tissues begins *within seconds* or *minutes* after contact with the antigen and disappears within one to two hours. There is little or no infiltration of leukocytes.

*b.* The tissues affected are primarily *smooth muscle, blood vessels* and *supporting tissues* such as cartilage and fibrous tissue, but other tissues may also be affected.

*c. Desensitization* is relatively easy though sometimes extremely dangerous (see *anaphylaxis*).

*d.* The reaction is due to antibodies that circulate in the blood (notably *precipitins*) and which, therefore, are readily *transferable* in serum from one animal to another.

**Passive Allergy.** Normal tissue cells may passively acquire the antibodies necessary to an immediate-type allergic reaction merely by receiving an injection of serum from an animal whose blood contains the specific antibodies. Within a few minutes the recipient is fully sensitized. Since in such cases the antibodies are passively received, the phenomenon is commonly called passive allergy. It is analogous to passive immunity.

## 26.4 ANAPHYLAXIS

One of the most-studied and best known, though still incompletely understood, manifestations of immediate allergy is *anaphylaxis.* The antibodies mainly involved appear to be precipitins or circulating antibodies like precipitins. The anaphylactic reaction received its name because it was first thought to be a paradoxical immune reaction *against immunity* (Gr. *ana* = against; *phylassein* = to protect. It is not, however, a paradox but a sort of perversion or over-reactivity of a truly protective mechanism. The sensitizing dose of allergen may be very small; the shocking dose must be relatively large if an acute reaction is to occur.

Anaphylaxis results apparently from antigen-antibody combinations in the shock tissues where antibodies concentrate. The eliciting dose of allergen can enter naturally, by the bites of venomous animals, but is generally brought about artificially by injection of antigen. Bee stings sometimes produce immediate-type, anaphylaxis-like reactions in hypersensitive people.

THE ANAPHYLACTIC REACTION. Within about five minutes after introduction of the toxic or shock dose of specific antigen, the laboratory animal (usually a guinea pig) becomes uneasy, scratches at its nose, coughs and is evidently embarrassed for air. Gagging movements occur, and the animal gasps for breath. Urination and defecation take place, the animal falls on its side and ceases to breathe. Death may occur within a few minutes. If the attack is not fatal, recovery is often abrupt and seemingly complete within an hour or two, and the animal will not exhibit hypersensitiveness for some days or weeks afterward. The animal is said to be *desensitized.*

*Histamine* and several other substances; *serotonin, bradykinin,* and a "slow-reacting substance in allergy" (SRS-A) are released by the cells involved in the antigen-antibody reaction; especially by mast cells* and platelets. Histamine and the related substances induce smooth-muscle contraction. Many of the symptoms of anaphylaxis result from histamine-induced contraction of smooth muscle fibers (i.e., smooth muscle is the most obvious shock organ in anaphylaxis); hence the value of antihistaminic drugs such as epinephrine in immediate-type allergic reactions. Large amounts of smooth muscle are present in the lungs of guinea pigs. Thus, constriction of the air passages and consequent asphyxia is a marked feature of the anaphylactic reaction in them, but not necessarily in other species of animals. In rabbits, dogs and other animals the picture varies, partly owing to differences in anatomical location of smooth muscle. In pregnant animals abortion often occurs because the uterus consists largely of smooth muscle. In dogs and man there is much damage to the liver, which alters the clinical picture markedly.

In all immediate-type allergy there is damage to blood vessels resulting in dilatation and escape of fluid into the tissues, causing swelling (*edema*) and, if extensive, *shock.*

There is also decreased ability of the blood to coagulate (*hemophilia*). This appears to result from the removal of fibrin components from the blood by *heparin,* a normal anticoagulant that is produced in excessive amounts by mast and liver cells during anaphylaxis.

**Wheal and Flare.** A common manifestation of the immediate type of allergic reaction

---

*Cells that resemble basophilic granulocytes, found in connective and other tissues and that, in allergic reactions, release histamine and probably heparin. Heparin reduces coagulability of blood.

is seen when a small amount of a specific antigen (e.g., horse dander) is introduced into the superficial layers of the skin of a person or animal whose tissues contain antibodies for that antigen. Within a few seconds or minutes there appear: first, a red flush; then a hard, white swelling, or *wheal,* surrounded by an irregularly shaped, and often quite extensive, zone of redness called a *flare.* These two signs (wheal and flare) appear to be caused by dilatation of the local capillary blood vessels (the flare) and release of fluid into the local tissues (edema) under sufficient pressure to cause intense itching by irritating the local sensory nerve endings. The pressure shuts off the local vessels, which excludes blood and thereby produces the white, central swelling (the wheal). These vascular responses are characteristic of virtually all types of immediate allergy. There is no local accumulation of leukocytes in immediate-type allergy. The whole wheal-and-flare reaction usually disappears within a few hours. It may be abruptly abolished by *antihistaminics.* (Why?)

This type of reaction is also commonly called a *hive. Hives* often seem to result from the introduction of antigen into the skin by the escape from the gastrointestinal tract of some undigested antigenic food substance to which the patient is allergic. Generalized hives may also occur in persons who have received doses of serum, such as tetanus antitoxin, for therapeutic purposes, and in other circumstances.

**Hay Fever and Asthma.**   These and some related disorders are common manifestations of the immediate type of allergic reaction. They occur in the respiratory tract of persons who have had repeated contacts with plant pollens; dust of hay; equine, canine or feline dander; and other antigens that have been inhaled. Some persons are much more likely to become sensitized in this manner than others. They are said to be *atopic.*

## 26.5   DELAYED-TYPE ALLERGY

Delayed-type allergy differs from immediate-type allergy both as to mechanism and to manifestation:

*a.* A demonstrable or visible reaction of hypersensitive tissue begins only *hours* or *days* following introduction of antigen and develops fully during one or more days and persists for days. There is marked infiltration of leukocytes.

*b.* Any vascular tissue may be affected.

*c. Desensitization* is difficult or impossible.

*d.* The reaction is due to antibodies called

*reagins* that are closely attached to or inside cells. These antibodies are not readily demonstrable or transferable in serum. They are transferable only in cells. The presence or absence of circulating antibodies has no relation to the delayed reaction.

The antibodies involved in delayed allergy are quite unlike any that we have yet described. They remain closely associated with or inside the cells that produce them and are not readily demonstrable in the blood. Not much that is definite is known of these antibodies. They are often spoken of as allergic *reagins.* The antigens that engender them are mainly cellular components and some other substances that are lipids or lipid-complexes. They are often called *allergens.**

For example, antigenic proteins associated with lipid particles typically engender delayed-type allergy. Such lipo-proteins occur in many bacteria; notably the waxy tubercle bacilli. Since bacteria and other microorganisms commonly contain lipo-proteins and regularly engender delayed-type allergy, this form of allergy is often called *infection allergy.*

**Adjuvants.**   Some proteins are not highly antigenic unless associated with lipids; e.g., the waxy substance in cells of dead tubercle bacilli or other species of *Mycobacterium;* lanolin; aqueous emulsions of vegetable oils or mineral oil. So effective are such lipids in enhancing antigenicity that they are often used to promote antibody production and are called *adjuvants.* A well-known type, called Freund's adjuvant, is an aqueous emulsion of mineral oil mixed with heat-killed tubercle bacilli. Such lipid adjuvants commonly promote delayed allergy. Since bacteria of the Genus *Mycobacterium* contain more waxy components than other bacteria, infection by any species of *Mycobacterium* is particularly likely to induce delayed allergy. Indeed, infection by *M. tuberculosis* produces the classical model of delayed or infection allergy; readily demonstrable as the *tuberculin reaction.*

**The Tuberculin Reaction.**   Allergic sensitivity to the protein of tubercle bacilli resulting from an infection, present, past or induced by BCG, may be demonstrated by introducing into or onto (not under) the skin, tuberculo-protein in the form of dead tubercle bacilli, or the sterile filtrate of broth in which they have grown, or purified protein derivatives (*PPD*) extracted from the bacilli (Fig. 26.1). These tuberculo-proteins are called *tuberculin.* At the site of their

---

*Some workers use the words *reagin* and *allergen* for all antibodies and antigens referred to in allergy.

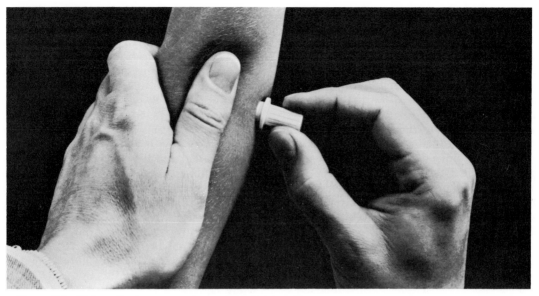

**Figure 26.1**   Tuberculin tine test employs a plastic holder with a stainless steel disk and four tines coated with Old Tuberculin and dried. The only preparation required is cleansing of the site of inoculation with alcohol. Methods such as the tine test, using disposable plastic units, offer distinct advantages in speed, accuracy and economy. (Courtesy of Lederle Laboratories, a division of American Cyanamid Company, Pearl River, N.Y.)

introduction into the skin a red, *indurated* (firm and swollen) spot at least 5 mm. in diameter appears after 24 to 48 hours. The red zone fades in a day or so but the induration may be palpated for several days. The reaction is called a *tuberculin reaction,* and is representative of the delayed type of allergy. Analogous skin tests for delayed-type allergy are used in several fungal infections: *histoplasmin* tests in histoplasmosis; *coccidioidin* tests in coccidioidomycosis (Chapter 11). All are tests for allergy to the respective organisms. (How is this type of reaction differentiated from the wheal and flare of the immediate allergic response?)

The tuberculin test is widely used in finding cases of tuberculosis. The tuberculin test, modified for ocular application, is also widely used to detect tuberculosis in cattle.

**Allergy and Tissue Destruction.**   Delayed allergy often results in necrosis of the tissues involved when the degree of hypersensitivity and dosage of allergen are sufficient. A tuberculin test in some persons may result in a large ulcer at the site of the intradermal injection.

Allergic necrosis of tissues occurs in numerous chronic infections. It is well exemplified by production of lung cavities in some tuberculous persons. Slowly progressive destructive lesions of bone, arteries and nerves are associated with syphilis, leprosy and other slowly progressive diseases. The allergy in such proc-

esses is often called *bacterial* or *infection allergy.* Histamine and like substances are not involved. In infection allergy the sensitivity may be purely of the delayed type, or both immediate and delayed sensitivity may be present in varying degrees. These situations may give rise to varying symptoms and complex, little-understood reactions.

Massive tissue destruction is not inevitable in infection allergy and is the conspicuous exception rather than the rule. Allergy is basically a defensive mechanism.

## 26.6   ALLERGY AS A DEFENSIVE MECHANISM

**Binding Power of Immune Tissues.**   Once the body has been subjected to an antigenic stimulus, the tissues, especially the more superficial tissues (skin or mucous membranes), acquire a greatly enhanced power to *bind* and *localize* the specific antigen when later brought into contact with it. The effectiveness of this *tissue immunity* is greatly enhanced by allergy. Dermal allergic reactions generally are illustrations of this heightened reactivity of superficial tissues. The antigen thus bound in the tissue of initial contact, although perhaps causing necrosis where bound, cannot spread throughout the body and thus cause injury to deeper and more vital tissues.

**Nonantitoxic Immunity to Toxin.**   An example of the effectiveness of the binding power of immune tissues is seen when rabbits and guinea pigs are made allergic by injections to somatic antigens of *Corynebacterium diphtheriae*. The animals are then able to survive *cutaneous* doses of live, *toxigenic* diphtheria bacilli which always kill normal animals. The toxin formed by the bacilli, instead of diffusing throughout the body as it does in the unimmunized animals, is held and bound in the skin of the allergic animals. Although it does severe damage locally, it cannot spread to the deep vital tissues, so the animals survive *in the complete absence of antitoxin.*

**The Koch Phenomenon.**   Another example of the binding power of hypersensitive tissues is the *Koch phenomenon.* A guinea pig is inoculated in the right groin with virulent tubercle bacilli, the bacteria gain a foothold, form a local abscess, and then proceed almost unopposed from the abscess to the lymph nodes of the abdominal cavity, to the spleen, the liver, the lymph nodes of the thorax and the lungs and kidneys; the pig dies of disseminated tuberculosis in six to eight weeks. Now, if on the second or third week of this progressive disease a second injection of tubercle bacilli is made into the left groin, there is a strong local allergic tissue reaction. The bacilli are *closely held* in the site where they are injected and *do not* progress farther although they may cause a local abscess. The tissues are highly defensive because of the allergy due to the first infection.

Unfortunately, guinea pigs are so susceptible to tubercle bacilli that they eventually die in spite of the valiant defense put up by the tissues. Human beings are in general much more resistant. Many adult persons, especially dwellers in thickly populated districts, have had a mild, unrecognized and long-since-healed infection with tubercle bacilli. Because of this they are much more resistant to tuberculosis than persons who have never had any contact with tubercle bacilli. The previously infected group are allergic (hence, resistant) to the bacilli, as shown by the fact that they react positively to tuberculin. The second group, those never previously infected and hence *tuberculin negative,* may be made allergic (resistant) to tubercle bacilli by giving them a very mild infection, as is done in BCG vaccination. They become *tuberculin positive.* Allergy is thus revealed as a potent defensive mechanism.

## 26.7   HARMFUL EFFECTS OF ALLERGY

Like many normal and beneficent physiological functions, allergic reactions may at times be so violent in some persons as to be harmful, "like an overzealous servant who, attempting to warm the living room with a good fire, burns the house down." These few violent reactions, like violent acts, create more comment and attract more attention than the enormous number of normal and helpful reactions that go on unnoticed constantly. For example, certain persons appear to become excessively allergic to hemolytic streptococci. The heart and joints appear to be shock tissues in such allergy. There is believed to be a close relation between this allergy to hemolytic streptococci and rheumatic heart disease, one of the most important causes of disability and death in the United States. Many chronic, disabling conditions, especially forms of asthma and joint disease such as rheumatoid arthritis, are thought to be related to allergic reactions of certain tissues to obscure microbial infection such as chronic sinusitis. Many of the rashes and eruptions seen in bacterial, viral and fungal diseases are allergic reactions of the delayed type. Reactions to poison ivy and poison oak are also allergic responses of the delayed type. Allergy, therefore, plays an important though "Jekyll and Hyde" part in infectious and other diseases.

**Autoallergy.**   As previously mentioned, autoantigens can sensitize some persons to certain of their own tissues: eye lens, sperm, nervous-system tissue, some connective tissues, possibly muscle. It is thought, on the basis of accumulating evidence, that such sensitizations are the basis of what are called autoimmune or autoallergic diseases: muscular dystrophy, multiple sclerosis, some forms of arthritis, some types of encephalitis or brain damage, and numerous other conditions of obscure etiology.

**Haptens in Allergy.**   Many allergens are entirely nonantigenic. Examples, among hundreds, are sulfonamides, certain cosmetics, certain dyes on fabrics, some plastics, penicillin and some other antibiotics. Hypersensitivity to these substances, or certain molecular groups resulting from their disintegration, is commonplace.

Although these allergens are not antigens such as previously described, it is thought that, as haptens, they can become conjugated with proteins and other body components, especially lipids (adjuvants), so that they act like complete antigens. Allergic reactions to such substances must be distinguished from the very similar reactions called *drug idiosyncrasies*. Some persons seem to have a genetic tendency to develop allergy to such substances. They are said to be *atopic*.

**Drug Idiosyncrasies.** Certain plant perfumes, cosmetics, detergents, drugs, rubber goods and dyes may cause immediate-allergy–like responses: hives, dermatitis, asthma. Such immediate reactions, although closely simulating allergy and sometimes actually a result of allergic mechanisms, may often be basically different from true immediate allergy and not primarily dependent on specific antibodies at all. Such reactions are usually limited to certain allergic (atopic) or asthmatic individuals. These allergy-like reactions are often referred to as *drug idiosyncrasies*. The exact mechanisms underlying such reactions and their relations to allergy are not fully understood.

## SUPPLEMENTARY READING

Benacerraf, B., and McCluskey, R. T.: Methods of immunologic injury to tissues. Ann. Rev. Microbiol., *17*:263, 1963.

Chase, M. W.: The Allergic State. *In:* Dubos, R. J.: Bacterial and Mycotic Infections of Man. 4th ed. J. B. Lippincott Co., Philadelphia. 1965.

Epstein, W. L.: To prevent poison ivy and oak dermatitis. Amer. J. Nursing, *63*:113, 1963.

Fireman, P., Boesman, M., Haddad, Z. H., and Gitlin, D.: Passive transfer of tuberculin reactivity in vitro. Science, *155*:337, 1967.

Kamin, P. B., et al.: Live, attenuated measles vaccine. J. Am. Med. Assn., *185*,8:647, 1963.

Klement, Z., and Goodman, R. N.: The hypersensitive reaction in relation to infection by bacterial plant pathogens. Ann. Rev. Plant Pathol., *5*:17, 1967.

Levine, B. B.: Antigen-antibody reaction: Nature of complex initiating delayed hypersensitivity. Science, *149*:205, 1965.

Milgrom, F., Centeno, E., Shulman, S., and Witebsky, E.: Autoantibodies resulting from immunization with kidney. Proc. Soc. Exp. Biol. Med., *116*:1009, 1964.

Raffel, S.: Immunity. 2nd ed. Appleton-Century Crofts, Inc., New York. 1961.

Ruddle, N., and Waksman, B. H.: Cytotoxic effect of lymphocyte-antigen interaction in delayed hypersensitivity. Science, *157*:1060, 1967.

Shaffer, J. H., and Sweet, L. C.: Allergic reactions to drugs. Amer. J. Nursing, *65*:100, 1965.

Slavin, R. G., and Garvin, J. E.: Delayed hypersensitivity in man: Transfer by lymphocyte preparations of peripheral blood. Science, *145*:52, 1964.

Thompson, P. E., Olszewski, B., and Waitz, J. A.: Functional studies of cultured brain tissues as related to "demyelinative disorders." Science, *148*:1242, 1965.

# Chapter 27

## MICROORGANISMS AND INFECTION

### 27.1 HOST-PARASITE RELATIONSHIPS

In biology the term *host* means any organism that is used by another organism for shelter or food. The second organism is called a *parasite*. The relationship of each plant and animal to each of the many other organisms with which it is in contact under natural conditions varies from complete mutual indifference or *neutralism* to lethal, mutal *antagonism* or antibiosis. A number of terms, familiar to the student of elementary biology, are used to describe the different types of relationships between these extremes: *commensalism,* in which one species benefits from the association, the other being unaffected; *mutualism* or *symbiosis,* in which both are benefited and often wholly interdependent; *antagonism* or *amensalism,* in which one species is injured, the other unaffected, by the association; *predation* (usually of large animals) as when hawks eat field mice or trouts eat minnows. In *parasitism* the *parasite* lives in or on the parasitized plant or animal (the *host*) at the expense of the host. Parasitism is not necessarily harmful to the host and often approaches commensalism. The term parasite is usually applied to small species such as lice, hookworms and microorganisms such as yeasts, molds, bacteria, viruses and amebas.

The first requisite of continued successful parasitism by microorganisms is the ability to live in or on the host without stirring up a defensive reaction on the part of the host with which the parasite cannot cope. In the absence of significant damage to the host this could be viewed as a kind of commensalism and is the commonest form of relationship of man to most microorganisms. If a violent defensive reaction is set up by the parasite, there are three possible outcomes: the parasite may be killed or cast out; the host may be killed; or the invasive and pathogenic properties of the parasite and the defensive mechanisms of the host may reach an equilibrium, during which the two live together in "peaceful coexistence" or "an armed truce." Either is a potential aggressor against the other if the equilibrium (the "balance of power") is disturbed.

*Infection* exists when parasites are enabled to penetrate or bypass the defensive barriers of, and to live inside, the host. Infection may or may not result in disease. When the host is visibly or sensibly injured by the parasite, *disease* exists and the parasite is said to be *pathogenic* (Gr. *pathos* = sadness or pain). Most microorganisms lack the physiological properties that might enable them to multiply within the tissues of (i.e., to *infect*) a plant or animal host. They are not infectious. An organism may, however, be highly infectious for one host and harmless for another or, in the same host, pathogenic at one time, commensal at another.

A parasite may be called a *primary pathogen* if it can, unaided, penetrate or evade the normal defensive mechanisms of the healthy, susceptible (i.e., not specifically immunized) body and establish an infection. It is highly *aggressive.* Examples would be measles virus, gonococci, or rickettsias of typhus fever. A *secondary pathogen* or *"opportunist"* is one that cannot, of its own powers, pass the normal defensive mechanisms of the healthy, susceptible host but that can infect and cause disease if defense mechanisms have been broken, as by wounds, prolonged disease, old age or poisons.

## 27.2   PARASITISM AND PATHOGENICITY

It is sometimes difficult to distinguish between parasitism and pathogenicity. A parasite may be or it may not be significantly pathogenic. For example, a mosquito might be regarded as a harmless parasite. But if its bite causes a severe allergic reaction it is a pathogen.

**Pathogenic Saprophytes.**   On the other hand, pathogenicity does not always involve parasitism. For example, certain organisms, such as the bacilli causing lockjaw (*Clostridium tetani*), cannot invade or live in normal tissues and are in no sense parasites. They can live only in dead (necrotic) material, such as might occur in a crushed foot; they are true saprophytes. They can cause fatal disease, however, because they give off a toxin that is absorbed from the site of their growth.

Similarly, the organism of food poisoning (*Cl. botulinum*) cannot as a rule multiply in the tissues or on the body, but produces a poison in foods outside the body. When such food is eaten the preformed toxin produces a highly fatal disease: food poisoning, or botulism. Such organisms are *pathogenic saprophytes.*

**Pathogenicity Is Fortuitous.**   Those not familiar with microbial disease sometimes consider microorganisms to be purposeful predatory creatures that invade the tissues and produce poisons for the sole purpose of causing harm, as though that were to their benefit in the sense that a tiger, snake or spider benefits from killing its prey. Microorganisms are sometimes thought to be endowed with special powers for injury. Like dandelions in the lawn, microbial growth occurs only where (and because) conditions permit. Dandelions, although highly irritating to people who cherish all–blue-grass lawns, have no evil intent. Their only interest is propagation of the dandelion; so also the microbe. If the lawn owner (or host) reacts against them with 2,4-D (or antibiotic) it is only because he is not adapted to them. Some people like the dandelion flowers or make delicious salads out of their leaves. However, excessive irritation to the host by plant or microbe usually is unfavorable to the parasite. The greatest advantage to the parasite results from *unnoticed* parasitism.

**Mutual Adaptation.**   The process of adaptation between host and parasite must be thought of as a mutual one, requiring many generations of natural selection of the most compatible. Microbial generations are sometimes very short, a few minutes or hours; human generations are long, about 25 years. Thus, microorganisms can become adapted to growth in contact with human tissues before man acquires species or racial resistance to invasive microorganisms.

We may imagine that a few species of microorganisms are just beginning the process of adaptation, since they stir up a violent reaction (acute disease) nearly every time they come into contact with the host and begin multiplying. Gonococci and measles virus are examples. The human host has not yet become adapted to them. Other parasites are better adapted; the host, through many generations of contact, seems to have become more used to having them growing within him, and chronic or slowly progressive disease ensues. Syphilis, tuberculosis and leprosy may be thought of as examples.

**The Carrier State.**   In still other instances an individual human host and dangerous pathogens, such as the typhoid bacillus, hemolytic streptococci, pneumococci and meningococci, rapidly become mutually adapted, with or without perceptible disease. They may live together for years with no evidence of disease. This is a very common situation and is referred to as the *carrier state.* The person or animal who thus carries infectious organisms (i.e., a *carrier*) although remaining well himself can often transmit the pathogens to others who may become very ill as a result.

Frequently carrier relationships represent in reality only a temporary "armistice" or a microbiological "cold war." If one side weakens, the other automatically takes advantage of the situation and serious infection of the carrier can occur. The important point here is that we are constantly in contact with microorganisms capable of making us very ill or of killing us. That they do not do so is because we have ample defensive mechanisms. Let these become weakened or breached, and disease, severe or mild, results.

## 27.3   FACTORS IN THE OCCURRENCE OF DISEASE

Besides the weakening of defensive mechanisms by various extraneous factors such as exposure, exhaustion, alcoholism and drug-addiction or too-frequent child-bearing, several other factors are important in the occurrence of infection: the means by which the parasite enters the body (*portal of entry*); parasite *virulence;* and *dosage,* or numbers of infecting organisms.

**Portal of Entry.**   The portal by which an organism enters the body is important in determining the occurrence and kind of disease. If the skin is kept intact, no ordinary microorganism can get through it. (Some few microorganisms are said to be able to penetrate the intact skin; probably they get into hair follicles and sweat glands.) But if any slight cut or scratch exists, then microorganisms can get into the tissues. The thin mucous membranes about the eye (*conjunctivae*), in the nose, throat, and lungs and in the genitourinary tract are less able to withstand invasion of some microorganisms than the tough outer skin. Numerous infections readily begin in such situations.

Certain microorganisms under ordinary circumstances can gain a foothold in the body *only* when they come into contact with the respiratory tract, others only through contact with the intestinal lining, and so on. For example, dysentery bacilli (*Shigella*) rubbed over the hands or even into a wound would ordinarily cause no infection, while if swallowed they might produce a fatal disease. On the other hand, *Neisseria gonorrhoeae* (cause of gonorrhea) might be swallowed without harmful effect, but if rubbed into the eye or genitalia it could cause gonorrheal infection of the mucous membranes.

**Virulence.** Virulence is a complex property which combines *infectiousness,* or the ability to initiate and maintain an infection in a host; *invasiveness,* or the power to progress farther into the host from the initial infection; and *pathogenicity,* or the ability to injure a host once an infection is established (Fig. 27.1). Pathogens that pass from one host to another (e.g., "animal passage") seem to acquire enhanced virulence. The mechanism is not clear but may result from the development of capsules or other properties.

INFECTIOUSNESS. Infectiousness depends on a complex of properties, several still obscure, that enable the parasite to establish an initial beachhead in the host by evading or overcoming local defensive measures such as normal antibodies, possibly specific antibodies, and phagocytes.

Infectiousness need not involve great virulence or pathogenicity. Infection and even invasion frequently occur without any perceptible disease. Indeed, very fortunately, this is the general rule. For example, yellow fever and poliomyelitis have been so widespread in some com-

munities that virtually all of the children under ten have become infected and have developed demonstrable antibodies, yet few have shown any perceptible evidence of disease at all. Before the advent of highly effective preventive measures that are commonplace today (i.e., prior to about 1940), most adult urban residents were immune to poliomyelitis, diphtheria and tuberculosis yet had never had a *recognized* case. Obviously, there are many mild, immunizing infections yet little disease. Thus, distinctions should be made when speaking of the infectiousness, pathogenicity and virulence of microorganisms. They are too commonly confused; everything is relative and dependent on something else.

INVASIVENESS. Invasiveness depends on characteristics that enable the parasite to leave the initial site of infection and grow in other tissues. Invasion of blood and tissues may or may not result in perceptible disease, depending on the character of the organisms and the resistance of the host.

Mutations undoubtedly occur that confer infective properties on an otherwise harmless commensal. Additional mutations can occur during the ensuing invasion, such that the invaders are selectively favored by conditions in the host. For example, such mutants often possess capsules that protect them from phagocytosis and antibodies. They can then grow into the lymph spaces, invading widely through the tissues. Others may invade and grow in the blood; then we have the condition called *viremia, bacteriemia* or *rickettsiemia, septicemia,* or "blood poisoning." Once microorganisms invade the blood they may be carried to various other points in the body (e.g., liver, spleen, bone marrow or lymph nodules of the intestine). Secondary abscesses (*secondary foci* of infection, or *metastatic infections*) may then result.

Invasiveness is enhanced by the production of certain exoenzymes that attack defensive measures. For example, several common bacterial pathogens produce enzyme-like substances called *leukocidins* that kill leukocytes. Many pathogens of plants produce the enzyme *protopectinase* that digests the supporting structures (middle lamella) of plants, causing soft-rot diseases. Streptococci such as those causing scarlet fever, erysipelas and septicemia produce an enzyme-activator called *streptokinase* or *fibrinolysin.* This helps to digest the fibrin of blood clots that surround and contain sites of injury and infection. Destruction of the retaining net of fibrin presumably enables the organisms to invade distant tissues. Other organisms produce trypsin-like,

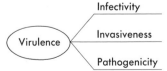

**Figure 27.1**   Factors in virulence. For explanation see text.

tissue-destroying, proteolytic enzymes. Hook-worms produce similar enzymes that enable them to penetrate the intestinal mucosa. Some bacteria produce enzymic complexes that kill and destroy the cells (fibroblasts) of defensive (or scar) tissues that tend to develop around foci of infection, forming retaining sacs.

*Hyaluronidase* is an enzyme that destroys hyaluronic acid, a clear, gummy, intercellular cementing substance of animal tissues which normally opposes progress of microorganisms through the tissues. For this reason hyaluronidase is often spoken of as a *spreading factor.*

There are other enzymes that are inimical to plant or animal tissues. Production of these various enzymes and others may be, in some cases, *constitutive* properties of the organisms involved; in some microorganisms the enzymes may appear as a result of *mutation;* in others they may represent *induction* by the substrates in the body tissues.

Some exoenzymes act in a toxic manner. For example, some organisms produce lipolytic enzymes such as *lecithinase.* This causes destruction of erythrocytes (*hemolysis*) with resulting anemia and anoxia. Such organisms are said to be *hemolytic.* Another effect of some lipolytic enzymes is to produce poisonous hydrolysis products from the lipids present in normal plasma. Other organisms are known to produce poisonous products of normal tissues by means of their exoenzymes. The production of *catalase,* an enzyme that decomposes $H_2O_2$ to $H_2O$ and $\frac{1}{2}O_2$, appears to be definitely associated with disease production by several species of bacteria pathogenic for man, though the exact mechanism is not yet clear. The line of demarkation between the pathogenic roles of exoenzymes and exotoxins is often vague.

PATHOGENICITY.   Like invasiveness, pathogenicity is a complex of factors, some known, others still to be elucidated. A principal cause of pathogenicity is the production of poisons called toxins, as well as of exoenzymes as just described. Microbial toxins may be secreted or released to the surrounding fluids as *exotoxins,* or remain attached to the cell as *endotoxins.*

*Exotoxins.*   Exotoxins are proteins and, like all typical proteins, are sensitive to temperatures above 70° C., 50 per cent alcohol and dilute acids. Exotoxins are strongly antigenic and evoke antitoxins. Some exotoxins, such as those of *Clostridium botulinum* and certain staphylococci, (causes of food poisoning) are harmful only when swallowed (except under unusual conditions such as experimental injection). Others, such as diphtheria and tetanus toxins, can be

taken by mouth with impunity, but if injected or adsorbed into the blood from infected lesions, even in very tiny doses, may cause death; additional evidence of the importance of portal of entry. Most bacterial exotoxins appear to have an affinity for nervous tissue and often for heart muscle, kidney and certain other specialized tissues. They cause damage principally to those tissues. Most of these toxins are much more potent than cobra venom. Indeed botulinal toxin is the most poisonous biological substance known (for mammals). Various toxins and toxin-like substances of specific organisms are discussed with the specific organisms that produce them.

*Endotoxins.*   The term *endotoxin* in a broad sense includes toxic substances of the cell body, i.e., *somatic toxins* as contrasted with toxins secreted or released into the surrounding medium, e.g., exotoxins. However, the term endotoxin as currently used is synonymous with the *haptenic* portion of the cell walls of gram-negative bacteria and is best known as the somatic or O antigens of the Enterobacteriaceae. Unlike the heat-labile, alcohol- and acid-sensitive, proteinaceous exotoxins and exoenzymes previously discussed, the endotoxins are lipo-polysaccharide complexes and are resistant to heat, alcohol and dilute acids. Being heteropolymers, they can have different sequences of the component units so that, as with proteins, they have different antigenic specificities in different species of organisms. Coupled with the cell proteins of their respective species they are complete, specific antigens that engender specific agglutinins. Neither lipid nor polysaccharide moiety of the heteropolymer is highly toxic per se, but the combination is very poisonous indeed.

The toxic effects of endotoxins have been widely investigated. Endotoxins are markedly *emetic* and *pyrogenic* (cause vomiting and elevations of temperature) and at first may temporarily stimulate an increase of activity of phagocytic cells, both of the reticuloendothelial system and the leukocytes. However, the reticuloendothelial system removes endotoxins from the blood rapidly and the cells are injured thereby. Thus, phagocytic activity is temporarily suppressed; so also is antibody formation. Repeated doses of endotoxins soon induce a tolerance that seems unrelated to antibody formation.

Endotoxins produce several of the effects of gastrointestinal infection with pathogens of the group of Enterobacteriaceae: weakness, nausea, diarrhea, lowered arterial blood pressure and intestinal hemorrhage. Infection of pregnant animals can induce abortion. Curiously, there seems to be little fixed relationship between pathogenicity and endotoxin content of an organism.

It is of interest that, in tumor-bearing animals, injection of endotoxin causes hemorrhage and necrosis of the *tumor*. Therapeutic use of the endotoxin is limited by its toxicity and the rapid appearance of tolerance.

Endotoxins are very important as *potentiators* of other infections (i.e., they greatly weaken the phagocytic and other defenses against pathogens). For example, infections with certain endotoxin-containing gram-negative rods of relatively little virulence (swine influenza bacilli) can cause an otherwise mild viral disease (swine influenza) to become a devastating scourge in a herd. Long-standing chronic bacterial infections (e.g., tuberculosis) may be suddenly converted to acute, quickly fatal infections by injecting minute amounts of endotoxins.

**Dosage.** This factor in establishing infection is a simple quantitative one, yet it also involves other factors. As a generality we may say that under ordinary circumstances the larger the dose of infective microorganisms the greater the chance that an infection will result. However, certain qualifications are necessary. For example, very large numbers of some organisms may be present in certain situations without causing any difficulty at all. The intestine contains thousands of billions of deadly bacteria at all times, yet if only a dozen or so of some of these are placed in the peritoneal cavity or injected into the brain, they can quickly set up a fatal infection (an example of the importance of portal of entry). Similarly, one might swallow three or four typhoid bacilli with impunity, yet a dosage of several hundred might overcome local resistance and cause typhoid fever. With some organisms a single cell or particle is invariably sufficient to infect. Obviously, much depends on the virulence of the particular organism involved and on the resistance of the tissues that it contacts, as well as on dosage alone. It is conceivable that among a thousand rough (R) unencapsulated, readily phagocytized bacilli or cocci, there might be one encapsulated smooth (S) mutant that by itself could initiate an infection.

## 27.4 KOCH'S AND RIVERS' POSTULATES

It is not always possible to be certain that the microorganisms isolated from a given disease lesion or from pus, blood or feces are the cause of the observed disease condition. Many harmless microorganisms are found growing in feces, sputum and ulcerating wounds. Some would not grow there unless the diseased condition existed first. Such adventitious organisms are called *secondary invaders*. To prove that a certain microorganism is the primary and unassisted cause of a given disease often requires careful study.

The question of the etiological relationship of various bacteria to specific diseases was a very live one long before the time of Koch, and there was much loose discussion and profitless argument regarding many bacteria and their relation to disease, due to unrecognized contamination of cultures. When Koch established the pure-culture technique it became possible to apply exact methods to the study of the etiology of disease. He was very conservative in stating the relationships of any given organism to any particular disease.

His ideas on the subject were crystallized largely by his studies of the relationship of tubercle bacilli (*Mycobacterium tuberculosis*) to tuberculosis. Koch, like others before him, observed the bacilli in the lesions of persons and animals dead of the disease. But he was not too ready to believe that he had discovered the cause of tuberculosis just because he found certain organisms present in the lesions of tuberculosis. Might not this bacillus appear in the tissues merely by accident because the host, being so ill, is too weak to resist its invasion? Might it not be merely a relatively harmless opportunist? Might it not represent contamination with a common saprophyte capable of living in the necrotic tissue? Koch, involved in a discussion of the problem, finally stated what he believed to be the evidence necessary to prove an organism to be the cause of a disease. The evidence consists of four postulates, generally called *Koch's postulates* today, and they are essentially as follows:

1. The organism must be associated with all cases of a given disease and in logical pathological relationship to the disease and its symptoms and lesions.

2. It must be isolated from victims of the disease in pure culture.

3. When the pure culture is inoculated into susceptible animals or man, it must reproduce the disease or engender specific antibodies. (Many such inoculations into man have been made on courageous volunteers. In others, accidental infections have occurred which have provided long-wanted evidence. The value of animal experimentation is here very evident.)

4. It must be isolated in pure culture from such experimental infections.

Even today the etiological relationship of

some bacteria to diseases that they are thought to cause has not been established on the basis of Koch's postulates. A notable example is the relation of so-called *Mycobacterium leprae* to leprosy. Only the first of Koch's postulates may be applied here.

**Rivers' Postulates in Viral Diseases.** Viruses were unknown at the time of most of Koch's major works, so he failed to take these invisible, noncultivable agents of disease into consideration when he stated the criteria by which the causal relationship of a pathogen to a disease might be determined. Rivers, in 1937, outlined criteria similar to Koch's postulates, which might apply in the cases of viruses. Essentially these are as follows:

1. The virus must be present in the host cells showing the specific lesions or in the blood or other body fluids at the time of the disease.

2. Filtrates of the infectious material (blood or tissue triturates) shown *not to contain bacteria or other visible or cultivable* * organisms must produce the disease or its counterpart, specific antibodies, in appropriate animals. (In response to infections, plants produce antimicrobial substances, though these are not true antibodies or proteins.)

3. Similar filtrates from such animals or plants must transmit the disease.

---

*In inanimate media.

## SUPPLEMENTARY READING

Abdulla, E. M., and Schwab, J. H.: Biological properties of streptococcal cell-wall particles. III. Dermonecrotic reaction to cell-wall mucopeptides. J. Bact. *91*:374, 1966.

Arredondo, M. I., and Kampschmidt, R. F.: Effect of endotoxins on phagocytic activity of the reticuloendothelial system of the rat. Proc. Soc. Exp. Biol. Med., *112*:78, 1963.

Bradley, S. G., and Watson, D. W.: Suppression by endotoxin of the immune response to actinophage in the mouse. Proc. Soc. Exp. Biol. Med., *117*:570, 1964.

Braun, A. C.: The role of toxins and other metabolites in the causation of disease in plants. Tr. N. Y. Acad. Sci., *21*(Ser. II):613, 1959.

Braun, W., editor: Biochemical aspects of microbial pathogenicity. Ann. N. Y. Acad. Sci., *88*(Art. 5):1021, 1960.

Burnett, G. W., and Scherp, H. W.: Oral Microbiology and Disease. The Williams & Wilkins Co., Baltimore. 1962.

Buxton, E. W.: Speculations on plant pathogen-host relations. Fourteenth Symposium, Microbial Behaviour in vivo and in vitro, page 145. Soc. Gen. Microbiol., London. 1964.

Crook, J. R., Otto, W. K., and Jones, R. S.: Potassium, lethal and tumor-necrotizing properties of *Klebsiella* polysaccharide. Proc. Soc. Exp. Biol. Med., *109*:552, 1962.

Davis, B. D., Dulbecco, R., Eisen, H. N., Ginsberg, H. S.,

and Wood, W. B.: Microbiology. Hoeber Medical Division, Harper and Row, New York. 1967.

Deverall, B. J.: Substances produced by pathogenic organisms that induce symptoms of disease in higher plants. Fourteenth Symposium, Microbial Behaviour in vivo and in vitro, page 165. Soc. Gen. Microbiol., London. 1964.

Faine, S., and van der Hoeden, J.: Virulence-linked colonial and morphological variation in *Leptospira.* J. Bact., *88*:1493, 1964.

Howie, J. W., and O'Hea, A. J., editors: Mechanisms of microbial pathogenicity, Fifth Symposium, Soc. Gen. Microbiol., London. 1955.

Keppie, J.: Host and tissue susceptibility. Fourteenth Symposium, Microbial behaviour in vivo and in vitro, page 44. Soc. Gen. Microbiol., London. 1964.

Landy, M., and Braun, W.: Bacterial Endotoxins. Rutgers University Press, New Brunswick, N. J. 1964.

Lippincott, J. A., Webb, J. H., and Lippincott, B.: Auxotrophic mutation and infectivity of *Agrobacterium tumefaciens.* J. Bact., *90*:1155, 1965.

MacLeod, C. M.: Pathogenic properties of bacteria and defense mechanisms of the host. In: Dubos, R. J.: Bacterial and Mycotic Infections of man. 4th ed. J. B. Lippincott Co., Philadelphia. 1965.

Manohar, M., Maheswaran, S. K., Frommes, S. P., and Lindorfer, R. K.: Platelet damaging factor, a fifth activity of staphylococcal α toxin. J. Bact., *94*:224, 1967.

Martin, W. J., and Marcus, S.: Relation of pyrogenic and emetic properties of enterobacteriaceal endotoxin and of staphylococcal enterotoxin. J. Bact., *87*:1019, 1964.

Maynell, G. G.: Phenotypic variation and bacterial infection. Eleventh Symposium, Microbial Reaction to Environment, page 174. Soc. Gen. Microbiol., London. 1961.

Nowotny, A.: Molecular biology of gram-negative bacterial lipopolysaccharides. Ann. N. Y. Acad. Sci., *133*(Art. 2): 277, 1966.

O'Leary, W. M., and Weld, J. T.: Lipolytic activities of *Staphylococcus aureus.* I. Nature of the enzyme producing free fatty acids from plasma lipids. J. Bact., *88*:1356, 1964.

Onoue, K., Kitagawa, M., and Yakamura, Y.: Chemical studies on cellular components of *Bordetella pertussis.* III. Isolation of highly potent toxin from *Bordetella pertussis.* J. Bact., *86*:648, 1963.

Smith, W. K.: A survey of the production of pectic enzymes by plant pathogenic and other bacteria. J. Gen. Microbiol., *18*:33, 1958.

Standfast, A. F. B.: The correlation of properties in vitro with host-parasite relations. Fourteenth Symposium, Microbial Behaviour in vivo and in vitro, page 64. Soc. Gen. Microbiol., London. 1964.

Sultzer, B. M., and Freedman, H. H.: Endotoxin-induced susceptibility to staphylococcal infection and its reversal by adrenergic blocking agents. J. Bact., *90*:1001, 1965.

Suzuki, T., Whang, H. Y., Gorzynski, E. A., and Neter, E.: Inhibition by lipopolysaccharide (endotoxin) of antibody responses of rabbits to common antigen of Enterobacteriaceae. Proc. Soc. Exp. Biol. Med., *117*:785, 1964.

Wallen, V. R.: Host-parasite relations and environmental influences in seedborne diseases. Fourteenth Symposium, Microbial Behaviour in vivo and in vitro, page 187. Soc. Gen. Microbiol., London. 1964.

Willoughby, D. S., Ginzburg, Y., and Watson, D. W.: Host-parasite relationships among group A streptococci. I. Hyaluronic acid production by virulent and avirulent strains. J. Bact., *87*:1452, 1964.

# Chapter 28

## SOURCES AND VECTORS OF INFECTION

In ancient times diseases of man and animals were thought to be caused by or transmitted by odors, vapors and miasmas from rotting organic matter or from swamps. The disease malaria is named for the Italian words *mala-aria* (for "bad air" or "air-disease"). Occult and mysterious influences were also blamed for disease. *Influenza* is the Italian word for influence. Today we know virtually all the sources of infection, the causative agents and their means of transmission.

**Sources of Infection.** The primary *sources* of infection of man and other animals are: (a) infected man and other animals and (b) the soil. Most infectious agents of man and other animals may be transmitted from one to another by various body fluids, which thus serve as *original* or *prime* or *direct* vectors. The principal sources of infectious body fluids, spoken of as *portals of exit,* are: the oral and respiratory tracts, including eyes and ears which are directly connected to the respiratory tract; the intestinal tract; the genitourinary tract; open lesions anywhere on the body; tissues, e.g., stillborn infected animals, fluids and placentas; eggs of birds; and blood and blood derivatives.

Soil is an important primary source of several dangerous agents of disease. Several species of pathogenic and invasive fungi are indigenous to the soil (see Chapter 11). Several pathogenic but *not invasive* bacteria are also commonly found in soil: *Cl. tetani,* the cause of tetanus or lockjaw; *Cl. botulinum,* the cause of food poisoning; *Cl. perfringens* and several similar organisms associated in causing gas gangrene of wounds. These soil organisms are more fully discussed under each specific disease.

**Transmission of Infection.** Among microorganisms, self-mobility is generally limited to distances of a few microns, inches or feet. Microorganisms cannot travel or swim long distances or fly or climb of their own volition. Unless they are transferred from one animal or plant to another by *direct contact,* they must depend on indirect transmission in (or on) extraneous *vectors,* which may be various *substances* (foods, water, milk), *objects* (hands, bedding, toys, eating utensils, cutting instruments), or certain *arthropods* contaminated with, or containing, the infectious agent.

Even though many pathogens are fairly durable in the outer world, especially those that form spores, conidia, or cysts, a great difficulty in travel for many pathogens, especially those of mammals, is that conditions in the world outside the body are too harsh. This is a penalty of extreme adaptation. Drying is fatal to some —meningococci, gonococci and syphilis spirochetes, for instance. Exposure to sunlight quickly kills many mammalian pathogens, such as tubercle bacilli. Others cannot live long in natural bodies of water, in soil or in feces. Others can travel only inside insects or animals.

Furthermore, not only are many infectious agents much restricted in the modes of travel available to them, but, if they are to infect, they must find a suitable *portal of entry* into a host at the end of their journey. The host must in addition be a *susceptible* subject, plant or animal. Nevertheless, in spite of their difficulties, like the lowly bedbug,* microorganisms get there just the same.

---

*The moth has wings of velvet;
  The butterfly, wings of flame.
  The bedbug has no wings at all,
  But he gets there just the same! (*Old rhyme*)

## 28.1   VECTORS OF INFECTION: AGENTS AND MECHANISMS

**Direct Contact.** Obviously, if one rubs against infectious material he runs a risk of infection. Diseases so transmitted are properly said to be *contagious* (L. *contagio* = touch or contact). However, the term *contagious* is often used interchangeably with *transmissible, communicable* and *infectious.* Transmission by direct contact is easy to guard against, especially if one avoids transferring the contagium to its special portal of entry. One does not voluntarily come into physical contact with feces, sputum or the visible sores of pustules of infected persons or the flesh or fluids of infected animals. If, in the course of professional or home-nursing duties, this cannot be avoided, one should wear rubber gloves or wash and disinfect the hands immediately afterward without touching anything first. However, an innocent kiss may transmit various respiratory diseases and all too often does, sometimes with tragic results to infants, young children and very ill or old persons. Common examples of diseases transmitted by direct contact among adults are several venereal diseases, including syphilis and gonorrhea, both spread by coitus; syphilis is spread by kissing, also, if there are open labial or oral lesions (Fig. 28.1).

HANDS. The practice of shaking hands doubtless transmits many pathogenic intestinal and respiratory organisms, notably poliomyelitis, bacillary dysentery and respiratory diseases. If hands are to be held they should be clean! (Fig. 28.2.)

Milk supplies and the food in any kitchen may become infected from the hands of careless milkers, dairymen or cooks who are carriers

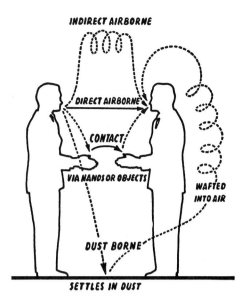

**Figure 28.2**   Transmission of infectious microorganisms of oral and respiratory tracts from one person to another. Absent from the picture but active, nevertheless, are contaminated foods, water and milk. (Courtesy of American Sterilizer Co.)

of respiratory or intestinal infectious microorganisms.

Washing the hands after defecation, urination or blowing the nose is a partial safeguard against transmission of intestinal and respiratory diseases, but careless and ignorant persons are often very lax in this respect.

Thorough cooking of foods followed by prompt eating or prompt refrigeration are other safeguards. Persons who handle foods for restaurants or institutions, as well as dairy workers, should be required by law to pass bacteriological examinations and are required to do so in many communities; however, enforcement is difficult and expensive. There is danger from enteric and respiratory infections in food handlers, but little from venereal disease or tuberculosis unless present in an open, acute or active stage.

**Saliva and Nasal Secretion.** The mucous secretions of the nose, throat, mouth and lungs, all combined to some extent with saliva, constitute one of the most formidable vectors of disease. Pneumococci, streptococci, meningococci, diphtheria bacilli and tubercle bacilli, as well as influenza virus, poliomyelitis virus, measles and mumps viruses and other organisms of respiratory disease are thus transmitted. These organisms are frequently carried in the upper respiratory tract by normal persons (Fig. 28.3).

We are all very careless in our habits in regard to mucus and saliva, far more so than we

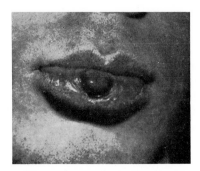

**Figure 28.1**   Primary syphilitic lesion (chancre) of the lip; typically swollen and firm or hard; contains *T. pallidum* and is highly infectious. (From Andrews and Domonkos: Diseases of the Skin. W. B. Saunders Co., 1963.)

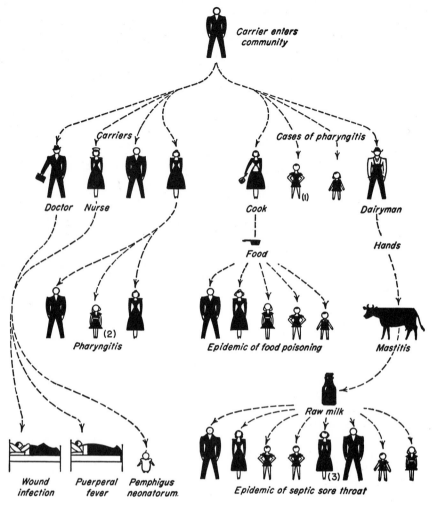

**Figure 28.3** Spread of streptococcal infection from a single carrier. Many persons became additional carriers and others developed various diseases. A child (1) with a case of pharyngitis also developed middle ear infection. A child (2) also developed the dreaded rheumatic fever. A woman (3) with a case of septic sore throat also developed subacute bacterial endocarditis, a frequently fatal heart infection. (From Witten: Microbiology with Application to Nursing. 2nd ed. McGraw-Hill Book Co.)

care to realize. The case has been stated vividly by a famous physician (Chapin):

If infection by contact is of such very great importance in the fecal-borne diseases, how much more important must it be in diseases in which the infective agent is found in the secretions of the nose and mouth, as is the case with diphtheria, scarlet fever, smallpox, mumps, measles, whooping cough, tuberculosis, influenza, and cerebrospinal meningitis. Everyone avoids feces and urine, but it is only the very few who have any objection to saliva.

Not only is the saliva made use of for a great variety of purposes, and numberless articles are for one reason or another placed in the mouth, but for no reason whatever, and all unconsciously, the fingers are with great frequency raised to the lips or to the nose. Who can doubt that if the salivary glands secreted indigo the fingers would continually be stained a deep blue.

DROPLET INFECTION. Droplets of saliva are presumably responsible for much disease transmission. Sneezing or coughing in public without a handkerchief is, like exceeding the speed limit, reprehensible but commonplace, and can have fatal results. Every cough or sneeze inevitably results in a microbe-laden spray. The smallest spray droplets remain suspended for some time in the air and may be carried many feet by draughts. The bacteria in such droplets may easily be demonstrated on an agar plate held near the sneeze and then incubated (Fig. 28.4). They land on food, lips, hands, furniture. After the microbe-laden droplets become dry the mucus-coated and protected bacteria and viruses that they contain then constitute what are called *droplet nuclei*. These may float about through the air for hours like very fine dust particles.

**Figure 28.4** Unstifled sneeze explodes a cloud of highly atomized, bacteria-laden droplets. Some droplets travel at such high speed that they are streaks even at 1/30,000 of a second. (Courtesy of M. W. Jennison, Department of Plant Sciences, Syracuse University.)

AIR DISINFECTION. The possibilities of disinfecting air in public places have been the subject of intensive and large-scale investigations. The two methods giving most promise are irradiation with ultraviolet light and the use of bactericidal vapors, sometimes called *aerosols*. Both methods are strongly bactericidal but neither is of significant value for practical purposes, except in special situations like operating rooms and other closed areas. These are discussed in more detail in Chapter 44.

**Dust.** From what has been said little imagination is needed to understand how disease may be transmitted by household or intramural dust. If not exposed to excessive heat or sunlight or other unfavorable influences, the organisms in droplet nuclei may survive in dust for considerable periods. When the dust is stirred up, persons inhaling it or getting it into operative or accidental wounds may suffer an attack of disease. One of the major problems of today in hospitals is the prevention of transmission of *Staphylococcus aureus* (the *"golden killer"* of popular newsprint) in air, dust and on fomites. Probably respiratory diseases like tuberculosis, pneumonia, diphtheria and scarlet fever are often transmitted by such means, since the organisms involved resist drying and exposure to diffuse daylight. Good examples of outdoor dustborne fungal diseases are coccidioidomycosis and histoplasmosis (Chapter 11). Infections transmitted directly or indirectly from person to person in institutions like hospitals are called *nosocomial* infections (L. *nosocomium* = hospital).

The dust in places where *psittacine birds* (e.g., parrots) are raised and sold can be a source of serious and often fatal infection with the organisms (see chlamydias) of *"parrot fever"* (*psitta-cosis*). The organisms occur in feces and nasal secretions of infected birds. These dry and are scattered as dust about the building. Strict federal laws of quarantine and control are now in effect.

In barracks and hospital wards dust and lint from clothing and bedding can be important means of disease transmission, especially of respiratory infections. One method of controlling this in certain situations is to impregnate bedding with imperceptible oils that tend to keep the dust from flying about. Floors and sweepings are also oiled. The oil merely controls dust; it does not kill microorganisms. Bactericidal sweeping compounds (oiled, disinfected sand or sawdust) are often used.

**Fomites.** Fomites are any inanimate objects or substances that serve to transfer infectious microorganisms from one host to another: man, animal or plant. Thus, soiled bed linen or clothing, eating utensils, toys, pencils and similar objects are dangerous after having been in contact with infected hosts harboring microorganisms that can be transmitted by such means, especially those of respiratory and intestinal diseases. Plant pathogens are transmitted by pruning instruments, gardener's gloves and the like.

**Eating Utensils.** Sanitization of public eating places has been developed on the basis of scientific study. Most restaurants have standardized dishwashing equipment that cleans and disinfects mechanically (Fig. 28.5). Proprietors of smaller restaurants, who have the well-being of their patrons in mind, either carefully scald all dishes after washing them or, after thoroughly washing them in *hot* water with a good detergent, rinse them in clean cool

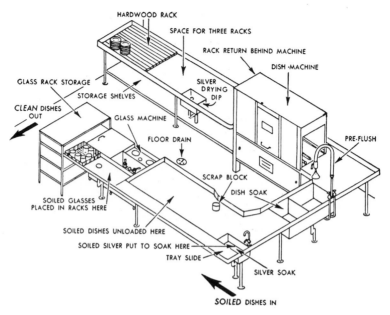

**Figure 28.5** One form of modern, sanitary dishwashing equipment. The working bench is of stainless steel. Soiled dishes are piled on the bench in the foreground. They are sorted and scraped, the larger scraps of food dropping into a barrel beneath the counter. Glasses are rinsed over rotating brushes, dipped in disinfectant and placed in trays in a rack (left). Silverware soaks in a pan of special detergent solution (right foreground). The dishes, arranged in baskets, are soaked and then given a preliminary rinse with *hard* streams of *hot* water (right). They then pass through a machine dishwasher (center, background). The silver, after soaking, passes through the same process as the dishes and is self-dried after a dip into a drying agent. Afterward all utensils are stacked and stored in dust-proof cabinets. Eating utensils handled in this way are virtually sterile. (From Wilson and Podas: Mod. Sanit., May, 1950.)

water containing at least 100 parts per million of available chlorine and dry by drainage. The odor of chlorine around a lunch counter is a favorable sign. Other disinfectants, without taste or odor, are also widely used.

EXAMINATION OF UTENSILS. Methods for measuring and controlling the amount of bacterial contamination of dishes are not yet exact. Most of the present methods for bacteriological examination of eating utensils center around some modification of the *swab-rinse technique*. In a simple procedure, a swab made of cotton or of a soluble material, such as calcium alginate, is moistened in a bland collecting fluid (water, broth or buffered saline solution). It is then used to wipe a certain prescribed area of the utensils shortly after they have been washed and dried. The swab is then shaken thoroughly in a known volume (10 ml.) of sterile saline solution or, better, broth, in a vial.

After shaking the swab in the collecting fluid, dilution-plate counts are made of the bacteria in the fluid. From the numbers of colonies obtained an estimate is made of the degree of contamination on the dishes. Commonly, a minimum standard of 100 organisms per utensil is recommended.

A standardized method taking these and other factors into consideration has been outlined by a committee of the American Public Health Association. This group specifies formulae for media, solutions, area swabbed, method of swabbing and cultural details. There are also other, direct methods (Fig. 28.6).

Unfortunately, there is no exact method of measuring the amount of disease spread by dirty dishes and eating utensils in unhygienic restaurants. From an esthetic viewpoint alone, one does not like to feel that a little saliva from previous patrons is being included, gratis, with his meal.

PAPER DISHES. The use of paper cups, dishes and eating utensils is an effective step toward eliminating the sanitary evils of public glass and chinaware and metal spoons and forks. Not only is expensive dishwashing equipment with its noise, sloppiness and heat eliminated, but labor and fuel costs are reduced, breakage costs are trifling and esthetic and sanitary standards enormously improved. Bacteriological studies of paper used for containers and tableware show negligible content of microorganisms, of which none is pathogenic. Paper dishes are used with success in many snack bars and smaller

**Figure 28.6** Direct bacteriological examination of eating utensils. Warm sterile fluid agar was poured into the plate. The fork was placed in the agar and moved about to dislodge contaminating material. The dish was then covered, the agar allowed to solidify and the dish incubated. The bacteria from the fork developed into colonies which are clearly visible. Among these hundreds of colonies there are undoubtedly pathogenic bacteria. (From Barton: Appl. Microbiol., vol. 2.)

restaurants but have not yet been perfected to the point where the public accepts them in place of china and glass at formal meals.

**Foods.** Foods that are moist and not very acid, e.g., soups, puddings, meat stew or pie (not pickles [acid] or bread [dry]), are excellent culture media for many microorganisms. The great majority of microorganisms in foods are harmless molds and saprophytic species of bacteria. They may cause the food to become sour, putrid or otherwise "spoiled" but do not cause infection. However, carriers of respiratory or intestinal pathogens may infect foods with the typhoid bacillus (*Salmonella typhi*) and dysentery bacilli (*Shigella* species) (Chapter 36); toxin-producing *Staphylococcus aureus* (Chapter 33); the hemolytic streptococci (*Streptococcus pyogenes*) which cause scarlet fever and septic sore throat (Chapter 33); the diphtheria bacillus (*Corynebacterium diphtheriae*) (Chapter 35); and others. The infection of foods with respiratory or enteric pathogens is often the result of carelessness by food handlers who are unrecognized carriers of the organisms and who sneeze or cough over foods or manipulate them with hands unwashed after toilet or after nose-blowing. Raw meats from infected animals are notorious sources of infection: cattle, bovine tuberculosis; swine and poultry, salmonellosis; wild rabbits, tularemia; cattle, swine and goats, undulant fever. (See the specific diseases for details.)

Foods may or may not be sterilized by cooking. The center of large masses of food, such as a deep pan of bread pudding, macaroni with cheese, or hash is not always raised to a bactericidal temperature by baking or boiling. Further, if the cooked food is infected during handling *after* it has cooled, and is left standing (actually, *incubating*) for hours in a warm kitchen, the persons who eat it might (in some instances) just as well drink a culture in the laboratory. In case of doubt, discard the food or, second best, recook it. Always keep perishable foods *covered* (avoiding contamination) and *refrigerated* (avoiding incubation).

FOOD POISONING.   Two other bacterial diseases associated with improperly handled foods are not infections like typhoid fever, scarlet fever and diphtheria but are *poisonings* caused by toxins preformed in the foods. One form of food poisoning, called *botulism,* is caused by *Clostridium botulinum* (Chapter 32). The other type of food poisoning, *staphylococcal food poisoning,* is caused by certain strains of staphylococci (Chapter 33). Botulism is highly lethal; staphylococcal food poisoning is not so fatal but is highly unpleasant and prostrating.

**Milk as a Disease Vector.**   Sterilized milk is often used in the laboratory as a culture medium, and it is a good one. It is thus clear why milk, incubated for hours in the sun on a loading platform, was, in days before general sanitation and pasteurization, the vector of scores of epidemics of diphtheria, typhoid fever, dysentery, scarlet fever and sore throat ("strep throat") derived from infected cattle and dairy workers. There are two principal methods by which milk may become infectious for man and cause epidemics:

The milk, as it is drawn from the udder, may contain pathogenic microorganisms which are infecting the udder of the cow. The organisms of most importance in this respect are: *Mycobacterium tuberculosis* var. *bovis; Brucella* (cause of undulant fever); *Coxiella burnetii* (the rickettsias of Q fever); *Streptococcus pyogenes* (cause of scarlet fever and septic sore throat), introduced into the udder by a milker carrying the organisms; and *Staphylococcus aureus,* cause of boils and mastitis.

Milk freshly drawn from a *normal* udder usually contains a few harmless contaminants but is free from pathogens. Pathogens of *human* origin may be introduced into the milk *after it is drawn,* by infected persons, utensils, wash-water or other vectors. The more important organisms of this sort are: *Salmonella* and *Shigella* (causes of typhoid fever and dysentery); *Streptococcus pyogenes; Corynebacterium diphtheriae; Staphylococcus aureus. S. aureus* usually does not *infect* but if allowed to grow extensively in the milk can make it very poisonous by excreting staphylococcal *enterotoxin* (page 414). The milk may also contain the toxin if secreted by a cow with mastitis caused by *S. aureus.*

PASTEURIZATION. As mentioned previously, pasteurization consists in holding the milk in tanks at 145° F. (63° C.) for 30 minutes and immediately refrigerating. Disinfection of milk is accomplished in many dairies by heating the milk rapidly in a coiled tube or in thin layers between metal plates to 71.6 to 80° C. and holding at that temperature for 15 to 30 seconds, then cooling. These high-temperature-short-time (HTST or *flash*) methods save time and money and are effective so far as sanitation of milk is concerned.

Pasteurization does not sterilize milk. Many bacteria, especially sporeformers, survive 63° C. for 30 minutes. These survivors will cause pasteurized milk to spoil if it is not properly refrigerated. However, pasteurization eliminates all of the *pathogens* referred to above. Staphylococcal enterotoxin is very thermostable and if already present in the milk, as in milk from an udder infected with staphylococci, is not inactivated by pasteurization. Never drink unpasteurized milk or *uncertified* raw milk. (See Chapter 45.)

**Blood and Blood Derivatives.** Blood not infrequently contains pathogenic microorganisms. In certain infectious diseases the etiologic agents circulate in the blood for varying periods. Typhoid bacilli are readily found in the blood during the first week of the disease. Meningococci not infrequently occur in the blood, even in the absence of meningitis. Rickettsias are present in the blood during typhus and Rocky Moun-

tain spotted fevers. Many viruses (e.g., yellow fever, dengue, encephalitis) and protozoa (malaria parasites or trypanosomes of sleeping sickness) also circulate in the blood.

Any organisms circulating in the blood may be transmitted by improperly sterilized cutting or piercing instruments. Rickettsias and many viruses and some protozoa are also transmissible in blood via certain blood-sucking arthropods, their natural vectors.

HOMOLOGOUS SERUM JAUNDICE. Two closely similar viruses occur over long periods in the blood of apparently healthy persons: (a) the virus of infectious hepatitis or, more accurately, of *epidemic viral jaundice* (also called hepatitis virus A); (b) the virus of homologous serum jaundice or serum hepatitis (also called hepatitis virus B).

These viruses can be carried in blood of donors, serum, plasma, blood-bank blood, and by syringes, needles or instruments not properly sterilized. Very rigid precautions must be taken in handling any human blood, tissues, derivatives thereof, or blood-contaminated instruments to avoid transmission of these viruses. Virus B has the property, rare if not unique among viruses, of being able to withstand boiling for some minutes; virus A may withstand near-pasteurization temperatures: 56° C. for 30 minutes, or more.

It is worth noting that hepatitis virus A, while sometimes transmitted in blood as noted, is most commonly transmitted by feces and sewage and food, including shellfish, contaminated by them, and causes serious epidemics; hence the term *epidemic* jaundice. Virus B is not transmitted in feces.

BLOOD-BANK BLOOD. Human blood may temporarily have many organisms in it immediately after any severe injury, after some tooth extractions or surgery, or even in the absence of any injury at all. Such organisms are normally quickly removed by phagocytes and natural antibacterial factors in the blood. Blood drawn at such times for blood-bank purposes may, if not properly refrigerated, contain large numbers of bacteria, because the few bacteria that may have been initially present soon multiply to thousands. Even refrigerated blood may support growth of some psychrophilic organisms. Sometimes blood is contaminated by bacteria introduced by the hypodermic needle from the surface of the skin. However, under proper conditions of collection, storage and use, danger from blood-bank blood is relatively remote.

## 28.2   INFECTED ARTHROPODS

**Arthropod Bites.**   As noted in the section on viruses, many plant diseases are transmitted by bites of leafhoppers and other insects. There are also many diseases of man and lower animals, which, in nature, are transmitted only by the bites of arthropods. In 1878 a mosquito (*Culex fatigans*) was shown to transmit the worm *Filaria bancrofti*, agent of one form of *filariasis* (a notorious symptom of which is *elephantiasis*). The classical observations of Smith and Kilborne in 1893 on transmission of Texas fever of cattle by the cattle tick (*Boophilus annulatus*) were the first on tick transmission of protozoan disease. Certain mosquitoes (*Anopheles*) were later found

to transmit malaria. Usually, but not always, each disease has its own *specific* insect vector. Several arthropods of importance as vectors of pathogenic microorganisms are shown in Figure 28.7.

Several arthropod-borne pathogenic agents are listed in Table 28.1.

**Arthropod Feces.**   Cockroaches were shown as early as 1914 to transfer cholera vibrios in their intestines for at least 48 hours after feeding on human cholera feces. Ants transmit cholera and probably other enteric diseases in the same manner. Flies have long been under indictment for the same crimes.

Many bloodsucking insects deposit feces on the skin when they feed. The feces of lice

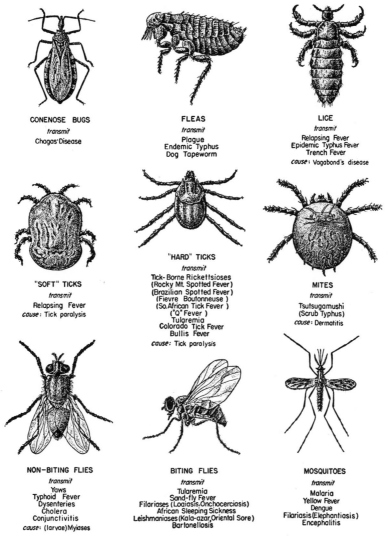

CONENOSE BUGS
*transmit*
Chagas'Disease

FLEAS
*transmit*
Plague
Endemic Typhus
Dog Tapeworm

LICE
*transmit*
Relapsing Fever
Epidemic Typhus Fever
Trench Fever
*cause*: Vagabond's disease

"SOFT" TICKS
*transmit*
Relapsing Fever
*cause*: Tick paralysis

"HARD" TICKS
*transmit*
Tick-Borne Rickettsioses
(Rocky Mt. Spotted Fever)
(Brazilian Spotted Fever)
(Fievre Boutonneuse)
(So.African Tick Fever)
("Q" Fever)
Tularemia
Colorado Tick Fever
Bullis Fever
*cause*: Tick paralysis

MITES
*transmit*
Tsutsugamushi
(Scrub Typhus)
*cause*: Dermatitis

NON-BITING FLIES
*transmit*
Yaws
Typhoid Fever
Dysenteries
Cholera
Conjunctivitis
*cause*: (larvae)Myiases

BITING FLIES
*transmit*
Tularemia
Sand-fly Fever
Filariases (Loaiasis,Onchocerciasis)
African Sleeping Sickness
Leishmaniases (Kala-azar,Oriental Sore)
Bartonellosis

MOSQUITOES
*transmit*
Malaria
Yellow Fever
Dengue
Filariasis(Elephantiasis)
Encephalitis

**Figure 28.7**   Types of insects that transmit disease. (From Stitt, Clough and Branham: Practical Bacteriology, Hematology, and Parasitology. McGraw-Hill Book Co.)

**TABLE 28.1** SOME REPRESENTATIVE ZOONOSES

| Diseases | Causative Organism | Animals Principally Involved | Transmitting Agent |
|---|---|---|---|
| *Viral:* | | | |
| Eastern equine encephalitis | Eastern equine virus | Birds, equines | Mosquitoes |
| Japanese B encephalitis | Japanese B virus | Birds, horses, swine | Mosquitoes |
| St. Louis encephalitis | St. Louis virus | Birds | Mosquitoes |
| "Jungle" yellow fever | Yellow fever virus | Monkeys | Mosquitoes |
| Influenza | Influenza virus A, B, etc. | Swine, horses | Oro-nasal secretions |
| Rabies | Rabies virus | Canines and other mammals | Infected saliva |
| *Rickettsial:* | | | |
| Murine typhus | *Rickettsia mooseri* | Rats | Rat fleas |
| Q fever | *Coxiella burnetii* | Domestic animals (cattle, sheep) | Infected milk, dust, ticks |
| Scrub typhus (tsutsugamushi) | *Rickettsia tsutsugamushi* | Rodents | Larval mites |
| Rocky Mountain spotted fever | *Rickettsia rickettsii* | Rodents, dogs | Ticks |
| *Chlamydial:* | | | |
| Psittacosis Ornithosis | Chlamydias | Psittacine birds, poultry, pigeons | Oro-nasal secretions, feces, infected dust |
| *Bacterial:* | | | |
| Anthrax | *Bacillus anthracis* | Domestic livestock | Infected tissues, fluids, dust, hair |
| Brucellosis | *Brucella* species | Domestic livestock | Animal fluids and tissues, milk |
| Bubonic plague | *Pasteurella pestis* | Rodents | Fleas, ticks |
| Leptospirosis | *Leptospira* species | Rodents, dogs, swine, wild mammals | Animal tissues, fluids, urine |
| Relapsing fevers | *Borrelia* species | Cave rodents | Ticks, lice |
| Salmonellosis | *Salmonella* species | Rats, poultry, dogs | Excreta, flesh, eggs |
| Tuberculosis | *Mycobacterium tuberculosis* | Domestic livestock | Milk, flesh |
| Tularemia | *Pasteurella tularensis* | Wild rabbits | Deer flies, various ticks, flesh |
| *Fungal:* | | | |
| Ringworm (tinea) favus | *Microsporum* species *Trichophyton* species | Various domestic animals | Contact, hair, dander |
| *Protozoal:* | | | |
| Leishmaniasis (various forms) | *Leishmania* species | Dogs, cats, rodents | Sand fly |
| Toxoplasmosis | *Toxoplasma gondii* | Wild mammals, birds | Unknown |
| Trypanosomiasis | *Trypanosoma* species | Man, wild game | Tsetse flies (Africa); "kissing bugs" (South America) |
| Malaria | Simian species of *Plasmodium* | Monkeys | Mosquitoes |

infected with typhus rickettsias will infect if scratched into the skin. Feces of infected fleas from rats, prairie dogs and similar rodents contain plague bacilli and may contaminate small wounds or scratches. Indeed, many bloodsucking insects may pass infective agents in the feces and may also cause infection by being crushed on the skin near or in an abrasion or wound. Engorged ticks on dogs are especially dangerous in this respect because they contain a relatively large volume of blood that can transmit the rickettsias of Rocky Mountain spotted fever.

**Bodies of Arthropods.**   Arthropods that fly or crawl from unsanitary, unscreened and undisinfected privies to hospitals or to dwellings may mechanically transmit intestinal and other disease organisms on their feet and bodies. In areas where flies abound, especially rural or city slum areas, if there is access to infectious sewage or feces, enteric fevers will usually be more prevalent during the summer months when flies are numerous. In places where city sewerage systems are not available, flyborne disease can be avoided to a large extent by the construction of screened and deep-pit or other sanitary types of privies or, better still, by the installation of sanitary plumb-

ing and septic tanks. Plans and specifications for such structures can be obtained from state health departments.

## 28.3   ZOONOSES

Animals constitute an enormous and ever-present reservoir of agents infectious for human beings. Diseases primarily of animals but transmissible to man are called *zoonoses.* A partial list of zoonoses is shown in Table 28.1.

**Animal Bites.**   Any animal (or human) bite will introduce a mixture of the microorganisms present in the saliva and on the teeth. There is always crushing of tissues and violation of the defensive barriers. The so-called "normal flora" of the mouth is introduced in large numbers. Several ordinarily "harmless" organisms, introduced under such circumstances, can become dangerous, invasive pathogens. Such bites are always infectious and should immediately be opened, cleaned, disinfected and covered with sterile gauze.

The most notorious pathogen transmitted by animal bites is the virus of *rabies,* or hydro-

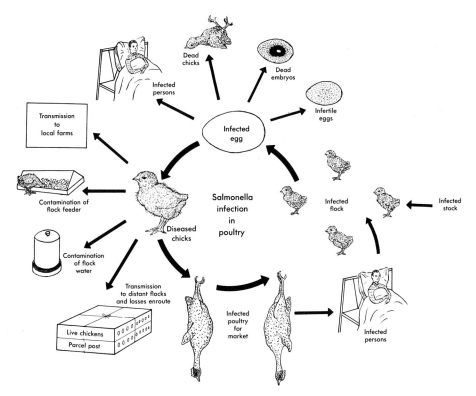

**Figure 28.8**   Transmission of salmonellosis to and from poultry and man. (Adapted from Williams, Zumbro and Mac-Donald, in: Animal Diseases. The 1956 Year Book of Agriculture, U. S. Dept. of Agriculture.)

phobia. All mammals are susceptible to rabies and can transmit it. Cats, dogs, foxes and wolves are particularly dangerous in this respect. Three varieties of bats—vampire, insectivorous and fruit-eating—have been shown to harbor and transmit rabies among themselves and to cattle, other animals and man.

**Eggs.** Even the fragile and inscrutable egg is guilty as a disease vector. Poultry are frequently carriers of *Salmonella* (paratyphoid and food-infection organisms). Numerous large outbreaks of food infection (diarrhea) due to *Salmonella* species have been traced to foods made with raw eggs (mayonnaise). Eggs often contain infectious organisms when laid by an already infected hen (Fig. 28.8).

**Rats.** Rats are well known as vectors of disease to man. Their feces transmit food infection (salmonellosis); their urine, leptospirosis or hemorrhagic jaundice. The fleas of rats transmit bubonic ("black") plague and murine typhus. Their bites, especially in the Orient, introduce the agent of sodoku or rat-bite fever.

Rats should be eliminated by poisoning and trapping and deprivation of food and breeding places through cleanliness and rat-proof construction. Their fleas may be temporarily exterminated by dusting runways and places of refuge with DDT.

**Domestic Environments and Diseases.** Infectious diseases, both of man and animals, are usually much more frequent and widespread in crowded, unsanitary living quarters than in clean spacious dwellings. This is well illustrated in the case of insect-borne diseases of man such as typhus (body lice) and plague (rat fleas) which are notoriously associated with low-grade living conditions, often as a result of wars. It is equally true of respiratory diseases and enteric infections. Microorganisms spread by oral and nasal secretions, as in sneezing and coughing, and by soiled hands can much more readily be transmitted from person to person in close, crowded, cold and damp rooms than in spacious, well-ventilated, warm and dry quarters.

Infection by enteric viruses (polio, hepatitis) and other microorganisms of the intestinal tract (dysentery, typhoid and related bacilli, intestinal worms and protozoa) are obviously transmitted by feces-soiled hands, clothing, soil, water or food. It is very significant that a direct correlation has been shown to exist between many of these diseases and the *availability of ample clean water for domestic purposes,* especially for washing of hands and installation of sanitary plumbing.

## SUPPLEMENTARY READING

Banfield, W. G., Woke, P. A., MacKay, C. M., and Cooper, H. L.: Mosquito transmission of a reticulum cell sarcoma of hamsters. Science, *148*:1239, 1965.

Bell, J. F., Moore, G. J., Raymond, G. H., and Tibbs, C. E.: Characteristics of rabies in bats in Montana. Amer. J. Pub. Health, *52*:1293, 1962.

Berg, G.: The food vehicle in virus transmission. Health Laby. Science, *1*:51, 1964.

Burrows, W., Moulder, J. W., and Lewert, R. M.: Textbook of Microbiology, 18th ed. W. B. Saunders Co., Philadelphia. 1963.

Busvine, J. R.: Insects and Hygiene, 2nd ed. Chapman and Hall, London. 1966.

Davé, K. H., and Wallis, R. D.: Survival of type 1 and type 3 polio vaccine virus in blowflies (*Phaenicia sericata*) at 40° C. Proc. Soc. Exp. Biol. Med., *119*:126, 1965.

Faust, E. C., Beaver, P. C., and Jung, R. C.: Animal Agents and Vectors of Human Disease. 2nd ed. Lea and Febiger, Philadelphia. 1962.

Gordon, J. E. (Chairman): Control of Communicable Diseases in Man, 10th ed. American Public Health Association, New York. 1965.

Gregory, P. H., and Monteith, J. L., editors: Airborne Microbes. Seventeenth Symposium, Soc. Gen. Microbiol., London. 1967.

Hagan, and Bruner, D. W.: Infectious Diseases of Domestic Animals, 5th ed. Cornell University Press, Ithaca, N. Y. 1961.

Herms, W. B., and James, M. T.: Medical Entomology, 5th ed. The Macmillan Co., New York. 1961.

Hoogstral, H.: Ticks in relation to human diseases caused by *Rickettsia* species. Ann. Rev. Entomol., *12*:377, 1967.

Hull, T. G.: Diseases Transmitted from Animals to Man, 5th ed. Charles C Thomas, Springfield, Ill. 1963.

Korff, R. S., and Sear, H. S.: Internal temperature of steamed clams. New Eng. J. Med., *276*:737, 1967.

Langmuir, A. D.: Airborne Infection: How important for public health? Amer. J. Pub. Health, *54*:1666, 1964.

Mackel, D. C., Langley, L. F., and Prchal, C. J.: Occurrence in swine of *Salmonella* and serotypes of *Escherichia coli* pathogenic to man. J. Bact., *89*:1434, 1965.

Ordinance and Code Relative to Eating and Drinking Establishments. U. S. Public Health Service Publication No. 37. Government Printing Office, Washington, D. C. 1950.

Pratt, H. D., Littig, K. S., and Marshall, C. W.: Introduction to arthropods of public health importance. U. S. Public Health Service Publication No. 772. Government Printing Office, Washington, D. C. 1960.

Proctor, D. F.: Airborne disease and the upper respiratory tract. Bact. Rev., *30*:498, 1966.

Rosebury, T.: Bacteria Indigenous to Man. *In:* Dubos, R. J.: Bacterial and Mycotic Infections of Man, 4th ed. J. B. Lippincott Co., Philadelphia. 1965.

Sadler, W. W., and Corstvet, R. E.: Second survey of market poultry for *Salmonella* infection. Appl. Microbiol., *13*:348, 1965.

Schwabe, C. W.: Veterinary Medicine and Human Health. The Williams & Wilkins Co., Baltimore. 1964.

World Health Organization: Joint WHO/FAO Committee on Zoonoses. Tech. Rept. Ser., No. 169. World Health Organization, Geneva, Switzerland, 1959.

Yoeli, M.: Animal infections and human disease. Sci. Amer., *202*:161, 1960.

# 4

---

## *The Parade of the Procaryons*

In this part of "Fundamentals of Microbiology" the principal actors in the drama (or comedy?) of Microbiology make their first definitive and personal appearance on the stage that has been set and lighted in the preceding sections. Here are the procaryons (exclusive of the previously discussed Cyanophyceae): the various Orders of the Class Schizomycetes and the related Tribe Rickettsiae and Family Chlamydiaceae. All are paraded to reveal their beauties and mysteries, their evil (to man and his allies) and their beneficence (to *Homo sapiens,* et al.).

As soon becomes evident, there is more in Microbiology than meets the eye; even through an electron microscope. The more we learn, the more we become aware that we are only at the beginning of the path of learning that leads to a solution of the eons-old mystery of life. As any student will find, if he examines the "Journal of Bacteriology" (a publication of the American Society for Microbiology) it was Louis Pasteur who said, "It is characteristic of Science and Progress that they continually open new fields to our vision." Nothing could be more true of the Science of Microbiology.

# Chapter 29

---

# THE BACTERIA
# Systematic Study

Ancient systems of biological classification were necessarily based almost entirely on characteristics discernible only with the naked eye. The inferences and classifications of those times were often erroneous but, as knowledge grew, so did accuracy in biological classifications. After the advent of microscopes over 300 years ago, ancient classifications of microorganisms had to undergo many revisions.

Today's identifying descriptions and classifications of all forms of life are, like those of the ancients, based primarily on form, size, motility, color, whether or not dependent on sunlight, and so on, but they are daily growing enormously more exact and complicated through extremely sophisticated researches with high powered electron microscopes in the fields of molecular biology, biochemistry, biophysics and genetics. Some of these parameters as to bacteria are outlined in the chapter on classification (Chapter 30). Classifications and identifying descriptions of viruses, chlamydias, rickettsias and fungi are discussed in the chapters dealing with those organisms. (See also Tables 29.1 and 29.2.) Here we present a simple example of a type of procedure commonly used and available in most laboratories for the isolation and identification of a common species of bacterium.

In spite of the fact that, as previously explained, identifying characteristics of bacteria vary, it is rare that all characters vary simultaneously. Further, variations are usually recognized for what they are. Under uniform conditions of laboratory study, and in spite of variations, bacteria generally retain their fundamental distinguishing characteristics (Chapter 30). It is necessary to know what these are and how to determine them in the laboratory.

## 29.1 PROCEDURES IN IDENTIFICATION

For purposes of discussion let us proceed as though we have been given an unknown organism for complete identification and systematic study.

**Initial Determination of Group.** The first important step in the systematic study of an unknown microorganism is to determine to which of the major groups of microorganisms it belongs and whether other species are present as contaminants. Much information can be obtained by simple microscopic examination. Let us assume that the organism we are investigating is a minute granule or sphere 1 to 2 $\mu$ in diameter and readily visible with an optical microscope equipped with an oil-immersion lens and giving a magnification of about 900 $\times$. It is therefore not a virus. Its size and shape are within the range of bacterial dimensions and form. It shows no evidence of yeastlike budding, distinct eucaryotic-type nucleus, branching filamentous structures or motility; therefore it is probably not a yeast, mold or protozoan. It is not pleomorphic and does not produce large bodies and elemental granules characteristic of PPLO. In all probability it is a bacterium (see Tables 29.1 and 29.2).

**Purification of Culture.** The next step in an exact study of any bacterium is to separate it from other forms with which it might be mixed. These would introduce error into various biochemical experiments or tests performed in the course of the identification. This process is spoken of as isolation in pure culture. Many a student* has fallen into difficulties by assuming the purity of a culture and neglecting this very

---

*As well as veteran researchers!

**TABLE 29.1** DISTINCTIVE PROPERTIES OF PROCARYOTIC PROTISTA*

| | Blue-green Algae | Bacteria† |
|---|---|---|
| Photosynthesis | All species contain chlorophyll *a* only, with phycocyanin and beta carotene; free oxygen given off; typically aerobic. | Only species of Suborder Rhodobacteriineae contain photosynthetic pigments bacteriochlorophyll or chlorobium chlorophyll; none contains chlorophyll *a* or phycocyanin; do not give off free oxygen; many anaerobic or facultative. |
| Cell differentiation | Slight; some "holdfasts"; some arthrospore-like resting cells: conidia, heterocysts, akinetes; no thermostable endospores; no sex cells known. | Very slight; conidiospores in moldlike Streptomycetales; extremely thermostable endospores in Family Bacillaceae; arthrospore-like microcysts in most Myxobacterales and in some *Azotobacter*. |
| Multiplication | Transverse binary fission; asexual so far as known. | Generally transverse binary fission; asexual, although genetic recombination by a primitive type of conjugation occurs. |
| Cell groupings | Many form trichomes, chains or irregular masses within slimy or gelatinous matrix; some unicellular species resemble bacteria. | Generally free, undifferentiated, single cells; some occur in sheaths or in irregular masses within slimy or gelatinous matrix; some form trichomes, some form moldlike mycelia; some form chains. |
| Cell walls | Thick, rigid, morphologically distinct; supporting fibers of mucopolysaccharide; occasionally cellulose(?), capsules or sheaths of pectic materials usually prominent. | *Except* Orders Myxobacterales, Spirochaetales, Mycoplasmatales and probably the chlamydias, thick, rigid, morphologically distinct, supporting fibers partly or wholly or mucopolysaccharide; capsules or sheaths in some species, usually of polysaccharides, polypeptides. |
| Motility (when present) | Gliding, bending, oscillatory; no cytoplasmic streaming; no flagella or cilia. | *Except* Orders Myxobacterales, Beggiatoales and Spirochaetales, which exhibit flexing, gliding, and rotation without flagella, actively progressive by means of flagella. |
| Size of cell | Generally smaller than eucaryotic cells; minimum commonly $> 5\mu$; readily visible with good optical microscopes ($50 \times$ to $600 \times$). | Much smaller than Cyanophyceae; maximum diameters commonly $<5\mu$, minimum, $>0.2\mu$; readily visible only with very good optical microscopes ($400 \times$ to $1200 \times$). |
| Cultivation and nutrition | Many species cultivable on inanimate media; typically autotrophic (photolithotrophic) though not necessarily obligately; holophytic. | *Except* Rickettsia and Chlamydiaceae, generally cultivable on inanimate media; holophytic; some photolithotrophic, some chemolithotrophic, some chemoorganotrophic, some photoorganotrophic; some obligately aerobic, some obligately anaerobic, some facultative. |

*Except viruses.
†Including rickettsias and chlamydias.

important step. Even cultures of animal tissue cells have been found infected with protozoa, viruses, bacteria and PPLO derived from the animal source of the tissue cells. Such cultures also frequently become accidentally contaminated with yeasts, molds and bacteria from extraneous sources. Microscopic examination of a smear stained by Gram's method may sometimes reveal the presence of contaminants and very often gives a valuable clue as to the genus or family of the organism, but it cannot be depended upon entirely since many different bacteria, including contaminants, look and stain exactly alike. The culture must be purified. The preparation of pure cultures is outlined in Chapter 4.

It is advisable to start with some solid nutrient substance that is known to support growth of a wide variety of organisms. A medium like meat-infusion agar containing 0.5 per cent glucose is very useful in such situations. If the unknown will not grow on it in the Petri plate, then it may be necessary to prepare a medium especially to resemble as closely as possible the material on which the organism originally grew, if this is known. If not known, autotrophic and other heterotrophic media must be furnished, supplemented with blood or yeast extract that contains vitamins and growth factors needed by some species of bacteria.

If contaminating bacteria are present, they will probably be evident as colonies of distinc-

**TABLE 29.2   GROUPS AND CHARACTERISTICS OF PROTISTA**

A. Protozoa (Animal Kingdom)—eucaryotic cell structure; no morphologically and chemically differentiated cell walls; cell cuticle or plasmalemma often contains chitin; typically without photosynthetic system; typically motile by ameboid, flagellate or ciliate action; nutrition may be holozoic or holophytic; typically organotrophic; diameters generally $>20 \mu$; sexual phenomena commonly evident; cells typically capable of independent mutiplication; exhibit cytoplasmic streaming.

B. Protophyta (Plant Kingdom)—eucaryotic or procaryotic cell structure; except PPLO, have morphologically and chemically differentiated cell walls; *except* the Eumycetes, most bacteria, and all rickettsias and chlamydias, have photosynthetic system; motility may be by flagella or by gliding, flexing, oscillatory or rotatory movements; nutrition typically holophytic; may be autotrophic or organotrophic; cells typically capable of independent multiplication.*

   I. "Higher" (green) Algae—eucaryotic cell structure; cell walls contain cellulose; chloroplasts with chlorophyll *a* and generally *b* or *c* and $\alpha$, $\beta$ and *c* carotenes; do not contain phycocyanin (phycobilin); diameters generally $>20 \mu$; motility when present due to flagella, no cilia; in photosynthesis split $H_2O$ and release *oxygen*; sexual phenomena commonly evident; aerobic; exhibit cytoplasmic streaming.

   II. Eumycetes (yeasts and molds)—eucaryotic cell structure; cell walls commonly contain chitin; no photosynthetic systems or phycocyanin; motility generally restricted to flagellate gametes of aquatic species; nutrition holophytic, organotrophic; diameters of filaments (hyphae) generally $>15 \mu$; sexual phenomena commonly evident; obligately or preferentially aerobic; exhibit cytoplasmic streaming.

   III. Cyanophyceae (blue-green algae)—procaryotic cell structure; cell walls principally mucopolysaccharide complex; chromatophores contain *only* chlorophyll *a*; $\beta$ carotene and phycocyanin present; diameters generally $<20 \mu$; motility when present is of gliding, bending and twisting type, slow, no flagella or cilia; in photosynthesis, split $H_2O$ and release oxygen; no sexual phenomena described; aerobic; no cytoplasmic streaming.

   IV. Schizomycetes (bacteria)—procaryotic cell structure; cell walls principally mucopolysaccharide and lipopolysaccharide complexes; may be photosynthetic or nonphotosynthetic; motility when present by flagella or alga-like bending, creeping or twisting or (in Spirochaetales) rapid rotatory motion; nutrition holophytic; may be photo- or chemolithotrophic, photo- or chemoorganotrophic; diameters typically $<5 \mu$; sexual phenomena primitive, no true gametes or zygotes; aerobic, anaerobic or facultative; no cytoplasmic streaming.

     a. Suborder Rhodobacteriineae—photosynthetic bacteria; photosynthetic pigments in purple and brown species are bacteriochlorophyll with accessory carotenes; in green species, chlorobium-chlorophyll with carotenes; no phycobilins (phycocyanin); photosynthesis active in red and infra-red; motility when present alga-like, no flagella; in photosynthesis split $H_2S$ and release S; no sexual phenomena described; typically anaerobic.

C. Viruses—not cellular in structure; incapable of independent multiplication.

    *Except rickettsias and chlamydias which are obligate intracellular parasites.

tive appearance after incubation of the plates. However, many different bacteria produce colonies of very similar appearance, and it may be necessary to examine stained smears made from selected colonies in order to obtain the desired organism. Even this may yield no useful information, because different species may produce colonies closely resembling each other, and also possess identical morphological and staining properties. In this case we must either decide which of the two (or more) kinds of bacteria in the sample is (are) the contaminant(s) or identify both (all) and decide afterward.

For present purposes let us inoculate the unknown culture onto three plates of blood-glucose-meat-infusion agar at pH 7.4. Such a medium supports the growth of a wide variety of (but not necessarily all) heterotrophic, saprophytic and parasitic bacteria. It cannot be depended on to support autotrophs. Let us also inoculate three plates of meat- or yeast-extract agar, without blood, in the same manner. If thought necessary, three silica-gel plates may be prepared from some of the solutions noted elsewhere to serve for the cultivation of strictly autotrophic bacteria such as *Nitrosomonas*. Similar media with organic energy source and agar but devoid of nitrogen source will serve for such autotroph-like species as *Azotobacter*, which obtains its nitrogen from the air. One plate of each kind of medium may now be incubated at 25° C., one at 37° C. and one at 55° C.

**Initial Observations of Growth.**   After 24 hours there may be no growth, in which case we may continue incubation for several days. But let us suppose that after 24 hours there is no growth on the plates prepared for autotrophs and near-autotrophs, very sparse or no growth on the extract and infusion plates incubated at 55° C., while good growth occurs on plates of both the extract and infusion media held at 25° C., and somewhat less growth at 37° C. These data tell us the approximate optimum temperature for growth and also give us an idea as to the kind of media and pH likely to be of use in dealing with our organism. Since it grows readily on simple, organic, nonliving culture media without serum it is neither rickettsia, chlamydia nor virus. Since it does not require sunlight for growth it is neither an alga nor a photosynthetic bacterium. It is clearly aerobic (or facultative), mesophilic as to temperature and pH, chemoorganotrophic, and probably a saprophyte (though possibly a pathogen). Apparently all of the colonies are alike and *presumably* (but not *certainly*) no contaminant is present. At least, they have not formed *distinctive* colonies under these particular conditions of growth.

Colonies (or any other sort of culture: agar, tissue-cell or otherwise) are not necessarily "pure" and may contain more than one species of morphologically and tinctorially identical cells. One or more colonies should be emulsified in broth and again streaked on a suitable solid medium and examined for purity.

An inspection of the growth on the agar gives an idea as to the size, shape, color and consistency of colonies. Let us say that the colonies are about 1 to 4 mm. in diameter, glistening, convex, circular, opaque, butyrous in consistency and lemon-yellow in color.*

**Study of Pure Culture.** By carefully transferring a portion of one of these colonies with a sterile needle into a tube of extract broth, we provide ourselves with a pure culture that may be studied further as described below.

If no growth occurred on any of the plates inoculated with the original material, we may assume that:

(a) No living bacteria were present in the inoculum; or

---

*Pigment is often beautifully shown on cubes of white potato sterilized with a few drops of water in the bottom of a tube.

(b) The temperatures used were not suitable; or

(c) Some other medium, possibly with a different pH, is necessary; or

(d) The bacteria may have been strict anaerobes.

Suitable adjustments of conditions must then be made until growth is obtained.

Now that we have a pure culture, the next step is a study of arrangement, motility, staining reaction and morphology. The first three characters may be determined by observation in a hanging-drop preparation of the growth in broth. Let us assume that our organism is a coccus, although this must be confirmed by microscopic examination of a stained preparation.

Arrangement and Motility. A hanging drop prepared with a young broth culture is a useful means of determining how bacteria are arranged and their form and motility. Chains of cocci or bacilli are readily observed, while cubical packets of *Sarcina* can be seen turning over and over like little bundles floating in the medium. *Micrococcus* and *Staphylococcus* groups appear to be very irregular in arrangements, like bunches of grapes, but may often appear singly or in pairs. Motility, if present, is easily seen in hanging drops. There are also critical tests for motility based on visible migration of the organisms in macroscopic masses through semisolid ("mushy") nutrient agar (about 0.1 per cent agar and 3 per cent gelatin) (Fig. 29.1). Let us assume that our unknown is nonmotile and morphologically resembles *Micrococcus* or *Staphylococcus*.

Staining Reaction and Morphology. The next step is to observe the staining reaction and confirm the morphology. Gram's stain is of great value, but one must bear in mind that the

**Figure 29.1** A test for motility. This meat-infusion medium contains 3 per cent gelatin and 0.1 per cent agar, with 0.2 per cent potassium nitrate ($KNO_3$) and an indicator of reduction, triphenyl tetrazolium chloride (TTC). The medium remains solid only at temperatures below 23° C. Each tube is inoculated while firm by a stab as shown. The tubes are incubated for 16 hours at 35° C. at which temperature the medium becomes liquid. Due to the agar and gelatin the position of the stab inoculation is maintained. Migration of organisms into the liquid medium (at 35° C.) indicates motility (tubes 1, 2, 3, 4, 5) and is seen as clouding of the medium and by reduction (precipitation and darkening) of the TTC if the organisms reduce the $KNO_3$. Reduction may also be tested for as described in this chapter. Gelatin liquefaction is indicated in any tube if the medium remains liquid at 5° C. (From Ball and Sellers: Appl. Microbiol., *14*:670, 1966.)

method requires experience and that the differentiations it gives are not absolute. Some organisms are gram-positive only when young or when cultivated on blood or serum media. Others are variable under nearly all conditions. Many lose gram-positiveness with aging, or in acid (fermented) cultures. Let us assume that the organism under discussion is gram-positive in well-grown but not aged cultures on agar containing no blood or fermentable sugar.

Other morphological features may be looked for at this point. If the organism is rod-shaped it may produce spores, especially if it is gram-positive. Because spores may not readily be seen or promptly formed, their presence or absence may often be determined by staining an old (at least one week) agar-slant culture with methylene blue or by a method of spore staining. A surer test is to emulsify some of the growth in 2 ml. of sterile water and heat it at 90° C. for 10 minutes, afterward inoculating some of the heated material into broth and incubating for several days. If growth occurs, it is practically certain that bacterial endospores were present, since no known vegetative cells or spores of other microorganisms withstand 90° C. for 10 minutes. Some bacterial endospores are considerably less heat-resistant.

Capsules may or may not be visible, depending largely on the culture medium and whether we are dealing with an R or S form. Sometimes capsules are seen only on organisms occurring in pathological material or when growing in media containing serum or milk. They may be demonstrated by capsule stains, negative stain with India ink or nigrosin, or by darkfield methods. Let us say our organism shows no demonstrable capsule under these particular conditions of growth.

The morphology of any organism always varies to some extent. A given variety of bacteria may, in any one culture, produce cells of varying size just as, in a group of men or horses, some may be large and some small. In logarithmic phases of growth, cells are usually small. If the bacteria are cocci, some of the individual cells may not be perfectly round; some may be oval. If bacilli, some may be long and thin, others short, oval and thick; some may occur singly, others in pairs or chains or long filaments. But the predominating form, size and arrangement of the cells in a pure culture are usually quite apparent, especially when seen growing under a variety of conditions and in different kinds of media, both fluid and solid. Form, size and arrangement of the individual cells are important and reliable differential characters if carefully determined.

Summarizing our knowledge at this point we may state that we are dealing with a non-motile, gram-positive, unencapsulated coccus that grows well aerobically in irregular clusters on plain meat-extract medium at a pH of about 7.4, producing opaque, glistening, lemon-yellow colonies and preferring a temperature around 25° C. There is still, however, a good deal to learn about our unknown before identification is complete.

## 29.2 BIOCHEMICAL TESTS

The experienced bacteriologist would know at once exactly what peculiarities to look for in dealing with a culture of gram-positive cocci that have the characters we have enumerated. For the present, however, we shall put ourselves in the place of a person to whom such a gram-positive coccus is a hitherto unknown bacterium.

Since presence (or absence) of certain enzymes characterizes certain genera and species of bacteria, we test the ability of our unknown organism to metabolize some of the common carbohydrates such as glucose (dextrose), sucrose (saccharose or cane sugar) and lactose (milk sugar). We examine also its power to utilize as hydrogen acceptors such substances as sodium nitrate and sodium nitrite. Its production of enzymes hydrolytic for gelatin, coagulated serum, the casein in milk, starch and fat should also be investigated. All of these are simple and commonly used procedures.

In any of these tests it is important that the medium and conditions of incubation support good, vigorous growth of the organism. A negative result in the absence of good growth is obviously of no value. In order that uniform, standard and authoritative results may be obtained, it is recommended that recognized, documented procedures such as those outlined in the "Manual of Microbiological Methods" (published under the auspices of the American Society for Microbiology) or later authoritative methods be used throughout. It should be emphasized that results obtained in empirical media of the complex organic type, such as extract or infusion broth, can vary with changes in the quantity and quality of such ingredients as peptones, yeast extracts and meat extracts; and that growth and enzymic activities are affected by presence or absence of certain kinds of hydrogen donors and acceptors, pH, temperature and other factors. These variables are always standardized as far as possible and are carefully recorded for comparative purposes by competent workers. Here, only general principles and a few illustrative procedures of tests for *fermentation* of carbohydrates, *hydrolysis* of proteins and lipids and *reduction* of various substrates will be outlined. A number of special test procedures are reserved to descriptions of particular organisms farther on in this book.

**Fermentation Tests.** As previously outlined, fermentation is the anaerobic, enzymic decomposition of organic compounds, typically carbohydrates, in which part of the substrate is oxidized, part reduced. Acids, alcohols and carbon dioxide are common products.

In the study of fermentative characters, tubes should contain a sufficient depth of broth containing the test substrate (e.g., glucose, lactose) to provide anaerobic conditions and should also contain a small inverted vial or other device (placed there *before* sterilization) to aid anaerobiosis and to catch any gas that may be formed as a result of the fermentation (Fig. 29.2). Gas might otherwise pass off into the atmosphere and not be detected. Two organisms, both of which ferment the same carbohydrate, may be sharply differentiated if one forms gas while the other does not.

When gas is produced from fermentable substrates by growing microorganisms, it is *prima facie* evidence of fermentation and is vir-

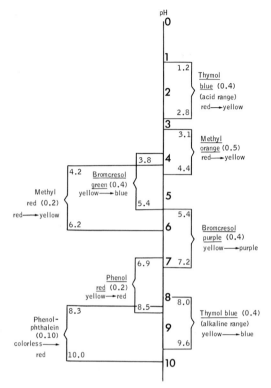

**Figure 29.3**   Some pH indicators commonly used in microbiology. Numbers in parentheses are recommended per cent concentrations of dye in solution. Color change for each indicator is given from maximum acid color (left) to maximum alkaline color (right). The pH range of each indicator is enclosed in a bracket. Probably the most generally useful indicators in microbiology are methyl red, bromcresol purple and phenol red.

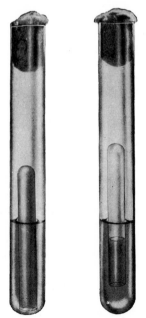

**Figure 29.2**   Durham fermentation tubes. Note that the inverted tube on the left is filled with liquid, whereas the one on the right is partially empty. What is the explanation for the difference between the two tubes? (From Smith: Principles of Microbiology, 5th ed., The C. V. Mosby Co., 1965.)

tually always accompanied by acid formation since the gas is derived from formic or other acid resulting from fermentation. However, fermentation often occurs without gas production, and then acid formation is our only evidence that the organism has metabolized the substrate. Sometimes only alkaline substances are produced from substrates.

Acid or alkali production in the culture may be detected by adding to the medium an indicator or dye such as bromcresol purple, which changes from purple to yellow in the presence of acid. The ranges of color of various indicators at various pH's are shown in Figure 29.3. Phenol red turns from yellow to red in the presence of alkali. The change in color of the indicator is our proof of fermentation or metabolic use of the substrate (see Fig. 36.2). However, some species can metabolize the acids produced by fermentation and cause a reversion from acid to alkaline. Others may produce ammonia from amino acids in sufficient quantity to mask acid production. In other instances, if too much buffer is used in the medium, it, too, will mask acid or alkali production. These and similar possibilities can be allowed for but must be kept in mind. Fresh serum added to the medium will vitiate the results because it often contains extraneous hydrolytic enzymes of animal origin and is also a potent buffer.

Observations of growth should be made every 24 hours in order that the culture may not revert to an alkaline reaction before acid-formation has been noted.

GASES PRODUCED BY BACTERIA.   Two gases commonly given off by bacteria during fermentation are carbon dioxide and hydrogen in varying, more or less distinctive, proportions. One may determine the ratio of carbon dioxide to hydrogen by first marking the level of gas in a fermentation tube and then adding strong sodium hydroxide solution to the tube. This absorbs the carbon dioxide, leaving hydrogen. The difference in level of fluid in the gas tube is readily measurable.

*Hydrogen Sulfide.*   Many organisms in their metabolism of sulfur-containing organic compounds liberate hydrogen sulfide in considerable amounts. This gas is one of the most noticeable odors in putrefactive processes. Some organisms may be differentiated from others by their production of hydrogen sulfide. For example, *Salmonella paratyphi B* (a cause of gastroenteritis) produces it, while *Salmonella paratyphi A,* a closely related species, does not. This test therefore has diagnostic value.

Two methods for detecting the formation of hydrogen sulfide are the *lead-acetate-paper* method and the *stab* method. In the paper method hydrogen sulfide arising from the culture blackens lead acetate dried on a strip of filter paper suspended above the medium. In the stab method lead acetate already incorporated in the agar is blackened (Fig. 36.2).

*Methane.*   Methane is another gaseous product of bacterial metabolism. However, production of methane is rarely determined in routine procedures because the procedures are complex and require special apparatus. Carbon is a good hydrogen acceptor and is readily reduced. In swampy places several species of strictly anaerobic bacteria attack the carbohydrates derived from dead vegetation. Cellulose is decomposed by the enzyme *cellulase,* yielding the disaccharide cellobiose which, in turn, is hydrolyzed to glucose. Carbon dioxide produced by fermentation of glucose can be reduced to methane by certain other bacteria (e.g., *Methanobacterium*). These

bacteria also produce methane by the fermentation of acetic acid and of methyl alcohol and sometimes large amounts of the gas are given off. The bubbles seen rising during the summertime in woodland swamps are largely methane. Cellulase is also produced by a number of species of bacteria found mainly (or only) in the rumen of cattle. Microorganisms in sewage digestion tanks at sewage disposal plants produce such large quantities of methane (*sewer gas*) that it is profitable to collect it in tanks and use it as fuel. (Sewage contains a large amount of cellulose.) Accumulations of methane ("fire damp") in coal mines have sometimes caused disastrous explosions.

*Ammonia and Nitrogen.*   Many bacteria, especially saprophytic species, produce ammonia and nitrogen from decomposition of proteins and other nitrogenous compounds. Some species can reduce sodium nitrate and sodium nitrite to nitrogen and ammonia. Like carbon, nitrogen is readily reduced. Ammonia and volatile amines may be detected by suspending a strip of litmus or other indicator substance in the culture tube above the medium.

## 29.3   PROTEOLYSIS

**Gelatin.**   The ability of a microorganism to hydrolyze the incomplete protein, gelatin, so that it no longer solidifies in the cold or coagulates, is commonly taken as evidence that the organism hydrolyzes proteins in general. This is often true but there are numerous exceptions. However, the gelatin decomposition test is much used as a test for proteolytic power because of its convenience.

A dependable method of detecting gelatin decomposition consists in preparing nutrient agar containing 1 per cent gelatin and then dispensing the gelatin-agar in 2-ml. amounts in small tubes. The tubed agar is sterilized and allowed to harden. Inoculation is by a stab with a heavy young growth from a 4- to 8-hour-old culture on agar. After one to five hours of incubation several drops of a strong coagulating fluid (acid-$HgCl_2$)* are added. Hydrolysis is indicated by a clear zone in the upper layer of the gelatin agar. Sometimes the zone is visible without the coagulant (Fig. 29.4).

**Serum Digestion.**   Serum is a mixture of proteins but is generally considered as one for purposes of proteolytic tests. Coagulated serum may be prepared by mixing three parts of horse

---

*$H_2O$, 100 ml; $HgCl_2$, 15 gm; HCl, 20 ml.

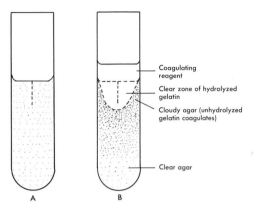

**Figure 29.4** Test for hydrolysis of gelatin. *A*, The tube of gelatin-agar just after having been inoculated by a stab at the top of the column. *B*, The tube after incubation and addition of the coagulating reagent. The gelatin-agar has become cloudy everywhere except in the zone of hydrolysis.

or beef serum with one part of nutrient broth. By careful heating, the serum is coagulated in slants and sterilized at the same time. The slants are inoculated when cool by smearing a loopful of growth over their surfaces. When hydrolyzed by microorganisms the serum usually becomes brownish and translucent, and the growth appears to sink inward. Total liquefaction sometimes occurs in 48 hours at 37° C., especially in cultures of molds and sporeforming, aerobic bacilli.

Serum digestion may also be detected by incorporating serum in nutrient agar in tubes and treating as in the test for gelatin-digestion previously described.

**Action on Milk.** Milk has a pH of about 6.8 when fresh. It is an ideal culture medium for many microorganisms. For use as a bacteriological culture medium, skim milk is tubed in 5-ml. amounts and sterilized by autoclaving (steam pressure cooker: 120° C. for 10 minutes). If an indicator such as litmus or bromcresol purple be added, fermentation of the lactose may be detected. Rennet production may be inferred if the milk is curdled (provided this is not due to souring, a point difficult to determine if fermentation of the lactose also occurs). Hydrolysis of the casein often follows coagulation. The milk then becomes brownish and translucent, and the clot disappears.

## 29.4   PLATE METHODS

A good method of testing the ability of many organisms to hydrolyze test substances like sugars, gelatin, fat or starch is to mix the test substance with agar, pour into Petri plates and, when solid, heavily inoculate the surface in streaks or spots. After good growth has occurred, a reagent reacting with the test substance to produce some distinctive appearance is flooded over the surface of the agar. Alternatively, the growth may be removed and the underlying surface treated with the reagent. If hydrolytic enzymes have been produced, the area of growth or the area surrounding the growth will show a distinctive reaction (or lack of reaction). For example, starch plates may be treated with Lugol's iodine solution. The starch-hydrolyzing colonies will be surrounded by colorless zones; the remainder of the plate will turn dark blue. In simple fermentation tests the carbohydrate to be tested and an acid indicator such as phenol red (yellow = acid; red = alkaline) are incorporated in the nutrient agar. After incubation, acid-forming colonies are surrounded by yellow zones. Gas formation is not indicated. The conditions of "fermentation" on the surface of an agar plate exposed to air are very different from those in the depths of a fermentation tube, and comparative tests made under the two conditions may not agree.

## 29.5   LIPOLYSIS

Many microorganisms produce enzymes that hydrolyze one or more lipids or esters. One of the inconveniences in studying lipases is difficulty in bringing the lipid substrate into intimate contact with the organism. This contact is necessary since lipases often appear not to diffuse well into solid culture media. It may be that they are inducible enzymes and appear only in contact with their substrate. Another difficulty is in making the lipolytic effect evident. Lipolysis has not been studied as much as it should be because of such technical difficulties and it is not commonly mentioned in keys. Several methods are shown in Figure 29.5.

A reliable method is a recent improvement of the procedure devised by Eykman in 1901. A specially prepared mixture of mono- and diglycerides in palm oil is spread and allowed to cool on the inside bottom of a Petri plate. Two ml. of a broth suspension of the organisms are then layered on the lipid and 6 to 7 ml. of melted (45° C.) agar of appropriate composition are thoroughly mixed with the suspension by tilting and rotating the plate. Time and temperature of incubation are adapted to the organism under test. Lipolysis is indicated by the appearance of white, opaque spots of fatty acids

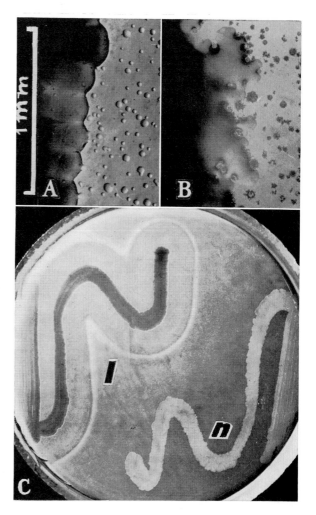

**Figure 29.5** Lipase production and its detection. *A*, The margin of a colony of *Micrococcus sp.,* on a plate of agar sprayed with a fine mist of olive oil. No lipase is evident since all the droplets of oil have remained unchanged, even in contact with the colony. *B*, The irregular margin of a colony of *Serratia* on agar sprayed with oil. Lipase activity has caused the oil droplets to become deformed and optically dense and refractive near, as well as at some distance from, the colony. *C*, A plate containing agar in which fat is emulsified and to which has been added a small amount of Nile blue sulfate (a dye which turns blue in the presence of lipolysis). On this plate are seen a strain of *Micrococcus* producing lipolysis (zone of color change and emulsion destruction, *l*), and a strain not producing lipolysis (no zone of color change or emulsion destruction, *n*). (*A*, From Bulder: Ant. Leeuw., vol. 21; *B*, same author, unpublished; *C*, From Davies: J. Gen. Microbiol., vol.11.)

or their calcium salts in and around the colonies. The method avoids the use of acid indicators that are toxic to some organisms and that introduce error if extraneous acids are formed from fermentable sugars in the medium.

## 29.6    MICROBIAL REDUCTIONS

A distinctive property of many microorganisms is the power to reduce various substances (i.e., to use them as electron [hydrogen] acceptors).

**Nitrate Reduction.** Reduction of nitrate is a result of the use of sodium nitrate as an electron acceptor by facultative bacteria in the absence of oxygen. Incubate the microorganisms being investigated in broth containing about 0.1 per cent of sodium *nitrate* ($NaNO_3$). The columns of broth in the tubes should be at least 5 cm. deep to exclude oxygen. After 48 hours, and at other intervals, a test is made for

the presence of *nitrites* ($NaNO_2$) by withdrawing a small sample of the culture from the bottom of the tube and immediately adding to that sample a drop of sulfanilic acid solution* and a drop of dimethyl-alpha-naphthylamine solution.† Alternately, the drops of sulfanilic acid and dimethyl-alpha-naphthylamine may be added to the culture and allowed to settle to the bottom. It is better to test the bottom layers of the culture rather than mixing the whole culture, because slight reduction sometimes occurs at the bottom of the tube and nowhere else, due to lower oxygen tension in the depths

---

\* Sulfanilic acid solution

| | |
|---|---:|
| Glacial acetic acid | 100.0 ml. |
| Water | 250.0 ml. |
| Sulfanilic acid | 2.8 gm. |

† Dimethyl-alpha-naphthylamine solution

| | |
|---|---:|
| Glacial acetic acid | 100.0 ml. |
| Water | 250.0 ml. |
| Dimethyl-alpha-naphthylamine | 2.1 ml. |

of the tube. The presence of oxygen often interferes with nitrate reduction.

The development of a red or brown color
denotes the presence of *nitrites,* but the failure
of this color to develop raises a question. Either
the nitrate has not been attacked, so that no
nitrite is present, or nitrite has been formed
but also attached and reduced to free nitrogen
or ammonia. A test to see whether any nitrate remains may be made by adding a little pulverized zinc. This reduces any remaining nitrate to
nitrite (which may be tested for as described) and
tells us whether the organism has reduced *all* of
the nitrate. If the test with zinc is positive (i.e.,
nitrate is still present), the original test for
nitrites having been negative, then it is clear
that the organism did not attack the nitrate at
all. If both the nitrate and nitrite tests are negative then it is obvious that the organism reduced
all the nitrate as well as nitrite to nitrogen or
ammonia which has dissipated.

**Nitrite Reduction.**  The latter point (i.e.,
ability of the organism to attack nitrite) may be
determined separately by testing the ability of
the organism to destroy the nitrite in cultures
known to contain it. This is done by incubating
deep broth cultures containing quantities of nitrite so small (about 0.002 per cent) as just
barely to be detectable. If the organism is capable of reducing nitrite, the culture will soon
lose its nitrite because the organism will quickly
reduce *all* of such a small amount of nitrite. A
sterile control tube should be tested at the same
time, since illuminating-gas fumes (as from
Bunsen burners) often contain nitrous acid,
which may be absorbed by the medium and
give a slight reaction.

**Reduction of Litmus.**  The ability of an organism to reduce other substances than nitrates
and nitrites is often investigated. Some strictly
anaerobic marine species and some found in
petroleum (*Desulfovibrio* sp.) can reduce sulfates
to hydrogen sulfide. Sulfur, like oxygen, carbon
and nitrogen, is readily reduced. Litmus serves
to show whether the organism has strong reduc-

ing powers by becoming entirely decolorized
when reduced. Litmus is used, like nitrates and
nitrites, as an alternative electron acceptor by
many facultative species. Just enough is added to
the medium before sterilization to give a definite
color.

**The "Reductase" Test.**  Standardized solutions of methylene blue are often added to
samples of market milk to estimate roughly
whether a few, a moderate number, or enormous
numbers of bacteria are present. When great
numbers are present, the blue color disappears
almost immediately. Several other oxidation-
reduction dyes are now used in addition to
methylene blue: tetrazolium salts, neutral red
and resazurin (see Chapter 45).

## INDOLE

Indole is derived from the amino acid, tryptophan, by certain species of bacteria (Fig. 29.6).
Most peptones contain tryptophan, but if a
medium is used in which it is not *known* to be
present, it must be added if one is to test for
indole production. Cultures are incubated for
48 to 72 hours. Indole reacts with acidified
solution of Ehrlich's or Kovac's reagent* to produce a pink compound.

The culture to be tested is first shaken with
1 ml. of xylol. Indole is soluble in xylol, and is
concentrated in it and carried to the surface by
the solvent after a minute of standing. Six drops
of Ehrlich's reagent are then *gently* added to the
culture and are made to remain in a layer between the xylol and the medium. If indole is
present, a pink color forms in a few minutes as
a ring at the junction of the xylol and reagent.
Pink compounds not caused by indole sometimes appear in the presence of reagent after
long contact.

---

*Ehrlich's reagent (and Kovac's modification)
  Amyl or butyl alcohol                75 ml.
  HCl (conc.)                          25 ml.
  Para-dimethyl-amino-benzaldehyde   5 gm.

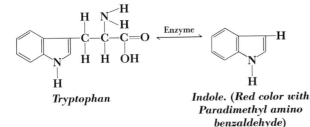

*Tryptophan*                    *Indole. (Red color with
                                Paradimethyl amino
                                benzaldehyde)*

**Figure 29.6**  Production of indole from tryptophan.

## CATALASE

Catalase is an enzyme which catalyzes the decomposition of hydrogen peroxide:

$$H_2O_2 \xrightleftharpoons{\text{catalase}} H_2O + \tfrac{1}{2} O_2$$

It is produced by many cells, especially aerobic cells, rarely anaerobic cells. It is common in human saliva. Its presence or absence is often a valuable distinguishing character, especially among the Lactobacteriaceae. Data are incomplete on this point in many other groups. Catalase activities of certain groups of bacteria are as follows:

| Bacteria | Catalase |
|---|---|
| *Micrococcus* | + |
| *Staphylococcus* | + |
| Lactobacilleae | − |
| Streptococceae | − |
| Propionibacteriaceae | + |
| Corynebacteriaceae | + |
| *Bacillus* | + |
| Actinomycetales | + |

In a simple means of demonstrating the presence of catalase a previously inoculated and incubated plate of nutrient medium is flooded with a 3 per cent solution of hydrogen peroxide. Evolution of bubbles of oxygen is evidence of the presence of catalase. Special attention must be given to pH, which must be near 7.0.

## 29.7   RAPID MICROTECHNIQUES

By certain modifications of procedure many of the tests described above may be made more quickly and more economically by rapid techniques, which are based on the principles that small amounts of culture and of reagent may be used in small tubes; and since microorganisms rapidly multiplying in the logarithmic phase are most active in all enzymic functions, one may greatly speed up their effects by adding to *prewarmed medium* containing the test substrate a heavy suspension of young, actively growing organisms gently removed from a young agar-slant culture with a few drops of broth or saline solution. Alternatively, billions of active organisms may be concentrated by centrifugation of 10 ml. of a young broth culture. They are resuspended in 0.5 ml. of broth or saline solution. Of this suspension, 0.2 to 1.0 ml. are added to 2 ml. of the test medium previously warmed to the incubator temperature. The mixture is held in a water bath during the period of incubation. The ready-made population consisting of billions of young, active organisms sets to work immediately and brings about the desired characteristic changes (production of acid, hydrolysis of urea or gelatin, nitrate reduction) within a few minutes or hours (Fig. 29.7).

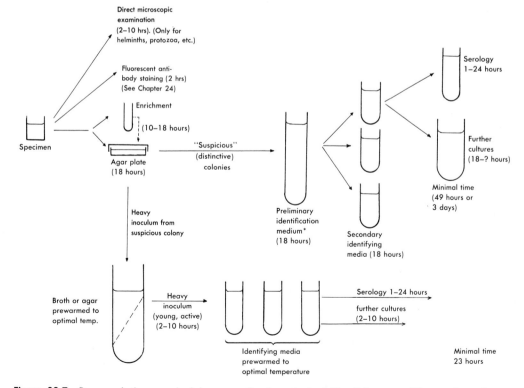

**Figure 29.7**   Steps and time required in conventional method of identifying a rapidly growing microorganism (e.g., typhoid bacilli) compared with steps and time required in "rapid" procedure. (Specimen is of feces.)

**Disk and Tablet Methods.** These methods simplify and expedite procedures by incorporating the culture medium or the test substrate and indicator in prepared, sterile, dried disks of filter paper or tablets of porous material. In one procedure, 15 ml. of melted nutrient agar at 40° C. in a tube are inoculated with a heavy suspension of young active cells. The agar is then poured into a Petri dish and allowed to solidify. One then places, on the surface, small paper disks or tablets previously dried and sterilized after saturation with solutions of test substrate and suitable indicator. The test substance and indicator diffuse into the agar around the disk or tablet and are quickly acted upon by the bacteria in the agar (Fig. 29.8).

This procedure is easily modified for fluid media in tubes. Sterilized disks of filter paper are prepared by drying upon them the ingredients of various kinds of nutrient media plus the test substance (e.g., lactose) and indicator (e.g., bromcresol purple). With sterile forceps one merely adds the desired kind of sterile disk to 2 to 5 ml. of sterile water in a tube. After a minute or two the ingredients in the disk dissolve and the tube is ready to be inoculated with a heavy suspension of active cells (Fig. 29.9). There are numerous ingenious modifications of

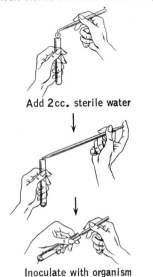

Insert sterile disk with desired reagent

Add 2cc. sterile water

Inoculate with organism

**Figure 29.9** A rapid disk cultural method. For explanation see text. (Courtesy of Pennsylvania Biological Laboratories, Inc., Philadelphia, Pa.)

these methods. In one, strips of filter paper are saturated with the test substance and indicator and then dried. Hundreds of these strips occupy little space and may be stored indefinitely. A test is made by placing on the prepared strip a heavy suspension of the organisms scraped from agar (Fig. 29.10), or from the sediment pellet of a strongly centrifuged, luxuriant, broth culture. Readings can be made in 30 to 60 minutes. Results are satisfactory for routine purposes and can be checked by additional tests.

## 29.8  IDENTIFICATION OF THE UNKNOWN ORGANISM

After completion of the tests, as described, a tabulation is made of the results. For the organism under investigation, let us assume that they are as follows:

Pigment (as observed in colonies on agar) —lemon yellow

Lactose—not fermented; no gas

Glucose—slight acidity; no gas

Sucrose—slight acidity; no gas

Gelatin—not hydrolyzed

Catalase—produced

Extract agar slant and cubes of potato— good growth, soft, moist and glistening; lemon yellow in color

Extract broth—turbid; sediment is yellow; faint pellicle (scum)

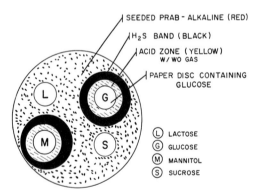

SEEDED PRAB - ALKALINE (RED)

$H_2S$ BAND (BLACK)

ACID ZONE (YELLOW)
W/ WO GAS

PAPER DISC CONTAINING
GLUCOSE

(L) LACTOSE
(G) GLUCOSE
(M) MANNITOL
(S) SUCROSE

**Figure 29.8** One form of disk method for identification of microorganisms. While still fluid at about 40° C. the base agar is heavily inoculated with young, active cells from a broth culture of the test organism. The agar contains an acid-base indicator and a source of sulfur (for $H_2S$ production) with an iron salt to turn black in the presence of $H_2S$. Sterile paper disks containing lactose, sucrose, glucose and mannitol, respectively, were placed on the surface of the agar before incubation. After overnight incubation the agar around the lactose and sucrose disks was colorless, showing that these sugars have not been fermented; agar around the glucose and mannitol disks showed a zone of yellow (indicator showed acid due to fermentation) and a black zone due to $H_2S$ production from the sulfur source in the agar. If gas is produced it may appear as tiny bubbles in the depths of the agar. (From Sanders, Faber and Cook: Appl. Microbiol., vol. 5.)

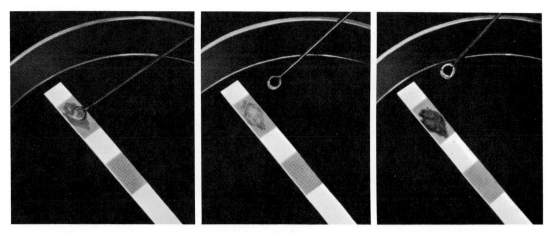

**Figure 29.10**   A rapid test for metabolic properties. A moist "paste" of pure culture of actively growing young cells is scraped from an agar surface with a loop and rubbed on the surface of a strip of test paper (in this case Patho-Tec) in the indicated zone. The zone contains test substrate (e.g., lysine) with an indicator that undergoes a distinctive change in color if the organisms decompose the substrate. The test in this case was for decarboxylation of the lysine (positive in case of *Salmonella.*) (Courtesy of General Diagnostics Division, Warner-Chilcott, Morris Plains, N. J.)

Milk—slightly acid; not coagulated
Nitrates—not reduced to nitrites
Indole—not produced

How are we now to determine the genus and species of the cocci which we have been studying?

**Use of Keys.** Although every experienced bacteriologist has at his finger tips, so to speak, all of the distinguishing cultural reactions and other identifying characters of the organisms with which he is working, it is unusual, to say the least, to find one who knows *all* the characters of *all* the species. When an unknown organism is encountered that must be identified, the main morphological and tinctorial features are determined in some such manner as just described and then recourse is had to *keys* or other reference works. A much used key for general bacteriological use in the United States is "Bergey's Manual of Determinative Bacteriology"; see page 381. As a valuable saver of time, and as more up to date, one should also consult "A Guide to the Identification of the Genera of Bacteria," second edition, 1967.

In order to use "Bergey's Manual" we should first determine to which of the ten orders of the Class Schizomycetes our culture belongs. On pages 33 and 34 of the 1957 edition of the manual is to be found a brief synopsis of the characters used to differentiate the 10 orders. Obviously the species in question does not occur in trichomes (threadlike filaments); it does not multiply by budding, neither is it sheathed or stalked (Orders II, III, VI). It does not branch, nor is it acid-fast (Order V). It is not characterized by formation of sulfur granules or

deposits, nor does it show gliding, jerky or flexuous movements (Orders VII and VIII). It is neither spiral (Order IX) nor highly pleomorphic (Order X). We are thus left to consider Orders I (Pseudomonadales) and IV (Eubacteriales). All species of Pseudomonadales (Bergey, p. 35) are gram-negative, and they are also mostly rod-shaped and motile. Coccuslike forms are not common. Thus we may eliminate Order I and examine Order IV (Bergey, pp. 281–282). Our unknown clearly does not belong in families I to VI, which are rod-shaped. We may eliminate family VIII as gram-negative, and IX to XIII as rod-shaped.

Family VII (Micrococcaceae), therefore, would seem to be our objective, and we are referred to page 454. Here we find that the descriptions of genera III to VI do not correspond with the organism in question, and that we must search in genera I and II. The organisms of these genera resemble each other so closely that it is necessary to consider carefully the characters of the individual species.

A short study of the data we have already obtained by our cultural tests shows that our organism corresponds closely with the description of *Micrococcus luteus* (page 456), since it produces a lemon-yellow pigment, grows best at 25° C., does not hydrolyze gelatin or ferment lactose, grows on potato with lemon-yellow pigment, does not reduce nitrates to nitrites and fails to produce indole.

A further check upon the identity of the culture may be made by making other tests and comparing various characters of organisms closely resembling it, such as *Micrococcus flavus.*

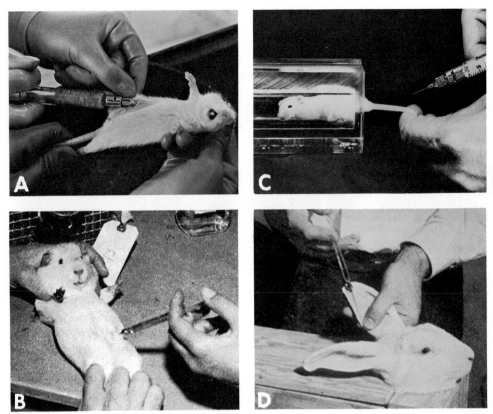

**Figure 29.11**   Tests for pathogenicity by injection of laboratory animals. *A* and *B*, Intraperitoneal injection of mouse and guinea pig, respectively. *C* and *D*, Intravenous injection of mouse (tail vein) and rabbit (marginal ear vein), respectively. (Courtesy of Ch. Pfizer & Co., Inc.)

A few repetitions of the tests usually serve to confirm the diagnosis or prove it to be in error, necessitating further study.

Pathogenicity may be determined if necessary by injecting 0.5 ml. of a 24-hour broth culture intravenously or subcutaneously into a rabbit, guinea pig or other animal (Fig. 29.11).

In all properly operated laboratories animals are maintained under most favorable conditions of nutrition, comfort and sanitation, and anesthesia is used as it would be for humans. Strict regulations are published by the U. S. Department of Health, Education and Welfare, Public Health Service.

If our unknown is truly pathogenic, abscesses will probably form or the animal may die (*M. luteus* is not pathogenic). Further details concerning micrococci will be given when these genera are taken up specifically.

## SUPPLEMENTARY READING

Animal Facilities Standards Committee of the Animal Care Panel.: Guide for Laboratory Animal Facilities and Care. U. S. Public Health Service Publn. No. 1024. Govt. Printing Office, Washington, D. C. 1963.

Breed, R. S., Murray, E. G. D., and Smith, N. R., et al.: Bergey's Manual of Determinative Bacteriology, 7th ed. The Williams & Wilkins Co., Baltimore. 1957.

Conn, H. J., editor: Manual of Microbiological Methods. McGraw-Hill Book Co., New York. 1957.

Harris, A. H., and Coleman, M. B., editors: Diagnostic Procedures and Reagents, 4th ed. American Pub. Health Ass'n, New York. 1963.

Halliwell, G., and Bryant, M. P.: The cellulolytic activity of pure strains of bacteria from the rumen of cattle. J. Gen. Microbiol., *32*:441, 1963.

Kaufman, L., and Weaver, R. H.: Rapid methods for the identification of clostridia. J. Bact., *79*:119, 1960.

McDade, J. J., and Weaver, R. H.: Rapid methods for the detection of gelatin hydrolysis. J. Bact., *77*:60, 1959.

Narayan, K. G., Guinée, P. A. M., and Mossel, D. A. A.: Use of reagent-impregnated ("Patho-Tec") test papers in the identification of Enterobacteriaceae and similar bacteria. Ant. Leeuw., *33*:184, 1967.

Skerman, V. B. D.: A Guide to the Identification of the Genera of Bacteria, 2nd ed. The Williams and Wilkins Co., Baltimore. 1967.

Smith, Jr., H. L., and Goodner, K.: Detection of bacterial gelatinases by gelatin-agar plate methods. J. Bact., *76*:662, 1958.

Starr, M. P., and Skerman, V. B. D.: Bacterial Diversity. Ann. Rev. Microbiol., *19*:407, 1965.

Steel, K. J., and Fisher, P. J.: A fallacy of the nitrate reduction test. Monthly Bull. Min. Health Pub. Health Lab. Serv., *20*:63, 1961.

Tuynenburg, G., and Willemse, H.: The detection and enumeration of lipolytic microorganisms by means of a modified Eykman-plate method. Ant. Leeuw. *31*:103, 1965.

# Chapter 30

## THE BACTERIA
## Classification

Biological classification, or *taxonomy,* is the systematic arrangement of organisms in groups or categories called *taxa* (singular, *taxon;* Gr. *taxis* = arrangement or grouping) according to some definite scheme. Scientific names are given to organisms and taxa after adequate study, publication of the descriptions, and other prescribed formalities. Systematic naming constitutes the science of *nomenclature.* Scientific names are, by mutual agreement among scientists, abbreviated definitions or descriptions of the named organisms. General agreement on the distinguishing properties of any specifically named organism is essential to any logical discussion of that organism.

Following a tradition and accepted rules in biology, scientific names are in Latin because in the past Latin has been the common language of the learned of all nationalities (i.e., Latin transcended language barriers). When and if English becomes a universal language it may supplant Latin in scientific nomenclature.

The protistologist turns to the zoologist for classifications of the protozoa, to the botanist for systematization of the procaryotic algae, and to the mycologist for arrangement of the eucaryotic fungi. When he attempts to begin his classification of bacteria with a clear, concise definition of a bacterium he immediately encounters difficulties. The first is at the border between the blue-green algae on the one hand and, on the other hand, photosynthetic bacteria and certain nonphotosynthetic microorganisms that, though classed as bacteria, closely resemble blue-green algae. These may really be forms of Cyanophyceae that have lost by mutation (or never gained?) the ability to form chlorophyll. He is equally puzzled when he reviews the moldlike properties of the Actino-

mycetales, the protozoa-like properties of the Spirochaetales and the bacteria-like (?) properties of the Eubacteriales and Pseudomonadaceae, to say nothing of the virus-like properties of the rickettsias, chlamydias and the PPLO. He may feel somewhat like a traveler in an illimitable forest that is traversed by anastomosing, sometimes barely visible, footpaths; a traveler who is without a compass and possesses only an obsolescent map. As one expert in the field (Sneath) has stated, concerning bacteria: ". . . bacterial classification is in such confusion that it seems doubtful whether any nonsense can make it much worse than it is." The zoologists and botanists have good guides to natural relationships among higher animals and plants based on demonstrable evolutionary and phylogenetic relationships. The structures and forms are usually patently related and fairly stable; and paleontology gives ample corroboratory evidence. The bacteriologist can only theorize as to the evolutionary and the phylogenetic history of his organisms; bacteria left no fossils; their origin is merely the subject of shrewd speculation; their evolutionary history debatable; their properties "subject to change without notice."

As for a definition of bacteria, the bacteriologist may not be accused of obscurantism or circular logic if he relies on five words and a letter: *bacteria are procaryons without chlorophyll a.* In giving this definition he must rely on the sophistication of his reader to realize that, although some bacteria are photosynthetic, they do not contain chlorophyll *a,* the type of chlorophyll that is found in all photosynthetic cells *except* bacteria; and that, except blue-green algae (which contain chlorophyll *a*), there are no other procaryons than bacteria (including as bacteria, PPLO, rickettsias and chlamydias). The viruses are excluded from this definition though they may be included in the Kingdom Protista "by courtesy."

Within the wide framework of this definition the bacteriologist draws up his systems of classification. Originally simple and limited in scope, the present systems have been built up during a century or more, little by little, being modified and extended constantly as new organisms were discovered and as more and more data about them came to hand from microscopists, biochemists, biophysicists, geneticists, immunologists and virologists. Because true genealogical relationships between bacteria have been generally obscure or moot, these classifications have evolved mainly as descriptive keys for identification of organisms. While artificial, these keys are, and have always been, indispensable for practical, systematic work.

## DIFFICULTIES OF BACTERIAL CLASSIFICATION

Organisms discovered within the last decade or so generally have clearly described properties determined by specified and generally available methods. Sample cultures are available from the American Type Culture Collection, the International Collection of Phytopathogenic Bacteria at Davis, California, and other sources around the world for other workers to study. Rules for nomenclature are clear. Classification under such circumstances may not be too difficult a task. If, however, the person originally naming a supposedly newly discovered organism failed, as has frequently happened in the past, to keep cultures available for study; used undescribed or misleading methods to determine color, motility or biochemical properties; and if in addition he was unacquainted with the *rules of nomenclature* and used incorrect names, or names already given to other organisms, it can be seen that confusion and disagreement are introduced. Many older descriptions are inadequate and might fit a dozen different species. On trying to duplicate them no exact descriptions of the methods used are to be found. "Definitions" of some genera and other groupings seem overinclusive. For example, in describing the members of a genus it suggests heterogeneity to say that *some* species are motile, *many* are gram-negative, *most* are encapsulated, *several* are pigmented, a *few* forms *tend to be* microaerophilic, and so on.

Even if a complete taxonomic system were finally agreed upon (*that* will be the day!), a new difficulty would arise because microorganisms are variable and an organism having one set of characters today may have others tomorrow.* Like the Cheshire cat in "Alice in Wonderland," properties of bacteria are apt to appear and disappear quite unexpectedly (and leave behind only a grin!). This is further complicated by the fact that some microorganisms may have some of the distinctive characters of others. A man-made difficulty arises when it is found that, by means of irradiation with ultraviolet light, and by artificial transfers of genetic material, it is possible to transmute one "species" of microorganism into another!

Any organisms may be arranged into *taxa*, according to shape, motility or other criteria. Among bacteria, form, motility, flagellation, spore formation, growth under certain absolute conditions such as complete lack of oxygen (anaerobiosis), and similar properties are called *qualitative unit characters*. Such characteristics are most useful in classification because they are not quantitative or variable as are size, rate of growth, the shade of color of a pigment or its intensity. They are present or not present; *as a general thing*, that is!

However, the situation is not as chaotic as might appear. Variation has definite limitations under ordinary circumstances. Certain characters of most species are surprisingly constant; possibly because the segments of DNA that control them are too large to be affected by single point mutations. The fact that certain organisms may be classed as species results from this fact. As pointed out by Skerman, "recognition of them as species has come through the gradual recognition of the constancy of certain characteristics which they display. . . . Variants have been recognized only because certain characters were selected as representative of a species." Classification is obviously possible, but it depends on cooperation among microbiologists, use of standardized procedures, and a knowledge of variable properties and of the principles and problems of taxonomy and nomenclature.

## 30.1 BACTERIAL NOMENCLATURE

The name of an organism is (or should be) a descriptive symbol. It should convey a definite idea of the organism named. This saves words,

---

*As stated by Leifson, "It would be naïve to expect universal agreement among bacteriologists on the definitive characteristics for all genera, not to mention species." Bact. Rev., *30*:257, 1966.

time and confusion. But it requires meticulous care to devise a name correctly, to avoid using the same name or previously used names for different organisms and to describe the organism itself fully and accurately.

In naming a bacterium, certain official rules are followed. Each species is allowed a "first" and "last" name only. The two-name (binomial) scheme was originated in 1760 under the leadership of Linnaeus (or Carl von Linné, 1707–1778). The first name of a bacterium refers to the genus (pl. genera), and is usually a Latin or latinized word based on the morphology of the organism, the name of the discoverer or some other distinguishing character, habitat or the like. It is always used in the form of a Latin noun, singular. It is written with a capital letter. The second name is the species name and is usually an epithet descriptive of the noun, referring to its color, source, disease production, discoverer or some other distinguishing point. The gender of the epithet must agree with that of the noun. It is not capitalized. Genus and species names are generally italicized. For example, the name *Bacillus anthracis* indicates that the organism is a gram-positive, sporebearing, aerobic rod (properties of the genus *Bacillus*); while *anthracis* calls attention to the fact that this species of the genus *Bacillus* produces the disease anthrax. The name *Spirillum rubrum* tells us that this species is a heterotrophic bacterium, rigid, spiral in structure, nonsporeforming, motile with polar flagella, and gram-negative (all properties of the genus *Spirillum*), and that the species named is characterized by a red color (*rubrum*). The name *Clostridium novyi* indicates a heterotrophic, gram-positive, sporeforming, rod-shaped organism, saprophytic or parasitic, and restricted to growth in the total absence of free oxygen. These are properties of the genus *Clostridium*. This particular species bears the name *novyi* in honor of F. G. Novy of the University of Michigan, who discovered the organism and its relation to the disease, gas gangrene. The practice of using personal names for newly discovered species of bacteria is obsolescent, although many generic names are derived from the discoverers or original students of the genus; for example the genus *Salmonella*, from an American microbiologist named *Salmon; Escherichia* from *Escherich,* a famous German scientist; *Shigella,* from the Japanese epidemiologist, *Shiga.* Sometimes an additional modifying term is added in the form of a varietal name; for example, *Streptococcus faecalis,* var. *liquefaciens,* a gelatin-liquefying variety of a fecal streptococcus.

In writing of bacteria, it is customary to abbreviate the generic name, using only the initial letter if it is clear what genus is meant; for example *B. anthracis* for *Bacillus anthracis.* Sometimes the abbreviation may be longer, as *Br. abortus* for *Brucella abortus.* (Bruce discovered the organism, named for him, which causes *abortion* in cattle and undulant fever in man.) Medical bacteriologists often dispense with these rules and designate organisms by the disease with which they are most frequently associated, for example, meningococcus, pneumococcus, gonococcus and typhoid bacillus. This is a convenient but loose custom not in accord with the rules of nomenclature.

## 30.2   CLASSIFICATION SCHEMES

Many systems of classification of microorganisms have been brought forward but none has remained long without revision and enlargement. One of the first schemes for bacteria was devised by Cohn, in 1872, based almost wholly on morphology. In 1897 Migula devised a scheme based not only on form but on color and some physiological characters such as nitrogen fixation. Orla-Jensen, in 1909, made up a system based largely on physiological properties; this has served as a model for all later schemes.

Stanier and Van Niel suggested the establishment of a new kingdom, the *Monera* (Gr. *moneres* = singular or unicellular) to include all procaryotic organisms (*Procaryota*), a very practical scheme. An older term, *Mychota,* has not been widely recognized. Here, for convenience, we shall adhere to the kingdom of Protista that originally (1866) included the protozoa, fungi, algae and bacteria but now includes all unicellular and noncellular microorganisms.

Modern schemes for classification of bacteria use a miscellany of properties: form, arrangement, Gram stain, motility, various enzymic properties, and any other sort of information that can serve to delimit an organism or group of organisms.

**"Bergey's Manual."**   A system of classification of Schizomycetes that is used by all bacteriologists and that has an international standing is "Bergey's Manual of Determinative Bacteriology" (commonly: "Bergey's Manual"). It represents the collaborative effort of over 100 of the best-qualified microbiologists at the time it was brought together and is a monumental work. It is based on the *International*

*Code of Nomenclature of the Bacteria and Viruses* established by the International Committee on Bacteriological Nomenclature in 1947. In 1959, a Committee on Terminology in Biological Nomenclature of the International Union of Biological Sciences met "to consider and report on possibilities of reconciliation of differing terminologies in the several International Codes (botanical, zoological, microbiological) of Biological Nomenclature."

So rapidly does microbiological science advance that "Bergey's Manual," in its seventh edition, has needed revision since its appearance in 1957. However, with the exception of some new names and changes that have come to be pretty generally used, bacteriologists continue to use Bergey's Manual simply because no other system has yet been put forward that is completed, officially sponsored, and as widely known. Other systems are in the making and the seventh edition of "Bergey's Manual" will no doubt soon be superseded. The situation is somewhat like a road map made 10 years ago. Names and numbers of many highways and byways have changed, some have ceased to exist, and new and better ones have been constructed. The old map is still of much service but must be used with care.

As outlined in "Bergey's Manual" the entire group of bacteria (Class Schizomycetes) comprises some 1500 species. These are divided into 10 orders differentiated from one another primarily on the basis of morphological characters and type of motility:

I.  Pseudomonadales—cells rigid; spheroidal or rodlike: straight, curved or spiral; some groups form trichomes; motile species have *polar* flagella.
II.  Chlamydobacteriales—rodlike cells in trichomes, often sheathed; deposit iron hydroxide in sheath; flagella *subpolar* when present.
III.  Hyphomicrobiales—cells spheroidal or ovoid, connected on stalks or threads; no trichomes; exhibit budding and longitudinal fission; flagella *polar* when present.
IV.  Eubacteriales—typically unicellular spheroid or rodlike cells (a few branching species); no trichomes, sheaths or other accessory structures; motile species have *peritrichous* flagella.
V.  Actinomycetales—cells branch; many species form mycelia and moldlike conidiospores and sporangiospores; *polar* flagellate sporangiospores in only one species.

VI.  Caryophanales—trichomes, often very long; prominent nuclear (?) material; *peritrichous* flagella.
VII.  Beggiatoales—alga-like trichomes or coccoid cells; accumulate elemental S; gliding and oscillatory or rolling motion; *no* flagella.
VIII.  Myxobacterales—cells coccoid, rodlike or fusiform; communal slime; fruiting bodies; cells flexuous; gliding motility in contact with solid surfaces; *no* flagella.
IX.  Spirochaetales—elongated, spiral cells; rotatory and flexing motions and translatory motility; *no* flagella.
X.  Mycoplasmatales(PPLO)—extremely pleomorphic, and easily distorted cells without cell walls; possibly complex life cycle; *nonmotile.*

In addition to the Class Schizomycetes, two groups that were included in the Class Microtatobiotes in 1957 are now regarded as modified, or closely related to, bacteria:

Class III.  Microtatobiotes
I.  Rickettsiales: Obligate intracellular parasites; gram-negative; *nonmotile.*
A.  Rickettsiaceae (rickettsias)—Very minute rods or cocci visible with optical microscopes; typically not filterable through bacteria-retaining filters; typically transmitted by arthropods; procaryotic-type cells and multiplication.
B.  Chlamydiaceae (P-L-T group or chlamydias)—pleomorphic coccoid forms barely resolvable with optical microscopes; several species filtrable; not transmitted by arthropods; cell-form and multiplication not eucaryotic or obviously procaryotic.

Each order is divided into families, and these into tribes, genera and species. Groups of similar species constitute genera; groups of similar genera constitute tribes, and so on. It is important to remember the endings attached to the names of taxa. These denote various grades:

Order . . . . . . . . . . . . . . . . . . . . . . .*ales*
(e.g., Pseudomonad*ales*)
Suborder . . . . . . . . . . . . . . . . . . . . . *ineae*
(e.g., Rhodobacter*ineae*)
Family . . . . . . . . . . . . . . . . . . . . . .*aceae*
(e.g., Thiorhod*aceae*)
Tribe . . . . . . . . . . . . . . . . . . . . . . . *eae*
(e.g., Escherichi*eae*)

These names are frequently used without other

explanation and may be confusing unless clearly understood.

The names of genera and species have no such distinctive endings (see farther on). Some names of species and genera are changed with successive revisions of the systems of classification, and different names are therefore sometimes used by different authors for the same organism, or two different organisms may be called by the same name. Thus there is some confusion in bacteriological literature. This is one of the signs of progress, like the confusion attendant on the repair of a downtown thoroughfare.

**Species and Genus.** In bacteriology the terms *species* and *genus* are used, but the concept of these is somewhat vague. Until the 1950's there was little exact knowledge of genetics in relation to bacteria, and no established knowledge of evolutionary and phylogenetic relationships. Species of higher animals and plants are generally established on the basis of their demonstrable common ancestry and their ability to breed *only* within the species. *Breeding,* as the term is commonly used (i.e., fusion of sex cells), is doubtful in bacteria, except among a few kinds. However, recent experiments on inter-species *hybridization* among bacteria are revealing some surprising relationships (see page 387).

In bacteriology a species is theoretically a single kind of bacterium, all individual cells of which are identical or nearly so. In actuality this identity of cells rarely exists. In any culture of a given species mutant cells may be found that, while having the outward form, staining properties and other obvious characters of most of the cells in the group, differ in subtle and obscure ways. For example, they often possess different metabolic properties or different antigenic composition, and so on. Usually these differences are not extreme and may represent only temporary fluctuations from the principal type. It must be remembered that many ordinary 5-ml. test-tube cultures of a "species" consist of billions of individuals and represent a "population" many "generations" old even in 18 hours of growth. Many mutations can occur during that period. A *generation* (i.e., time required for one cell fission or division to occur) is as short as 20 minutes in many common species of bacteria. In terms of human generations of approximately 20 years, an 18-hour-old culture of bacteria would represent nearly 1100 years or 54 human generations!

When two bacteria have one or more well-marked morphological differences, and exhibit important metabolic or other differences between them that are constant, the two may be regarded (by some!) as distinct species. But who is to determine what character or characters are "well-marked," constant, and of sufficient importance to be the basis of differentiation between species or genera? The same differences may be used as a basis of generic, tribal or even familial distinction between some other kinds of bacteria. Bacterial species, therefore, are rather ill defined.

The concept of genera among bacteria is in many instances equally nebulous. A genus is theoretically and ideally a group of species all of which bear sufficient resemblance to one another to be considered closely related and easily distinguishable from members of other groups or genera. The boundaries of some genera are sharply defined by as few as three characteristics, as in the genus *Bacillus:* (1) aerobic, (2) endosporeforming, (3) rods. These (under certain defined conditions of growth!) are very definite, distinct, constant and readily determined characters. The boundaries of other genera are sometimes more difficult to define, for example, the genera *Salmonella, Escherichia, Shigella* and *Aerobacter.* All of these are nonsporeforming, gramnegative, facultative (capable of growing aerobically or anaerobically) rods of identical size and appearance, nonpigmented and fermenting glucose. All occur more or less frequently in the intestinal tract. None forms pigment. Many possess certain O antigens (Chapter 24) in common. All are motile except *Shigella.* But sometimes nonmotile variants of the others occur. In such a situation some experts prefer using the word *group* to avoid the restrictions imposed by rules of nomenclature and the definitions of *genus* and *species.* As stated by Taylor: ". . . . the situation is similar to the use of the terms 'boyfriend' and 'betrothed'; the former is carefree, the latter is a legal state with defined responsibilities." An organism of one genus may thus possess several of the important (?) characters of two or three or more other genera; its proper allocation to one of these is often difficult and must be decided on an arbitrary basis.

**Strains.** A term frequently used in microbiology is *strain.* A strain of microorganisms is a particular example, specimen or *culture* of a given species. For example, we might isolate a culture of *Staphylococcus aureus* (causes boils) from Mr. Jones and, later, another culture of the same species from Miss Smith. We may call the first culture the "Jones" strain; the latter the "Smith" strain. They may or may not show temporary or minor differences, which are referred to as *strain differences.*

**Clones.** A clone is a strain of microorganism derived from a single cell and therefore asexually propagated. Clones of mammalian tissue cells are much used in tissue cultures for virology.

**Type Species.** These are certain central types of bacteria as, for example, *Streptococcus pyogenes, Bacillus subtilis, Clostridium butyricum* and the like. Each of these is a well-known, thoroughly studied, easily identifiable species representative of a genus or a group of species. It is spoken of as the *type species* of that genus or group of organisms. Usually it is the first-described member of the species. Cultures of type species are usually maintained in various institutions (among them the American Type Culture Collection in Washington, D.C.) for purposes of comparison.

To every experienced microbiologist the name of a type species conveys a very definite idea as to the characters of the group. However, ill-defined, partly studied organisms distinguishable from the type species or from each other only with the greatest difficulty, or not at all, are often included in such groups. On the other hand, organisms differing so markedly from the type species that the relationship seems very vague may also be included. Endless arguments often arise concerning such matters.

In certain new systems of classification (numerical or Adansonian classification) such groups are defined as "clusters," "taxospecies," "pleista" or "phenons"; all equivalent terms.

## 30.3   NUMERICAL (ADANSONIAN) TAXONOMY

In this system traditional, highly standardized methods are used to determine as many as possible of the phenotypic (visible or demonstrable) properties of as many as possible specimens of each of the organisms to be classified. Degrees of *relatedness* are determined by numbers of similarities between various properties of the organisms. Difficulties arise when some phenotypic properties are highly variable under different conditions of cultivation or when they vary as to degree of intensity of reaction: "+", "++", or "+++."

Selection of properties that are invariably present or + (A) or absent or − (B) simplifies analysis, but variable properties cannot always be ignored; personal judgement (frequently a source of error in any human endeavor) inevitably complicates the picture.

Once the distinctive (?) properties are selected, determined in the laboratory and tabulated, they are coded for computer or numerical analysis. If definitely + or − they are given code letters (e.g., A or B) for each type of reaction. Other symbols (e.g., C, D, E) are given for varying degrees of intensity or degrees of reaction or to other properties. Different values may be given to the various properties, depending on the judgement of the investigator. Each property of each organism is then compared with each property of each of all the other organisms.

Tabulations are made showing those organisms in which all properties agree (100 per cent similarity), those which differ in only one property, those that differ in two properties, and so on. Electronic computers are often used in such compilations. Percentage similarities (%S) of the organisms are calculated and are expressed as a *matching coefficient* or *%S value* for each organism:

$$\%S = \frac{Nsp}{Nsp + Nd} \times 100$$

or

$$\%S = \frac{Nsp + Nsn}{Nsp + Nsn + Nd} \times 100$$

Nsp = Number of similar positive matches (i.e., both positive); Nsn = Number of similar negative matches (i.e., both negative); Nd = Number of dissimilar matches (i.e., one positive, one negative).

These values (%S) may then be tabulated to show the relationship of each organism to all of the others in the group under investigation (Fig. 30.1). The data may be arranged in various ways such as a coded diagram (Fig. 30.2) or to form a sort of genealogical tree or *dendrogram* (Fig. 30.3) that graphically expresses degrees of relatedness; or other arrangements may be made. Whatever arrangement of the data is made, it is usually found that various groups of species appear in which the organisms have many similarities among themselves and dissimilarities from organisms of other clusters.

That there is not complete agreement on Adansonian classification is suggested by Marmur, Falkow and Mandel:

. . . numerical taxonomy is tedious in its practice, limited in its concepts, and has produced no new principles, nor has it as yet led to a meaningful improvement in the definition of taxonomic categories.*

---

*Ann. Rev. Microbiol., *17*:329, 1963.

```
C. diphtheriae gravis       1  100
C. diphtheriae mitis        2   87 100
C. diphtheriae P.W.8        3   77  76 100
C. diphtheriae intermedius  4   67  58  51 100
C. ulcerans                 5   60  62  50  40 100
C. flavidum                 6   53  46  48  53  41 100
C. renale                   7   46  40  38  51  37  57 100
C. xerosis                  8   49  45  45  45  46  56  46 100
Nocardia sp. (oral)         9   35  44  50  47  37  32  34 100
C. hofmannii (231)         10   45  40  40  36  38  44  41  55  35 100
C. hofmannii               11   36  33  34  33  31  45  40  49  31  86 100
C. equi                    12   30  29  31  39  41  39  36  51  33  54  50 100
Nocardia sp. (soil)        13   39  34  40  37  49  37  37  42  41  48  39  61 100
Jensenia canicruria        14   48  38  42  42  45  44  36  48  39  55  48  59  59 100
Mycobacterium smegmatis    15   47  39  48  37  41  41  34  38  36  45  48  53  61  57 100
M. butyricum               16   43  36  45  36  43  42  36  41  39  46  39  51  65  61  66 100
M. phlei                   17   41  33  38  36  39  39  43  35  35  46  40  41  55  54  54  65 100
M. lacticola               18   47  38  46  39  44  47  40  44  38  40  35  43  49  62  58  60  63 100
C. ovis                    19   37  33  30  42  30  46  46  41  30  34  39  27  23  27  22  26  30  36 100
C. murium                  20   31  27  29  31  29  36  36  35  28  34  35  32  22  24  24  31  27  28  41 100
C. helvolum                21   36  32  32  29  40  37  41  35  26  42  36  35  40  49  36  43  36  41  19  26 100
C. viscosum                22   28  26  23  33  36  38  42  38  26  41  37  35  36  41  35  39  38  42  26  38  54 100
C. fascians                23   33  30  25  42  38  37  38  37  40  32  25  40  40  42  42  40  39  40  25  33  38  40 100
C. betae                   24   16  20  13  23  30  33  33  38  29  26  21  35  48  32  38  34  30  30  24  26  30  36  46 100
C. rathayi                 25   13  14  14  16  26  28  21  30  25  33  29  37  39  35  26  35  24  22  20  25  48  33  36  48 100
C. michiganense            26   14  17  15  19  25  32  24  34  27  32  28  43  40  36  28  30  26  23  21  21  31  32  40  61  68 100
C. segmentosum             27   25  26  20  27  31  28  25  34  38  41  41  35  37  35  23  28  29  27  30  40  37  38  28  26  39  30 100
Arthrobacter sp. (1233)    28   31  33  31  35  34  40  28  43  31  43  40  44  43  50  31  36  41  38  39  32  50  48  33  36  46  43  62 100
Arthrobacter sp. (1234)    29   33  27  25  34  34  30  38  31  27  35  28  37  35  48  29  36  34  36  28  28  48  48  36  30  41  35  52  57 100
C. bovis                   30   25  27  26  30  31  32  35  38  26  42  38  35  37  33  41  28  32  29  34  23  32  25  22  25  33  32  46  51  41 100
C. fimi                    31   31  31  27  29  33  32  21  33  33  18  16  26  29  26  29  30  23  32  19  13  26  26  28  31  26  29  16  27  20  22 100
C. pyogenes                32   10  13  13  13  20  19  25  19  13  13  13  17   8  16   9   9   8  17  20  14  17  25  13  19  24  18  16  18  16  16  25  15 100
C. haemolyticum            33   14   9  11  10  15  18  17  20  14  12  14   7   8  12  12  11   7  11  16  13  15  13  10   7  20  15  14  15  16  20   4  48 100
                                 1   2   3   4   5   6   7   8   9  10  11  12  13  14  15  16  17  18  19  20  21  22  23  24  25  26  27  28  29  30  31  32  33
```

**Figure 30.1**   The similarity matrix of some corynebacteria and related organisms. The similarity values are expressed as percentages. (From Harrington: J. Gen. Microbiol., *45*:31, 1966.)

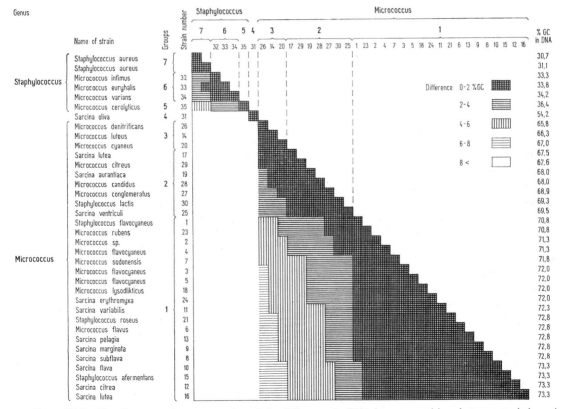

**Figure 30.2**   The diagrammatic representation of the differences in DNA base compositions between staphylococci and micrococci. The strains not differing from each other by more than 2 per cent guanine + cytosine (GC) are believed to have a similar DNA base composition. (From Rosypal, Rosypalová and Hořejš: J. Gen. Microbiol., *44*:281, 1966.)

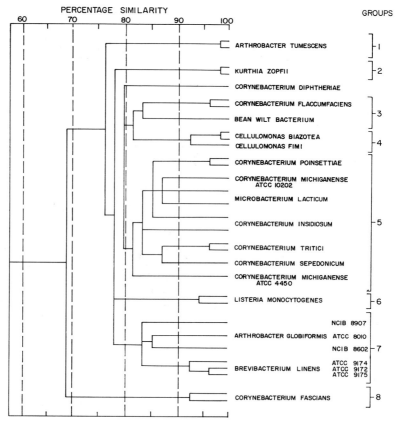

**Figure 30.3** Dendrogram depicting the phenetic resemblance among species of coryneform bacteria. The horizontal lines represent the taxa and the levels at which they unite to form groups. The broken vertical lines indicate the phenon levels. (From Da Silva and Holt: J. Bact., *90*:921, 1965.)

## 30.4   GENETIC CLASSIFICATIONS

Attempts are at present being made to determine relationships between organisms not merely on the basis of relatively superficial phenotypic (e.g., enzymic) similarities but on the more fundamental property of likeness or *homology* between the genetic materials, i.e., the DNA's. One line of such investigations is concerned with the *DNA base per cent composition;* another with degree of *hybridization* between DNA strands of different organisms.

**DNA Base Per Cent Composition.** Current studies of the molecular composition of the genetic material itself, especially the relative percentages of complementary pairs of guanine + cytosine (or G + C) in the DNA of each species (*mean DNA base per cent composition; %G + C*), are revealing relationships and differences between microorganisms never hitherto suspected on the basis of tests of phenotypic

properties. DNA base per cent composition of a species is presumably a fundamental and fixed property of each cell, dependent only on DNA base sequences and independent of age and all external influences except mutagenic agents.

Pure DNA can be extracted from cells that have been ruptured mechanically, as by osmotic shock; generally according to a method described by Marmur in 1961. Because of the three H-bonds in the $G \equiv C$ pairs these pairs require a higher temperature to separate them; they have a higher "melting point" than $A = T$ pairs. The per cent of G + C can therefore be calculated from the "melting point" (Tm), i.e., the mean temperature at which the DNA is denatured (thermal denaturation). Tm is determined by noting changes in optical density or light absorbance of a solution of DNA at a certain wave length of monochromatic light (260 m$\mu$) during the heating period (Fig. 30.4). The mean Tm is directly related to per cent G + C:

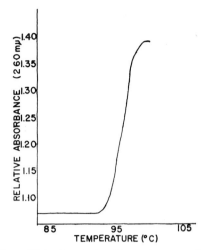

**Figure 30.4**  A typical melting point cruve. Organism represented is *Micrococcus* sp. L. A. 9.1. In this diagram the mean melting temperature (Tm), as measured by increase in turbidity from 1.10 to about 1.24 (i.e., relative absorbancy of light of wave length 260mµ), is about 96° C. (From Auletta and Kennedy: J. Bact., *92*:28, 1966.)

Tm = %G + C × 0.42 + 69.3. DNA base per cent composition may also be determined by hydrolyzing the DNA with formic acid and separating and measuring the resulting nucleotides by paper chromatography; also by other methods. Details of these complex and elegant methodologies are beyond the scope of this discussion. (See supplementary reading.)

Species of phenotypically similar organisms each having a %G + C in the range of 66 per cent to 68 per cent would theoretically be genetically very closely related; all being species in one genus. In another series, six species in a similar genus ranged from 64 per cent to 75 per cent G + C; fairly close. Species in a very different genus might be in a narrow range but at a very different level: 36 per cent to 41 per cent. It seems that strains that differ by more than 10 per cent G + C cannot be related phylogenetically. But unfortunately, certain wholly different organisms may have identical %G + C.

**Hybridization.**  In a different procedure, estimates of genetic relatedness may be made by measuring the extent of *hybridization* or recombination between single strands of sheared (split) DNA helices of different organisms.

Hybridization is a term that was for long wholly foreign to bacteriology since there was supposed to be no means of genetic recombination between bacteria. As explained in Chapter 14, it is now clear that there are several means of genetic recombination among bacteria: con-

jugation, transformation, transduction. Mechanisms for genetic recombination appear to exist also among cells of rickettsias, between different viruses and probably between certain cells of higher animals. It should be noted, however, that among bacteria such intercellular transfers of genetic material are limited to *genetically* related or *compatible* groups. There must be considerable agreement or *homology* between their DNA nucleotide sequences if recombination is to occur. Such groups of bacteria might be termed *genetic species* or *genospecies.*

Hybridization is not a means of intercellular genetic transfer but a means of measuring the degree of similarity (homology) between the nucleotide base sequences in separated or sheared single strands of DNA from two different organisms. If the nucleotide sequences are absolutely identical, the two strands should theoretically combine or hybridize 100 per cent. Lesser degrees of agreement or homology would result in correspondingly lesser percentages of hybridization.

Degree of homology is determined by mixing the two kinds of single sheared strands of DNA and then measuring the extent to which they recombine (if at all). In the double-stranded DNA produced by this recombination or hybridization the two single strands involved may be differentiated, if one is previously made radioactive by "feeding" the source organism with a pyrimidine base, say uracil, that has been artificially synthesized with $C^{14}$.

For example, purified isotopic (with $C^{14}$ uracil) DNA is prepared from one organism (A) and ordinary DNA is prepared from a closely related but different organism (B). The two kinds of DNA are mixed in a test tube containing pure 3 per cent agar and heated at a temperature above the Tm of either (105° C. for 10 minutes) to shear or break the H bonds between the complementary strands in each helix of DNA. Four single strands result. The mixture is cooled to about 70° C. to permit whatever hybridization or recombination (*annealing*) might occur between the sheared strands. The mixture is then treated with an enzyme (phosphodiesterase) that hydrolyzes all the *single*-stranded (i.e., the *unhybridized* or unrecombined) DNA; the enzyme does *not* affect the newly hybridized or recombined *double* helices. Without going into the technical details, which (as is very evident) are complex and beyond the scope of the present description, it may be pointed out that more or less hybridization may occur and that the degree of hybridization is determined by measuring the amount of isotopic DNA of the one organism (A) that combines (*per cent binding*) with ordinary DNA of the other organism (B).

Hybrids are formed only between single strands of DNA from closely related organisms having almost identical nucleotide sequences. For example, a single strand of DNA from *Pseudomonas fluorescens* (a common saprophyte of ditch and river water) will hybridize 100 per cent with isotopic single strands of DNA of its own species, and 83 per cent with strands from another species of the same genus; but *Ps. fluorescens* DNA will hybridize only 19 per cent with DNA of an organism of a different genus, even though of the same tribe or family, and not at all with a more distantly related and very different species. The degree of *genetic homology* (similarity of nucleotide sequences or "*microhomology*") is high in one case, low or absent in the others (Table 30.1). Strains that differ by more than about 2 per cent G + C composition cannot form DNA hybrids.

On the basis of similar genetic considerations, taxonomic groupings can also be made by means of transformation and transduction. These phenomena, like hybridization, are genetic recombination in which DNA from one organism merges with that of another; only the means of transfer differ. Whatever the method of transfer, recombination occurs only between organisms of which the G + C base composition and nucleotide sequences are within certain, rather narrow, limits of similarity.

## 30.5   ANTIGENIC STRUCTURE

In attempts to introduce still greater accuracy into systems of classification, immunology has been extensively drawn upon. Striking antigenic differences between organisms formerly believed to be identical, and vice versa, have been found.

Immunological methods often reveal very subtle differences between individuals of a given species. For example, as previously described all pneumococci (*Diplococcus pneumoniae*, cause of lobar pneumonia) were thought to be identical until it was found that the polysaccharides constituting their capsules fell into some 75 or more distinct antigenic groups because of differences in molecular structure of the capsular polysaccharides. The different sorts are called *types:* Type I, Type II, etc. Such types, based solely on antigenic differences, are often spoken of as *serotypes* because the antibodies used to

**TABLE 30.1**   THE DEGREE OF DNA HOMOLOGY OF SEVERAL FREE-LIVING NITROGEN-FIXING ORGANISMS WITH *PSEUDOMONAS FLUORESCENS* AND *P. PUTIDA.* *

| Organism | Strain number | Hybridization with $C^{14}$-DNA fragments from *P. fluorescens* 488 | | Hybridization with $C^{14}$-DNA fragments from *P. putida* 520 | |
|---|---|---|---|---|---|
| | | Labeled DNA bound | %DNA bound relative to *P. fluorescens* | Labeled DNA bound | %DNA bound relative to *P. putida* |
| *Pseudomonas fluorescens* | 488 | 68.4 | 100 | 43.2 | 83 |
| *Pseudomonas putida* | 520 | 48.2 | 70.5 | 52.0 | 100 |
| *Derxia gummosa* | III | 8.2 | 12 | 8.3 | 16 |
| *Azotobacter vinelandii* | C–1 | 27.4 | 40 | 26.0 | 50 |
| *Azotobacter beijerinckii* | B–2 | 31.4 | 46 | 21.3 | 41 |
| *Azotobacter chroococcum* | 9125 | | | 25.5 | 49 |
| *Azomonas macrocytogenes* | 8200 | 30.8 | 45 | | |
| *Azomonas macrocytogenes* | 9128 | 23.9 | 35 | 23.9 | 46 |
| *Azomonas macrocytogenes* | 9129 | 24.6 | 36 | 29.6 | 57 |
| *Azomonas insignis* | 9127 | 32.1 | 47 | 25.0 | 48 |
| *Beijerinckia derxii* | | 19.2 | 28 | 15.1 | 29 |
| *Beijerinckia fluminensis* | | | | 9.9 | 19 |
| *Azotococcus agilis* | K | 13.0 | 19 | 10.9 | 21 |
| *Azotococcus agilis* | S | 15.1 | 22 | 17.2 | 33 |
| *Azotococcus agilis* | 9 | 21.2 | 31 | 18.2 | 35 |
| *Pseudomonas azotogensis* | | 2.7 | 4 | 3.6 | 7 |
| agar | | 0.7 | 1 | 0.5 | 1 |

*(From De Ley and Park: Ant. Leeuw., *32:*6, 1966.)

determine the different types are found in serum. An analogous situation exists among hemolytic streptococci. We now speak of Group A or Group B hemolytic streptococci (*Streptococcus pyogenes,* cause of "strep throat"), depending on the chemical nature of their carbohydrate antigens. Some humans are of blood group A, and some of group O, and so on.

## BACTERIOPHAGE TYPES

As indicated in the section on bacteriophages (Chapter 18), within a species, and even within a clone or serotype, intraclonal or intraserotypic differentiations can be established on the basis of differing susceptibilities to type-specific bacteriophages. These hyper-specific *phage types* to a certain extent parallel serotypes, since phage type susceptibility appears to be closely related to specific cell wall antigen content and this, in turn, to DNA base sequence and content. However, phage typing often goes beyond serotyping. Certain strains of bacteria of great importance in industry and medicine are, at present, identifiable *only* by means of phage typing.

## SUPPLEMENTARY READING

Ainsworth, G. C., and Sneath, P. H. A., editors: Microbial Classification. Twelfth Symposium, Soc. Gen. Microbiol., London. 1962.

Bergey's Manual of Determinative Bacteriology. (See Supplementary Reading, Chapter 29.)

Bogdanescu, V., and Racotta, R.: Identification of mycrobacteria by overall similarity analysis. J. Gen. Microbiol., *48*:111, 1967.

Campbell, C. B. G.: Taxonomic status of tree shrews. Science, *153*:436, 1966.

Colwell, R. R., Citarella, R. V., and Ryman, I.: Deoxyribonucleic acid base composition and adansonian analysis of heterotrophic, aerobic pseudomonads. J. Bact., *90*:1148, 1965.

De Ley, J.: The quick approximation of DNA base composition from absorbancy ratios. Ant. Leeuw., *33*:203, 1967.

Focht, D. D., and Lockhart, W. R.: Numerical survey of some bacterial taxa. J. Bact., *90*:1314, 1965.

Friedman, S., and De Ley, J.: "Genetic species" concept in *Xanthomonas*. J. Bact., *89*:95, 1965.

Heberlein, G. T., De Ley, J., and Tijtgat, R.: Deoxyribonucleic acid homology and taxonomy of *Agrobacterium, Rhizobium,* and *Chromobacterium.* J. Bact., *94*:116, 1967.

Iglewski, W. J., and Franklin, R. M.: Denaturation and renaturation of viral ribonucleic acid. J. Virol., *1*:793, 1967.

Ikawa, M.: Bacterial phosphatides and natural relationships. Bact. Rev., *31*:54, 1967.

Leifson, E.: Bacterial taxonomy: A critique. Bact. Rev.: *30*:257, 1966.

Marmur, J., Falkow, S., and Mandel, M.: New approaches to bacterial taxonomy. Ann. Rev. Microbiol., *17*:329, 1963.

Pfister, R. M., and Burkholder, P. R.: Numerical taxonomy of some bacteria isolated from antarctic and tropical seawaters. J. Bact., *90*:863, 1965.

Rosypalová, A., Boháček, J., and Rosypal, S.: Deoxyribonucleic acid base composition and taxonomy of violet-pigmented cocci. Ant. Leeuw., *32*:105, 1966.

Skerman, V. B. D. (See Supplementary Reading, Chapter 29.)

Sokal, R. R.: Numerical Taxonomy. Sci. Amer., *216*:106, 1967.

# Chapter 31

---

# ORDER EUBACTERIALES: THE BACILLACEAE

All species of bacteria are important but we can here describe only some representative groups or species that have attracted particular attention by their role in diseases of man, or of plants or animals of value to man, or by their importance in industry, the fertility of the soil, and so on.

In contemplating the formidable array of some 1500 species of bacteria listed in "Bergey's Manual" we may do as logicians do, and proceed from the simple to the more complex. If any of the Class Schizomycetes may be called simple then possibly those that are grouped in the Order Eubacteriales may be the simplest (or most primitive) in terms of over-all form, arrangement and life history. They will be used as a convenient starting point for our discussion of the bacteria.

Bacteria of the Order Eubacteriales occur in only two basic forms: (1) unicellular spheres or spheroids (*cocci;* singular, *coccus;* Gr. *kokkos* = grain; berry); (2) simple, unicellular rods or rodlike forms (*bacilli;* singular, *bacillus;* L. *bacillum* = small rod); various modifications and distortions of both forms are frequent. The Order Eubacteriales as classified in the 1957 edition of "Bergey's Manual" contains 69 genera and subgenera divided into 13 families containing over 600 species. There have been changes since 1957 but the main structure of the system is still used.

At this point it may be well to emphasize that the term bacillus refers indiscriminantly to any rod-shaped bacterium regardless of its other properties, whereas the term *Bacillus* refers only to the genus of aerobic, rod-shaped bacteria that form heat-resistant endospores, i.e., the Genus *Bacillus.* The word bacterium refers to any of the Schizomycetes regardless of form or properties.

Of the hundreds of species of Eubacteriales one or more is to be found almost anywhere on the surface of the earth: in the soil, thousands of feet in the air, in rivers and lakes and in the most profound marine depths (six miles or more), in mines, on mountain tops, in and on plants and animals, from pole to pole.

The Eubacteriales, as indicated by the name of this order, have what may well be called *typical* bacterial characteristics, being independently unicellular, undifferentiated cocci or rods. They are microscopic in size (about 0.5 to 2.0 $\mu$ in diameter; 5 to 20 $\mu$ in length if rod-shaped), enclosed in rigid, relatively thick strong cell walls of or containing mucopolysaccharide, and are holophytic chemoorganotrophs in nutrition. They multiply by transverse binary fission.

All motile species are *peritrichously* flagellate. This is one of the major characters differentiating all Eubacteriales from all species of the other great group of typically unicellular bacteria of similar form and size, the Order Pseudomonadales. All Pseudomonadales, when motile, are *polar*-flagellate. (See Table 37.1.)

Among the Eubacteriales are found both gram-positive and gram-negative species, species which are encapsulated or unencapsulated, aerobes and anaerobes, sporeformers and nonsporeformers, mesophils, thermophils and cryophils, parasites and saprophytes, and so on. Of all of the families of Eubacteriales one of the most interesting is the Family Bacillaceae.

## 31.1 FAMILY BACILLACEAE

This is one of the largest groups of the Order Eubacteriales, comprising over 100 species. Most species are gram-positive; a few are gram-negative or gram-variable. The family is divided into two genera: *Bacillus* (25 species) all strict or facultative aerobes; and *Clostridium* (L. *closter* = a small spindle) (93 species), all more or less strict anaerobes.

With the exception of a single species of sporeforming cocci (*Sporosarcina ureae*), these two genera, *Bacillus* and *Clostridium,* are the *only* bacteria that form *heat-resistant* endospores. *Endospores* must be distinguished carefully from conidiospores and sporangiospores of molds and Actinomycetales, from ascospores of yeasts and from conidia (often called spores) of the Streptomycetaceae. True bacterial endospores (Family Bacillaceae) generally have a high degree of resistance to chemical disinfectants and to temperatures used in baking and sterilizing. None of the other spore types approaches this degree of resistance.

Because of the vast difference in thermostability between mature endospores and vegetative cells, presence or absence of these spores is most conclusively demonstrated by means of heat. Growth of a culture after exposure to 90° C. for 10 minutes in aqueous fluid (Chapter 29) proves the presence of spores. Many spores are killed at lower temperatures or by shorter exposures to 90° C. *All* vegetative cells are killed by this exposure.

It was the heat-resistant spores of Bacillaceae that misled Needham and others to support the view that life began spontaneously in the infusions that they thought they had sterilized by heating. Even experienced bacteriologists are sometimes embarrassed by the appearance of sporeforming rods (*Bacillus* spp.) in supposedly sterile material or in pure cultures of bacteria. This is usually due to carelessness in the sterilizing room or to short-cuts in heating processes.

**Structure of Bacillaceae.** The electron microscope shows that species of *Bacillus* and of *Clostridium* have structures typical of nonphotosynthetic, cellular, independently living procaryons, i.e., bacteria, as previously described in Chapter 13.

**Spores of Bacillaceae.** Knowledge of the thermal resistance of spores, of their formation and germination and of the factors affecting both of these is of great importance in various preserving industries, manufacturing processes, medicine and other human activities. In the strictly aerobic species of *Bacillus,* formation of spores (sporulation) occurs *only* under aerobic conditions. In the strictly anaerobic *Clostridium* it occurs only anaerobically. In some of the aerobes that are facultative, sporulation may occur aerobically or anaerobically.

SPORULATION. The process of *sporulation* in Bacillaceae has been admirably elucidated in great detail with the electron microscope. Sporulation is much alike in both *Bacillus* and *Clostridium.* Commonly the process begins by elongation of the cell as though about to undergo fission. In *Bacillus* spp., which have been most used as models, many granules of poly-beta-hydroxybutyric acid (pbha) now appear. These are used as reserve food for energy required in the late and maturation phases of spore formation. By virtue of stored pbha, sporulation in *Bacillus* species can go to completion in the absence of extraneous food sources, e.g., sporulation can be completed in distilled water (*endotrophic sporulation*). In *Clostridium* spp., such internal food reserves have not been found and these species require exogenous food sources during all stages of sporulation (*exotrophic sporulation*).

FORESPORE. In the elongated cell about to sporulate, the nuclear material is redistributed from end to end as an axial mass and is then divided so that one complete nucleus appears to be concentrated at one end of the cell (Fig. 31.1, a). The cell membrane now appears to grow inward, possibly from a mesosome, and to grow around the nucleus, forming a complete, *two-layered septum* segregating the nucleus, and a portion of the cytoplasm containing ribosomes, mesosomes and enzymes, from the remainder of the cell. The material thus enclosed is now a *forespore,* a new cell, and the septum is a *forespore membrane* (Fig. 31.1, b). The forespore DNA becomes distinctively rearranged. Water may be withdrawn during forespore formation or at some other stage of the process; the mature spore is considerably but not wholly dehydrated.

SPORE COATINGS. Between the outer and inner layers of the forespore membrane there now is laid down a thick shell or *cortex* that forms between the layers and, like a cell wall, encloses the spore protoplast. The spore cytoplasm, ribosomes and nuclear material are enclosed within the cortex and the *inner layer* of the forespore membrane which now appears to serve as, or to produce, a protoplast membrane.

Around the cortex, and exteriorly to the *outer* forespore layer, there is formed a *spore coat* (Fig. 31.1, c). This appears first in the form of segments, later as a complete, continuous, two-layered covering. Outside the spore coat a membrane is formed that is scalloped or rippled (*sculptured*) and that thickens and becomes multilaminate and often voluminous (Fig. 31.1, d).

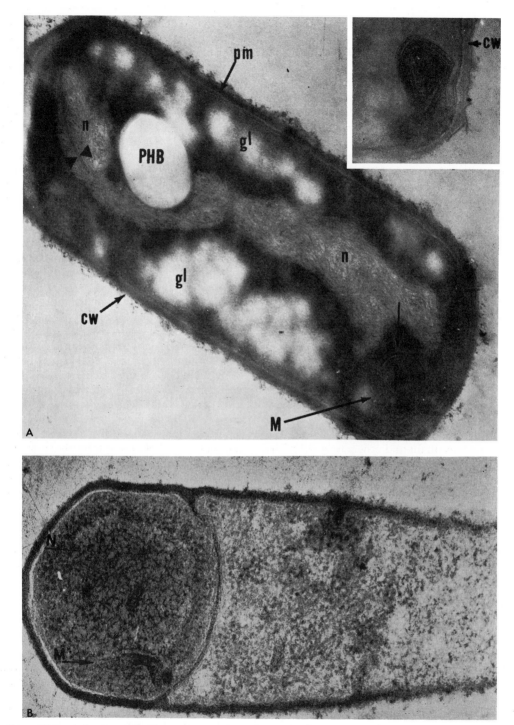

**Figure 31.1**   *A,* Section of *Bacillus cereus* grown in a glucose-glutamate-glycine-salts medium and fixed by the agar block method of Kellenberger, Ryter and Séchaud. The cell is at stage 1 in sporulation, with the nuclear material (n) arranged in the form of an axially disposed filament of fine fibrils and associated at one end with a mesosome (M). A strand of membrane (triangles) is embedded in the nuclear fibrils. The characteristic cell wall (cw), cytoplasmic membrane (pm), poly-beta-hydroxybutyrate inclusion (PHB) and smaller electron-dense areas (gl) believed to contain glycogen are also shown. ✕ 69,800. Inset is an enlargement showing a more clearly defined, concentric, laminated mesosome from a stage 1 cell. ✕ 87,000. *B,* Thin section of a sporulating rod of *Clostridium pectinovorum,* showing the spore nuclear body (N) trapped behind the apparently completed forespore septum. ✕ 100,000.

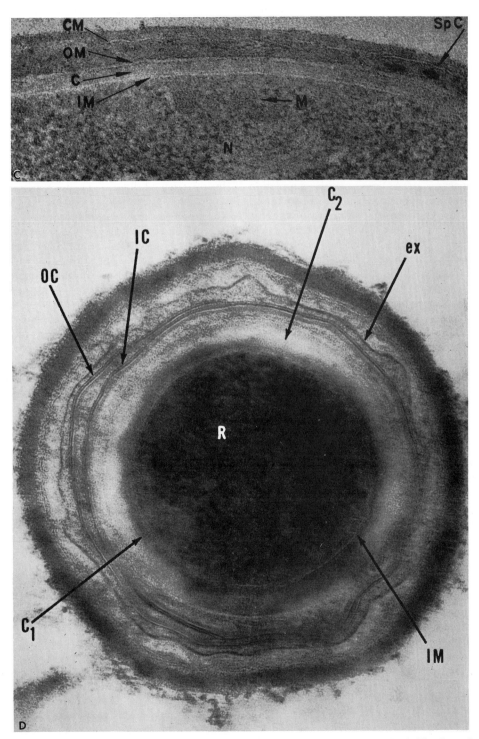

**Figure 31.1** *Continued. C,* Cortex and spore formation in *C. pectinovorum* stained with lead. The formation of the cortex (C) between the inner (IM) and outer (OM) forespore membranes is visible. The cytoplasmic membrane (CM) is seen under the cell wall. Small areas of a spore coat (SpC) and part of a nuclear body (N) are seen. The intraspore mesosomes (M) are barely detectable. × 142,000. *D,* A transverse section of a cell at stage 6 grown as in *A.* The outer (OC) and inner (IC) coats are well defined and appear separated. The less dense cortical layer (C₂) and the inner dense layer (C₁) are apparent. Other structures are: ex, exosporium; R, ribosomal aggregate; IM, inner membrane. × 125,000. (*A* and *D* from Ellar and Lundgren: J. Bact., *92*:1748, 1966; *B* and *C* from Fitz-James: J. Bact., *84*:104, 1962.)

The cortex appears to contain the dipicolinic acid (DPA*) that is an essential and important component of bacterial endospores. DPA is liberated as calcium dipicolinate (CaDPA) in considerable amounts when the spore germinates and grows (see page 396). CaDPA may contribute to the thermostability of bacterial endospores. DPA was for some time thought to be a unique and distinctive component of bacterial endospores; it has since been found in considerable quantities as a waste product of the growth of the mold *Penicillium citreo-viride*.

PROPERTIES OF SPORES. With completion of the spore wall, and following maturation and probably dehydration, the spore acquires three distinctive properties: (1) high refractive index, or *refractility;* (2) impenetrability to ordinary stains, such as methylene blue, and to many disinfectants; (3) high degree of resistance to heat. These properties are all associated with *dehydration* of protoplasm.

Spores vary enormously in heat resistance. Not only do spores of different species differ in resistance but spores of the same species and in the same culture may vary a hundred-fold or more. Part of the latter variations may be due to different degrees of maturity, hydration, DPA content and unknown factors. Greatest thermal resistance appears to be associated with moisture content of about 5 to 10 per cent of dry weight.

The process of sporulation is complete in about 5 to 13 hours depending on species and on growth conditions. In some species the mature spore escapes from the now-empty *sporangium;* in others the sporangium remains as an outer covering of the spore.

FACTORS IN SPORE FORMATION. Endospores are formed most readily under good growth conditions. Their formation appears to require some energy and carbon source such as glucose. Nitrogenous food substances (as certain amino acids) are also required. In some species manganese ions are requisite; in others, $Fe^{++}$, $Cu^{++}$, $Zn^{++}$ and $Mo^{++}$ greatly increase spore formation. At least part of the spore contents appear to be newly synthesized and are not merely old material of the vegetative cell. The fact that by far the largest numbers of spores are usually found in well-matured cultures several days old indicates that spores generally represent a mature stage of cell development.

They do not necessarily represent a response to unfavorable conditions, because they often germinate and grow in the same medium in which they were produced. They appear to be merely an alternate form of existence in what may be thought of as a primitive life cycle.

**Staining Spores.** As noted previously, mature spores cannot be stained by ordinary methods such as Gram's. A rod with a spore inside, when stained by ordinary methods, may appear to have a hole in it (Fig. 31.2). However, the outer surface of the spore may readily be colored; in stained smears *free* spores may appear as tiny, blue or red rings. There are special stains for spores. The Ziehl-Neelsen acid-fast stain often penetrates. Another method is outlined in the footnote.*

**Spore Outgrowth.** If it were known how to make all spores promptly germinate and grow into vulnerable vegetative cells, methods of sterilization and preserving of foods and industrial materials could be much simplified at tremendous savings of time and money. The change from a dormant spore to an active vegetative cell involves at least three distinct stages: (1) *activation;* (2) *germination* and (3) *outgrowth,* or *postgermination development.* In some ways spores suggest an automobile with switch off and engine not running. The mechanism is ready for *activation.*

ACTIVATION. Under natural conditions, activation of endospores in aqueous media appears to occur only occasionally, slowly and intermittently during hours or days at temperatures from 20 to 35° C. Activation of all or nearly all the spores in a group occurs within a few minutes if the spores are heated in an aqueous fluid at about 65° C. for 15 to 60 minutes; higher temperatures (105 to 120° C.) are used for thermophilic spores. Spores so treated are said to be *heat activated* or *heat shocked.* Activation may also be brought about by certain chemicals, e.g., L-alanine, adenosine, glucose and some reducing agents.

Activation is a reversible process. Unless agencies are present that induce the activated spores to germinate after being activated, the spores revert to dormancy and may require reactivation. The mechanism of activation is not

---

*The chemical name of dipicolinic acid is 2,6-pyridine dicarboxylic acid:

$$HOOC \underset{N}{\bigcirc} COOH$$

Do not confuse with diaminopimelic acid (DAP), a lysine derivative that occurs in bacterial cell walls.

---

*Spore stain: Apply saturated malachite green (about 7.6 per cent) for 10 minutes. Flame until warm. Rinse with tap water for about 10 seconds.

Apply 0.25 per cent aqueous safranin for 15 seconds. Rinse with tap water, blot dry.

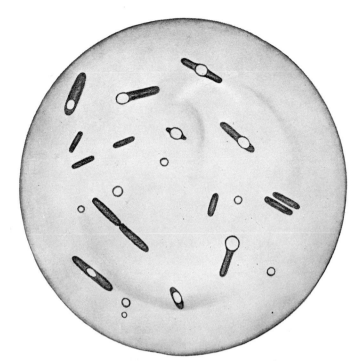

**Figure 31.2**   Various types of bacterial spores. Some of the spores have escaped from the sporangia. Stained with methylene blue, which does not penetrate inside the spore, only the outer surface of the spore is stained (about × 1000).

fully understood, but may involve reversible alterations in the tertiary structure of certain of the enzyme proteins in the spore. Activation of a spore may be likened to the driver of a car getting into the car and inserting the key in the switch.

GERMINATION.   Germination is an irreversible change from the activated but still inert state to the beginning of enzyme action. Germination occurs only *after* activation. Water is imbibed, metabolic activity begins and nutrients are required: sources of P, N, S and C and energy. Extending the automobile analogy, we may say that the switch has been turned on and the starter is running.

Germination of heat-activated cells may be triggered by a variety of chemical agents: various hexoses, potassium nitrate and some others but most notably, and specifically, L-alanine. The presence of electrolytes and of L-alanine is usually essential. D-alanine, on the contrary, can suppress germination. An enzyme, referred to as a *germination enzyme*, that causes germination of *Bacillus* spores has been described.

Germination of all species of *Bacillus* can occur in the presence of air; many clostridia germinate only anaerobically in the presence of carbon dioxide. Water is essential in any case. Germination is not necessarily followed by outgrowth, and agents that trigger germination do not necessarily support outgrowth and vice versa.

The process of germination may be divided into two stages: (1) the *microlag*, extending from addition of triggering agent to the first visible change in the spore: *beginning* loss of refractility; (2) the *microgermination time*, which extends from first loss of refractility to *complete* loss of refractility. The spore has by now also lost its thermostability and it can also be stained with ordinary dyes. Swelling occurs, presumably caused by imbibition of water.

DIPICOLINIC ACID AND SURFACTANTS.   It has been known for some time that dipicolinic acid and calcium form about 5 to 15 per cent and 1 to 3 per cent, respectively, of the dry weight of spores, and that these substances are released in considerable amounts, apparently from the cortex, when spores germinate and grow out. That DPA and calcium play a critical role is indicated by the observation that adding DPA, and chelates of calcium, magnesium or strontium to washed spores, aerobic or anaerobic, induces 100 per cent germination within about 20 minutes at pH 7.0 and temperatures of 25 to 35° C. in the absence of any activating agent. Equally fast or faster germination is induced, in the absence of heat-shocking or L-alanine, by some surface-tension reducers, notably, *n*-dodecylamine at pH 7.0 and temperatures from 37 to 70° C. The mechanisms of these actions are under intensive investigation.

POSTGERMINATIVE GROWTH.   As a seed may sprout in perfectly non-nutritious, sterile distilled water but fail to develop further, so ger-

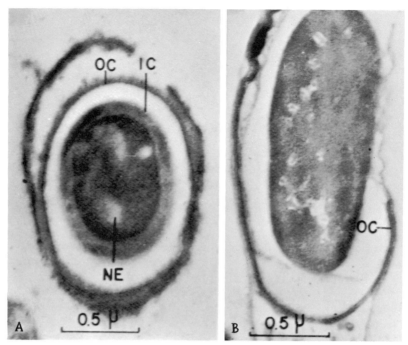

**Figure 31.3**   Electron micrograph of ultrathin section of spores of *Clostridium butyricum* during the germination process. *A,* Nuclear elements have become less dense and are more clearly seen. Both inner spore coat and cortex are less readily seen. Incubation time: 5 min. *B,* The spore has become a vegetative cell and is escaping through the ruptured spore coat. Incubation time: 30 min. (From Takagi, Kawata and Yamamoto: J. Bact., vol. 80.)

mination of a spore does not necessarily imply postgerminative development into a bacterium. *Postgerminative* outgrowth of the spore occurs only if conditions for cell nutrition and growth are favorable. Assuming such favorable conditions, the postgerminative changes consist of swelling of the spore, increasing enzymic activity, splitting of the spore wall, elongation of the developing cell and, finally, emergence of the actively growing vegetative cell. The method of splitting of the spore wall may be distinctive of species (Fig. 31.3). As we extend our automobile analogy, the engine is running, the car is beginning to move; fuel is needed. Amino acids, especially glutamic acid, with other fuels such as glucose and minerals, are essential for cells.

The DPA chelates mentioned above may be added to a good nutrient broth, thus achieving activation, germination and outgrowth in one operation.

## 31.2   GENUS *BACILLUS*

All species of *Bacillus*\* are more or less strictly aerobic, gram-positive or gram-variable, endo-

---

\*In order to avoid confusion of names, the student is urged to re-read the paragraph on page 390 concerning the use of the terms *bacillus, Bacillus* and *bacterium.*

spore-forming rods. Most species are motile and many contain numerous fat globules. Just prior to sporulation, they form many granules of poly-beta-hydroxybutyric acid, conspicuous if properly stained; e.g., by fat stains. From the standpoint of cultivation in the laboratory, or growth in natural habitats, most species of *Bacillus* are not fastidious. They grow well in aqueous extracts of soil, in vegetable or yeast extracts, or in simple peptone media.

They are active and versatile producers of hydrolytic enzymes and consequently can utilize as food a wide variety of proteins, carbohydrates, lipids, glucosides, alcohols and organic acids. They are thus seen to be of great importance as scavengers. Some of their enzymes are produced in quantity commercially and are used in industrial processes (leather, paper, silk, textiles, coffee). Several species are both famous and respected in the community because they produce valuable antibiotics: bacitracin and polymyxin, for instance. Others (sometimes the same) are both infamous and shunned because they grow in many sorts of valuable commodities (paper, various foods and drugs, wood, leather), producing spoilage and economic loss to human beings. One species, *B. anthracis,* is the cause of anthrax or "malignant pustule."

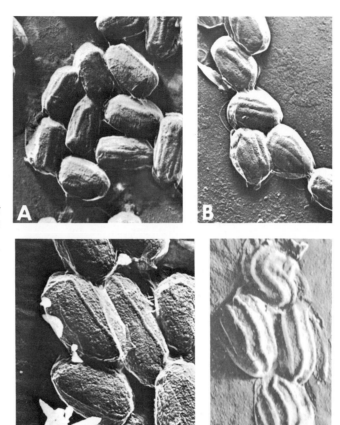

**Figure 31.4** Distinctive sculpturing of spores of *Bacillus* species: *A, subtilis*, × 12,000; *B, subtilis*, × 7500; *C, brevis*, × 9000. *D. polymyxa.* × 5000. (From Bradley and Williams: J. Gen. Microbiol., vol. 17.)

**Classification.** These organisms are among the most difficult to classify. Not only do the physiological and morphological properties of various "species" overlap, but it requires the greatest care concerning composition of medium, its pH, temperature of incubation, age of culture and numerous other factors to obtain reproducible results in the study of these species.

Partly for these reasons, primary groupings are often based on the diameter and shape of the endospores (oval or spherical) and their location in the sporangium.

Electron-microscopic studies of the distinctive surface ridges or sculpturings of spores (Fig. 31.4) and investigations of chemical constitution and enzymic content, are introducing taxonomic order among these confused species. On an Adansonian basis (Chapter 30), several clusters of these organisms are discernible, each centering around a fairly well-defined species, for example: the *B. cereus* group which includes numerous variants such as *B. cereus* var. *anthracis;* the *B. subtilis* group vars. *niger,* etc.; the *B. thuringiensis* group comprising variants *sotto* and *alesti,* among others.

## 31.3 IMPORTANT SPECIES OF *BACILLUS*

Most species of *Bacillus* are harmless saprophytes of the soil. Their heat-resistant spores are ubiquitous and often plague the food-preserving industries, surgeons, microbiologists and others who must work with sterile materials. Only one species is definitely pathogenic for animals: *B. anthracis,* the cause of anthrax (Gr. *anthrax* = carbuncle).

**Anthrax.** Primarily a disease of farm animals, anthrax is transmissible to man, especially workers in hide, hair and wool industries. In man, the spores most commonly gain entrance to the body from infected soil, dust or animal hair or tissues, through a cut in the skin. The spores first germinate and grow at the point of entrance, forming a very rapidly progressive, angry, inflamed carbuncle or pustule (*malignant pustule*) which, when well developed, is covered with a black crust. This pustule teems with anthrax bacilli which are heavily encapsulated. The initial pustule frequently heals, but in other cases the bacilli invade the blood, multiply enormously, and are spread through all the organs of the body, where they tend to form local lesions which serve as further centers for dissemination unless the leukocytes and other defensive mechanisms of the body overcome them. When growing in the body (i.e., in the absence of free $O_2$) or in cultures in the presence of atmospheres containing 50 per cent carbon dioxide, they produce *no spores* but develop large protective capsules. They also produce a group of potent exotoxins: I, II and III. These occur only in the blood of infected animals or in certain complex, semisynthetic media.

Anthrax in farm animals (cattle, sheep) may be prevented by injections of *B. anthracis* bacterins (formaldehyde-killed bacilli) or by injections of spore-vaccines made with *living* spores of graded, attenuated virulence or by the use of serum for temporary, passive immunity. Animals dead of anthrax should be handled with care to avoid contaminating the premises and infecting the handlers and dust with the spores. The bacilli sporulate rapidly when exposed to air. They can survive many decades dried in soil.

## 31.4   *BACILLUS* SPECIES PATHOGENIC FOR ARTHROPODS

Pasteur was one of the first to make scientific studies of infectious diseases of arthropods, especially diseases of the valuable silk worms. Today, infection of arthropods is important from two opposite viewpoints:

First, as in Pasteur's day, it is essential to *protect* from infection such valuable arthropods as silk moths and honey bees. Second, it is now known that specific infection is an important means of killing certain arthropod pests: (a) vectors of diseases and (b) arthropods that destroy crops. While there are numerous effective chemical insecticides, some have toxic effects on man and livestock and are expensive. Further, many noxious insects, notably malaria-transmitting mosquitoes and house flies (*Musca domestica*), tend to become resistant to certain insecticides. To avoid some of these disadvantages, bacteria and viruses that are harmless to mammals and useful arthropods, but lethal to undesirable arthropods, are now being used more and more for pest control. The ideal microbial insecticide should be: (1) virulent and lethal at all times; (2) not sensitive to the environment where it is to act (sunshine, dryness or dust); (3) persistent in the area of use, e.g., *sporeforming;* (4) fast-acting; (5) harmless to man, plants, and useful insects; (6) capable of mass production at low cost. There are few, if any,

such agents; some have several of these desirable attributes.

There are several species of *entomogenous* bacteria (bacteria that live in insects) that cause disease of their insect hosts. Best known at present are species of *Bacillus* that cause (a) infection or (b) intoxication.

**Infection.** Infection is caused by the growth, in the larvae of the arthropod, of bacilli from ingested spores. At first, rapid growth occurs in the gut. This is followed by penetration of the gut wall and generalized invasion, with slow but massive growth of the bacilli in the hemolymph ("blood") of the larval stage. The invasion process is usually slow, requiring days or weeks to kill. Although some toxic substance may be produced by bacilli causing this type of disease, death appears primarily due to overwhelming invasiveness on the part of the bacilli.

MILKY-WHITE DISEASE. A "useful" disease, milky-white disease is typical of the infection just described. It is caused by *B. popilliae* and *B. lentimorbus.* These are used to combat Japanese beetles (*Popillia japonica*). The bacilli grow to prodigious numbers in the "blood" of the larvae causing it to appear milky-white. For use against the beetles, the infected larval juices, containing billions of spores, are dried, ground and mixed with chalk dust or other powder. This is applied to the soil as a spray or dust. The beetles have disappeared almost entirely in areas where the spores have been applied.

Methods for production of large numbers of *spores* of the organisms by using artificial culture media have recently been developed. As a curious sidelight, these bacilli are confirmed drug-addicts, i.e., they require barbiturates for vegetative growth in synthetic media.

FOULBROOD. This illustrates an undesirable aspect of infection of arthropods. *Bacillus alvei* is one of several organisms that cause, or are associated with, a disease (*foulbrood*) of bees which results in great losses to beekeepers annually. There are several forms of the disease. American foulbrood is caused by a related organism, *B. larvae,* while *B. alvei* causes European foulbrood; certain streptococci (*S. apis*) also appear to cause the disease. The larvae of bees contain the infecting organisms in large numbers. This sort of disease appears to parallel the type of slowly progressive infection of Japanese beetle larvae just mentioned.

**Intoxication.** This is caused by a protein toxin produced by *B. thuringiensis, B. entomocidus* and their several variants. Within a few minutes after ingestion by larvae, the toxin causes a paralysis of the gut with cessation of feeding

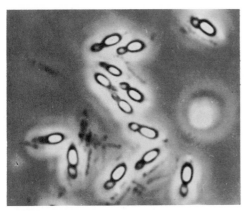

**Figure 31.5** Phase contrast microphotograph of unstained spores (larger light ovals) of *Bacillus popilliae* with parasporal bodies attached (× 2425). (From Steinkraus: J. Bact., vol. 74.)

and, within a few hours, total paralysis and death. Many species of larvae of *Lepidoptera* (moths and butterflies), including the valuable silk worms (*Bombyx mori*) and some species of flies, are susceptible to the toxin. An enzyme, phospholipase C, is also produced and appears to have a noxious effect. Unlike milky-white disease, infection and invasion ordinarily play little or no part in the lethal process.

The toxin (presumably a metabolic waste product) is formed *in the sporangium* of the bacilli

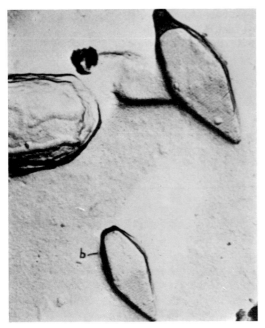

**Figure 31.6** Electron micrograph of spore and crystals of *Bacillus thuringiensis,* var. thuringiensis Berliner. (From Monro, R. E.: The formation of protein inclusions in *Bacillus thuringiensis.* Ph.D. Thesis. Cambridge University, 1959.)

as a cuboidal, triangular or diamond-shaped crystal lying beside the spore. It is called a *parasporal* body (Figs. 31.5 and 31.6.) Bacilli producing such crystals are said to be *crystalliferous.* Parasporal bodies are formed in the sporangia of many species of *B. cereus*-like bacilli, e.g., *B. popilliae,* but in *B. popilliae* the parasporal body does not appear to be very toxic, at least for Japanese beetles. Possibly it may be so for other species of insect, a good field for investigation in applied entomology.

The use of *B. thuringiensis* in the control of insects differs from the use of *B. popilliae* in that *B. thuringiensis* must be cultivated in large amounts to obtain sufficient toxic crystals. These, like any other insect poison, are sprayed repeatedly on crops. *B. popilliae,* on the contrary, is used in smaller amounts merely to start a self-propagating infection which maintains and spreads itself from year to year. The production of *B. thuringiensis* toxin is now a considerable industry in some countries.

## OTHER IMPORTANT BACILLUS SPECIES

*Bacillus subtilis* is the type species of the genus and is found in dusty places everywhere. If hay be soaked in warm water for a day or two, the water will be found teeming with organisms of many kinds, including many beautiful protozoa. *B. subtilis* and other species of *Bacillus* will also be found.

*Bacillus subtilis* often forms long chains of bacilli sometimes called *streptobacilli.* Since the bacilli are motile, such chains swim with a writhing motion. Owing to avidity for oxygen, *B. subtilis* and many other species of *Bacillus* grow in a scum, or *pellicle,* at the surface of fluid media.

Because of its active attack on organic nitrogenous compounds, cultures of *B. subtilis* smell of ammonia. On slants of potato it grows luxuriantly, with a yellowish or pink color and a warty or vesiculated appearance.

*B. subtilis* is important as the source of the antibiotic, *subtilin.* Bacitracin is produced from a strain very like *B. subtilis,* often called *B. licheniformis.*

*Bacillus coagulans* is a species of importance as a cause of spoilage of canned foods. It is notable for its ability to grow in acid foods such as tomatoes. Since it produces no gas, spoilage (souring) is not discovered until the container is opened. *B. coagulans* is said to cause *flat sours,* so termed because the ends of the can do not bulge as they would if gas were formed

under pressure by the fermentation. Spores of
*B. coagulans* are very heat resistant and thus
sometimes survive commercial processing.
*B. coagulans* is either a facultative anaerobe or it
can grow sufficiently in the small residuum of
air enclosed in cans at the time of processing to
produce its results.

*B. stearothermophilus* is also well known as
a nuisance and a source of flat sours in the
canning industry. Since it is exceptionally heat
resistant, its spores are often used to check the
efficiency of heat sterilizing processes.

## SUPPLEMENTARY READING

Angus, T. A., and others: Symposium on microbial insecticides. Bact. Rev., *29*:364, 1965.

Bradley, D. E., and Franklin, J. G.: Electron microscope
survey of the surface configuration of spores of the
genus *Bacillus*. J. Bact., *76*:618, 1958.

Buono, F., Testa, R., and Lundgren, D. G.: Physiology of
growth and sporulation in *Bacillus cereus*. I. Effect of
glutamic and other amino acids. J. Bact., *91*:2291, 1966.

Campbell, L. L., and Halvorson, H. O., editors: Spores
III. Amer. Soc. Microbiol., Ann Arbor, Mich. 1965.

Curran, H. R., and Knaysi, G.: Survey of fourteen metabolic inhibitors for their effect on endospore germination in *Bacillus subtilis*. J. Bact., *82*:793, 1961.

Day, L. E., and Costilow, R. N.: Physiology of the sporulation process in *Clostridium botulinum*. II. Maturation of
forespores. J. Bact., *88*:695, 1964.

Fey, G., Gould, G. W., and Hitchins, A. D.: Identification
of D-alanine as the auto-inhibitor of germination of
*Bacillus globigii* spores. J. Gen. Bact., *35*:229, 1964.

Fitz-James, P. C.: Morphology of spores of *Bacillus apiarius*
Katznelson. J. Bact., *78*:765, 1959.

Gibbs, P. A.: Factors affecting the germination of spores of
*Clostridium fermentans*. J. Gen. Microbiol., *37*:41, 1964.

Gould, G. W., Hitchins, A. D., and King, W. L.: Function
and location of a 'germination enzyme' in spores of
*Bacillus cereus*. J. Gen. Microbiol., *44*:293, 1966.

Haines, B. W., Klein, F., and Lincoln, R. E.: Quantitative
assay for crude anthrax toxins. J. Bact., *89*:74, 1965.

Halvorsen, H. O., Vary, J. C., and Steinberg, W.: Developmental changes during the formation and breaking
of the dormant state in bacteria. Ann. Rev. Microbiol.,
*20*:169, 1966.

Haynes, W. C., and Rhodes, L. J.: Spore formation by
*Bacillus popilliae* in liquid medium containing activated
carbon. J. Bact., *91*:2270, 1966.

Jaye, M., and Ordal, Z. J.: Germination of spores of *Bacillus megaterium* with divalent metal-dipicolinate
chelates. J. Bact., *89*:1617, 1965.

Kolodziej, B. J., and Slepecky, R. A.: Trace metal requirements for sporulation of *Bacillus megaterium*. J. Bact.,
*88*:821, 1964.

Mitruka, B. M., Costilow, R. N., Black, S. H., and Pepper,
R. E.: Comparisons of cells, refractile bodies, and
spores of *Bacillus popilliae,* J. Bact., *94*:759, 1967.

Murrell, W. G., and Scott, W. J.: The heat resistance of
bacterial spores at various water activities. J. Gen.
Microbiol., *43*:411, 1966.

Rode, L. J., and Foster, J. W.: Influence of exchangeable
ions on germinability of bacterial spores. J. Bact.,
*91*:1582, 1966.

Sussman, A. S., and Halvorson, H. O.: Spores: Their Dormancy and Germination. Harper & Row, New York.
1966.

Takagi, A., Kawata, T., and Yamomoto, S.: Electron microscope studies on ultrathin sections of spores of the
*Clostridium* group with special reference to the sporulation and germination process. J. Bact., *80*:37, 1960.

Torriani, A., and Levinthal, C.: Ordered synthesis of proteins during outgrowth of *Bacillus cereus*. J. Bact.,
*94*:176, 1967.

Wax, R., Freese, E., and Cashel, M.: Separation of two
functional roles of L-alanine in the initiation of
*Bacillus subtilis* spore germination. J. Bact., *94*:522,
1967.

Wilson, J. B., and Russell, K. E.: Isolation of *Bacillus
anthracis* from soil stored 60 years. J. Bact., *87*:237,
1964.

# Chapter 32

# ANAEROBIOSIS AND ANAEROBIC BACTERIA

## 32.1 ANAEROBIOSIS

The isolation of oxygen by Priestley in 1774, and subsequent observations by Lavoisier about 1775 on the role of oxygen in combustion and respiration, led to the conclusion that free oxygen (air) is necessary to all life. In 1861, however, Pasteur proved that certain yeasts and bacteria could multiply in the absence of air. He devised the term *anaerobiosis* to describe life without air. This was one of the epoch-making discoveries in biological science. Subsequent studies of the physiology of cells living in situations devoid of free oxygen revolutionized ideas of cell physiology and metabolism.

Since Pasteur's researches, many microorganisms capable of living without air have been discovered. These include many common species of bacteria.

**Relations to Oxygen.** Microorganisms may be divided into several groups with respect to their relation to free oxygen (Table 32.1):

STRICTLY AEROBIC SPECIES. Aerobic microorganisms cannot grow without free oxygen to act as final hydrogen acceptor. Their enzyme systems can transfer hydrogen to free oxygen only. They are said to have an aerobic type of metabolism, and the substrate is usually completely oxidized to carbon dioxide and water or hydrogen peroxide.

FACULTATIVE ORGANISMS. The facultatives grow either aerobically as above or, in the absence of free oxygen, they can use some other easily reducible substance (e.g., sulfur, carbon or sodium nitrate) as hydrogen acceptor, i.e., they have the *faculty* of growing aerobically or anaerobically. This appears to be because they possess both aerobic and anaerobic enzyme systems. However, they generally grow better aerobically (the so-called *Pasteur effect*), i.e., complete

oxidation yields more energy than incomplete oxidation. During anaerobic growth the facultatives exhibit the less efficient fermentative type of metabolism, i.e., the substrate is not completely oxidized (Chapter 9).

TABLE 32.1 OXYGEN RELATIONSHIPS OF SOME BACTERIAL TYPES

1. Strict Aerobes
   Most species of the genus *Bacillus*
   Several species of the genera *Pseudomonas, Xanthomonas*
   Genus *Brucella*
   Genus *Azotobacter*
   Family Nitrobacteraceae
   Genus *Thiobacillus* (except *Th. denitrificans*: facultative with NaNO₃ as H acceptor)
   Genus *Acetobacter*
   Genus *Mycobacterium*
   *Bordetella pertussis*
   Genus *Micrococcus*
   Family Streptomycetaceae
   Genus *Nocardia*
   Order Myxobacterales (except *Cyto. fermentans*)

2. Facultative
   Family Enterobacteriaceae
   Tribe Streptococceae (a few are strict anaerobes; mostly *indifferent*)
   Genus *Spirillum*
   Genus *Staphylococcus*
   Genus *Neisseria*
   Genus *Alcaligenes*
   Tribe Lactobacilleae (mostly *indifferent*)

3. Strict Anaerobes
   Genus *Clostridium*
   Genus *Actinomyces*
   Family Bacteroidaceae
   Genus *Desulfovibrio*
   Family Thiorhodaceae
   Family Chlorobacteriaceae

4. Microaerophils
   Genus *Leptospira*
   Genus *Lactobacillus*

STRICTLY ANAEROBIC SPECIES. Anaerobic organisms have two peculiarities: (a) oxygen is *toxic* to them probably because certain of their enzymes can be blocked by oxygen; (b) their enzyme systems cannot transfer hydrogen to free oxygen. With some possible minor exceptions they must use other hydrogen acceptors.

*Hydrogen Peroxide and Anaerobiosis.* Bio-oxidation in the presence of free oxygen commonly results in the formation of hydrogen peroxide, if free oxygen is used as hydrogen acceptor. $H_2O_2$ is very toxic. Thus, strict anaerobes, while possibly capable of some aerobic growth, immediately commit suicide by producing $H_2O_2$ when they attempt it!

"But," you say, "$H_2O_2$ is produced by many *aerobic* bacteria. Why do *they* not die?" Ah! But most of these produce *catalase,* an enzyme which immediately decomposes $H_2O_2$! And you (being a well-informed student) say, "True, but many vigorous aerobes do *not* produce catalase. Why does *their* $H_2O_2$ not kill *them?*" A valid question! We reply, "These are not sensitive to $H_2O_2$." You would like to ask, "Why aren't they sensitive?" and we would say, "Because they have enzyme systems not affected by $H_2O_2$." Unfortunately we do not yet know exactly why these enzyme systems are not affected by $H_2O_2$. Some organisms can use $H_2O_2$ as a hydrogen acceptor: $H_2O_2 + 2(H) \longrightarrow 2H_2O$.

*Indifferent Organisms.* With (as usual!) "a few exceptions," organisms of the genera *Streptococcus* and *Lactobacillus* are unique in their relation to free oxygen. Ordinarily they can grow in the presence of air but, like the strict anaerobes, do not contain the cytochrome system that would enable them to use free oxygen as a hydrogen acceptor; they neither require nor utilize oxygen. Consequently, when growing aerobically they do not produce $H_2O_2$ (at least in significant amounts). This is lucky for them because they do not produce catalase, either. Very few bacteria can grow in the presence of air unless they protect themselves from $H_2O_2$ by also producing catalase. Since the streptococci and lactobacilli neither need free oxygen nor are adversely affected by it, they are *indifferent* to it (they can take it or leave it); they do not exhibit a Pasteur effect. Note, however, that some substances, e.g., glycerol, are used by these organisms with the production of much $H_2O_2$. Unless the $H_2O_2$ is removed they die.

MICROAEROPHILIC SPECIES. These require limited or lowered oxygen tension but not strict anaerobiosis. This peculiarity has not been explained fully, but probably reflects a sensitivity to blockage of some of their enzymes by free oxygen, as in the case of strict anaerobes, but to a lesser degree.

## 32.2  CULTIVATION OF ANAEROBIC BACTERIA

Many types of anaerobic devices exist, but only one fundamental purpose is involved: the removal of free oxygen from the immediate environment of the bacteria, or the maintenance of a low oxidation-reduction (O-R) potential by adding a reducing or oxygen-absorbing agent to the medium itself.

**Oxidation-Reduction Potentials.** Oxidation and reduction can occur in the absence of oxygen and are, as previously pointed out (Chapter 9), basically electrical phenomena; i.e., they are dependent on electron transfers. The electron-yielding or electron-accepting potentialities (O-R potential) of any given material such as a bacterial culture or, what is actually the same thing, sewage, can readily be measured. An electrode is placed in it and it thus becomes a half-cell. The cell is then completed by means of a U-tube with salt-agar between this half-cell and a *reference half-cell* of known potential. The potential of the complete cell thus formed is the tendency of electrons to flow from one half-cell to the other, the direction and force of flow (EMF) depending on their relative electron pressures, or O-R potentials. To measure the EMF of the culture, the EMF of this complete cell is balanced against that of a *known (Weston) standard cell* by means of a slide-wire resistance and a potentiometer (Fig. 32.1). Knowing the potential of the reference half-cell and of the standard cell, the potential of the half-cell consisting of culture or other material is easily calculated (see literature cited).

**Oxidation-Reduction Requirements of Microorganisms.** Anaerobic organisms require absence of oxygen or low O-R potentials (i.e., an electron-accepting or reducing environment) for growth. Some are much more sensitive to oxygen (high O-R potentials) than others. For example, a negative O-R potential of $-0.2$ volt is optimum for the initiation of growth by most species of anaerobes; some will start to grow only at $-0.4$ volt. Anaerobic spores usually require low O-R potentials for outgrowth. Once growth has started, the O-R potentials of cultures of all bacteria decline. This is especially marked in cultures of anaerobes, since these use every available hydrogen (electron) acceptor (tend to release electrons) in their respiratory processes (Fig. 32.2).

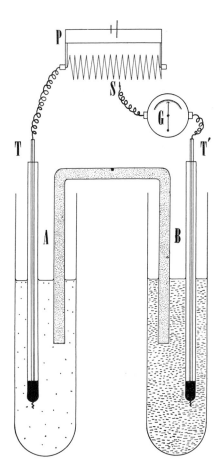

**Figure 32.1**   Apparatus for measuring redox potentials. In this assembly the bacterial culture half-cell (A) is connected by a salt-agar bridge to a calomel half-cell (B)* previously standardized ($E_{st}$) against a hydrogen half-cell whose potential is arbitrarily given a value of zero. The potential of the culture (A) is designated as $E_h$ since it is to be stated in reference to the hydrogen half-cell ($E_o$). The EMF of the potentiometer (P) ($E_1$) is derived from a battery previously adjusted to equal a Weston reference cell of EMF 1.0186 v. at 20° C. After making all connections the EMF of the potentiometer (indicated on a dial) is varied by means of the slide wire (S) of known resistance per unit of length, until it just balances the EMF of the A/B system. At this point the galvanometer (G) needle does not swing toward either pole when the circuit is completed by a push-button switch. $E_1$ is then read on the dial. Then, $E_1 = E_h - E_{st}$ or $E_h = E_1 + E_{st}$. Knowing $E_1$ and $E_{st}$, $E_h$ may be calculated.

---

*A calomel half-cell ($E_h$ at 20° C and 3.5% KCl = 0.254 v.) is used in place of the hydrogen half-cell for reasons of convenience and economy. Appropriate allowance is made for the voltage of the calomel half-cell in the calculations.

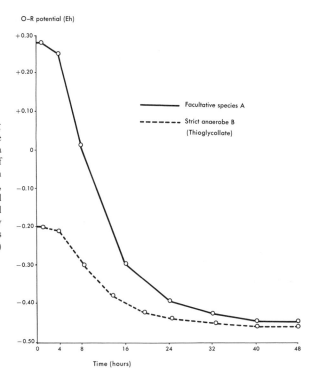

O–R potential (Eh)

— Facultative species A

---- Strict anaerobe B
(Thioglycollate)

**Figure 32.2**   Changes in O–R potential during growth of a facultative species (*A*) and a strict anaerobe (*B*). The medium for *A* at time of inoculation has a relatively high oxidizing (+) potential. The O–R of the medium for *B* is necessarily reduced to begin with to about −0.20 by the addition of the reducing agent, sodium thioglycollate. In each culture, after an initial lag of 1 to 2 hours, logarithmic growth begins and the O–R potential of each culture drops precipitately to a relatively strong reducing (−) level. This illustrates in part the origin of the biological oxygen demand (BOD) characteristic of municipal sewage (Chapter 42).

Time (hours)

## 32.3   ANAEROBIC METHODS

Anaerobic conditions in culture media are brought about by numerous ingenious variations of two basic procedures: (1) use of substances that combine with free oxygen, i.e., reducing agents; and (2) mechanical exclusion of free oxygen. Most procedures involve combinations of (1) and (2), as shown in the following examples:

Cultures may be enclosed in an airtight vessel with *sticks of phosphorus* or with a freshly made mixture of *potassium hydroxide and pyrogallol.* These substances absorb large amounts of oxygen and leave mainly the inert gas, nitrogen, and a partial vacuum.

The *combustion of small amounts of alcohol* or the burning of a *small candle* in a closed jar containing the cultures will use up some of the free oxygen. Combustion ceases when the carbon dioxide content approximates 7 per cent. This method results in only partially anaerobic conditions. It is widely used to increase the carbon dioxide content of the atmosphere, a condition favorable to many organisms, both aerobic and facultative, since most require some carbon dioxide for cell synthesis. The reduction of oxygen tension favors microaerophilic organisms rather than strict anaerobes.

**Hydrogen Jars.**  A means of *absolute anaerobiosis* is to allow a fine stream of hydrogen to enter a closed vessel containing the cultures, impinging, as it enters, on a small mass of some catalytic agent such as finely divided platinum that causes it to combine with the free oxygen, forming water. The platinum catalyst acts rapidly only when heated. Heat is usually applied by means of an electric current. A drying agent is enclosed in the vessel to absorb the water that is formed. There is no vacuum, the remaining gas being a mixture of hydrogen and nitrogen.

In a modern, simplified form of jar, hydrogen and carbon dioxide are evolved from a mixture of dry chemicals in a plastic (Gaspak) envelope (Fig. 32.3). Ten ml. of water are added to the contents of the bag and the jar is immediately closed and sealed. The evolved hydrogen combines catalytically at room temperature with all the free oxygen in the jar. A dye indicates, by a change of color, when all the free oxygen has been removed. There is no vacuum; the remaining atmosphere consists of nitrogen and carbon dioxide.

**Thioglycollate.**  A widely used and effective method of anaerobiosis depends on chemical absorption of oxygen from air trapped by a

**Figure 32.3**  Simplified form of anaerobe jar utilizing hydrogen and carbon dioxide from the "Gaspak" envelope. Combination of hydrogen and oxygen in the jar is catalyzed at room temperature. (Courtesy of Baltimore Biological Laboratories, Division of Becton-Dickinson Laboratories, Baltimore, Md.)

specially shaped cover in a very thin layer over the surface of special agar medium in a Petri dish (Fig. 32.4). The oxygen in this air is absorbed by sodium thioglycollate, or some similar compound (e.g., cysteine) having an affinity for oxygen, incorporated in the agar. By this means the O-R potential of the medium is held very low and even the most sensitive anaerobes will grow on the agar surface. The method is especially useful in obtaining pure cultures of strict anaerobes.

Fluid Reducing Media.  Unless we are cultivating some of the strictly chemolithotrophic anaerobes, the addition of sodium thioglycollate (0.1 per cent), sodium formaldehyde sulfoxalate (0.1 per cent) or cysteine hydrochloride (0.2 per cent) to dextrose broth or other similar fluids adapts them to anaerobic requirements. These substances maintain a satisfactorily low O-R potential. (Why are such media unsuitable for strict autotrophs?) The further addition of 0.1 per cent agar creates a very slight

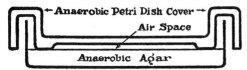

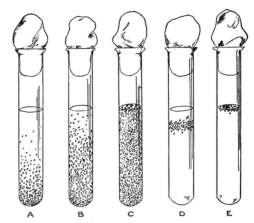

**Figure 32.4** Cross section showing Brewer anaerobic Petri dish cover in use. The anaerobic agar contains the reducing agent, sodium thioglycollate. Note that, at the periphery of the agar surface, the Petri dish cover is in contact with the agar, thus sealing the air space. The thioglycollate absorbs the oxygen from the air space. (Courtesy of Baltimore Biological Laboratories.)

**Figure 32.5** Deep tubes of agar inoculated with bacteria of various oxygen relationships. *A,* Fairly strict anaerobe, like *Cl. botulinum; B,* less strict anaerobe, like *Cl. perfringens; C,* Facultative aerobe-anaerobe, like *Esch. coli; D,* microaerophilic organism like *Br. abortus; E,* strict aerobe, like *Pseudomonas fluorescens.*

viscosity which reduces aeration of the solution by convection currents from the air surface.

For chemoorganotrophic anaerobes, organic media such as milk, infusion broth and infusion agar with blood, with the addition of reducing reagents, are recommended, since these organisms require not only low O-R potential but media rich in organic matter with a pH of about 7.2. Chopped brain, fish or other tissues are also often used. The addition of dextrose provides a readily available source of carbon and energy which promotes the growth of nearly all heterotrophic anaerobes.

DEEP MEDIA. Anaerobiosis in tubes of broth is satisfactory if the medium for heterotrophic species contains bits of chopped tissue: *cooked-meat medium.* The tissue acts as a reducing agent. The meat also serves as pabulum for the bacteria. Most heterotrophic anaerobic bacteria grow well in cooked-meat medium.

If the columns of medium in the tubes are 10 to 15 cm. deep, all that is necessary is to heat the medium in boiling water for 10 minutes to drive off dissolved air and decompose "organic peroxides," cool rapidly, and inoculate in the depths.

SHAKE TUBES. Deep tubes of dextrose-infusion agar are also used to cultivate anaerobes. Infusion agar in tubes 8 to 10 cm. in depth is melted and cooled to about 40° C. The inoculum is put in and mixed thoroughly. The agar is then made to solidify rapidly in cold water and is incubated. Strict anaerobes will grow only in the depths and will not appear at all within a centimeter or more of the surface. Less strict anaerobes will grow in the depths and will also grow somewhat nearer to the surface, while facultative anaerobes will grow on the surface as well as in the depths. Organisms having a narrow zone of tolerance to both oxygen and strict anaerobiosis (*microaerophils*) may grow in a narrow zone some distance below the surface (Fig. 32.5). Such preparations are often spoken of as *shake tubes* because shaking is used to mix

the agar and the inoculum. Formation of foam is carefully avoided. (Why?)

## 32.4 STRICTLY ANAEROBIC BACTERIA

Strictly anaerobic bacteria are found in several orders of the Class Schizomycetes. Some of these (e.g., some of the Suborder Rhodobacteriineae; Genus *Actinomyces;* some of the Family Micrococcaceae and others) are discussed elsewhere. Here we shall give some attention to several obligately anaerobic species of the Order Eubacteriales. In this order most anaerobic species are rod-forms grouped in the Genus *Clostridium* and in the Family Bacteroidaceae. Some clostridial spores have curious appendages.

### GENUS CLOSTRIDIUM

*Clostridium* is a large group, comprising nearly 100 "species." Many species are probably identical or are mere variants of each other. The group of clostridia is sometimes divided into physiological groups on the basis of enzymic properties, especially in relation to fermentation and proteolysis. Some representative species and distinctive properties are shown in Table 32.2. All clostridia are obligately anaerobic, gram-positive, sporebearing rods. Nearly all are motile. They vary somewhat in size and shape in the manner, say, of cigars but average around 0.5 $\mu$ by 10 $\mu$ in dimensions. They require complex organic media such as cooked-meat medium, blood-glucose-infusion agar or broth, and the like. The group includes the organisms producing tetanus (lockjaw), gas gangrene and botulism (food poisoning). The majority of clostridia are harmless and helpful saprophytes. Many of them produce enzymes, chemicals and industrial fermentations of great value. All occur widely distributed in the soil. Some of them also live in the intestinal tract of man and animals. They are metabolically active and versatile.

**Clostridium butyricum.** *Cl. butyricum* is one of the earliest species of *Clostridium* to be studied (Prazmowski, 1880) and is the type species of the genus. It represents the group of industrially important clostridia. In general they are plump, actively motile rods having oval, excentric spores which swell the sporangium. They grow well in media made of dilute molasses or grain extracts, with starch and suitable nitrogenous and mineral (and sometimes vitamin) supplements. All ferment carbohydrates, with the production of one or more commercially valuable substances, e.g., *butyl, ethyl, amyl* and *propyl* alcohols; *acetic, formic* and *lactic* acids; *acetone; carbon dioxide* and *hydrogen.* The products of fermentation depend on the species or variety of *Clostridium* used and the condition of the fermentation, i.e., pH, temperature and substrate. The industrial uses of these species of *Clostridium* are more fully discussed in Chapter 47.

**Anaerobic Nitrogen Fixation.** An interesting property of some of these organisms is the power to fix atmospheric nitrogen. That is, they are not, like most other organisms, restricted to the use of nitrogen combined in the form of ammonia, nitrates or amino acids, as are "higher" (more dependent!) plants and animals, but possess the power to cause free nitrogen of the air to combine in the synthesis of their cell substance. Several other microorganisms of the soil are even more important in nitrogen fixation. As will be seen later, without microbial

nitrogen fixation there might be no human race at all. (See Nitrogen Cycle, Chapter 43.)

## SOME PATHOGENIC CLOSTRIDIA

An important paradox is that although they are highly dangerous pathogenic organisms, *Clostridium botulinum* and *Cl. tetani* are not *parasites,* but *strict* saprophytes. They grow only in dead matter and cannot invade live tissue to a significant degree. They are commonly found in the soil and in human and other animal feces. The spores, consequently, are widespread in manured and sewage-polluted lands.

**Clostridium tetani and Tetanus (Lockjaw).** *Clostridium tetani* is one of the strictest anaerobes. Morphologically, the organism is distinguished by its spherical spore that occurs at the very tip end (*terminal*) of the rod. The round, terminal spore gives to the organisms what has been called a *drumstick* appearance (Fig. 32.6).

*Cl. tetani* gives off a potent exotoxin. Tetanus toxin is particularly active in the motor nerve centers, irritating them so that the muscles (most conspicuously those of the jaws) connected with them are thrown into a state of violent and continuous contraction (*tetanic convulsion,* or *tetanus*). The use of antitoxin in the treatment and prevention of tetanus is a classical example of passive immunity and was the first to be discovered (von Behring and Fränkel, 1890).

Tetanus organisms gain entrance to the body with dirt or dirty objects when these are forced into the tissues, as in gunshot or shrapnel wounds, deep, extensive and dirt-contaminated burns, or various other accidental means. Under such circumstances some tissue is killed locally by the injury, and in deep wounds the low O-R potentials favor growth of anaerobic bacteria. *Cl. tetani* grows as a saprophyte on the necrotic (dead) tissue in the wound, liberating

TABLE 32.2   REPRESENTATIVE SPECIES AND PROPERTIES OF CLOSTRIDIA*

| Species | Glucose | Lactose | Sucrose | Proteolysis | Motility | Capsules |
|---------|---------|---------|---------|-------------|----------|----------|
| *Cl. tetani* | − | − | − | − | + | − |
| *Cl. histolyticum* | − | − | − | + | + | − |
| *Cl. novyi (A)* | + | − | − | + | + | − |
| *Cl. putrefaciens* | + | − | − | + | − | − |
| *Cl. botulinum* | + | − | − | + | + | − |
| *Cl. septicum* | + | + | − | + | + | − |
| *Cl. perfringens* | + | + | + | − | − | + |
| *Cl. butyricum* | + | + | + | − | + | − |

*Note that species in the upper part of the table (except *Cl. tetani*) can be grouped as "proteolytic, nonsaccharolytic"; those in the lower part of the table as "saccharolytic, nonproteolytic." There are numerous other species in each group as well as many intermediate species.

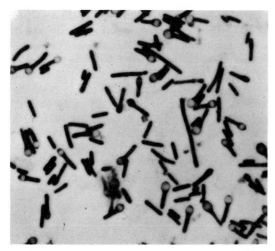

**Figure 32.6** *Clostridium tetani,* a gram-stained smear showing terminal spores that swell the rods and produce the typical drumstick appearance. Cells of this species range from 0.3 to 0.8 by 2.0 to 5.04. (Courtesy of General Biological Supply House, Chicago, Ill.)

its deadly toxin which is absorbed by the blood or nerves or both.

Tetanus toxin is one of the most potent poisons known. It requires only about 0.00025 gm. of tetanus toxin to kill a man, while it requires twenty times as much cobra venom and about one hundred and fifty times as much strychnine.

TETANUS IMMUNIZATION. Alum-precipitated fluid toxoids, in all respects analogous to diphtheria toxoids (Chapter 24), are useful in producing active immunity to tetanus. Protection depends particularly on the action of a *primary* stimulus consisting of at least one, preferably two or three, doses of tetanus toxoid a month or so apart. This is routinely given on entering the armed forces. A booster dose is sometimes given about a year later.

To a *secondary* stimulus (such as entrance of tetanus toxin into the body as the result of infection of a wound) the toxoid-conditioned, antibody-producing cells respond quickly with the production of antitoxin. Similarly, a dose of toxoid is often used as prophylaxis in dealing with any fresh wound in previously immunized persons. Because of allergy, it is preferable to avoid the use of *serum* in dealing with wounds unless tetanus seems imminent. However, in case of severe, very dirty wounds, passive prophylactic antitoxin may be used. Even if serum has to be used, toxoid should also be given. (Why?) Antibiotics may be used to suppress growth of the bacteria in the wound.

**Clostridium perfringens (Cl. welchii).** *Cl. perfringens* is a rather short, thick rod with rounded

**Figure 32.7** Tube of milk inoculated with *Clostridium perfringens* showing "stormy fermentation." For explanation see text. (Photo courtesy of Communicable Disease Center, U. S. Public Health Service, Atlanta, Ga.)

ends. It usually grows singly, never in long chains or filaments. It forms oval, central or subterminal spores which do not swell the cell. With perhaps a dozen uncommon or medically unimportant exceptions it is the only nonmotile species in the genus.* It is rare also among clostridia in that it reduces sodium nitrate to sodium nitrite.

The constant presence of *Cl. perfringens* in feces has led at times to its consideration as an indicator of human fecal pollution when found in water (Chapter 42). *Cl. perfringens* produces much hydrogen by fermentation and is often called the "gas bacillus" (Fig. 32.7).

Some strains of *Clostridium perfringens* have been implicated as causes of food poisoning in

---

*In attempting to determine motility of anaerobic bacteria, care must be taken not to expose the hanging drop to the air for more than a few seconds, as motility is destroyed by access to free oxygen.

man and animals, especially by meat dishes in Great Britain. Typical symptoms are gastroenteritis with diarrhea. The particular strains involved in Britain are described as Type A, distinguished by producing very heat-resistant spores and gamma or alpha type colonies in blood agar (see streptococci). In the United States, food-poisoning strains seem to be uncommon and to differ in several respects from British strains, especially in not producing highly thermostable spores regularly. The mechanism of the poisoning is still obscure. Apparently no exotoxin is involved.

Methods for isolation and enumeration of the organisms include 24 hours of anaerobic incubation of inoculated, highly selective, agar medium containing sodium sulfite, polymyxin and sulfadiazine. Colonies blackened by reduction of the sulfite are transferred as pure cultures and tested for presence of gram-positive, nonmotile, sporeforming rods that reduce sodium nitrate to sodium nitrite. Animal tests for food-poisoning toxins in foods have not yet yielded useful results.

*Cl. perfringens,* common in the soil, always accompanies *Cl. tetani* in dirty wounds. Like *Cl. tetani, Cl. perfringens* grows as a saprophyte in deep, dead tissues and gives off several toxins: the enzyme *lecithinase* (α toxin) which causes hemolysis, the "egg-yolk" reaction (p. 414) and tissue necrosis; κ toxin, an enzyme (*collagenase*) that digests collagen protein fibers in tendons; μ toxin or *hyaluronidase,* an enzyme destroying hyaluronic acid (see *spreading factor*); and several others.

GAS GANGRENE.   In dirty wounds, in addition to *Clostridium perfringens* and *Cl. tetani,* there are nearly always one or more of about a score of similar species of clostridia of the soil, such as *Cl. novyi* and *Cl. histolyticum.* Some of these are able to digest dead tissue rapidly; these and others produce toxins and hemolysins. Some (*Cl. novyi, Cl. septicum*) can actually invade the blood. All of these bacteria are spoken of as gas-gangrene organisms.

The combined, unchecked growth of gasgangrene organisms in dirty wounds such as crushed limbs, shell wounds and nail punctures, where the lesion is deep, and there is much dead tissue, produces pain, profound shock, toxemia and the rapidly fatal condition known as *gas gangrene.* It used to be much feared by soldiers wounded on the battlefield but is now controlled (virtually eliminated) by prompt cleansing, surgery, antitoxins and antibiotics.

A most important development in the treatment of gas gangrene has been the discovery and use of the fact that exposure of seriously ill gasgangrene patients to an atmosphere of pure oxygen under 45 lb. pressure per sq. inch completely suppresses the formation of alpha toxin and the growth of anaerobes in the infected tissues. Oxygen content of the plasma rises from a normal of 0.3 to 6.2 per cent, and the O-R potential in the tissues rises to a level that is inhibitory to the anerobes. Cure of the gas gangrene is rapid and complete. Use of compressed oxygen can be very dangerous physiologically and explosively.

**Clostridium botulinum.**   One of the two organisms (*Staphylococcus aureus* and *Cl. botulinum*) that cause food poisoning, *Cl. botulinum* is a strict anaerobe and forms large, oval spores in a subterminal position, often giving the sporangium a shape that is said to resemble a snowshoe (Fig. 32.8). These spores are very heat-resistant. The exotoxin that it produces is the most poisonous biological substance known. It derives its name from the Latin word for sausage (*botulus*), which was given because the organism was first found in sausages that were the cause of an outbreak of fatal food poisoning (*botulism*) in persons who had eaten them at a picnic. *Cl. botulinum* does not infect. The interior of a sausage (or canned foods if not sterilized) obviously presents an ideal place for the growth of anaerobes, including *Cl. botulinum.*

BOTULISM.   Botulism is not an *infection* but is *poisoning** by a bacterial exotoxin that is formed in foods under conditions of improper processing and storage in which strict anaerobes may find good pabulum and good anaerobiosis. The microorganisms are introduced into the containers when soiled foods are used. If the containers are not sufficiently heat-processed (autoclaved) and if storage (as is usual with canned goods) is at warehouse or household temperatures, anaerobic bacteria can grow and cause spoilage. This in itself is usually harmless. On the other hand, *Clostridium botulinum* may be present. The spores of this bacterium are often found in the soil and are likely to be present on any soil-contaminated food. Sometimes their growth is not sufficient to spoil the food noticeably and it may be eaten. This has often proved fatal.

Botulinal toxin is absorbed directly from

---

*Food poisoning due to botulinal toxin and staphylococcal enterotoxin must be distinguished from food *infections* due to *Salmonella* and other invasive pathogens. Both food poisoning and food infection are commonly called "food poisoning."

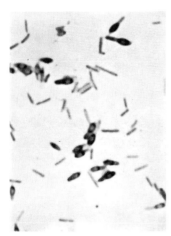

**Figure 32.8** Gram-stained smear of *Clostridium botulinum* cultivated in cooked-meat medium (× 1000). The morphology of *Cl. butyricum* is very similar and, indeed, the two species are alike in many other respects, pathogenicity being a striking difference. (Photo courtesy of Communicable Disease Center, U. S. Public Health Service, Atlanta, Ga.)

the stomach and intestines. It affects the nerve-muscle complex, producing a flaccid paralysis, particularly of the face, eyes and throat, and respiratory system. As in diphtheria and tetanus, after advanced symptoms appear antitoxin is of little value therapeutically.

There are at least six serological types of botulinal toxin: A, B, C, D, E, and F. Types A and B are the most common in the United States, though cases due to type E in fish have occurred. There is a specific antitoxin for differential diagnosis of each type, but *polyvalent* antitoxin is commonly used in treatment.

The four home-canned foods most commonly responsible for botulism are corn, beans, beets and asparagus. Note that none is an acid food and that three of them are often contaminated with soil. Botulinal toxin is heat-labile and can be destroyed by heating to boiling for ten minutes (compare with staphylococcal enterotoxin). Botulism caused by commercially preserved foods is rare in the United States due to perfection of processing by the trades concerned.

*Cl. botulinum* ordinarily will not grow if foods are preserved in brines stronger than 10 per cent sodium chloride or that have an acidity greater than that represented by pH 4.5. Some foods that might be ruined by long processing are therefore acidified to a greater degree than pH 4.5 and processed for a much shorter period. The acidity makes the short heating more effective.

## FAMILY BACTEROIDACEAE

Unlike the clostridia, Bacteroidaceae are strictly anaerobic, nonsporeforming and gram-negative. They are small, usually rod-shaped and very pleomorphic; sometimes branching or filamentous. Some species are motile with peritrichous flagella. There are five genera, only two of which are common or familiar: *Bacteroides* and *Fusobacterium*. Of the others, the Genus *Sphaerophorus* (or *Necrobacterium*) has properties and habitat much like *Bacteroides*.

**Genus Bacteroides.** Most species of *Bacteroides* occur in enormous numbers in the normal intestinal tract. The species present in normal feces grow on ordinary laboratory media but are *extremely* sensitive to oxygen.

Various species of both *Bacteroides* and *Necrobacterium* are frequently found as apparently causative agents in lesions of the mucous membranes, in septicemia, in appendicitis, in abscesses of liver, lungs, and in necrotic lesions in other parts of the body. These pathogens are often overlooked in diagnostic microbiology because they grow only under *very* strictly anaerobic conditions on media containing blood or ascitic fluid; the colonies are small, inconspicuous and colorless; the organisms are fragile and it is difficult to maintain them alive.

**Genus Fusobacterium.** These are much like *Bacteroides* and *Necrobacterium* in general properties but, as the name implies, they have distinctly pointed ends. A familiar species, *Fusobacterium fusiforme* (Fusobacterium plautivincenti), is regularly found in the normal human mouth in association with *Borrelia vincentii*, a spirochete. The combination has been thought to cause ulcerative conditions of the buccal cavity, especially Vincent's angina, or "trench mouth," but there is doubt of the primary etiological status of the bacteria; they are secondary invaders.

***Streptobacillus moniliformis.*** The systematic position of this curious organism is not yet clear. Although much resembling *Mycoplasma*, it was included in the Family Bacterioidaceae in 1957 mainly because of its *Bacteroides*-like filamentous character and pleomorphism, gram-negative stain and heterotrophism. However, it is aerobic and facultatively anaerobic. It resembles *Bacteroides* also in growing best on blood or serum media. It is not motile.

Its most interesting characteristic is the fact that, when first studied by Klieneberger (later Klieneberger-Nobel) in 1935, there was associated with it what was thought to be a symbiotic species of PPLO. Klieneberger, working at the Lister Institute in London, called the supposed symbiont $L_1$, L being the initial of the Lister Institute named for Lord Lister, pioneer in aseptic surgery. The $L_1$ organism was later shown by Klieneberger and others to be a stable protoplast or L-form of *Streptobacillus moniliformis*. The two forms interchange under proper growth conditions. The letter L continues in bacteriological terminology for L-forms of bacteria in general. (See Chapter 41.) (Do not confuse L-forms of bacteria with L cells, a clone of animal tissue-culture cells.)

## SUPPLEMENTARY READING

Brill, W. J., Wolin, E. A., and Wolfe, R. S.: Anaerobic formate oxidation: A ferredoxin-dependent reaction. Science, *144*:297, 1964.

Dack, G. M.: Food Poisoning, 3rd ed. University of Chicago Press, 1956.

Dolman, C. E.: Botulism. Amer. Jour. Nursing, *64*:119, 1964.

Eller, C., Rogers, L., and Wynne, E. S.: Agar concentration in counting *Clostridium* colonies. Appl. Microbiol. *15*:55, 1967.

Foster, E. M., and Sugiyama, H.: Recent developments in botulism research. Health Lab. Sci., *4*:193, 1967.

Gunner, H. B., and Alexander, M.: Anaerobic growth of *Fusarium oxysporum.* J. Bact., *87*:1309, 1964.

Hall, H. E., and Lewis, K. H.: *Clostridium perfringens* and other bacterial species as possible causes of foodborne disease outbreaks of undetermined etiology. Health Lab. Sci., *4*:229, 1967.

Kim, C. H., Cheney, R., and Woodburn, M.: Sporulation of *Clostridium perfringens* in a modified medium and selected foods. Appl. Microbiol., *15*:871, 1967.

MacLennan, J. D.: The Histotoxic Clostridial Infections of Man. Bact. Rev., *26*:177, 1962.

McClung, L. S., and Lindberg, R. B.: The Study of Obligately Anaerobic Bacteria. *In:* Manual of Microbiological Methods. Society of Amer. Bacteriologists (Amer. Soc. for Microbiol.), McGraw-Hill Book Co., New York. 1957.

Omata, R. R., and Braunberg, R. C.: Oral fusobacteria. J. Bact., *80*:737, 1960.

Pheil, C. G., and Ordal, Z. J.: Sporulation of "thermophilic anaerobes." Appl. Microbiol., *15*:893, 1967.

Prevot's Manual for the Classification & Determination of the Anaerobic Bacteria, Fredette, V. (translator): Lea & Febiger, Philadelphia. 1966.

Rosebury, T., and Reynolds, J. B.: Continuous anaerobiosis for cultivation of spirochetes. Proc. Exp. Biol. Med., *117*:813, 1964.

Stadtman, T. C.: Methane fermentation. Ann. Rev. Microbiol., *21*:121, 1967.

van Unnik, A. J. M.: Inhibition of toxin production in *Clostridium perfringens* in vitro by hyperbaric oxygen. Ant. Leeuw., *31*:181, 1965.

Yolton, D. D., Pope, L., Williams, M. G., and Rode, L. J.: Further electron microscope characterization of spore appendages of *Clostridium bifermentans*. J. Bact., *95*:231, 1968.

# Chapter 33

# THE MICROCOCCACEAE AND
# THE NEISSERIACEAE

A few species of spherical or spheroidal bacteria occur scattered among the several orders of Schizomycetes, but the great majority of cocci are grouped together in the Order Eubacteriales (Families Micrococcaceae and Neisseriaceae) and in the Tribe Streptococceae or streptococci (Family Lactobacillaceae; Chapter 34). In this chapter we shall discuss the Micrococcaceae and Neisseriaceae, leaving the streptococci to a later chapter. All three families contain species of importance and renown (and some of notoriety!) in medicine and industry and in human welfare and woe.

## 33.1 THE FAMILY MICROCOCCACEAE

The Micrococcaceae are gram-positive and are mostly free-living saprophytes of the outer world. They are nonsporeforming except one curiosity, *Sarcina* (or *Sporosarcina*) *ureae* that probably should be grouped in the Family Bacillaceae. It is a gram-positive, motile (?), endospore former but is morphologically a coccus.

The Micrococcaceae are usually spherical or nearly so and, unlike the Streptococceae, typically divide in two or three planes. If the divisions are in planes at irregular angles, irregular clusters or masses of cocci are formed, resembling bunches of grapes in arrangement (genera *Micrococcus* and *Staphylococcus*). If the divisions are in *two horizontal planes* at right angles, flat, square groups of four (tetrads) are formed (Genus *Gaffkya\**). Divisions in two horizontal planes and a perpendicular plane at right angles, produce cubical packets of eight

or more cocci (Genus *Sarcina\**) (Fig. 33.1). During rapid growth many single cells occur; and cells of any genus in the process of division may often appear in pairs, temporarily simulating diplococci.

In general, the Micrococcaceae are aerobic or facultative. Most of the aerobic and facultative species produce catalase. A few species of strict anaerobes (Genus *Methanococcus*) live in black mud in marshes, sewage sludge and similar stagnant habitats. They are active producers of the bubbles of methane (marsh gas, or sewer gas). Carbon dioxide and hydrogen are often mixed with methane in the bubbles. Another genus of strictly anaerobic proteolytic cocci (*Peptococcus†*) is associated with feces and with foul, septic tissue infections which they may cause or complicate. The family also includes the notorious pathogen, *Staphylococcus aureus,* to be described.

### SAPROPHYTIC MICROCOCCACEAE

**Genus *Micrococcus.*** The cocci of Genus *Micrococcus* are enzymically versatile and are physiologically heterogeneous and able to thrive under a wide range of conditions including dairy products, soil, dust, sea water, pickling brines and many foods not too acid or alkaline (pH 6.5 to 8.0), at temperatures from about 22 to 38° C. Most are killed by pasteurization, but some thermoduric species can survive. Of course, various species vary somewhat in these toler-

---

\**Gaffky* was the German bacteriologist who first described these organisms.

\*L. *sarcina* = packet.

†Do not confuse with *Peptostreptococcus,* described on page 425.

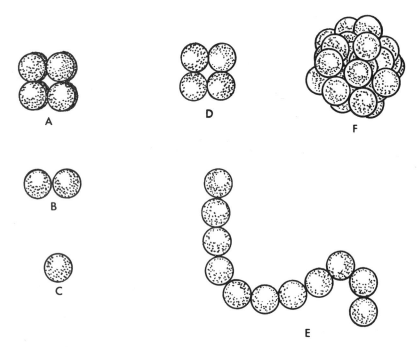

**Figure 33.1**   Arrangement of cocci showing: *A*, fission in three planes at 90 degrees, forming cubical packets, e.g., *Sarcina;* *B*, fission in one plane, forming diplococci, e.g., *Diplococcus pneumoniae* or *Neisseria* sp., *C*, a single coccus, basis of all the arrangements and frequently seen in any of them; *D*, fission in two planes at 90 degrees, forming tetrads, e.g., *Gaffkya tetragena; E*, fission in one plane with adherence of the cocci, forming chains of streptococci, e.g., *Streptococcus pyogenes; F*, fission in various planes, forming irregular groupings or clusters, e.g., *Staphylococcus* sp., or *Micrococcus* sp. (From Frobisher, Sommermeyer and Blaustein: Microbiology for Nurses, 11th ed. W. B. Saunders Co., 1964.)

ances. All are organotrophic and grow well on ordinary peptone or meat-infusion media as commonly used in the laboratory. They are strict aerobes and cannot utilize glucose or mannitol anaerobically. They are distinguished from staphylococci by this, by their failure to be lysed by the enzyme-like antibiotic *lysostaphin* and by failure to produce coagulase. These three properties are of importance in diagnostic and other aspects of differential bacteriology.

On solid media most species of *Micrococcus* form opaque, butyrous colonies with white or yellow pigments; various shades of red and orange are also common, e.g., *M. roseus, M. agilis* and *M. morrhuae.* Many species have a marked tolerance for sodium chloride and can be isolated from mixed cultures on selective media containing 5 to 8 per cent salt, a concentration that inhibits growth of many other organisms. Several species occur in sea water and salt lakes (e.g., *M. morrhuae*).

The micrococci, and the very similar cocci of the Genus *Sarcina,* are of importance mainly as scavengers. Common in dust, they are familiar airborne contaminants in laboratory cultures.

Many of them actively digest proteins such as gelatin and casein and attack various carbohydrates and numerous other organic substances. Some species of *Micrococcus* (*M. flavus, M. caseolyticus*) are of commercial importance in the ripening and flavoring of cheese, since they attack casein and lactose with the production of aromatic substances having pleasing flavors. They are said to be *acidoproteolytic.* On the other hand, some micrococci produce various undesirable slimy conditions such as *ropy milk* (*M. freudenreichii* and other slime producers, sometimes called *M. cremori-viscosi*).

### PATHOGENIC MICROCOCCACEAE

In this family the principal pathogens are in the strictly anaerobic Genus *Peptococcus,* occasionally found in or on humans, and in the genera *Staphylococcus* and *Gaffkya.*

**Genus Staphylococcus.**   As previously stated, *Staphylococcus* is differentiated from *Micrococcus* by the ability of *Staphylococcus* to utilize glucose, mannitol and pyruvate anaerobically

**TABLE 33.1** CHARACTERISTICS OF SOME MICROCOCCACEAE*

| | *Micrococcus* | *S. epidermidis* | *S. aureus* |
|---|---|---|---|
| Oxygen relationship | aerobic | facultative | facultative |
| Coagulase production | − | − | + |
| Anaerobic utilization of glucose and pyruvate | − | + | + |
| Fermentation of mannitol | − | − | + |
| Lactase production | − | ±† | + |
| Phosphatase production | − | ± | + |
| Lecithinase production | ± | − | + |
| Hydrolysis of gelatin and casein | ± | − | + |
| Growth in 15 per cent NaCl | + | + | + |
| Growth at 10° C. | + | − | + |
| Growth at 45° C. | + | + | + |
| Lysozyme production | − | − | + |
| Reduction of NaNO₃ | | | |
| to NaNO₂ only | + | + | .. |
| to NH₃ | − | − | + |
| Lysostaphin sensitivity | − | + | + |
| Animal pathogenicity | − | slight | marked |
| DNA-ase production | − | − | + |

*Properties given are "typical" of the named types; no single one, two, three or even four characters can be used as entirely definitive. Irregularities are common.
† ± = variable.

and by its sensitivity to *lysostaphin* (Table 33.1). Microscopically the two species are virtually identical, although cells of staphylococci are slightly smaller than those of micrococci. Staphylococci are usually to be found on the skin or mucous membranes of the animal body, especially of the nose and mouth, where they often occur in large numbers even under normal conditions. There are two principal species. *Staphylococcus aureus,* distinguished primarily by its golden pigment, is notorious as the cause of suppurative (*pyogenic* or pus-forming) conditions: *mastitis* of women and cows, *boils, carbuncles, infantile impetigo, internal abscesses* and *food poisoning.* S. *epidermidis* (S. albus) is a lesser pathogen or commensal on the skin and mucous membranes.

**Staphylococcus aureus.** Staphylococci isolated from pathological materials are generally S. aureus. These cocci typically: (1) *ferment mannitol and lactose;* (2) are *proteolytic;* (3) produce *coagulase* (an enzyme-like principle that causes citrated blood plasma to coagulate); (4) produce *golden pigment;* (5) produce *lipase;* (6) produce wide zones of *beta hemolysis* (see streptococci) aerobically in blood agar plates; (7) grow in media containing *10 per cent sodium chloride.*

S. *aureus* may be isolated from contaminated material by first cultivating in a selective, protein-digest, broth medium containing 10 per cent NaCl. Growth in such a selective fluid may then be streaked on "Staphylococcus medium 110." This medium is specially designed to

select *Staphylococcus aureus* and reveal some of its distinctive properties. It contains: protein digest (Trypticase or Tryptone), 1 per cent; yeast extract, 0.25 per cent; gelatin, 3 per cent; D-mannitol, 1.0 per cent; lactose, 0.2 per cent; NaCl, 7.5 per cent; K₂HPO₄, 0.5 per cent; agar, 1.5 per cent. Phenol red may be added as an indicator. Simple, 1.0 per cent mannitol–7.5 per cent NaCl agar may also serve. Distinctive colonies on these media may be fished to pure cultures for tests of coagulase production.

Production of wide zones of beta-type hemolysis on blood-agar plates is a dramatic property but is also seen in several harmless, saprophytic species, e.g., *Bacillus* spp. Staphylococci from pathological materials produce other noxious substances, notably *leukocidins* that destroy leukocytes. Under aerobic conditions they form *alpha toxin,* which has three distinct effects that are *demonstrable in rabbits: hemolysis; rapid lethality;* localized dermal *necrosis* on subcutaneous injection. Most pathogenic strains also produce the enzyme *lysozyme* and a fibrin-digesting enzyme activator called *staphylokinase* (see also *streptokinase,* page 348). Coagulase production is often, but not necessarily, associated with virulence of S. *aureus.*

COAGULASE. Staphylococcal coagulase acts only in conjunction with a serum factor called *coagulase reacting factor* (CRF). Normal, physiological coagulation of blood results from a complex series of reactions, the last two of which are:

prothrombin + prothrombinase + CaCl$_2$ $\longrightarrow$
$$\text{thrombin}$$
thrombin + fibrinogen $\longrightarrow$ fibrin (= clot)

The role of staphylococcal coagulase appears to be to displace both prothrombinase and prothrombin. Coagulase first combines with CRF, a substance much like prothrombin:

CRF + coagulase $\longrightarrow$ CRF · coagulase

This complex then replaces thrombin in the formation of fibrin:

CRF · coagulase + fibrinogen $\longrightarrow$
$$\text{fibrin (= clot)}$$

A substance commonly called "bound coagulase" that causes *Staphylococcus* cells to clump together in the presence of fibrinogen during the coagulase test is more correctly called *clumping factor*. There is no demonstrable relationship between clumping factor and coagulase.

*Demonstration of Coagulase.* Many methods for detecting coagulase have been described. A simple technique consists of mixing 0.5 ml. of a vigorous, young, broth culture, or a heavy suspension of young growth on agar, with 0.5 ml. of fresh or lyophilized citrated plasma (preferably human). The plasma must be known, by previous and simultaneous control tests, to be rich in CRF and fibrinogen (i.e., coagulable by known coagulase) and to be free from fibrinolytic (staphylokinase) properties and coagulase inhibitors. Pooled human plasmas suitable for such purposes are available commercially. Numerous organisms other than staphylococci will cause citrated plasma to clot, but this commonly results from their metabolic destruction of the citrate which thus liberates the Ca$^{++}$ (essential in coagulation) from the citrate · CaCl$_2$ chelate.

THE EGG-YOLK REACTION. All staphylococci produce some lipase. However, of *Staphylococcus aureus* strains from acute purulent lesions that produce coagulase and ferment mannite, about 95 per cent produce relatively large amounts of lipases that act on lipids and esters of the lipovitellenin of hens' egg yolk. Coagulase-negative strains from the same sources and staphylococci from nonpurulent sources are much less frequently active producers of lipases.

Lipase production by staphylococci may be demonstrated by streaking the strain to be tested on the surface of peptone agar containing about 3 per cent of filtered, aqueous, egg-yolk solution. This is rich in lecithin. After about 24 hours of incubation a positive "egg-yolk reaction" is seen around the growth as a clear zone that broadens on further incubation. A distinctive, opalescent clouding then appears close to the colony and later extends into the clear zone. The two-zone reaction extends and intensifies up to 48 hours of incubation. It should be noted that this reaction is not peculiar to staphylococci but is produced by any organisms that produce similar lipases, e.g., numerous species of *Clostridium* and *Bacillus.*

ANTIBIOTIC-RESISTANT *Staphylococcus aureus.* When penicillin first came into clinical use about 1944 during World War II, virtually every strain of *S. aureus* was highly sensitive to it. A few mutants were resistant, however, and it was found that these were usually vigorous producers of an enzyme, *penicillinase,* that very rapidly destroys penicillin. It was then discovered that penicillinase production is readily induced by contact with the drug. As a result, with more and more widespread use of antibiotics, especially penicillin, most strains of *S. aureus,* especially in hospitals, are now completely resistant to penicillin. The genetic mechanism for penicillinase production is transmissible, like an episome (Chapter 15).

These penicillin-resistant strains became widespread in hospital personnel and in the environmental dust, on walls, floors, bedding and furniture. Infection with such strains has been a major problem in many institutions, especially in maternity wards and nurseries, where they often cause mastitis and impetigo or pemphigus neonatorum. Control requires the most assiduous attention to handwashing, elimination of infected personnel and disinfection of premises, clothing and bedding. Fortunately the resistance of staphylococci to penicillin is being overcome successfully by the development of semisynthetic penicillins (Chapter 22) that are not vulnerable to penicillinase and that are fully as effective as natural penicillin.

**Staphylococcal Food Poisoning.** Staphylococci are notorious as a cause of food poisoning. This is because some strains of staphylococci release a heat-stable exotoxin called *enterotoxin* when growing in many common foods: "tenderized" hams, milk, custards, "cream" fillings, soups, stews. Excessive growth of the organisms in an abnormal intestinal tract can cause similar symptoms. When absorbed, staphylococcal enterotoxin causes nausea, vomiting, diarrhea and prostration. Staphylococcal food poisoning is seldom fatal but it has ruined many a dance date! The symptoms come on usually within 2 to 12 hours after eating the toxin. This permits differentiation from salmonellosis, which produces very similar symptoms, but only after a necessary incubation period, usually of 12 to

24 hours. Approximately 30% of strains of *S. aureus* produce enterotoxin.

There are at least three immunological types of enterotoxin, A, B and C, analogous to the several types of botulinal toxin. Unlike the thermolabile botulinal toxin, all staphylococcal enterotoxins are exceptionally thermostable proteins. They withstand boiling for at least 30 minutes. Distinguish carefully between staphylococcal *enterotoxins*, which are *exotoxins*, and the *endotoxins* of Enterobacteriaceae (Chapter 36).

Considerable growth of the cocci is necessary to produce enough enterotoxin to cause symptoms. Staphylococcal food poisoning therefore usually involves stale, moist, not-too-acid foods that have been contaminated from a human source and then held for several hours (incubated) at room temperature (22° to 40° C.) (Chapter 28). There is only one dependable proof that a suspected food caused an outbreak of staphylococcal food poisoning; i.e., demonstration of enterotoxin in the food. Second-best evidence is demonstration of staphylococci in enormous numbers in the suspected food and proof that the isolated strain is capable of producing enterotoxin.

The most satisfactory method for demonstrating enterotoxin in suspected foods is by means of extraction, purification and concentration followed by immunodiffusion techniques using specific-antitoxin serum. Older methods involve cat and monkey feeding tests that are difficult and not very reliable.

Most strains of enterotoxigenic staphylococci (usually, but not always, *S. aureus*) are distinguished by the production of DNA-ase capable of resisting autoclaving (121° C. for 5 minutes). Demonstration of this enzyme in foods strongly indicates the growth of pathogenic staphylococci in the food.

Growth or enterotoxin production by staphylococci tends to be suppressed in foods in which large numbers of the various harmless saprophytes common in foods are actively multiplying, especially at temperatures between 15° and 25° C. Saprophytes whose growth is especially inhibitory to staphylococci include species of *Escherichia, Proteus, Klebsiella*, lactic streptococci, *Pseudomonas, Micrococcus* and enterococci. Some species of *Bacillus* appear to stimulate staphylococci, others to inhibit them.

There is no wholly reliable, single laboratory test for identification of strains of staphylococci that are pathogenic for man. Coagulase production is commonly, but by no means invariably, associated with pathogenicity; further, its actual inimical effect, if any, remains obscure.

**Staphylococcus epidermidis.** *S. epidermidis* typically does not ferment mannitol or produce coagulase, alpha toxin or lipase. It forms chalky white pigment, whence its older name *S. albus.* Gelatin liquefaction is slow or absent; hemolysis is slight or absent. Pathogenicity is slight as a rule.

**Genus Gaffkya.** *Gaffkya* is generally regarded as saprophytic so far as man is concerned. However, some species are very pathogenic for mice and some other forms of life. For example, *Gaffkya homari* (*Homarus* = genus of lobsters) is highly pathogenic for lobsters, producing a commercially costly disease with a high fatality rate.

## 33.2  THE FAMILY NEISSERIACEAE

This family derives its name from a German bacteriologist, *Neisser*, who in 1879 discovered and studied one of the most important species: *N. gonorrhoeae*, the cause of gonorrhea. The Family Neisseriaceae includes two genera, *Neisseria* and *Veillonella*. The latter are small, gram-negative, anaerobic diplococci that occur chiefly in the normal mouth of mammals.

**Genus Neisseria.** Cocci of the Genus *Neisseria* are rather small, gram-negative diplococci, each cell characteristically flattened where it is in contact with its mate, each cell having somewhat the shape of a coffee bean (Fig. 33.2). The various species of *Neisseria* are indistinguishable morphologically. They are aerobic, reluctantly facultative, and grow best at 35° to 37° C. Unlike the ubiquitous and busy Micrococcaceae, all but one species of *Neisseria* are found only in the human upper respiratory tract. The exception is *N. gonorrhoeae*, which is associated mainly but not exclusively with the genital tract and gonorrhea.

Of the several species of *Neisseria*, two commonly cause disease: *N. gonorrhoeae* (the gonococcus) and *N. meningitidis* (the meningococcus). The latter causes epidemic meningitis, or cerebrospinal fever. *N. gonorrhoeae* and *N. meningitidis* are very much alike; one is probably a minor variant of the other.

These two species are classical examples of fragile microorganisms that have become highly adapted to an existence as parasites of man. In moist, warm material such as pus, urine, serum, or cultures in incubators, the meningococci and gonococci autolyze and die in a few hours. They are extremely fragile in the outer world. Unless special protective methods are used they do not survive for more than 2 to

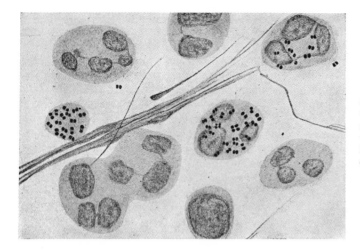

**Figure 33.2** Gonococci in leukocytes in smear of pus from case of gonorrhea, stained with methylene blue. The long, fibrous objects are shreds of fibrin and mucus in the pus. Note that the gonococci are nearly all *within* the leukocytes. (× 1000.) (From Ford: Bacteriology.)

6 hours outside the body, since drying is very deleterious to gonococci; chilling, to meningococci. Their nutritive requirements are complex. They grow only at 35° to 37° C., on *infusion media* containing blood heated to 90° C. (*"chocolate agar"*) or other special mixtures of a similar nature. Some contain selective antibiotics and nutrient supplements such as yeast autolysate and vitamins, e.g., Thayer-Martin medium. Incubation must be in a very humid atmosphere with 5 to 10 per cent carbon dioxide. The colonies are from 1 to 4 mm. in diameter, clear, colorless, moist and watery looking (Fig. 33.3).

These cultural characteristics serve to differentiate the meningococci and gonococci from all other species of the Genus *Neisseria: N. flava, N. catarrhalis* and *N. sicca.* These three species, and a few similar ones, grow well on blood-free media at temperatures as low as 25° C., and are

relatively resistant to drying, chilling and light. Several species are pigmented. These species, while parasites in a broad sense, being restricted to a life on a mammalian host, are usually quite harmless (Table 33.2).

However, as is true of many bacteria generally regarded as harmless, some of these respiratory *Neisseria* under certain conditions may cause meningitis, and some can cause nonvenereal infections of the genitalia in preadolescent girls, these infections being sometimes confused with gonorrhea, with tragic results. Therefore, no diagnosis of gonorrhea, especially in females, can be said to be complete and accurate without a full bacteriological study of the organism involved. Institutional outbreaks of vulvovaginitis in female children are often caused by fomite-borne infections of *N. catarrhalis, N. flava,* or *N. sicca.*

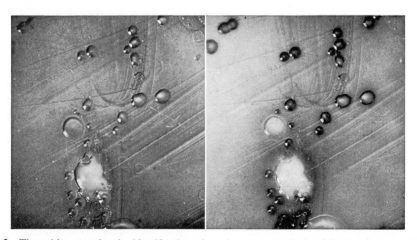

**Figure 33.3**   The oxidase test for the identification of meningococcus colonies. Mixed culture on blood agar. *Left,* colonies of meningococci and contaminants before the application of tetramethyl-*p*-phenylenediamine solution. *Right,* the same colonies after the application of the reagent. Note that the meningococcus colonies show the development of color first about the edges, and there is slight discoloration of the medium (× 5). (From Burrows: Textbook of Microbiology, 17th ed., W. B. Saunders Co.)

**TABLE 33.2**  CHARACTERS DIFFERENTIATING SPECIES OF NEISSERIA

| Species | Normal Habitat | Fermentation of | | | Growth at 25° C. | Growth on Plain Agar |
|---|---|---|---|---|---|---|
| | | Glucose | Sucrose | Maltose | | |
| *N. gonorrheae* | Genital tract | + | − | − | − | − |
| *N. meningitidis* | Respiratory tract | + | − | + | − | − |
| *N. catarrhalis* | " | − | − | − | + | + |
| *N. flavescens* | " | − | − | − | + | + |
| *N. sicca* | " | + | + | + | + | + |
| *N. flava* | " | + | − | + | + | + |

THE OXIDASE TEST. All of the *Neisseria* produce an enzyme (*oxidase* or indophenol-oxidase) that causes a 1 per cent solution of tetramethyl-paraphenylene-diamine to turn, successively, pink, rose, magenta, and finally black. The oxidase test is applied by moistening a colony of the suspected organism with a drop of the dye solution. The changes in color begin in a few moments (Fig. 33.3). The same test for oxidase can be made on all sorts of microorganisms in addition to *Neisseria* and is a valuable differential method for general use.

THE CATALASE TEST. The test for catalase is made by putting a drop of hydrogen peroxide on any suspected colony. If catalase is present, bubbles of oxygen will appear almost instantly. All *Neisseria* produce catalase. So do many other aerobic organisms: *Micrococcus, Staphylococcus,* various Myxobacterales, *Corynebacterium* and *Bacillus.*

## PATHOGENIC NEISSERIA

**Gonorrhea.** This is one of several diseases commonly spoken of as *venereal diseases,* deriving this appellation from the name of Venus, goddess of love. The inappropriateness of this term will become obvious in the discussion of the infections.

Gonorrhea is an acute inflammatory disease due to infection, by *N. gonorrhoeae,* of the mucous surfaces and adjacent glandular structures of the reproductive organs of men and women. Much pus forms, and appears as a white discharge (*leukorrhea*) from the genitalia. It is an alarmingly prevalent disease, with well over a million cases under medical care in the United States in 1968. There are a million or more unreported and untreated cases. Teenage venereal disease is common and is sometimes a sign of stupidity or ignorance, irresponsibility or social and psychological maladjustment.

Infection of the genitalia with *N. gonorrhoeae*

results from sexual contact with an infected person. Gonorrhea is seldom fatal but is sometimes difficult to cure. Patients often believe themselves cured only to find later that the disease has reappeared in a chronic form. The sulfonamide drugs promised for a time to eliminate gonorrhea, but drug-fast strains of gonococci rapidly developed, and indiscriminate use of the drugs by the medically ignorant has robbed such therapy of its effectiveness. Penicillin now offers the best hope for cure in all cases, although penicillin-resistant strains have been reported.

It can be readily understood that stupid, careless, ignorant or malicious people can spread gonorrhea widely. *Prostitution* is one of the chief means by which the disease is propagated. Adequate medical treatment with penicillin very close to the time of exposure will prevent many cases from developing. Inadequate treatment is in several respects worse than none.

Gonorrhea, untreated, often results in sterility. The intense inflammation caused by the organism destroys the tissues lining the genito-urinary tract, the tissue being replaced with scars. Such scars contract strongly and obstruct the *fallopian tubes* of the female and the *vas deferens* of the male (tubes through which the reproductive cells pass). Such scarred obstructions are called *strictures.* Stricture of the urethra in the male interferes with urination and may require surgical intervention. Gonococci sometimes invade the body, localizing in the joints and the heart valves. In the former case, a very painful and stubborn type of arthritis results, while in the latter case a very damaging disease of the heart occurs, with permanent injury and sometimes death.

GONORRHEAL OPHTHALMIA. An intensely painful acute inflammatory infection of the eye (*ophthalmia*) results when gonococci are rubbed into the eye. Loss of sight usually results in a few days unless treatment is prompt. A gonorrheal mother may infect her child's eyes at birth. Infection of the eye of the newborn is called *ophthalmia neonatorum.* Much blindness has been caused by gonorrheal ophthalmia neonatorum. To prevent this, most cities, states and countries require physicians, nurses or midwives attending births, *regardless of any circumstances,* to instill into the eyes of the infant a few drops of weak (1 per cent) silver nitrate, penicillin, or other legally approved disinfectant solution. This rapidly destroys gonococci (and other organisms) before they can start an infection in the eye. Approved disinfectants are obtainable at any health department or drug store, ready for use.

**Laboratory Diagnosis of Gonorrhea.** The diagnosis of *acute* gonorrheal infection in the adult male is usually based on microscopic examination of the pus stained by Gram's method. The gram-negative gonococci appear within the leukocytes (Fig. 33.2). Such organisms found in adult males with acute urethritis are usually gonococci. In the female genitourinary tract many other organisms are present, and gonococci are frequently not discoverable with the microscope. By the use of a method employing antigens washed with saline solution from the surface of freshly isolated gonococci and deposited on the surface of tanned erythrocytes (see *indirect hemagglutination*), hemagglutinating antibodies are readily detected in the body fluids of persons *chronically* infected by *N. gonorrhoeae.*

As noted previously, respiratory *Neisseria* may cause gonorrhea-like infection in preadolescent girls, being transmitted by hands and towels soiled with oral or nasal secretions. Isolation and complete cultural and serological identification of the organism is therefore of especial importance under such circumstances.

**Tribe Mimeae.** Certain gram-negative, pleomorphic rods found during diagnostic studies of gonorrhea were originally classed as a new tribe, Mimeae. They are not found in "Bergey's Manual" and their systematic position, and even the existence of some of them as distinct species, is dubious. They grow vigorously on blood-free media and some may at times be confused morphologically with *Neisseria,* although in cultures of Mimeae both rod and coccal forms occur together. None is motile. On the basis of physiological characters three genera, of one species each, were designated: *Mima polymorpha, Herellea vaginicola* and *Colloides anoxydana* (probably *Escherichia freundii*). *Mima polymorpha* produces oxidase-positive colonies like *Neisseria* and has certain nutritive peculiarities that might cause it to be confused with *Neisseria. Herellea* is closely similar to, and may be identical with, a gram-negative rod called *Bacterium anitratum* that in many respects re-

sembles some species of *Achromobacter* or *Alkaligenes.* Like *Mima polymorpha, Herellea* fails to ferment glucose or lactose in the usual 1 per cent concentration and does not reduce nitrates to nitrites.

Members of the Tribe Mimeae are frequently found associated with other bacteria in pathological (also normal) materials, but appear to have little or no primary pathogenicity per se; they appear to be mainly saprophytes or secondary invaders.

**Meningitis and *Neisseria meningitidis.*** The term meningitis is drawn from pathology and means, simply, inflammation of the membranes (meninges) covering the brain and spinal cord. Meningitis may result from mechanical irritations or infection by viruses or many kinds of bacteria, both pathogens and saprophytes, which may localize in the meninges. The meningococcus is the only common cause of *epidemics* of meningitis. The organisms are transmitted, as are other respiratory microorganisms, in oral and nasal secretions.

Carriers of meningococci are common, but meningitis is not. There is evidence that the meningococcus often causes conditions like rhinitis, catarrh or purulent colds, which heal and attract no particular attention because the etiological agent is unsuspected.

The meningococci gain entrance to the meninges from the upper respiratory tract. Diagnosis is based on clinical appearance of the patient and is confirmed by observing the meningococci in gram-stained smears of pus cells in the spinal fluid. Chemotherapy is instituted on this basis. Meningococcal meningitis is too rapidly progressive and fatal to await cultivation of the organisms, although this is done for confirmatory purposes.

Serological Types. The meningococci are separable into four main serological groups: A, B, C, and D, on the basis of agglutination reactions. The *quellung reaction* (see in next chapter) for grouping is available, analogous to that used in typing pneumococci, since freshly isolated strains of meningococci possess type-specific carbohydrate capsules.

## SUPPLEMENTARY READING

Albert Neisser and the Gonococcus. Editorial. Am. J. Pub. Health, *45*:95, 1955.

Bayliss, B. G., and Hall, E. R.: Plasma coagulation by organisms other than *Staphylococcus aureus.* J. Bact., *89*:101, 1965.

Bergdoll, M. S., Borja, C. R., and Avena, R. M.: Identification of a new enterotoxin as enterotoxin C. J. Bact., *90*:1481, 1965.

Branham, S. E.: Milestones in the history of the meningococcus. Can. J. Microbiol., *2*:175, 1956.

Casman, E. P., and Bennett, R. W.: Detection of staphylococcal enterotoxin in food. Appl. Microbiol., *13*:181, 1965.

Catlin, B. W.: Genetic studies of sulfadiazine-resistant and methionine-requiring *Neisseria* isolated from clinical material. J. Bact., *94*:719, 1967.

Chesbro, W. R., and Auborn, K.: Enzymatic detection of the growth of *Staphylococcus aureus* in foods. Appl. Microbiol., *15*:1150, 1967.

Crisley, F. D., Peeler, J. T., and Angelotti, R.: Comparative evaluation of five selective and differential media for the detection and enumeration of coagulase positive staphylococci in foods. Appl. Microbiol., *13*:140, 1965.

Hall, H. E., Angelotti, R., and Lewis, K. H.: Detection of the staphylococcal enterotoxins in food. Health Lab. Science, *2*:179, 1965.

Henderson, A.: The *Moraxella lwoffi* group of bacteria; a review. Ant. Leeuw., *31*:395, 1965.

Hirshberg, N., and Harper, K. W.: Hemagglutination tests—the detection of antibodies to *N. gonorrhoeae*. Pub. Health. Lab., *23*:212, 1965.

Ivler, D. (Chairman): The Staphylococci: Ecologic Perspectives. Ann. N. Y. Acad. Sci., *128* (Art. 1):1, 1965.

Jay, J. M.: Production of lysozyme by staphylococci and its correlation with three other extracellular substances. J. Bact., *91*:1804, 1966.

Mazanec, K., Kocur, M., and Martinec, T.: Electron microscopy of ultrathin sections of *Sporosarcina ureae*. J. Bact., *90*:808, 1965.

McCoy, D. W., and Faber, J. E.: Influence of food microorganisms on staphylococcal growth and enterotoxin production in meat. Appl. Microbiol., *14*:372, 1966.

Rotter, J., and Kelly, F. C.: Serological reactions associated with the clumping factor of *Staphylococcus aureus*. J. Bact., *91*:588, 1966.

Schindler, C. A.: The role of NaCl in the lysis of *Staphylococcus aureus* by lysostaphin. J. Gen. Microbiol., *40*:199, 1965.

Shah, D. B., and Wilson, J. B.: Egg yolk factor of *Staphylococcus aureus*. I. Nature of the substrate and enzyme involved in the egg yolk opacity reaction. J. Bact., *85*:516, 1963.

Shinefield, H. R., and Ribble, J. C.: Current aspects of infections and diseases related to *Staphylococcus aureus*. Ann. Rev. Med., *16*:263, 1965.

Thayer, J. D., Frank, P. F., and Martin, Jr., B. A.: Thayer-Martin selective medium for the cultivation of *Neisseria meningitidis* from the nasopharynx. Am. J. Pub. Health, *55*:923, 1965.

# Chapter 34

---

# THE STREPTOCOCCEAE

The Tribe Streptococceae is a division of the large and important Family Lactobacillaceae. The name of this family is drawn from the Latin word, *lactis,* for milk. Not only are many of the species of this family found in milk and dairy products, but they all ferment carbohydrates such as glucose and lactose (sugar of milk) with the formation of considerable amounts of L(+) lactic acid (the acid of sour milk). All such bacteria are often spoken of together as the *lactic-acid bacteria,* or the *lactics,* because of their production of lactic acid in the fermentation of common hexoses.

All are typical eubacteria, the few motile species possessing peritrichous flagella. All are gram-positive. They are heterotrophs and generally facultative or strict anaerobes *indifferent to oxygen* (Chapter 32). Although generally regarded as catalase-negative, several types have been shown to produce a distinctive type of hydrogen peroxide-decomposing enzyme, unlike the heme-iron catalase common in many cells. Lactobacillaceae generally require carbohydrates for vigorous growth. None forms spores or conidia.

Because of their fermentative type of metabolism they do not fully utilize the energy of carbohydrates by decomposing them completely to carbon dioxide and water. Glucose is changed to pyruvate and this is hydrogenated to form lactate. Most species convert about 90 per cent of lactose or glucose into lactic acid, with little or no production of $CO_2$ or acetic or other acids:

$$C_{12}H_{22}O_{11} + H_2O \longrightarrow$$
$$4CH_3 \cdot CHOH \cdot COOH.$$

These species are therefore said to be *homofermentative.* Species of the Genus *Leuconostoc* convert lactose or glucose into about 50 per cent lactic acid, about 25 per cent $CO_2$ and about 25 per cent acetic acid and ethyl alcohol. *Leuconostoc* species are therefore said to be *heterofermentative.* Differentiation between heterofermentative and homofermentative activities may depend somewhat on conditions of growth and nutrition. In fermenting *pentose* sugars instead of hexoses, for example, both types may produce lactic and acetic acids:

$$C_5H_{10}O_5 \longrightarrow$$
$$CH_3 \cdot CHOH \cdot COOH + CH_3COOH$$

**Divisions of Lactobacillaceae.** In spite of the family name, which is based on a long-standing compromise, some species of Lactobacillaceae are definitely streptococci. These are segregated in the Tribe Streptococceae described in this chapter. The rod-forms are grouped in the Tribe Lactobacilleae (Chapter 35).

## 34.1 THE TRIBE STREPTOCOCCEAE

Members of the Tribe Streptococceae divide in parallel vertical planes and tend to cling together after fission, thus forming chains of spheres like beads on a string. Chains may consist of only three or four cells or up to thousands, depending on species and growth conditions. Streptococci are often pleomorphic (Fig. 34.1); under some growth conditions several species of streptococci elongate and form chains of cells indistinguishable from lactobacilli and diphtheroids (Chapter 35). Streptococci are most strongly gram-positive in young cultures, especially in media containing blood or serum. They often appear gram-negative in old or acidified cultures. They have complex nutritive requirements, including specific amino acids, vitamins and, for several pathogenic species, factors found in blood or serum.

The Tribe Streptococceae is divided into

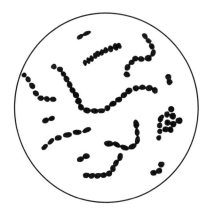

**Figure 34.1** Representative forms and arrangements of various species of *Streptococcus*. Note variations in size, and that many cells are ovoid. Others are spherical and still others are flattened together. (Composite drawing of gram-stained cultures in serum broth.) (About × 1500.)

five genera: *Streptococcus, Diplococcus, Peptostreptococcus, Leuconostoc* and *Pediococcus*. The first three genera (*Streptococcus, Diplococcus* and *Peptostreptococcus*) are characteristically parasitic in and on animals; some are dangerous pathogens. However, two species of *Streptococcus* (*S. lactis* and *S. cremoris*) are probably of plant origin and are common in dairy products and are harmless. The genera *Leuconostoc* and *Pediococcus* are also probably of plant origin and are important in the dairy and brewing industries.

## GENUS STREPTOCOCCUS

There are three major groups in this genus. The first, the *pyogenic* (pus-forming) *group,* includes dangerous pathogens of man and animals. This group is commonly divided into the hemolytic or *S. pyogenes* group and the *viridans* or "nonhemolytic" group, though all are pyogenic and all are hemolytic (see *blood-agar* types). The second, or *fecal group,* commonly called *enterococci,* includes commensal species always found in feces of normal man and animals; also a few that are potentially pathogenic. The third group is the entirely harmless *lactic group,* associated with *Lactobacillus* and other lactic-acid bacteria in dairy products and in fermenting plant products such as sauerkraut and pickles. These groups are differentiated on the basis of properties shown in Table 34.1.

**Blood-Agar Types.** The terms *hemolytic, viridans* and *indifferent* streptocci refer to the action of colonies of the streptococci in plates of infusion agar containing about 5 per cent mammalian blood.

BLOOD-AGAR PLATES. To determine the blood-agar type, a tube containing about 15 ml. of melted meat-infusion agar, cooled to 45° C. (still fluid, yet not hot enough to injure the microorganisms), is inoculated with a loopful of pus, milk, broth culture, or other material containing the desired streptococci. About 5 per cent sterile defibrinated blood is added aseptically and well mixed with the agar. The mixture is poured into plates and incubated *aerobically* for 24 hours at 25° C. for lactic streptococci and 37° C. for others.

ALPHA-TYPE HEMOLYTIC STREPTOCOCCI. Colonies of these streptococci are surrounded by a nearly colorless zone of hemolysis resulting from destruction of erythrocytes, and a zone of *discolored,* but *intact,* erythrocytes close in around the deep colonies. These erythrocytes have a green or brownish green color; hence the term *viridans* (*S. viridans*) (L. *viridis* = green) often (incorrectly) used for *alpha-type hemolytic streptococci,* especially pathogens. Peripheral to the inner ring of discolored cells the outer zone of clear, almost colorless hemolysis may be of great or small extent, and may sometimes be so small as to coincide with the zone of green cells. It usually widens on refrigeration of the plate (Fig. 34.2, W and X).

Only the use of a microscope can be relied upon to make the distinction and *only colonies that are deep in the agar* are always thus characterized, surface colonies sometimes producing deceptive appearances or growth spreading over and hiding hemolytic zones.

BETA-TYPE HEMOLYTIC STREPTOCOCCI. The hemolytic zones around deep colonies of streptococci of this type in blood-agar plates are seen to be entirely clear, almost colorless, and *free from any intact erythrocytes* (Fig. 34.2, U and V). Such streptococci are loosely spoken of under the general term of *Streptococcus hemolyticus,* or "hemolytic strep."

DOUBLE-ZONE BETA-TYPE STREPTOCOCCI. Certain species, almost exclusively of bovine origin and not uncommon in dairy products, after producing a zone of hemolysis like that of other beta-type streptococci and then allowed to cool, produce a second ring of hemolysis separated from the first by a ring of red erythrocytes. This is sometimes called "hot-cold" hemolysis.

GAMMA-TYPE STREPTOCOCCI. When deep colonies of streptococci in blood-agar pour plates show no visible change in the blood cells surrounding the colony, they are said to be of the *gamma, indifferent* or *nonhemolytic* type.

**TABLE 34.1** DIFFERENTIAL CHARACTERS OF STREPTOCOCCI

| Group Designation | Action on Blood Agar* | Grow well at 10 | Grow well at 45 | Opt. Temp. (°C.) | Survive 60° C. | 6.5% NaCl | pH 9.6 | 0.1% Meth. bl. | 40% bile | Decarboxylate Tyrosine | Representative Species | Lancefield Groups | Lactose | Mannitol | Salicin | Maltose | Trehalose | Sorbitol | Inulin | Sod. hippur. | l-serine | Gelatin | Pyruvate | Red. litmus | Tolerate 0.04% KTe | Form hexosan slimes or capsules | Bile-soluble |
|---|---|---|---|---|---|---|---|---|---|---|---|---|---|---|---|---|---|---|---|---|---|---|---|---|---|---|---|
| 1. Pyogenic group: A. (Beta-type hemolytic streptococci) "Str. hemolyticus" | β | − | − | 37 | − | − | − | − | − | − | S. pyogenes | A, E, F, G | + | − | + | + | + | − | − | − | .. | − | .. | − | .. | − | − |
| | | | | | | | | | | | S. agalactiae‡‡ | B | + | − | + | + | + | − | − | + | .. | − | .. | − | .. | − | − |
| | | | | | | | | | | | S. equi | C | − | − | + | + | + | − | − | − | .. | − | .. | − | .. | − | − |
| | | | | | | | | | | | S. equisimilis | C | + | − | + | + | .. | − | − | − | .. | − | .. | − | .. | − | − |
| B. Viridans group (Alpha-type hemolytic streptococci) "Str. viridans" | α | − | + | 37 | − | − | − | − | − | − | S. mitis | | + | − | + | + | + | − | − | − | .. | − | .. | − | .. | − | − |
| | | | | | | | | | | | S. salivarius† | | + | − | + | + | + | − | − | − | .. | − | .. | − | .. | + | − |
| | | | | | | | | | | | S. equinus‖ | | − | − | + | + | + | − | ± | − | .. | − | .. | − | .. | − | − |
| | | | | | | | | | | | S. bovis‡‖ | | + | − | + | + | + | + | + | − | .. | − | .. | − | .. | + | − |
| | | | | | | | | | | | S. thermophilus¶ | | + | − | − | + | + | − | + | − | .. | − | .. | − | .. | − | − |
| | | | | | | | | | | | D. pneumoniae† | | + | − | + | + | .. | − | + | − | .. | − | .. | − | .. | + | + |
| 2. Fecal group (enterococci) | α, β | + | + | 35 | + | + | + | + | + | + | S. faecalis†† | D | + | + | + | + | + | + | − | + | + | ± | + | + | + | − | − |
| | | | | | | | | | | | S. faecium | D | + | + | + | .. | + | + | − | + | + | + | .. | − | − | − | − |
| | | | | | | | | | | | S. durans** | D | + | − | ± | + | .. | − | − | + | .. | − | .. | − | − | − | − |
| 3. Lactic group | γ | + | − | 25 | + | − | − | + | + | − | S. lactis | N | + | ± | ± | + | + | − | − | − | .. | − | .. | + | .. | − | − |
| | | | | | | | | | | | S. cremoris§ | N | + | ± | ± | − | + | − | − | − | .. | − | .. | + | .. | ± | − |

\* Incubated aerobically.
† Does not grow at 45° C.
‡ Some strains not hemolytic (γ).
§ Differs from S. lactis in failure to grow at 40° C., in 4 per cent NaCl or at pH 9.6 and in not fermenting maltose.
¶ Distinguished by (a) growth at 50° C.; (b) failure to ferment maltose. A nuisance in dairies.
‖ These are commonly included as fecal streptococci; they tolerate 40% bile; S. bovis also survives 30 min. at 60° C.
** β-hemolysis
†† Includes S. liquefaciens and S. zymogenes.
‡‡ Tolerates 40% bile.

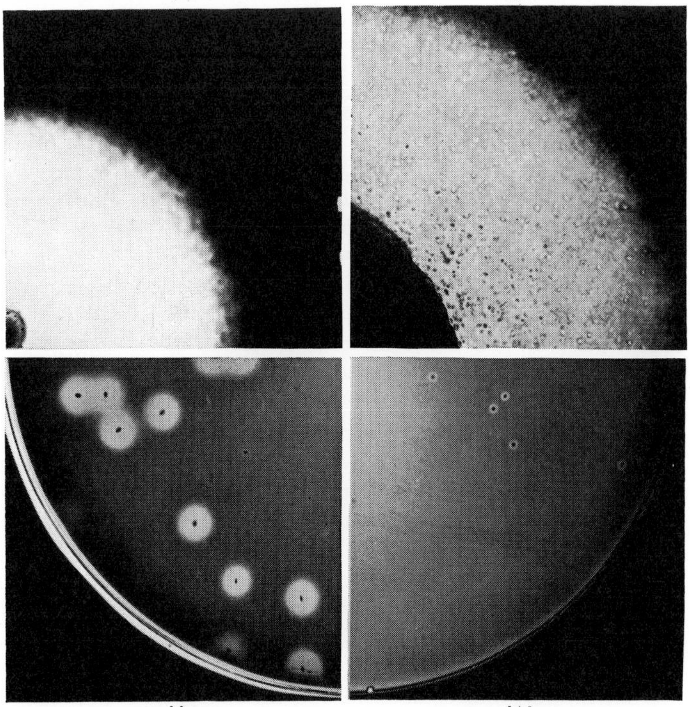

**Figure 34.2** Colonies of hemolytic streptococci in blood agar. *U,* Clear zones of complete hemolysis around colonies of beta type (*Strep. pyogenes,* Lancefield group A), natural size. *V,* One beta-type colony enlarged to show edge of colony at lower left and absence of erythrocytes in clear hemolyzed zone. *W,* Small hemolytic zones of alpha-type colony, *Strep. mitis,* natural size. *X,* One alpha-type colony enlarged to show edge of colony at lower left, with many intact erythrocytes in hemolyzed zone. (Preparations by Dr. Elaine L. Updyke. Photo courtesy of Communicable Disease Center, U. S. Public Health Service, Atlanta, Ga.)

## 34.2   THE PYOGENIC STREPTOCOCCI

Any agent, living or inanimate, that stimulates an increase in leukocytes locally or generally is said to be *pyogenic*. With reference to the streptococci the term is generally understood to mean the beta-type hemolytic streptococci. However, some alpha-type streptococci sometimes produce pyogenic infections. In addition, some species of the fecal group can produce pyogenic lesions but are not usually very important pathogens. For convenience they are not included in the pyogenic group referred to here. Thus, the pyogenic group here includes both alpha- and beta-type streptococci.

The pyogenic streptococci differ markedly from those of the lactic and fecal groups in being more highly dependent on a parasitic life in the mammalian body. They are less able to grow and survive under conditions of very low surface tension, high osmotic pressure, low pH or high and low temperatures. Such influences as these are encountered in the intestinal tract, ripening cheese, fermented and brined food products and the outer world, which environ the fecal and lactic groups. (See Table 34.1.) The fastidious and delicate pathogens of the pyogenic group are best cultivated at 37° C.

in meat-infusion agar or broth containing serum or blood and 0.1 per cent glucose, in an atmosphere containing 5 to 10 per cent carbon dioxide. Their colonies on blood or serum agar are generally about 1 to 2 mm. in diameter, colorless or greyish, watery, translucent and inconspicuous. They may be mucoid, smooth or exhibit different degrees of roughness.

**Lancefield Groups of Beta-Type Streptococci.** Lancefield made extracts of cultures of beta-type streptococci from different sources by means of hot, 0.2N HCl. These extracts contain specific, somatic antigen (*carbohydrate* or C substances). The extracts are used as antigens in precipitin tests. The corresponding antibodies are obtained by injecting the antigens into animals.

By means of such precipitin tests several distinct groups of beta-type hemolytic streptococci can be differentiated with respect to origin. Lancefield designated these groups by letters: A, B, C, D, E, F, G and so on, according to source or other characters. They are accordingly known as *Lancefield groups*. There are nearly a score of such groups. A few alpha-type streptococci and some other organisms have also been found to contain some of these antigens. For example, *S. faecalis,* an alpha-type fecal streptococcus, contains Lancefield group D antigen;

*S. lactis* of the lactic group contains Lancefield group N antigen. Only two of the Lancefield groups need be described here.

Group A Streptococci. Biological properties distinguishing group A streptococci from others are shown in Table 34.1. *S. pyogenes* causes scarlet fever, septic sore throat, empyema, blood poisoning, puerperal sepsis, and many other serious, epidemic and acute pyogenic diseases in human beings. *S. pyogenes* can also infect the udder of cows. The unpasteurized milk of such cows then becomes a dangerous vector of streptococcal disease.

*M-Types of Group A.* Two colony forms of *S. pyogenes* have been discerned: a smooth, glossy form and a dull, granular form called *matte* or M. Different strains of the M forms contain different protein, somatic antigens. These M antigens evoke *type-specific* precipitins. Over 40 serological types (*M types*) of *S. pyogenes* (all group A) have been found. Several physiological varieties of *S. pyogenes* were formerly given various names such as *S. scarlatinae, S. erysipelatus* and *S. epidemicus.*

The importance of determining the M-type of *S. pyogenes* becomes clear when it is realized that resistance to *S. pyogenes* infection is M-type-specific. For example, one may have resistance to a type 6 *S. pyogenes* yet succumb in a type 19 epidemic with what *clinically* appears to be the same disease. The importance of typing in the study of group A streptococcal disease can scarcely be overestimated. For example, the whole problem of the control of rheumatic heart disease appears to be bound up with the epidemiology of *S. pyogenes* infection of various M types. Other protein antigens in the cell walls of group A streptococci are designated T and R.

*Streptolysins.* The hemolytic toxins (streptolysins) of group A streptococci are of two sorts: (1) *streptolysin S,* unstable in the presence of heat and acids, and (2) *streptolysin O,* unstable in oxygen. Streptolysin S produces beta-type hemolysis in blood-agar plates. It is not antigenic. Streptolysin O is an antigen. In persons infected with group A streptococci, antibodies to streptolysin O are generally found and easily measured. The measurement (titration) of antibodies against streptolysin O, especially when the titer rises sharply over a period of two weeks or so in connection with an illness such as sore throat, affords not only a valuable diagnostic test but also a measure of the reaction of the patient. Over 80 per cent of rheumatic fever patients have a considerable titer of antistreptolysin O.

Group B Streptococci. Streptococci of group B differ from all other pyogenic streptococci (except enterococci) in hydrolyzing sodium hippurate and in producing double zones of beta hemolysis.

Hemolytic streptococci of group B are usually of bovine origin, but are occasionally found in human infections. *S. agalactiae,* an important member of group B, is of particular interest to the farmer because it causes severe mastitis in cattle and stoppage of milk flow. Of minor pathogenic significance for man, *S. agalactiae* may be confused with *S. pyogenes* by workers seeking to eliminate *S. pyogenes* from milk supplies.

**The Pyogenic Alpha-Type (Viridans) Streptococci.** The alpha-type hemolytic streptococci of the pyogenic group must be distinguished from those of the enterococcus group, which are physiologically very different. As represented by *S. mitis,* the pyogenic alpha-type streptococci are generally delicate, fragile, highly adapted parasites found mainly in the normal mammalian upper respiratory tract. Usually regarded as lesser pathogens, they sometimes produce serious infections, often of a chronic nature. For example, in man alpha-type streptococci are frequently found in abscessed teeth, infected sinuses and diseased tonsils. From teeth and tonsils they may be carried to the joints and produce rheumatic conditions (arthritis). They can also infect injured heart valves and cause a serious heart disease, *bacterial endocarditis. S. faecalis* (a viridans species of the fecal group) is also sometimes involved in such conditions.

*Streptococcus salivarius,* representative of the harmless "salivary" streptococci, forms thick, slimy or gummy colonies if cultivated on media containing 5 per cent sucrose. The gumminess results from the synthesis of viscous polysaccharides (generally dextrans or levans) from the sucrose, and is a good example of the ability of many bacterial species and all plants to synthesize extracellular polysaccharides.

*S. bovis* and *S. equinus* occur in the alimentary tract of animals and man, and are more vigorous growers than other salivary streptococci. *S. bovis* is potentially pyogenic; *S. equinus* probably not.

## 34.3　GENUS *DIPLOCOCCUS*

The only species in this genus is *Diplococcus pneumoniae.* It is a cause of lobar pneumonia and, like *Streptococcus pyogenes,* group A, causes numerous other serious, acute pyogenic conditions: meningitis, septicemia, empyema and peritonitis. It was a frequent cause of death before the ad-

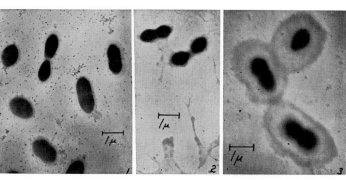

**Figure 34.3** Electron micrographs of *Diplococcus pneumoniae*. The first picture shows the capsules in their normal state. The center picture shows the capsules virtually unaffected by serum of a heterologous type. The picture on the right shows the effect of homologous-type serum on the capsules—a well-marked quellung reaction. (From Mudd, Heinmets and Anderson; J. Exp. Med., vol. 78.)

vent of chemotherapy and is still a dangerous killer.

Some writers logically refer to *Diplococcus pneumoniae* as *Streptococcus pneumoniae* since the organisms often form short chains of ovoid diplococci and produce alpha-type colonies on blood-agar plates. The chains are usually made up of from two to eight pairs of cocci. They are encapsulated, the capsule consisting of a polysaccharide. The pneumococci are rarely spherical, commonly having the form of short artillery projectiles placed base to base. Methods of cultivation and study are like those used for other pyogenic streptococci. *D. pneumoniae* is found in the saliva and sputum of patients with lobar pneumonia and, like other viridans streptococci, also occurs frequently in the normal mouth and throat.

**Diagnosis.** Pneumococci are extremely pathogenic for white mice when freshly isolated from the body. Advantage is often taken of this fact to isolate pneumococci from sputum of patients for diagnosis. The sputum is injected into the mice intraperitoneally. After six to twenty-four hours the mice die or become very ill, and enormous numbers of pneumococci are found in the peritoneal cavity and heart blood. The cocci found on the peritoneum of the mouse may be identified by: (1) their morphology; (2) their *capsules* (Fig. 34.3); (3) their *solubility* in bile or in solutions of various other surface-tension reducers; (4) ability to ferment inulin (see Table 34.1).

SEROLOGICAL TYPES OF PNEUMOCOCCI. Pneumococci may be divided into more than 70 serological types which are designated by Roman numerals. These are analogous to the Lancefield groups of streptococci. Serological type-specificity of pneumococci is conferred by their capsules.

QUELLUNG REACTION. If encapsulated pneumococci or other organisms with type-specific capsular antigens are mixed with a *type-specific* immune serum, swelling of the capsules is seen (Fig. 34.3). This is spoken of as a quel-

lung (German for *swelling*) reaction. It was first described by Neufeld so is sometimes called the Neufeld reaction.

*Transmission of pneumonia* is chiefly through droplets of infected saliva and nasal and pulmonary mucus, and by inhalation of infected dust. Kissing undoubtedly transmits the infection as well as other respiratory pathogens but, obviously, not every such infection results in disease. Romance has a powerful ally in natural resistance to respiratory disease.

## THE GENUS PEPTOSTREPTOCOCCUS

Peptostreptococci (Gr. *pepto* = to digest; i.e., proteolytic) occur mainly in pyogenic, putrefactive and gangrenous lesions and wounds. Most are highly pathogenic. Physiologically the group is somewhat heterogeneous. Except in being strongly proteolytic, peptostreptococci resemble streptococci of the pyogenic group; some are hemolytic, others not. Most species are distinguished by being, when first isolated from pathological material, *rigidly anaerobic* though they often later become aerotolerant.

## 34.4   THE FECAL (ENTEROCOCCUS) GROUP

As the name implies, these are streptococci commonly found in feces of man and other animals. They also occur on plants. They are regularly found in the normal mouth, whence they probably get into the intestinal tract. These are all relatively hardy organisms capable of resisting growth conditions wholly inhibitory to the more fragile pyogenic group (Table 34.1).

Many of the enterococci have a tendency to produce short chains and pairs of plump, ovoid cocci, and are commonly found in clumps suggestive of micrococci; some were first described as micrococci.

Unlike the highly adapted pyogenic streptococci, enterococci are characterized by wide tolerance of heat and cold and other influences unfavorable to other streptococci: 60° C.; 6.5 per cent sodium chloride solution; bile (low surface tension); the presence of 0.1 per cent methylene blue; pH 9.6; and conditions of life in feces and the outer world. (See Table 34.1.) Enterococci are even more hardy than the lactic groups.

The enterococci are typified by *Streptococcus faecalis.* This is most commonly found in the intestinal tract of man and lower vertebrates and on plants. A closely similar species, found primarily in the intestinal tract of lower vertebrates but also in man and on plants, is called *S. faecium.* Properties that distinguish between *S. faecalis, S. faecium* and its variant, *S. faecium* var. *durans,* are shown in Table 34.1.

Varieties of *S. faecalis* are *liquefaciens* and *zymogenes,* the last differing from other enterococci in producing beta-type zones in blood agar. Varieties *liquefaciens* and *zymogenes* hydrolyze proteins. As a result, they give rise to strong bitter flavors in cheese. They have been found occasionally in certain pathological conditions. The present tendency is to include these variants in the species *S. faecalis.*

All contain Lancefield group D antigen. They grow readily at 22° to 40° C. on meat infusion and similar organic media commonly used in the laboratory.

*S. equinus* and *S. bovis,* previously mentioned as salivary streptococci, are also found in large numbers in the intestinal tract of equines and bovines, respectively. Thus they are fecal streptococci and as such are as resistant to bile as are the true enterococci. They are also heat resistant like the enterococci. However, they have other properties that ally them to the *S. salivarius*-like commensals of the viridans group. Thus, while *fecal* streptococci, they are not regarded as true *enterococci.*

**Fecal Streptococci in Water Supplies.**  Because fecal streptococci, especially *S. faecalis,* are constantly present in the human intestines in enormous numbers, survive for weeks in feces-polluted water supplies and are easily cultivated and identified in the laboratory, their presence in water is commonly used as an indication of fecal or sewage pollution. Identifying tests are easily done. (See pages 422, 442.)

## 34.5   THE LACTIC GROUP

This group contains: (a) *Streptococcus lactis,** the common, milk-souring streptococcus useful

in the dairy industry; (b) a very similar species called *S. cremoris;* and (c) the thermoduric *S. thermophilus.* These species are usually of the gamma type in blood agar but some variants may produce green colonies.

**S. lactis.**  A gamma-type streptococcus, *S. lactis* contains Lancefield group N antigens. *S. lactis* is always present in market milk, even of the best quality. It occurs in cow dung, dust and soil, and on plants and utensils; its entrance into the milk is easily explained. Its persistence in such environments shows that it is a relatively hardy organism. It is quite harmless to man. *S. lactis* and *S. cremoris* (see below) are, together, responsible for pleasant flavors in dairy products such as butter and cottage cheese. The important role of these two species and of *S. thermophilus* in the dairy and food industries is discussed in Chapters 46 and 47.

*S. lactis* sometimes forms long chains but occurs chiefly in short chains or pairs and the cells are oval. It grows rapidly in milk at 28° C. (82° F.), causing souring of the milk. The acidity usually suppresses the development of other organisms, some of which might otherwise cause the milk to putrefy. Contributing to the suppression of undesirable gram-positive organisms in milk is the potent antibiotic *nisin* produced by some varieties of *S. lactis. S. lactis* can readily be cultivated on agar containing milk, whey or tomato juice. It grows best in the presence of glucose or lactose.

**S. cremoris.**  *S. cremoris* is one of numerous lactic-acid streptococci that are similar to *S. lactis. S. cremoris* tends to form very long chains. It may be differentiated from *S. lactis* by characters given in Table 34.1.

**S. thermophilus.**  Common in dairy products, *S. thermophilus* is perfectly harmless. Although not truly thermophilic, it is thermoduric. It has the property of surviving temperatures as high as 63° C. (pasteurization) and may appear in large numbers in pasteurized milk, giving the false impression that the milk has not been properly pasteurized. It forms "pinpoint" colonies in agar plates used to determine the numbers of bacteria in milk. On the other hand, it is very useful in the ripening of cheeses made with high processing temperatures, such as Swiss cheese, because it grows well at about 45° C.

## 34.6   GENUS *LEUCONOSTOC*

The name of Genus *Leuconostoc* is derived from the name of a common blue-green alga, *Nostoc,* and the Greek *leukos,* meaning white or

---

*\*S. lactis* represents a *cluster* of variants or closely similar species.

colorless. *Nostoc,* the alga, is characterized by tangled trichomes of spherical green (chlorophyll-containing) cells with a thick, firm, gelatinous outer coating. *Leuconostoc,* the bacterium, resembles *Nostoc* in forming spherical cells in tangled chains and in generally forming thick outer coatings of slime or gum (dextrans, *L. dextranicum* and *L. mesenteroides*) in sucrose media (Fig. 34.4) (compare *S. salivarius*). However, *Leuconostoc* cells are colorless and small (1.0 to 1.5 $\mu$) whereas *Nostoc* cells are relatively enormous: 25 to 200 $\mu$ compared with *Leuconostoc* cells. *Leuconostoc* is much like *Lactobacillus* (see next chapter) in most respects, even in morphology; *Leuconostoc* is pleomorphic and often closely resembles lactobacilli. *Leuconostoc* is distinguished among the lactic acid bacteria in being heterofermentative. There are various types of *Leuconostoc,* differentiated serologically and by colony form, the amount and molecular nature of gum formed, and by amount of carbon dioxide produced. They produce both levo- and dextrorotatory lactic acid.

**L. mesenteroides and L. dextranicum.** These two important species are widely distributed on growing plants and, like *S. lactis,* are commonly found in dairy products and vegetable products. They ferment actively and produce acid in such carbohydrate-rich plant materials as sauerkraut, ensilage, and in such plant juices as are used in making cane sugar and beet sugar. They constitute a great nuisance in the sugar refining industry because their slime and gum formations clog vats, pipes and machines. Indeed, so much of the specific carbohydrate of *Leuconostoc* is left in commercial cane, beet, and other sugars that specific precipitin tests can be obtained by mixing a little "sugar water" with immunologically specific serum.

**L. citrovorum.** This species produces little or none of the gum that is so characteristic of other species of *Leuconostoc*. It so closely resembles *S. lactis* that some workers have regarded it as a streptococcus (*S. citrovorum*). (It has also been classified as a species of *Pediococcus*, a sarcina-like lactic-acid coccus most commonly found in spoiled beer and beer wort.) A very closely related variety has often been called *L. paracitrovorum*. These organisms are closely allied to *S. cremoris,* are commonly found in its company and have some of its principal characters and produce characteristic flavors.

**Lactic-Acid Bacteria and Diacetyl.** The important point about *L. citrovorum* and *S. cremoris* is that they decompose citric acid (usually present in small amounts in normal milk) with the formation of acetic acid, carbon dioxide and, most important, *diacetyl*. Diacetyl is re-

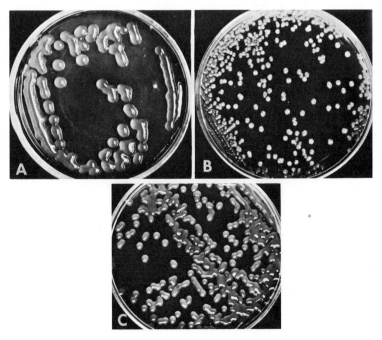

**Figure 34.4** Colonies of *Leuconostoc* sp., growing on carbohydrate agar. Note the large amount of gummy, polysaccharide capsule-like material around the colonies in A and C. B is a species like *L. citrovorum* that produces little gum. Compare with pneumococci (Fig. 34.3). (Photo courtesy of American Society for Microbiology.)

sponsible for the pleasant, buttery flavor of dairy products. Consequently, pure cultures of *L. citrovorum* and *S. cremoris* are commonly added to milk or cream that is to be made into butter or cheese. Citric acid also is often added to increase the amount of diacetyl formed. The overall reactions are shown in Figure 34.5.

Citric acid is first decomposed to yield acetylmethyl-carbinol and other products. Acetylmethyl-carbinol is then oxidized in the presence of acid to diacetyl. Since diacetyl is best produced in an acid medium, sometimes a little acetic or other harmless acid is added to ensure proper pH. Also, aeration is necessary or, as shown in the foregoing reaction, the acetylmethyl-carbinol, instead of being *oxidized* to diacetyl, is *reduced* to 2:3 butylene glycol, which is tasteless. These facts are of vital importance to dairymen.

An important branch of the dairy industry is the selection, propagation, maintenance and sale of pure cultures of *S. lactis, L. cremoris, L. citrovorum,* various lactobacilli, and mixtures of these, for the manufacture of butter, fermented milks, yoghurt and cheeses. (See Chapter 45.) On the other hand, these organisms are nuisances in the citrus and other fruit juice in-

dustries, imparting "sour milk" and "buttermilk" flavors to the products.

LEUCONOSTOC AND VITAMIN ASSAY. Like many species of *Lactobacillus,* some *Leuconostoc* species are important because of syntheticenzyme deficiencies; for example, nicotinic acid is necessary for *L. mesentericus,* and the so-called citrovorum factor (CF) or leucovorin (the vitamin, folinic acid) is required by *L. citrovorum.* The organisms are commonly used in the assay of these vitamins. (See Table 35.2 and Chapter 47.)

## GENUS PEDIOCOCCUS

*Pediococcus* (Gr. *pedion* = plane) is characterized by division in parallel vertical planes, forming short chains, or in two vertical planes at right angles, forming tetrads. Pediococci have often been called *Sarcina,* though the formation of cubical packets like *Sarcina* probably does not occur. In some respects pediococci resemble *Leuconostoc citrovorum,* although pediococci are homofermentative. Pediococci have the general properties of Family Lactobacillaceae. Pediococci are of considerable importance as nuisance

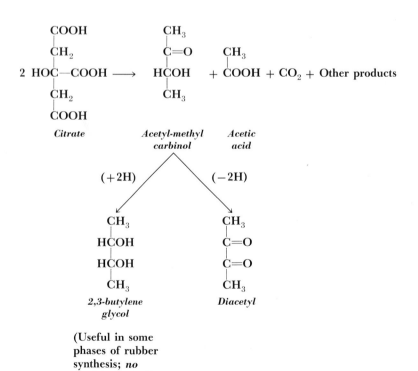

**Figure 34.5** Overall reactions in production of diacetyl from citrate. For explanation see text. Diacetyl can also be produced from pyruvate.

saprophytes in fermenting vegetable products, notably sauerkraut, fruit juices, beer and beer wort. They produce acidity, turbidity and diacetyl and, consequently, buttery odors and flavors ("sarcina odor") in fruit juices and beer. Most true beer connoisseurs *despise* buttermilk-flavored beer!

## SUPPLEMENTARY READING

Burrows, W.: Textbook of Microbiology; 18th ed. Chapters 17 and 18. W. B. Saunders Co., Philadelphia. 1963.

Deibel, R. H.: The group D streptococci. Bact. Rev., *28*:330, 1964.

Moody, M. D., Padula, J., Lizana, D., and Hall, C. T.: Epidemiologic characterization of Group A streptococci by T-agglutination and M-precipitation tests in the public health laboratory. Health Lab. Science, *2*:149, 1965.

Mundt, J. O.: Occurrence of enterococci on plants in a wild environment. Appl. Microbiol., *11*:136, 1963.

Slanetz, L. W., and Bartley, C. H.: Detection and sanitary significance of fecal streptococci in water. Amer. J. Pub. Health, *54*:609, 1964.

Smith, D. T., Conant, N. F., and Overman, J. R.: Zinsser Microbiology. 13th ed. Appleton-Century Crofts, Inc. New York. 1964.

Whittenbury, R.: Differentiation of *Streptococcus faecalis* and *S. faecium.* J. Gen. Microbiol., *38*:279, 1965.

# Chapter 35

## THE LACTOBACILLEAE
## AND THE
## CORYNEBACTERIACEAE

### 35.1 TRIBE LACTOBACILLEAE

The organisms of the Tribe Lactobacilleae as outlined in the 1957 edition of "Bergey's Manual" are divided into five genera: *Eubacterium, Catenabacterium, Ramibacterium, Cillobacterium* and *Lactobacillus*. All are gram-positive, nonsporeforming rods. Some are motile, some nonmotile. The systematic position of the first four genera is doubtful. These four genera are strict anaerobes, and occur mainly in the intestinal tract. They are physiologically rather heterogeneous. Some are pathogenic. They probably should be considered as belonging in a single genus, *Ramibacterium,* and transferred to the Family Propionibacteriaceae (see below). Here we shall consider in detail only the Genus *Lactobacillus*. The Tribe Lactobacilleae and some other gram-positive, nonsporeforming rods are compared in Table 35.1.

### GENUS LACTOBACILLUS

The species of Genus *Lactobacillus* are among the most important and most studied of the Lactobacilleae.

Lactobacilli are usually long, slender, nonmotile rods, often forming filaments of cells (Fig. 35.1). Several species that are motile with peritrichous flagella have been described. Lactobacilli are pleomorphic; under some growth conditions they form chains of cells that resemble streptococci or *Leuconostoc*. Encapsulated strains of lactobacilli have been described. Lactobacilli occur in soil, in dust, on plants, in the vertebrate intestinal tract and in foods and dairy products. Most species are homofermentative; a few, e.g., *L. fermenti* and *L. pastorianus,* are heterofermentative. Many species such as *L. fermenti, L. bulgaricus, L. brevis, L. delbrueckii, L. plantarum* and *L. lactis* are quite acid-resistant and thermoduric. As a result they can grow in warm and acid situations such as curing ensilage and sauerkraut; fermenting beer, wine and whiskey mashes; and fruits and vegetables and their juices as prepared for canning. Several species are resistant to high osmotic pressures and grow well in salt-pickling vats and meat corning and curing brines, in sugar refining vats and salty cheeses.

*Lactobacillus* species are rarely of pathogenic significance, with the possible exception of a few oral species, e.g., *L. casei* which, with acid-forming oral streptococci, appear to be involved in the production of dental caries. The principal role of lactobacilli is in industry. In many ways lactobacilli resemble *Leuconostoc* and are often found associated with *Leuconostoc* in dairy products and fermenting plant materials. At least one species of lactobacilli, *L. casei,* produces a specific capsular polysaccharide analogous to but less conspicuous than that of *Leuconostoc.*

**Nutrition of Lactobacillus.** Several species of *Lactobacillus* and of *Leuconostoc* are important because of curious deficiencies in their synthetic-enzyme equipment. In the laboratory they generally do not grow well on the usual peptone and meat-extract media. Instead they require vitamin-containing vegetable or fruit juices, yeast extracts, whey or milk, as well as carbon dioxide for carbon and carbohydrates as sources of carbon and energy. While some can use ammonium

**TABLE 35.1**   COMPARISON OF SOME GRAM-POSITIVE NONSPOREFORMING RODS*

| Characteristics | Lactobacilleae | Propionibacteriaceae | Brevibacteriaceae | Corynebacteriaceae |
|---|---|---|---|---|
| Morphological peculiarities | Lactobacilleae: long, slender rods; pleomorphic | Short rods, occasional branching; pleomorphic | Short rods, red, yellow and orange pigments; pleomorphic | Short rods; pleomorphic; metachromatic granules; club forms |
| Distinctive metabolic products or characters | Lactic acid | Propionic or butyric acids; ferment lactic acid | Lactose not fermented | As Propionibac. |
| Proteolysis | Little or none | As Lactobac. | Active | Various |
| Catalase production | −† | + | + | + |
| Relation to oxygen | Indifferent or microaerophilic | Anaerobic to microaerophilic | Aerobic and facultative | Strictly aerobic to microaerophilic or facultative |
| Special nutritive requirements | Numerous vitamins and amino acids | As Lactobac. | | Few |
| Habitat (saprophytic species) | Feces, soil, dairy products, fermenting vegetable matter | As Lactobac. | As Lactobac. | Soil, plants, dairy products |
| Pathogenesis | Some pathogenic on mammals | None | None | Several species on animals and plants |

*There are some exceptions to nearly all of the properties listed.
†Some catalase activity has been described in some species.

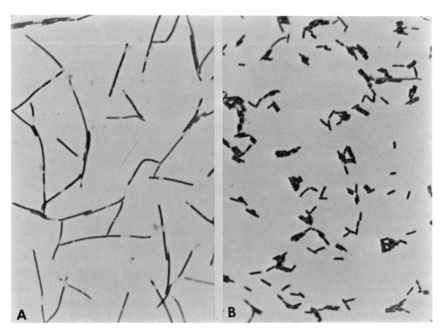

**Figure 35.1**   Comparison of morphology of *Lactobacillus leichmannii* grown in media of different compositions, *A*, Cells from complex medium containing thymidine and (*B*) cells from complex medium containing vitamin $B_{12}$. (From Diebel et al.: J. Bact., vol. 71.)

**TABLE 35.2** SOME ESSENTIAL GROWTH REQUIREMENTS OF CERTAIN LACTOBACILLACEAE

| Specific Growth Requirement | Species |
|---|---|
| Para-aminobenzoic acid | *Lactobacillus plantarum* |
| Folic acid | *Lactobacillus casei; Streptococcus faecalis* |
| Folinic acid | *Leuconostoc citrovorum* |
| Nicotinic acid (Niacin) | *Leuconostoc mesenteroides Lactobacillus plantarum* |
| Riboflavin (vitamin B₂) | *Streptococcus lactis* |
| Thiamin (vitamin B₁) | *Lactobacillus fermenti* |

salts as a source of nitrogen, and from them synthesize all necessary amino acids and proteins, others are *absolutely dependent* on certain ready-formed amino acids that they cannot synthesize. Others are similarly dependent on certain specific vitamins or other specific compounds (purines and fatty acids), the specific requirements depending on species (see Table 35.2). Nutritive conditions often determine specific requirements. For example, some species do not require the amino acid L-serine if the vitamin folic acid is present. It would seem that if they have folic acid they can synthesize their own L-serine.

Because of these specific nutritive requirements, various species of lactic-acid bacteria are of immense value and are widely used in *assaying* (measuring) the vitamin and amino acid content of foods and drugs for industrial and pharmaceutical purposes. More details of the many industrial aspects of lactic-acid bacteria are given in Chapter 47.

### 35.2   FAMILY PROPIONIBACTERIACEAE

Members of the Family Propionibacteriaceae are much like *Lactobacillus:* gram-positive, nonmotile, nonsporeforming. They are generally short rods with rounded ends but may assume very pleomorphic, club-shaped and branched forms. Unlike the Family Lactobacillaceae, most of these organisms produce catalase. They are nutritionally fastidious, are facultative anaerobes, and are heterofermentative. In the 1957 edition of "Bergey's Manual" the family includes two genera: *Butyribacterium* and *Propionibacterium.* In a new edition of "Bergey's Manual" the family will probably be somewhat enlarged and altered. Unlike *Lactobacillus* they do not

*produce* lactic acid but ferment it, producing carbon dioxide, acetic acid and either butyric acid (genus *Butyribacterium*) or propionic acid (genus *Propionibacterium*).

Species of *Propionibacterium* are common in dairy products. *P. freudenreichii* (type species), *P. shermanii* and some others are commonly found in various hard cheeses. During the ripening of these, *Propionibacterium* contributes flavors with its fermentation products, among them propionic acid. For example, the distinctive sweet and bitter flavor of Swiss cheese is thought to be due, in part at least, to propionates. The "eyes" of Swiss cheese are largely caused by carbon dioxide. Pure cultures of *Propionibacterium* are added to milk in the manufacture of Swiss, Münster, and similar cheeses.

### 35.3   FAMILY BREVIBACTERIACEAE

The Genus *Brevibacterium* (L. *brevis* = short) is the most important genus of this family. These organisms are similar to *Propionibacterium* in being short, pleomorphic, gram-positive, nonsporeforming rods. A few species are motile with peritrichous flagella. Unlike typical lactic-acid and propionic-acid bacteria, brevibacteria commonly produce red, yellow or brown pigments, and do *not* ferment lactose. Like *Lactobacillus* and *Propionibacterium*, species of *Brevibacterium* are widely distributed in nature and occur in dairy products, where they are important members of the cheese-making community. Unlike anaerobic or microaerophilic *Lactobacillus* and *Propionibacterium*, brevibacteria are aerobic and grow well on outer surfaces. For example, *Brevibacterium linens* (type species) grows with a yellow-orange pigment on the outside surfaces of ripening cheeses such as Limburger and Camembert. Since the organism is proteolytic it contributes to the softening and flavoring of such cheeses.

### 35.4   FAMILY CORYNEBACTERIACEAE

The name of the Family Corynebacteriaceae is derived from the Greek word *koryne* for club, and refers to the bizarre club-shaped cells often formed by some species, notably *Corynebacterium diphtheriae.* Typical corynebacteria could be included in the group of lactobacilli since they produce small amounts of lactic acid from glucose. However, they differ in producing catalase and in other characteristics (Table 35.1).

The family contains six genera: *Corynebacterium*, of which *C. diphtheriae*, the cause of diphtheria, is type species; *Listeria*, of which *L. monocytogenes*, the cause of listeriosis in man and animals, is the only species; and *Erysipelothrix*, of which the cause of swine erysipelas, *E. rhusiopathiae* (*E. insidiosa*), is the only species. Three other genera, *Microbacterium*, *Cellulomonas* and *Arthrobacter* are saprophytes of dairy products, the soil, dust and the skin, and are common as accidental contaminants of laboratory cultures.

All are gram-positive (or gram-variable), nonsporeforming, generally short, nonmotile, plump rods ranging around 1.0 by 8.0 μ in dimensions and exhibiting various degrees of pleomorphism. All are heterotrophic. Most species grow best on infusion media at 25° to 40° C. (pH 7.0 to 8.0) particularly if serum (or blood) and dextrose are added. Most species are aerobic or facultative and catalase-positive.

## 35.5   GENUS CORYNEBACTERIUM

Species of Genus *Corynebacterium* that are of importance to the farmer and veterinarian are: *C. pyogenes*, which is common in purulent lesions of cattle, swine and sheep; *C. equi*, causing pneumonia in foals; and *C. renale*, which causes a necrotic disease of the urinary tract in domestic livestock. In addition, the genus includes a number of important plant pathogens, such as *C. michiganese*, the cause of tomato wilt and canker, and *C. insidiosum*, cause of a destructive disease of

alfalfa. A few of the species from plants are motile. (Should they be included as species of true *Corynebacterium?*)

Except for motility, differentiations between species of corynebacteria are commonly made on the basis of morphology, fermentation reactions, pigment formation, gelatin liquefaction, pathogenesis and antigenic composition. In general, corynebacteria are not very active in attacking carbohydrates, proteins or fats.

From the standpoint of human health the two most important species are *C. diphtheriae*, cause of diphtheria, and the anaerobic *C. acnes*, implicated as a partial cause of acne, so often a temporary thorn in the flesh of the young and therefore beautiful.

*C. diphtheriae* is usually distinguishable by: (1) great variation in *length* of the cells, from coccoid to spindles or clubs 10 to 15 μ in length; (2) great variation in shape, from club-shaped to spermlike, needle-shaped or boomerang-shaped forms; (3) irregularity of arrangement often described as "Chinese-character configuration"; (4) conspicuous intracellular granules, bars and masses of *volutin** (Fig. 35.2) having marked affinity for *methylene blue*. The result of this affinity is that the granules, bars or the entire cell (depending on the distribution of the material in the cell) stain a *very intense blue or metachromatic* (red) color.

**Diphtheroids.** Species of corynebacteria having more regular length, form and arrangement, properties that distinguish them from

---

*Polymetaphosphates.

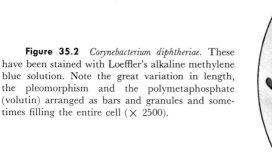

**Figure 35.2** *Corynebacterium diphtheriae.* These have been stained with Loeffler's alkaline methylene blue solution. Note the great variation in length, the pleomorphism and the polymetaphosphate (volutin) arranged as bars and granules and sometimes filling the entire cell (× 2500).

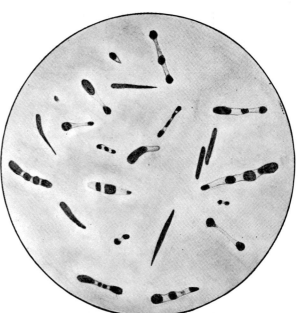

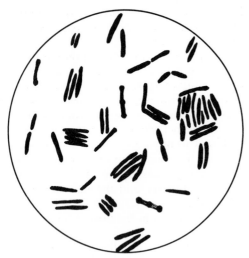

**Figure 35.3** *Corynebacterium xerosis,* a typical diphtheroid common in the normal throat of man. Compare with *C. diphtheriae* (Fig. 35.2). Note the comparative uniformity in size and shape and the occasional *C. diphtheriae*-like beaded cell. (Magnification about × 2000.) (Drawing of a methylene-blue-stained smear.)

*C. diphtheriae,* are spoken of collectively as *diphtheroids* (Fig. 35.3). They characteristically arrange themselves side by side in distinctively regular parallel rows spoken of as "palisade configuration." This is thought to result from their method of fission, in which incomplete breakage of the cell coatings leaves the two cells attached by a fragment that acts as a hinge, like the bark of a partly broken green twig, on which the two cells swing around by a "snapping movement" to lie side by side. Diphtheroids are generally nonpathogenic for man. Two common species found in humans are *C. xerosis* and *C. pseudodiphtheriticum.* Most species of *Corynebacterium* have similar *diphtheroidal* morphology.

The colonies of corynebacteria on solid media such as blood infusion agar are generally white or yellowish, opaque, round and range in diameter from about 1 mm. to 3 or 4 mm. They are usually soft and butyrous, but some species form irregular and brittle (R) colonies. Many species, especially the saprophytic species, form brilliant pigments.

## 35.6  DIPHTHERIA

Diphtheria is a specific disease caused by *Corynebacterium diphtheriae.* The organisms are transmitted in the same manner as others causing respiratory disease, i.e., by secretions of the upper respiratory tract. Healthy carriers are not uncommon and are doubtless sources of infection. The bacteria establish themselves on the mucous membranes, most commonly of the tonsils or pharynx and larynx and nares. In a susceptible person the bacilli set up an intense local inflammation with swelling and fibrinous, purulent exudate that forms a spreading *pseudomembrane.* As the bacteria grow they release diphtherial exotoxin. As pointed out in Chapter 15 the property of toxigenicity in *C. diphtheriae* is a result of *phage conversion.*

The toxin of *C. diphtheriae* is one of the most powerful biological poisons known. When the organisms infect the mucous membranes, this poison is absorbed by the blood and damages heart, kidneys, adrenals and nerves, and may cause death unless antitoxin is (a) already present as a result of previous infection or artificial immunization or (b) is developed rapidly by the cells of the patient as an anamnestic or secondary response or (c) is injected into him in the form of antitoxic serum from some outside source (passive immunity). The toxin is also very poisonous to rabbits, mice, guinea pigs and to chicks and other birds.

*Corynebacterium diphtheriae* is a classical illustration of virulence depending almost entirely on toxigenicity. This organism, although often growing extensively on the surfaces of the respiratory and other mucous membranes, has little ability to invade the tissues beyond the mucous membranes.

**Types of C. diphtheriae.**  Several types of *C. diphtheriae* have been recognized: gravis, mitis, minimus and intermedius. They are differentiated by characters shown in Table 35.3. The gravis types were thought to cause more severe and fatal diphtheria than the other types, but extensive studies in the United States have failed to support that view, since no constant correlation between cultural type and clinical severity of diphtheria has been found. All produce the same toxin.

**Immunity to Diphtheria.**  Some persons possess *natural, active,* specific immunity to diphtheria, resulting from *subclinical* attacks during early childhood. They retain their immunity throughout life, probably as a result of repeated reinfection. Their blood usually, but not always, contains a small amount of antitoxin, which helps combat ordinary infection.

**Active Artificial Immunization.**  Because today there are few cases and carriers of diphtheria, *natural* active immunization and repeated reinfections are much diminished. It is therefore desirable, and sometimes required by law for community protection, to immunize *artifi-*

**TABLE 35.3   CULTURAL CHARACTERS DIFFERENTIATING PRINCIPAL TYPES OF CORYNEBACTERIUM DIPHTHERIAE**

| Type | Sucrose | Fermentation of Glucose | Fermentation of Glycogen | Fermentation of Starch | Colonies* | Hemolysis in Broth† | Formation of Pellicle in Broth | pH of Broth‡ |
|------|---------|---------|----------|--------|-----------|---------------------|--------------------------------|--------------|
| Gravis | − | + | + | + | Low, rough; 2 to 4 mm. | − | + | 7.5 to 8.4 |
| Mitis | − | + | − | − | Domed, smooth; 1 to 2 mm. | + | − | 6.5 to 7.4 |
| Intermedius | − | + | − | − | Low, smooth; 0.5 to 1 mm. | + | − | 6.5 to 7.4 |
| Minimus | − | −§ | − | − | Flat, rough or smooth; less than 0.5 mm. | − | − | 6.5 to 7.4 |

\* On heated blood agar with tellurite.
† Mix 0.5 ml 48-hour broth culture with 0.5 ml 2 per cent washed human erythrocytes.
‡ In absence of glucose, after 5 days at 37°C.
§ In infusion broth, initial pH 7.8.

*cially.* The antigens used consist of harmless toxoids and are generally mixed with antigens against whooping cough and tetanus. Polio vaccine may be included also.

Any physician or health department will do this on request. The process requires only two (preferably three) injections of toxoid, alum-precipitated, given four to six weeks apart. Since this immunity wears away in time, it is customary to reimmunize with repeated small doses ("booster doses") one year later, and then every two to three years through 12 to 15 years of age.

**Passive Immunization.**   A child exposed to the disease by proximity to a diphtheria patient may have immediate need of antibodies to combat the disease or ward off infection. Endangered persons may, under special circumstances to be judged by the physician, receive immediate protection through injections of serum that contain large quantities of antitoxin. Injections of serum for any purpose are always to be avoided if possible because of dangers of allergy; Chapter 26.

### 35.7   GENUS *LISTERIA*

The organisms of Genus *Listeria,* named for Joseph, Lord Lister, British scientist, founder of aseptic surgery, are in most respects much like diphtheroids except that they are more regular in form and are *motile. Listeria* grows readily on blood and serum media at 37° C. and is facultative with respect to oxygen.

**Listeriosis.**   *Listeria* appears to be regularly pathogenic for man and lower animals, causing a febrile disease characterized especially by swollen lymph nodes and necrotic lesions in various organs (glandular fever) and the appearance in the blood of the organisms and large numbers of white cells, called *monocytes* —hence the type species name, *Listeria monocytogenes.*

### 35.8   GENUS *ERYSIPELOTHRIX*

The name of Genus *Erysipelothrix* (Gr. *erysipelo* = erysipelas; *-thrix* = thread) refers to the inflammation produced and the often-filamentous appearance of the organism. A farmer who has raised many hogs or poultry for market probably knows about swine erysipelas. Only the fortunate farmer has escaped the infection himself. *Erysipelothrix insidiosa,* the causative organism, is widely distributed in soil, dung, dust and sewage, and can infect sheep, birds, rodents and fish. It is a common cause of infection in commercial-fish handlers.

*E. insidiosa* in many respects resembles the diphtheroids. However, it is often pleomorphic and filamentous, like lactobacilli, especially in the R phase. It is nonmotile. Because of its tendency to filament formation it has sometimes been classified in the Actinomycetales. It is facultatively aerobic. It is quite resistant to preservatives like smoking, pickling, drying and outdoor conditions generally and therefore can persist stubbornly in barns, vats, dust and dirt of animal pens, buildings and vehicles where infected animals have been kept. It probably lives in soil as a saprophyte. It is transmitted by inhalation and ingestion of infected dirt and animal products, and by way of cuts and scratches.

**Swine Erysipelas.**   Swine erysipelas, caused by *E. insidiosa,* is usually slowly progressive, though the infection at times is highly and rapidly fatal in swine herds (and very costly to stock raisers). It can be isolated on blood agar from the dung, urine and lesions of infected animals. Because the reddish skin lesions are often roughly diamond-shaped, swine erysipelas is sometimes called *diamond disease.*

## SUPPLEMENTARY READING

Davis, J. G.: The Lactobacilli. Progr. Industr. Microbiol., *2*:1, 1960.

Foster, E. M., Nelson, F. E., Speck, M. L., Doetsch, R. N., and Olson, Jr., J. C.: Dairy Microbiology. Prentice-Hall, Inc., Englewood Cliffs, N. J. 1957.

Frazier, W. C.: Food Microbiology. 2nd ed. McGraw-Hill Book Co., New York. 1967.

Gemmell, M.: The physiological characters and flagellar arrangement of motile homofermentative lactobacilli. J. Gen. Microbiol., *35*:519, 1964.

Gray, M. L., and Killinger, A. H.: *Listeria monocytogenes* and listeric infections. Bact. Rev., *30*:309, 1966.

Hagan, W. A., and Bruner, D. W.: The Infectious Diseases of Domestic Animals. 4th ed. Cornell University Press, Ithaca, N. Y. 1961.

Hammond, B. F., Rosan, B., and Williams, N. B.: Encapsulated lactobacilli. II. Specific capsular reaction of *Lactobacillus casei.* J. Bact., *88*:1807, 1964.

Johnston, M. A., and Delwiche, E. A.: Distribution and characteristics of the catalases of Lactobacillaceae. J. Bact., *90*:347, 1965.

Rogosa, M., Franklin, J. G., and Perry, K. D.: Correlation of the vitamin requirements with cultural and biochemical characters of *Lactobacillus.* J. Gen. Microbiol., *25*:473, 1961.

# Chapter 36

# THE ENTEROBACTERIACEAE AND OTHER GRAM-NEGATIVE EUBACTERIALES

In the five foregoing chapters we have discussed mainly gram-positive bacteria belonging to the Order Eubacteriales. Here we turn to the Family Enterobacteriaceae and several other families of Eubacteriales that are gram-negative, nonsporeforming rods. Many of the species are extremely important in human activities such as medicine, agriculture and industry. They exhibit a wide variety of properties. Some are adapted to very specialized situations such as sea bottoms at 4° C. and thousands of pounds pressure per square inch, others to sun-warmed soils or heaps of decaying matter at 35° to 40° C. Many are adapted to very special ecological niches such as the intestinal tract of man and lower animals; some are highly specialized and fastidious parasites. Many species are motile; these species have *peritrichous* flagella. Nearly all are aerobic or facultative with respect to oxygen. An outstanding exception is the strictly anaerobic Family Bacteroidaceae that was discussed in Chapter 32 with the anaerobic bacteria. The other families, as arranged in the 7th edition of "Bergey's Manual" (1957) are: (1) Azotobacteraceae, (2) Rhizobiaceae, (3) Achromobacteraceae, (4) Enterobacteriaceae, (5) Brucellaceae. Some of their properties are listed for comparison in Table 37.1.

The Families Rhizobiaceae and Azotobacteraceae contain very highly specialized species that are important as causes of diseases of agricultural plants, e.g., *Agrobacterium,* and also the extremely valuable genus of *Rhizobium,* species of which are involved in the fixation of atmospheric nitrogen in symbiosis with leguminous plants. The Family Azotobacteraceae is highly important in nonsymbiotic fixation of nitrogen in the soil. Both these families are more fully discussed in Chapter 43, dealing with microbiology of the soil.

The Family Achromobacteraceae contains five genera: *Alkaligenes, Achromobacter, Flavobacterium, Agarbacterium* and *Benecka,* comprising species that in general are small (0.5 by 1.0 to 4.0 $\mu$) rods widely distributed, especially in aquatic and marine habitats, on seaweeds, in fish slime and soil. They are almost exclusively harmless saprophytes. Some are motile, others nonmotile. In spite of the family name, some produce red, yellow or orange carotenoid pigments. Most grow at temperatures ranging from 4° to about 30° C. All are aerobic or facultative. As a group they are not very active in fermentations, and rarely attack glucose or lactose anaerobically. One group (*Agarbacterium*) has the uncommon property of hydrolyzing the polysaccharide *agar,* a component of certain seaweeds (and of bacteriological culture media). Another group (*Benecka*) actively hydrolyzes *chitin,* the skeletal material of crustacea and of fungal cell walls. Several groups, especially *Flavobacterium* and *Agarbacterium,* are actively proteolytic. Altogether, the Family Achromobacteraceae constitute a group of well diversified and important scavengers.

Most species of the Family Enterobacteri-

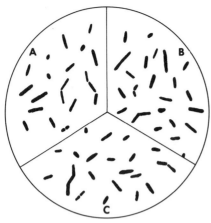

**Figure 36.1**   Representative forms and arrangements of: *A,* Enterobacteriaceae; *B,* Achromobacteraceae; *C,* Pseudomonadaceae. Drawing of smears from cultures; stained with methylene blue. (Magnification about × 1000.) Note that these organisms are morphologically indistinguishable.

aceae differ from the specialized, restricted and aerobic Rhizobiaceae and Azotobacteraceae in being able to thrive in a wide variety of habitats and under a wide range of environmental conditions. The Enterobacteriaceae are generally active fermenters of glucose and many other sugars and alcohols; many ferment lactose. Many Enterobacteriaceae can grow in simple mineral solutions with a little glucose or peptone, and they are also readily cultivable in a variety of media at temperatures from 25° to 37° C. at pH of 6.5 to 8.0. In size, Enterobacteriaceae commonly range from 0.5 to 2.0 $\mu$ in diameter and lengths of from 1.0 to 10 $\mu$ (Fig. 36.1). They have one other property that distinguishes them from many other facultative and aerobic bacteria: failure to produce either cytochrome oxidase or pectinase. Pectinase is produced by some pathogens of plants, the Genus *Erwinia,* which was formerly included with the Family Enterobacteriaceae. Other pectinase producers are found in the Family Pseudomonadaceae (Chapter 37).

## 36.1    THE FAMILY ENTEROBACTERIACEAE

Whereas many species of Enterobacteriaceae are primarily environmental saprophytes and scavengers, all are sometimes (i.e., from rarely to invariably) found in the intestinal tract of man or lower animals, hence the family name. Some are dangerous primary pathogens, others are potential or secondary pathogens. Because of the relationship to environmental

sanitation and to enteric diseases (typhoid fever, paratyphoid fevers, dysentery and infant diarrhea) and to infections of the urinary tract and other organs, a major facet of interest in, and research concerning, the Enterobacteriaceae centers around their taxonomy and the isolation and identification of the different species.

As arranged in "Bergey's Manual" (1957), there are some 60 species of Enterobacteriaceae. Numerous revisions of the 1957 arrangement have since been proposed. One now widely used was published in 1962 and represents the work of many authorities on Enterobacteriaceae. In this system the Enterobacteriaceae are arranged in four major divisions, each subdivided into two to four groups. These may be identified on the basis of physiological and biochemical properties shown in Table 36.1. It is evident that no single biochemical test or physiological property can be used alone to identify any member of the family. It is to be noted also that the demonstrability of various physiological and biochemical properties is greatly influenced by the cultural conditions and methods used for such purposes. As stated by Edwards and Ewing: "A source of difficulty in work with enteric bacteria is the great lack of uniformity in methods employed . . . in different laboratories . . . ." This is true of other groups, also.

**Selective Isolation.**   In practical diagnostic and sanitary bacteriology a time-honored (though imperfect) means of differentiation between the groups of Enterobacteriaceae has been the test for prompt (within 24 to 48 hours at 35° C.) fermentation of lactose. This property is the basis for selective media used for the isolation and preliminary identification of Enterobacteriaceae from feces, foods, water or sewage. Scores of selective media, both fluid and solidified with agar, have been devised over nearly a century of work with these organisms. Basically they all consist of peptone or meat extract or infusion broth containing 0.5 to 1.0 per cent lactose; substances such as bismuth sulfite, desoxycholate, citrate and eosin-methylene blue that inhibit extraneous organisms such as gram-positive cocci and sporeforming bacilli; and an acid-alkali indicator such as litmus, sulfite-reduced fuchsin or phenol red to detect acid formed by decomposition of the lactose. Most of the media are solidified with agar and are inoculated by streaking the agar in Petri dishes. They are then incubated 24 to 48 hours at 35° C.

Colonies of species that do not promptly ferment lactose are small, translucent and colorless on such media, whereas colonies of prompt

## TABLE 36.1 SUBDIVISIONS OF THE ENTEROBACTERIACEAE*

### Differential Properties (by Major Subdivision)

| Major Subdivisions | Indole[1] | Methyl Red | Acetyl-methyl-carbinol | Utilize Citrate | Splits Urea[2] | H$_2$S[1] | Phenylalanine deaminase[1] |
|---|---|---|---|---|---|---|---|
| Shigella-Escherichia | +(−)[8] | + | − | − | − | − | − |
| Salmonella-Arizona-Citrobacter | − | + | − | + | − | + | − |
| Klebsiella-Aerobacter-Serratia | − | − | + | + | − | − | − |
| Proteus-Providence | +(−) | + | − | +(−) | +(−) | ± | +(−) |

### Biochemical Properties of Genera and Groups

| Groups or Genera | β-D-galactosidase (ONPG test) | Lactose | Glucose (with gas) | Sucrose | Motility | Mannitol | KCN[3] | Gelat. | Urea[2] | Phenylalanine deaminase | H$_2$S[1] | Decarboxylates l-lysine | Deaminates l-lysine | Extracellular DNA-ase |
|---|---|---|---|---|---|---|---|---|---|---|---|---|---|---|
| Shigella | | −[4] | − | −[4] | − | ±[5] | − | − | − | − | − | −(+) | − | − |
| Escherichia | | + | + | + | + | + | − | − | − | − | − | + | −(+) | − |
| Salmonella | − | −[4] | +[6] | − | + | + | − | − | − | − | + | + | − | − |
| Arizona group | | +[4] | + | − | + | + | − | + | − | − | + | + | − | − |
| Citrobacter group | + | +[4] | + | ± | + | + | + | − | + | − | + | − | − | − |
| Klebsiella (Aerobacter B) | | + | + | + | − | + | + | − | + | − | − | + | − | − |
| Aerobacter A | | + | + | + | + | + | + | + | − | − | − | + | − | − |
| Haffnia[7] | | + | + | : | + | : | : | − | − | − | − | + | − | − |
| Serratia (Aerobacter C) | | − | ± | + | + | + | + | + | − | − | − | + | − | + |
| Proteus group | | − | ± | ± | + | ± | + | + | + | + | ± | +(−) | − | ± |
| Providence group (Proteus inconstans) | | − | + | −[4] | + | − | + | − | − | + | − | ± | −(+) | − |

*It must be understood that in describing any group of bacteria allowance must be made for variation, modification and mutation. Forms of any species not infrequently occur that are aberrant with respect to any physiological characteristic.

[1] Produced.
[2] Rapidly hydrolyzed.
[3] Grows in the presence of KCN.
[4] Some slowly positive.
[5] ± = variable.
[6] S. typhi acid but no gas.
[7] At 22° C.
[8] + or − in parentheses = some variants

lactose fermenters are usually deeply colored by the indicator. Colonies of desired types are fished to other media for further purification, gram-stain, verification of action on lactose, and species identification.

**Identification.** The several tests necessarily used in identification have been ingeniously arranged in numerous schemes, each an improvement over previous ones because of newer knowledge. In a scheme devised in 1966 the pure culture is first stab-and-streak inoculated into a slant of Kligler's iron-agar. This medium contains an iron salt (ferrous sulfide) that turns black if hydrogen sulfide is produced. It also contains lactose and sucrose and an acid-alkali indicator. After 24 to 48 hours at 35° C., rapid lactose or sucrose fermenters (e.g., *Escherichia coli* or *Aerobacter* sp.) produce gas and acid throughout the slant culture. If the butt (anaerobic part) is acid while the slant (aerobic part) is alkaline and ferrous sulfide has blackened the medium, the organism may be *Salmonella* or certain others (Fig. 36.2). Further group and species identifications are made on the basis of additional tests for motility, gelatin liquefaction, sugar fermentations, production of various enzymes such as urease, lysine decarboxylase, lysine deaminase and DNA-ase (Table 36.1).

Some species of Enterobacteriaceae do not ferment lactose rapidly but may do so after 4 to 7 days of incubation at 35° C. in lactose media. This may result from their containing genetic units that permit induction of beta-D-galactosidase (lactase) (Chapter 5), or the selection of lactose-fermenting mutants, or the induced formation of appropriate permeases by cells genetically capable of fermenting lactose but not permeable to it. Among slow-lactose-fermenting Enterobacteriaceae are some strains of *Escherichia coli*, the Arizona group, Haffnia, Citrobacter, *Shigella*, and *Serratia*. By the preliminary selective plating methods that have been described, these types can easily be mistaken for true nonlactose-fermenters because their colonies on lactose-indicator plates after 24 to 48 hours at 35° C. are colorless like those of the true nonlactose-fermenters. Special consideration and tests must be used to detect and identify such organisms.

Of the species that do not ferment lactose rapidly many are pathogenic: the typhoid bacillus (*Salmonella typhi*), paratyphoid bacilli (*Salmonella paratyphi A*), other *Salmonella* species and most dysentery bacilli (*Shigella* species). Slow-lactose-fermenters such as *Proteus*, Providence and Haffnia species are also pathogenic but usually cause only secondary, though often very

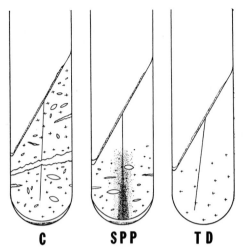

**Figure 36.2** Cultures of Enterobacteriaceae in an agar medium designed to differentiate major groups. The medium is triple-sugar-iron (T-S-I) agar. It contains lactose, glucose and sucrose with acid-alkali indicator. $FeCl_3$ is added to detect the formation of $H_2S$. The slants are inoculated on the surface and by a stab of the needle into the depths of the butt of the agar. *C* shows the reaction of coliform organisms: gas bubbles and acid (crosses) throughout the agar. Note that the volume of gas formed has rent the agar slant at several places and pushed the butt of the agar slant away from the bottom of the tube, where a few drops of bacterial suspension have collected. *SPP* shows the reaction typical of *Salmonella* organisms and also of some strains of *Proteus* and Arizona group: acid and gas, with formation of $H_2S$ (shading) in the butt; alkaline slant (upper portion). *TD* shows the reaction of *Salmonella typhi* and of the genus *Shigella* (typhoid-dysentery): acid butt, alkaline slant; no gas, no $H_2S$. Further differentiations are made on the basis of serological and additional biochemical tests.

troublesome, infections. *Serratia* (Aerobacter C) is rare in the intestinal tract but has caused numerous serious infections of other tissues. Many strains of *Serratia* are distinguished by the production on starchy media, at 22° C., of blood-red pigment; nonpigmented strains are common and can resemble pathogenic Enterobacteriaceae.

The rapid-lactose-fermenting types (*Escherichia, Klebsiella, Aerobacter* and Citrobacter) constitute the so-called "coliform" or "coli-aerogenes" groups. They are generally non-pathogenic (except certain strains of *Escherichia coli* that cause infant diarrhea and other diseases; see farther on).

## THE ESCHERICHIA COLI GROUP

**Genus *Escherichia*.** This genus comprises *E. coli* and several variants. All are of particular interest to the sanitarian since they occur commonly in the normal intestinal tract of man and animals. Their presence in foods or drinking water, therefore, may indicate fecal pollution. *Escherichia coli* is the most distinctively fecal species and is *always* found in the normal intestinal tract. Certain strains of *E. coli* cause mild to severe diarrhea, especially in infants. Although *E. coli* is also found in sewage and materials recently polluted by feces, it is not well adapted to continuous life in the outer world.

ESCHERICHIA COLI. *E. coli* is distinguished from all the other coliforms by its *inability* to utilize *citrate* in place of glucose as a *sole* source of carbon in an otherwise wholly inorganic medium. Other distinctive properties of *E. coli* and related organisms are given in Table 36.2.

ESCHERICHIA FREUNDII. *E. freundii* (Citrobacter group) is very similar to *E. coli* but commonly lives in the outer world as well as in the intestinal tract. Consequently its presence in foods or drinking water may or may not indicate fecal pollution. *E. freundii* is placed in the Citrobacter group and is called an *intermediate* because it has properties of the definitely fecal *E. coli,* on the one hand, and of the much less fecal *Klebsiella* and *Aerobacter* species, on the other hand. It is called *Citrobacter* because, although coli-like, it can utilize *citrate* as a sole source of carbon like the other coliforms (*Aerobacter* and *Klebsiella*).

AEROBACTERS A AND B. Aerobacters A and B are much like the coliforms but are more commonly found in soil and water than in the intestine. Aerobacter A is also known as *A. cloacae.* Closely similar to it is Aerobacter B or *Klebsiella aerogenes.* They differ mainly in that Aerobacter A (*A. cloacae*) is proteolytic, unencapsulated and motile, while Aerobacter B (*Klebsiella*) is nonproteolytic, capsulated and nonmotile. *Klebsiella* has dangerous pathogenic potentialities and is

a cause of pneumonia. It has long been known as *K. pneumoniae* or "Friedlander's bacillus."

**Differentiation of Coliforms.** The procedures for differentiating between the various coliforms are not technically difficult. Having obtained satisfactory pure cultures from either the standard or membrane filter method (page 442), tests are made of indole production, methyl-red reaction, the Voges-Proskauer reaction and ability to utilize sodium citrate as a sole source of carbon (Table 36.2). Technical details may be found in the supplementary reading at the end of this chapter.

IMViC FORMULA. A mnemonic (memory-aiding) device, IMViC, is often used with plus and minus signs to express differences between coliform organisms by means of a "formula." *I* stands for indole reaction; *M*, for methyl-red reaction; *V*, for the acetyl-methyl-carbinol test (originated by Voges-Proskauer); *i* is for the sake of euphony; and *C* stands for growth in mineral solution containing citrate as a sole source of carbon.

Thus, an organism of the coliform group designated as "IMViC + + − −" would be *E. coli*, since this gives positive indole and methyl-red reactions but negative Voges-Proskauer and citrate reactions. These symbols are used in Table 36.2.

THE EIJKMAN REACTION. A useful differential method, the *Eijkman reaction* is a good example of a temperature-dependent enzymic action. It is based on the fact that most strains of the fecal species of *E. coli* produce gas from lactose in a special, buffered broth when incubated at *exactly* 45.5° C.; whereas very few of the less frequently fecal strains of *Aerobacter, Klebsiella* and intermediates (e.g., *E. freundii*) do so.

A pure culture of the organism to be tested is inoculated into 0.3 per cent lactose-tryptose

**TABLE 36.2**  DISTINCTIVE PROPERTIES OF COLIFORM AND ASSOCIATED ORGANISMS

| Species | Lactose | Glucose | Sucrose | I | M | V | C | Gelatin | Motility |
|---|---|---|---|---|---|---|---|---|---|
| *Esch. coli* | ⊕ | ⊕ | ⊕ | + | + | − | − | − | + |
| *Esch. freundii* | ⊕ | ⊕ | ⊕ | − | + | − | + | − | + |
| *Klebs. aerogenes* | ⊕ | ⊕ | ⊕ | − | − | + | + | − | − |
| *Aero. cloacae* | ⊕ | ⊕ | ⊕ | − | − | + | + | + | + |
| *Proteus vulgaris* | − | ⊕ | ⊕ | + | − | − | + | + | + |
| *Providence group* | − | ⊕ | ⊕ | + | + | − | + | − | + |
| *Pseudomonas aeruginosa†* | − | − | − | − | − | − | ·· | + | + |

+ = Positive test.

− = Negative test.

⊕ = Acid and gas formed.

†Produces two water-soluble pigments; blue *pyocyanin* and yellow *fluorescein*. (See Chapter 37, Order Pseudomonadales.)

broth prewarmed to 45.5° C. and buffered at pH 7.4. The culture is held at 45.5° C. for 48 hours. The production of gas is a *positive* result (i.e., *Escherichia coli* is present). The reaction is extremely temperature-dependent, 0.2° C. downward fluctuation in temperature vitiating the test. The production of indole can be determined concomitantly if tryptophan-containing peptone is used.

## 36.2 POLLUTION AND THE COLIFORM GROUP

**Index Organisms.** Pollution of foods or water with fecal material, whether infected or not, is obviously undesirable, both from the standpoint of danger of infection and for purely esthetic reasons. The detection of fecal bacteria of any kind in food or domestic water is therefore of importance in determining its suitability for human consumption. For every typhoid bacillus or other pathogen (e.g., *Entamoeba histolytica,* or viruses of polio or hepatitis) in polluted water supplies or in any foods there are usually millions of coliform organisms or fecal streptococci. Either or both may serve as an *index of fecal pollution.* Methods for their detection and enumeration in water and foods are carefully prescribed by the American Public Health Association and affiliated societies, and are used daily in every health department laboratory. A series of steps (tests for coliforms), the *presumptive test, confirmed test* and *completed test,* are carried out systematically. These tests are applicable to any properly prepared samples of foods, water, fruit juices or dairy products (Fig. 36.3).

**Other Index Organisms.** Three other groups of bacteria invariably present in human (and animal) feces are: (a) fecal streptococci, especially *S. faecalis;* (b) *Clostridium,* especially *Cl. perfringens;* and (c) certain species of anaerobic lactobacilli (*L. bifidis*). These species are easily isolated from water, foods or dairy products by the use of relatively simple methods of selective cultivation and are readily identified. The first two especially are used frequently as indices of fecal pollution both in waters and foods.

STREPTOCOCCI. The enterococci are readily isolated by the use of selective media such as sodium-azide glucose broth. Sodium azide inhibits gram-negative bacteria especially. Tubes of such broth are often inoculated as a *presumptive test.* Streptococci growing in this medium are transferred to ethyl-violet-azide glucose broth. Ethyl violet and azide inhibit virtually all bacteria except fecal streptococci. This serves as a *completed test.* Streptococci growing in ethyl-violet-azide broth are almost certainly of human or fecal origin. Enterococci are rarely found in any but human feces, while *S. bovis* and *S. equinus* generally occur only in bovine, equine or other animal feces (see Table 34.1).

**Significance of Index Organisms.** The survival time of these indicator organisms in water is of significance (Fig. 36.4). The *fecal streptococci* seem unable to multiply significantly in open water and do not survive long. The *bifid lactobacilli* are quite unable to multiply and survive only a short time. Their presence in considerable numbers, therefore, suggests relatively recent pollution—a few hours or days. The *coliforms* generally outnumber the streptococci and, possibly being able to multiply to some extent in open polluted waters, may survive for weeks or months depending on conditions in the water. *Cl. perfringens,* because of its resistant spores, can survive indefinitely. The presence of this organism in the absence of the others, therefore, suggests pollution that may have existed for a considerable time if it occurred at all. Clostridia grow naturally in many soils and polluted waters.

None of these organisms is a perfect index of human pollution because all occur in the soil or in animal dung, or both, as well as in human excrement. Examination of any water or food for these index species must be supplemented by a sanitary survey-examination of the terrain for their proximity to sources of pollution. It is essential to know the danger of human fecal pollution before final conclusions can be drawn or legal restrictions on the use of a water supply or food instituted.

**The Membrane Filter Method.** Some of the difficulties in determining the presence of coliform organisms by the procedure shown in Figure 36.2 lie in the facts that: (a) only relatively small samples can be examined at one time; (b) several days are required for the incubations of the successive cultures; (c) the test is largely qualitative; only relatively rough estimates of numbers of coliform organisms being feasible; (d) it requires considerable amounts of expensive medium and equipment; (e) it is not readily done in the field on the spot, but necessitates transportation of samples to the distant laboratory, with accompanying risk of deceptive changes in coliform content of the samples.

By means of membrane filters (see Chapter 20) it is possible to filter rapidly, on the spot, and immediately after collection, large samples of water or other fluid samples to be tested for coliform or, indeed, any and all organisms that

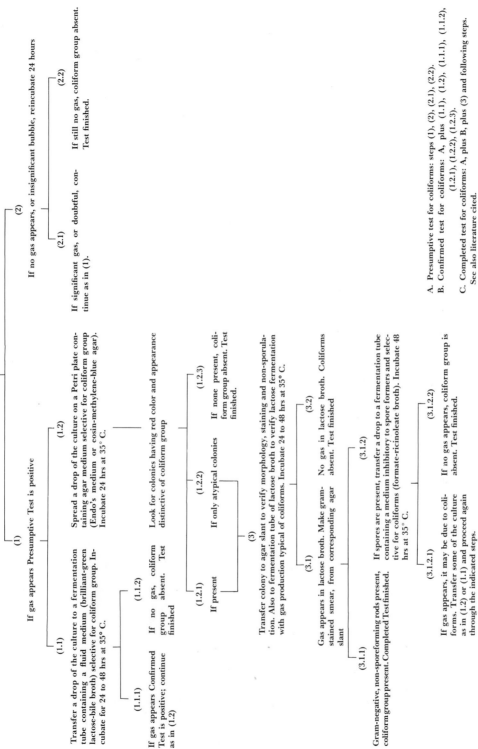

**Figure 36.3** Outline of official completed test for coliform organisms in fluids. (Adapted from "Standard Methods for the Examination of Water and Waste-water." 12th Edition, 1965, American Public Health Asso., New York 19, N.Y.)

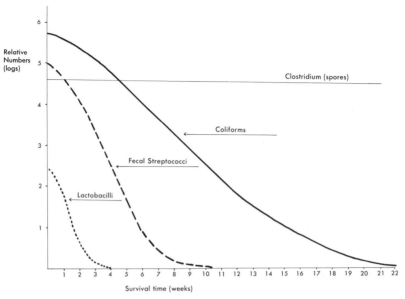

**Figure 36.4**   Approximate curves of survival of various organisms used as indices of sewage pollution of water. These are merely hypothetical curves, based on data from various situations and types of pollution, and so are subject to considerable variation.

will grow under these particular conditions. The bacteria in the sample are held on the surface of the filter membrane (Fig. 36.5). By methods, adopted as standard by the American Public Health Association in 1965, it is possible, within 24 hours at 35° C., not only to enumerate the coliform colonies by their distinctive color but to finish the procedures involved in the confirmed test in the procedure outlined in Figure 36.3.

Filter membranes cannot be used with water or other fluids (e.g., whole blood, fruit juice) containing any considerable amount of algae, silt or sediment likely to clog the filter, or with samples heavily contaminated with noncoliforms. The standard lactose-broth test and the standard membrane filter method do not measure the same flora, and neither gives results that, on the basis of present knowledge, may be expressed accurately in terms of the other. However, each is a recognized and reliable method.

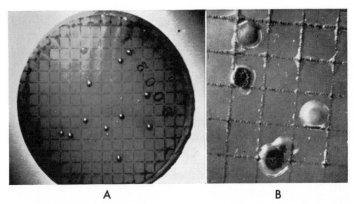

**Figure 36.5**   *A,* Membrane or ultrafilter disk with colonies of *Escherichia coli.* The disk is on a circular pad saturated with Endo medium, which is selective for coliform organisms. *Esch. coli* colonies are seen here as dark and glistening (about actual size). They are actually deep magenta in color and have a green-violet metallic iridescence. *B,* Section of membrane filter disk with colonies of coliform organisms. *Escherichia coli* colonies appear here as whitish, opaque, and slightly mounded. *Klebsiella aerogenes* are larger, more mucoid, with dark centers (× 4). (Photos courtesy of Environmental Health Center, U. S. Public Health Service, Cincinnati, Ohio.)

## 36.3   GENUS *PROTEUS*

*Proteus* species, although common in decaying matter, soil and water, also are often found in the human intestine and in infections of the urinary or intestinal tract; they also cause diseases in lower animals. Most *Proteus* species are active in fermentation and, since they also actively decompose proteins, they are valuable scavengers. As shown in Table 36.1, they fail to ferment lactose and, being actively motile, are sometimes mistaken for *Salmonella* (paratyphoid) species. The power to *hydrolyze urea rapidly* is a distinctive character of *Proteus* that is used in differential diagnosis. Cultures of *Proteus* usually have a disagreeable, fetid odor.

**H and O Colonies.**   Many strains of *Proteus* are distinctive in that their colonies usually spread rapidly in the microscopic film of moisture on the surface of freshly poured solid media, forming a thin, grey, almost transparent film which may escape notice entirely unless it is especially sought. This form of growth is designated as the *H form*, or *swarming* (Fig. 36.6). The bacilli are actively motile. An aflagellate, nonmotile variant form of *Proteus* occurs (called the *O form*), of which the colonies are small, discrete and circular. These terms, H and O, are of importance in taxonomic and diagnostic work. They refer to flagellar (H) antigens and somatic (O) antigens. (See page 317.)

## 36.4   PATHOGENIC ENTEROBACTERIACEAE

The most important pathogens of the family Enterobacteriaceae are comprised in the genera *Salmonella* and *Shigella*.\*

---

\*The apparently meaningless generic names *Salmonella* and *Shigella* are derived from names of famous bacteriologists. *Salmon* was an American microbiologist noted for his work on hog cholera (1885). *Shiga* was the Japanese bacteriologist who first determined the cause of highly fatal epidemics of dysentery in Japan in 1896.

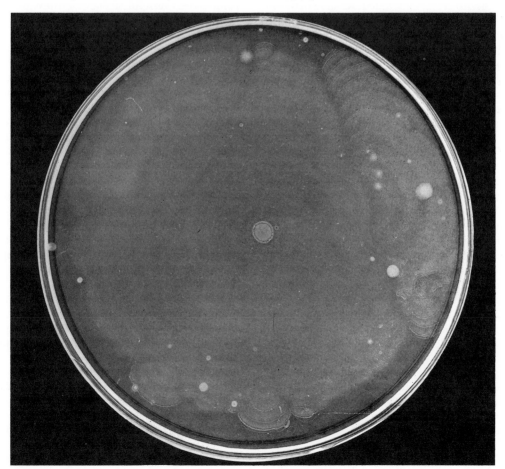

**Figure 36.6**   Speading ("Hauch" or H) form of growth of *Proteus* sp., over the surface of moist agar (largest portion). Sectors are also seen showing a modified or adapted form of growth appearing toward the periphery as the medium dries. (Approximately actual size.) (From Hughes: J. Gen. Microbiol., vol. 17.)

**TABLE 36.3**   DIFFERENTIAL PROPERTIES OF SOME SALMONELLAS*

| Species | Xylose | Trehalose | Arabinose | H₂S | Citrate Agar† | Gas in Dextrose |
|---|---|---|---|---|---|---|
| *S. typhi* | v | + | – | + | – | – |
| *S. paratyphi A* | – | ⊕ | ⊕ | – | – | + |
| *S. paratyphi B* | ⊕ | ⊕ | ⊕ | + | + | + |
| *S. paratyphi C* | ⊕ | ⊕ | ⊕ | + | + | + |
| *S. enteritidis* | ⊕ | ⊕ | ⊕ | + | + | + |
| *S. typhimurium* | ⊕ | ⊕ | ⊕ | + | + | + |
| *S. cholerae-suis* | ⊕ | – | – | – | + | + |

⊕ = Acid and gas.

+ = Positive test or acid only.

v = Variable.

*Variants are not rare

†Growth with citrate as sole source of carbon.

The genera most likely to be confused with *Salmonella* and *Shigella* because of slight, slow or absent fermentation of lactose are *Proteus* and species of the Providence group. These are readily differentiated by the physiological characters shown in Table 36.1.* All of the Enterobacteriaceae are closely allied, as shown by the fact that antigenic relationships are commonly found between species in all genera in the family. Further, some species have identical biochemical properties. Consequently, in identifying species it is frequently necessary to go through a complex serological process called *antigenic analysis,* using adsorbed sera (Chapter 24), before the true status of an organism is known; even then the position of some is left in doubt.

**Genus Salmonella.** The salmonellas cause infections (commonly called *salmonellosis*) in man and many species of domestic and wild animals. The resulting diseases are characteristically gastrointestinal, but may be septicemic (bloodborne) and completely generalized in the body. Salmonellosis may range in severity from almost imperceptible intestinal discomfort to fatal disease (notably in typhoid fever). The habitat of the organisms is mainly the intestinal tract and tissues of infected animals, but the organisms can grow in feces-polluted foods and may survive in polluted or infected foods, waters and on fomites for periods of from a few hours to days.

Of the salmonellas, *S. typhi* (the cause of typhoid fever) and the so-called "food-poisoning," or paratyphoid, group (*S. paratyphi A, S. paratyphi B, S. paratyphi C, S. typhimurium, S. enteritidis,* and *S. cholerae-suis*) are among the most important. There are over 300 named types (serotypes) including the above. New types are frequently reported. Many of these names are derived from the place where the organism was found, as for example, *senftenberg, newport, kentucky* and *mississippi.* Representative species of principal groups of *Salmonella* may be differentiated by the biochemical tests shown in Table 36.3. Further differentiations (serotypes) are based on antigenic structure.

**Antigenic Analysis.** With a collection of adsorbed, monovalent agglutinating sera (Chapter 24), each representing a single different antigenic component of the various species of *Salmonella,* one may test any given organism for the presence of different H and O antigenic components, and assign to it a "formula" expressing the antigenic complex of which it is composed.

**Kauffmann-White Schema.** By means of such antigenic analyses the salmonellas have been arranged in a series called the *Kauffmann-White Schema.* In this schema the O (somatic) antigens are given Arabic numbers. The flagellar (H) antigens have two series of numbers, depending on *phase variations:* small letters if in phase I; Arabic numbers if in phase II. The antigenic structure of any given species may therefore be expressed in terms of these numbers and letters. For example, *S. typhimurium* has the antigenic formula, 1, 4, 5, 12: i; 1, 2 (see Table 36.4). Species having one or more *somatic* antigens in common are placed in convenient groups: A, B, C and so on.

Similar antigenic schemes are found in other groups of bacteria such as *Clostridium, Shigella, Klebsiella, Corynebacterium,* and *Escherichia.*

VARIATION OF SPECIES. A confusing feature of such antigenic analysis is the fact that by various procedures, including transduction, one type may readily be changed into another! Un-

---

*It must be understood that in describing any group of bacteria allowance must be made for variation, modification and mutation. Aberrant forms of any species may occur.

**TABLE 36.4   ANTIGENIC FORMULAS OF SOME SALMONELLA SPECIES**

| Group | Species | O Antigens | H Antigens Phase I | H Antigens Phase II |
|-------|---------|-----------|------------------|-------------------|
| A | *S. paratyphi A* | 1, 2, 12 | a | ... |
| B | *S. paratyphi B* | 1, 4, 5, 12 | b | 1, 2 |
|   | *S. typhimurium* | 1, 4, 5, 12 | i | 1, 2 |
| C₁ | *S. paratyphi C* | Vi, 6, 7 | c | 1, 5 |
|   | *S. choleraesuis* | 6, 7 | c | 1, 5 |
| D | *S. enteritidis* | 1, 9, 12 | g, m | ... |
|   | *S. typhi* | Vi, 9, 12 | d | ... |
| E₄ | *S. senftenberg* | 1, 3, 19 | g, s, t | ... |

doubtedly such changes also occur in nature. New types are constantly being found.

Closely associated with the O antigens of Enterobacteriaceae is another antigen common to all species of these bacteria. It is called a "common antigen" (CA). CA differs from O antigen in being soluble in 85 per cent alcohol. It is highly antigenic when separated from O antigen, has marked opsonic activity and can be identified by hemagglutination tests. Its presence is masked by the presence of overlying group-specific O antigens.

## SALMONELLOSIS

*Salmonella,* like all of the Enterobacteriaceae, is transmitted by feces or urine, or both, of patients or carriers. A common vector for all of them is feces-soiled hands. Another is food that has become infected and allowed to stand in a warm place after little or no cooking so that the organisms can grow. These organisms grow well at warm room temperatures (65° to 100° F.). Infection of the food is sometimes by unwashed hands of a person with a very mild infection, or a human carrier.

Food *infection* (often incorrectly called "food poisoning") may also be caused by introduction of excrement of dogs, mice, rats, flies or cockroaches that harbor, particularly, *S. typhimurium* as well as other salmonellas. So-called "meat-poisoning" often results from eating or handling raw or improperly cooked flesh of cattle, swine, poultry, fish, or other animals suffering from infection with these organisms, especially *S. cholerae-suis* and *S. enteritidis.* These species are among the most commonly occurring in the United States. Even hens' eggs are often infected, before being laid, by maturation in an

infected hen. The eating of raw egg or egg products is therefore not wise, and has resulted in large outbreaks of salmonellosis caused by raw eggs in mayonnaise used in sandwiches (Fig. 26.2).

Obviously, avoidance of these diseases means cleanliness in the kitchen; sanitary habits on the part of food handlers; care to see that food is properly cooked to kill all organisms, even those in the center of large masses; proper refrigeration of stored food; and avoidance of uncooked hand-prepared foods at club suppers or on picnics. Foods are often prepared during the morning or previous evening and then unwittingly incubated in the kitchen or in transit. *Salmonella* food infections are very common. Characteristically the onset is at least 10 (usually 18 to 24) hours after eating the infected food. The bacteria multiply during this incubation period.

**Typhoid Vaccination.**   Probably most students will have received typhoid "shots" at some time before studying microbiology, especially if they have seen military service. These injections are a good example of a method of active artificial immunization. The material injected is saline solution containing about one billion *Salmonella typhi* per milliliter killed by heating at about 65° C. for 30 minutes, or with formaldehyde. Sometimes included are killed *S. paratyphi A* and *S. paratyphi B.*

For initial immunization two doses (0.5 ml., and 1.0 ml.) at 3 to 6 week intervals are required. Revaccination with small doses every 3 or 4 years (0.1 ml. intracutaneously or 0.5 ml. subcutaneously) is recommended in order to maintain immunity at an effective level. This is a good example of the use of the secondary antigenic stimulus, or booster dose (Chapter 25).

## GENUS SHIGELLA AND BACILLARY DYSENTERY

The organism discovered by Shiga in 1896 during a frightful epidemic of dysentery in Japan with over 22,000 fatalities is now called *Shigella dysenteriae.* It is the type species of the genus. The principal distinguishing characteristics of the genus are shown in Table 36.5. After Shiga's discovery many other kinds ("species") of dysentery bacilli were discovered by Flexner, Boyd, Sonne and others. Except *S. sonnei,* each represents several serotypes. The classification and differentiation of these species and serotypes present problems analogous to those related to classification of the salmonellas. H antigens are not involved. (Why?)

TABLE 36.5   SOME CULTURAL REACTIONS OF THE SHIGELLAS*

| Serological Group | Principal Species | Mannitol | Lactose | Sucrose | Indole Production |
|---|---|---|---|---|---|
| A | *Shigella dysenteriae* | − | − | − | − |
|   | *Shigella ambigua* | − | − | − | + |
| B | *Shigella flexneri* | + | − | − | ± |
| C | *Shigella boydii* | + | − | − | ± |
| D | *Shigella sonnei* | + | Slowly + | Slowly + | − |

\* There are exceptions to most of the reactions, in aberrant strains.

**Bacillary Dysentery.** The shigellas cause intestinal disturbances ranging from very mild diarrhea to severe and sometimes fatal dysentery with intense inflammation and ulceration of the large bowel, often with scar formation and stricture of the bowel after recovery. Unlike *Salmonella typhi,* which always causes bacteremia, *Shigella* does not commonly invade the blood. In some epidemics of bacillary dysentery, especially those caused by *S. dysenteriae,* the fatality rate is high.

The transmission and prevention of bacillary dysentery are similar to those aspects of salmonellosis, except that animals do not transmit dysentery.

DYSENTERY VACCINATION. Vaccination against bacillary dysentery appears to be much less satisfactory than typhoid vaccination and is rarely practiced in the United States.

### ESCHERICHIA COLI

If given a large enough dosage and sufficient opportunity, such as a very dirty wound or an old, slowly healing ulcer, *Escherichia coli* may act as a secondary invader, especially if the patient's general health and nonspecific resistance are low. *Escherichia coli* may cause more serious trouble by invading the bladder and pelvis of the kidney after surgery or instrumentation. It produces a stubborn and dangerous inflammation. In the bladder this is called *cystitis;* in the pelvis of the kidney, *pyelitis. Proteus* and *Pseudomonas* species are often also involved.

Extensive studies of bacteria in the feces of infants with diarrhea show that many cases of infantile diarrhea can be traced to certain particular kinds of *Escherichia coli.* These pathogenic strains can be distinguished from other strains of *E. coli* only by immunologic studies of their antigenic structure. Some of these strains of *E. coli* are designated as O26:K60(B6):H11; O55:K59(B5):H6; O111a, 111b:K58(B4):HZ

and so on. The numbers and letters refer to O, K and H antigens in the organisms. At least 12 such strains are known.

These organisms and *Pseudomonas aeruginosa* are particular nuisances in children's institutions and nurseries. They are spread about by hands and fomites, as are other enteric pathogens, and at times are very difficult to eradicate.

### 36.5   GENUS *ERWINIA*

This important group is named for one of America's outstanding pioneers in the field of plant microbiology and pathology, Erwin F. Smith. *Erwinia* was formerly included in the Family Enterobacteriaceae because it resembles the coli-typhoid-dysentery organisms in some respects. Erwinias differ in that they are not typically found in the intestines but in the soil associated with infected plants. They invade the tissues of living plants, producing various pathologic and destructive conditions. Representative species are *E. carotovora* which, by means of a pectolytic enzyme common in *Pseudomonas* and *Xanthomonas* (Chapter 37) but not found in Enterobacteriaceae, liquefies the tissues of carrots, cabbage, iris and egg-plant, causing the condition called *soft rot* (Fig. 37.3); and *E. tracheiphila,* which grows so extensively in the sap channels of cucumber, melon and related plants as to occlude the channels and, like *Pseudomonas,* cause the disease known as *wilt* (Fig. 37.4). *Erwinia* is not now included with Enterobacteriaceae though it is still listed among Enterobacteriaceae in the 1957 edition of "Bergey's Manual." Its exact systematic position remains to be established.

### 36.6   FAMILY BRUCELLACEAE

Like the Enterobacteriaceae, these organisms are small, straight, asporogenous, gram-negative rods (Table 37.1). Only one species is motile. Unlike the Achromobacteriaceae, Pseudomonadaceae and Enterobacteriaceae, these organisms represent the highly evolved or specialized type of bacteria that require complex organic media and special nutrients for their optimum growth. They are not markedly fermentative or proteolytic. In general, unlike most Enterobacteriaceae, they lack the enzymic versatility and the ruggedness necessary for significant *growth* in the outer world, although they may *survive* for some time. No saprophytic species in this family is known. All appear to cause disease in man or lower mammals.

**Genus *Pasteurella*.**   *Pasteurella* is named for Pasteur, who founded the science of immunology on his studies of vaccination against *Pasteurella avicida,* the cause of fowl cholera. *P. avicida* is now regarded as a variant of the type species of the genus, *P. multocida.* Other variants of *P. multocida* previously named for animals in which they were found as the cause of disease were: *P. bovicida* (cattle), *P. suilla* (swine), *P. muricida* (rats). They differ from one another only slightly in biochemical properties. *P. multocida* and its variants are highly pathogenic for most birds and animals; less so for man. They may be transmitted by blood, pathologic exudates and bites of animals. They can inflict tremendous losses on the stock and poultry industries by causing *hemorrhagic septicemia* ("shipping fever"). The species causing *bubonic plague* in man is *P. pestis.* Any infection with any species of *Pasteurella* is properly spoken of as *pasteurellosis.*

The morphology of *Pasteurella* is distinctive. In pathological material the organisms are short, oval rods about 0.5 by 3 $\mu$, which tend to stain most heavily at the tips (*bipolar staining*). In cultures the bipolar appearance is often less definite (Fig. 36.7).

*Pasteurella multocida* can survive in, and is transmitted by, infectious dust, fomites and animal secretions from stables, railroad cars and stockyards. The organisms invade the lymphatic system and blood (*septicemia*), and may easily be cultivated on infusion media from all of the organs and body fluids of heavily infected animals. There are many small hemorrhages on various internal mucous surfaces, in the skin and in the internal organs—hence the name *hemorrhagic* septicemia. In the animal disease there is much exudation of fluid from nose, mouth and eyes.

## PASTEURELLA PESTIS

From the standpoint of human disease the most important member of the genus is *P. pestis,*

the cause of bubonic and pneumonic plague in man. Morphologically and culturally, *P. pestis* resembles *P. multocida* but is slower and less vigorous in its growth and somewhat less active biochemically.

**Bubonic Plague.**   This malady is the classic example of a bacterial disease transmitted by the bite of an insect. It is primarily a disease of rodents; a *zoonosis.* It is conveyed to human beings by the bite of infected fleas, commonly *Xenopsylla cheopis* and *Ceratophyllus fasciatus,* the rat fleas. The fleas usually derive the plague bacilli from the blood of infected rats, notably *Mus norvegicus* (sewer rat) and *Mus rattus* (house rat). When the rats are infected they show lesions similar to those found in man.

Rats and rat fleas maintain plague as an epizootic disease, much like hemorrhagic septicemia, among themselves for long periods and act, therefore, as an *animal reservoir* of plague bacilli. When rats become excessively prevalent in any community, human plague is apt to occur because the opportunity for rat fleas to bite human beings greatly increases. Crowded populations living near dumps or in dirty, unsanitary conditions suffer most. Conditions following the devastation of war, with breakdown of disease-control systems, are ideal for the development of rats and therefore of rat-borne diseases. The pages of history are filled with disasters to armies and civil populations attacked by plague. Daniel Defoe's "Journal of the Plague Year" and Winsor's "Forever Amber" give dramatic descriptions of the plague in London in 1665. The rats often die in great numbers from the disease, and the fleas leave the cooling bodies by jumping on to the first warm animal which passes. Dead or dying rats are, therefore, potentially dangerous.

In 1900, plague was first found in human beings in this country. It has since been found in rats and in rodents other than rats, especially ground squirrels or prairie dogs. Many human cases have since been traced to contact with wild rodents. The disease in woodland- or wild-living creatures is often spoken of as *sylvatic* (forest) or *campestral* (prairies) plague. The control of plague in wild rodents is a field problem of great importance.

## PASTEURELLA (FRANCISELLA) TULARENSIS

This organism much resembles *P. pestis* and *P. multocida* but is somewhat more exacting in its nutritional requirements. As discovered by Francis, little or no growth occurs unless cystine or (what amounts to the same thing) some compound containing the sulfhydryl ($^-$SH) group,

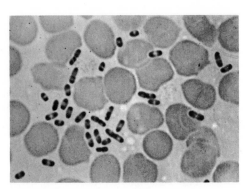

**Figure 36.7** Stained smear of blood of mouse with septicemia due to *Pasteurella pestis.* Note minute size (about 1 by 2 μ) and distinctive bipolar staining. (Courtesy of Naval Biological Laboratory.)

is added. Tryptose broth with thiamine, cysteine, glucose, ferric sulfate, potassium chloride, histidine, tris buffer and agar can be used with excellent results. This medium is also good for *P. pestis,* *Brucella* sp. and other fastidious bacteria.

*P. tularensis* is found in much the same ecological relationship to rodents (rabbits, gophers, mice), biting insects (wood, dog and rabbit ticks; rabbit lice, deer flies, horse flies) and man as are *P. pestis,* fleas, and rodents. *P. tularensis* causes a disease called *tularemia.* (The name is derived from the Tulare swamps in California where early observations were made on this disease.)

**Tularemia ("Rabbit Fever").** This is a plague-like disease in many American rodents and other wild animals. As in other pasteurelloses, there are enlargements of regional lymph nodes, swelling of the spleen, and the appearance of tubercle-like nodules in spleen, liver and elsewhere. The bacilli invade the blood from these foci as in other pasteurelloses. *P. tularensis,* the etiological agent, can also infect man.

One common means of transmission of tularemia is through the handling of infected wild rabbits, as in the marketing of these animals for food and pelts; hence *rabbit fever.* In some sections of the country the disease is known as *deer fly fever,* being transmitted largely by the deer fly, *Chrysops discalis.* In Arkansas and adjacent regions the disease is largely tick-borne. It causes enormous losses among sheep if they graze in areas where there is tick-infested undergrowth. *P. tularensis* has been isolated from forest streams. The water is apparently infected by the carcasses of infected wild animals dying in the stream or on its nearby banks, another reason for disinfecting drinking water from questionable sources during field trips.

## 36.7   GENUS *BRUCELLA*

*Brucella melitensis* and two closely related species, *Br. abortus* and *Br. suis,* cause *Malta fever* or undulant fever in man, a disease common in most parts of the world. The generic name of the causative organisms is derived from the discoverer, Bruce, a British scientist. Bruce first (1887) found the organism now called *Br. melitensis* on the island of Malta* in the spleens of persons infected by the organisms in goats' milk. Brucellas are very small (0.3 to 0.5 μ long), nonmotile, nonsporeforming rods without distinctive morphological features.

*Br. abortus* was first known as the cause of abortion in farm animals, especially cattle. It was discovered by a Danish worker, Bang, in 1895 and is still often called *Bang's bacillus,* and the disease in cattle, *Bang's disease.*

*Br. suis,* commonly found in swine, was first observed by Traum in the United States in 1914.

The fact that the organisms discovered in 1887 in Malta, in 1895 in Denmark, and in 1914 in America are all closely similar species or variants of one type was revealed in 1918 by Evans in the United States.

Because of the frequent presence of these organisms in the blood and tissues of farm animals, persons in contact with them are likely to become infected. Thus meat packers, cattlemen, hog raisers, persons who drink uncertified or unpasteurized milk, bacteriologists and veterinarians most frequently contract the disease.

**Isolation.** Brucellas grow rather slowly on first isolation from the blood, milk or tissues of infected animals, or from the blood of man. They may be cultivated on slightly acid (pH 6.8) beef-liver infusion agar, or on tryptose or trypticase soy agar or broth. (See also under *P. tularensis.*) Exemplary selective media are used in isolating *Brucella* from contaminated material like feces. Selective agents may include polymyxin B, penicillin, Actidione, brilliant green or crystal violet. These inhibit contaminants but not *Brucella* or *Pasteurella.* *Brucella* can also be isolated from blood by injecting it into living chick embryos. *Brucella abortus* will grow at first *only* in an atmosphere containing about 7 to 10 per cent carbon dioxide. The three species are closely similar but may be distinguished by special tests (Table 36.6). Specific phages (brucellaphages) have been found useful in the differentiation of these organisms.

---

*Malta was called Melita by the ancients because of the fine honey (Gr. *meli* = honey) found there; hence, *Melitensis.*

**TABLE 36.6**   USUAL DIFFERENCES BETWEEN BRUCELLA SPECIES*

|  | *Br. abortus* | *Br. melitensis* | *Br. suis* |
|---|---|---|---|
| *Sensitive to:*† |  |  |  |
| Thionine | + | − | − |
| Fuchsine | − | − | + |
| Saffranine O | − | − | + |
| Pyronin | − | − | + |
| Crystal violet | − | − | + |
| *Ferment:* |  |  |  |
| Inositol | + | − | − |
| Maltose | − | − | + |
| *Requires* $CO_2$‡ | + | − |  |
| *Produce:* |  |  |  |
| Urease (4 hours) | + | − | + |
| $H_2S$§ | 2–4 days + | 1–2 days + | 4–8 days + |
| *Brucellaphage* ‖ | + | − | +** |

\*There are "unusual" types in *all* biological groupings.
†Cannot grow on agar containing the dye.
‡For initial isolation.
§Expressed as days of incubation during which $H_2S$ is continuously produced
from culture media.
‖ Undiluted
\*\*Negative if highly diluted (critical dilution).

**Survival and Distribution.**   *Brucella* species can survive for considerable periods in dairy products, water, soil, dung, dust and meats, and are transmitted by these vectors. The blood of infected man and animals and tissues and fluids associated with aborted animals are highly infectious.

The three species, though originally associated with certain animals, are not restricted to those animals, but each may occur in any of the three species mentioned, as well as in man, dogs, horses and possibly poultry.

## 36.8   GENERA *HAEMOPHILUS*, *BORDETELLA* AND *MORAXELLA*

All the organisms in these genera are morphologically similar small (0.3 by 2 $\mu$) rods, though they are pleomorphic and often vary from coccoid to long, filamentous or distorted forms. Only one species (which probably should be classified elsewhere) is motile (to be discussed). None forms spores. They are among the most highly adapted and fragile parasitic and pathogenic bacteria, with fastidious nutrient requirements. Most grow well on *"chocolate agar"* (i.e., infusion agar, with about 10 per cent blood, heated to 90° C. for 10 minutes) though some require special nutrition. They are aerobic and facultative.

The Genus *Haemophilus* (Gr. *haemo* = blood; *philus* = requiring) includes *H. influenzae*\* and

several other pathogenic species, notably *H. ducreyi*, cause of the venereal disease, *chancroid* (soft chancre).

The hemophils are excellent instances of the highly adapted and dependent bacterial parasite. For example, *H. influenzae* cannot live without certain blood components. One of these, long known as the *X factor*, is the iron complex called *heme*, which is part of the red coloring matter of erythrocytes. Besides heme, *Haemophilus* requires for growth a *V factor*, identified as coenzyme I or nicotinamide-adenine-dinucleotide (NAD) or NADP, found in the electron-transfer system of many types of cells: plants, yeasts, many bacteria. *H. ducreyi* requires X but not V (Table 36.7).

*Moraxella*† is a very similar organism that causes infectious conjunctivitis (*"pink eye"*). It has been suggested that the organisms of the group of Mimeae (see page 418) be included in this genus.

**Bordetella.**   Genus *Bordetella* includes *Bor. pertussis*, the cause of whooping cough, discovered by Belgian scientists Bordet (Nobel Prize winner) and Gengou in 1906. On initial isolation from patients these organisms are truly and rigidly hemophilic like *H. influenzae*, but on subculture soon become adapted to growth without either X or V factor. They do, however, require nicotinic acid ("niacin"), a part of the NAD coenzyme molecule. On potato–glycerine–20 per cent blood agar the colonies are distinctive, being hemolytic and resembling minute pearls.

---

\*Formerly thought to cause influenza. Influenza is now known to be caused by influenza virus.

† Morax was a famous French ophthalmologist.

**TABLE 36.7**  SOME DIFFERENTIAL PROPERTIES OF *HAEMOPHILUS* AND *BORDETELLA*

| Organism | Usual Habitat | Production of | | Growth Factors Required | | | Motility | Brown Color in Peptone Agar | Urease Produced | Colonies on Blood Agar | Fermentation of Glucose |
|---|---|---|---|---|---|---|---|---|---|---|---|
| | | Indole | NaNO$_2$ | X | V | Nicotinic Acid | | | | | |
| *H. influenzae* | Resp. tract (man) | ± | + | + | + | − | − | − | − | Small, "dewdrop" (some hemolytic) | + |
| *H. ducreyi* | Genitalia (man) | − | | + | − | − | − | − | − | Small, gray, hemolytic | ± |
| *B. pertussis* | Resp. tract (man) | − | − | +* | +* | + | − | − | − | Tiny, pearl-like, hemolytic | − |
| *B. parapertussis* | Resp. tract (man) | − | − | +* | +* | + | − | + | + | Resemble *B. pertussis* | − |
| *B. bronchiseptica* | Resp. tract (animal) | − | + | − | − | + | + | − | + | Large, white, like *E. coli* | − |

*Requires neither after subcultivation.

(Adapted from Ripins: Medical Licensure Examinations, 10th ed. J. B. Lippincott Co., Philadelphia, 1965.)

Two other species (*Bor. parapertussis* and *Bor. bronchiseptica*) are similar to *Bor. pertussis* antigenically and in causing pertussis-like disease. *Bor. bronchiseptica* differs markedly in being actively motile and able to grow on simple organic media such as peptone solution. It has at different periods been classified as a species of *Alcaligenes*, *Brucella* and *Haemophilus;* a sort of taxonomic orphan waif.

## SUPPLEMENTARY READING

Drinking Water Disinfection. U. S. Public Health Service Publn. No. 387. Govt. Printing Office, Washington, D. C.

Edwards, P. R., and Ewing, W. H.: Identification of Enterobacteriaceae. 2nd ed. Burgess Publishing Co., Minneapolis. 1962.

Edwards, W. M., et al.: Outbreak of typhoid fever in previously immunized persons traced to a common carrier. New England J. Med., *267*:742, 1962.

Ewing, W. H., Johnson, J. G., and Davis, B. R.: The occurrence of *Serratia marcescens* in nosocomial infections. U. S. Public Health Serivce, Com. Dis. Center, Atlanta, Ga. 1962.

Guinée, P. A. M., Kampelmacher, E. H., Willems, H. M. C. C., and Spithout, H.: Twelve new *Salmonella* types. Ant. Leeuw. *30*:168, 1964.

Guinée, P. A. M., and Mossel, D. A. A.: The reliability of the test of McKenzie, Taylor, and Gilbert for the detection of faecal *Escherichia coli* strains of animal origin in foods. Ant. Leeuw. *29*:163, 1963.

Henderson, A.: *Pasteurella multocida* infection in man; a review of the literature. Ant. Leeuw., *29*:359, 1963.

Hoogendijk, J. L.: *Pasteurella* strains isolated from human sputum. Ant. Leeuw., *28*:315, 1962.

Huddleson, I. F.: Enhancement of colonial growth of brucellae on beef liver agar. J. Bact., *88*:540, 1964.

Johnson, J. G., Kunz, L. J., Barron, W., and Ewing, W. H.: Biochemical differentiation of the Enterobacteriaceae with the aid of lysine-iron-agar. Appl. Microbiol., *14*:212, 1966.

Jones, H. E., and Park, R. W. A.: The influence of medium composition on the growth and swarming of *Proteus*. J. Gen. Microbiol., *47*:369, 1967.

Parnas, J.: *Brucella* Phages, Properties and Application. Albert J. Phiebig, P. O. Box 352, White Plains, N. Y. 1963.

Pickett, M. J., and Calderone, J. G.: Criteria for the identification of *Brucella* species. Amer. J. Pub. Health, *53*:655, 1963.

Pickett, M. J., and Goodman, R. E.: $\beta$-Galactosidase for distinguishing between *Citrobacter* and *Salmonella*. Appl. Microbiol., *14*:178, 1966.

Prost, E., and Riemann, H.: Food-borne salmonellosis. Ann. Rev. Microbiol., *21*:495, 1967.

Rothberg, N. W., and Swartz, M. N.: Extracellular deoxyribonucleases in members of the Family Enterobacteriaceae. J. Bact., *90*:294, 1965.

Smith, R. S., and Bodily, H. L.: Use of a methylene blue azide medium for isolation of enterococci. Appl. Microbiol., *15*:1087, 1967.

Steele, J. H., and Galton, M. M.: Epidemiology of food-borne salmonellosis. Health Lab. Sci., *4*:207, 1967.

Tresselt, H. B., and Ward, M. K.: Blood-free medium for the rapid growth of *Pasteurella tularensis*. Appl. Microbiol., *12*:504, 1964.

Valu, J. A.: Use of the deoxyribonuclease test as an aid in the differentiation of Paracolobactrum (*Hafnia*) from *Serratia*. J. Bact., *91*:467, 1966.

von Graevenitz, A., and Strouse, A.: Isolation of *Erwinia* spp. from human sources. Ant. Leeuw., *32*:429, 1966.

# Chapter 37

## THE PSEUDOMONADACEAE
## AND THE SPIRILLACEAE

The Order Pseudomonadales (Gr. *pseudes* = imitating; *monas* = a monotrichous, flagellate protozoan) as arranged in the 1957 (7th) edition of "Bergey's Manual" is the largest and most heterogeneous of the ten orders of the Class Schizomycetes. A radical rearrangement of this order has been proposed. Like the Enterobacteriaceae, the bacteria of this order are generally simple, undifferentiated, rod-shaped (a few are curved or spiral) cells with diameters of 0.7 μ and lengths of 8 μ, though some species approach 15 μ in diameter and lengths up to 100 μ (Table 37.1). None forms spores and all are gram-negative. Motile forms have single or several *polar* flagella that may be mono- or lophotrichate. Unlike the Enterobacteriaceae, Pseudomonadaceae are never peritrichate.

The order is divided into two suborders. The members of the Suborder Rhodobacteriineae (Chapter 38) are alga-like in that they contain photosynthetic pigments. None contains chlorophyll *a*, which is found in *all other*

photosynthetic cells. *Bacteria\* might therefore be defined as procaryons without chlorophyll a.* So far as is known none of the Suborder Rhodobacteriineae is pathogenic for plants or animals. The Suborder Pseudomonadineae does not contain any species with photosynthetic pigments, but many of the species, unlike any other bacteria, produce blue, greenish and yellow pigments that are water-soluble and diffusible and sometimes fluorescent. Some species form nondiffusible, carotenoid pigments. Most of the Suborder Pseudomonadineae are saprophytes of the environment; a few species of the Genus *Pseudomonas* are pathogenic for man or lower animals. Many of the Genus *Xanthomonas* are pathogenic for plants: none for animals.

Several specialized groups of the Order Pseudomonadales are discussed elsewhere in this book: Suborder Rhodobacteriineae; Families

---

*Including rickettsias and chlamydias.

**TABLE 37.1**   PROPERTIES OF ENTEROBACTERIACEAE AND SOME OTHER GRAM-NEGATIVE EUBACTERIALES

| Family | Gram stain | Spores | Metabolism | Form | Flagellation (if motile) | Relation to oxygen | Pigment formation |
|---|---|---|---|---|---|---|---|
| Enterobacteriaceae | Neg. | — | Fermentative | Straight rod | Peritrichous | Facultative | Few species |
| Achromobacteraceae | Neg. | — | Oxidative | " | " | " | Many species |
| Brucellaceae | Neg. | — | " | " | " | " | None |
| Pseudomonadaceae | Neg. | — | " | " | Polar | Aerobic | Common |
| Spirillaceae | Neg. | — | " | Curved or spiral; rigid* | Polar | Facultative | Few species |
| Azotobacteraceae | Neg. | — | Oxidative; fix N | Rods; pleomorphic | Peritrichous | Strict aerobes | Brown |
| Rhizobiaceae | Neg. | — | Some fix N symbiotically in root nodules | Rods; pleomorphic | Peritrichous | Facultative aerobes | One species violet |

* Distinguish from *flexible* Spirochaetales.

Caulobacteraceae, Siderocapsaceae and families that contain species of autotrophs that are highly specific in respect to inorganic source of energy: oxidation of $^-NH_3$ and $^-NO_3$ (Family Nitrobacteraceae); oxidation of $H_2S_2O_3$, S, $FeSO_4$ (Thiobacteraceae); oxidation of $H_2$, CO, $CH_4$ and $CH_3OH$ (Methanomonadaceae) and several others. Here we shall discuss only the Family Pseudomonadaceae. These are generally chemoorganotrophic and aerobic or facultative, having the general characters of the Suborder Pseudomonadineae given above.

## 37.1   FAMILY PSEUDOMONADACEAE

Pseudomonadaceae is a very large group comprising some 150 species of the Genus *Pseudomonas*, 75 of the Genus *Xanthomonas* and about 35 other species in 10 genera ("Bergey's Manual," 1957 edition). Most species of *Pseudomonas* are of importance mainly as scavengers in sewage and in marine and fresh waters, the soil and in decomposing organic matter generally. Many species in the Family Pseudomonadaceae are of marine origin and many are very tolerant of high (3 to 30 per cent) salt concentrations, i.e., *halotolerant*. Some are parasitic on fish.

Some others that exhibit remarkable properties are:

1. Acetomonas (polar flagellate *Acetobacter* —the "vinegar bacteria") that oxidize alcohols to vinegar (Chapter 47);
2. *Aeromonas*, parasitic on fish, that produce acid and gas from glucose and are often confused with *Aerobacter* species of Enterobacteriaceae although they do not produce gas from lactose (anaerogenic *Aerobacter?*);
3. *Azotomonas*, agriculturally important soil species that can synthesize their own proteins using the nitrogen of the air (nitrogen fixation);
4. *Photobacterium*, marine species that are associated with luminescence of light-organs of deep-sea fish and with luminosity of many other fish and decaying organic matter;
5. *Zymomonas*, that produce ethyl alcohol like yeasts;
6. *Halobacterium*, obligate halophils restricted to a life in nutrient solutions containing at least 12 per cent of salt, commonly found in the Dead Sea, Great Salt Lake (27 per cent salinity), salted fish, and pickling brines (30 per cent salinity).

Several of these microbiological curiosities are discussed elsewhere in this book.

The aerobic pseudomonads have been investigated intensively with a view to additional knowledge and an improved taxonomic arrangement. An exhaustive study by Stanier et al. included *Pseudomonas, Xanthomonas, Methanomonas, Hydrogenomonas, Comamonas, Vibrio, Acetomonas, Alginomonas, Cellulomonas* and *Cellvibrio*. Eliminated were: Caulobacteraceae, Siderocapsaceae, Chlamydobacterales, *Aeromonas, Zymomonas, Photobacterium*, some *Vibrio, Desulfovibrio*, Rhodobacteriineae, Nitrobacteraceae, Thiobacillaceae and chemoheterotrophic spirilla.

The organisms included are, with few exceptions, strict aerobes that never exhibit fermentative metabolism, but utilize carbohydrates oxidatively (unlike Enterobacteriaceae). The included genera are sufficiently alike in all other basic properties of the Pseudomonadaceae to constitute a distinct taxonomic group. They do not produce indole or acetyl-methyl carbinol and are methyl-red negative. This group is further characterized by the ability of these species to use, as sources of carbon and energy, scores of different organic compounds of many different chemical types under aerobic conditions of growth. The enzymes involved appear to be inducible.

These organisms may be divided into three major groups as shown in Table 37.2. Most of the species mentioned can be further divided into biotypes on the basis of additional physiological tests: organic compounds used, egg-yolk reaction, lipase production, reduction of sodium nitrate, base composition of DNA, and others.

Here we may briefly describe, as representative of the Pseudomonadaceae, two of the largest genera in the Class Schizomycetes: *Pseudomonas* and *Xanthomonas*.

### GENUS PSEUDOMONAS

Members of the Genus *Pseudomonas* are among the most common and widely distributed bacteria. As previously indicated, they are enzymically active, metabolizing a wide variety of proteins, fats, carbohydrates and other organic compounds including such aromatic compounds as phenol and naphthalene, and hydrocarbons. Thus they are excellent and ubiquitous scavengers. They are principally aerobic; a few are facultative. They are found in soil, fresh waters and ocean waters and decomposing fish and other organic matter, including sewage. Only two representative species can be detailed at

**TABLE 37.2**   DIFFERENTIAL CHARACTERS OF AEROBIC PSEUDOMONADS††

| Groups | Grow at | | Utilize pbha* | Produce phenaz.† | Pigment fluor.‡ | Oxidase | Catalase |
| | 4° C. | 41° C. | | | | | |
|---|---|---|---|---|---|---|---|
| **Fluorescent:** | | | | | | | |
| *Pseudomonas aeruginosa* | −(+) | +(−)§ | − | +(−) | + | + | + |
| *P. fluorescens* | | | | | | | |
| *P. putida* | | | | | | | |
| others | | | | | | | |
| **Acidovorans:** | | | | | | | |
| *P. acidovorans* | −** | −** | + | − | − | + | + |
| *P. testosteroni* | | | | | | | |
| others | | | | | | | |
| **Alcaligenes:** | | | | | | | |
| *P. alcaligenes* | − | + | − | − | − | + | + |
| *P. pseudoalcaligenes* | | | | | | | |
| *P. multivorans* | | | | | | | |
| *P. stutzeri* | | | | | | | |
| *P. maltophila* | | | | | | | |

\* Poly-beta-hydroxybutyric acid
† Phenazine
‡ Fluorescent
§ (+) = a few +; (−) = a few negative
\*\*Grow well at 20 to 30°C.
††Adapted from Stanier, Palleroni and Doudoroff (see references).

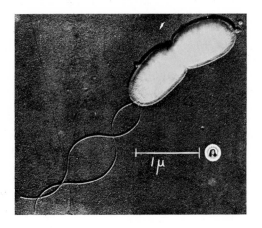

**Figure 37.1** Electron micrograph of *Pseudomonas fluorescens,* a dividing cell. Note the polar flagella. The cytoplasm appears to have shrunken away from the cell wall, probably due to drying. Note the line indicating 1μ at this magnification and the small portrait of Leeuwenhoek, the symbol of the American Society for Microbiology. (Courtesy of The American Society for Microbiology and Drs. Houwink and Van Iterson.)

**Figure 37.2** Phage-like autoplaques (AP) produced by spontaneous autolysis of a mucoid (M) strain of *Pseudomonas aeruginosa* (strain M⁺AP⁺) on agar medium in a Petri dish (upper portion of plate). In the lower portion is seen the growth of a variant that fails to produce AP (strain M⁺AP⁻). Some nonmucoid strains may also produce plaques (M⁻AP⁺). The phenomenon may be related to phage but the exact role of phage if any remains to be demonstrated. (From Berk and Gronkowski: Ant. Leeuw., *30*:141, 1964.)

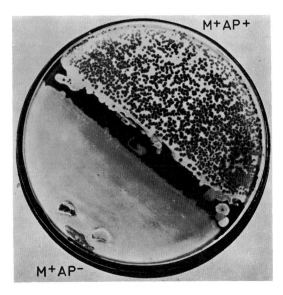

this point. One of the commonest species is *Pseudomonas fluorescens.*

Most strains of *Pseudomonas fluorescens* produce a greenish-yellow, water-soluble, fluorescent pigment in cultures. *Ps. fluorescens* grows best at about 22° C. and not at 37° C. There are numerous similar species, widely distributed and extremely important as causing decomposition of petroleum fuels, asphalt and many foods and other substances (Fig. 37.1).

**Pseudomonas aeruginosa.** *Ps. aeruginosa* is type species of the genus. In addition to the greenish-yellow pigment characteristic of many *Pseudomonas,* it produces a turquoise-blue pigment, *pyocyanin,* which may be extracted from broth culture with chloroform. When cultivated on agar media it typically produces phagelike plaques (autoplaques) of self-lysis (Fig. 37.2).

*Ps. aeruginosa* is a common saprophyte but is not infrequently found as an opportunist or secondary or even primary invader in wounds or ulcers that have not healed promptly in animals or man. The two pigments of the organism give a blue-green color to the pus (hence the name of the pigment: *pyo* = pus; *cyanin* = blue). *Ps. aeruginosa* does not grow at 30° C. but grows well at 37 to 42° C.

Some outbreaks of diarrhea in adults and especially among newborn children are said to be caused by this organism. *Ps. aeruginosa* is also able to cause a leaf-rot disease in tobacco and lettuce and a fatal disease in poultry. The organism may be isolated on agar media containing $K_2HPO_4$, $MgSO_4$, $K_2SO_4$, asparagine, proline and alcohol.

Thus, this versatile organism illustrates several of the properties common in this family: production of *water-soluble* pigments, activity as a general scavenger in a wide range of habitats, pathogenicity for plants and also for animals. Some of its other properties are shown in Table 36.2.

U. S. military activities in Vietnam have given prominence to a curious and dangerous disease called *meloidosis.* It is caused by a Pseudomonas-like organism called *P. pseudomallei,* and is contracted from lower animals.

## GENUS XANTHOMONAS

There are about 75 species of *Xanthomonas,* many of which are extremely important as pathogens of plants. They cause great losses to farmers, fruit-growers, horticulturists, lumber industries and others dependent on the vegetable kingdom. In most respects *Xanthomonas* is very

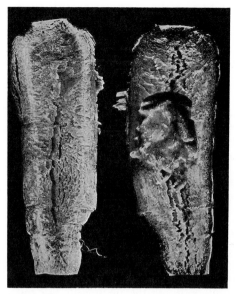

**Figure 37.3**   *Right,* soft rot of carrot due to inoculation with *Erwinia carotovora* and incubation for 3 days at 23° C. The inoculum was taken from a rotting raw potato. The carrot was first washed, soaked in disinfectant and then cut with a cold, sterile knife. The uninoculated part (*left*) remained sound. (Erwin F. Smith.)

much like *Pseudomonas;* several *Xanthomonas* were formerly classified as *Pseudomonas* and vice versa. The name *Xanthomonas* is derived from the Greek word, *xanthus,* for yellow, since *Xanthomonas* characteristically produces a *water-insoluble* yellow pigment on suitable media.

**Xanthomonas and Plant Disease.** Several species of *Xanthomonas* (and also several of molds, *Pseudomonas* and *Erwinia*) produce protopectin-

**Figure 37.4**   Bacterial wilt disease in a tomato plant due to *Pseudomonas solanacearum.* Note the wilted stems and leaves. (Courtesy of U. S. Dept. of Agriculture, Bureau of Plant Industry.)

**TABLE 37.3   SOME BACTERIAL PLANT PATHOGENS**

| Bacterium | Disease Produced |
|---|---|
| *Erwinia tracheiphila* | Wilt of cucumbers and melons |
| *Erwinia carotovora* | Soft rot of many species of plants |
| *Pseudomonas solanacearum* | Rot of potato and tomato |
| *Pseudomonas savastanoi* | Blight of olives |
| *Xanthomonas hyacinthi* | Yellow rot of hyacinth bulbs |
| *Xanthomonas pruni* | Blight of plums and peaches |

hydrolyzing enzymes. Protopectins are a group of gumlike polysaccharides constituting the intercellular cement substance that binds plant cells together. When the protopectin is destroyed by protopectinase the plant cells fall together in a slimy mass; the plant is said to have a *soft rot* and often dies (Fig. 37.3). *Protopectinases* are, so far as plant pathology is concerned, analogous to the hyaluronidases produced by several bacterial pathogens of mammals: *Staphylococcus aureus, Streptococcus pyogenes* and *Clostridium perfringens.* Hyaluronidases decompose *hyaluronic acid,* which is an intercellular cement substance of animals, analogous in function to protopectins of plants. Microorganisms that produce hyaluronidase are thus better able to penetrate between the tissue cells of animals and invade the host.

Numerous other species of *Xanthomonas,* which may or may not produce protopectinase, are the cause of destructive leaf spots, wilts (Fig. 37.4), and other diseases in many species of plants. Examples of some bacterial diseases of plants and the causative organisms are listed in Table 37.3. Some plant pathogens produce soluble toxic substances also.

## 37.2   FAMILY SPIRILLACEAE

Species of the Family Spirillaceae are curved or spiral rods. Otherwise, most have the general properties and habitats of the Family Pseudomonadaceae as described earlier in this chapter. The line of demarkation between the two families, especially the curved rods, is often obscure. Most species of Spirillaceae are saprophytes. However, there are a few dangerous pathogens of man and lower animals: *Vibrio comma,* cause of Asian cholera; *V. fetus,* cause of infectious abortion in farm animals and capable of infecting man; *Spirillum minus,* cause of rat-bite

fever or *sodoku* in man. There are also important soil-scavenger species: *Cellvibrio* and *Cellfalcicula,* which, as their names imply, digest cellulose as well as other organic wastes, including substances related to paraffin and phenol; the sulfate-reducing *Desulfovibrio,* mentioned elsewhere (Chapter 43) in connection with sulfur bacteria; curious species (*Methanobacterium*) in mud and stagnant water, which produce methane by the *reduction* of carbon compounds (compare Methanomonadaceae that *oxidize* methane); marine species such as *V. luminosus,* which give off an eerie blue-green light when growing on sea-water media or dead fish. (See also *Photobacterium* in Pseudomonadaceae.)

## GENUS VIBRIO

The name of the Genus *Vibrio* is derived from the exceptionally rapid to-and-fro motility of these organisms (L. *vibrare* = to vibrate). Vibrios are short rods that are typically curved like a comma; each is a portion of a spiral turn (Fig. 37.5). They often remain attached end to end after fission, forming long spirals. The length of the individual vibrios seldom exceeds 10 $\mu$, their diameter 1.0 to 1.5 $\mu$. Some are strictly aerobic, some facultative and some strictly anaerobic. They are principally saprophytic, and are world-wide in distribution in polluted rivers and lakes. Most grow readily in peptone media.

Many so-called "species" greatly resemble each other, having similar habitats, physiological properties, and sharing several somatic and flagellar antigens. Many are named for the place where they were isolated: *V. danubicus, V. gindha* and *V. massauah.* Some vibrios, like

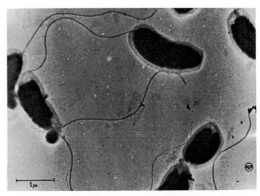

**Figure 37.5** Electron micrograph of typical vibrios (*Vibrio comma*). Note curved cells and polar flagella. Compare with Figure 37.1. (Courtesy of American Society for Microbiology and Drs. Anderson and Pollitzer.)

*V. metchnikovi* (named for its discoverer, *Metch-nikoff*), are pathogenic for guinea pigs and pigeons, which is not true of *V. comma* unless special methods of injection are used.

**V. comma.**   *Vibrio comma* (discovered in the feces of cholera patients by Koch in 1884) is the cause of Asian or classical cholera. It resembles other vibrios in living for long periods, possibly multiplying, in polluted river and lake waters. Various strains of *V. comma* are recognized: the Inaba, Ogawa and Hikojima varieties and others. These differ mainly in protein and carbohydrate structure (Linton groups) and in antigenic structure. The H or flagella antigens are not highly specific; the O antigens are. Three type-specific O antigens are recognized: A, B, C. The Inaba group is AC; the Ogawa group, AB; the Hikojima type, ABC.

EL TOR VIBRIOS.   The *El Tor* vibrios (isolated from pilgrims at a quarantine station at El Tor on the Sinai peninsula) are another cause of cholera or "paracholera" prevalent in the regions around Malaysia and India. El Tor vibrios and *V. comma* and the diseases they cause are very similar indeed. Considerable confusion exists as to the distinction between El Tor vibrios and the classical *V. comma*. The El Tor vibrios are strongly hemolytic when broth cultures are mixed with a suspension of sheep or goat erythrocytes and incubated for 4 to 6 hours (the Greig test). *V. comma* is not hemolytic (Greig negative) under these conditions. However, nonhemolytic variants of El Tor vibrios are not uncommon. Other tests may be used (Table 37.4). In tests of hemolysis in blood-agar plates the El Tor vibrio usually produces hemolysis and no *hemodigestion; V. comma* causes destruction of the erythrocytes but by a process of hemodigestion rather than lysis. The relation between El Tor vibrios and *V. comma* remains to be fully clarified.

**Isolation.**   Most intestinal vibrios (and especially *V. comma*) grow at the surface of nutrient liquids in response to need for oxygen.

They prefer a pH of 8 to 9. This pH retards the growth of many of the bacteria associated with vibrios in fecal material. These vibrios also metabolize peptone and hydrolyzed egg rapidly. Therefore, very rapid growth occurs at the surface of alkaline-egg-peptone solutions (Dieudonné medium) inoculated with feces of cholera patients. Transfers from the surface film of such cultures after six to eight hours of incubation often yield almost pure cultures of *V. comma*. This is a good example of selective *enrichment*.

The colonies on agar are small, colorless and distinctively translucent. Most intestinal vibrios, including *V. comma*, are markedly proteolytic, liquefying gelatin and digesting casein.

**Classic (Asiatic) Cholera.**   Cholera is characterized by an intense diarrhea and prostration, due to toxins of the vibrios. These are intracellular substances that are liberated by mechanical disruption of the cells. Great damage is done to the patient by the excessive and rapid dehydration which is a consequence of the diarrhea. The stools are thin, watery and turbid with mucus, and are frequently described as *rice water stools*. They contain large numbers of microscopically demonstrable cholera vibrios. Cholera is transmitted primarily by feces and sewage-polluted drinking water and foods.

Less than a century ago, cholera was to be found in practically every large city in the world. It occurred often in places with a large transient population, or in centers for religious, military or other concentrations of large numbers of people with no effective sanitary provisions with regard to sewage and pollution of water and food. In medieval Europe and later in America, cholera was an ever-present and often widespread and fatal scourge. It has played a sinister and strictly nonpartisan role in many disastrous military campaigns.

Cholera is found today mainly in the Orient. Sanitary engineering of sewage disposal and water supplies and constant vigilance by inter-

**TABLE 37.4**   DIFFERENTIATION OF EL TOR VIBRIO FROM *V. COMMA*

|  | El Tor | *V. comma* |
|---|---|---|
| Hemolysis {Tube | + (−)* | − |
|           {Plate | + (−) (no hemodigestion) | − (hemodigestion) |
| Susceptibility to phage specific for *V. comma* (phage type IV) | − | + |
| Slide agglutination of chicken erythrocytes | + | − |
| Virulence for chick embryos | + | − |
| Agglutination with Ogawa (O group I (A) serum) | + | + |
| Resistant to polymyxin antibiotic | + | − |

*A few are negative.

national health authorities and the activities of federal, state, and local sanitary administrations in North, Central and South America have succeeded in eliminating cholera from the Western Hemisphere. One case was reported in the United States in 1965. By contrast, during an epidemic of cholera in 1958 there were nearly 50,000 (known) cases and over 20,000 (known) deaths in India, East Pakistan, Thailand, Cambodia and Burma. Travelers from the United States to cholera areas are required to be vaccinated against cholera.

**V. fetus.**   *Vibrio fetus* is an important species because it causes abortion and considerable reduction in fertility in sheep, cattle and horses and consequent serious economic losses among stock raisers in the United States. It can infect humans handling tissues of infected animals.

*V. fetus* is a rather highly adapted parasite. It apparently thrives only in the genital organs of male and female domestic mammals (possibly also in wild animals). The infection appears to be transmitted only by coitus. The organisms grow only on very moist organic media in small, translucent, colorless colonies. The slender, curved, individual cells are morphologically much like *V. comma*. The best means of diagnosis is by isolation of the organisms from the animals suspected. Chemically defined media for isolation and growth of *V. fetus* are now available.

**Bdellovibrio bacteriovorus.**   One of the most interesting species of vibrios was first described in 1962. It is called *Bdellovibrio bacteriovorus* (Gr. *bdella* = leech; L. *vorare* = to eat). *B. bacteriovorus* is a minute (0.3 by 2.0 μ) comma-shaped rod with a single polar flagellum. It is unique among all known bacteria in being an obligate, predatory parasite of bacteria. It has not so far been cultivated in the absence of living cells. It has been found in activated sludge (Chapter 42). It appears to be most commonly associated with species of *Pseudomonas* and a few other gram-negative bacteria, including *Salmonella.*

Unlike organisms that in nature require the mere presence of growth products of associated bacteria (e.g., *Spirillum volutans*), these minute vibrios actually absorb the contents of other bacteria like leeches, hence their name. The vibrios move at very high speeds. With phase microscopy they can be seen to collide violently with the host (perhaps *victim* is a better term) bacterial cell, become attached and cause prompt lysis of the attacked cell. The attachments of the vibrios to their prey are sometimes reversible and repeatable and often multiple. The predators apparently live on the contents of the lysed cells; the vibrios continue to multiply long after the disappearance of all intact cells. The vibrios can also penetrate inside the host cells and metabolize the entire cell contents (Fig. 37.6).

If a culture of susceptible bacteria is mixed with a few cells of *Bdellovibrio* and the mixture then spread to grow as a "lawn" on an agar surface, the lawn will show plaques closely resembling plaques of phage (Fig. 37.7). The plaques are sites of the lytic action of the vibrios. That the plaques are not due to phage is clear from the facts that: plaques appear only after two days of incubation (*B. bacteriovorus* grows slowly) instead of within 18 hours or less as is true of phage plaques; the parasitic vibrios can be isolated from the plaques in greatly increased numbers; the plaque-forming units can easily be filtered or centrifuged out of the suspended growth so that the supernatant fluid or filtrate has no plaque-forming power. This is the reverse of phage. Unlike phage, the vibrios can also lyse heat-killed cells, if provided with some sterile lysate from another culture as a "starter" on which to grow before any of the new cells are lysed.

## GENUS SPIRILLUM

With the single exception of *Spirillum minus,* this genus contains only harmless saprophytes and scavengers living, along with vibrios, in stagnant or polluted water and putrefying materials.

**Morphology.**   Most saprophytic spirilla are relatively large, ranging from 5 to 40 μ in length though only 0.5 to 3 μ in diameter. They are spirally twisted through one to five complete turns (Fig. 37.8), rigid, and are motile by means of one or more flagella at one or both poles.

**Cultivation.**   *Spirillum* species usually grow with difficulty on first isolation, are generally catalase-positive and require aerobic conditions and organic sources of carbon and energy. Some of them have been obtained in pure culture from infusions of stagnant water, dung or sewage enriched with peptone, meat or fish. After a few days at 25° to 30° C. the fluid usually swarms with these and other microorganisms. In one method for obtaining pure cultures, the surface fluid from such an infusion is sterilized and used as a medium by solidifying it with 2 per cent agar. It is poured into Petri dishes. Colonies of some species of *Spirillum* can be obtained by inoculation of the agar surface with the unsterilized infusion.

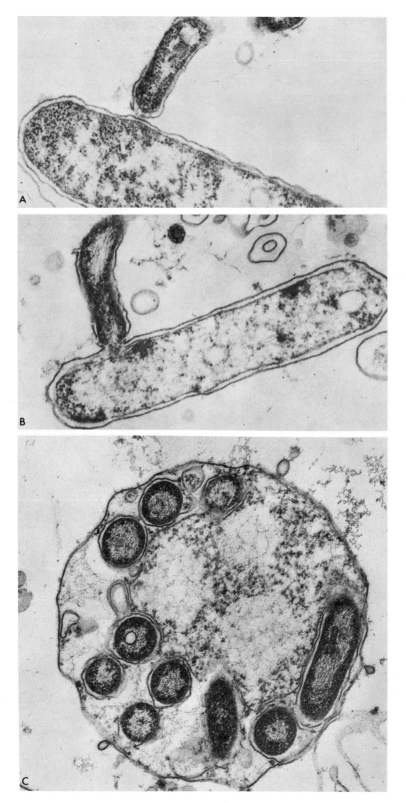

**Figure 37.6** Sequences in the interaction between *Bdellovibrio bacteriovorus* strain 233 and *Pseudomonas tabaci*. × 60,000. *A*, initial contact; *B*, entrance of *Bdellovibrio* through pore; *C*, complete invasion of the host and multiplication of the vibrios (numerous dark bodies) inside the *Pseudomonas* cell. (From Starr and Baigent: J. Bact., *91*:2006, 1966.)

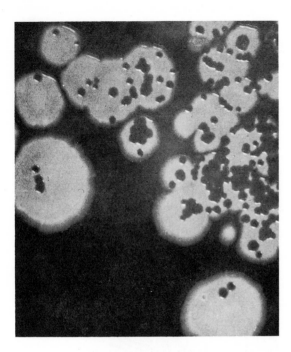

**Figure 37.7** Lytic action of *Bdellovibrio bacteriovorus* on *Escherichia coli,* after streaking a mixture of parasites and host bacteria on nutrient agar. The colonies of *E. coli* are the larger light areas; colonies ("plaques") of the vibrios are small and dark. (From Stolp and Starr: Ant. Leeuw., *29*:217, 1963.)

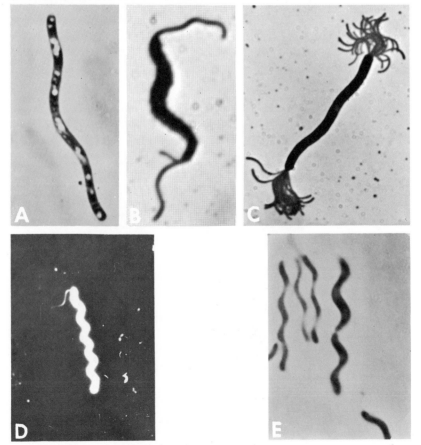

**Figure 37.8** Various species of saprophytic spirilla. *A, S. serpens,* darkfield, live, flagella not visible. *B, S. beijerinckii,* Leifson's flagella stain ($\times$ 1250). *C, S. serpens,* Leifson's flagella stain; compare to *A. D, S. sinuosum,* darkfield microphotograph ($\times$ 600). *E, S. lunatus,* live, dark phase contrast microphotograph. (*A, B, C* and *E* from Williams and Rittenberg: Internat. Bull. Bact. Nomenclat. & Taxon., vol. 7. *D* courtesy of A. Pijper, Institute for Pathology, Pretoria, South Africa.)

***Spirillum volutans.*** *Spirillum volutans* (Ehrenburg, 1832) is of interest because of its active, tumbling volutions and its large metachromatic granules from which the term *volutin* (polymerized phosphates) in reference to the species, is derived. The rotatory and to-and-fro motility and the form of these spiral organisms are well demonstrated in hanging-drop and darkfield preparations. Negative staining is useful in demonstrating their form and arrangement (not motility). Until recently this species could be cultivated *in vitro* only in association with other bacteria or their dialyzable products. In 1965 it was grown in a completely bacteria-free medium under special *microaerophilic* conditions. Similar species have been isolated by allowing them to grow through membrane filters lying on the surface of semisolid (0.1 per cent) agar medium. Some species grow in relatively simple synthetic media.

***Spirillum minus* and Rat-bite Fever.** *Spirillum minus,* one of the most minute species, causes a disease in man (rat-bite fever or *sodoku*) having several of the clinical features of a typical spirochetal disease (syphilis). *Sp. minus* has never been successfully cultivated. It is gram-negative.

*Sp. minus* occurs in the blood of rats, mice and possibly other animals, and is transmitted from them to each other and to man by their bites. In man it causes intermittent fever and *spirillemia.*

## SUPPLEMENTARY READING

Canale-Parola, E., Rosenthal, S. E., and Kupfer, D. G.: Morphological and physiological characteritics of *Spirillum gracile,* sp.n. Ant. Leeuw., *32*:113, 1966.

Chambers, J. S.: The Conquest of Cholera. The Macmillan Co., New York. 1938.

Drake, C. H.: Evaluation of culture media for the isolation and enumeration of *Pseudomonas aeruginosa.* Health Lab. Science, *3*:10, 1966.

Felsenfeld, O.: The Cholera Problem. Warren H. Green, St. Louis, Mo. 1967.

Fletcher, R. D., and Plastridge, W. N.: Chemically defined medium for some microaerophilic vibrios. J. Bact., *85*:992, 1963.

Hegeman, G. D.: Synthesis of the enzymes of the mandelate pathway by *Pseudomonas putida.* I, II, III. J. Bact., *91*:1140, 1155, 1161, 1966.

Hoadley, A. W., and McCoy, E.: Studies of certain gram-negative bacteria from surface waters. Health Lab. Science, *2*:20, 1966.

Mandel, M.: Deoxyribonucleic acid base composition in the genus *Pseudomonas.* J. Gen. Microbiol., *43*:273, 1966.

Powell, Jr., C. J., and Finkelstein, R. A.: Polymyxin agar as an adjunct in the isolation of El Tor vibrios. J. Bact., *87*:1249, 1964.

Redfearn, M. S., Palleroni, N. J., and Stainer, R. Y.: A comparative study of *Pseudomonas pseudomallei* and *Bacillus mallei.* J. Gen. Microbiol., *43*:293, 1966.

Rosenberg, C. E.: The Cholera Years. Chicago University Press, 1962.

Shilo, M., and Bruff, B.: Lysis of gram-negative bacteria by host-dependent ectoparasitic *Bdellovibrio bacteriovorus* isolates. J. Gen. Microbiol., *40*:317, 1965.

Smibert, R. M.: Nutrition of *Vibrio fetus.* J. Bact., *85*:394, 1963.

Stanier, R. Y., Palleroni, N. J., and Doudoroff, M.: The aerobic pseudomonads: A taxonomic study. J. Gen. Microbiol., *43*:159, 1966.

Stolp, H., and Starr, M. P.: Problems in speciation of phytopathogenic pseudomonads and xanthomonads. Ann. Rev. Phytopathol., *3*:287, 1965.

Sutter, V. L., Hurst, V., and Lane, C. W.: Quantification of *Pseudomonas aeruginosa* in feces of healthy human adults. Health Lab. Sci., *4*:245, 1967.

Takeya, K., Shimodori, S., and Zinnaka, Y.: New method for early diagnosis of Celebes type El Tor vibrio carriers. J. Bact., *90*:824, 1965.

# Chapter 38

## SUBORDER RHODOBACTERIINEAE
### (and Other Alga-like Bacteria)

The term "alga-like" used as the title of this chapter has no taxonomic status or significance. It is merely a term of convenience in bringing together for discussion certain groups of bacteria that, though quite widely separated in "Bergey's Manual" (in different orders or suborders) (Table 38.1), have certain more or less superficial similarities to blue-green algae. All of the organisms discussed in this chapter are properly classed as bacteria, not algae, because: (1) their *diameter* is typically 1 to 5 $\mu$ and seldom exceeds 10 $\mu$; (2) their cellular structure is procaryotic; (3) they typically multiply only asexually by *transverse*, binary fission; (4) except for the relatively few photosynthetic species they are chemosynthetic.

The several curious nonphotosynthetic bacteria described in this chapter resemble the Cyanophyceae in the formation of trichomes, filaments or branching stalks, in exhibiting gliding, nonflagellate motility and in aquatic habitat. None resembles molds or "moldlike" bacteria (Family Streptomycetaceae) in producing mycelia or conidiospores and none resembles protozoa or "protozoa-like" bacteria (Order Spirochaetales) in having thin, flexible cell walls or self-flexing movements. None produces thermostable endospores or *peritrichate* motile cells. One ambiguous group, Order Myxobacterales, resembles Cyanophyceae in having gliding, nonflagellate motility and in forming a slimy, enveloping matrix. This group is, however, discussed in this book with the protozoa-like bacteria because the organisms in it are characterized by thin, flexible cell walls and by producing communal vegetative and "fruiting" groupings that are strikingly, though only superficially, similar to analogous vegetative and fruiting structures of certain true, eucaryotic, ameba-like protozoa, the Mycetozoa (Order Acrasiales).

The photosynthetic bacteria (Suborder Rhodobacteriineae) described in this chapter resemble the Cyanophyceae in that both utilize solar energy. The Rhodobacteriineae differ from the Cyanophyceae and, indeed, from all other photosynthetic cells in their method of using radiant energy. Before examining bacterial photosynthesis let us review the usual type of photosynthesis that is familiar to all students of elementary biology.

### 38.1 PHOTOSYNTHESIS

Chemosynthetic and photosynthetic forms of metabolism, seemingly so different, are basically much alike. They differ only in the means by which energy is obtained. Once energy is made available in either type of cell, the energy is taken up in chemical bonds in the ADP-ATP system and in strongly reduced coenzymes, and is used in synthetic processes that are essentially alike in both forms of metabolism.

As every student of elementary biology knows, in photosynthesis by familiar green plants the energy of sunlight, especially of wave lengths in the blue (around 450 m$\mu$) and red (around 660 m$\mu$), and even shorter (around 400 m$\mu$; violet), is trapped by the green pigment *chlorophyll* (actually two cooperating chlorophylls, *a* and *b* that act, as it were, in tandem). The trapped energy is then used in the synthesis of substances such as starch.

**TABLE 38.1**   BACTERIA SIMULATING OTHER CLASSES OF MICROORGANISMS

| Order | Sub-order | Representative family | Distinguishing Properties |
|---|---|---|---|
| *Protozoan-like* | | | |
| Spirochaetales | | | Thin, flexible cell wall or sheath; fibrillar structure; flexing, rotatory and translatory motility; no flagella |
| Myxobacterales | | | Thin, flexible cell wall; flexing and gliding motility; no flagella; form pseudoplasmodium and fruiting bodies |
| *Mold-like* | | | |
| Actinomycetales | | Streptomycetaceae, Actinoplanaceae | Branching, mycelial growth; formation of conidia and/or motile sporangiospores |
| *Alga-like* | | | |
| Chlamydobacteriales | | Chlamydobacteriaceae | Formation of free and sessile trichomes; aquatic habitat; sheath formation; motile swarm cells |
| Beggiatoales | | Beggiatoaceae | Free and sessile trichomes; gliding motility; aquatic habitat |
| Pseudomonadales | Rhodobacteriineae | | Cellular aggregates; aquatic habitat; photosynthesis |
| | Pseudomonadineae | Caulobacteraceae | Formation of branching stalks; aquatic habitat; free and sessile; accumulation of metallic oxides. |
| | | Siderocapsaceae | Aquatic habitat; accumulation of metallic oxide |
| Hyphomicrobiales | | Hyphomicrobiaceae | Aquatic habitat; formation of stalks or fiaments; free or sessile; photosynthesis in one species |
| Caryophanales | | Caryophanaceae | Motile trichomes; distinctive nuclear structure; gonidia; aquatic habitat |

The process of photosynthesis is thus divided into two phases: (1) the *light phase* in which radiant energy is trapped by chlorophyll and transferred into ATP with concomitant formation of NADH and NADPH; (2) the *dark phase,* in which the energy stored in ATP is used in the synthesis of organic compounds as summarized in the well known equation:

$$CO_2 + 2H_2O \xrightarrow[\text{energy}]{\text{light}} (CH_2O) + H_2O + O_2 \text{ or}$$

$$6CO_2 + 12H_2O \xrightarrow[\text{(Light and dark phases)}]{\text{photosynthesis}}$$

$$\underset{\text{(glucose)}}{C_6H_{12}O_6} + 6H_2O + 6O_2.$$

The dark phase is independent of light and occurs alike in both photosynthetic and chemosynthetic cells when energy in the form of ATP is provided.

**The Light Phase.**   The first effect of radiation of chlorophyll is to raise the energy level of certain of its electrons to such a pitch that one electron leaves each molecule of chlorophyll. "Excited" electrons are potent reducing agents. Each is immediately taken up by an electron

acceptor. The "extra" energy of the excited electrons is used in two processes: cyclic phosphorylation and noncyclic phosphorylation. Each process generates ATP. Noncyclic phosphorylation also generates reducing potential in the form of NADPH (Fig. 38.1).

CYCLIC PHOSPHORYLATION.   In this process the "high energy" electrons driven out of chlorophyll by light are passed along an electron transfer system consisting in part of flavin nucleotides and cytochromes, analogous to the electron-transport systems in bio-oxidation. The electrons are transferred from coenzyme to coenzyme, yielding energy at each step. The energy of each electron generates two ATP from two ADP and two $H_3PO_4$. ($H_3PO_4$ is here indicated by Pi = inorganic phosphoric acid.) The electron then returns to the chlorophyll, completing the cycle.

NONCYCLIC PHOSPHORYLATION.   In this reaction the electrons are taken up by ferredoxin. Ferredoxin is an iron-containing metalloprotein having enzyme-like properties and a uniquely high capacity for electrons; i.e., it thus becomes a potent reducing agent. The electrons acquired

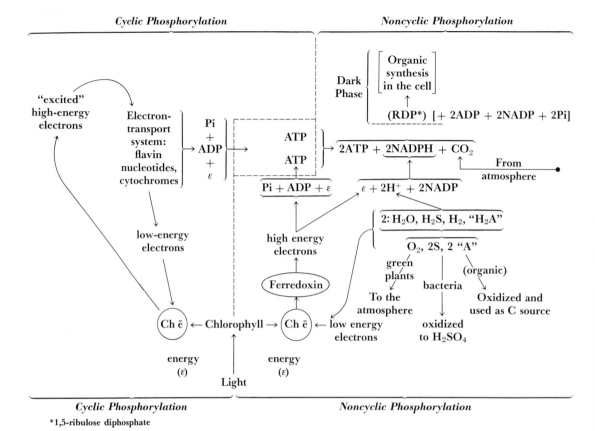

*Cyclic Phosphorylation*                    *Noncyclic Phosphorylation*

*Cyclic Phosphorylation*                    *Noncyclic Phosphorylation*

*1,5-ribulose diphosphate

**Figure 38.1**   Cyclic and noncyclic photophosphorylation. For explanation see text.

by ferredoxin from irradiated chlorophyll are immediately transferred along two paths. Most of the energy is used to generate ATP from ADP and Pi. The remaining energy is used to "split" (oxidize) $H_2O$, yielding $2H^+$ and $O^{--}$. The hydrogen ions are then reduced by electrons from ferredoxin and combine with NADP to form NADPH. With energy from ATP this carries the hydrogen that is used to reduce $CO_2$ as it is incorporated into organic compounds in the cell (see Dark Phase).

The electrons left attached to the oxygen after water is split are immediately returned, at a very low energy level, to restore the chlorophyll that was robbed of its electrons by sunlight. The oxygen, minus its electrons, is given off as gaseous molecular oxygen. This terminates the light phase of photosynthesis.

**The Dark Phase.**   The ATP, NADH and NADPH resulting from the light phase reaction cooperate to introduce $CO_2$ into organic combination in the cell. This process can proceed in the dark as well as in the light. At least two processes appear to be involved. In one, that has been most thoroughly studied by means of $C^{14}O_2$ by Calvin (Nobel Prize winner) and others, $CO_2$

is added directly to 1,5-ribulose diphosphate, a 5-carbon ketose. The 6-carbon compound thus formed is immediately split by the enzyme carboxydismutase into two molecules of 3-phosphoglyceric acid (PGA) (see Figure 38.2 and the Embden-Meyerhof scheme for anaerobic dissimilation of glucose, Chapter 9).

Using energy stored in ATP formed during the photophosphorylation reactions previously described, and apparently reversing the energy-yielding processes that occur during exothermic decomposition of glucose (Chapter 9), the 3-phosphoglyceric acid molecules are reduced by NADPH and combined with phosphoric acid to form, first, triose phosphate and from this, 6-carbon compounds such as fructose and glucose. These are polymerized as described elsewhere to produce sucrose, starch or cellulose. PGA is also reduced to form fatty acids which are the basis of lipids (Fig. 38.2).

In another, and possibly simultaneous process $CO_2$ is reduced directly by ferredoxin in the presence of acetyl-CoA and an enzyme called *pyruvate synthetase*. The $C_3$ compound, pyruvic acid (pyruvate), is formed (see the Krebs or citric acid cycle). As previously explained,

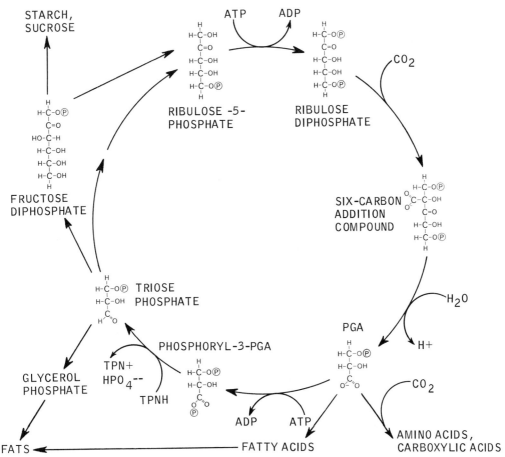

**Figure 38.2** Dark-phase reactions in photosynthesis. For explanation see text. (From The Path of Carbon in Photosynthesis, by J. A. Bassham. Copyright © 1962 by Scientific American, Inc. All rights reserved.)

pyruvate is a starting point for the synthesis of amino acids, the basis of proteins; fatty acids, the basis of lipids; and numerous other organic compounds that appear in the photosynthetic cell within a few seconds of exposure to light (Fig. 38.3). In Figure 38.3 the ferredoxin is reduced by activated electrons from irradiated chlorophyll. $H_2O$ is split and ATP is formed much as in Figure 38.1. $CH_2O$ is merely a symbolic compound representing carbohydrates finally formed by the reduction of $CO_2$.

It is to be noted that chlorophylls are not the only light-trapping pigments in photosynthetic cells. In many eucaryotic green plants there are ancillary pigments such as the yellow carotenes and xanthophylls (relatives of vitamin A). These absorb radiant energy of other wave lengths. These pigments, though incapable of photosynthesis, transfer the energy that they absorb to chlorophyll. In Cyanophyceae, the unique pigment *phycocyanin* appears to play a similar accessory part. Other accessory pigments of various colors function in other species, including photosynthetic bacteria.

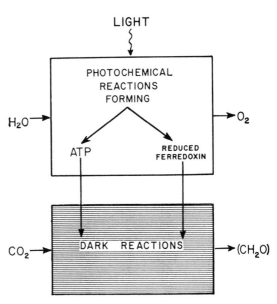

**Figure 38.3** Diagrammatic representation of the light and dark reactions of photosynthesis in chloroplasts. For explanation see text. (From Arnon: Science, *149*:1460, 1965.)

## 38.2  BACTERIAL PHOTOSYNTHESIS

Photosynthetic bacteria do not contain any of the chlorophylls found in eucaryotic green plants or in the Cyanophyceae; the last contain only chlorophyll *a* plus accessory phycocyanin. Instead, the photosynthetic bacteria contain the structurally similar pigments *bacteriochlorophyll* or, depending on species, *chlorobium chlorophyll* (Fig. 38.4). Unlike eucaryotic photosynthetic cells, bacterial chlorophylls and the

chlorophyll *a* of Cyanophyceae are not contained in complex, membrane-enclosed, highly differentiated, independently replicating chloroplasts, but in vesicular particles or disks or tubular structures in the cytoplasm called *chromatophores* (Gr. *chroma* = color; *phoros* = carrier) or, in the case of *Chlorobium* species, ovoid or spindle-shaped bodies called "*Chlorobium* vesicles." In all groups the chromatophores appear to be associated with the cytoplasmic membrane and to contain oxidative and syn-

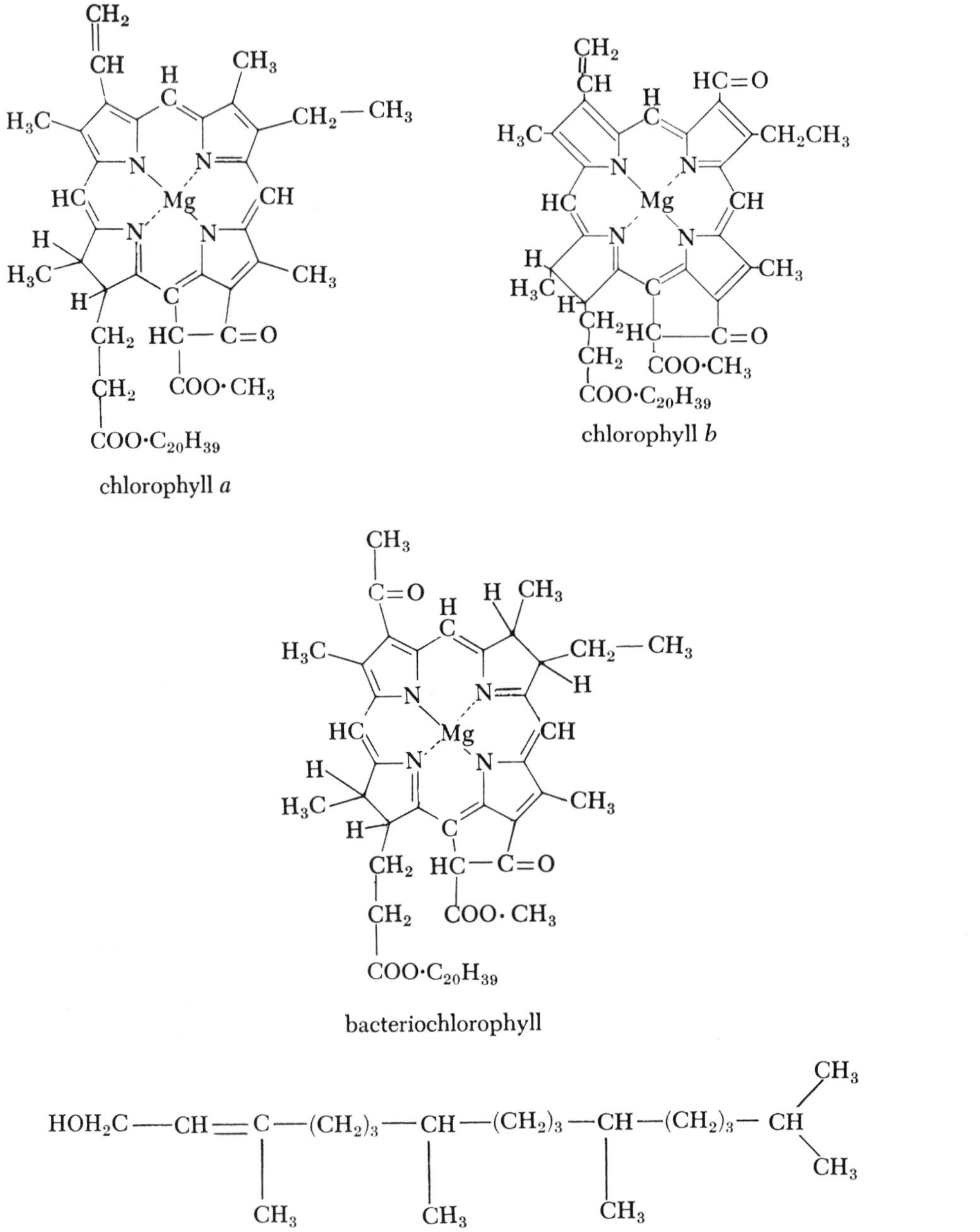

chlorophyll *a*

chlorophyll *b*

bacteriochlorophyll

**Figure 38.4**  Chlorophylls *a* and *b* and bacteriochlorophyll. The structure of phytol ($C_{20}H_{39}OH$), part of each, is shown separately. (From Lascelles: Tetrapyrrole Biosynthesis and Its Regulation, Benjamin, 1964.)

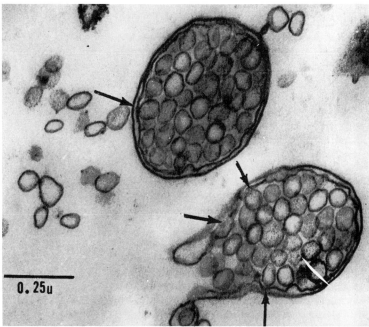

**Figure 38.5** Transverse section of the photosynthetic bacterium *Rhodospirillum rubrum* grown in the light and ruptured by osmotic shock. The rupture of the cell wall is evident in one of the cells. The intracytoplasmic membranes (chromatophores) are still retained in the opened cell. Arrows indicate possible peripheral connections of the chromatophores to the peripheral membrane. × 85,000. (From Holt and Marr: J. Bact., *89*:1402, 1965.)

thetic enzymes characteristic of cell membrane and photosynthesis. Procaryotic chromatophores are now seen to be very suggestive of the eucaryotic chloroplast. The structures differ in different families of bacteria and are under active investigation (Figs. 38.5 and 38.6).

The chlorophylls of bacteria absorb most light energy in the very far red (720 to 750 m$\mu$; green chlorobium chlorophyll) and invisible infrared (purple bacteriochlorophyll, 850 to 950 m$\mu$) zones. Light of these relatively long wave lengths may have been the very first to reach the primeval earth and permit development of primitive forms of photosynthesis. Since the energy of radiations is inversely proportional to their wave length, it is evident that the chlorophylls of bacteria furnish less energy than the chlorophylls of green plants which use light of much shorter wave lengths. The energy trapped by bacteriochlorophylls is, in fact, insufficient to split $H_2O$, a process that requires high-level energy. Consequently, photosynthesis by bacteria differs from that of all eucaryotic plants and of Cyanophyceae. The photosynthetic bacteria cannot use water as a source of hydrogen to reduce $CO_2$ and therefore do not give off free oxygen as a result of photosynthesis. However, they can and do split $H_2S$, a chemically analogous substance ($2H^+ + S^{--}$), or thiosulfates or certain organic compounds, as hydrogen donors in an equivalent manner; some can use molecular hydrogen directly. These relationships have been summarized by Van Niel as analogous to eucaryotic plant photosynthesis in a generalized formula:

1. Green-plant photosynthesis:

$$CO_2 + 2H_2O \longrightarrow (CH_2O) + H_2O + O_2$$

2. Bacterial photosynthesis:

$$CO_2 + 2H_2A \longrightarrow (CH_2O) + H_2A + A_2$$

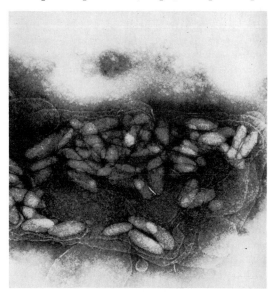

**Figure 38.6** Cells of the photosynthetic bacterium, *Chloropseudomonas ethylicum* (grown in the light and negatively stained with phosphotungstic acid) opened by mechanical (ballistic) disintegration. Note the distinct, ovoid vesicles. × 88,400. (From Holt, Conti and Fuller: J. Bact., *91*:311, 1966.)

In reaction 2, A may be sulfur or an organic residue, depending on species. Some sulfide-splitting species make themselves conspicuous by storing the sulfur as intracellular globules.

## 38.3   THE PHOTOSYNTHETIC BACTERIA

### ORDER PSEUDOMONADALES, SUBORDER RHODOBACTERIINEAE

Morphologically, the photosynthetic bacteria of the suborder Rhodobacteriineae are much like the bacteria that are their very common, numerous and *nonphotosynthetic* cousins, the Families Pseudomonadaceae and Spirillaceae. They occur as unicellular, undifferentiated cocci, rods, vibrios and spirilla (do not confuse with spirochete). Some secrete copious gelatinous material around themselves; in this respect resembling the Cyanophyceae.

All Rhodobacteriineae contain photosynthetic pigment. All can grow *anaerobically* (many are strict anaerobes) in the presence of light; some can also grow aerobically in light or dark. Obviously, photosynthesis cannot occur in the dark, so these aerobic species can grow in the dark like their nonphotosynthetic congeners; i.e., they are facultative phototrophs and facultative aerobes. Like all species of the Order Pseudomonadales, the Rhodobacteriineae have *polar flagella* when motile. The flagella may occur at either or both poles, singly or in tufts (compare *peritrichously* flagellate Eubacteriales). All Pseudomonadales, including Rhodobacteriineae, are gram-negative. None forms endospores or conidiospores.

As Van Niel states: "If, under certain conditions, one of the nonsulfur-storing photosynthetic bacteria should fail to produce its prominent pigment system, it would thereby become indistinguishable from a typical *Pseudomonas, Vibrio* or *Spirillum* species." It is interesting to note that nonphotosynthetic (pigment-free) mutants of photosynthetic bacteria have been discovered and that they are virtually indistinguishable from ordinary, nonphotosynthetic bacteria of the same morphological types. One may therefore imagine that photosynthetic bacteria evolved from corresponding nonphotosynthetic species by the acquisition (through mutations) of photosynthetic pigments. Back-mutation (loss of pigment) has also been observed, and this produces the primitive, nonphotosynthetic forms again.

The Rhodobacteriineae are divided into three families* (Thiorhodaceae, Athiorhodaceae and Chlorobacteriaceae) on the basis of the role of $H_2S$ or other sulfur compounds as hydrogen donors in their photosynthetic processes and the nature of their photosynthetic pigments:

1. $CO_2 + 2H_2S \xrightarrow{\text{light}}$

$(CH_2O) + H_2O + 2S$ (free or intracellular globules)

2. $3CO_2 + 2S + 5H_2O \xrightarrow{\text{light}}$

$$3(CH_2O) + 2H_2SO_4$$

*Thiorhodaceae* (Gr. *theîon* = sulfur; *rhodon* = red or rose) contain the photosynthetic pigment *bacteriochlorophyll* and red, brown and *purple* carotinoid pigments. The Thiorhodaceae are generally called the *sulfur purple bacteria*. The reactions which follow are *overall* expressions of photosynthesis by these organisms. In this process $H_2S$ serves in place of water as an extraneous donor of hydrogen to reduce $CO_2$. The sulfur resulting from the oxidation of (removal of H from) $H_2S$ is stored as intracellular globules of elemental sulfur that is later oxidized as a source of energy to sulfuric acid. Thiorhodaceae are typically (but not invariably) *autotrophic*, strict *anaerobes* and strict *phototrophs*.

*Athiorhodaceae* contain bacteriochlorophyll and purple and brown carotenoid pigments. They are essentially like the Thiorhodaceae but, as *athio* in their name implies, lack the ability to utilize $H_2S$. They therefore do not store sulfur intracellularly or excrete it extracellularly. These bacteria obtain their hydrogen and their carbon for photosynthesis from organic compounds. Fatty acids are often used.

Both Thiorhodaceae and Athiorhodaceae can use molecular hydrogen in photosynthesis:

$$CO_2 + 2H_2 \longrightarrow (CH_2O) + H_2O.$$

Some Athiorhodaceae are not strict phototrophs but can grow aerobically in the dark. Athiorhodaceae are often called the nonsulfur purple and brown bacteria.

*Chlorobacteriaceae* is a small group containing green chlorobium chlorophylls and γ-carotene. Like the Thiorhodaceae, these bacteria metabolize $H_2S$ and sulfites, but deposit free sulfur extracellularly instead of intracellularly. The S is often oxidized to sulfuric acid. They cannot grow without $H_2S$ or other sulfides or sulfites. They are often called the *sulfur green bacteria*. They are strictly anaerobic, strictly photosynthetic and autotrophic.

---

*"Bergey's Manual of Determinative Bacteriology," 7th ed. Baltimore, Williams & Wilkins Co., 1957.

**TABLE 38.2** SOME PROPERTIES OF PHOTOSYNTHETIC BACTERIA

| Family | Photosynthetic Pigment | Carotinoid Pigments | Obligate Photosynthesis | Obligate Anaerobe | Litho-troph | Organo-troph | S Deposit | H$_2$S Dependent |
|--------|------------------------|---------------------|------------------------|-------------------|-------------|--------------|-----------|------------------|
| Thiorhodaceae | Bacteriochlorophyll | Red, brown, purple | All | All | Most | Some | Intra-cell. | No |
| Athiorhodaceae | Bacteriochlorophyll | Brown, purple | Most | Most | Some | Most | No | No |
| Chlorobacteriaceae | Two types of chlorobium chlorophyll | γ-carotene | All | All | All | None | Extra-cell. | Yes |

These data are summarized in Table 38.2. **Habitat and Functions of Rhodobacteriineae.** Species of photosynthetic bacteria are commonly found in sunlit fresh and marine waters, stagnant lakes, polluted bays, sea water and brackish ditchwater, where H$_2$S is being plentifully produced by organic decomposition and where the O-R potential is very low because of chemosynthetic metabolism. The Rhodobacteriineae are mainly lithotrophic. They have no special industrial, agricultural or medical interest, but are of great importance as scavengers and deodorizers since they utilize H$_2$S in photosynthesis. They are much used by students of the enormously important process of photosynthesis.

Although the photosynthetic bacteria are of no immediate importance to medicine or "the economy," these organisms are of no inconsiderable importance to humanity at large. Photosynthesis on land is but a small portion (perhaps 25 per cent) of the world total. Probably well over 100,000,000,000 tons of glucose alone, and an even larger amount of oxygen, are produced in the seas annually from photosynthesis by both eucaryotic and procaryotic algae and other marine plants. Without their photosynthesis there might be very little oxygen in our atmosphere. The millions of tons of agricultural crops of all kinds, starches, lumber, paper, livestock, and so on, would be unknown to us. In

**Figure 38.7** Carbon and energy cycles. Two ultimate sources of energy are available to living organisms: radiant energy for photosynthetic organisms; chemical energy for chemosynthetic organisms. In both types of organism the energy is first taken up into the ADP-ATP system whence it may be stored in organic compounds such as carbohydrates, fats or proteins, or used by the cell in other ways. Organic compounds (e.g., glucose) are decomposed exothermically by bio-oxidation in plants and animals, releasing the CO$_2$ and H$_2$O to repeat the cycle. Other sources of CO$_2$ and H$_2$O are combustion and rain; other sources of H$_2$ donors for photosynthesis are H$_2$S, H$_2$, and certain organic compounds for photosynthetic bacteria.

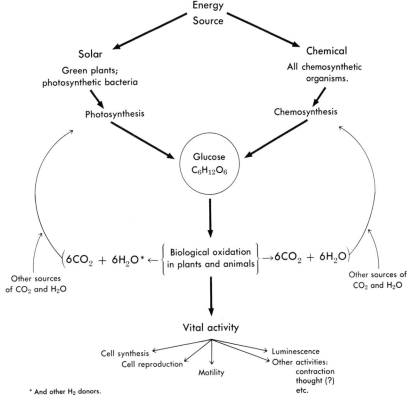

* And other H$_2$ donors.

fact, there would be no people; a sad (or not so sad?) truth!

Although the photosynthetic bacteria cannot be credited with contributing to the oxygen supply of our atmosphere, they certainly play a role, though doubtless only a "bit part", in the grand spectacle of world synthesis of organic compounds (Fig. 38.7). The microbic cosmos on which humanity depends works unseen and unheard, never goes on strike or receives wages and is beyond the control *even of Congress* (except very locally). The nation that first learns how to harness sunlight to synthesize its foodstuffs artificially, i.e., without plant life, on a commercially feasible basis can rule the world; "moon shots" or no moon shots!

### 38.4  SOME NONPHOTOSYNTHETIC ALGA-LIKE BACTERIA

#### "SULFUR BACTERIA"

Inorganic sulfur is available to bacteria in various stages of oxidation and reduction, ranging from the most reduced, $H_2S$, through elemental S, thiosulfates and tetrathionates to the most oxidized form, sulfates. Any of these except sulfates may be oxidized as energy sources by various bacteria; and any except $H_2S$ may be reduced as electron acceptors by other bacteria.

Bacteria that metabolize elemental sulfur or its inorganic compounds are often called *sulfur bacteria.* The term is used merely as a convenience and includes a heterogeneous group of species that have little else in common. We have already discussed photosynthetic sulfur bacteria. The relations of these and nonphotosynthetic sulfur bacteria are summarized in Table 38.3.

**Habitat of Sulfur Bacteria.**  Nonphotosynthetic sulfur-utilizing bacteria, both sulfur-storing types, oxidizing and reducing, are common in sewage and other polluted waters, in decomposing organic matter and in swampy

soils all over the world where putrefactive organisms are releasing $H_2S$ from dead plants and animal wastes, or where sulfur-reducing species (*Desulfovibrio*) are reducing sulfates to $H_2S$. Some sulfur bacteria that are not at all like algae are found around free sulfur deposits, in oil wells or in sulfur springs. Some occur in acid coal mine waters, others in garden soil. (See Family Thiobacteriaceae, Chapter 43; also Table 38.3.) The strictly anaerobic photosynthetic species, of course, thrive in the sunlit situations where oxygen has been removed by chemosynthetic organisms and where $H_2S$ occurs.

**Beggiatoales.**  We shall describe, as alga-like, some *nonphotosynthetic* sulfur bacteria of the order Beggiatoales (named for the Italian scientist, F. S. Beggiatoa). This order, as outlined in "Bergey's Manual" (1957) consists of four families:

Beggiatoaceae, Vitreoscillaceae, Leucotrichaceae and Achromataceae.

A great majority of species of Beggiatoales form long, multicellular threads called trichomes. A *trichome* (Gr. *trichos* = hair) is a single, multicellular organism consisting of undifferentiated cells attached end-to-end like railway cars and clearly an entire multicellular structure. The term includes flagellate, nonflagellate and gliding organisms. It does not include chains of obviously independent cells such as streptococci, individual cells of which have clung together accidentally after fission. In two species of Beggiatoales, relatively large, single ovoid cells are typical. None of the Beggiatoales is ensheathed and none branches. Most of the filamentous species are structurally so very like the blue-green algae, *Oscillatoria,* that many authors regard the filamentous Beggiatoales as nonphotosynthetic variants of the *Oscillatoria.* In fact, some species are said to contain some photosynthetic pigments. Except the filamentous, heterotrophic Family Vitreoscillaceae, which oxidize organic compounds as energy sources, all usually

**TABLE 38.3**  RELATIONS OF THE SULFUR BACTERIA

| Oxidize Sulfur and its Inorganic Compounds | | | | Reduce Sulfates | Produce $H_2S$ From Organic Sulfur Compounds |
|---|---|---|---|---|---|
| Intracellular Sulfur Granules | | No Intracellular Sulfur Granules | | | |
| Photo-synthetic | Not Photo-synthetic | Photo-synthetic | Not Photo-synthetic | | |
| Thiorhodaceae | Beggiatoaceae (filamentous) Achromatiaceae (non-filamentous) | Chlorobacteriaceae* Athiorhodaceae | *Thiobacillus* | *Desulfovibrio* *Sporovibrio* (?) | Various pathogenic and saprophytic (putrefactive) species: *Proteus, Serratia, Clostridium* |

*Free sulfur deposited extracellularly.

live together in the same habitats, where $H_2S$ is plentiful.

Only two families of Beggiatoales are sulfur storers: the filamentous Beggiatoaceae and the nonfilamentous Achromatiaceae. They oxidize S and $H_2S$ as sources of energy, probably according to the equations:

$$2H_2S + O_2 \longrightarrow 2H_2O + 2S$$
$$2S + 3O_2 + 2H_2O \longrightarrow 2H_2SO_4$$

The acid combines with other substances to form sulfates. Sulfates are invaluable as the principal sulfur compound available to higher plants.

*Beggiatoa alba* is a good representative of the sulfur-metabolizing filamentous species. It is common in all sewage and other polluted waters containing $H_2S$. It is microaerophilic (i.e., requires some free oxygen as indicated in the above equations). Whether or not it is lithotrophic remains to be determined. Typical trichomes of *B. alba* range in diameter from 3 to 5 $\mu$ and up to several millimeters in length (Fig. 38.8). The cells are gram-negative. Reproduction is primarily by transverse binary fission of the individual cells constituting trichomes; secondarily by fragmentation of the trichomes. In contact with solid surfaces the trichomes show slow gliding and rotatory motility (Fig. 38.9). They also show slow, bending and waving movements. Flagella are absent. Cultivation of *Beggiatoa* is usually in enrichment cultures from sewage. Catalase has been found to favor growth and viability.

Like the sulfur purple bacteria, Thiorhodaceae, when $H_2S$ is abundant *B. alba* stores colloidal globules of sulfur inside its cells, giving the organisms a distinctive milky appearance, hence the name *alba*, or white. When $H_2S$ is scanty, the stored $H_2S$ is oxidized; when $H_2S$ is absent the organisms grow poorly or die.

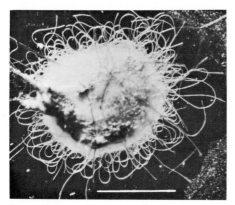

**Figure 38.8**   A dried colony of *Beggiatoa alba* showing loops of trichomes at edge of colony. The line indicates 1 mm. at this magnification. (From Faust and Wolfe: J. Bact., vol. 81.)

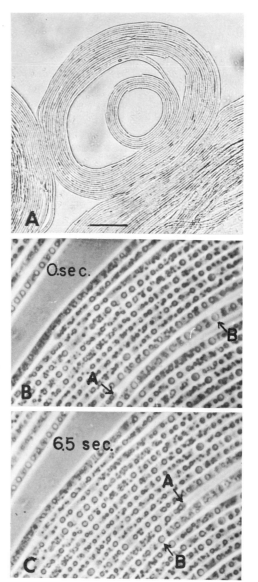

**Figure 38.9**   *Beggiatoa* growth on moist agar surface. *A*, Manner of coiling of the trichomes. *B* and *C*, Selected frames from a 16-mm. motion picture film showing motion of gliding trichomes. In the course of 6.5 seconds point A passed point B. Note the sulfur granules in the trichomes. (Dark phase-contrast photomicrography.) The line in *A* indicates 50 $\mu$; in *B* and *C* a similar line would indicate 10 $\mu$. (From Faust and Wolfe: J. Bact., vol. 81.)

## "IRON BACTERIA"

Like the term "sulfur bacteria," "iron bacteria" is a term of convenience for bringing together some aquatic, alga-like bacteria that exhibit a curious relationship to iron in their metabolism but that are otherwise quite dissimilar. They are nonphotosynthetic and occur world-wide in fresh, sea or brackish waters, especially waters rich in ferrous iron. Several species oxidize ferrous or manganous salts or organic compounds of iron or manganese as a source of energy and deposit $Fe(OH)_3$ or manganese oxides, not inside their cells but in *extracellular* structures. The yellow or reddish slime found on the mud and stones or water plants in iron-bearing waters is usually caused by ferric hydroxide in the sheaths or stalks or the gum of iron-accumulating bacteria growing there.

On the basis of the form of their extracellular structures three groups of these bacteria are recognized: (1) *sheaths* in the order Chlamydobacteriales (Gr. *chlamys* = cloak or covering); (2) *gummy, capsule-like masses* in the family Siderocapsaceae (Gr. *sideros* = iron; L. *capsa* = box or casing); (3) *stalks* in the family Caulobacteraceae (L. *caulis* = stalk).

The role of iron (or manganese) in the physiology of these organisms is interesting but is still under investigation. According to one view, the three groups of bacteria under discussion do not oxidize iron as a source of energy at all. They appear to utilize organic compounds containing iron but do not oxidize the iron itself.

For example, most Chlamydobacteriales and Siderocapsaceae can grow without gross amounts of iron or manganese, and then their sheaths or casings do not contain these metals. Young growths are free from iron or manganese. The deposition of the metals is a conspicuous and common feature of mature growths but clearly not an essential part of their physiology. The iron or manganese residue from the organism's metabolism remains outside the cell in the sheath, stalk or gum. According to one group of opinions, the metals are oxidized to ferric iron [or $Mn(OH)_3$] not by the cell but by free oxygen extraneous to the cell. The metals yield no energy to the cell. Such organisms are not true *iron bacteria* but might be called *iron-depositers*.

According to a logical view, only those organisms that oxidize *inorganic ferrous* iron compounds as a source of energy should be classed as true iron bacteria. A reaction often given to explain this process is:

$$4FeCO_3 + O_2 + 6H_2O \longrightarrow 4Fe(OH)_3 + 4CO_2$$

The iron is oxidized from the ferrous ($Fe^{++}$) to the ferric ($Fe^{+++}$) state. There are several such species but they are not at all alga-like. They occur especially in acid drainage waters of iron and coal mines and are discussed elsewhere. (See *Ferrobacillus*, Chapter 43.)

**Functions of Iron-Depositing Bacteria.** These organisms are not pathogenic but are of great economic importance as scavengers because they decompose organic matter in water. They are also important economic nuisances because they grow in water-distributing pipe systems and create obstructions. Some large geologic iron deposits ("bog-iron") may represent the accumulation of iron over long periods by these microorganisms.

### SHEATHED BACTERIA (CHLAMYDOBACTERIALES)

There are numerous types of sheathed "iron" organisms. Their taxonomy is under active investigation. Some of the many "species" are undoubtedly variants of a few central species. Two main types are *Leptothrix* and *Sphaerotilis*.

**Sphaerotilis natans.** *S. natans* is a common, much-studied and representative species.

It occurs world-wide in sewage and other polluted waters and becomes especially recognizable when those waters contain organic iron. It is aerobic or microaerophilic, organotrophic and nonsporeforming.

The sheath of *S. natans* is flexible, looking and behaving much like a clear, cellophane or paper tube such as a drinking straw. Chemically, it is a protein-polysaccharide-lipid complex, without muramic acid. It is neither cell wall nor capsule; a unique structure (Fig. 38.10).

The individual cells inside the sheath are of the same order of size as typical rod-shaped bacteria (1 $\mu$ by 2 to 10 $\mu$), though the trichomes may be several millimeters in length. The rods when motile possess one or more *polar* flagella. When the growth of *S. natans* is young, the filaments may resemble hyphae of coenocytic molds, though bacterial in diameter (1 to 3 $\mu$). As the growth matures, the protoplast becomes more obviously divided into bacilli with lophotrichous flagella. These cells multiply by binary fission. The resulting motile bacilli, often called *swarm cells*, slip out at the ends of the sheaths or are liberated at the sides as the sheaths disintegrate. Sometimes the young cells cling to the outside of the sheath of origin and grow off at an angle. This is called *false branching*. In one variety, called *S. dichotomus* (possibly identical with *S. natans*), the false branching appears to be dichotomous.

*S. natans* usually does not accumulate much iron in the sheath except in matured filaments. *Leptothrix ochracea*, a species similar in several respects, deposits much larger amounts until it forms dense, ochre-colored masses. Some workers have regarded *L. ochracea* as matured *S. natans*.

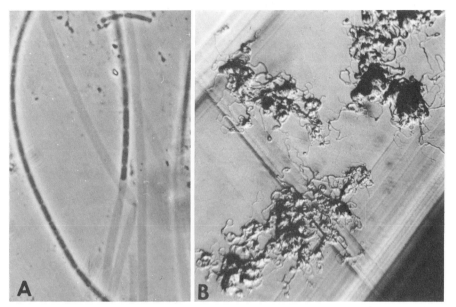

**Figure 38.10**  *Sphaerotilis natans. A*, Sheaths and bacillus-like cells within sheaths. Note also empty sheaths (about × 1000). *B*, Young colonies on nutrient agar after 24 hours at 28° C. (about × 50). (From Dondero, Phillips and Heukelekian: Appl. Microbiol., vol. 9.)

It is of interest to note that *S. natans* has also been described as a sulfur bacterium, depositing sulfur granules like *Beggiatoa alba. S. natans* also synthesizes prominent granules of poly-beta-hydroxybutyric acid.

*S. natans* is a tremendous nuisance when, because of its excessive growth, the tangled, filamentous masses cause blockage ("bulking") in the flow of sewage in disposal plants that use activated sludge. (See Chapter 42.)

### STALK-FORMING BACTERIA (CAULOBACTERACEAE)

**Gallionella ferruginea.** *G. ferruginea* is a common and representative species of the stalk-forming family. Similar organisms are *Sidero-phacus* and *Nevskia*. Each cell of *Gallionella* forms a stalk which, as the plant matures, becomes encrusted with $Fe(OH)_3$. *Gallionella* does *not* form a sheath. It is said by some observers to be a true iron-oxidizing bacterium, but this is doubted by others. However, it grows only in waters bearing reduced iron (i.e., iron that can be oxidized as a source of energy). A curious metabolic feature is that all species require vitamin $B_{12}$ (cyanocobalamin).

The cells of this organism are bean- or kidney-shaped and about 0.5 by 2 $\mu$ in size. Like other bacteria, they multiply by transverse binary fission. When motile, they resemble *Pseudomonas* and have polar flagella. From the concave side or end of each cell a flat, mucilag-inous ribbon or stalk is excreted. This is attached by the distal end to some solid object. As each cell divides, dichotomy of the stalk occurs, so that complex tangles or rosettes of long stalks streaming from a common object are formed. The stalks are sometimes 0.2 to 0.3 mm. in length (Fig. 38.11).

From the complex fibrillar structure of these stalks and their occasional independence of the cell, it is inferred by some workers that these stalks or their fibers may possibly be living matter and play a role in the life cycle of the organism.

The stalks of *Gallionella* have the remarkable habit of twisting so that they resemble a loosely coiled rubber band. Large amounts of $Fe(OH)_3$ are later deposited in these stalks, giving them the appearance of a series of loops or string of beads. The twisting habit renders identification of *Gallionella* easy, since no other organism of similar character is known to twist in just this way. As stated by Thimann: ". . . the gallionellas are more notable for their excreta than for themselves."

*Gallionella* is found in nature as widely distributed as *Sphaerotilus*. Like other iron-accumulating bacteria, *Gallionella* can multiply in water pipes and often causes extensive deposits and incrustations of iron which may eventually occlude the pipes. It is also responsible in part for the fouling of ship bottoms.

**Caulobacter vibrioides.** *C. vibrioides* and

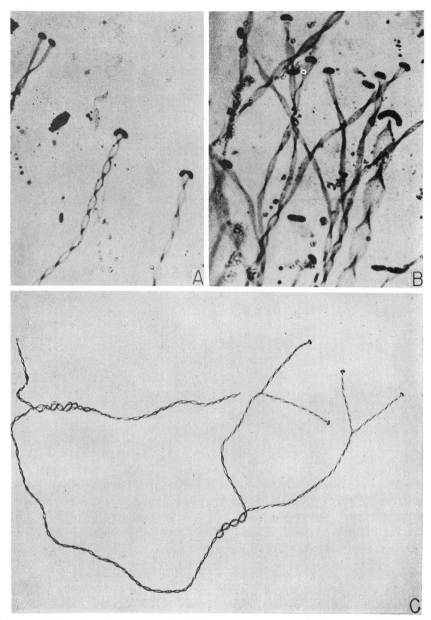

**Figure 38.11**   *A, Gallionella minor,* × 1100. *B, Gallionella major,* × 1100. *C, Gullionella ferruginea,* × 650. (All from N. Cholodny, 1929. Reproduced by R. L. Starkey.) In Thimann: The Life of Bacteria. 2nd ed., The Macmillan Co., 1963.

several similar species of stalk-formers are neither sulfur nor iron bacteria. The cells are typically *Vibrio*-like: ellipsoidal, rodlike, fusiform or banana-shaped. They resemble common species of *Pseudomonas* in size and procaryotic structure. They are chemoorganotrophic and multiply by transverse binary fission. They are nonspore-forming and have single, unipolar flagella when motile. Electron micrographs reveal such familiar structural details as cell wall, cell membrane, ribosomes and nuclear area as seen in other bacteria.

The caulobacters differ from all other known procaryotic organisms in the unique character of their stalks. Unlike the excreted stalks of *Gallionella,* the stalk of the caulobacters is not an excretion but a distinct *part of the cell itself,* a narrow, flexible tubular outgrowth closely associated with, or possibly (as the cell matures) *including,* the polar flagellum. The stalk wall is

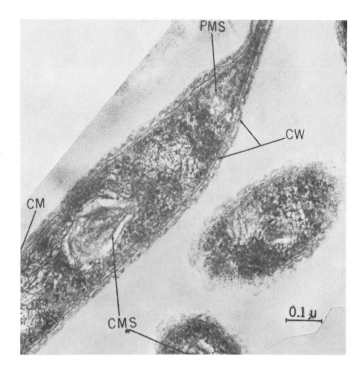

**Figure 38.12** Electron micrograph of section of bacteroid (*Caulobacter*) strain CB11. CW, cell wall; CM, cell membrane; CMS, membrane structure within cell; PMS, membrane structure at base of stalk of flagellum. (From Poindexter: Bact. Rev., *28*:231, 1964.)

a continuation of the cell wall itself; the core of the stalk is an extension of the cytoplasm, especially of its membranous parts (Fig. 38.12).

Formation of stalk and flagellum is related to what appears to be a primitive "life cycle" or cyclic type of cell division. In this cycle, a mature, stalked, *nonflagellate, vegetative* cell is attached by a strongly adhesive "holdfast" at the tip of its stalk, to some solid object. This cell elongates and then divides transversely near the middle of the long cell. The new, distal cell is without a stalk but contains the accumulated stalk-forming material at its distal end. At that end an adhesive "holdfast" material and an active flagellum also appear (Fig. 38.13). The new cell, now a motile "swarmer," separates from the parent cell and swims away. The older cell remains attached by its stalk and continues to repeat this vegetative process.

The young swarmers soon attach to solid objects, usually other microorganisms such as protozoa, algae, fungi, other bacteria; most

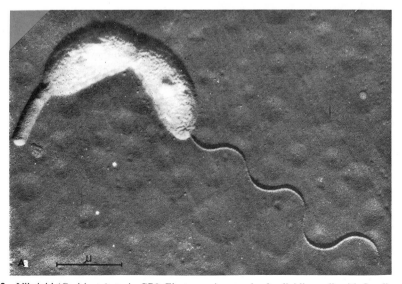

**Figure 38.13** Vibrioid (*Caulobacter*) strain CB2. Electron micrograph of a dividing cell, with flagellum at one pole and stalk at the other. (From Poindexter: Bact. Rev., *28*:231, 1964.)

**Figure 38.14**   Vibrioid (*Caulobacter*) strain CB2. Stalked cells in a rosette, the cells adhering to the common mass of holdfast material by the tips of the stalks. (From Poindexter: Bact. Rev., *28*:231, 1964.)

commonly, to each other. They thus form characteristic rosettes (Fig. 38.14). The new stalk, attached to the solid object by the holdfast, now develops from the cell, increasing the distance between the cell and the solid object. The stalked, sessile cell is now mature and begins the vegetative process described above. Swarmers do not undergo fission until they become sessile.

Caulobacters in which the stalk arises in line with the central, long axis of the cell are included in the genus *Caulobacter;* those in which the stalk arises excentrally are grouped in a new genus, *Asticcacaulis* (Gr. *stichos* = alignment). Adhesion of the stalks of caulobacters to other bacteria, especially gram-positive species, suggested at one time that the caulobacters became predatory by inserting the stalk into other cells as a "sucking proboscis." However, it now appears that attachment to other organisms is a purely mechanical process without ill effect on the organisms so invested by the caulobacters.

### NONSTALKED, NONSHEATHED IRON-DEPOSITERS

**Siderocapsa treubii.**   *S. treubii* is a coccobacillus about 0.5 by 2 μ in size. It is hardly algalike but is representative of aquatic, iron-accumulating bacteria that grow in gummy masses, the Siderocapsaceae. *S. treubii* envelops itself in a thick, slimy or gelatinous extracellular substance and grows in fresh water in the form of a

compact mass attached to some object such as a water plant or a stone. Sometimes these growths are extensive, and iron or manganese is deposited in large amounts around them. Like *Gallionella* and *Leptothrix,* they are important in the fouling of pipes but their growth is not so extensive as *Gallionella* or *Leptothrix* or *Sphaerotilis.*

### OTHER ALGA-LIKE BACTERIA

In addition to the organisms already discussed, two other groups of alga-like bacteria may be briefly described.

**Order Hyphomicrobiales.***   Organisms of the Order Hyphomicrobiales are common in freshwater ponds, streams and muds; also in soil and sewage. One species has been isolated from sea water in Barcelona harbor. Most are saprophytes; some species parasitize aquatic fauna.

Bacteria of the Order Hyphomicrobiales are distinguished by the formation of yeastlike *buds* at the tips of mature, bacillus-like cells or from the tips of *filaments,* or *stalks,* which develop at the tips of cells; or from the filaments themselves, which often connect two cells (Fig. 38.15). Branching of the stalks thus often occurs. The cells generally occur in aggregates; free-floating or attached by their filaments to a stone or other base. The cells are gram-negative, ovoid

---

*Gr. *hyphe* = thread.

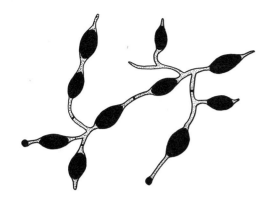

**Figure 38.15**   Structure of Hyphomicrobiales (diagrammatic). (See text.)

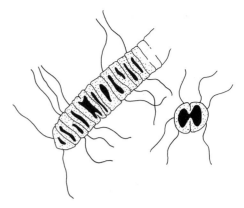

**Figure 38.16**   Structure of Caryophanales (diagrammatic). The prominent, disk-like nuclei are shown as dark objects. Note also the multicellular trichome, nuclei undergoing division and peritrichous flagella.

or spherical, with diameters of 0.5 to 1.0 $\mu$. When motile they have a single polar flagellum. Unlike any other bacteria, fission in Hyphomicrobiales is *longitudinal* instead of transverse.

Similar stalked, aquatic species are grouped in the genera *Pasteuria* and *Blastocaulis.* One species, *H. neptunum,* exhibits a life cycle reminiscent of that of the caulobacters. A nonflagellate "mother" cell sends out a stalk at the tip of which a budlike cell appears. This develops a flagellum, usually at the distal tip. The flagellate "daughter" cell ("swarmer"?) swims away. It eventually discards the flagellum and repeats the cycle. Some modifications of the cycle have been described.

Hyphomicrobiales are mainly aerobic, nonsporeforming, and have simple organic nutrient requirements; however, one genus, *Rhodomicrobium,* is photosynthetic. This genus thus combines properties of Caulobacteraceae (stalks) and Rhodobacteriineae (photosynthesis). Such overlappings of properties illustrate some of the difficulties in classifying microorganisms. Some species of Hyphomicrobiales have been found in association with heavy deposits of insoluble manganese compounds in fresh-water pipes.

**Order Caryophanales.*** Like Beggiatoales, the Caryophanales generally occur as unsheathed, long (in some species up to 2000 $\mu$ or 2 mm.), alga-like trichomes, typically with rounded ends. However, one species resembles the Chlamydobacteriales in forming a sheathed trichome containing bacillus-like cells. The individual cells are cylindrical or discoid, and each contains a distinctive, *conspicuous,* disk-shaped or ringlike body that resembles a nucleus (Fig. 38.16). The trichomes in some species are motile with peritrichous flagella. Multiplication is by

transverse division of the trichomes and by bacillus-like swarm cells (hormogonia or gonidia) released from the trichomes. Some species form spores. None is photosynthetic. They are generally nonpathogenic saprophytes and occur in dung, the oral mucous membranes of mammals and in decaying organic matter.

## SUPPLEMENTARY READING

Brock, T. D., and Mandel, M.: Deoxyribonucleic acid base composition of geographically diverse strains of *Leucothrix mucor.* J. Bact., *91*:1659, 1966.

Burton, S. D., Morita, R. Y., and Miller, W.: Utilization of acetate by *Beggiatoa.* J. Bact., *91*:1192, 1966.

Gibson, K. D.: Electron microscopy of chromatophores of *Rhodopseudomonas spheroides.* J. Bact., *90*:1059, 1965.

Jensen, S. L.: Biosynthesis and function of carotenoid pigments in microorganisms. Ann. Rev. Microbiol., *19*:163, 1965.

Johnson, A. H., and Stokes, J. L.: Manganese oxidation by *Sphaerotilus discophorus.* J. Bact., *91*:1543, 1966.

Leifson, E.: *Hyphomicrobium neptunum* sp. n. Ant. Leeuw., *30*:249, 1964.

Morita, R. Y., and Stave, P. W.: Electron micrograph of an ultrathin section of *Beggiatoa.* J. Bact. *85*:940, 1963.

Mulder, E. G., and van Veen, W. L.: Investigations on the *Sphaerotilis-Leptothrix* group. Ant. Leeuw., *29*:121, 1963.

Pfennig, N.: Photosynthetic bacteria. Ann. Rev. Microbiol., *21*:285, 1967.

Romano, A. H., and Peloquin, J. P.: Composition of the sheath of *Sphaerotilis natans.* J. Bact., *86*:252, 1963.

Schmidt, J. M., and Stanier, R. Y.: Isolation and characterization of bacteriophages active against stalked bacteria. J. Gen. Microbiol., *39*:95, 1965.

Thimann, K. V.: The Life of Bacteria, 2nd ed., Chapter 23. The Macmillan Co., New York. 1963.

Tyler, P. A., and Marshall, K. C.: Microbiol oxidation of manganese in hydroelectric pipelines. Ant. Leeuw., *33*:171, 1967.

Valentine, R. C.: Bacterial ferredoxin. Bact. Rev., *28*:497, 1964.

Van Iterson, W.: *Gallionella ferruginea* in a Different Light. N. V. Noord-Hollandsche Vitgevers Maatschappij, Amsterdam. 1958.

---

*Gr. *caryum* = kernel; *phanus* = conspicuous.

# Chapter 39

---

# ORDER ACTINOMYCETALES (Moldlike Bacteria)

The name of the Order Actinomycetales is derived from the term *Actinomyces* (Gr. *actino* = radial emanations, e.g., sunlight; *mykes* = fungus; hence "ray-fungus"). The term Actinomyces was first used by Harz in 1878 to describe an organism found in the pus of cattle suffering from the disease now called *actinomycosis* or "lumpy jaw." Harz used the term Actinomyces as descriptive of the *radial* arrangement of the branching, moldlike threads of the organism when growing in infected tissues. The term has since been adopted as the name of one genus of the Order Actinomycetales.

The Actinomycetales differ from most other bacteria in that *true branching*, a distinctly moldlike character, is normally found in all of its species. Unlike any of the bacteria discussed in the foregoing chapter, none of the Actinomycetales is sheathed, stalked or photosynthetic; none accumulates sulfur, iron or other free elements in or on the cells. All of the Actinomycetales are chemoorganotrophic, although many will grow on simple mineral media with an organic carbon source. The cells are of the same order of diameter as typical Eubacteriales or Pseudomonadineae: 0.5 to 5 $\mu$, although the branching filaments of some species may reach lengths of several millimeters. Septa are formed by some, but many are coenocytic. All are gram-positive. Only one or two species are motile. All but a few species are harmless saprophytes, widely distributed in decomposing organic matter in soil, dung and marine and fresh waters. None forms endospores, although some species form moldlike conidia (or conidiospores) borne on *conidiophores* (or *sporophores*) (Table 39.1). The whole order is often referred to casually as the actinomycetes.

**Molds and Actinomycetes.** Striking and constant *differences* between the moldlike Actinomycetales and true molds (Eumycetes) are: (1) the minuteness of the filaments of Actinomycetales (1 to 5 $\mu$ in diameter and seldom more than a few millimeters in length; true molds range around 10 to 20 $\mu$ in diameter and their mycelia are often several inches in extent); (2) the procaryotic structure of Actinomycetales; (3) the cell walls of Actinomycetales contain mucopolysaccharide, like bacteria, and are not chitinous as in molds and contain both muramic and diaminopimelic acids, found only in bacteria; (4) sexual phenomena such as occur in many molds are absent.

These branching bacteria are at present grouped in four families as listed in Table 39.1.

## 39.1 FAMILY STREPTOMYCETACEAE

There are two distinct genera in this family: *Streptomyces* and *Micromonospora*. A third, *Thermoactinomyces,* is sometimes merged with the first two.

*Streptomyces* forms long, much-branched, aerial mycelia consisting of very moldlike, non-fragmenting, very fine, typically coenocytic filaments. Their cell walls contain some of the components of chitin, a major constituent of cell walls of Eumycetes, but are not true chitin. Multiplication is by conidia produced asexually at the tips of *conidiophores* or *sporophores*. The conidia form long, straight, curved or coiled chains,

**TABLE 39.1**   THE ORDER ACTINOMYCETALES (TRUE BRANCHING)

| | |
|---|---|
| 1. Family Streptomycetaceae (filament and mycelium formers; do not readily fragment) <br>    Genus *Streptomyces* (well developed aerial mycelia; curled chains of conidia; many produce antibiotics). <br>    Genus *Micromonospora* (single conidia; subsurface mycelia) <br>    Genus *Thermoactinomyces* (50° to 65° C.) <br> 2. Family Actinoplanaceae (spores formed in sporangia) <br>    Genus *Actinoplanes* (no aerial mycelium; spores motile) <br>    Genus *Streptosporangium* (much aerial mycelium; spores nonmotile) | Conidia or Spores present |
| 3. Family Actinomycetaceae (limited mycelia that fragment readily) <br>    Genus *Actinomyces* (anaerobic; cause actinomycosis) ⎫ <br>    Genus *Nocardia* (aerobic; some cause nocardiosis) ⎬ (slightly acid-fast) <br> 4. Family Mycobacteriaceae (mycelial character limited to occasional branching cells: T, Y) <br>    Genus *Mycobacterium* (strongly acid-fast; tuberculosis, leprosy) <br>    Genus *Mycococcus* (not acid-fast) | No Conidia or Spores |

giving a curious appearance to the mycelium as a whole (Fig. 39.1). The directions and forms of the coils are fairly constant for any given species under standard cultural conditions and are important in the classification of *Streptomyces*.

The conidia of *Streptomyces*, when examined with the electron microscope at magnifications of 8000 ×, reveal striking surface configurations, "sculpturing," or "ornamentations." They are of at least four types: spiny, hairy, warty and smooth (Fig. 39.2). Under standardized cultural conditions these characters are fairly constant as to species and can serve as an aid in classification; usually a frustrating process when based only on the notoriously variable biochemical characters of *Streptomyces*.

The conidia of *Streptomyces* and other Actinomycetales are not as heat resistant as the endospores of true bacteria, being killed by 10 to 30 minute exposures at 65° C., a temperature only slightly higher than that required to kill the vegetative mycelium.

The colonies of *Streptomyces* are usually tough, dense-textured, and often very adherent to the medium owing to vegetative (subsurface) mycelia. They have a woolly or velvety appearance because of the mycelial structure. The growth of many species is brilliantly colored: red, orange, yellow. Colonies usually range in diameter from less than 1 mm. to several millimeters, definitely smaller than the huge colonies of true molds.

The colonies on infusion or extract agar are often papillate, and frequently the surface is thrown into radial folds or ridges. They give off a distinctive, musty odor characteristic of damp cellars and newly turned soil. This has been ascribed to a neutral volatile oil called *geosmin*.

Most species of *Streptomyces* are saprophytes

and are active in decomposition of a wide range of organic materials. A few species are pathogens in animals or plants. *Streptomyces scabies,* for example, produces a troublesome disease ("scab") of potatoes.

Growth is usually best at temperatures about 25° C., although some thermophilic soil species (Genus *Thermoactinomyces*) grow well at

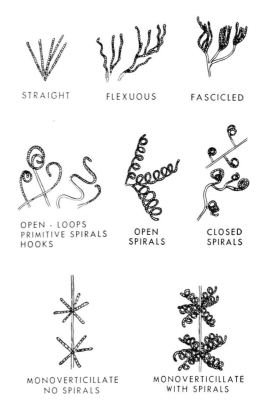

STRAIGHT     FLEXUOUS     FASCICLED

OPEN - LOOPS <br> PRIMITIVE SPIRALS    OPEN     CLOSED <br> HOOKS       SPIRALS     SPIRALS

MONOVERTICILLATE     MONOVERTICILLATE <br> NO SPIRALS        WITH SPIRALS

**Figure 39.1** Distinctive arrangements of conidial filaments of various types of *Streptomyces*. (Adapted from Pridham, Hesseltine and Benedict: Appl. Microbiol., vol. 6.)

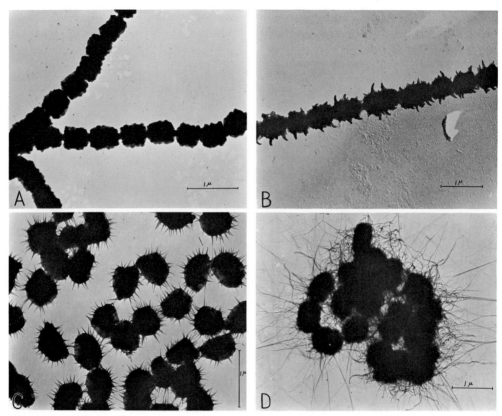

**Figure 39.2** Examples of distinctive "sculpturing" on the surfaces of conidia of various species of *Streptomyces*. *A, S. olivaceus; B, S. purpurascens; C, S. diastatochromogenes; D, S. albogriseolus.* (From Tresner, Davies and Backus: J. Bact., vol. 81.)

temperatures as high as 65° C. Unlike most true molds, optimal growth occurs at pH 8 or 9, and is greatly depressed by reactions near pH 5.

It is obvious from the optimal pH that liming of acid soils will encourage growth of the saprophytic actinomycetes of all families. Their growth increases fertility since they actively decompose complex organic materials so that other bacteria and farm crops can make use of them. The various species causing *scab* of potatoes and other root crops are also encouraged by liming of soil so that one must consider both the nature of the crop to be raised and soil pH before indiscriminate liming. As the Streptomycetaceae and other actinomycetes of the soil are aerobic, it is apparent why draining swamp lands in addition to liming increases the fertility of such soils.

*Streptomyces and Antibiotics.* The Genus *Streptomyces* is one of the most extensively investigated groups of bacteria, because various species produce antibiotics of immense value in human or veterinary medicine, in the control of plant diseases and industrial spoilage by molds

and bacteria, and in scientific research (see Chapters 22 and 43).

MICROMONOSPORA. The organisms of this genus are similar to *Streptomyces* in many respects. *Micromonospora* filaments are coenocytic. Mycelial growth is not conspicuously aerial but is extensive in the substrate; the conidia occur singly or in small clusters at the tips of short branches.

## 39.2   FAMILY ACTINOPLANACEAE

Some of the species of Family Actinoplanaceae are among the most moldlike of bacteria. They are commonly found in soil and in aquatic habitats or growing as saprophytes on dead leaves. They form a much-branched, occasionally septate, inconspicuous but widespreading *vegetative* mycelium and a more or less conspicuous aerial mycelium.

As in the Phycomycetes (Eumycetes), asexually reproductive *sporangiospores* are formed by Actinoplanaceae in sacs or sporangia (Fig. 39.3) under aerobic conditions. In the Genera

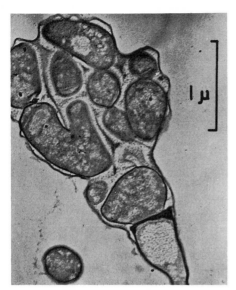

**Figure 39.3**   Electron micrograph of a section through a mature sporangium of a strain of *Actinoplanes*. (From Lechevalier and Holbert: J. Bact., *89*:217, 1965.)

*Actinoplanes, Ampulariella* and *Spirillospora* these spores are actively motile with polar flagella when released from the sporangium (Fig. 39.4). This is suggestive of the aquatic mold *Saprolegnia* which also forms motile sporangiospores (*zoospores*). However, electron micrographs of *Actinoplanes* show it to be procaryotic, not moldlike (eucaryotic), in structure.

## 39.3   FAMILY ACTINOMYCETACEAE

The Family Actinomycetaceae includes two genera of mycelium-formers: the aerobic Genus *Nocardia* and the strictly anaerobic Genus *Actinomyces*.

**Genus Nocardia.**   Nocardias differ from *Streptomyces* in that: (1) the filaments, at first coenocytic, later become septate and tend to fragment readily into bacillus-like and coccuslike segments (Fig. 39.5); (2) no conidia or spores are formed.

Differentiation between some species of *Nocardia* and *Streptomyces* is often difficult, but may be made on the basis of differing forms of diaminopimelic acid present in their cell walls.

Most of the nocardias are saprophytes that live in the soil as scavengers, decomposing complex organic substances of a great variety such as cellulose, proteins, polysaccharides, lipids, paraffins and even carbolic acid (phenol), naphthalene, rubber and cresol as sources of energy and carbon. Except for these curious sources

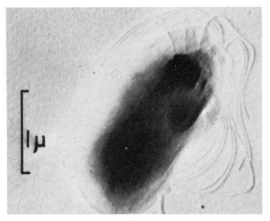

**Figure 39.4**   Electron micrograph of flagellate, motile sporangiospore of *Actinoplanes* strain P128. (From Lechevalier and Holbert: J. Bact., *89*:217, 1965.)

of carbon and energy their minimal food requirements are simple minerals.

Like the Actinoplanaceae, nocardias tend to grow on, and in, the surface of solid media such as agar, rarely producing much aerial mycelium.

Several *Nocardia* species are parasitic in man or animals, causing tuberculosis-like diseases or ulcerative lesions (*nocardiosis*). Saprophytic species of *Nocardia* are frequently found as contaminants in laboratory cultures. The mycelial fragments are often rod-shaped with some branching. Misshapen, clubbed and knobbed forms are easily mistaken for *Corynebacterium diphtheriae, Lactobacillus* and other gram-positive rods. A few species are somewhat acid-fast, especially in pathologic exudates (see *Mycobacterium*).

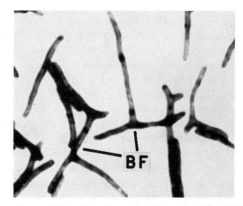

**Figure 39.5**   *Nocardia erythropolis*, stained by Webb's cell wall stain. Microphotograph of an 18-hour culture, with filaments exhibiting true branching and septum deposition after branching. BF, branching filament. Many of these fragment into bacillus-like bodies. × 2500. (From Adams and McClung: J. Bact., *84*:206, 1962.)

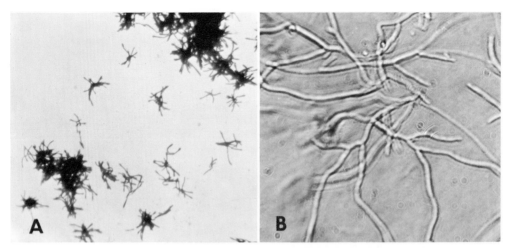

**Figure 39.6**   A pathogenic actinomycete, *Actinomyces israelii. A,* Smear from anaerobic (thioglycollate broth) culture ($\times$ 650). *B,* A very young colony on agar incubated anaerobically with 5 per cent $CO_2$ plus 95 per cent N at 37° C. ($\times$ 1750). Note the true-branching mycelia. (From Howell, Murphy, Paul and Stephen: J. Bact., vol. 78.)

Many species, as do *Streptomyces,* form brilliant pigments. The colonies of *Nocardia* on agar, however, are usually not mycelial but butyrous like those of true bacteria, ranging in diameter from 1 to 10 $\mu$.

**Genus Actinomyces.**   Species of Genus *Actinomyces* are distinguished among Actinomycetales by being strictly anaerobic and by requiring complex organic foods, such as chopped meat in broth. They are associated with the disease *actinomycosis* in man and animals. They are much like *Nocardia* in morphology and colony form (Fig. 39.6).

*Actinomyces bovis,* the cause of *"lumpy jaw"* or *actinomycosis* in cattle, is one of the few Actinomycetales rarely if ever found free in the environment. It occurs as a normal inhabitant in the oral cavity of cattle and other animals and man. Thence it may be introduced into the flesh of the jaws or tongue of cattle by thorns, splinters and the like. Swellings are produced by the growing *Actinomyces,* and the surrounding tissues become hard and indurated; hence the colloquial term *"wooden tongue"* for actinomycosis of the tongue in cattle. Eventually the infected tissue becomes riddled with abscess-like cavities which are filled with pus.

"Sulfur Granules."   The organisms, in contact with the defensive substances in the tissues, grow in compact, granular masses that acquire a bright yellow color. They are commonly called "sulfur granules." Crushed, they are seen with the microscope to consist of masses of mycelium held in a hard matrix of a polysaccharide-protein complex that is rich in calcium phosphate. The embedded mycelia

tend to send out filaments radially; hence the origin of the term "ray fungus." the tips of the filaments appear at the surface of the granules; coated with the cement-like calcified substance they appear club-shaped.

## 39.4   FAMILY MYCOBACTERIACEAE

This family contains only the bacterium-like Genera *Mycobacterium* and *Mycococcus.* The Genus *Mycobacterium* includes soil saprophytes, some unclassified species, and two pathogenic species: *Mycobacterium tuberculosis,* cause of tuberculosis, and the closely related *Mycobacterium leprae,* cause of leprosy. The mycobacteria rarely form true mycelia but sometimes exhibit limited branching. Any short filaments that are formed tend to break up at once into bacillus-like fragments.

Species of *Mycobacterium* are distinguished from all other bacteria by a peculiar staining property called *acid-fastness* (Chapter 2). This is associated with the waxy components in their cell walls. Occasionally acid-fast cells or fragments are found in other actinomycetes, especially some nocardias, but their staining is not like the definite, strong and constant acid-fastness of *Mycobacterium.*

Mycobacteria are gram-positive, nonmotile, aerobic, and nonsporeforming. Morphologically they are much like ordinary bacteria except for being somewhat curved and spindle-shaped, and sometimes beaded or granular, the beads and granules being probably artifacts resulting from staining processes. None forms conidia or

aerial hyphae. Most species are harmless saprophytes living in the soil, where they are very
important as scavengers that bring about decomposition of a wide variety of complex organic
compounds. Saprophytic mycobacteria may also
be found in acid-fast-stained smears of material
from preputial secretions (*Mycobacterium smeg-
matis*) or from folds of the skin as in the but-
tocks or axillae. Other saprophytic acid-fast
bacilli (*Myco. phlei*) are found in dust, soil,
butter, manure or on hay.

**Cultivation.**  Mycobacteria are commonly
cultivated on rich, solid organic media (Petroff's,
Petragnani's, Lowenstein-Jensen) made with
eggs, milk and potatoes and containing selectively inhibitory dyes. Any species may also be
cultivated in simple, aqueous, mineral solutions
containing an organic source of carbon or nitrogen, e.g., ammonium citrate plus glucose and
bovine albumin. The surface tension of the fluid
must be lowered with a surfactant substance
such as Tween-80* or WR1339 so that the fluid
*wets* the waxy bacilli. Most species, both saprophytes and pathogens, grow rapidly in such
fluids with a smooth, diffuse turbidity. Virulent
tubercle bacilli distinctively form long *cords* of
growth in such media (Fig. 39.7). This is of
great value in diagnosis.

***Mycobacterium tuberculosis.***  The organism
causing tuberculosis, *Myco. tuberculosis* is typical
of the Genus *Mycobacterium*. It is the most strongly
acid-fast species of the genus. It was first isolated
and shown to be the cause of tuberculosis by
R. Koch in 1882.

Tubercle bacilli may remain alive for long
periods outside the human or animal body. In
dried sputum in dark corners they may live six
to eight months; in particles of dried and
powdered sputum which can float through the
air as dust, they can remain alive for days and
may be inhaled. Exposure to sunlight for a few
hours kills them; so does pasteurization. This is
of importance since they can infect cows' udders
and hence their milk, thus transmitting the disease from the cattle to persons who drink unpasteurized or improperly supervised (uncertified) raw milk.

TYPES OF TUBERCLE BACILLI.  There are
several kinds of tubercle bacilli, varying according to the animal infected. For example, there
is the human type, *Mycobacterium tuberculosis* (or
*Myco. tuberculosis*, var. *hominis*) and the bovine

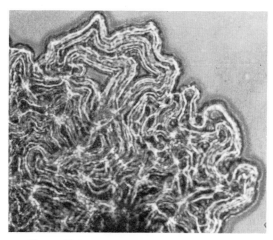

**Figure 39.7**  Tubercle mycobacteria, human strain
at 21 days on WR 1339 medium, showing thick cords
formed. × 100. (From Lorian: Appl. Microbiol., *14*:603, 1966.)

type, *Myco. bovis* (or *Myco. tuberculosis*, var. *bovis*).
The BCG bacillus used for vaccination (Chapter
25) is a modified bovine strain. A third mammalian type, called the *vole** bacillus (*Myco.
microti*), was discovered in 1937. This organism
is highly virulent for voles but produces only a
mild *immunizing* infection in man and has been
used in place of BCG. (See Chapter 25.) There
is also a bird or avian type (*Myco. avium*), that
grows well at about 40° C., and fish (*Myco.
marinum*) and other cold-blooded animal types
that grow well at lower temperatures (18° to
30° C.). All look alike microscopically and may
be cultivated on similar media. The cold-
blooded animal types do not as a rule infect the
warm-blooded animals or birds, and vice versa;
a good example of *species* (not of *specific*) resistance to infection.

**Atypical Acid-fasts.**  Some species of mycobacteria (e.g., *Myco. fortuitum, Myco. ulcerans,
Myco. kansasii*) are found associated with lesions
in the lung resembling tuberculosis and with
nodular lesions in cattle and other animals.
These mycobacteria are spoken of by medical
microbiologists as *atypical, unclassified* or anony-
mous *acid-fasts*. Their etiological relationship to
such lesions has long been in question, but organisms of Groups I and possibly III of the
Timpe-Runyon classification appear to be
definitely pathogenic for man.

The atypical acid-fasts have been divided
into several groups, primarily on the basis of
pigment formation and rate of growth on solid
media.

---

*Tween-80 (Atlas Powder Co.) is a surface-tension
reducer, a polyoxyethylene derivative of sorbitol mono-
oleate, a sort of liquid soap.

---

*A vole is a species of field mouse.

**TABLE 39.2  DISTINCTIVE PROPERTIES OF VARIOUS MYCOBACTERIA**

| Organisms | Pigment Formation in Relation to Light at 35° C. | | Produce aryl-sulfatase enzyme | Produce catalase§ in presence of isoniazid | Produce niacin | Decompose salicylate | Sensitive to: | | Rate of colony growth on solid media at 35° C. (days) | Pathogenic action in: | | |
| | Growth in dark | Growth in light | | | | | hydroxyl-amine | 8-azaguan-ine | | Man | Guinea pig** | Rabbit** |
|---|---|---|---|---|---|---|---|---|---|---|---|---|
| **"Typical" acid-fasts:** | | | | | | | | | | | | |
| M. tuberculosis | buff | buff | − | − | + | − | + | + | 14 | Tb‖ | Tb‖ | slight |
| M. bovis | none | none | − | − | − | − | + | + | 21 | Tb‖ | Tb‖ | Tb‖ |
| M. avium | little; yellow | little; yellow | − | + | − | − | + | + | 7 | rare in mammals | | |
| **"Atypical" acid-fasts:** | | | | | | | | | | | | |
| M. kansasii* | little or none | bright yellow or red-orange | + | + | − | − | + | + | 10 | ? | −¶ | − |
| M. fortuitum | little; yellow | little; yellow | + | + | − | + | − | − | 2 | ? | −¶ | − |
| Skotochromogens† | orange-yellow | orange-red | + | ± | − | − | ± | ± | 14 | ? | −¶ | − |
| Nonchromogens‡ | none | none | + | −, ± or + | − | − | − | − | 2–12 | ? | −¶ | − |
| **Saprophytes:** | | | | | | | | | | | | |
| M. phlei | orange, yellow | orange, yellow | + | + | − | − | − | − | 2–4 | − | − | − |
| M. smegmatis | orange, yellow | orange, yellow | + | + | − | − | − | − | 2–4 | − | − | − |

\* Group I photochromogens of the Runyon classification.
† Group II of the Runyon classification.
‡ Groups III and IV of the Runyon classification; including the "Battey" strains (from Battey Hospital, Georgia).
§ Applies only to isoniazid-resistant strains since only these grow in the presence of isoniazid. All strains produce some catalase in the absence of niazid.
‖ Progressive tuberculosis.
¶ May be a local abscess; no progressive disease.
** Using pure culture as inoculum.

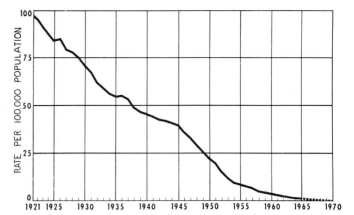

**Figure 39.8** Decline in tuberculosis mortality in the United States since 1921, with prospective decline to 1970. Note that this applies to *deaths,* not to new or existing cases. (From Dublin: Am. J. Pub. Health, vol. 48, and Statistical Bureau, Metropolitan Life Insurance Co.)

**Differentiation between Mycobacteria.** In the control of tuberculosis, both human and bovine, it is clearly necessary to differentiate between the pathogens, possible pathogens such as the atypical acid-fasts, and the harmless saprophytes. Several tests used in such differentiations are summarized in Table 39.2. Space does not permit a detailed description of these tests but data may be found in the literature cited. It is important to note that, as in many microbiological differentiations, no *single* test is wholly reliable by itself.

The atypical acid-fast bacilli produce a tuberculin-type of allergy detectable with tuberculin-like antigens prepared from the appropriate strains, but often cross-reacting with tuberculin from *M. tuberculosis.*

## TUBERCULOSIS

Tuberculosis is much more common than is generally supposed. While *deaths* in the United

States have declined greatly in four decades (Fig. 39.8) because of improved methods of finding cases, diagnosis and treatment, the number of *newly reported cases* each year remains appallingly high; over 50,000 in 1968, with nearly 10,000 deaths. Undoubtedly, many more infections (actual and potential cases), possibly 350,000 are *unreported* (Fig. 39.9).

**Tubercles and Tuberculosis.** When tubercle bacilli gain a foothold in an uninfected but susceptible animal or person, the tissues in which the bacilli settle immediately react against the organisms in a very characteristic way. Numbers of tissue cells begin to grow around the bacilli in an attempt to incarcerate them, or wall them in. A tiny, pearly gray mass of cells is thus formed with tubercle bacilli at the center. This lesion is called a *tubercle.* Such infections occur very commonly. In a large majority of people, in good health and environments, resistance is high. Under such circumstances these infections

**Figure 39.9** Reported tuberculosis mortality, incidence and prevalence in the United States, 1956. (U. S. Public Health Service, Pub. No. 639, 1958.)

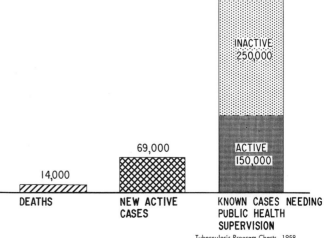

heal and confer immunity. The tuberculin test becomes positive (see Chapter 26).

If the resistance of the host is low, because of malnutrition, overwork, or other debilitating factors, the tissues are unable to arrest the bacilli. They continue to grow, killing the surrounding cells and destroying the fibrous walls. Numbers of adjacent tubercles may thus coalesce. The dead tissue at the center of such masses of tubercles becomes cheesy and yellowish and is said to be *caseated.* It may rapidly involve the major part of the infected organ. If the tubercle is in a lung, the necrosis (death of tissue) may extend till it invades and breaks through the wall of a bronchus. The caseous material, which may contain millions of living tubercle bacilli, is discharged with the sputum by coughing. A cavity is left behind (*cavitation*).

Sometimes the caseous process breaks through the wall of an artery and then hemorrhage of the lung occurs, which may be fatal. In the vast majority of human beings these tuberculous processes tend to heal and to form lifelong scars whether the patient recovers or not. Sometimes they remain latent only to start up again later in life under stress of illness and other weakening influences.

## Hansen's Disease (Leprosy)

While leprosy is infrequent in the United States (possibly 40 new cases in 1966; probably 2000 in all), it is estimated that there are up to 20,000,000 cases in the world, mainly in the tropics: Central Africa, India, China, Burma, Asia, Brazil. The World Health Organization conducts world-wide studies of the disease and its control and cure.

**Etiology.** *Mycobacterium leprae* was discovered in 1874 by the Norwegian physician, *Hansen.* The disease and the bacillus are often referred to as *Hansen's disease* and *Hansen's bacillus.* Morphologically and in degree of acid-fastness the bacillus is almost exactly like the tubercle bacillus, but differs from it in being an *obligate intracellular parasite.* It has never been artificially cultivated in a *virulent form.* (Compare Reiter treponeme in relation to syphilis in Chapter 40.)

*Mycobacterium leprae* is always present in leprous tissue and never occurs in normal tissue. For many years this has been the only one of Koch's postulates to be demonstrated in connection with the etiology of leprosy. Demonstration of this organism in histological sections or

*biopsy* material (live tissue removed during life) is the most useful and conclusive diagnostic procedure.

There are several strains of so-called *Myco. leprae,* isolated from lepers, which may be cultivated easily on ordinary culture media. They are not virulent and have the properties of saprophytic species of *Mycobacterium.* Several reports of successful inoculation of human beings with cultures of *Myco. leprae* and even with leprous material have appeared. None has ever been confirmed. It is interesting to note that leprous lesions occur principally in the outer parts of the body that are relatively *cool:* skin, peripheral nerves and nasal passages. Artificial inoculation into cool tissues, e.g., foot-pads of mice, human skin (tattooing), is said to produce infections.

The method of transmission of leprosy under natural conditions is obscure. Contrary to a notion as old as history, Hansen's disease is *not* highly contagious. The rate of conjugal infection is low. Many children who become infected heal spontaneously, as in tuberculosis. Also as in tuberculosis, the outcome of infection depends greatly on the resistance of the individual. Lesions and nasal discharges contain the bacilli in large numbers and probably transmit the disease. However, prolonged (months or years) close contact appears to be necessary. Persons under 25 years of age are more likely to contract the disease. The incubation period appears to range from a few months to as long as 20 years.

**Allergy in Hansen's Disease.** As in tuberculosis, allergy of the delayed type develops in Hansen's disease. A skin test, the *lepromin test,* in some ways analogous to the tuberculin test, is used in diagnostic work. The antigen may be made from the bacilli themselves (*bacillary lepromin*) or, preferably, from leprous tissue (*integral* or *Mitsuda-Hayashi* lepromin). These antigens act not only to detect allergy but also, it seems, to induce some degree of immunity. BCG can induce lepromin positivity and there is encouraging evidence that BCG vaccination may be a valuable weapon in immunizing against this ancient enemy of mankind.

**History.** Hansen's disease is well known to students of the Bible and medieval history. Fear and horror of lepers have been a human tradition since antiquity. In former days many disfiguring diseases were confused with leprosy: various fungal infections, yaws, protozoal infections, and so on. The loathing of leprosy arises in great part from the disfigurement of

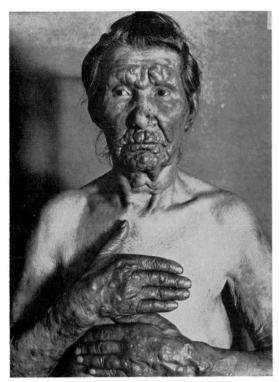

**Figure 39.10** An advanced lepromatous case with leonine face, both furrowed and nodulate, and with marked involvement of the forearm and hands, less of the upper arms and still less of the body. (From Hunter, Frye and Swartzwelder: Manual of Tropical Medicine 4th ed., 1966, W. B. Saunders Co.)

the body and destruction of tissue, with scar formation, which accompanies it (Fig. 39.10). Modern surgery is doing much to combat this.

In ancient times lepers were excluded from all public contacts and left to die of exposure and starvation. In some areas they still are excluded, but provisions for their comfort and well-being are being greatly improved in developed areas. There are now drugs (sulfones, antibiotics) that are of great assistance, but much remains to be done.

## SUPPLEMENTARY READING

Brown, J. A. K., and Stone, M. M.: BCG against leprosy. British Med. J., *1*:7, 1966.

Christensen, W. B., Street, A. W., and Leach, R. E.: Simplified medium and method for determining niacin production by *M. tuberculosis.* Pub. Health Lab., *24*:124, 1966.

Cochrane, R. G., and Davey, T. F.: Leprosy in Theory and Practice, 2nd ed. The Williams & Wilkins Co., Baltimore. 1964.

Dubos, R.: Acquired immunity to tuberculosis. Amer. Rev. Resp. Dis., *90*:505, 1964.

Gerber, N. N., and Lechevalier, H. A.: Geosmin, an earthy-smelling substance isolated from actinomycetes. Appl. Microbiol., *13*:935, 1965.

Hopwood, D. A., and Glauert, A. M.: Electron microscope observations on the surface structures of *Streptomyces violaceoruber.* J. Gen. Microbiol., *26*:325, 1961.

Lechevalier, H. A., and Lechevalier, M. P.: Biology of actinomycetes. Ann. Rev. Microbiol., *21*:71, 1967.

Lester, W.: Unclassified mycobacterial diseases. Ann. Rev. Med., *17*:351, 1966.

Mallman, V. H., Mallman, W. L., and Robinson, P.: Relationship of atypical bovine and porcine mycobacteria to those of human origin. Health Lab. Science, *1*:11, 1964.

Moore, R. T., and Chapman, G. B.: Observations of the fine structure and modes of growth of a streptomycete. J. Bact., *78*:878, 1959.

Mushlin, I., and Amberson, J. B.: Tracking down tuberculosis. Amer. J. Nursing, *65*:91, 1965.

Olitzki, A. L., Godinger, D., Israeli, M., and Honigman, A.: In vitro effects of some chemotherapeutic agents on mycobacteria. Appl. Microbiol., *15*:994, 1967.

Pine, L., and Overman, J. R.: Determination of the structure and composition of the 'sulphur granules' of *Actinomyces bovis.* J. Gen. Microbiol., *32*:209, 1963.

Shepard, C. C.: Leprosy, a world health problem. Amer. J. Nursing, *63*:112, 1963.

Stergus, I.: Relation of atypical acid-fast bacteria to disease. Pub. Health Lab., *24*:100, 1966.

Takimura, Y., and Thompson, J. R.: Photochromogenic mycobacterial pulmonary infection in a group of hospitalized patients in Chicago. Amer. Rev. Resp. Dis., *91*:582, 1965.

Tsukamura, M.: Conversion of salicylate to catechol by *Mycobacterium fortuitum.* J. Gen. Microbiol., *41*:317, 1965.

Tsukamura, M.: Differentiation of mycobacteria by susceptibility to hydroxylamine and 8-azaguanine. J. Bact., *90*:556, 1965.

Waksman, S. A.: The Actinomycetes. A Summary of Current Knowledge. Ronald Press Co., New York. 1967.

# Chapter 40

## ORDERS MYXOBACTERALES AND SPIROCHAETALES
### (Protozoa-like Bacteria)

Like the terms "alga-like" and "moldlike," the term "protozoa-like" has no taxonomic significance, but is merely one of convenience for considering together two groups of bacteria, Spirochaetales and Myxobacterales, that have in common some characteristics that are suggestive of protozoa: thin, flexible cell walls and active, self-flexing movements. The Spirochaetales are characterized, in addition, by relatively complex helicoidal forms and elastic, keratin-like "skeletons" and by active rotatory as well as translatory motility. They do not exhibit flagellar or gliding motility (Table 38.1).

The Myxobacterales also have thin, flexible, cell walls and definite, translatory motility without flagella. They are distinguished from Spirochaetales by their alga-like, gliding motility in contact with solid objects. They are distinguished from all other bacteria by their relatively complex life cycle that superficially but strikingly resembles the life cycle of certain protozoa, the ameba-like slime molds or myxamebas of the Order Acrasiales (see *Mycetozoa*, this chapter).

Because of the flexing activity of myxobacters, it has been suggested that they might be included, with other bacteria that show both gliding and flexing motility, in a proposed subclass, the Flexibacteria. As an extension of this idea, it has also been suggested that all of the procaryons be brought together into a new kingdom, the Procaryota or Mychota; a logical and progressive idea.

The Spirochaetales and Myxobacterales are not photosynthetic, nor do they form trichomes, branching filaments, mycelia, flagella, conidia or endospores. They are not sheathed, or stalked, nor do they accumulate granules of sulfur, iron or other elements. With a few exceptions they are bacterial in dimensions and, so far as is known, procaryotic in structure. All multiply by transverse binary fission and are organotrophic. True sexuality has not been observed. Not all have been cultivated but several representative species have been grown on artificial media at mesophilic temperatures and pH of about 7.2. Most species are harmless saprophytes of the soil or of marine or fresh aquatic muds, and are active as scavengers in decomposing organic matters. A few species of Spirochaetales are among the most dangerous and widespread pathogens; a few species of Myxobacterales are pathogenic on fish or plants.

### 40.1 ORDER MYXOBACTERALES

The Myxobacterales (myxobacters) (Gr. *myxo* = slime) are coccus-like or often fusiform rods, varying in length from 3 to 12 μ (Fig. 40.1), and are especially characterized, in addition to the aforementioned peculiarities, by the production of distinctive masses of slime in which they live communally. These communal structures consist of flat, spreading, slimy colonies with lobular extensions, and are usually called a *swarm stage* or *pseudoplasmodium*. The latter term is derived from their resemblance to a similar structure called a *plasmodium* formed by true

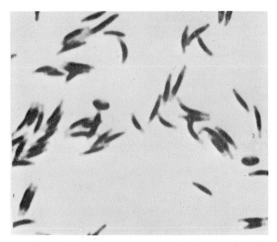

**Figure 40.1** Electron micrograph of vegetative cells of a species of myxobacteria. Mature cells stained to show chromatinic intracellular (presumably nuclear) structures. (Robinow-Giemsa stain) ($\times$ 3,000). (From Loebeck and Ordal: J. Gen. Microbiol., vol. 16.)

eucaryotic protozoa, Mycetozoa (see farther on). The pseudoplasmodium is one stage of the life cycle of myxobacters.

**Life Cycle.** These curious organisms undergo alternations of form: the *swarm stage* and the *encystment stage,* suggesting *alternation* of *generations* of eucaryons.

SWARM STAGE.   This growth may occur on any decaying organic matter. In this stage the bacteria multiply by binary fission and secrete a slimy matrix in which they all live together. The slime appears to be formed within the cell wall and extruded to the exterior. This slimy material is "A distinct, firm, hyaline, gelatinous base, secreted by the colony as it extends itself, over which the individuals may move or in which they may become imbedded, and is so coherent a structure that whole colonies may be stripped intact by means of it, from the surface of nutrient agar, for example" (*Thaxter*) (Fig. 40.2). The swarm stage lasts for periods varying from a day to a week. Under favorable growth conditions the swarm stage continues and the growth may cover an area of several square centimeters. Encystment then begins, apparently as a result of increased nutritional deficiencies.

ENCYSTMENT OR FRUITING STAGE.   Except in two groups: Family Cytophagaceae (no cysts or fruiting bodies) and Genus *Sporocytophaga* (individual cells form dormant *microcysts*), the rods gather together at different points in the slimy matrix and heap themselves up. The heaps may become raised above the substratum. In some genera, e.g., *Myxococcus,* this primitive fruiting body never develops beyond a low, rounded microscopic hump (Fig. 40.3). In others, e.g., *Chondromyces,* it grows into elaborate, branched, hobgoblin, treelike structures up to 2 mm. in height (Fig. 40.4). The rods push to the uppermost portions. The rods then become shortened, rounded and dormant *resting cells.* In the family Myxococcaceae these become oval, deeply staining, thick-walled *microcysts.* The gelatinous slime dries as an envelope about the resting cells. In some genera, e.g., *Angiococcus,* masses of the resting cells are enclosed in separate, fruitlike cysts. Within the fruiting body they resist drying and other unfavorable conditions. After a resting period, if moisture is present the enclosing slime softens and the rods emerge, become vegetative, and form new swarm stages.

**Cultivation of Myxobacterales.**   Some species have never been cultivated. Of many species only the fruiting stage is known. The initial *enrichment* of some fruiting species is not difficult. (Enrichment of any organism involves stimulation of rapid and pre-emptive growth of the desired organism in a mixed culture by providing nutrients and environmental conditions which favor it.) For many species of myxobacters, one enrichment method is to place pellets of sterilized rabbit feces close together on the sur-

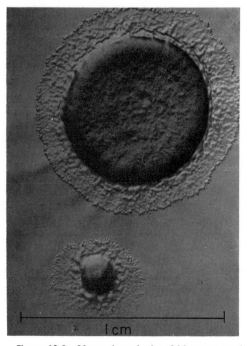

**Figure 40.2** Vegetative colonies of *Myxococcus xanthus,* strain FB. (From Dworkin: J. Bact., *86:*67, 1963.)

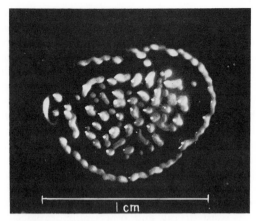

**Figure 40.3** Fruiting bodies of *Myxococcus xanthus,* strain FB. (From Dworkin: J. Bact., *86*:67, 1963.)

For the isolation of a cellulose-utilizing, soil-inhabiting species of *Cytophaga,* an initial enrichment in a solution containing inorganic sources of all necessary elements except carbon will suffice. Such a solution may consist of the following:

| Ingredient | Grams |
| --- | --- |
| $KNO_3$ | 0.1 |
| $K_2HPO_4$ | 0.1 |
| $MgSO_4$ | 0.02 |
| $CaCl_2$ | 0.01 |
| $FeCl_3$ | 0.002 |
| Water | 1000 |

Adjust pH to 7.5.

face of fresh soil in covered dishes, keeping the whole quite moist for a week or two at about 35° C. Many species grow well at 10° to 20° C. Pure cultures of some species may be obtained on rabbit-dung agar or on infusion agar. The field is an interesting one for the student of cryptogamic botany.

To this are added some bits of sterile filter paper (cellulose) as a source of carbon.

One species (*Cytophaga columnaris*), of importance because it is a pathogen of fish of commercial value, has been cultivated on media containing peptone (*Tryptone*), yeast and meat extracts and sodium acetate. Such media may be fluid or solidified with agar. The colonies of these organisms are beautifully stellate or arbo-

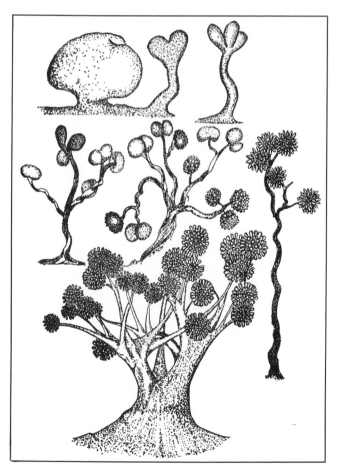

**Figure 40.4** Various mature forms of Myxobacterales. (Redrawn from Thaxter.)

rescent, especially when floating in a fluid medium.

Sometimes they swing by one end from a fixed surface and oscillate like a pendulum. It is of interest that a bacteriophage (*myxophage*) active in the lysis of *C. columnaris* has been demonstrated, the first to be observed in any species of Myxobacterales.

**Lytic Action of Myxobacterales.**   Many of the fruiting myxobacters produce lysis of the cells of true bacteria (Eubacteriales) and of some higher fungi. They utilize as food the substances thus liberated. Practical use of this is made to cultivate myxobacters on agar containing heavy suspensions of bacteria, living or dead. Curiously, vegetative growth of the myxobacters is not abundant, but fruiting bodies are readily formed on such nutriment; further evidence that fructification is induced by nutritional deficiencies.

This lytic action must be of great importance in the interrelationship (ecology) of all organisms in the soil, where myxobacters live in contact with other microorganisms, though its full significance has not yet been entirely clarified. The lytic action is reminiscent of the polypeptide, cell-wall-destroying antibiotics produced by *Streptomyces* and *Bacillus* species from the soil, and suggests that the myxobacters may be a rich source of valuable antimicrobial products. In some species the lytic agent resembles lysozyme.

**Functions of Myxobacterales.**   Except a few parasitic species, myxobacters are of great importance to humanity as scavengers. As a group they are very active in the decomposition of *insoluble* organic materials such as dead vegetable matter (cellulose, agar) and the exoskeletal material (chitin) of insects and crustacea, as well as a wide variety of other animal and vegetable matter, thus not only removing waste matters but obligingly transforming them into predigested soluble foods for plants.

## 40.2   THE MYCETOZOA

### (MYXOMYCETES)

The mycetozoa are true, eucaryotic protozoa that have a strange resemblance to myxobacters. The two are all too frequently confused. In these animals a swarm stage is found that consists of a mass of *living protoplasm* (a true *plasmodium,* not a pseudoplasmodium consisting of inert slime), in which are thousands of diploid *nuclei.* These masses of multinucleate protoplasm are capable

of ameboid motion and, like true amebae, can ingest solid particles of food including bacteria. These are distinctly *animal* characters. The mycetozoa live on rotten logs and the like in much the same situations as myxobacters and move about in the moisture and shade like amebae.

After several days of plasmodial existence they cease to move, and fructification begins. The protoplasm sends up *stalks* on the tips of which *sporangia* (spore-bearing cysts) are formed, in a great variety of the most graceful and delicate forms and of the most brilliant colors. Each sporangium contains many spores; each spore contains a haploid nucleus and is surrounded by a cellulose wall. The spores are dispersed by the wind. In water, each germinates, forming a separate, naked, flagellate or ameba-like swarm cell. These forms multiply rapidly by cell division. They later conjugate. Eventually they reaggregate to form the *multinucleate swarm stage* again.

Generally, cultivation of these organisms in both vegetative and fruiting stages is possible only if living bacterial cells (or, to a much less extent, dead cells or extracts of bacteria) are provided as pabulum. Without bacteria, development of the vegetative stage was not possible until 1962, when one species was cultivated through both stages on an axenic medium containing embryo extract, serum albumin, Tryptose, glucose, certain vitamins and necessary minerals (see cultivation of tissue cells and animal cells).

The resemblance between the myxobacters and mycetozoa is so close, yet so superficial, as to suggest the idea that a comparative study in morphology and function might have been in progress; an example of *convergent evolution.*

## 40.3   ORDER SPIROCHAETALES

### SPIRAL, FLEXIBLE BACTERIA

The term *spirochete* is often used in a general sense to include all species of the Order Spirochaetales. It will be so used here. All spirochetes are flexible *and* spiral. Differentiate the term spirochete from the name of the Genus *Spirillum,* Order Pseudomonadales (page 454). *Spirillum,* though spiral, is not flexible. On the other hand, Myxobacterales, while flexible, are not spiral.

The Order Spirochaetales is divided into two families: (a) Spirochaetaceae, which includes three genera of relatively large, saprophytic spirochetes: *Spirochaeta, Saprospira* and *Cristaspira;* and (b) Treponemataceae, which includes three genera of relatively small, slender spirochetes, some of which are dangerous and widespread pathogens: *Treponema, Leptospira* and *Borrelia*.

## FAMILY SPIROCHAETACEAE

**Genus *Spirochaeta*.**　The name *Spirochaeta* is derived from the term "Spirochaeta," by which name Ehrenberg, in 1833, designated a very long (100 to 500 $\mu$) slender (0.5 to 1.0 $\mu$) spiral and flexible organism that he found free-living in stagnant water. This organism, now the type species of the Genus *Spirochaeta*, is called *Spirochaeta plicatilis*. The ends are blunt. Large intracellular granules of "volutin" or inorganic polyphosphates and fat are present (Fig. 40.5). Motility is achieved by creeping and twisting movements. The organism may be found in sewage and stagnant and brackish water. Pure cultures have been made on medium containing extracts of leaves, and on 1.5 per cent agar with red blood cells. It grows as a thin film on the agar, rarely forming ordinary colonies. *Spirochaeta* is microaerophilic and grows in a pH range of 6 to 9 at about 26° C., and is entirely saprophytic.

**Genera *Saprospira* and *Cristispira*.**　These entirely saprophytic organisms resemble the foregoing in habitat and overall morphology. They are somewhat shorter and thicker than *Spirochaeta*.

Saprospiras appear to have septate or chambered protoplasm. This could represent separate cells or convolutions of helicoidal, end-to-end bundles of fibrils. End-to-end fibrils are characteristic of all spirochetes. Their form, numbers and arrangements vary with species, and are described more fully farther on. Saprospiras have never been cultivated in pure culture.

The habitat of *Cristispira* is restricted to a hyaline structure, called the crystalline style,

in the esophagus of oysters and related mollusks. Cristispiras are distinguished by a *crista*, a sort of keel or end-to-end membrane, apparently constructed of fibrils, which winds spirally about the organism from one end to the other, one edge free, the other attached to the cell (Fig. 40.5). This structure is suggestive of the undulating membrane seen in one genus of pathogenic protozoa, the trypanosomes.

## FAMILY TREPONEMATACEAE

Members of the Family Treponemataceae are the smallest and most tenuous of all of the spirochetes. There are three genera: *Treponema, Borrelia* and *Leptospira;* each contains dangerous and widespread pathogens of man and lower animals.

**Structure.**　Because of the minute diameters of these organisms, the details of their cell structure have had to await the development of very high-powered electron microscopes. Studies of various species show that treponemas, leptospiras and borrelias, while differing in size and form, have analogous structures. All appear to consist of three principal parts: (1) An *outer envelope* or sheath that is trilaminate like a "unit membrane" in some species. In other species the sheath is thin, vague, fragile and easily removed by washing or agitation, more like a capsule than a cell wall (Fig. 40.6). Differences in appearance may result from differences in preliminary treatment of the cells. (2) The cell proper appears to be a *protoplasmic tube* or cylinder (Fig. 40.7) enclosed in a very thin membrane that serves as a cytoplasmic membrane (Fig. 40.8). Like the outer structure, this also appears to be multilayered or of the "unit membrane" type; in some species it appears double. In *Treponema* it is easily destroyed by surfactants (emulsifying agents) and may be rich in lipids. Differentiation of a cell wall is not clear; in this spirochetes resemble protozoa. (3) All species have an *axial filament* that may consist of from 2 to 20 fibrils, depending on species and perhaps on extraneous factors.

These fibrils appear to arise, like flagella, from discs or basal granules or groups of granules close to one end of the protoplasmic cylinder and to be wound spirally, close around the outer surface of the protoplasmic cylinder, inside the outer envelope from one end of the cell to the other (Fig. 40.8). When the cells divide, extensions of these fibrils sometimes appear beyond the tips of the cells as "terminal fibrils," once regarded as flagella. The fibrils from

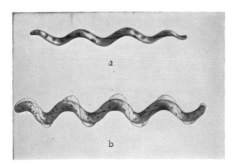

**Figure 40.5**　Forms of saprophytic spirochetes. *a, Spirochaeta; b, Cristispira.*

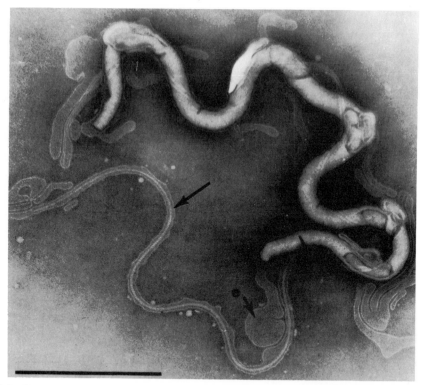

**Figure 40.6**    Flagellum-like projection of one axial fibril (arrow) in *Treponema microdentium*, probably following recent division. Note that sheath surrounding fibrillar protrusion is of a structure similar to that of disrupted envelope (e). Negative contrast. × 70,000. (From Listgarten and Socransky: J. Bact., *88*:1087, 1964.)

opposite ends of a pair of dividing cells appear at times to overlap on the protoplasmic cylinders. Fibrils may consist of many subfibrils that sometimes become frayed and resemble flagella, or the fibrils may be solid or have a distinct core. These appearances seem to be variable. Some spirochetes appear to have many large axial fibrils that seem to be tough and elastic and may consist of keratin-like proteins (e.g., horn or fingernails). In all species motility appears to be caused by the contractility and elasticity of the fibrils and the rotation of the helical cell. Similarities are seen by some workers between fibrils and flagella.

The internal structure of the protoplasmic cylinder appears granular or homogeneous in some species; markedly laminate or membranous in others. The nuclear material seems to be of the procaryotic type.

**Genus Treponema.** Genus *Treponema* contains the organisms that cause venereal syphilis, nonvenereal syphilis (bejel), the widespread tropical scourge, yaws, and some other diseases of man and other animals.

Treponemes are slender (0.25 to 0.4 $\mu$ in diameter) and seldom exceed a length of about 15 $\mu$. Their size is therefore comparable with

that of true bacteria. The organisms have neither crista nor septa. The 8 to 14 spirals found in *Treponema* are close and regular unless the contractions that characterize these organisms change them. The ends of the organisms are drawn out to extremely fine fibrils. These terminal fibrils have no function in the motility of the organism (Fig. 40.9). They are probably extensions of the axial filaments as previously mentioned.

*Treponema* is not easily stained or seen in moist, unstained preparations by ordinary illumination. Indeed, the first *Treponema* to be described, that causing syphilis (Schaudinn, 1905), was named *Treponema pallidum* because of its pale appearance. Other methods are therefore used to demonstrate treponemas microscopically. One is the method of negative staining; another, widely used to examine exudate from lesions of syphilis for diagnostic purposes, is the darkfield apparatus. A third, used mainly by the pathologist to demonstrate spirochetes in infected tissues, is termed *silver impregnation* (Fontana's method or Levaditi's method).

RESISTANCE AND CULTIVATION.    *T. pallidum* is a relatively fragile, highly parasitic organism. It has never been with certainty cultivated in a

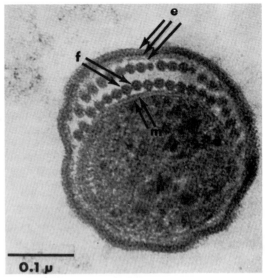

**Figure 40.8** Cross-section through large spirochete in gingival lesion of acute necrotizing ulcerative gingivitis. Note substructure of axial fibrils (f) suggestive of the presence of a dense central core. Fibrils are located between three dense layers of outer envelope (e) and two dense layers of membrane (m) covering protoplasmic cylinder (p). Kellenberger fixation. × 216,000. (From Listgarten and Socransky: J. Bact., *88*:1087, 1964.)

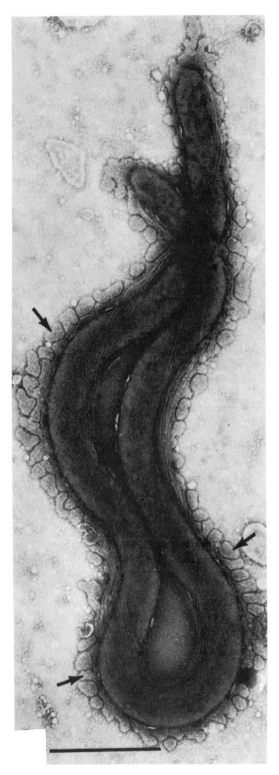

**Figure 40.7** Spirochete of intermediate size in gingival debris, demonstrating overlap of axial fibrils from opposite ends of what is probably a dividing cell. Note disrupted outer envelope (arrows). Negative contrast. × 29,900. (From Listgarten and Socransky: J. Bact., *88*:1087, 1964.)

virulent form in artificial media, in chick embryos or in tissue cultures, although it may be maintained alive and virulent, without multiplication, for several days in certain artificial media; an important factor in the diagnosis of syphilis.

*T. pallidum,* under ordinary circumstances, can survive for only very short periods outside the tissues of man or experimentally infected animals; hence, nonvenereal infection of man is rare. However, when quickly frozen and maintained at −76° C. by means of solid carbon dioxide, syphilis spirochetes, as well as many other bacteria and viruses, remain viable and fully infectious for years. *T. pallidum* does not long survive drying. Surface-tension reducers, such as ordinary soap and bile salts, quickly cause lysis of *T. pallidum,* suggesting that the membrane of the protoplasmic tube may be rich in lipids. The organism is quickly killed by ordinary disinfectants. In citrated blood stored in blood banks the spirochetes quickly die out.

REITER TREPONEME. Some similar spirochetes, possibly mutants of *T. pallidum* (notably the Reiter treponeme), have been cultivated and grow vigorously, but none of these is able to cause infection. The Reiter treponeme is of especial importance because it appears to be antigenically almost identical with *T. pallidum.*

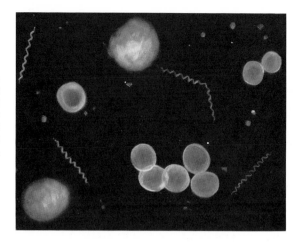

**Figure 40.9** Scrapings from a syphilitic chancre as seen in the microscope with darkfield illumination. The spirochetes are *Treponema pallidum.* The eight small rounded objects are erythrocytes; the two larger, rounded objects are tissue cells or pus cells; the smallest irregular objects are salt crystals, cell detritus and other bacteria. (Courtesy of Chas. Pfizer and Co., Inc., Brooklyn, N. Y. In J.A.M.A., vol. 157.)

It is therefore of great value in the diagnosis of syphilis by means of specific serological tests. Media used for cultivating the Reiter treponeme are complex organic mixtures containing numerous amino acids, fatty acids, vitamins, salts and serum. The organism is strictly anaerobic.

## 40.4   THE TREPONEMATOSES

Infection of humans or other animals by any species of treponeme is properly spoken of as *treponematosis.* The most important of these diseases in humans are syphilis and bejel (*T. pallidum*), yaws (*T. pertenue*), and pinta or carate (*T. carateum*). The treponemes causing them are identical or very closely related, and all cause a positive reaction to the standard serological tests for syphilis as well as very extensive destruction of body tissues. There is considerable cross immunity between syphilis and yaws. With the possible exception of pinta all may be transmitted by contact with open (infectious) lesions: syphilis, venereally; yaws and bejel, nonvenereally; the last two are probably also transmitted by biting flies. All are extensively distributed: syphilis world-wide, yaws in tropics around the world, bejel in southeast Mediterranean areas, and pinta, a discoloration of the skin, in the tropics of the Americas.

**Syphilis.**   Syphilis is usually transmitted by sexual intercourse. When so transmitted, and when it develops typically, it begins as a small ulceration on the mucosal surface of the genitalia within two to eight weeks after exposure. The spirochetes rapidly migrate from there to the deeper tissues of the body.

The ulcer increases in size, becoming rather hard (*indurated*) and flat. Upon removal of the crust, serous fluid oozes from the surface. This, upon examination with a darkfield apparatus, is found swarming with *Treponema pallidum* (Fig. 40.9). When syphilis is acquired through kissing, the ulcer may appear on the lip. The primary ulcer, oral or genital, is spoken of as a hard chancre (pronounced shank′er). It tends to heal spontaneously because of the development of antibodies after two to six weeks. The victim may believe himself cured. Attempts are made by the regional lymph nodes to arrest the migrating spirochetes. The nodes become swollen and firm and are sometimes called *buboes.* Their efforts, unfortunately, are futile.

What really happens is that by this time a certain degree of immunity has developed. The treponemes have long since migrated from the primary lesion, probably within less than an hour after exposure, and have been carried all over the body. They localize in various organs, particularly the liver, spleen, walls of arteries, heart, brain, skin and mucosal surfaces, setting up *secondary lesions.* These begin to manifest themselves after two to four months. When situated on the skin these often appear as red blotches or an extensive rash and may be very infectious if open or moist, since they contain the treponemes. White patches may also appear in the mouth and genitalia. In such conditions of the mouth, kissing of other persons results in infection of the lips, tongue or gums. The teeth may loosen and come out, as well as the hair. Probably these and later lesions represent a reaction of delayed allergy. After a time, weeks or months, these outwardly visible secondary lesions slowly disappear in great part and the patient may again believe himself cured. Spontaneous cure actually may occur but this is not the usual outcome.

In untreated syphilis the treponemes usually slowly cause extensive *tertiary lesions,* called *gummata,* in various internal organs and on the skin. These tend to heal and form scars as the process continues. The liver becomes damaged and scarred (syphilitic *cirrhosis* of the liver), and bulges appear in the aorta where lesions in the layers of the vessel have weakened it. These bulges are called *aneurysms.* When they burst, death from hemorrhage ensues. Gummata also occur in many of the bones.

The treponemes also damage the brain and spinal cord. Various nerve centers are slowly destroyed and characteristic forms of insanity and paralysis result. Death follows, sometimes after a period of many years. Mothers recently infected practically always have miscarriages, stillbirths or sickly, syphilitic children.

PREVALENCE AND CONTROL.   This picture of syphilis is not pleasant and, indeed, the disease is one of the most insidious and dangerous. It is an epidemic disease of major importance (Fig. 40.10). Many more persons die annually of this disease in the United States than of poliomyelitis, diphtheria, mumps, measles, scarlet fever, typhoid fever and malaria combined. Over a million known new cases develop each year and many more are never recorded. Venereal disease is *not* beaten. It is on the increase, especially among young people and teenagers, because of complacency, ignorance and general laxity, including homosexuality and drug addiction.

As in the case of gonorrhea, prostitution and sexual promiscuity are the chief means by which syphilis is spread. In spite of sustained efforts by federal, state and local authorities to educate the public to the dangers of syphilis and to enlist the aid of legislatures, medical and civic authorities, and of *the people themselves* who are endangered by it, many new cases appear each year.

As one great physician has said, "The greatest obstacles to Public Health are the ignorance and indifference of the public!"

SYPHILIS SEROLOGY.   The *diagnosis of syphilis* after the disappearance of the primary lesion in which the spirochetes are easily demonstrable microscopically is made by means of serological tests.

*The Precipitin Test Applied to Syphilis.*   In complement fixation tests, including the Wassermann test for syphilis, the complement is fixed because it is adsorbed onto finely divided particles of antigen-antibody precipitate. In the Wassermann test the precipitate is not visible. It would be a great advantage if we could see the precipitate directly, as in other precipitin reactions. This can be arranged.

A specially prepared and very concentrated alcoholic antigen is used in which the reactive substances are present but in the form of large, unstable colloidal complexes. These are brought by proper dilution with saline solution to a state where in contact with syphilitic serum they precipitate in a visible form. Generally, no precipitation occurs in the presence of normal serum

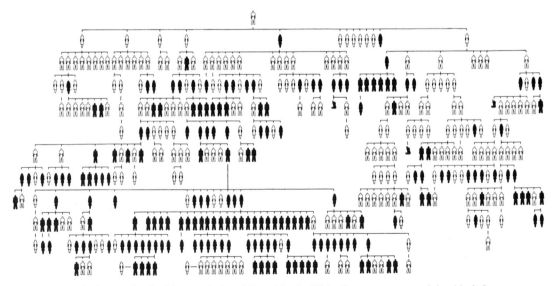

**Figure 40.10**  Persons involved in a typical syphilis epidemic. White figures represent adults; black figures represent persons under 20; small black figures represent infants. (Courtesy of U. S. Public Health Service Task Force on Eradication of Syphilis, L. Baumgartner, M.D., Chairman.)

*under proper circumstances.* Tests based on this principle are the Kahn test, Eagle test, Hinton test, Mazzini and V.D.R.L.

It is worth noting that the antigen used in these tests is not specific. Commercial antigens used in the tests are derived from normal beef hearts and are called *cardiolipins.* They can give false-positive reactions, with always distressing, sometimes tragic, results. The advantages of tests using *specific* antigens are therefore obvious.

Three *specific* tests are now available for the exact diagnostic study of syphilis, great steps forward in syphilology. All are dependent on *specific* antibodies against *T. pallidum.* One is the *T.P.I.* (*Treponema pallidum* immobilization) *test;* another, the *immune adherence phenomenon;* the third, a *complement fixation test,* differing fundamentally from the Wassermann test in using extracts of *T. pallidum* as a specific antigen. A near-specific test is the complement-fixation test using purified antigens extracted from the Reiter treponeme. These are available commercially. Reiter treponemes are also used as antigen in detecting syphilis by the fluorescent-antibody staining technique.

## 40.5   BORRELIOSIS AND LEPTOSPIROSIS

**Genus *Borrelia*.**   Borrelias resemble treponemes in many respects. However, *Borrelia,* unlike treponemes, can be stained readily by Gram's method or by means of polychrome stains (Jenner's stain, Wright's stain) used for protozoa. Borrelias are gram-negative. They often have a less definite spiral form, being more wavy and open than treponemes, especially in microscopic stained preparations (Fig. 40.11). In death they seem to relax and lose their regular, coiled form. They are also somewhat thicker and coarser-looking than *Treponema.* Cultivation of some has been accomplished in media with sterile tissue, although it is not very satisfactory. They grow well in living chick embryos.

Commensal species of *Borrelia* occur, often in large numbers, in the normal mouth (*Borrelia buccalis*) and on the external genitalia (*B. refringens*). Some of these so closely resemble *Treponema pallidum* in appearance as to create confusion at times in the diagnosis of syphilis by microscopic methods. They appear to be harmless. They are sometimes designated as *Spirillum, Spirochaeta* or *Treponema.* Leeuwenhoek probably was the first to observe these.

BORRELIOSIS.   Most species of pathogenic *Borrelia,* like *B. recurrentis* and *B. novyi,* are blood

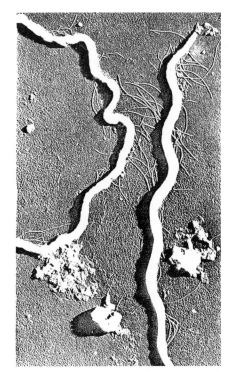

**Figure 40.11**   *Borrelia recurrentis* (relapsing fever) (× 50,000). The flagella-like objects are presumably parts of intracellular fibrils of the spirochetes extruded as a result of mechanical damage to the cells. (From Martin: Thirteen Steps to the Atom. Franklin Watts, Inc.)

parasites causing fever of a recurrent nature (relapsing fever). Many species infect lower mammals and birds. The spirochetes occur in large numbers in the blood during the numerous febrile relapses characteristic of the disease. In North America they are transmitted mainly by certain ticks; in Asia, Africa and South America, by body lice (thus they are good examples of *arthropod-borne zoonoses*).

TRENCH MOUTH.   Some anaerobic species of *Borrelia* (notably *B. vincentii*) are found associated with ulcerative conditions (*trench mouth,* or *Vincent's angina*) in the mouth. They may be seen readily in gram-stained smears from such conditions, mixed with gram-negative fusiform bacilli (*Fusiformis fusiforme*). The name *trench mouth* originated from the frequent occurrence of outbreaks of the disease in soldiers in trenches during World War I. The disease was thought to be transmitted by unclean eating utensils and other articles that carry saliva directly from mouth to mouth. It seems more correctly to be associated with dietary deficiencies, or the microorganisms may act merely as secondary invaders of lesions due to other causes such as caries or herpes.

**Genus Leptospira.** *Leptospira* is the smallest of the spirochetes. The spirals of leptospiras are so fine and so closely wound that when observed in the darkfield with optical microscopes only the outer curves of the spirals are seen, and the organisms appear like strings of minute, illuminated beads. The leptospiras are further characterized by being bent into a hook at one or both ends (Fig. 40.12). Their motion consists of a writhing and flexing movement and a rapid rotation around the long axis. Their progression from place to place is rapid and can be readily explained on the basis of their screwlike form and their rotation (Fig. 40.13).

The structure of Leptospira is much like that of other Treponemataceae but is distinctive in that the long, cylindrical cell or protoplasmic cylinder is wound as a helix around an extracellular, apparently unifibrillar, axial filament. The arrangement has been likened to a segment of plastic hose wound around a thinner segment of rather rigid wire.

Species and Serotypes. Numerous species of leptospiras have been named in the past, but differentiation between many of them is difficult or impossible with methods presently available. As a matter of convenience two species are recognized: one, representing the harmless, free-living saprophytic types, *Leptospira biflexa;* a second, representing the pathogenic types, *Leptospira icterohaemorrhagiae.* *L. biflexa* and others are not sensitive to the purine analogue 8-azaguanine; pathogenic species are highly sensitive. *L. icterohaemorrhagiae* is divided into several serological (antigenic) groups and serotypes. Over 100 serotypes or subserotypes are recognized. Many of these were formerly given species names (see Table 40.1).

Distribution. *L. biflexa* (and related species or variants) is widely distributed in river and lake waters, mine drainage, bilge, stagnant

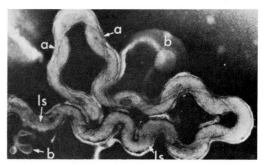

**Figure 40.13** *Leptospira pomona* in potassium phosphotungstate negative stain. Terminal portion of a cell exhibiting a variety of detail. Complex lamellar structures (ls) occupy an extensive volume of the protoplasmic cylinder. The axial filament (a) is readily discerned and its position exterior to the cylinder is clearly seen. (b), sheath bleb. × 140,000. (From Ritchie and Ellinghausen: J. Bact., *89:*223, 1965.)

ponds, sewage and the like as a normal habitat where it appears to multiply. *L. icterohaemorrhagiae* probably does not normally grow significantly in such situations but is often found there as a result of pollution by the urine or dead bodies of infected mammals. *L. icterohaemorrhagiae* can live for months in polluted water, and can infect humans and animals drinking or bathing in that water.

Cultivation. Leptospiras may readily be cultivated in simple mineral solutions with peptone and serum—for example, Korthof's medium, which contains $NaCl$, $NaHCO_3$, $KCl$, $CaCl_2$, $KH_2PO_4$, $Na_2HPO_4$ and 1 per cent peptone. All such media also require 10 per cent rabbit serum containing some hemoglobin. Leptospiras may also be cultivated in colony form on the surface of 1 per cent agar containing tryptose phosphate and serum. The colonies give a positive oxidase reaction (see page 417).

As a differential character, the saprophytes will also grow in media such as hay infusion, dilute feces and egg water, without serum and at 10 to 15° C. Some can be cultivated with minerals, vitamins and tryptose phosphate and no serum. The pathogenic species require serum, prefer temperatures around 30° C., and will not grow in mixed cultures such as feces or hay infusion. All are morphologically identical. Aside from the above cultural differentiations the different types are distinguishable only by special serological procedures.

Filtrability. Certain of the spirochetes (e.g., *Leptospira* and *Borrelia*) are readily filtrable through porcelain or Seitz-type filters which hold back ordinary bacteria. It is thought by some that the filtrability of these organisms is a

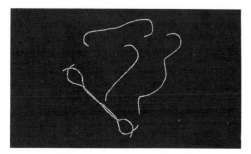

**Figure 40.12** *Leptospira icterohaemorrhagiae.* Appearance of the organism on a darkfield preparation (about × 1000).

**TABLE 40.1** SOME COMMON LEPTOSPIROSES

| Serotype | Usual Animal Host | Disease* |
|----------|-------------------|----------|
| *icterohaemorrhagiae* | Rats | Weil's disease |
| *canicola* | Dogs | Canicola fever |
| *pomona* | Cattle, swine, horses | Swineherd's disease |
| *autumnalis* | Rats | Autumnal fever |
| *hebdomadis* | Field mice, other rodents | Seven-day fever |
| *grippotyphosa* | Field mice, other rodents | Swamp fever |

* Terms commonly used for various leptospiroses.

result of the formation of minute granules which may represent phases in a life cycle. Material (e.g., lake water) that has been filtered and found on microscopic examination to contain no visible spirochetes has later been shown to contain spirochetes by cultural methods or animal inoculation. However, this does not prove conclusively that *only* invisible granules were present, since microscopic examination of a drop or two of fluid might easily fail to detect the presence of a few spirochetes in the greater, unexamined portion.

Small buds or granules appear to form at the end or on the side of some species, possibly as part of a reproductive cycle. Some of these may be merely blebs in the spirochetal sheath (Fig. 40.13). Such granules may form in *Leptospira* and *Borrelia* and, if truly viable, account for their filtrability.

**Leptospirosis.** Infection with any species or serotype of *Leptospira* is properly called *leptospirosis*. (See Table 40.1.) Leptospirosis in man is fairly common, though often wrongly diagnosed.

The various forms of leptospirosis are basically alike, although the symptoms vary. In general, the infection is common among numerous species of mammals. It is most commonly transmitted from animal to man through the urine or bodies of infected animals and by anything so polluted (water, food) coming into contact with the skin or being ingested. Leptospirosis is thus another typical zoonosis. Doubtless the same mode of transmission occurs among animals. Many wild and domestic animals carry leptospiras in their urine. Transmission from man to man is uncommon.

## SUPPLEMENTARY READING

Baseman, J. B., Henneberry, R. C., and Cox, C. D.: Isolation and growth of *Leptospira* on artificial media. J. Bact., *91*:1374, 1966.

Dworkin, M.: Biology of the myxobacteria. Ann. Rev. Microbiol., *20*:75, 1966.

Felsenfeld, O.: Borreliae, human relapsing fever, and parasite-vector-host relationships. Bact. Rev., *29*:46, 1965.

Follett, E. A. C., and Webley, D. M.: An electron microscope study of the cell surface of *Cytophaga johnsonii* and some observations on related organisms. Ant. Leeuw., *31*:361, 1965.

Hanson, A. W., and Cannefax, G. R.: Isolation of *Borrelia refringens* in pure culture from patients with condylomata acuminata. J. Bact., *88*:111, 1964.

Hardy, Jr., P. H., Lee, Y. C., and Nell, E. E.: Use of a bacterial culture filtrate as an aid to the isolation and growth of anaerobic spirochetes. J. Bact., *87*:1521, 1964.

Hart, B. A., and Zahler, S. A.: Lytic enzyme produced by *Myxococcus xanthus*. J. Bact., *92*:1632, 1966.

Hohl, H-R., and Raper, K. B.: Nutrition of cellular slime molds. II. Growth of *Polysphondylium pallidum* in axenic culture. J. Bact., *85*:199, 1963.

Jahn, T. L., and Bovee, E. C.: Movement and locomotion of microorganisms. Ann. Rev. Microbiol., *19*:21, 1965.

Johnson, R. C., and Harris, V. G.: Differentiation of pathogenic and saprophytic leptospiras. J. Bact., *94*:27, 1967.

Kerr, N. S.: The growth of myxamoebae of the true slime mold, *Didymium nigripes*, in axenic culture. J. Gen. Microbiol., *32*:409, 1963.

Soriano, S., and Lewin, R. A.: Gliding microbes: some taxonomic reconsiderations. Ant. Leeuw., *31*:66, 1965.

World Forum on Syphilis and other Treponematoses, Proceedings. Govt. Printing Office, Washington, D. C. 1964.

# Chapter 41

# ORDER MYCOPLASMATALES (PPLO);

# RICKETTSIAS;

# CHLAMYDIACEAE

## PLEUROPNEUMONIA ORGANISMS

In 1898 the French scientists Nocard and Roux, studying pleural fluids of cattle suffering from a disease called pleuropneumonia, discovered organisms that were unlike any other microorganisms then known. The organisms were aerobic and were cultivable only on rich organic media containing about 20 per cent of animal serum. When cultivated on plates of such specially prepared agar these organisms were sometimes found to be spheroid in form, but they also produced a bewildering variety of minute granules, thin, branching filaments, stellate or asteroid structures and many other highly irregular forms (Fig. 41.1). Pleomorphism (Gr. *pleo* = many; *morphe* = forms) is now recognized as one of the outstanding properties of these organisms. The species discovered by Nocard and Roux was called *Asterococcus mycoides*, meaning, "rounded and stellate forms with radial, moldlike filaments."

## 41.1 PLEUROPNEUMONIA-LIKE ORGANISMS

After the original description of the bovine pleuropneumonia organisms, similar organisms were found in various other animals: sheep, goats, dogs, rats, mice, human beings. They are associated with various pathologic conditions, especially rheumatic or arthritic diseases, in-

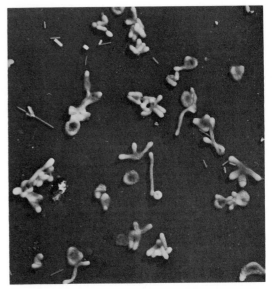

**Figure 41.1** A species of *Mycoplasma* showing a variety of forms, including one or more minimal reproductive units as well as stellate, filamentous, branching and bud-like forms and corpuscle-like bodies. Compare Figure 41.4. (Courtesy of Dr. E. Klieneberger-Nobel.)

fections of the mammary glands, respiratory tract and adjacent tissues, and inflammations of the genitourinary system. Similar organisms were found growing as saprophytes in decaying organic matter. All of these organisms are now referred to as *pleuropneumonia-like organisms*, commonly called PPLO or mycoplasmas.

**Classification of PPLO.**   Because long, branching, filamentous structures are prominent morphological features of PPLO, they were at one time thought to belong to the group of moldlike bacteria, the Actinomycetales. Their taxonomic position is still under discussion. In one system of classification they are placed in a separate order of Schizomycetes or bacteria, the Mycoplasmatales, Family Mycoplasmataceae, Genus *Mycoplasma* (i.e., "fungus substance"). The original species of Nocard and Roux is now called *Mycoplasma mycoides.*

In 1966 the International Committee on Nomenclature of Bacteria approved a Subcommittee on the Taxonomy of Mycoplasmatales. The Subcommittee recommended that these organisms be no longer considered as stabilized L-phase bacterial variants and that they be grouped in a new Class, the Mollicutes, coordinate with the Class Schizomycetes and the blue-green algae (Class Schizophyceae). The recommendation is based on a number of distinctive properties of PPLO, including the requirement of many of them, especially pathogens, for sterols for growth; similarities among PPLO in per cent G + C; absence of cell wall and mucopeptides. They differ from Schizomycetes also in having much smaller content of nucleic acids. There will be some discussion before final action is taken.

**Cultivation of PPLO.**   PPLO are best cultivated on solid (agar) medium, although they will grow, usually reluctantly, in liquid media. In general, media for their growth must be fairly concentrated and have a considerable osmotic pressure. A rich meat-infusion agar, pH 7.8, containing about 1 per cent peptone and 25 per cent serum, is satisfactory. Yeast extract, about 25 per cent, is often added, especially for forms parasitic on the animal body. Incubation is at about 37° C. and may be aerobic, although an increased (5 per cent) content of carbon dioxide is usually helpful. Some species are anaerobic.

The addition of unsaturated fatty acids to the medium facilitates growth and, for all parasitic species, cholesterol or a related sterol is essential; an important differential point of these organisms. PPLO are also readily cultivated in living chick embryos and, as previously mentioned, in tissue-cell cultures (Chapter 16).

SUBCULTURE.   Because, as will be explained, colonies of PPLO adhere strongly to agar media, subculture of PPLO is most convenient if a small agar block containing the desired colony is carefully cut out of an agar plate. It may be used to inoculate an appropriate fluid medium by macerating it in the fluid. However, it is usually more satisfactory to inoculate agar by sliding the piece of colony-containing agar, inverted, over the surface of the fresh medium.

**Staining.**   PPLO can be seen much more readily if they are stained with an aniline dye. A good method of staining is that of Dienes, one of the first investigators of L bodies. Cut out a block of agar on which the colonies are growing and place it upon a slide. Then invert upon it a cover slip on which is dried methylene blue-azure (deposited from alcoholic solution).* The microscope is focused on the inverted cover slip. Most species of living bacteria decolorize the stain; PPLO do *not.*

**Colony Form.**   In addition to extreme pleomorphism a very distinctive property of PPLO is the form of their colonies on agar medium. Growth is commonly initiated just beneath the surface of the agar. Expanding, it erupts onto the surface and spreads outward, the filaments tending to penetrate into the agar (Fig. 41.2). Thus the colony appears densest at its central point and, when mature, is removed from the agar only with difficulty. Unlike colonies of other organisms cultivable on agar, individual cells of PPLO are not visible in their colonies even with high-powered optical microscopes. The mature colony reveals a dark center and, over the nearby agar, many rounded or pleomorphic bodies ranging in size from barely visible to large, vacuolated or apparently empty sacs; regarded by some as stages in a reproductive cycle, by others as degenerate, nonviable, involution forms. The whole colony is said to have a "fried egg" or lacy appearance and is highly distinctive of PPLO (Fig. 41.3). Colonies are always extremely minute, ranging from about 10 to 600 $\mu$; usually resembling fine dust on the agar surface. They must be differentiated from *pseudocolonies;* minute crystals or other specks and irregularities that are common on agar surfaces. One group of PPLO called T strains is distinguished by its Tiny colonies.

**Morphology and Structure.**   PPLO, like animal cells, have no demonstrable cell wall. Their sole retaining structure is the cytoplasmic membrane which, like most other cell membranes, is of the three-layered or "unit" type (Fig. 41.4). The membrane of PPLO is extremely thin, "limp," (Fig. 41.5) plastic and elastic, hence the extreme pleomorphism of PPLO. Because of the fragility of this membrane PPLO are very

---

*Dienes' stain.

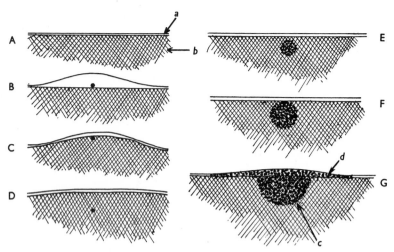

**Figure 41.2** Diagrammatic illustration of development of L-form colonies. *A,* A greatly magnified vertical section through the agar (*a,* a film of water on the surface; *b,* substance of the agar gel). *B, C* and *D,* The penetration of a live L-form a few microns into the agar. *E* and *F,* Development of new L-forms in a subsurface colony. *G,* Eruption of the deep growth (*c*) onto the surface and its spread in the film of water (*d*). (From Razin and Oliver: J. Gen. Microbiol., *24*:225, 1961.)

liable to mechanical distortion of form (as, for example, in laboratory manipulations) and also to osmotic rupture, unless the surrounding fluid has a considerable protective osmotic tension. (See Protoplasts, Chapter 13.)

It is noticeable that lobule and filament formations by PPLO are enhanced by "feeding" the organisms increased amounts of unsaturated fatty acids. The resulting increased lipid content of the membrane seems to make the membrane more elastic and thus more easily distorted but less likely to rupture. Low temperatures and polyvalent cations also seem to strengthen the PPLO membrane. Because of the large amount of lipid in the cell membrane, many PPLO are markedly sensitive to lipid solvents like alcohol,

or to lipid-emulsifying agents such as bile salts and detergents.

INTERNAL STRUCTURE. The internal structure of PPLO, as revealed by the electron microscope, is typical of procaryons generally and closely resembles that of bacteria. Nuclear structures are present but are less evident in PPLO than in bacteria. Mesosomes are conspicuously absent. This may result from the elasticity of the cell membrane, which "stretches" so that invaginations of the membrane, such as mesosomes, cannot occur (Fig. 41.4).

Enzyme systems and metabolic characteristics of PPLO differ somewhat from those of familiar bacteria but, in general, the differences are not extreme and, like many properties of

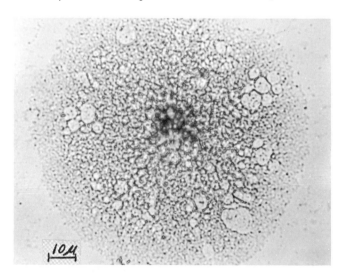

**Figure 41.3** Surface view of a colony of PPLO growing on agar and stained to show various structures in the colony. See text for details. (From Clark, Fowler, and Brown: J. Bact., vol. 81.)

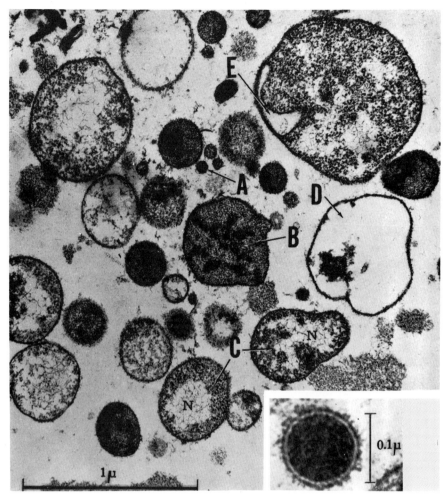

**Figure 41.4**   Culture of *Mycoplasma hominis* showing a variety of forms. At (A) is a small dense form ("elementary body"). One type of the large forms (B) has a finely granular protoplasm divided into light and dark areas. A second major type (C) has its protoplasm divided into a central nuclear area (N) of netlike strands and a cytoplasm (C) containing ribosome-like granules. The internal material in several of the large forms has a watery appearance, and sometimes only an empty plasma membrane is seen (D). One of the organisms in this field has a membrane-bound vacuole (E) at its periphery. × 53,000. Inset shows body similar to A at a higher magnification (× 200,000). (From Anderson and Barile: J. Bact., *90*:180, 1965.)

**Figure 41.5**   One form of PPLO. This strain was isolated from a case of urethritis in a human being by Dr. L. Dienes. Cultivated on agar medium as described in text (× 20,000). Note the relatively large, thickened granules in the larger organism. These are probably nuclear material. There is no evidence of a definite cell wall. (From Morton, Lecce, Oskay and Coy: J. Bact., vol. 68.)

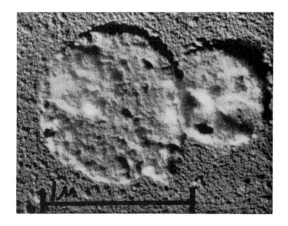

PPLO, can be ascribed to the physiological adaptation of PPLO to life without a cell wall.

**Reproduction of PPLO.** The dimensions of mature cells of PPLO are of the same order as those of true bacteria. However, cells of PPLO divide unevenly. Very minute bodies, called *elementary bodies* or *minimal reproductive units,* are commonly formed inside the *large bodies* or mature cells. These elementary bodies range in size from 100 to 300 m$\mu$. The smaller sizes of these can pass through bacteria-retaining filters like viruses but are viable on ordinary media. The elementary bodies have bacteria-like structures. These minute, living bodies of PPLO are often cited as the smallest independently living entities (viruses are not independently living). PPLO are thought to contain the minimal number of molecules needed by any microorganism to maintain an independent existence and multiply.

These minute bodies represent a stage in the life cycle of PPLO. They enlarge to form long filaments and mycelia and chains of minute spheres like conidia but much smaller. It is thought by some that these conidia-like bodies are liberated and that each increases in size to become a large body several microns in diameter inside which new elementary bodies are formed. These are released by rupture of the membrane of the large body (Fig. 41.4). There are other views of the reproductive cycle of PPLO, including ordinary, bacterium-like, binary fission or yeastlike budding.

**Relation to Antibiotics.** PPLO, like typical viruses and animal cells, are completely resistant to penicillin. Since the principal action of penicillin is to stop synthesis of the mucopolysaccharide complex of the procaryotic cell wall, it is understandable that it would have no effect on organisms without any cell wall. That PPLO are not resistant to all antibiotics in general is shown by their sensitivity to the tetracyclines and to other antibiotics that do not depend for their effect on elimination of cell walls e.g., kanamycin.

Unlike many bacteria, PPLO are not susceptible to infection by bacteriophage. This follows from the absence of a cell wall with its specific receptors for bacteriophage. It is questionable whether PPLO can undergo conjugation of the bacterial type, since this appears to involve the cell wall.

## 41.2  PATHOGENIC PPLO

PPLO have usually been found in pathologic conditions of lower animals. A few harmless saprophytic species are known, a common one being *Mycoplasma laidlawi* (named for discoverer, Laidlaw). A number of species have also been found associated with a variety of diseases of various organs in man but their etiological relationship, while probable, remains to be established in most cases. One species, *M. hominis,* is especially common in such situations.

The first undoubted human pathogen of the PPLO group is the agent causing primary atypical pneumonia (PAP). Many viruses (e.g., influenza) cause pneumonias of this type, and it was long thought that only viruses were involved. About 1950 it was discovered by Eaton that many cases of PAP were caused by an agent that, like viruses, was filterable, was (at first) not visible with optical microscopes and which, like viruses, could infect cells in tissue cultures. However, it was completely unlike true viruses in that, although insusceptible to penicillin, it was fully susceptible to other antibiotics. It was called "Eaton's agent." In 1962 it was shown to be cultivable on inanimate media and to be, in fact, a PPLO. It has since been called *Mycoplasma pneumoniae.* This brief history shows the importance of looking for PPLO in conditions in which other microorganisms cannot be demonstrated. In a recent study, for example, PPLO have been isolated from, and observed in, benign human tumors. The observation is stimulating but the exact etiological role of the PPLO remains to be fully investigated.

Other PPLO have since been found as important and insidious contaminants in many tissue cultures, including some used in the propagation of viruses for human vaccines. These tissue cultures had formerly been thought to be "pure" cell lines. (Compare the difficulties with contamination experienced by Koch, Pasteur and others a century ago.) In contaminated tissue cultures the PPLO apparently live intracellularly unrecognized although some produce definite CPE. The commonest source of these contaminations (mainly *M. hominis* and a species called *M. orale*) appears to be the oropharynx of persons working with the cell cultures. Only the most assiduous aseptic technique can eliminate these contaminants. Contaminated cultures may be "cured" by using PPLO-immune serum (see Chapter 24) or antibiotics to which the PPLO are sensitive. Contamination may be detected by several means, including culture methods on agar of appropriate composition; also by microscopic examination of tissue cultures stained with fluorescent antibodies *specific* for the PPLO involved (see fluorescent antibody staining, Chapter 24).

## 41.3   L-FORMS

The status of *Mycoplasma* as a separate and distinct group of microorganisms was brought into question by the observation, about 1953, that cell walls of many species of bacteria can be removed, or their synthesis inhibited, by a number of substances. As explained in Chapter 13, bacteria so treated become *protoplasts* or *L-forms*. Eucaryotic fungi may also grow as L-forms (Fig. 41.7).

Some bacteria undergo spontaneous mutation to loss of cell walls. For example, some bacterial mutant auxotrophs (Chapter 15) require diaminopimelic acid (DAP) among their nutrients in order to form their cell walls. DAP is peculiar to bacterial cell walls. If DAP is withheld, *and* the medium is *osmotically protective,* the bacteria grow *without* a cell wall; i.e., they are L-forms of the bacteria from which they were derived (Figs. 41.6 and 41.8). If DAP is fed to them they revert to their original form. Like PPLO, none forms colonies on ordinary media but colonies are formed on media *osmotically protective;* i.e., media with about 3 per cent sucrose

or other nontoxic osmotically active substance. L-forms possess virtually all of the distinguishing features of PPLO (Figs. 41.9 and 41.10).

**Stability of L-forms.**   Usually, when separated from the influence of the agent that removed (or prevented formation of) their cell walls (penicillin is commonly used), L-forms more or less rapidly revert to their original status as bacteria, identical in virtually all respects with the bacteria from which they originated. Such forms are said to be "transition" or "unstable" L-forms. However, under certain conditions of cultivation in the laboratory some may retain the wall-less state tenaciously for considerable periods without reversion. They become fairly well stabilized as L-forms even when cultivated in ordinary media. Such well-stabilized L-forms, if not known to have originated previously from bacteria, would be called PPLO. *No undoubted PPLO has ever been demonstrated to originate from, or revert to, a bacterium.* However, several organisms long supposed to be PPLO have lost their status as PPLO by reverting to common types of bacteria and back again. Thus some workers, understandably, regard L-forms and PPLO as

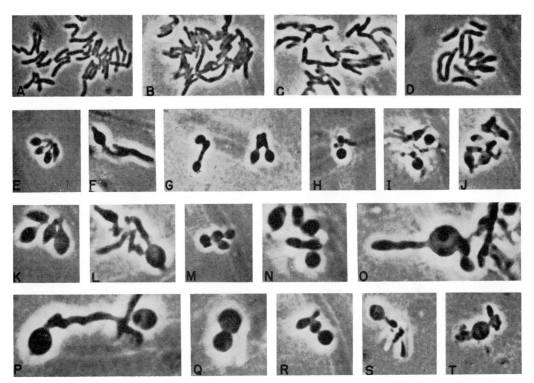

**Figure 41.6**   Formation of stabilized spheroplasts of *Mycobacterium tuberculosis* by cultivation in a low-surface-tension fluid medium containing lysozyme and ethylene diamine tetra-acetate (EDTA) with tris buffer, Mg$^{++}$ and osmotically protective (0.34M) sucrose. Changes in morphology from normal bacillary form (A, B, C) to swollen translucent forms at 6 days (E) and 10 days (F, L) and to globular and spheroidal (spheroplast) forms after incubation for 14 days (P-T) are clearly shown. (From Thacore and Willett: Proc. Soc. Exp. Biol. Med., *114*:43, 1963.)

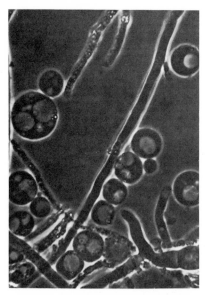

**Figure 41.7** Protoplasts of *Fusarium culmorum.* Note the variation in size of the protoplasts and the large vacuoles in some of them. × 3000. (From Rodriguez Aguirre, Garcia Acha, and Villanueva: Ant. Leeuw., *30*:30, 1964.)

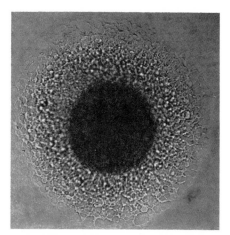

**Figure 41.9** Unstained L colony induced from a penicillin G-resistant strain of *Staphylococcus aureus* in a medium containing 500 μg/ml. of methicillin. × 115. (From Kagan, Molander and Weinberger: J. Bact., vol. 83.)

identical, differing only in origin and stability of the wall-less state and in other relatively minor properties. The differentiation depends largely on the knowledge of origin and future state of an L-form or PPLO.

**Colony Types.** In the bacterial species *P. mirabilis,* at least two types of L-forms are differentiated by their colonies: 3A and 3B. Type 3A L-forms induced by penicillin require serum

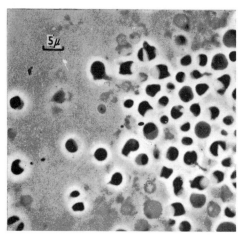

**Figure 41.8** Photomicrograph of a common bacterium (*Escherichia coli*) growing in broth containing sucrose (15 per cent w/v) but devoid of diaminopimelic acid which the bacterium requires in order to synthesize its cell wall. *E. coli* is ordinarily a slender, cigarette-shaped bacillus, quite uniform in shape and size (× 1000). (From McQuillen: J. Gen. Microbiol., vol. 18.)

for growth and initially produce in agar very small subsurface colonies containing minute, deeply staining granules. The subsurface growth appears on the surface later.

These L-forms are so slow and reluctant to revert to the parent bacterial forms that they could be regarded as *stable* or *permanent* L-forms (PPLO if their origin were not known).

Type 3B L-forms produce larger surface colonies that are definite in outline and slightly raised, having a dark, vacuolated or granular center, with a central density caused by growth beneath the surface. The peripheral surface growth may appear granular in the center, lacy and vacuolated at the periphery (Fig. 41.9). Type 3B L-forms do not require serum, and readily revert to the parent bacterial form when grown in the absence of penicillin.

## 41.4   THE RICKETTSIAS

As described in the 1957 edition of "Bergey's Manual of Determinative Bacteriology," the Order Rickettsiales, of the Class Microtatobiotes, includes four families of basically similar organisms: Rickettsiaceae, Chlamydiaceae, Bartonellaceae and Anaplasmataceae. All are believed to be obligate parasites, generally intracellular, in tissue cells of vertebrates and arthropods, the hosts depending upon the species of microorganism. Only members of the Tribe Rickettsieae will be described here, since it is fairly representative of the entire order.

The Tribe Rickettsieae includes two genera:

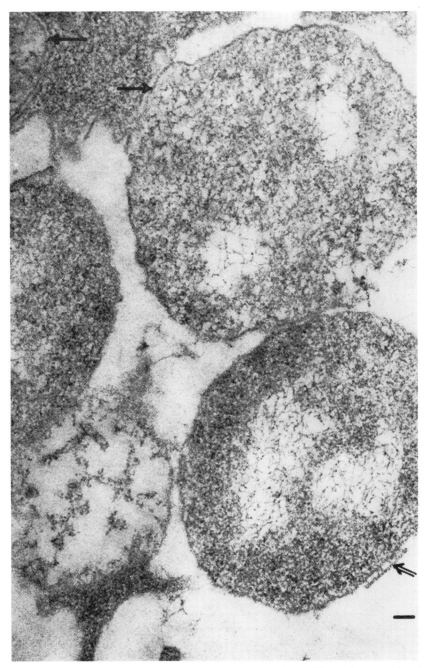

**Figure 41.10** Protoplasts prepared from a marine *Pseudomonas* species by washing and resuspending in 0.5M sucrose (osmotically protective) and then by treatment with EDTA (which removes an outer, probably lipopolysaccharidic, part of the cell wall that is impermeable to lysozyme) and then with lysozyme (the mucopeptide-hydrolyzing enzyme). The double arrow points to a small portion of retained outer layer of cell wall; the single arrows point to cytoplasmic membranes of rounded-up or highly pleomorphic protoplasts in contact. Note the similarities to PPLO in Figure 41.4. The black line indicates 0.1 $\mu$. (From Costerton, Forsberg, Matula, Buckmire, and MacLeod: J. Bact., *94*:1764, 1967.)

*Rickettsia,* which is not filtrable, and *Coxiella,* which is filtrable through bacteria-retaining filters.

## GENUS RICKETTSIA

**Discovery.** Howard Taylor Ricketts, an American medical scientist, while studying Rocky Mountain spotted fever in 1909, described as the causative agents of that disease a group of microorganisms that differed from any that had been previously described. A year later he discovered similar organisms as the cause of typhus* fever while working in Mexico. During the latter studies he contracted the disease and died.

In 1916, H. da Rocha-Lima, a Brazilian scientist, made further observations of the organisms described by Ricketts and named the genus *Rickettsia,* in honor of its discoverer. He also gave the species name *prowazekii* to the rickettsias associated with louse-borne or classical typhus fever, in honor of another scientist, Stanislaus von Prowazek, of Hamburg, who had lost his life in the study of that disease. The causative agent of louse-borne typhus fever is therefore called *Rickettsia prowazekii.* It is the type species of the Genus *Rickettsia.*

### PROPERTIES OF RICKETTSIAS

The rickettsias are not yeasts, molds, protozoa, PPLO, algae or viruses. They have most of the distinctive properties of bacteria and probably should be grouped as a suborder or family of the Order Eubacteriales or as a separate order of the Class Schizomycetes.

**Morphology and Staining.** The rickettsias are much smaller than typical bacteria, having diameters of about 0.5 to 1.0 $\mu$ and lengths seldom exceeding 5 $\mu$ and often much less than this. However, they are larger than any of the viruses and can be seen readily with ordinary microscopes at magnifications around 1000$\times$. They multiply by transverse binary fission, like bacteria. They are variously shaped: cigarette- or rod-shaped, spherical or ovoid (Fig. 41.11). They may cling in pairs or chains after fission. Sometimes relatively long filaments are formed.

*Do not confuse *typhus fever,* a blood and tissue disease due to rickettsias, with *typhoid fever,* an intestinal infection due to a bacterium, *Salmonella typhi.* The name of typhoid fever was conferred by a French physician contemporary with Marie Antoinette (*Dr. Pierre Louis*) because the stuporous symptoms of typhoid in some ways resemble those of typhus (Gr. *typhos* = stupor).

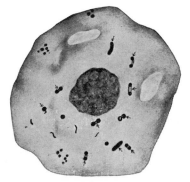

**Figure 41.11** Drawing of epithelial cell showing rickettsiae in the cytoplasm. Typical rickettsiae are indicated by arrows (about $\times$ 3000).

No spores are produced. Rickettsias are not motile.

Unlike most bacteria, it is difficult to stain rickettsias with ordinary basic aniline dyes. They can, however, be colored very well with Giemsa's* or Machiavelli's stain. If stained by Gram's method they are gram-negative. The rod forms tend to stain more intensely at the tips, often giving short rods the appearance of a pair of minute spheres or cocci (bipolar staining).

Electron microscope studies of ultrathin cross sections of *Rickettsia* (magnifications around 100,000$\times$) indicate that rickettsias possess a "unit" type (three-layered) cell membrane and a two- or three-layered cell wall. Biochemical studies show that, like true bacteria, the rickettsial cell walls contain mucopolysaccharide as the main supporting component, and also the amino-sugar, muramic acid, that occurs only in bacterial cell walls. The internal structure as seen in ultrathin sections closely resembles that of true bacteria, and includes ribosomes and nucleoids of the procaryotic type (Fig. 41.12). Invaginations of the cell membrane suggest mesosomes or a primitive endoplasmic reticulum.

**Growth.** In the matter of growth, rickettsias resemble the viruses and chlamydias in that they are not cultivable on nonliving material. However, rickettsias, like many bacteria, are easily cultivated in *live chick embryos.* They will also grow to some extent in *living* cells of tissue-cultures, such as those used to cultivate viruses (see Chapter 16). They appear to grow best in the live cells lining the egg-yolk sac. Yolk-grown rickettsias are widely used as antigens in procedures for the serological diagnosis of rickettsial diseases and for the preparation of *rickettsial vaccines.*

*Special stains used for blood and protozoa.

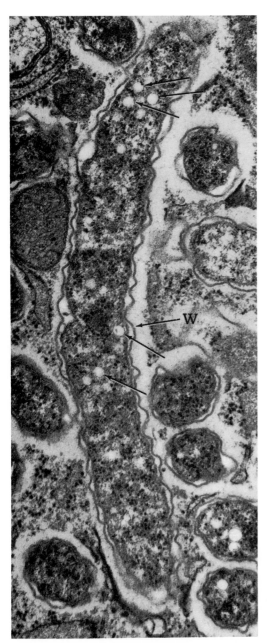

**Figure 41.12**  Longitudinal section through *Rickettsia prowazeki* which is 4 μ long. Several cross-sections are also included in the field. The rippled cell wall (W) is obvious, and the underlying plasma membrane which bounds the rickettsial cytoplasm is easily seen in several places. The internal material consists of ribosomes and DNA strands, and this species also has electron-lucent spherical structures, some of which are indicated with arrows. × 45,000. (From Anderson et al.: J. Bact., *90*:1387, 1965.)

**Metabolism and Antibiotics.** Rickettsias have been shown to have autonomous, though incomplete, metabolic activity. Though they appear to have lost* their own independent systems of digestive and synthetic enzymes, they have apparently retained (or gained?) at least some energy-mediating enzymes, since they are markedly susceptible to antibiotics that interfere with energy-mediating enzymes.

**Habitat.** Rickettsias appear to be primarily parasites of insects, and to appear only secondarily in man and other animals. The microorganisms characteristically inhabit the cells lining the intestines and other tissues of arthropods. Rickettsias not pathogenic for man have been found in ticks, fleas, lice, bedbugs, spiders and mosquitoes. Human pathogenic species of rickettsias primarily inhabit arthropods that bite man or animals or both.

Some species of pathogenic rickettsias are found in the salivary glands of biting arthropods whence they may be transmitted to man. Other species of *Rickettsia* occur in the intestinal contents of sanguisugent (L. *sanguis* = blood; *sugere* = to suck) arthropods and appear in the feces. Transmission of rickettsias to animal hosts may thus be obtained by bites or by rubbing or scratching the fecal deposits of arthropod vectors into the skin. Some rickettsias pathogenic for man are also pathogenic to their insect hosts; e.g., *R. prowazekii* kills body lice.

## Genus Coxiella

There is only one species in this genus, *Coxiella burnetii*. The genus is named for Herald L. Cox, co-discoverer of the organism in the United States; the species is named for F. M. Burnet (Nobel Prize winner), who first studied the organism in Australia. *Coxiella burnetii* causes an influenza-like disease of the respiratory tract. The disease is called *Q fever,* Q standing for *Query.* The word was applied to the unknown diagnosis of the first cases to be observed by Derrick in Australia. Q fever is world-wide in distribution. While often temporarily disabling, it is seldom fatal.

*Coxiella burnetii* differs from *Rickettsia* species mainly in being: (1) filtrable; (2) transmitted by inanimate vectors as well as by arthropods (see Table 28.1); (3) more resistant to heat, drying and chemical disinfectants.

---

*Or never to have had?

**TABLE 41.1   COMPARISON OF SEVERAL TYPES OF PROCARYONS**

|  | Viruses | Chlamydias | Rickettsias | Schizomycetes |
|---|---|---|---|---|
| Depend on host NA for multiplication | + | − | − | − |
| Visible with optical microscope (× 1500) | − | + | + | + |
| Cultivable in inanimate media | − | − | − | +* |
| Obligate intracellular parasites | + | + | + | −† |
| Synthesize proteins by own enzymes | − | + | + | + |
| Energy metabolism, e.g., synthesize ATP | − | − | + | + |
| Contain both DNA and RNA | − | + | + | + |
| Binary fission | − | + | + | + |
| Cell wall mucopolysaccharide | − | + | + | + |

*A few possible exceptions, e.g., *Treponema pallidum.*
†A few possible exceptions, e.g., *Mycobacterium leprae.*

## 41.5   THE P-L-T (PSITTACOSIS–LYMPHOGRANULOMA VENEREUM–TRACHOMA) GROUP

### FAMILY CHLAMYDIACEAE, GENUS CHLAMYDIA

The organisms of this group were, for many years, regarded as viruses. They were called "large" viruses (250 to 450 mμ) because of their size relative to true viruses; or "mantle viruses" because of their complex, mantle-like, outer structure. They are just within the range of visibility with optical microscopes, and they are gram-negative, indicating the presence of a bacterium-like cell wall. Like rickettsias and viruses, they are not cultivable in inanimate media and are obligate intracellular parasites.

The group was originally named for a type of pneumonia now called *psittacosis* and known for many years to be contracted by humans from infected birds of the psittacine type (L. *psittacus* = parrot); popularly called "parrot fever." The causative agent was positively identified in 1932 by Bedson and Bland. Since the original identification, similar organisms have been found as the cause of psittacosis-like pneumonias (*ornithosis*) in many nonpsittacine birds such as pigeons, and in man and other mammals. Closely related organisms also have been found to cause diseases of the eyes of man: *trachoma* and *inclusion conjunctivitis* or *blennorrhea*, and a venereal disease, *lymphogranuloma venereum*. There are other members of the group and probably many more still undiscovered.

The group has been called the P-L-T group and classified in the Genus *Chlamydia* (Gr. *chlamys* = a cloak) of the Family Chlamydiaceae (cloak or mantle viruses.) All of the chlamydias are very much like the psittacosis or ornithosis organism in morphology, structure, developmental cycle, and in protein (*group* antigen) composition. The various species causing the different diseases named can be distinguished only by minor differences in protein (*species* antigen) composition and by their host specificity and distinctive pathologic effects. In fact, all appear to be minor modifications of a single ancestral type.

The chlamydias are no longer regarded as viruses but, like rickettsias, as derivatives from a bacterial type modified and adapted to a life of obligate, intracellular parasitism. They must live intracellularly and cannot grow in inanimate media. Their great reduction in size, like that of rickettsias, would be a logical result of their loss of many of the physiological mechanisms necessary to an extracellular existence.

Further evidence of their close relationship to bacteria is the fact that, like the rickettsias, they have retained some autonomous enzymic systems. This is indicated not only by their bacterium-like and rickettsia-like susceptibility to several chemotherapeutic agents known to inhibit synthesis of proteins, but by data from numerous other indirect tests for enzyme activity. Unlike all other cells, including rickettsias, but like viruses, chlamydias apparently depend, at least to a large extent, on the host cell for their *energy*, i.e., they cannot synthesize their own ATP.

MULTIPLICATION.    Like rickettsias and other cells, chlamydias appear to multiply, in at least one phase of their developmental cycle, by a modified type of binary fission. They also exhibit a yeastlike budding process. Additional

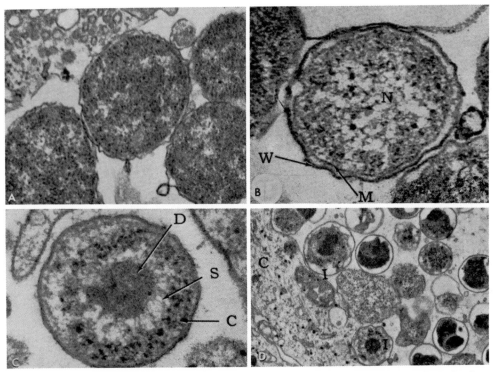

**Figure 41.13**   *A*, Initial bodies of ornithosis. They are confined to a membrane-lined space in the host-cell cytoplasm in which are seen, at upper left, a Golgi apparatus and a mitochondrion. × 45,000. *B*, Higher magnification of an initial body of ornithosis. Note the cell wall (W) and the cell membrane (M). In this initial body, the DNA strands are concentrated centrally to form a nuclear area (N) while the cytoplasmic components have migrated peripherally. × 90,000. *C*, Intermediate form of ornithosis. Homogeneous dense material (D) has formed within a central area of DNA strands (S), and the peripheral cytoplasmic components (C) include prominent ribosomes. × 90,000. *D*, Portion of a vacuole containing ornithosis in late stages of development. Many elementary bodies are seen, along with a few intermediate forms (I) and initial bodies. The membrane lining the vacuole is obvious in several places. The thin rim of host-cell cytoplasm (C) contains several mitochondria and other organelles. × 15,000. (From Anderson et al.: J. Bact., *90*:1387, 1965.)

phases of their multiplicative processes involve "small bodies," "large bodies" and intermediate (developmental?) sizes somewhat suggestive of the developmental cycles of PPLO and L-forms (Fig. 41.13). Intracellular binary fission, budding and variously sized particles are clearly visible in electron micrographs. The growth cycle, as seen in electron micrographs, suggests intracellular, virus-like eclipse and latent (lytic) periods and a long lag period. The large particles appear early in the presumed "eclipse" period and are of low infectivity; the small particles appear late in the latent period and seem to be of high infectivity. Unlike infection by viruses, the nucleus of the chlamydia-infected cell is not necessarily affected. It is worth noting that chlamydias can complete their growth cycle in cells deprived of their nucleus, indicating that chlamydias, unlike viruses, do not depend on host DNA for their synthesis.

Like all cells, and totally unlike viruses, the chlamydias contain both RNA and DNA. They also contain about 40 per cent lipids and 35 per cent proteins. Nuclei are like bacterial nucleoids, as would be expected of such procaryons. Ribosomes also are evident; antibiotics that inhibit the ribosomes of rickettsias and bacteria also inhibit chlamydias. The presence of muramic acid, found exclusively in the cell walls of bacteria and Cyanophyceae, is indicated by the susceptibility of chlamydias to penicillin. (Why?) Electron micrographs of ruptured chlamydias show cytoplasmic membranes and structures closely resembling bacterial cell walls but much less rigid; "resembling discarded grape skins" (Moulton) (Fig. 41.13).

A virus-like aspect of infection of susceptible cells and animals with chlamydias is the establishment of *latency* (do not confuse with latent or lytic period of viral growth cycle). In latent infections the organisms often remain for long periods apparently wholly inactive, though fully viable inside infected cells. This appears not to be analogous to lysogeny of phages; the mechanisms of latency of *Chlamydia* infections remains to be fully elucidated.

For comparative purposes (Table 41.1) we may think of viruses as intracellular parasites that depend almost wholly on the host for materials for synthesis and can utilize only the host's energy sources and mechanisms (utilization of host's ADP-ATP system). Chlamydias seem to have much more effective cell-synthesizing mechanisms, including RNA, DNA and proteins, but cannot synthesize their own ATP and therefore depend on the host for their energy. Rickettsias can synthesize themselves and can form their own ATP, but require certain micronutrients that can be found only inside living cells. Bacteria are, in general, "self-supporting" though some, as the leprosy bacillus and the syphilis spirochete, appear to require intracellular micronutrients if they are to multiply in an *infective* state.

## SUPPLEMENTARY READING

Anacker, R. L., Fukushi, K., Pickens, E. G., and Lackman, D. B.: Electron microscope observations of the development of *Coxiella burnetii* in the chick yolk sac. J. Bact., *88*:1130, 1964.

Bartnicki-Garcia, S., and Lippman, E.: Liberation of protoplasts from the mycelium of *Phytophthora.* J. Gen. Microbiol., *42*:411, 1967.

Dienes, L., and Madoff, S.: Development and growth of L forms of bacteria and PPLO on membrane filters. Proc. Soc. Exp. Biol. Med., *121*:334, 1966.

Eaton, M. D.: Pleuropneumonia-like organisms and related forms. Ann. Rev. Microbiol., *19*:379, 1965.

Edward, D. G. ff., Chairman, Subcommittee on the Taxonomy of Mycoplasmatales. Recommendations on nomenclature of the Order Mycoplasmatales. Science, *155*:1694, 1967.

Fogh, J., and Fogh, H.: A method for direct demonstration of pleuropneumonia-like organisms in cultured cells. Proc. Soc. Exp. Biol. Med., *117*:899, 1964.

Giménez, D. F.: Gram staining of *Coxiella burnetii.* J. Bact., *90*:834, 1965.

Guze, L. B.: Microbial Protoplasts, Spheroplasts and L-Forms. The Williams and Wilkins Co., Baltimore, Md. 1967.

Hatten, B. A., and Sulkin, S. E.: Intracellular production of *Brucella* L forms. II. Induction and survival of *Brucella abortus* L forms in tissue culture. J. Bact., *91*:14, 1966.

Hayflick, L., and Chanock, R. M.: *Mycoplasma* species of man. Bact. Rev., *29*:185, 1965.

Hummler, K., Armstrong, D., and Tomassini, N.: Cytopathogenic mycoplasmas associated with two human tumors. II. Morphological aspects. J. Bact., *90*:511, 1965.

Kim, K. S., Clyde, W. A., Jr., and Denny, F. W.: Physical properties of human *Mycoplasma* species. J. Bact., *92*:214, 1967.

Lackman, D. B., Bell, E. J., Stoenner, H. G., and Pickens, E. G.: The Rocky Mountain spotted fever group of rickettsias. Health Lab. Science, *2*:135, 1965.

Lynn, R. J., and Muellenberg, M. B.: Immunological properties of an L-form of a group A beta-hemolytic streptococcus. Ant. Leeuw., *31*:15, 1965.

Moulder, J. W.: The relation of the psittacosis group (Chlamydiae) to bacteria and viruses. Ann. Rev. Microbiol., *20*:107, 1966.

Ormsbee, R. A., and Peacock, M. G.: Metabolic activity in *Coxiella burnetii.* J. Bact., *88*:1205, 1964.

Pratt, B. C.: Cell-wall deficiencies in L-forms of *Staphylococcus aureus.* J. Gen. Microbiol., *42*:115, 1966.

Razin, S., Cosenza, B. J., and Tourtellotte, M. E.: Variations in *Mycoplasma* morphology induced by long-chain fatty acids. J. Gen. Microbiol., *42*:139, 1966.

Razin, S., Tourtellotte, M. E., McElhaney, R. N., and Pollack, J. D.: Influence of lipid components of *Mycoplasma laidlawii* membranes on osmotic fragility of cells. J. Bact., *91*:609, 1966.

Rodwell, A. W.: The stability of *Mycoplasma mycoides.* J. Gen. Microbiol., *40*:227, 1965.

Rogul, M. McGee, Z. A., Wittler, R. G., and Falkow, S.: Nucleic acid homologies of selected bacteria, L forms, and *Mycoplasma* species. J. Bact., *90*:1200, 1965.

Shepard, M. C.: Human *Mycoplasma* infections. Health Lab. Science, *3*:163, 1966.

Tamura, A.: Isolation of ribosome particles from meningopneumonitis organisms. J. Bact., *93*:2009, 1967.

Weibull, C., and Gyllang, H.: Metabolic properties of some L forms derived from gram-positive and gram-negative bacteria. J. Bact., *89*:1443, 1965.

# 5

---

*Microorganisms at Work*

As regards work, in one way microorganisms resemble the dormouse at the Mad Hatter's tea party in "Alice in Wonderland":

"You might just as well say," added the Dormouse, which seemed to be talking in its sleep, "that 'I breathe when I sleep' is the same thing as 'I sleep when I breathe'!" "It *is* the same thing with you," said the Hatter.

With microorganisms, to live is to work, and to work is to live; multiplication is their life's work and sole occupation. They are *always* at work—for themselves. But by the title of this section we mean *at work for us.* We may except, perhaps, as an appropriate part of a discussion of work, the chapter on Microorganisms of the Atmosphere since the atmosphere is, for microorganisms, merely a means of rapid transit; a sort of aerial commuter service, as unpredictable as some commuter services on wheels or wings.

Many ways have been found, and more are constantly being developed, to exploit the vital activities of microorganisms for our own profit and welfare. By using information outlined in foregoing sections millions of dollars are being made annually from the synthetic, fermentative, proteolytic and other enzymic processes carried on by microorganisms. Although only a glimpse of these may be afforded here, this section should give the student real respect for microorganisms as benefactors of the economy and as industrial tycoons, as well as reveal some of the activities and potentialities of certain microorganisms as members of an underworld of microscopic saboteurs of commodities and products.

# Chapter 42

# WATER SUPPLIES AND
# WASTE DISPOSAL

## 42.1 NATURAL WATERS

The numbers and kinds of microorganisms in natural waters depend largely on the available nutrient supply, the environment, other organisms present, and physical factors.

Of primary importance are the available nutrient substances in the water (e.g., ferrous iron for certain "iron bacteria," $H_2S$ for sulfur-oxidizing bacteria; $CH_4$ for methane oxidizers; decaying vegetation or animal matter or sewage for organotrophic saprophytes; and so on). Most natural waters contain all of the minerals necessary for all microscopic life.

As pointed out in Chapter 4, nutrient substances dissolved in water tend to accumulate at solid surfaces and in minute interstices and niduses (microenvironments) in porous materials. Hydrolytic and other enzymes secreted by microorganisms, which would otherwise be lost by dilution and removed by water currents, tend to remain more concentrated and effective in such microenvironments. Consequently, the largest numbers and greatest variety of microscopic plants and animals are found on and near the bottoms and banks of lakes and rivers. In the sea microorganisms are most numerous generally within a few miles from shores, river outlets and other sources of nutriment. The numbers of microorganisms (especially bacteria) in the open sea and far out in great inland lakes are usually small. The species in mid-ocean are usually indigenous (i.e., specifically adapted to this environment). Bacteria from such waters are often difficult to cultivate in the laboratory unless sterilized aged sea water is included in the medium.

Some waters contain substances unfavorable to certain microorganisms. For example, sea water or water from the Dead Sea is too saline for many species, whereas hydrogen sulfide produced from organic matter by putrefactive microorganisms is toxic to algae and some other microorganisms.

Acidic and metallic industrial wastes kill not only microorganisms but tons of larger aquatic and marine plants and fish. Acids, such as $H_2SO_4$ from certain sulfur-oxidizing bacteria, or organic acids, alcohols and other products of fermentations occurring in muds or stagnant ooze, are unfavorable to many microorganisms as well as macroorganisms.

The microscopic flora and fauna of waters also depend to some extent on the kinds and numbers of other living things. For example, most plankton organisms feed on bacteria, algae and one another. Among themselves they maintain an equilibrium between life and death. *Protozoa* and *bacteriophages,* and possibly bacterial predators like *Bdellovibrio,* in water destroy billions of bacteria. Probably some species of marine and aquatic bacteria and other microorganisms produce *antibiotic substances* that destroy other species. Several bacteriophages specific for certain marine bacteria have been found. The role of *bacteriocins* may be of importance but is still to be evaluated.

Physical factors are of critical importance. The kinds and numbers of microorganisms in waters are inevitably determined to a great extent by temperature, pH, osmotic pressure (salinity), hydrostatic pressure (depth), aeration and penetration of sunlight.

Thus, the microbiology of natural waters is an exceedingly complex subject and much remains to be learned about it. However, it is obvious that the microscopic flora and fauna of a shallow, sun-warmed river below the out-

fall of a large sewage-disposal plant will differ
from that of water from the middle of the Atlantic Ocean, the Great Salt Lake of Utah,
icy water from the Mendenhall glacier in Alaska,
or water from the hot sulfur springs of Yellow-
stone Park.

## 42.2   AQUEOUS ENVIRONMENTS

**Fresh Waters.**   Part of the flora of any surface water is introduced periodically by rain
wash from adjacent land surface, some by dust
from the air, some by continuous growth of
indigenous organisms.

**Unpolluted Waters.**   In lakes and rivers free
from sewage pollution (if any such now exist!)
the concentration of nutrients in solution is usually much lower than in polluted streams like
the Hudson, Danube or Ganges rivers. Consider
a placid woodland pool fed by surface run-off
and springs. The water is clear and looks "pure."

The number of bacteria floating free in the
water away from zones of nutrition at the bottom
and shores is often quite limited, perhaps only
a dozen or so per milliliter. These may include
various species of soil saprophytes that can grow
to some extent in the small amount of organic
and mineral substances in solution in the water:
species of *Micrococcus, Flavobacterium, Achromobacter,
Bacillus, Proteus, Pseudomonas, Leptospira* and
others. If there is much decaying organic matter
at the bottom, species of *Clostridium* and other
anaerobes, strict and facultative, are often found,
including sulfur bacteria and sulfate-reducing
species (*Desulfovibrio*). Caulobacteraceae and
Chlamydobacteriales   and   other   "alga-like"
forms may be found growing on the surfaces of
rocks and logs near the shore. If hydrogen sulfide is being produced by anaerobic decomposition of organic matter at the bottom and if the
pool is not too shaded, species of photosynthetic
bacteria (Rhodobacteriineae) may be present.

When during a summer windstorm a large
tree falls into the water and stirs up the bottom
sediment of a pool, the whole flora changes almost instantly. The organic matter stirred up
from the bottom furnishes a rich and varied
pabulum. Cellulose-digesters and fermentative
types thrive. Numerous species of saprophytes,
previously present in small numbers, multiply
enormously and some, previously numerous,
are suppressed by newly multiplying, antagonistic species. Total numbers of microorganisms
per milliliter may rise to 100,000 or more until
an equilibrium is again reached.

In a high mountain stream derived from
melting snow the numbers and variety of microorganisms to be found are ordinarily small.
Unless the stream runs over polluted soil or soil
rich in decaying vegetable matter, the water is
likely to be almost sterile. It may contain a few
spores of *Bacillus,* Streptomycetaceae, molds or
yeasts, but they will not be very actively ger-
minating because of the low temperature. They
have probably been caught from the air by the
falling rain or snow. A few other microorganisms
such as micrococci, corynebacteria (diphtheroids) or gram-negative rods (mostly from dust
of the air or from soil), caught by snow or rain,
might be found. However, they would not be
multiplying either, because of cold and lack of
dissolved   nutrient   substances.   Psychrophilic
species would predominate in the indigenous
flora.

**Polluted Waters.**   The lower Hudson River
(among others!) has for decades had a flora
representative of sewage pollution. One may assume that *Escherichia coli* and other Enterobacteriaceae, as well as fecal streptococci and various
species of intestinal *Clostridium,* are present in
large numbers. Many soil saprophytes such as
*Spirillum, Vibrio, Sarcina, Micrococcus, Mycobacterium,
Bacillus,* yeasts, molds, Streptomycetaceae, *Leptospira* and other spirochetes, *Beggiatoa, Sphaerotilus,*
and many moldlike and alga-like species would
also find the organic matter in raw or treated
sewage or garbage found in such rivers to be
good pabulum.

In the mud and ooze at the bottom, the
O-R potential is low and anaerobic species
exist: *Clostridium, Desulfovibrio* and various facultative bacteria, the species depending on the
physicochemical nature of the sediment.

In the more aerated surface layers, strict
anaerobes do not thrive, and the odors and tastes
of putrefaction and fermentation are not so
perceptible. The total numbers of microorganisms may reach into the millions per milliliter
of water.

There is nothing constant or necessarily
predictable about the flora of such a body of
tidal water except within wide limits. Conditions
change hourly and the flora changes in response
to tide and pollution. The temporary pollution
from large passenger ships is a case in point.

In any body of water, saprophytic organisms
serve the purpose of scavengers. They decompose organic wastes and make them available
as food for other organisms in the water: algae,
higher plants, protozoa and worms. These in
turn support fish and other commercially use-

ful marine or aquatic life, and so contribute to human welfare. The suppression of aerobic (i.e., nonputrefactive and nonfermentative) saprophytic microorganisms and other aquatic life by excessive sewage pollution, with its demands on every atom of dissolved oxygen (BOD; i.e., Biological Oxygen Demand), and by microbicidal industrial waste is one of the major problems of the progress of civilization.

**Marine Waters.** Marine bacteria (i.e., those indigenous to the sea) have been described as those that will not grow on media without sea water. For general studies of many species of marine bacteria a representative medium contains: sea water (aged) 1000 ml.; peptone, 5.0 gm.; soluble starch, 2.0 gm.; $KNO_3$, 1.0 gm.; $FePO_4$, 0.1 gm.; agar, 15 gm. Adjust to pH 7.9 and sterilize. Marine bacteria appear to have a distinctive, specific requirement for $Na^+$ and other ions in sea water. Many seem to be otherwise identical with familiar terrestrial species but to be, in comparison, osmotically fragile.

MARINE ZONES. The sea has been divided into *biotic zones:* the *benthic zone,* or sea floor (benthos); the *pelagic,* usually thought of as the upper layers; the *oceanic,* or open sea; the *neritic,* or shallow (200-meter) or coastal waters; the *littoral,* or close-in, beach or tidal inland waters; a *euphotic,* or lighted zone; and an *aphotic,* or dark zone. The largest numbers and varieties of microorganisms are found in the shallow waters near land (neritic or littoral). Food is more plentiful there.

*Temperatures.* These range from 40° C. in some sun-warmed littoral waters of the tropics to −2° C. in polar regions (sea water freezes at about −2° C.).

*Salinity.* Most truly marine bacteria are sensitive to small changes in salinity above or below that of sea water (i.e., they are *stenohaline*). Some bacteria peculiar to salt lakes (e.g., Dead Sea) *require* salinities of 13 per cent or more (*halophilic*).

Many species of halophilic *Spirillum* may be found in tidal bays. Some are able to pass through very fine filters (0.45 $\mu$ but not 0.22 $\mu$). Some marine species appear to exist as protoplast-like forms. The salinity of sea water would cause the water to be osmotically protective.

*Pressures.* At the floor of the profoundest depths, pressures become very high. At a depth of one mile the hydrostatic pressure is about 2000 pounds per square inch. Yet many bacteria thrive in the bottom muds at six miles and deeper, where the temperatures range about

3° C. These bacteria seem to be very well adapted to these conditions. For example, in the laboratory, many grow only at 3° C. and 15,000 pounds pressure per square inch. Those requiring such high pressures are said to be obligately *barophilic.* (See Chapter 19.)

It is curious that obligate thermophils, thought of as growing only at temperatures of 50° C. or over, are found both in polar seas and in samples of mud from the sea floor at depths of over 30,000 feet, where the temperature ranges constantly *below 10° C.* Numerous strictly aerobic bacteria are also found. Some of these species may have reached the ocean floor from above as spores carried by ocean currents.

PHOTOGENIC BACTERIA. There are several species of photogenic bacteria indigenous to the sea. They may be cultivated upon sea-water agar with peptone. *Photobacterium phosphoreum* from various marine fish, and various species of *Vibrio* (e.g., *V. pierantonii*) are isolated from luminous marine fish. Many of the photogenic species luminesce only in waters with salinity equivalent to that of sea water (about 3 per cent).

MARINE BACTERIA AND PETROLEUM. Very interesting observations have been made concerning the possible role of marine microorganisms in the formation of petroleum. Marine bacteria as a group are enzymically active, like most soil and sewage bacteria. The various organisms inhabiting deep ocean beds and marine sediments can, as a group, attack almost any sort of organic matter. There is some evidence, although it is not conclusive, that these marine anaerobic microorganisms can transform certain organic substances into petroleum-like matter. (See also Chapter 11.)

## 42.3   SANITATION OF WATER FOR DOMESTIC USE

We have pointed out in previous chapters that many enteric pathogens (viruses, bacteria, protozoa) are transmitted via water used for domestic purposes.

Bodies of water are convenient places for the disposal of sewage and other refuse. Springs, streams, lakes and wells also become polluted through the drainage or seepage into them of infected surface washings. The water for domestic use in many cities is therefore collected in reservoirs and then is usually filtered, especially if not perfectly clear and clean all the year round. In most cases, it must finally be disinfected with chlorine.

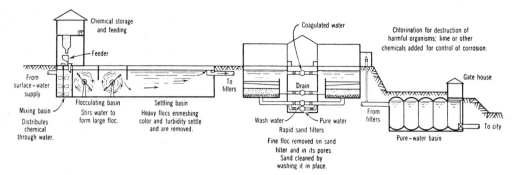

**Figure 42.1** Essential elements in a municipal water purification system. Flow is from left to right. Floc-forming chemicals (coagulants) are mixed with the water which then passes to a settling basin and then to rapid sand filters. On its way to the storage basin the filtered water receives a disinfecting dose of chlorine. (Fair and Geyer in Water Supply and Waste-water Disposal. John Wiley & Sons, Inc.)

## FILTER PLANTS

Although the construction and operation of apparatus for filtration and disinfection of water are primarily engineering problems, the processes they are designed to carry out are based in part on microbiological principles (Fig. 42.1). In purifying and disinfecting drinking water for municipalities, three major operations are generally carried out.

**Sedimentation and Flocculation.** This may occur primarily in large impounding reservoirs unless the water is derived from driven wells. In a large reservoir, silt, dead animal and vegetable matter and other suspended materials settle to the bottom and the water is largely clarified. When the water arrives at the filter plant from the reservoir, substances like iron salts ($FeSO_4$) and alum may be added to form a sticky, flocculent precipitate which settles in large sedimentation basins, taking down with it vegetable color and many microorganisms.

**Filtration.** The clarified water is then passed through sand filters, of which there are several types.

THE SLOW SAND FILTER. Large sand and gravel beds an acre or more in area are built up over drain pipes, starting with coarse gravel at the bottom and graduating in size to fine sand at the top (Fig. 42.2). The water is led onto the sand and allowed to trickle slowly through. The area of the slow sand filter is necessarily large because the water passes slowly through it.

As filtration proceeds, day after day, there accumulates, around each grain of sand and in the interstices, especially in the upper three or four inches of sand, a slimy, gelatinous film called a *schmutzdecke* (German for "dirt layer") composed of millions of bacteria, protozoa and other microorganisms. This slowly closes up the

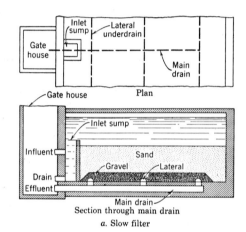

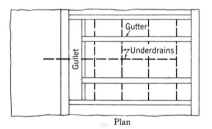

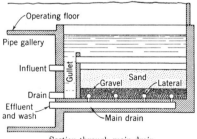

**Figure 42.2** Plan and section of (*a*) slow sand filter and (*b*) rapid sand filter. The total depth of water above the main drain in each is about 7 feet. Compare with Figure 42.3. (Fair and Geyer in Water Supply and Waste-water Disposal. John Wiley & Sons, Inc.)

pores between the sand grains and makes the filter bed more and more effective. At best, slow sand filters yield about three million gallons of filtered water per acre per day.

Through the action of enzymes, biological oxidation and reduction processes, and the ingestion of bacteria by myriads of protozoa inhabiting the slimy film, the bacterial and chemical content of the water is greatly reduced. When the gelatinous film finally becomes too thick, the filter is thrown out of service and the schmutzdecke is removed by cleaning machines.

The effectiveness of the filtration is constantly tested by bacteriologists in the plant, who determine the numbers and kinds of bacteria present in the water during different stages of the filtration process as well as in the finished product. Procedures are described in Chapter 36. The filters can remove 99 per cent of the bacteria present in the raw water.

The Rapid Sand Filter. The rapid sand filter is similar to the slow sand filter in principle, but its area is much less and it does not depend on the growth of a schmutzdecke. It filters water much more rapidly per unit of filter-bed area, about 130 million gallons per acre per day. The filters remain in service for several hours or days, and then are washed by a flow of water and air forced upward through them. Figures 42.2 and 42.3 show rapid sand filters.

**Chlorination.** In neither process is the filtered water sterile, nor can it be guaranteed free from pathogenic microorganisms. With few exceptions in public water systems in enlightened civilizations, after filtration the water is treated with chlorine. Enough must be added to leave a *residual* of 0.2 to 1.0 mg. per liter of free chlorine after all microorganisms and extraneous organic matter have been saturated with chlorine (*break-point* chlorination). The chlorinated water is commonly stored in underground cisterns. Highly polluted waters may be made potable, crystal clear and almost sterile by these devices, and it is largely because of these, as well as improved methods of sewage disposal, that typhoid fever, dysentery, both bacterial and amebic, cholera and other water-borne enteric diseases remain at a low level or absent in cities with properly operated water filtration plants.

**Combination Processes.** In newer processes the extensive basins needed for coagulation or floc formation and the long time and large tanks required for settling, plus the necessity of cleaning sand filters, are to a great extent overcome. *Tank machines* (often called *package plants*) are used in various engineering devices.

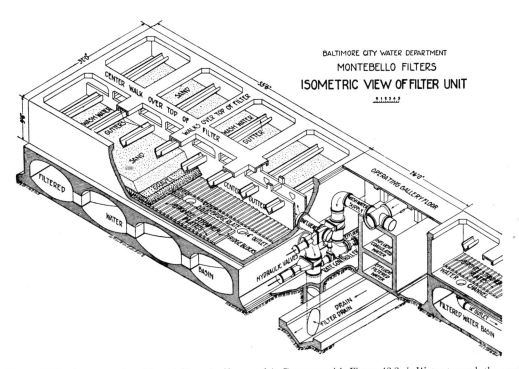

**Figure 42.3** A battery of rapid sand filters (uniform scale). Compare with Figure 42.2, *b*. Water to wash the sand is introduced beneath through a separate pipe system and is drawn off in the wash-water gutters above the sand. (Hopkins and Schulze in The Practice of Sanitation. The Williams & Wilkins Co., 1958.)

## 42.4  SEWAGE AND ITS DISPOSAL

**Composition of Sewage.**  The sewage of a city is about 99 per cent water and is handled in pumps and tanks much as is drinking water.

Fresh urban sewage contains dilute excrement, along with other city wastes: comminuted garbage, laundry water, and the like. Consequently it contains the flora and fauna of the intestinal tract as well as many soil and water species, and much organic matter. The pH is usually near the neutral point; temperature varies seasonally (5° to 25° C.). Of the solid material, after removal of silt, gravel, bottles and the like by preliminary settling and screening, nearly half is cellulose.

**Microorganisms in Sewage.**  These include many aerobes, strict anaerobes and facultative anaerobes, mostly saprophytic organotrophs. Common types of sewage bacteria derived from soil and intestine are: Enterobacteriaceae, fecal streptococci, *Clostridium, Bacteroides, Cytophaga, Micrococcus,* Pseudomonadaceae, spirochetes, Lactobacillaceae, Achromobacteraceae, yeasts, molds and others.

*Sphaerotilus, Crenothrix, Beggiatoa* and filamentous Rhodobacteriineae (if sunlight is present) characteristically form slimy growths on the sides and bottoms of sewage-containing ditches, pipes and tanks. They are often called *sewage fungi.* Certain real fungi (Phycomycetes), *Saprolegnia* and *Leptomitus,* are often found among them. All the organisms aid in decomposition of organic matter in the sewage.

At least 60 types of enteric viruses have been found in sewage, mainly polioviruses, ECHO and Coxsackie viruses, as well as hepatitis and adenoviruses. Unless very heavy chlorination is used, these can appear in the final effluent.

Most cities have separate sewerage systems to drain off storm waters. Industrial wastes (from dairies, tanneries, paper mills, etc.) are usually disposed of in plants specially designed for the particular material involved.

## 42.5  WASTE WATER DISPOSAL PLANTS

If raw domestic or "sanitary" sewage is discharged without previous *oxidative* treatment directly into lakes or streams, the water becomes a vector of disease, the available oxygen and other hydrogen acceptors in the water are soon used by the microorganisms living in the sewage, and foul-smelling, anaerobic processes develop and create a nuisance. Further, growth of fish and other forms of higher aquatic life is impossible, and considerable economic loss results. Still further, the water that receives the sewage is ruined for drinking or recreational purposes. Sewage disposal plants (Fig. 42.4) are therefore operated to accomplish several ends as follows:

**Screening.**  It is necessary to remove bulky foreign matter such as bottles, paper, wooden boxes and other extraneous refuse as well as to allow grit and gravel to settle out in *grit chambers* or *preliminary settling* basins. This is largely a matter of mechanics and does not concern us.

**Separation.**  Various kinds of *preliminary settling* or sedimentation tanks are employed, all designed to allow the solid matter to settle out as much as possible. The sewage is held in these tanks usually from 2 to 10 hours. This is a modification of the natural process of sedimentation that goes on constantly in rivers, lakes and the ocean. *Flotation* of fats, wood and the like may also occur, and surface-skimming is often an important part of preliminary settling. From 40 to 60 per cent of the solid matter of sewage settles out of suspension as sludge in three hours in these tanks. A small septic tank of this nature is shown in Figure 42.5.

Two-Story Tanks.  Some tanks for sedimentation purposes are made in two compartments, an upper and a lower. The upper portion is like a long, double, V-shaped trough and serves to introduce fresh sewage (Fig. 42.6). The solid matter settles out through slots at the bottom of the V's into a deep *sludge-slump* as the fluid flows along the trough. The solid matter, after settling to the lower compartment, is held there for some time to permit digestion and decomposition. The sludge is periodically removed to other digestion tanks. The best known device of this form is the *Imhoff* tank.

**Sludge Digestion.**  As we have seen, many of the common saprophytes of soil, water and the intestinal tract are anaerobic or facultative and, acting together, possess marked powers of hydrolysis of proteins, fats and related compounds. Nearly all forms of saprophytes can hydrolyze one or more carbohydrates. The woody materials in sewage are decomposed by numerous species capable of hydrolyzing cellulose. A piece of linen fabric or a thick sheet of cellulose filter paper will be digested and disappear completely in active sewage in five to seven days; faster in warm weather or in warmed sewage. Several species of microorganisms in sewage together hydrolyze all manner of organic matter: phenol, rubber, paraffin and so on. Some

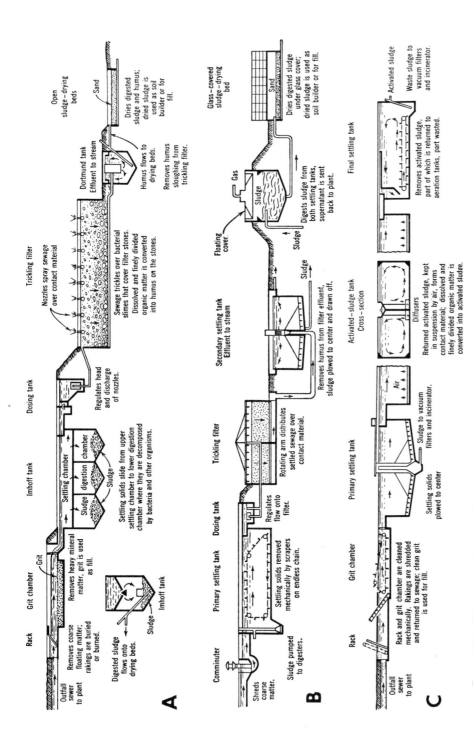

**Figure 42.4** Three types of sewage disposal systems accomplishing the same thing; they differ mainly in the method used to aerate the sewage. In *A* are seen a coarse screen (rack) and settling basin for grit, followed by a series of Imhoff tanks (Fig. 42.6). The fluid then is admitted under control (dosing tank) to a trickling aerating filter. The aerated fluid then passes through a secondary settling tank (Dortmund tank) from which residual solids (humus) are removed to sludge-drying beds. In *B* the solids are comminuted mechanically and collected mechanically from a primary settling tank. The aerating filter is of the sparger type. A secondary settling tank removes residual sludge or humus to a digestion tank which has a "floating" cover to trap sewer gas for use as fuel. The sludge is finally removed to a covered sludge drier. In *C* the partly clarified fluid is aerated and treated by the activated sludge process instead of by trickling filters. (Fair and Geyer in Water Supply and Wastewater Disposal. John Wiley & Sons, Inc.)

523

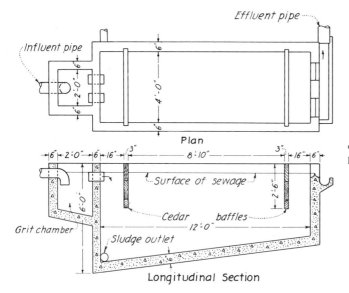

**Figure 42.5** Typical septic tank for school or factory. (Bulletin No. 16, Engineering Experiment Station, University of Washington.)

of these organisms have been mentioned. Others, especially certain gram-negative, anaerobic, cellulose-digesters of sludge, are still imperfectly known.

**Syntrophism.** The waste products of hydrolysis and metabolism produced by one organism are excellent pabulum for still another species, and so on. This is a form of *syntrophism* or mutual nutrition. The original molecules of wood, fat, meat or starch in sewage are finally changed, usually through the combined actions of several species, into soluble, relatively simple substances available to algae and other plants.

AEROBIC PROCESSES.   Under aerobic conditions, as in aerating filters and activated sludge (page 525), all of the complex, putrescible and organic matters in sewage are eventually changed largely into oxidized, inorganic ma-

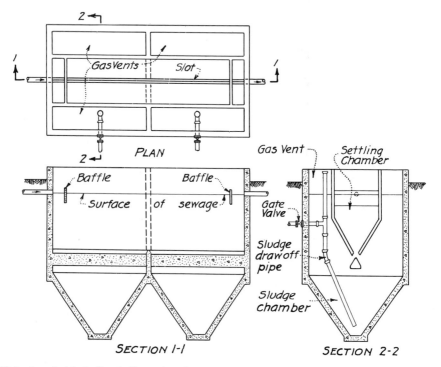

**Figure 42.6** A typical Imhoff tank. For explanation see text. (Keefer in Sewage Treatment—How It Is Accomplished. Smithsonian Institution Publication No. 4281.)

terials: sulfates, phosphates, nitrates, carbon dioxide and water: i.e., they are *mineralized.*

ANAEROBIC PROCESSES.    If the digestive process is anaerobic (as in tank-digested sludge) reduced compounds are formed: e.g., hydrogen sulfide, nitrogen, nitrates and methane. These are volatile. Other products of decomposition consist of microbial substance and reduced non-living materials rich in nitrogen, sulfur and phosphorus.

**Sludge Disposal.**    Sludge is removed from the tank and disposed of on sludge-drying beds, or it may be "dewatered" in large, heated drums and pulverized, incinerated or sold as fertilizer. The heating kills enteric pathogens. *Milorganite* is a good example of such fertilizer. Important constituents are various soluble compounds of nitrogen, phosphorus and potassium; essentials of plant growth.

**Gas Collection.**    Gas from various forms of sludge-digestion tanks contains about 75 per cent methane, produced by reduction of carbon compounds by anaerobic bacteria. In large plants it is piped to gas tanks and used as fuel. It furnishes steam and electric power for the disposal plant.

**Aeration of Fluid.**    Aeration is the key note in sewage disposal. The fluid part of the sewage, after passage through the sedimentation tanks or above the sludge compartment of the Imhoff tank, still contains much putrescible organic matter subject to oxidation. It may be recirculated through the system. The clarified fluid is subjected to various aeration treatments. Common are *activated sludge, aerating filters* and oxidizing lagoons.

## ACTIVATED SLUDGE

If large volumes of compressed air are forced through sewage in a tank, aerobic conditions are maintained throughout the liquid (Figs. 42.7 and 42.8). Particles of suspended matter flocculate, after a time, into small, gelatinous masses swarming with aerobic microscopic life and capable of oxidizing organic matter readily. These gelatinous masses are called *activated sludge.* As the process continues, the volume of the floc, or activated sludge, increases as more and more sewage and air are passed through the tank.

**Activated Sludge Organisms.**    The particles of floc in activated sludge consist of mixed species of bacteria which embed themselves in a mass of polysaccharide gum called *zoogloea* (Gr. *zous* = living; *gloea* = glue; hence, "living glue").

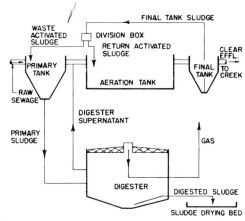

FLOW DIAGRAM—ACTIVATED SLUDGE PLANT

**Figure 42.7**  A "compact" activated-sludge plant. Raw sewage enters a primary tank where sludge settles into a digester (below) with sludge drying bed and gas collector. Activated sludge is introduced and the mixture is then aerated in the aeration tank. After a secondary settling (final tank) the supernatant fluid is led away and the sludge is recirculated. (Tapleshay: Total oxidation treatment of organic wastes. Sewage & Indust. Wastes, vol. 30.)

One of the principal zoogloea-forming organisms are *Pseudomonas*-like bacteria called *Zoogloea ramigera* and *Comamonas.* These organisms have complex nutritional requirements. They oxidize sewage materials very rapidly and are very active in forming floc. Numerous other familiar microorganisms may also form (or are found in) zoogloeal masses under the conditions of activated sludge: *Escherichia,* various species of *Pseudomonas, Alcaligenes* and *Bacillus* and filamentous organisms like *Sphaerotilis* as well as numerous types of protozoa (Fig. 42.9). The sticky zoogloeal material formed by these species gathers up, by adhesion and by adsorption, much of the colloidal material, bacteria, color and odors of the sewage fluid.

Rapid clarification, enzymic decomposition, oxidation and decrease in bacterial content are achieved, provided aeration continues and enough activated sludge is intimately mixed with the flowing sewage. The basic principle of the process is similar to that of aerating filters, the stones of sewage filters being replaced by the living particles and air in the activated sludge.

The fluid part of the activated sludge-sewage mixture is at length passed into a final settling tank. Part of the activated sludge is retained in the activated sludge tank as "seed," to reinoculate new sewage with the floc-forming bacteria, and the excess is removed.

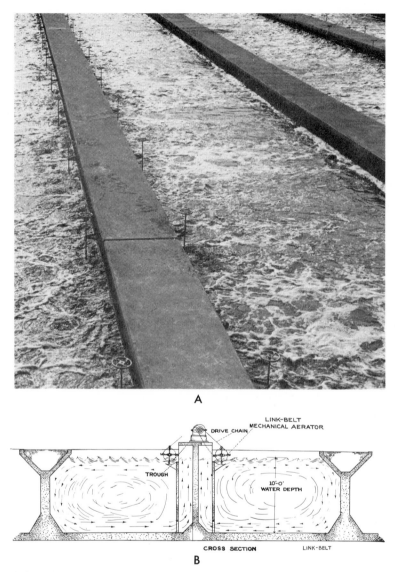

A

B

**Figure 42.8** *A*, Sewage aeration tanks in Pontiac, Michigan, equipped with valve orifices at the bottom for air diffusion. Note the uniform aeration pattern. (Courtesy of Pacific Flush Tank Co., Chicago.) *B*, Link belt mechanical top aeration agitators used in some activated sludge tanks. (Keefer in Sewage Treatment—How It Is Accomplished. Smithsonian Institution Publication No. 4281.)

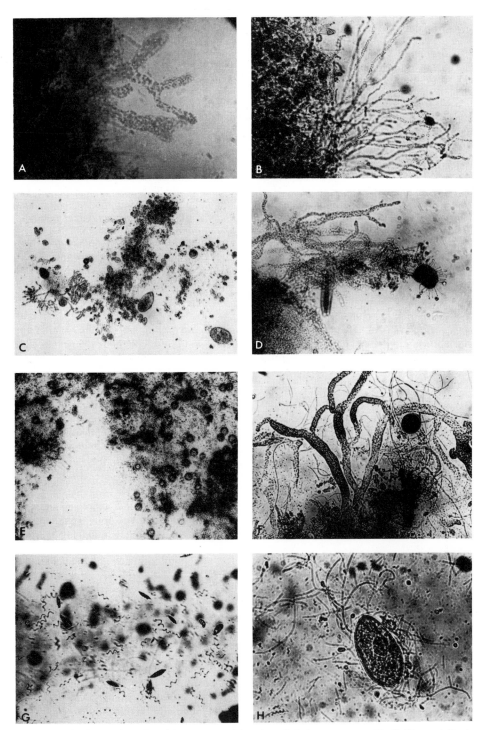

**Figure 42.9** *A, Zoogloea ramigera* from laboratory model activated sludge process. × 64. *B,* Fingered *Zoogloea* colonies from untreated raw sewage. × 64. *C,* Fingered *Zoogloea* colonies with protozoans. × 32. *D,* Fingered branching *Zoogloea* colonies with *Podophyra fixa.* × 64. *E,* Fingered *Zoogloea* colonies with *Vorticella microstoma* and other protozoans. × 26. *F,* Fingered branch-bearing *Zoogloea* colonies with the filamentous *Sphaerotilus natans.* × 64. *G,* Spirilla with flagellated protozoans. × 64. *H,* Long rods with Paramecium species. × 64. (From Amin and Ganapati: Appl. Microbiol., *15*:17, 1967.)

**Figure 42.10**   A typical trickling filter equipped with Dorrco rotary distributor (sparger). (Keefer in Sewage Treatment—How It Is Accomplished. Smithsonian Institution Publication No. 4281.)

### AERATING FILTERS

The fluid from any form of settling tank may be sprayed onto, and allowed to trickle and splash, continuously or intermittently, through artificial beds of broken stone or coke. The filtrate is collected by drains much as in slow-sand filtration of water. The pieces of stone become coated with a living film of aerobic, strongly oxidative microorganisms much like the schmutzdecke in a slow-sand water filter or floc inactivated sludge. These organisms feed upon and oxidize the organic matter of the sewage, the result being a much less offensive liquid (Fig. 42.10).

**Oxidation Lagoons.**   Raw sewage or preliminarily treated wastes are often led into broad, shallow, open, artificial *oxidation ponds,* or lagoons, there to undergo (partly) aerobic oxidative processes. Such lagoons and lakes have been found very effective in the removal of viruses.

### CHLORINATION AND FINAL DISPOSAL

Unless chlorinated and poured into some convenient body of water, the final effluent may be disposed of, where a porous and dry soil is available, by surface ditches or by a subsurface irrigation system of tile pipes, furnishing excellent fertilizer for farm crops raised on the land. There is little danger of infection, as typhoid, dysentery and cholera organisms are largely killed by the antagonistic action of protozoa or bacteria in the settling tanks or soil, or are filtered out by the soil and die. However, tubercle bacilli, *Salmonella* and poliovirus have been isolated from Imhoff-tank effluent as well as from secondary effluents. Promiscuous use of undisinfected sewage effluents is therefore not entirely safe. Epidemic (infectious) hepatitis virus is common in untreated water (Fig. 42.11).

**Water Reclamation.**   As the human population grows, and more and more water is demanded for both industrial and domestic uses, the natural sources of supply threaten to become inadequate as well as excessively polluted (Fig. 42.12). In addition to methods of desalinization of sea water, various Public Health agencies are now conducting research into means of using "used" and polluted waters by processes of *water reclamation.* In one such project municipal sewage is treated by an activated-sludge process and then stored in an oxidation and sedimentation pond for about 30 days. Water from this is well chlorinated and passed through a gravel percolation area. Thence it flows through soil and a river into a succession of lakes. It is then suitable (and much used) for recreational purposes. Other similar processes are projected.

As an interesting sidelight on conservation of food and utilization of solar energy (a "pet" subject for engineering research), attempts are usually made to reclaim waste water by cultivating algae (*Chlorella, Scenedesmus*) on the surface of photosynthetic reactors or ponds fully exposed to sunlight, on a large and intensive scale (Figs. 42.13 and 42.14). Bacteria in the sewage release carbon dioxide and soluble nutrients from the organic matter of the sewage. The algae growing on the surface use the carbon dioxide in photosynthesis and the soluble nutrients in the synthesis of their own complexes. From their photosynthetic process they return oxygen to the bacteria. The mass of algal growth may be harvested and dried to furnish feed for stock. Thus protein, a very expensive part of stock food, may be produced cheaply from sewage and sunlight. A difficulty is that if excessively large crops of algae are not removed, their death and disposal in the lagoons becomes a real problem.

The cultivation of algae with ultraviolet lamps in enclosed spaces such as spaceships and

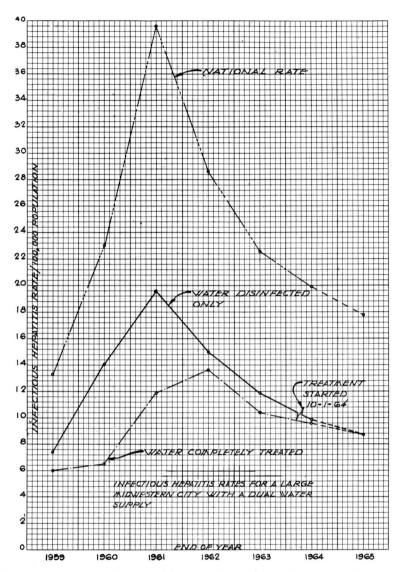

**Figure 42.11** Correlation between frequency of infection by epidemic (infectious) hepatitis virus and type of treatment of municipal water supply over a six-year interval including an epidemic period. Disinfection of the water, and the combination of disinfection with other procedures of purification in this city markedly lowered the local rate below the national rate even during the epidemic year. (From Taylor et al.: Amer. J. Pub. Health, *56*:2093, 1966.)

**Figure 42.12** Interrelationships of resources and products to total human activity. (From Mattoni, Keller and Myrick: Bioscience, June 1965, p. 405.)

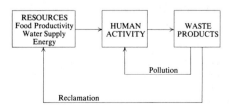

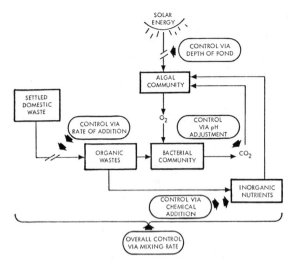

**Figure 42.13**  Industrial photosynthesis process. Organic wastes from clarified domestic sewage in an oxidation lagoon are decomposed in the bacterial community to furnish carbon dioxide and inorganic (mineralized) nutrients that are used in the surface-living algal community exposed to the sunlight. The resulting photosynthesis furnishes oxygen for the underlying bacterial community. Several self-explanatory factors that control the process are shown. (From Mattoni, Keller and Myrick: Bioscience, June 1965, p. 405.)

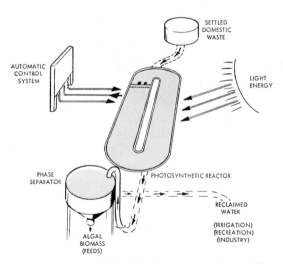

**Figure 42.14**  Industrial photosynthesis process. The "photosynthetic reactor" receives controlled volumes of clarified domestic sewage. Algae, with light energy, form masses of growth in the reactor and are removed by means of a "phase separator" and, after drying and other processing, serve as stock feeds. The reclaimed water serves for irrigation, recreation, industry, etc. (From Mattoni, Keller and Myrick: Bioscience, June, 1965, p. 405.)

submarines has been mentioned and is under intensive study. Not only is carbon dioxide removed from the air and replaced with oxygen but a source of food is provided from waste matter.

### DETERGENTS IN WATER

One phase of water pollution involves the use of synthetic detergents in household and industry. These can cause foaming of water in the house, in natural bodies of water and in sewage plants. The problem in respect to drinking waters is almost entirely one of esthetics; and in respect to sewage disposal it is one of mechanics. The actual amounts of detergents, even in sewage polluted water, are relatively minute. Detergents as ordinarily used are not harmful, although some persons are allergic to certain detergents. Fundamentally the problem of disposal is a bacteriological one and centers around "biodegradation" of the detergents, i.e., their decomposition by the microorganisms in sewage disposal plants or soil.

The effective agents in most household synthetic detergents are anionic surface tension reducers (surfactants). They may be mixed with perfumes, colors, complex phosphates and whiteners. None is toxic in ordinary use. Until recently they were of the class of polypropylene (alkyl) benzyl sulfonates (ABS); long, *branched-chain* molecules (tetrapropylene derivatives).

The long, branching, alkyl-benzene chains either resist direct enzymatic attack by microorganisms or are too large to permeate into the microbial cells. Hence they are not readily decomposed by microorganisms in sewage. They are said to be "hard" (difficult) detergents. Bacteriological studies show that some of these can be destroyed by certain specially adapted species of bacteria. Straight-chain detergents, i.e., *linear* alkyl sulfonates (LAS), were found to be much more easily decomposed ("biodegradable") than the branched-chain compounds; LAS are called "soft" detergents. As a result, progressive detergent manufacturers are using more of the LAS, such as sodium lauryl sulfate. These are up to 84 per cent biodegradable in ordinary disposal plants as against only about 50 per cent or less of ABS.

### 42.6   PREVENTION OF WATERBORNE DISEASE IN ABSENCE OF FILTRATION

Disease transmission by water in the absence of elaborate filtration and chlorination systems (as on camping trips) is easily prevented. With the single possible exception of hepatitis virus, all of the common intestinal pathogens are readily killed by boiling for five minutes as well as by contact for at least two hours with 2 to 5 ppm of chlorine, iodine or other suitable disinfectants. Probably 30 minutes boiling would eliminate even hepatitis virus, although this remains to be experimentally established.

Ice made from polluted water is as dangerous as the water itself. Water for camp use, provided it is clear and clean, may be treated with chlorine or iodine by using one of the numerous disinfectants for the purpose available on the market: *HTH, B-K, Wescodyne* or *Globaline*. A teaspoonful of fresh chloride of lime in 25 to 50 gallons of water will also prove an adequate safeguard, unless the water is very heavily polluted or dirty. At least an hour must be allowed for the chlorine to act. Ordinary laundry bleaches (5 per cent sodium hypochlorite) will also serve. Directions are found on the labels of the bottles.

To persons contemplating a camping trip, or travel in countries where water and sanitation are poor, publications of the Public Health Service of the Department of Health, Education and Welfare can be of great assistance.

## SUPPLEMENTARY READING

Askew, J. B., Bott, R. F., Leach, R. E., and England, B. L.: Microbiology of reclaimed water from sewage for recreational use. Amer. J. Pub. Health, *55*:453, 1965.

Berg, G.: Virus transmission by the water vehicle. III. Removal of viruses by water treatment procedures. Health Lab. Science, *3*:170, 1966.

Chen, P. K., Citarella, R. V., Salazar, O., and Colwell, R. R.: Properties of two marine bacteriophages. J. Bact., *91*:1136, 1966.

Collins, V. G.: Planktonic bacteria. In: A symposium on Plankton. J. Gen. Microbiol., *16*:265, 1957.

Coughlin, F. J.: Detergents and water pollution abatement. Amer. J. Pub. Health, *55*:760, 1965.

Fair, G. M., et al.: Water and Wastewater Engineering, Vol. 1: Water Supply and Wastewater Removal. John Wiley & Sons, New York, 1966.

Finstein, M. S.: Growth and flocculation in a *Zoogloea* culture. Appl. Microbiol., *15*:962, 1967.

Gaudy, Jr., A. F., and Gaudy, E. T.: Microbiology of waste waters. Ann. Rev. Microbiol., *20*:319, 1966.

Hopkins, E. S., and Bean, E. L.: Water Purification Control, 4th Ed'n. The Williams & Wilkins Co., Baltimore, Md. 1967.

Isherwood, J. D.: The fate of Coxsackie virus A-13 in water reclamation. Amer. J. Pub. Health, *55*:1945, 1965.

MacLeod, R. A.: The question of the existence of specific marine bacteria. Bact. Rev., *29*:9, 1965.

McKinney, R. E., and Pfeffer, J. T.: Effect of biological waste treatment on water quality. Amer. J. Pub. Health, *55*:772, 1965.

McLean, D. M., and Brown, J. R.: Virus dispersal by water. Health Lab. Science, *3*:182, 1966.

Meyer, G. H., Morrow, W. B., and Wyss, O.: Antarctica: The microbiology of an unfrozen saline pond. Science, *138*:1103, 1962.

Morgan, G. B., Gubbins, P., and Morgan, V.: A critical appraisal of the membrane filter technic. Health Lab. Science, *2*:227, 1965.

Oppenheimer, C. H., editor: Symposium on Marine Microbiology. Charles C Thomas, Springfield, Ill. 1963.

Payne, W. J., and Feisal, V. E.: Bacterial utilization of dodecyl sulfate and dodecyl benzene sulfonate. Appl. Microbiol., *11*:239, 1963.

Prakasam, T. B. S., and Dondero, N. C.: Aerobic heterotrophic bacterial populations of sewage and activated sludge III. Appl. Microbiol., *15*:1128, 1967.

Rowan, W. B.: Schistosomiasis and the chlorination of sewage effluent. Amer. J. Trop. Med. Hyg., *13*:577, 1964.

Slanetz, L. W., and Bartley, C. H.: Survival of fecal streptococci in sea water. Health Lab. Science, *2*:142, 1965.

Standard Methods for the Examination of Water and Wastewater, 12th ed. Amer. Pub. Health Assn., New York. 1965.

Theios, E. P., Morris, J. G., Rosenbaum, M. J., and Baker, A. G.: Effect of sewage treatment on recovery of poliovirus following mass oral immunization. Amer. J. Pub. Health, *57*:295, 1967.

Working Party of the Pub. Health Lab. Serv.: A bacteriological survey of swimming baths in primary schools. Monthly Bull., Min. of Health and Pub. Health Lab. Serv., London, *24*:116, 1965.

# Chapter 43

## MICROBIOLOGY
## OF THE SOIL

### 43.1 THE SOIL AS AN ENVIRONMENT

In Chapter 4 it was pointed out that many substances useful as food for microorganisms tend to be adsorbed upon surfaces immersed in fluid media. A mass of tiny particles, such as sand or charcoal in a fluid culture medium, furnishes multitudes of tiny, protected niduses and extensive surfaces where foods become abundant and digestive enzymes tend to be concentrated. A comparable relationship occurs in soil. Each particle of soil has its film of moisture and its swarm of microorganisms on its surface. On a rainy day, in angles and depressions in the soil, tiny pools or puddles may develop and persist for a day or so. In this fluid myriads of microorganisms grow in warm weather.

The topsoil is indeed an entire universe where billions of minute organisms—algae, bacteria, viruses, protozoa, nematodes and fungi—for millions of years have lived their pigmy lives, multiplied in their minute-long generation times, struggled together for space, food and survival and have finally died, only to be replaced by others. Nevertheless, like each human being, however obscure, each microorganism leaves its effect on the universe.

Most soil microorganisms occur in the upper few inches or feet of soil. In a fertile loam in central New Jersey, for example, few microorganisms are found below three feet (Table 43.1) and none at five feet, unless accompanying plant roots or other extensions from the surface. Their numbers and species vary. Good, fertile, moist loam may contain from 100,000 live microorganisms of all classes per gram of soil to half a billion or more, depending on moisture and food. Each type of soil is a special study in itself.

**Composition of Soils.** The soil consists primarily of inorganic particles derived from disintegrating rocks (mainly complex aluminum silicates) ranging in size from large boulders through gravel and sand to microscopic specks, mixed in varying proportions, all more or less compacted together, but having interstices between them as a result of their irregularity in shape. These interstices contain more or less water and air, carbon dioxide, hydrogen sulfide, ammonia and other gases in small amounts, the proportions of each depending on rainfall, drainage, barometric pressure, winds, temperature, atmospheric humidity, microbial activity and other factors (Fig. 43.1).

**Soil as a Culture Medium.** The water in good agricultural soil contains, in solution, ions like $K^+$, $Na^+$, $Mg^{++}$, $Ca^{++}$, $Fe^{++}$, $S^{--}$, $NO_3^-$, $SO_4^{--}$, $CO_3^{--}$, $PO_4^{---}$ and others, depending on the composition of the original rocks, on

**TABLE 43.1 MICROORGANISMS IN FERTILE LOAM SOIL AT VARIOUS DEPTHS**

| Depth (Inches) | Bacteria (per Gram*) |
|---|---|
| 1 | 4,000,000,000 |
| 4 | 3,000,000,000 |
| 8 | 2,000,000,000 |
| 12 | 1,000,000,000 |
| 20 | 500,000,000 |
| 30 | 1,000,000 |
| 72 | 100 |

*These figures rounded to nearest billion or hundred thousand. They represent only viable cells capable of growth on the particular medium provided, found in the particular sample of soil examined. Wide variations must be allowed for time of year, moisture, recent manuring, cropping, etc.

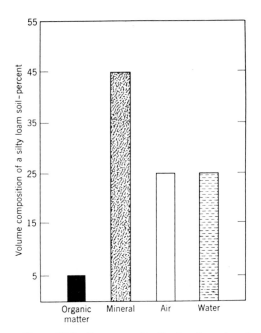

**Figure 43.1** Percentage distribution (by volume) of important classes of constituents of a representative silty, fertile loam soil. (From Waksman and Starkey; courtesy of Dr. S. A. Waksman in Soil Microbiology. John Wiley & Sons, Inc., 1952.)

farm cropping, on manuring and fertilizing practices, on the microscopic and macroscopic flora and fauna, and on other factors. These ions, it will be seen, represent elements essential in culture media for all forms of life. In a fertile soil these elements, in mineral form, are supplemented by a variety of organic compounds derived from the decomposition of animal and plant residues and from the synthetic activities of microorganisms: carbohydrates ranging in complexity from glucose to starches, cellulose and polysaccharide gums; nitrogenous compounds ranging from urea to amino acids, peptones and complex proteins; fats; waxes; organic acids such as acetic; pyrimidines; B-group and other vitamins; and so on. Thus, the ground water in a fertile soil (aqueous extract of soil) is actually an excellent culture medium for many microorganisms.

**Variations in Soil.** The soil environment is a highly variable one. Obvious variables are daily and seasonal temperatures and water content. It is clear also that if a heavy crop of clover and timothy grass is plowed under, the soil is aerated, some moisture is lost and an enormous amount of readily assimilable soluble substances in the plant juices is introduced. These soluble substances (proteins, carbohydrates, lipids, minerals and vitamins) quickly undergo hydrolysis

and other complex changes of metabolism. There is a resulting great increase in internal temperature of the soil; in its acidity, resulting from fermentation; in content of $CO_2$, $NH_3$ and ammonium salts; and in relatively simple organic food substances: various fatty and amino acids, peptones and alcohols. These support a tremendous upsurge in numbers of all heterotrophic forms as well as of facultative autotrophs capable of thriving in such an actively fermenting, acid, partly aerobic, partly anaerobic environment.

Oxidative microorganisms soon use up all the immediately available free oxygen. *Clostridium* spores can germinate, and strict, as well as facultative, anaerobes can thrive. If all air is excluded, as in swamps, heavy clays and compacted soils, then fermentative processes predominate and the soil becomes acid. Drainage, aeration and liming aid in *sweetening* such soils. Later, the acids are metabolized or neutralized, carbonates are formed, and the initial acidity reverts to alkalinity, especially if the soil is well aerated by tillage and drainage.

The tremendous growth of microorganisms that occurs after plowing under manures and green crops temporarily depletes the soil water of its soluble compounds, especially those of nitrogen, phosphorus, potassium and sulfur, which are combined as new microbial substance. As a result, for two weeks or more most newly planted crop plants find the soil a rather unfavorable medium. However, many of the microorganisms soon die, especially nonsporing species, and release the elements for crop use. Finally, a more or less complete equilibrium of dormancy or low-level activity is re-established, awaiting the next change, perhaps the planting of a corn crop with liberal application of lime or commercial fertilizer, to stir things up once again.

Prominent in this residual community are the various saprophytic Myxobacterales, Actinomycetales and Eumycetes, all of which are active in decomposing many resistant substances including cellulose, chitin, keratin, lignin* and even paraffin and vulcanized rubber!

The numerous protozoa in soil convert much organic matter into "protoplasm." A principal item of their diet is bacteria; thus

---

*Lignins are a class of substances that bind together the cellulose fibers in wood. They are complex heteropolymers of p-hydroxycinnamyl alcohol residues *distantly* related chemically to plastics such as *Bakelite* and *Formica*. Lignins are much harder, tougher and more resistant to hydrolysis than cellulose. Lignins occur especially in the roots and hearts of trees and woody plants.

protozoa are the basis of an important ecological control relationship in soil, as they are in sewage. Another control mechanism active in soil, as also in water and sewage, consists of bacteriophages, antibiotics and, probably bacteriocins.

Many worms, ranging from microscopic nematodes to large earthworms (night crawlers, the delight of fishing enthusiasts) eat organic matter. They digest it with the aid of their own enzymes and intestinal bacteria and return part of it to the soil in the form of simpler, more soluble substances as food for plants. Similarly, burrowing animals and the larvae of insects such as Japanese beetles help to transform organic matter in the soil.

## 43.2 SYNTROPHISM IN THE SOIL

*Syntrophism* (Gr. *syn* = mutual or together; *trophe* = nourishment) is that ecological rela-

tionship in which organisms provide nourishment for each other. In so varied a community as a fertile loam soil the nutritional relationships can be exceedingly complex.

For example, *cellulose,* a principal component (with lignin) of wood, is a complex polymer of glucose. Numerous species of soil bacteria (*Cellulomonas, Cellvibrio* and Actinomycetales), with numerous species of Eumycetes, hydrolyze the cellulose molecule into molecules of cellobiose, a disaccharide resembling maltose. *Starch* likewise is hydrolyzed into maltose and dextrins.

Some organisms can utilize cellobiose, maltose and dextrins, as such. Cellobiose, maltose and dextrins may also be further decomposed by other organisms to glucose. This is an almost universal source of energy, and under anaerobic conditions (fermentation) it is decomposed by microorganisms into a great variety of still smaller molecules that can be used as food by one organism or another. At each stage in the

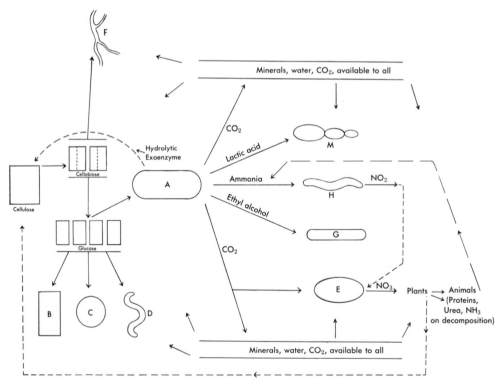

**Figure 43.2** Some of the many complex syntrophic relationships occurring in the soil. Heterotrophic organism *A* (left of center) secretes a cellulolytic enzyme (curved dash line) which hydrolyzes cellulose to cellobiose. Cellobiose is used directly by some organisms and is also hydrolyzed to glucose by organism *A* as well as by various other species not shown. Organisms *B, C,* and *D* as well as *A* then ferment the glucose with the production of various waste products ($CO_2$, etc.) (center of diagram). These serve as foods for still other species represented by *M* and *G*. Ammonia (center) may be produced from protein if organism *A* or any of the other species attacks proteins or amino acids. Ammonia so produced is oxidized to $NO_2$ as a source of energy by organism *H*. This $NO_2$ is oxidized to $NO_3$ by autotroph *E*. The $NO_3$ is then used by plants (lower right) which nourish animals; the plants and animals producing more cellulose and more protein for organism *A*, thus renewing a cycle of foods. Syntrophic relationships in the soil are so complex that to place in one diagram all that we know about would result in an almost solid mass of tangled lines.

decomposition of cellulose or starch a new group of microorganisms is found, capable of metabolizing the products of decomposition produced by other organisms. In the microscopic world, the waste of one is the indispensable food of another (Fig. 43.2).

*Proteins* are built up of amino acid units much as cellulose is built up of glucose units. Like cellulose, proteins are hydrolyzable and metabolically decomposed to peptones, polypeptides and amino acid molecules. Each product may be used by many species as sources of energy, carbon and nitrogen.

**Satellitism.** Syntrophism is not confined to microorganisms in the soil, but is found wherever complex mixtures of organisms live together. Syntrophism in a simplified form is well illustrated by the phenomenon often called *satellitism.* Inoculate, with organism A, a plate of agar medium that lacks an essential metabolite (let us say, NAD) of organism A. Then *spot inoculate* the plate with organism B, that is known to produce NAD. After incubation, colonies of A appear as satellites *only* around the spot of growth of B, *nowhere else.* B is obviously a syntrophe of A (Fig. 43.3).

Many other such interrelationships are seen in nature. *Lichens* are examples in which a fungus and an alga live together and in some instances

**Figure 43.3** Minute colonies of *Haemophilus influenzae* growing as satellites around colonies of *Staphylococcus aureus* on agar in a Petri Plate. Colonies of *H. influenzae* are barely seen except in areas around the two larger *S. aureus* colonies at upper and lower right that liberate into the agar an essential metabolite (NAD) absolutely required by *H. influenzae.* Organisms (not *S. aureus*) in the large colonies at upper and lower left liberate little or no NAD. (From unpublished work; courtesy of Drs. H. E. Morton and E. E. Long and from collection of American Society for Microbiology.)

will not live separately. Various animals are dependent on synthesis of several B-vitamins and essential amino acids by bacteria of the gastrointestinal tract; this is notably true of equines and in that very complex ecological system, the bovine rumen. Man depends on intestinal bacteria for vitamin K (unless he buys it in "7-a-week" capsules).

**Formation of Humus.** The least digestible parts of plant tissues (e.g., lignin, resins) and of animal carcasses (e.g., waxes, hair, horn and bone) undergo slow decomposition. The mixture of slowly decaying remains make up a soft, spongy, brownish residual material called *humus.* It improves the texture of the soil, making it more friable; it holds moisture like a sponge; it also serves as a reserve store of slowly released food for microorganisms and crop plants.

## 43.3 MICROBIOLOGICAL EXAMINATION OF SOIL

Fertile soil contains such a wide variety of microorganisms that no single method can be given for cultivating or enumerating soil microorganisms in general.

**Plating Methods.** Plating methods have been previously described in Chapter 4. They are applicable to the enumeration and isolation of bacteria, yeasts and molds in any substance, including soil. Suitable modifications are made to meet the cultural requirements of the kinds of microorganisms that it is desired to enumerate.

Selective methods are often used to cultivate or isolate some particular species from the soil. For example, to enumerate soil microorganisms capable of metabolizing cellulose, a weighed sample of soil is placed in water and well shaken. One-milliliter amounts of serial dilutions of this water are placed in tubes of medium containing cellulose as the only source of carbon. Hence only cellulose-metabolizers can grow. From the highest dilution showing growth one may estimate the "indicated" number of cellulose digesters in that sample of soil.

One may follow (and adapt to other uses as the student's ingenuity may suggest) the clever scheme of Winogradsky to select and enumerate autotrophic organisms that obtain energy by oxidizing ammonia to nitrite. An inorganic medium is prepared with $(NH_4)_2SO_4$ as the sole source of energy. Since these organisms are strict autotrophs and will not grow (in the laboratory) in contact with organic matter like agar or gelatin, the medium is solidified with silica gel. The surface is coated with powdered chalk, giving it a white, opaque appearance. As the $NH_3$ [$(NH_4)_2 SO_4$] is oxidized to $HNO_2$ by the growing colonies of ammonia-oxidizers, the $CaCO_3$ is destroyed and a clear zone appears around each colony.

**Microscopic Examination.** By making stained smears of soil and examining them with the microscope, we may count various morphological types of bacteria and other microorganisms, especially filaments of fungi. Since dead as well as living cells are counted, microscopic counts are higher than plate-culture counts. Error may arise in microscopic counts from difficulty of staining some species, and confusion of bacteria with soil particles. This

source of error may be largely eliminated, and the organisms specifically identified and observed in their natural relationships by staining soil preparations with specific, fluorescent antibodies.

## 43.4   CYCLES OF THE ELEMENTS

All the elements that are essential components of protoplasm undergo cyclical alternations between an inorganic state, free in nature, and a combined state in living organisms. Many of these elements also alternate between an oxidized and a reduced condition and can

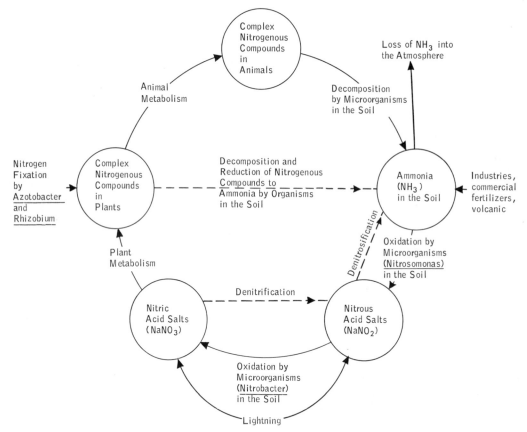

**Figure 43.4**   The nitrogen cycle. At the right, ammonia is brought into the cycle. This is nitrogen in its most reduced form. It is derived, in part, from protein decomposition, some volcanic sources, commercial fertilizers and various industries.

Proceeding in a clockwise manner, the process of *nitrosification*, carried on by soil bacteria (*Nitrosomonas*, etc.), oxidizes $NH_3$ to nitrites. Other soil bacteria (*Nitrobacter*, etc.) oxidize the nitrites to nitrates (*nitrification*). Nitrates and nitrites are also produced from atmospheric O and N by lightning flashes. Nitrogen in the form of nitrate is available to plants (left of diagram). Facultative and anaerobic bacteria of the soil are constantly acting to reverse these processes, as indicated by the lines marked "denitrification" and "denitrosification." After nitrogen is at last incorporated in plants as protoplasm, etc., it is converted into animal tissues (top of diagram). When plants and animals die, and their wastes decay, the saprophytic microorganisms in the soil convert the nitrogen back into the form of ammonia and other nitrogenous compounds, and the cycle recommences.

At the left of the cycle are shown the means by which atmospheric nitrogen is converted directly into living matter by soil microorganisms: *Clostridium, Pseudomonas, Aerobacter, Achromobacter, Azotobacter, Rhizobium,* some species of fungi, blue-green algae, etc. Once it is in this form, it follows the same course in the cycle that other vegetable proteins do.

thus serve some organisms as sources of energy by oxidation; others as electron (H) acceptors by reduction. Some of these cycles involve several stages. The nitrogen cycle is a familiar example (Fig. 43.4).

## 43.5   THE NITROGEN CYCLE

This cycle comprises three main processes: nitrogen reduction (nitrogen fixation; ammonification and denitrification) and nitrogen oxidation. Each process is carried on by certain groups of organisms (see Table 43.2).

## 43.6   NITROGEN REDUCTION

### I. Nitrogen Fixation: Nonsymbiotic

*Nitrogen fixation* is the process of causing free nitrogen gas to combine chemically with other elements.

In the atmosphere over one acre of soil it is estimated that there are some 35,000 tons of free nitrogen. Yet, though absolutely essential to life, not a molecule of it can be used as such by higher plants, animals or man* without the intervention of the nitrogen-fixing microorganisms. Nitrogen-fixers enzymically combine atmospheric nitrogen with other elements to form organic compounds in living cells. In organic combinations nitrogen is more reduced than when it is free. From these organic compounds, upon their decomposition, the nitrogen is liberated in a *fixed* form available to farm crops either directly or through further microbial action. It is of interest that some of these nitrogen-fixing enzymes are inducible or adaptive in contact with nitrogen.

The first microorganism discovered (by Winogradsky, 1895) to possess the property of fixing atmospheric nitrogen without symbiotic aid was the anaerobic species *Clostridium pasteurianum,* common in boggy soils. Aerobic nonsymbiotic nitrogen-fixing bacteria (*Azotobacter*) were discovered in the soil by Beijerinck in 1901. Since those discoveries the phenomenon of nonsymbiotic nitrogen fixation has been observed in numerous other *Clostridium* species; also in most blue-green algae; in many photosynthetic bacteria like *Rhodospirillum;* in *Desulfovibrio;* and in many other bacteria. One of the most interesting is Beijerinck's *Azotobacter.*

**Genus Azotobacter.** *Azotobacter* thrives in all well-aerated, neutral or slightly alkaline (pH about 7.5) arable soils. It is pleomorphic, strictly aerobic, normally encapsulated, nonsporing and motile with peritrichous flagella. An especially distinctive feature is the formation of thick-walled, spherical, dormant *cysts.* These have some properties suggestive of primitive spores but, although very resistant to ultraviolet and gamma radiations and sonic vibrations as well as drying, they are not highly thermostable as are true bacterial endospores (Fig. 43.5). The cysts contain a central body that appears to be a resting, shrunken (partly dehydrated?) cell within a dense, two-layered protective coating. The cysts are formed only by encapsulated cells.

In the soil *Azotobacter* species grow almost autotrophically; however, organic substances are needed as energy source. These energy sources are probably derived from the decomposition of cellulose, starches and the like by other microorganisms of the soil. Carbohydrates

**TABLE 43.2**  PRINCIPAL MICROORGANISMS AND PROCESSES INVOLVED IN THE NITROGEN CYCLE

I. *Nitrogen fixation:*
  A. Nonsymbiotic (independently living bacteria)
    1. Azotobacteraceae
      *Azotobacter*
      *Beijerinckia*
    2. Miscellaneous others
      Certain species of *Aerobacter, Nocardia, Rhodobacteriineae, Clostridium,* certain fungi, most blue-green algae
  B. Symbiotic (bacteria living symbiotically with leguminous plants)
    1. *Rhizobium meliloti, R. trifolii,* and so forth
II. *Nitrogen oxidation* (production of nitrites and nitrates):
  A. Nitrobacteraceae
    1. $NH_3$ to $NO_2$
      *Nitrosomonas*
      *Nitrosococcus*
      *Nitrosocystis*
    2. $NO_2$ to $NO_3$
      *Nitrobacter*
  B. Miscellaneous others ($NO_2$ and $NO_3$)
    Nocardias, *Streptomyces*
    *Aspergillus* sp., and other molds and higher fungi
III. *Nitrogen reduction* (Ammonia production and denitrification):
    Various microorganisms causing ammonification by producing $NH_3$ from decomposition of proteins, and denitrification by use of $NO_3$ and $NO_2$ as hydrogen acceptors.

---

*This refers to man in his primitive state. Since becoming "civilized" he has learned to *fix* atmospheric nitrogen by artificial means.

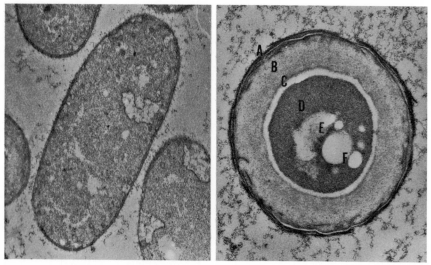

**Figure 43.5**   Electron micrograph of ultrathin sections of vegetative cells (left) and of a cyst (right) of *Azotobacter* sp. The vegetative cells show the internal structure commonly seen in vegetative bacteria. In the cyst are seen: *A*, a rough, laminated, external coat (exine); *B*, an intermediary layer without definite structure; *C*, a space, possibly due to drying of the section; *D*, an integrated central body; *E*, nuclear matter; *F*, globules of lipid substance. (From Scolofsky and Wyss: J. Bact., vol. 81.)

added to the soil in a form such as molasses or starch wastes stimulate the accumulation of nitrogen in the soil through the growth of the *Azotobacter* and other nonsymbiotic, nitrogen-fixing organisms. The nitrogen combined in their structures is taken from the atmosphere and is released in organic form as secretions and on the death of the bacteria.

*Azotobacter* grows readily in such nitrogen-free solutions as the following:

| | | |
|---|---|---|
| $H_2O$ | 1000.0 | ml. |
| Mannitol (or other organic | | |
| source of energy and carbon) | 15.0 | gm. |
| $K_2HPO_4$ | 0.2 | gm. |
| $MgSO_4 \cdot 7H_2O$ | 0.2 | gm. |
| $CaCl_2$ | 0.02 | gm. |
| $FeCl_3$ (10 per cent aqueous | | |
| solution) | 0.05 | ml. |
| Molybdenum salt | Trace | |

Adjust to pH 7.2; for solid medium add 15 gm. of agar or silica gel before adjusting the pH.

In the absence of molybdenum, nitrogen-fixation will not occur; the metal ions appear to activate an enzyme (*nitrogenase*) essential in the fixation process. Molybdenum can be replaced only by vanadium.

## II. Nitrogen Fixation: Symbiotic

**Genus Rhizobium.*** When young and actively growing, these bacteria are organotrophic,

aerobic, nonsporing, pleomorphic, gram-negative rods. They are usually motile with variably placed flagella. Enzymically they are restricted and feeble. Their pleomorphism is regarded by some as evidence of a somewhat complex life cycle. They grow on ordinary, organic, laboratory media, especially if made with yeast extracts, at 20° C. and pH 7.2.

Their most characteristic activity and form are seen when they grow in the tissues and within the cells of leguminous plant roots. In the plant cells they are morphologically distinctive as *bacteroids*. In stained smears made from crushed *nodules* from the roots of leguminous plants they are often seen as large, oddly angular, stellate, budding or Y, V, T, X and L forms. These contain metachromatic masses and bands which are thought by some to represent special reproductive mechanisms. Others regard these swollen forms as degenerative: the end of the supposed life cycle (Fig. 43.6).

**Nodule Formation.**   Although they invade plant roots, *Rhizobium* species are unable to hydrolyze the cellulose of plant cell walls. However, they appear to find noncellulosic points at the tips of root hairs of legumes. Through these, entrance into the root tissue is made.

INFECTION THREADS.   The bacteria utilize various carbohydrates found in the soil or juices of the host plant to synthesize gummy coatings around themselves. These coverings help the bacteria to invade plant roots. The rods advance endwise, several abreast in their gummy coating, into the plant-tissue cells. A long, gummy thread

---

*Gr. *rhiza* = root; *bios* = life; hence, "living in roots."

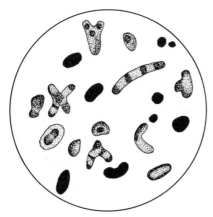

**Figure 43.6**  Representative forms of *Rhizobium*. Drawing from cultures (branched and banded forms from root nodules) (about × 1200). Flagella not revealed by staining method used.

is formed. This is surrounded by a tube of cellulose produced by the plant cells. The whole constitutes what is called an *infection thread*. These threads penetrate well into roots (Fig. 43.7) and into the plant cells. The infection thread inside a cell bulges and then ruptures, and the bacteria are liberated intracellularly. Each bacterium becomes a *bacteroid*, and undergoes fission

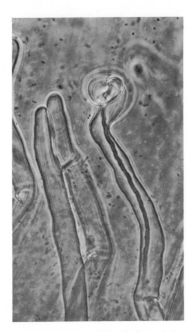

**Figure 43.7**  Infection threads formed in root hairs of a legume by *Rhizobium trifolii* about two weeks after inoculation. The right-hand thread clearly shows the matrix of the thread surrounded by a thin, plant-derived, cellulose wall, and the column of bacteria (dark line) inside the matrix. Many bacteria have escaped into the cell cytoplasm from the matured hairs. (Phase contrast microscopy, about × 600.) (From Fahraeus: J. Gen. Microbiol., vol. 16.)

while encysted within a double-layered membrane produced by the plant cell (Fig. 43.8). The presence of the bacteria stimulates multiplication of the plant cells around the localization, with resulting formation of a protective *nodule* of tissue (Fig. 43.9). Nutrients from the plant juices nourish the bacteria.

**Symbiotic Nitrogen Fixation.**  The rhizobia, when thus growing in leguminous plant nodules, take nitrogen directly from the air. By combined action of plant cells and bacterial cells, this is built into nitrogenous compounds such as amino acids and polypeptides that are found in the plants, the bacteria and the surrounding soil. Neither bacteria nor legumes can alone fix nitrogen. If combined nitrogen is not available in the soil, nonlegumes die. In contrast, if proper species of *Rhizobium* are present, legumes not only thrive in nitrogen-deficient soil but enrich it with fixed nitrogen while doing so.

**Soil Inoculation.**  Because of the value of nitrogen fixation by legumes with the bacteria, it is customary to inoculate virgin soils, or soils not known to support good growth of legumes, with the proper species of *Rhizobium* preparatory to planting such crops as alfalfa or soybeans for the first time. Once introduced, the bacteria continue to live in the soil.

SPECIES SPECIFICITY.  There are several species or varieties of the Genus *Rhizobium*. They exhibit considerable specificity as to the species of legume that they can infect. For example, *Rhizobium japonicum* produces nodules only on the soybean, whereas *Rhizobium meliloti* will not do so.

A few species of nonleguminous plants can form nitrogen-fixing root nodules in symbiosis with *Streptomyces* sp.

**Value of Nitrogen Fixation.**  A well-nodulated crop such as red clover may introduce as much as 100 pounds of organically combined (fixed) nitrogen per acre per season. In the form of a commercial fertilizer this nitrogen would cost in the neighborhood of four hundred dollars.

Inoculation of swampy, acid soils is money wasted because *Rhizobium* will survive and grow only in fertile, well-drained, aerated and nearly neutral soils. Crops of nonlegumes grown in association with legumes (as vetch and rye, or clover and corn) have been known for centuries to be superior.

### III. AMMONIFICATION AND DENITRIFICATION

Were all fixed nitrogen to remain inextricably bound up as organic matter, then the agricultural use of manures, animal carcasses, fish and fertilizer would be of no avail. Dead

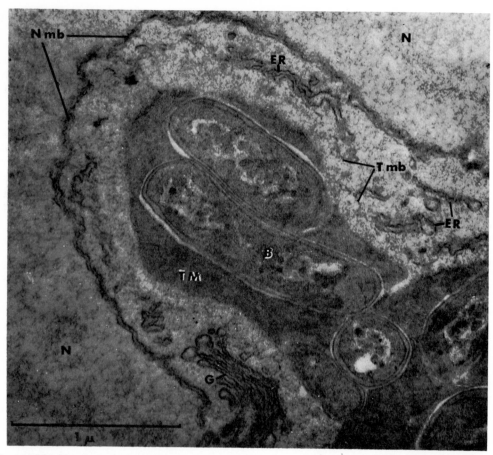

**Figure 43.8**   Tip of an advancing infection thread pushing into the nucleus of a host cell. The host cell nucleus is seen at N, N, while the nuclear membrane is seen at Nmb. The thin membrane surrounding the infection thread is visible at Tmb. The *Rhizobium* bacteria (B) are seen embedded in their gummy matrix, TM. As the nodule matures the bacteria are released into the cell cytoplasm and become pleomorphic bacteroids. The matrix of the advancing thread is surrounded by host cell cytoplasm containing ribosomes and organelles: endoplasmic reticulum (ER) and a Golgi body seen at G. Approximately × 50,000. (From Mosse: J. Gen. Microbiol., *36*:49, 1964.)

animals would not decay, manure would not rot, and dead fish would remain dead fish. The only forms of combined nitrogen available for living organisms would be the rare ammonia produced by lightning. All of the non-nitrogen-fixing forms of life would have to await the slow activities of the nitrifying and nitrogen-fixing microorganisms in order to obtain properly combined nitrogen. Such, however, is not the case. As soon as any organism ceases to live, and as soon as any organic waste matter returns to the soil, it begins to undergo biological decomposition; its fixed nitrogen is released.

**Ammonification.**   Protein and some other organic nitrogenous compounds are hydrolyzed to amino acids and similar compounds, and these are broken down to other, simpler compounds when they are metabolized by microor-

ganisms. The amino groups ($^-NH_2$) are split off to form ammonia ($NH_3$). Note that the nitrogen is in its most reduced form.

Urea ($O=C-NH_2 \cdot NH_2$), a waste product found in the urine of man and other animals, is also decomposed by numerous microorganisms (e.g., *Proteus* species and *Micrococcus ureae*), with liberation of ammonia. An ammoniacal odor is an outstanding impression in an uncleaned stable or in the infant's not-promptly-changed diaper wet with urine due to rapid decomposition of urea.

**Denitrification.**   Agriculturally, the most valuable and expensive form of nitrogen is in its most oxidized state, nitrate. Nitrates may be purchased expensively as fertilizer but are furnished free of charge by common nitrogen-oxidizing bacteria of the soil. This process of

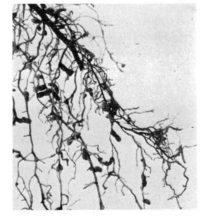
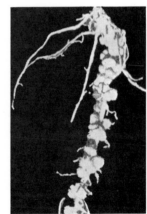

**Figure 43.9** Different types of root nodules formed by *Rhizobium* sp., on leguminous plants. (From Waksman: Soil Microbiology. John Wiley & Sons, Inc.)

bacterial oxidation, so agreeable to the farmer, is called *nitrification* (see next section). The reverse of nitrification is referred to as *denitrification*. In denitrification, nitrates are used by various facultative and anaerobic soil microorganisms as hydrogen acceptors, and are reduced from nitrates to nitrites, to gaseous nitrogen or to ammonia, the extent of reduction depending on the species involved and the availability of free oxygen. These processes are *not* agreeable to the farmer!

The reduction of nitrates accounts in part for the lack of fertility of constantly wet soils that support growth of nitrate-reducing anaerobic species. Some of these species are *Thiobacillus denitrificans* and various species of *Clostridium.*

As mentioned previously, part of the fixed nitrogen represented by ammonia, whether the ammonia is derived from decomposing organic matter or by denitrification, escapes into the atmosphere. More would be lost to the living cycle were it not for its immediate combination in the soil as ammonium salts, and for the nitri-

fying microorganisms (see next section) that oxidize ammonia to nitrites and nitrates (Fig. 43.4), in which form it is again available for plants; thus it re-enters the organic cycle.

## 43.7  NITROGEN OXIDATION

**Family Nitrobacteraceae.** These bacteria are common in fertile soils. They are so called because they are concerned in *nitrification* (i.e., the oxidation of ammonia to nitrates). Nitrates are the most useful and most expensive (and for many crops, the *only*) form of nitrogen for crop plants though some plants can use ammonia and/or nitrites if necessary.

The Nitrobacteraceae are strictly autotrophic. None forms spores. Some are simple rods, motile with polar flagella, others are spirals or cocci; some are gram-positive, others gram-negative.

The oxidation of ammonia to nitrates in the soil by Nitrobacteraceae involves two distinct stages, each stage carried out by different genera. The first stage, the oxidation of ammonia to nitrites, is sometimes called *nitrosification:*

$$2NH_3 + 3O_2 \longrightarrow 2HNO_2 + 2H_2O +$$
$$79,000 \text{ cal.}$$

**Oxidation of Ammonia to Nitrite.** *Nitrosomonas* and *Nitrosocystis* (representative genera) are very small oval rods, each with a single, polar flagellum. They are strictly aerobic and are very sensitive to acidity. Since oxidation of ammonia, and especially of ammonium sulfate, creates acidity caused by $HNO_2$ and $H_2SO_4$, *Nitrosomonas* and *Nitroscystis* soon cease growth unless a soil is well limed or otherwise buffered. The optimum pH is around 8.6.

These species are chemolithotrophic and can be cultivated in a solution of minerals such as the following:

| Ingredient | Per Cent |
|---|---|
| $(NH_4)_2SO_4$ (source of energy and nitrogen) | 0.20 |
| $K_2HPO_4$ (buffer) | 0.10 |
| $MgSO_4$ | 0.05 |
| $FeSO_4$ | 0.04 |
| NaCl | 0.04 |
| $CaCO_3$ | 0.10 |
| $MgCO_3$ | 0.10 |

This medium may be solidified with silica gel but not with agar, since all Nitrobacteraceae are strict autotrophs.

Some of these bacteria, notably *Nitrosocystis oceanus,* a marine species, exhibit very complex intracellular and pericellular membranous structures or organelles that are suggestive of the photosynthetic structures in eucaryotic chloroplasts or bacteria (Fig. 43.10).

**Oxidation of Nitrite to Nitrate.** This process is called nitrification. Both nitrosification and nitrification are sometimes spoken of together as nitrification. Most higher plants cannot utilize nitrites as their source of nitrogen. In fact, nitrites are toxic to many plants and animals. The most immediately useful form of nitrogen for agricultural purposes is nitrate. Since nitrate does not commonly occur spontaneously in soil, its development is dependent on the presence of the Genus *Nitrobacter,* which oxidize nitrites to nitrates:

$$HNO_2 + \tfrac{1}{2}O_2 \longrightarrow HNO_3 + 21,600 \text{ cal.}$$

A difficulty with nitrates as fertilizers is that they are very soluble and are quickly leached from the soil.

Nitrobacters are nonmotile rods. They occur in soil, rivers and streams, and are worldwide in distribution. Under laboratory conditions they grow well only in the entire absence of organic matter. *Nitrobacter* may be cultivated in solutions such as the preceding by substituting sodium nitrite for ammonium sulfate as a source of energy.

**Other Nitrogen Oxidizers.** In addition to the Nitrobacteraceae, certain heterotrophic bacteria have been shown to oxidize ammonia to nitrite (e.g., *Streptomyces* and *Nocardia* species). Nitrification as a sole source of energy appears to be carried out only by species of *Nitrobacter* and *Nitrocystis* (do not confuse with *Nitrosocystis*). However, several species of eucaryotic fungi (*Aspergillus flavus, Penicillium* sp., *Cephalosporium* sp.) carry out both steps, oxidizing *organic* nitrogen (possibly first forming ammonia from it?) to nitrite and nitrate.

## 43.8   THE SULFUR CYCLE

In many respects the sulfur cycle is analogous to the nitrogen cycle. Sulfur is as essential to protoplasm* as nitrogen and undergoes similar alternations between organic and elemental states and between oxidation and reduction. Like nitrogen also, sulfur is most available to green plants in its most oxidized form, i.e., as sulfates. Sulfur is commonly added to agricultural soils as gypsum or as ammonium sulfate. In nature sulfur is often found in the elemental state or in volcanic ("medicinal") waters as hydrogen sulfide ($H_2S$) and other sulfides. It is released from organic compounds (e.g., proteins) by anaerobic decomposition (putrefaction) in its most reduced state, $H_2S$, analogous to ammonia ($NH_3$). Sulfates are also reduced to $H_2S$ by certain bacteria. Like nitrates, fully oxidized sulfur (sulfate) is expensive and quickly leached (dissolved) from soil by rains.

### OXIDATION OF SULFUR

We have already discussed photosynthetic bacteria (Chapter 38) that oxidize various forms of sulfur, especially hydrogen sulfide, to sulfates. Other important sulfur oxidizers are grouped in the Family Thiobacteriaceae of the Order Pseu-

---

*If sulfur becomes a vital part (say, part of a chromosome) of a living cell, is the sulfur then alive? Is *any* element or substance, no matter how complex, that is part of a living organism, alive? If not, then just what part of us *is* actually alive? What differentiates the *alive* part from the *not-alive* part? What is meant by "alive"?

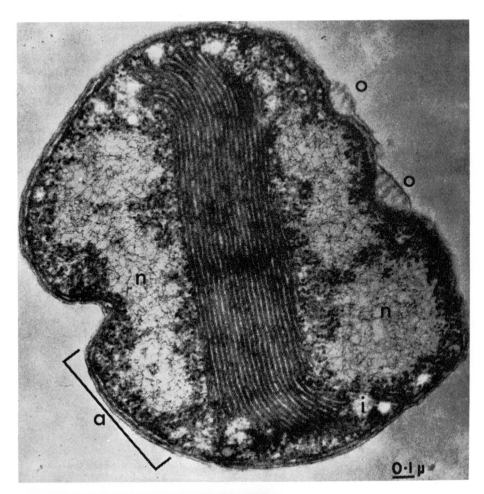

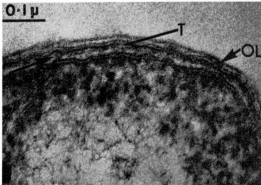

**Figure 43.10**  The nitrosifying and nitrifying bacteria are complex in structure and contain remarkably large, elaborate and orderly lamellar organelles that are probably derived, as are some other laminated intracellular structures, both eucaryotic and procaryotic, from the cell membrane. Many appear to be associated with energy-yielding processes in the cell: in the Nitrobacteraceae presumably with the complex processes of oxidation of $NH_3$ to $^-NO_2$ and of $^-NO_2$ to $^-NO_3$. In the upper electron micrograph of a thin section of *Nitrosocystis oceanus* nuclear material is seen at n, n; cell-wall organelles whose origin, structure and functions are not yet fully clarified are seen at o, o. A segment of the cell wall (a) is shown enlarged below. The wall is multilayered and consists of four or more layers. An outer envelope is seen at OL and a triplet layer of the wall at T. (From Murray and Watson: J. Bact., *89*:1594, 1965.)

domonadales. Thiobacteriaceae are single, in-dependent, gram-negative, cocci, straight or curved rods, or spirals, generally about 0.5 $\mu$ by 10.0 $\mu$ in dimensions. Motile species have polar flagella. Many are strict or facultative chemolithotrophs. Some interesting representatives are found in the Genus *Thiobacillus.*

**Genus Thiobacillus.** Thiobacilli thrive in mud, sea water, sewage, boggy places, coal-mine drainage, sulfur springs and so on where sulfur and its reduced compounds occur naturally or as a result of microbial metabolism.

Thiobacilli oxidize sulfur or its reduced inorganic compounds as energy sources in a variety of ways depending on species:

1. $5Na_2S_2O_3 + H_2O + 4O_2 \longrightarrow$
$$5Na_2SO_4 + H_2SO_4 + 4S$$
2. $2Na_2S_2O_3 + \frac{1}{2}O_2 + H_2O \longrightarrow$
$$Na_2S_4O_6 + 2NaOH$$

The sulfur in equation 1 above may be further oxidized by other thiobacilli to sulfuric acid.

3. $2S + 3O_2 + 2H_2O \longrightarrow 2H_2SO_4$

All thiobacilli are strict autotrophs. Aqueous solutions such as the following meet all of their nutritive requirements.

| Ingredients | Per Cent |
|---|---|
| S | 1.000 |
| $Na_2S_2O_3$ | 0.500 |
| $(NH_4)_2SO_4$ | 0.030 |
| $KH_2PO_4$ | 0.025 |
| $CaCl_2$ | 0.050 |
| $FeSO_4$ | 0.001 |
| KCl | 0.050 |
| $MgSO_4$ | 0.020 |
| $Ca(NO_3)_2$ | 0.050 |

Note the absence of carbon source. This diet and metabolism are truly marvellous when compared with the complex organic requirements of heterotrophic bacteria or man. Instead of lipids, carbohydrates and proteins and their derivatives as sources of energy and cell substance, thiobacilli use a few minerals. Instead of complex organic wastes in urine and feces, these organisms excrete corrosive $H_2SO_4$!

The metabolism of *Th. denitrificans* is of special interest, since this represents one of the factors responsible for losses of fertility in certain anaerobic (swampy) soils (*denitrification*, or reduction of nitrates):

$5S + 6HNO_3 + 2H_2O \longrightarrow$
$$5H_2SO_4 + 3N_2 (+ \epsilon)*$$

---

*$\epsilon$ = energy.

*Thiobacillus thiooxidans* oxidizes sulfur and thiosulfates to sulfuric acid *aerobically*. As sulfuric acid is formed in considerable amounts, it might be thought that the organisms would quickly inhibit their own further growth. This species, however, is of interest in having a great resistance to acid. It is "distinctive in that it is able not only to tolerate but to produce higher concentrations of acid than any other living organism yet known" (*Starkey*). Some growth is said to occur at a pH of 1, and it grows readily at pH 3. Another species, *Th. intermedius*, requires both organic and reduced inorganic sulfur for best growth (Fig. 43.11).

An interesting physiological question arises, and remains unanswered, as to how sulfur particles, water-insoluble, pass through the bacterial cell wall and membrane. In spite of their strange properties these organisms have the same general structures as familiar, heterotrophic, gram-negative bacteria. Could pinocytosis operate in a cell coated by a cell wall?

An important aspect of acid formation by any microorganism lies, on the debit side, in the corrosive and destructive properties of the acids on industrial steel, pipes, and other acid-sensitive products. On the credit side is the very desirable solvent action of acids on phosphate rocks that contain the indispensable element phosphorus in otherwise insoluble forms. (See Phosphorus Cycle, page 547.)

*Thiobacillus ferrooxidans*, a species closely similar to *Th. thiooxidans*, is found in acid drainage waters of iron and bituminous coal mines. *Th. ferrooxidans* can oxidize ferrous iron salts as well as sulfur:

$4FeSO_4 + 2H_2SO_4 + O_2 \longrightarrow$
$$2Fe_2(SO_4)_3 + 2H_2O$$
$Fe_2(SO_4)_3 + 6H_2O \longrightarrow$
$$2Fe(OH)_3 + 3H_2SO_4$$

Similar species called *Ferrobacillus ferrooxidans* and *Fer. sulfooxidans* have been described. These are all true "iron bacteria," i.e., they oxidize iron as a source of energy (Fig. 43.12).

## 43.9  BACTERIAL REDUCTION OF SULFUR

Sulfate-reducing species of bacteria are few but they are widely distributed, especially in sewage and other polluted waters, the sea and marine muds from pole to pole, in oil wells and in the bovine rumen. There are two general types; one, Genus *Desulfotomaculum*, includes sporeforming rods, one species of which was formerly known as *Clostridium nigrificans;* the

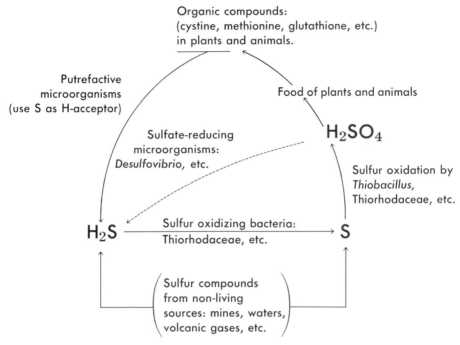

Organic compounds:
(cystine, methionine, glutathione, etc.)
in plants and animals.

Putrefactive
microorganisms
(use S as H-acceptor)

Food of plants and animals

Sulfate-reducing
microorganisms:
*Desulfovibrio*, etc.

$H_2SO_4$

Sulfur oxidation by
*Thiobacillus,*
*Thiorhodaceae,* etc.

$H_2S$ — Sulfur oxidizing bacteria:
*Thiorhodaceae*, etc. → S

Sulfur compounds
from non-living
sources: mines, waters,
volcanic gases, etc.

**Figure 43.11**   The sulfur cycle. At left, $H_2S$ enters the cycle from nonliving sources (bottom) and from living sources (top). It is oxidized to sulfur (right) by various sulfur-oxidizing microorganisms. Sulfur also enters the cycle from inorganic sources (bottom). Sulfur is oxidized by microorganisms to $H_2SO_4$ which may enter organic structures in plants and animals (top) or be reduced to $H_2S$ (left) by sulfate reducers.

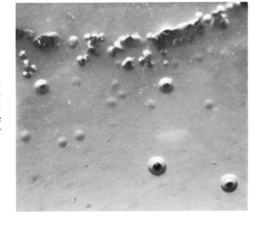

**Figure 43.12**   Colonies of *Ferrobacillus sulfooxidans,* an autotrophic, sulfur- and iron-oxidizing bacterium. The colonies are on a wholly inorganic nutrient agar (pH 4) containing $FeSO_4 \cdot 7H_2O$ as the sole source of energy. Note the red (dark) central areas of oxidized iron in the larger colonies ($\times$ 50). (From Kinsel: J. Bact., vol. 80.)

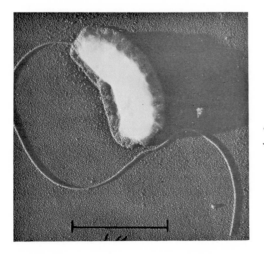

**Figure 43.13**   Electron micrograph of *Desulfovibrio desulfuricans* ($\times$ 18,540). (From Campbell, Frank and Hall: J. Bact., vol. 73.)

other is a group of pleomorphic, curved-rod (vibrio-like) organisms classified as *Desulfovibrio.* Like other vibrios they are motile with polar flagella (Fig. 43.13). Of these, *Desulfovibrio desulfuricans,* the best known species, is anaerobic though it has cytochrome systems like oxidative organisms. Like all typical anaerobes it requires low O-R potentials and must have iron for its cytochrome. Organic materials are dehydrogenated and the hydrogen is transferred to sulfites, sulfates and thiosulfates, which are reduced to $H_2S$.

$$2CH_3 \cdot CHOH \cdot COONa + H_2SO_4 \longrightarrow$$
*Sodium lactate*

$$2CH_3 \cdot COONa + H_2S + 2CO_2 + 2H_2O$$
*Sodium acetate*

Some sulfate reducers can use molecular hydrogen in the reduction of sulfate:

$$4H_2 + H_2SO_4 \longrightarrow H_2S + 4H_2O$$

## 43.10   THE CARBON CYCLE

Carbon is introduced into the organic system from its most oxidized state, carbon dioxide, and is reduced in organic combination, mainly by photosynthesis. A lesser amount of carbon is taken as atmospheric $CO_2$ into some species of chemosynthetic bacteria and some other cells. As a result of these various biological synthetic activities involving carbon, and in the passage of hundreds of millions of years, vast quantities of carbon are stored in coal, peat, petroleum oils and gases ("fossil fuels") and in coral, limestones, marble and other carbonate rocks to say

nothing of the carbon in today's living organisms (and to say still less of the carbon in diamonds!). In all of these forms, carbon is more reduced than it is as $CO_2$. A number of anaerobic bacteria use organically combined carbon as an electron (H) acceptor and reduce it still further to methane ($CH_4$). As mentioned elsewhere, methane is a major component of natural gas, including marsh and sewer gases, being produced by such species as *Methanobacterium, Methanococcus* and some species of *Clostridium.* Note that these are methane *producers.*

If all existing supplies of $CO_2$ in the atmosphere or dissolved in the waters of the earth were to be continuously removed from the atmosphere and combined in organic matter or in carbonate rocks, life on the earth would cease in a generation or so. But carbon is continuously reoxidized and returned to the atmosphere, and thence to the seas, as $CO_2$ in a variety of familiar ways: mainly by combustion of coal and organic fuels and biooxidations, and also by volcanic activities, all of which liberate $CO_2$. Biological activities include not only fermentations that yield $CO_2$, but metabolism by certain rare bacteria that oxidize methane as a source of energy, e.g., *Pseudomonas* or *Methanomonas methanica.* Some of these are *wholly dependent* on the *methyl* group as in methane or methanol, e.g., *Methylococcus capsulatus.* $CO_2$ is released from carbonate rocks by acids resulting from geological action and also by acids formed during fermentations and by such bacteria as the species in the nitrogen and sulfur cycles that produce $HNO_3$ and $H_2SO_4$.

Carbon monoxide is a relatively rare gas under ordinary conditions and results commonly

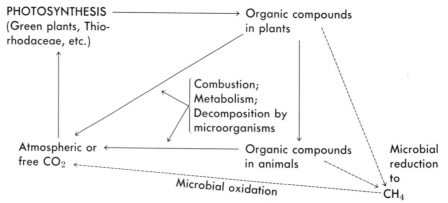

**Figure 43.14**   The carbon cycle. Atmospheric or free $CO_2$ (lower left) is combined as organic matter by photosynthesis (upper left). These organic compounds either remain as plant material (upper right) or are taken up by animals (lower right, solid lines). In either case the carbon is eventually released to the atmosphere again by combustion, metabolism of higher plants or animals, or by microbial decomposition of plant and animal wastes and remains (diagonal solid line). The dash lines at lower right show a sort of extraneous cycle carried on by anaerobic microorganisms which either *reduce* carbon to $CH_4$ in bio-oxidation or *oxidize* $CH_4$ to $CO_2$ as a source of energy in bio-oxidation.

from partial combustion. Exceedingly poisonous for most aerobic organisms including man, it is relished as a source of energy and carbon by at least one autotrophic bacterial species, *Carboxydomonas oligocarbophila,* that oxidizes CO to $CO_2$. So the carbon "goes 'round and 'round," alternating between organic and inorganic, reduced and oxidized, like sulfur and nitrogen (Fig. 43.14).

## 43.11  THE PHOSPHORUS CYCLE

The phosphorus cycle involves an alternation in form of phosphorus between soluble and insoluble as well as between organic and inorganic. No organisms are known that reduce phosphates or oxidize phosphorus as a source of energy. Phosphorus enters the soil in relatively insoluble, inorganic forms as phosphates in the rock from which the soil is derived. It is added to agricultural soils as $Ca_3(PO_4)_2$ in the form of *bone meal* and in commercial fertilizers as *rock phosphates.*

Phosphorus is liberated from such insoluble compounds [e.g., $Ca_3(PO_4)_2$] by acids formed during nitrification and during oxidation of sulfur (and also by fermentations) in the soil as follows:

$$Ca_3(PO_4)_2 + 2HNO_3 \longrightarrow$$
$$2CaHPO_4 + Ca(NO_3)_2$$
$$Ca_3(PO_4)_2 + 4HNO_3 \longrightarrow$$
$$Ca(H_2PO_4)_2 + 2Ca(NO_3)_2$$
$$Ca_3(PO_4)_2 + H_2SO_4 \longrightarrow$$
$$2CaHPO_4 + CaSO_4$$

Decomposing vegetable and animal materials liberate *soluble* compounds of phosphorus such as DNA and RNA, ADP and ATP.

The soluble forms of phosphorus are used by both higher plants and microorganisms.

## 43.12  THE RHIZOSPHERE

The rhizosphere is a zone of increased microbial growth and activity in the soil around the roots of plants. Sometimes the microorganisms form a sort of living mantle close around the roots. The rhizosphere may extend several inches into the soil around the roots. There are many interrelationships and interactions between plant roots and soil microorganisms. Some are favorable to plants, some indispensable; some are unfavorable, others lethal.

We know, for example, that some bacteria or fungi make nitrogen available to plants as nitrates or in organic form. Sulfur oxidizers make sulfur available as sulfates. Heterotrophic metabolism makes carbon available as carbon dioxide for photosynthesis. Production of acids by microbial action makes rock or bone phosphorus available as soluble phosphates. Some bacteria synthesize auxins or phytohormones (e.g., indole-acetic acid) which greatly stimulate root growth, and certain fungi (*Gibberella* species) synthesize the growth auxin, *gibberellic acid* (Fig. 43.15).

Plant roots reciprocate in kind. The roots of leguminous plants secrete soluble, organic nitrogenous compounds into the soil around them

**Figure 43.15**  Effect of gibberellin on plant growth. The first (left) lima bean seedling was grown from seeds dusted with plain talc. The talc used to dust the seeds of seedlings 2, 3 and 4 contained, respectively, 10, 20 and 40 gm of gibberellic acid. (Courtesy of Boyce Thompson Institute for Plant Research Inc.)

to be used by microorganisms and other plants. Many plant roots appear also to give off simple soluble carbon compounds (foods for bacteria) such as malic acid, pentoses and phosphatids.

The sloughing off of bark and root coverings, as well as death of roots, provides a rich source of carbohydrates and derivatives to support a luxuriant flora of nitrogen-fixers and other helpful forms close around the plant roots. The cellulose-digesters, amylolytic, and other hydrolytic forms transform plant material into humus, glucose, and other valuable foods for plants and microorganisms. A good heavy growth of microorganisms absorbs nitrogen, sulfur, phosphorus, potassium and other elements in soluble forms which might otherwise be removed (*leached*) from the soil by rain and drainage. While the organisms withhold these elements temporarily from plant use (sometimes with damage to the plants), the elements are eventually released on death of the microorganisms. Thus, the higher plants act as a food manufacturer and storage-warehouse for microorganisms of the soil and rhizosphere, while microorganisms act as collectors, processors and treasurers of foods for the higher plants.

## 43.13   PLANT DISEASES

Among the unfavorable relationships between higher plants and soil organisms are (a) *parasitism* of plants by pathogenic microorganisms such as many species of *Xanthomonas* and *Erwinia* (rots, wilts, blights and spots), *Agrobacterium* (galls, hairy root), eucaryotic fungi (rusts, rots, wilts), viruses (mosaics, curly top); and (b) *predation* by insects, rodents, nematodes and the like.

The organisms causing plant diseases live in the soil, often as saprophytes. They possess protopectinolytic* enzymes and other properties enabling them to live in or upon plant tissues, causing disease.

**Genus Agrobacterium.** Interesting and important bacteria, *Agrobacterium* species are much like *Rhizobium* and live in, or closely associated with, plant tissues. The type species, *A. tumefaciens,* is well known to the floral and horticultural industries as the cause of crown galls and tumors on plants such as the Paris daisy and many other families. Growth of *A. tumefaciens* in the plant tissues stimulates local overgrowth

(tumors) of the tissues much as *Rhizobium* stimulates nodule growth on roots. *Agrobacterium* species do not fix atmospheric nitrogen. Studies of the tumorigenic effects have given some interesting leads in research on human neoplasms (Fig. 43.16).

A related species, *Agrobacterium rhizogenes,* stimulates abnormal *root* growth, probably by the synthesis of a hormone-like factor (*auxin* or *phytohormone*). It causes *hairy root* of pomaceous plants (apples and pears).

## 43.14   ANTAGONISMS

There are many antagonisms among soil microorganisms that benefit the plant grower (Fig. 43.17). For example, soil infested with *Phytophthora parasitica,* the fungal cause of *damping-off* of tomato seedlings, may be virtually rid of the pest by inoculation with *Penicillium patulum,* which is antagonistic to the parasitic fungus. A genus of eucaryotic fungi, *Trichoderma,* produces a substance that greatly reduces infectivity of tobacco mosaic virus. Many similar examples are found in the literature.

**Antibiotics and Plant Diseases.** Many plant pathogens are quite susceptible to antibiotics, including some antibiotics that are used for treating infections in higher animals (streptomycin,* griseofulvin, cycloheximide, the tetracyclines). We know that many of these antibiotics are produced by soil microorganisms: *Strepto-*

---

*Streptomycin suppresses formation of chlorophyll and thus has a *bleaching effect* in some plants.

**Figure 43.16** Tumor (crown gall) on a species of chrysanthemum inoculated seven months previously with *Agrobacterium tumefaciens.* (About one-fourth natural size.) (Erwin F. Smith.)

---

*Protopectin is a plant gum or cementing substance that holds the plant structures in place.

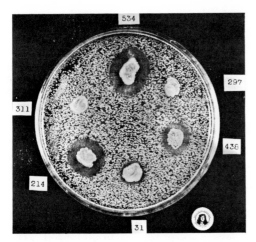

**Figure 43.17**   Microbial antagonism. The entire surface of the plate was inoculated with *Shigella paradysenteriae.* "Spot" inoculations were then made with various cultures of *Escherichia coli.* After incubation, growth of the *Shigella* appeared as grey "pebbling" except in zones around certain antagonistic cultures: 534, 214, 31 and 438. Cultures 311 and 297 showed no antagonism. (Compare with Figures 18.2 and 43.3.) (Courtesy of Dr. S. P. Halbert and the American Society for Microbiology.)

*myces, Penicillium, Bacillus* and numerous others. Other antibiotics not suitable for use in human or veterinary medicine are excellent for control of various plant pathogens when used as sprays, dusts or dips. It is scarcely to be doubted that the antibiotic-producers of the soil produce their antagonistic agents in their natural habitat and that they exert a tremendous influence on the soil microflora. They undoubtedly control plant pathogens to a great degree.

Antibiotics added to the soil or water in which plants or cuttings are growing are soon taken up in the plant and distributed to all parts. Obviously, if a heavy growth of organisms that produce penicillin or streptomycin or polymyxin is present in the rhizosphere, not only is it likely to prevent growth of pathogens in the soil but it may also prevent growth of desirable species.

## 43.15   MICROBIOLOGY AND PETROLEUM

No final conclusions as to the mode of origin of petroleum may be reached on the basis of present knowledge. However, it is generally held that it originated from living organisms and that microorganisms had a part in it. Crude petroleum contains many hydrocarbons (e.g., paraffin, kerosene) as well as compounds of nitrogen, *reduced* sulfur, phosphorus and other elements in proportions and relations suggestive of deriva-

tion from organic matter. Studies of the subject strongly indicate that: (a) the temperature of petroleum formation was within a range compatible with microbial life (30° to 80° C.); (b) pressures up to 100,000 pounds per square inch or more are within the limit of microbial viability; (c) petroleum was formed in or near its present locations that at the time were probably sea bottom; (d) conditions were highly anaerobic; (e) salinities were probably elevated (5 to 10 per cent?) but not excessive. A question is whether any known microorganisms could produce any of the higher homologues in the hydrocarbon series. While some experimental evidence suggests that this could occur, no conclusive demonstrations on the point have been made.

All higher plants synthesize fats and carbohydrates. Huge vegetable deposits like those that formed coal, when decomposed by certain microorganisms, could conceivably liberate large amounts of the hydrocarbons found in petroleum, but the exact mechanism is not clear.

**Destruction of Petroleum.**   While microorganisms may or may not have produced petroleum, there is a large group of organisms that actively attack and destroy petroleum hydrocarbons. We have already noted some species that oxidize methane. Others, common in the soil near petroleum wells, vigorously oxidize ethane (*Mycobacterium* species and *Pseudomonas* species). Others, as *Desulfovibrio,* oxidize higher homologues such as petroleum oils and paraffin.

Many microorganisms can decompose the hydrocarbons in gasoline, and are of considerable importance in the petroleum industry as causes of spoilage. Among these are *Pseudomonas* and *Achromobacter* species, also *Alcaligenes, Mycobacterium, Aspergillus, Monilia* and *Sarcina.* Several species of microorganisms capable of metabolizing petroleum hydrocarbons cause pitting and erosion of tanks, including fuel tanks of aircraft, due to acid formation.

**Prospecting for Petroleum.**   Microorganisms that utilize ethane and higher hydrocarbon vapors as carbon and energy source are sometimes used to find hidden sources of petroleum. Culture mixtures, complete in all respects *except carbon source,* are placed in flasks and inoculated with an appropriate species of organism able to utilize only petroleum vapors as carbon source. On being lowered into suspected oil-bearing strata and left for some days, growth will occur if petroleum vapors are present. Patents have been issued for some processes of this kind. Error can arise from the fact that methane produced by anaerobic microorganisms of the surrounding soil, e.g., *Methanobacterium,* can confusingly support growth of some hydrocarbon-users quite as well as hydrocarbon vapors from deep oil deposits.

The finding of large numbers of hydrocarbon-oxidizing microorganisms in soil also suggests the presence of hydrocarbons from petroleum deposits below the surface.

## SUPPLEMENTARY READING

Alico, R. K., and Liegey, F. W.: Growth of *Desulfovibrio desulfuricans* under heterotrophic and anaerobic conditions. J. Bact., *91*:1112, 1966.

Ayers, W. A., and Papavizas, G. C.: Violet pigmented pseudomonads with antifungal activity from the rhizosphere of beans. Appl. Microbiol., *11*:533, 1963.

Brisbane, P. G., and Ladd, J. N.: The role of microorganisms in petroleum exploration. Ann. Rev. Microbiol., *19*:351, 1965.

Burris, R. H.: Biological nitrogen fixation. Ann. Rev. Plant Physiol., *17*:155, 1966.

Bond, G.: The root nodules of non-leguminous angiosperms. Thirteenth Symposium, Symbiotic Associations, page 72. Soc. Gen. Microbiol., London. 1963.

Colmer, A. R.: Relation of the iron oxidizer, *Thiobacillus ferrooxidans,* to thiosulfate. J. Bact., *83*:761, 1962.

Davis, J. B.: Petroleum Microbiology. American Elsevier Publishing Co., New York, 1967.

Eklund, C., Pope, L. M., and Wyss, O.: Relationship of encapsulation and encystment in *Azotobacter.* J. Bact., *92*:1828, 1966.

Foster, J. W., and Davis, R. H.: A methane-dependent coccus, with notes on classification and nomenclature of obligate, methane-utilizing bacteria. J. Bact., *91*:1924, 1966.

Freudenberg, K.: Lignin: Its constitution and formation from p-hydroxycinnamyl alcohols. Science, *148*:595, 1965.

Gilmour, C. M., and Allen, O. N., editors: Microbiology and Soil Fertility. Oregon State University Press, Corvallis. 1965.

Goodchild, D. J., and Bergersen, F. J.: Electron microscopy of the infection and subsequent development of soybean nodule cells. J. Bact., *92*:204, 1966.

Henry, S. M.: The significance of microorganisms in the nutrition of insects. Tr. N. Y. Acad. Sci., Ser. II, *25*:676, 1962.

Hill, I. R., and Gray, T. R. G.: Application of the fluo-rescent-antibody technique to an ecological study of bacteria in soil. J. Bact., *93*:1888, 1967.

Holm-Hansen, O.: Algae: Nitrogen fixation by antarctic species. Science, *139*:1059, 1963.

Jordan, D. C., Grinyer, I., and Coulter, W. H.: Electron microscopy of infection threads and bacteria in young root nodules of *Medicago sativa.* J. Bact., *86*:125, 1963.

Mahoney, R. P., and Edwards, M. R.: Fine structures of *Thiobacillus thiooxidans.* J. Bact., *92*:487, 1966.

McCalla, T. M., and Haskins, F. A.: Phytotoxic substances from soil microorganisms and crop residues. Bact. Rev., *28*:181, 1964.

McLaren, A. D.: Biochemistry and soil science. Science, *141*:1141, 1963.

McKenna, E. J., and Kallio, R. E.: The biology of hydrocarbons. Ann. Rev. Microbiol., *19*:183, 1965.

Melin, E.: Some effects of forest tree roots on mycorrhizal basidiomycetes. Thirteenth Symposium, Symbiotic Associations, p. 125. Soc. Gen. Microbiol., London. 1963.

Nicholas, D. J. D.: The biochemistry of nitrogen fixation. Thirteenth Symposium, Symbiotic Associations. p. 92. Soc. Gen. Microbiol., London. 1963.

Nutman, P. S.: Factors influencing the balance of mutual advantage in legume symbiosis. Thirteenth Symposium, Symbiotic Associations. p. 51. Soc. Gen. Microbiol., London. 1963.

Parker, L. T., and Socolofsky, M. D.: Central body of the *Azotobacter* cyst. J. Bact., *91*:297, 1966.

Parle, J. N.: A microbiological study of earthworm casts. J. Gen. Microbiol., *31*:13, 1963.

Postgate, J. R., and Campbell, L. L.: Classification of Desulfovibrio species, the nonsporulating sulfate-reducing bacteria. Bact. Rev., *30*:732, 1966.

Rovira, A. D.: Interactions between plant roots and soil microorganisms. Ann. Rev. Microbiol., *19*:241, 1965.

Silver, M. P., Margalith, P., and Lundgren, D. G.: Effect of glucose on carbon dioxide assimilation by *Ferrobacillus ferrooxidans.* J. Bact., *93*:1765, 1967.

Stevenson, L. H., and Socolofsky, M. D.: Cyst formation and poly-β-hydroxybutyric acid accumulation in *Azotobacter.* J. Bact., *91*:304, 1966.

Stewart, W. D. P.: Nitrogen-fixing Plants. Science, *158*: 1426, 1967.

Stonier, T., Beardsley, R. E., Parsons, L., and McSharry, J.: *Agrobacterium tumefaciens* Conn. III. Effect of thermal shock on bacteria in relation to tumor-inducing ability. J. Bact., *91*:266, 1966.

Wieringa, W. T.: Solid media with elemental sulphur for detection of sulphur-oxidizing microbes. Ant. Leeuw., *32*:183, 1966.

# Chapter 44

# MICROBIOLOGY OF THE ATMOSPHERE

No organisms are indigenous to the atmosphere. Microorganisms of the air within 300 to 500 feet of the earth's surface are merely organisms of soil that have become attached to fragments of dried leaves, straw or dust particles light enough to be blown about by the wind. Live microorganisms are more numerous in air in dry weather than just after a rain, because rain washes them out of the air and settles the microbe-laden dust. Species vary considerably in their sensitivity to any given degree of relative humidity, temperature and exposure to sunlight. Many microorganisms, to say nothing of us humans, are unfavorably affected by the horrible exhalations of some industries that now pollute parts of our atmosphere. Microorganisms found in air over populated land areas, below altitudes of about 500 feet, in clear weather with moderate breeze include spores of *Bacillus* and *Clostridium,* ascospores of yeasts, fragments of mycelium and conidia of molds and Streptomycetaceae, pollen, cysts of protozoa, unicellular algae, and some of the more resistant nonspore-formers such as *Sarcina lutea* and *Micrococcus luteus,* nonpathogenic species of *Corynebacterium* (diphtheroids), and some few gram-negative rods such as some coliform species, Achromobacteraceae, and so forth. In fact, almost any of the microorganisms discussed in this book except certain of the more fragile parasitic and aquatic species may at times be found in the atmosphere. Much depends on the location where air samples are collected, weather, speed and direction of air currents, especially strong updrafts related to thunderstorm activities, and population. For example, on the Atlantic coast in a howling nor'easter, marine bacteria, plankton and seaweed as well as sand and sea water are to be found in the atmosphere well inland.

In the dust and air of theaters, schools, hospital wards or the rooms of persons suffering from infectious diseases, such organisms as tubercle bacilli, streptococci, pneumococci and staphylococci have been demonstrated. These respiratory bacteria are dispersed through the air in the droplets of saliva and mucus that are always produced by coughing, sneezing, talking and laughing. Viruses of the respiratory tract and probably (to some extent, at least) those of the enteric tract are also transmitted by dust and air.

Microorganisms of the upper air have been collected by means of airplanes or other aerial devices. For the collection of microorganisms in the upper layers of the atmosphere, special apparatus must be used that excludes contamination of the sample by dust from the aircraft or its occupants, that prevents damage to organisms by impact at the high speeds of today's planes, and that operates efficiently at all altitudes and atmospheric temperatures.

More microorganisms are found in air over land masses than far at sea, although Darwin, during his famous voyage on the *Beagle,* found various microbial spores in the air a thousand miles at sea west of Africa. Spores of fungi, especially *Alternaria, Hormodendrum, Penicillium* and *Aspergillus,* are more numerous than other forms over the sea within about 400 miles of land in both polar and tropical air masses at all altitudes up to about 10,000 feet. Total numbers of aerial organisms at such altitudes may range from less than one per cubic foot of air over oceans to several hundred per cubic foot over land. Much of the microflora of the lower air strata tends to settle out as land air moves out over the sea, leaving relatively more microorganisms in the upper levels.

Such information and such research is of enormous importance to agriculturists, since the spores of many pathogenic fungi causing costly crop diseases, plant pollens and seeds, and probably animal pathogens can be transmitted from continent to continent by air currents. Many larger objects of biological importance are also carried long distances by high winds and air currents: fragments of soil with seeds and plant pathogens; parts of plants, often diseased; soil nematodes; virus and bacteria-infected insects; birds; and even parts of small rodents and fish. The potentialities in biological warfare by the use of airborne pathogens of man and his crops and domestic animals thus become all too obvious.

## 44.1   COLLECTION AND ENUMERATION OF AERIAL MICROORGANISMS

Microorganisms in air at low levels may be collected by the simple method of allowing dust to settle on an open Petri dish containing nutrient agar (Fig. 44.1). This is useful in enclosed spaces. Dust and microorganisms may also be collected by drawing air through a tube containing a filter of wet sand or cotton (Fig. 44.2). The cotton or sand is then shaken in broth. This is one of the oldest and simplest devices.

There are many other types of device for collecting microorganisms in the air. One *impingement device* consists of an agar-covered cyl-

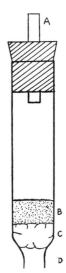

**Figure 44.2** Tube for collecting dust from the air for bacteriological analysis. Air enters at *A*, and deposits its dust on the sand (*B*), which is supported by a cotton plug (*C*). The air leaves at *D*. The sand is later washed with broth, from which a plate count is made.

inder rotating slowly around its axis vertically. An air stream, carrying dust and microorganisms, impinges on the sticky agar surface as the drum rotates. There are also *bubbling devices, atomizing devices* and *electrostatic devices*. In addition, the *membrane filter* (Chapter 4) is adaptable to direct collection by filtration of air. Some representative devices are illustrated here (Figs. 44.3 to 44.5). None of the devices collects and counts all the microorganisms in the air sample tested. Some microbial cells pass entirely through, or are destroyed in, all the processes.

## 44.2   DUST, DROPLETS AND DROPLET NUCLEI

Dust in and around urban dwellings usually arises from ash and soot, soil, lint from bedding, clothing and carpets. Most dust particles are relatively large (i.e., 10 to 100 $\mu$) and tend to settle rapidly. If inhaled, large (i.e., above about 5 $\mu$) dust particles tend to be trapped in the upper respiratory tract and removed by mucus, saliva and sneezing. Only the smallest (less than 2 $\mu$) reach the lungs.

*Droplets* are usually formed by sneezing, coughing and talking. Each consists of saliva and mucus and each may contain hundreds of microorganisms. Most are relatively large (about 100 $\mu$) and, like dust, tend to settle rapidly in quiet air. Inhaled, they are trapped in the de-

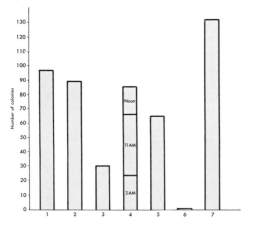

**Figure 44.1** Approximate numbers of colonies of microorganisms expected to appear on Petri plates containing "standard methods agar" incubated 18 hours at 35° C. after remaining open for 1 hour under the conditions indicated: *1*, broom sweeping, busy railway station, 10 A.M.; *2*, crowded downtown lunch room, noon; *3*, large secretarial room, 10 A.M.; *4*, main corridor, large city hall, at hours indicated; *5*, busy downtown street, summer, humid; *6*, open country after snowstorm; *7*, Broadway subway car, winter, 5 P.M.

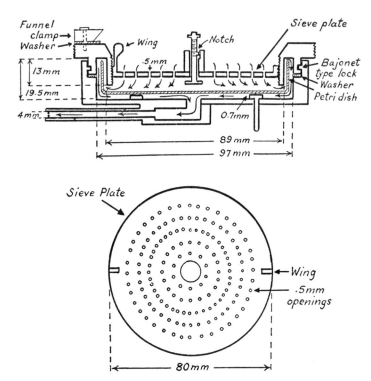

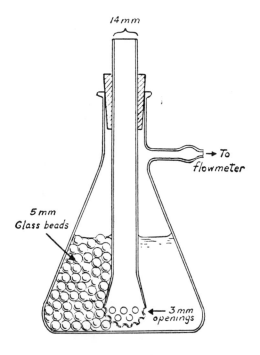

**Figure 44.3** Sieve device (a form of impingement device), with box and cover, containing a standard Petri dish with agar on which most of the particles of dust impinge. Arrows show the course of air through the perforations, along the agar surface, and out beneath the Petri dish. Sieve plate with wings is drawn separately. (From duBuy, Hollaender, and Lackey: Supplement No. 184, U. S. Public Health Service.)

**Figure 44.4** Bead-bubbler device, consisting of a 250-ml. suction flask containing broth, glass beads 5 mm. in diameter, and a glass bubbler kept in place by a rubber stopper. A plate count is made from the broth after sufficient air has been sampled. (Reproduced from Wheeler et al.: Science, vol. 94.)

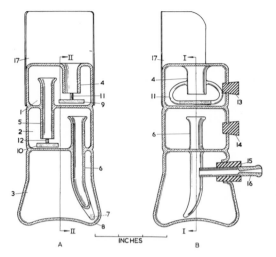

**Figure 44.5** A multistage, liquid impingement device. B is a sectional drawing at 90 degrees to A, B being rotated counterclockwise to reveal A; about one-half actual size. Three chambers (stages) (1, 2, 3,) are arranged vertically. Access to each is through rubber bungs 13, 14, 15. Air entering stages 1 and 2 flows over the surface of disks of sintered glass (9, 10) sticky with collecting fluid, the upper surface of the fluid being below the surface of the disks. The air then passes through the nozzle (7) and across a shallow layer of fluid in stage 3. Under prescribed conditions of operation particles of graded sizes are caught on the two wetted disks and in the fluid in stage 3. (From May: Bact. Rev., *30*:599, 1966.)

fensive hairs and mucus of the upper respiratory passages of persons inhaling them.

Small droplets in a warm, dry atmosphere are dry before they reach the floor and thus quickly become *droplet nuclei.* These are small (i.e., 2 to 5 $\mu$) and light and may float about for many minutes or even hours. The microorganisms in them are protected by the dried mucus which coats them. Being very small, droplet nuclei tend to pass the mechanical traps of the upper respiratory tract and enter the lungs.

The size, weight, moisture content and opacity to ultraviolet light of airborne particles are of importance in considerations of methods of sampling air for bacteriological examination and of methods for disinfecting air. For example, with respect to sampling, impingement methods will tend to catch the larger and heavier particles but not very small and light ones. With respect to disinfection, ultraviolet rays or sunlight may reach and kill organisms in droplets or nuclei if they are very small. Ultraviolet-opaque coatings and opaque dust particles will protect microorganisms from ultraviolet irradiation which, as we have seen (Chapter 19), has little power to penetrate. Humid atmospheres (about 50 per cent) have been shown to be more lethal than very dry or very moist atmospheres

(20 or 80 per cent), though both bacteria and viruses differ in this respect.

## 44.3  AIR POLLUTION

The crystal pure air our forefathers breathed is now subject to pollution from the industrial smokestack, the domestic chimney, and dust storms arising from uncropped land, to say nothing of liquors, garlic, tobacco, motor fumes, atomic explosions, radioactive fallout and "flying machines." Control over these involves engineering and other considerations foreign to this discussion. We may, however, consider the contribution of the individual human being to the all-enveloping pall of smog, perceptible or imperceptible, which now surrounds him in this day of advanced civilization, "from cradle to grave."

It is clear that the main source of dangerous microbial air pollution, so far as normal, peacetime human sources are concerned, is the mixture of saliva and mucus from their upper respiratory tracts. Aside from methods of air sampling already discussed, two important questions in studies of pollution of indoor atmospheres by human beings are: (1) what organism shall serve as an index of pollution by saliva and respiratory mucus? (compare use of *Escherichia coli* and *Streptococcus faecalis* as indices of sewage pollution, Chapter 42); and (2) what shall be used as a standard culture method to isolate and identify the organisms from the air? Final answers to these questions have not been formulated. As a test organism *Streptococcus salivarius,* one of the usually harmless oral, viridans-type streptococci (Chapter 34), has been proposed. Objections to it are that it may occur elsewhere, and that it is a fragile organism which soon disappears from the air. In other words, does its presence truly indicate salivary (and *only* salivary) pollution; does its absence prove the reverse?

Various media have been proposed for enumeration of airborne bacteria of sanitary significance. For general purposes the media used in milk or water examination are often used. As in all such enumerations, only those microorganisms capable of growth under the cultural conditions provided will be counted. However, the problem has not been fully explored and offers a good field for the ingenious and well-informed student.

## 44.4  CONTROL OF AIRBORNE INFECTION

Thorough *dilution* of contaminated air by *ventilation* is a very effective means of controlling airborne diseases indoors. However, it is sometimes expensive because of costs of heating or the installation of air ducts and blowers.

Under certain conditions disinfection or, more rarely, sterilization of air is desirable. Three general methods in addition to ventilation are available for the control of microorganisms in the air of rooms and buildings. This does not take into consideration such procedures as passing air through mechanical (e.g., fiberglass) filters or spray-washing devices. These reduce the numbers of organisms in air but do not necessarily disinfect or sterilize it.

**Radiation.** Irradiation with *ultraviolet light,* as pointed out in Chapter 19, is lethal to numerous microorganisms. A radiation wave length 2537 Å is generally used, as this is sufficiently microbicidal and at the same time not excessively irritating. Ultraviolet-producing electric lamps are attached to walls, overhead or at other strategic points. Deflectors are used to prevent direct exposure to the rays, which can cause serious "sunburn," and to protect the eyes, which may be seriously and permanently injured by prolonged, direct observation of an ultraviolet source. A difficulty arises from the necessity that in occupied rooms the microorganisms must circulate in air well above the heads of the people in the room in order to come within the range of action of the lethal rays. Only the lighter particles do this. Also, dust is little affected, and only places directly exposed are disinfected. Actually bactericidal, ultraviolet irradiation is difficult to apply with general effectiveness except under very special situations in storage facilities, hospitals, industry and research. If air is to be *recirculated* it may be first filtered and then passed through a tube where it is irradiated by powerful ultraviolet sources. These devices appear to be effective.

**Bactericidal Vapors.** Many substances are lethal to microorganisms in the vapor phase (formaldehyde, ethylene oxide, beta-propiolactone). Probably the most effective for disinfection of air are propylene glycol and triethylene glycol. These are odorless, tasteless, nonirritating, nontoxic and not explosive or corrosive. They are highly effective in killing bacteria in the air in the form of *vapor,* although (curiously enough) relatively ineffective in the form of concentrated aqueous solutions *in vitro.* It is the vapor molecules and not droplets of fine mist of these substances that are the effective disinfecting agent. As little as 0.5 mg. of propylene glycol vapor per liter of air can virtually sterilize heavily contaminated air in 15 seconds. Triethylene glycol is almost 100 times as effective.

Difficulties in the use of these vapors are chiefly of an engineering nature. Air conditioning appears inevitable to their effective use. The temperature and humidity of the air are important factors. If the air is cold and dry or excessively humid, the effectiveness of aerosols is reduced. Relative humidities of about 40 per cent at about 76° C. are favorable.

Other agents such as orthophenylphenol and related compounds have been recommended for *surface* application to supplement aerosols, especially as the phenylphenols cling to surfaces on which dust settles and render the surfaces bactericidal for prolonged periods under ordinary atmospheric conditions. Creation of persistent films of disinfectant on floors and other surfaces is undoubtedly of importance in control of dustborne disease (page 275).

**Dust Control.** In Chapter 28 it was pointed out that dust control is important in preventing disease transmission, and the fact is re-emphasized here. Methods were described in the earlier discussion (page 355).

## EFFECTIVENESS OF METHODS

Each of the methods just mentioned has been shown beyond doubt to be effective in reducing the number of aerial bacteria, both in experimentally contaminated laboratory atmospheres under various controlled conditions and in such places as barracks, schoolrooms, and hospital wards. When it comes to reduction of *disease,* however, data are less conclusive.

A great difficulty is that a person may spend his day-time hours in a protected environment such as an air-conditioned building with sterile air, but as he goes home in crowded subways or bus all of the expensive protection is nullified. This is well supported by published experience.

## SUPPLEMENTARY READING

Fulton, J. D., and others: Microorganisms of the upper atmosphere. Five papers. Appl. Microbiol., *14:*229, 232, 237, 241, 245, 1966.

Gregory, P. H., and Monteith, J. L., editors: Airborne Microbes. Seventeenth Symposium, Soc. Gen. Microbiol. 1967.

Lepper, M. H., and Wolfe, E. K., editors: Second International Conference on Aerobiology (Airborne Infection). Bact. Rev., *30:*11, 1966.

Won, W. D., and Ross, H.: Effect of diluent and relative humidity on apparent viability of airborne *Pasteurella pestis.* Appl. Microbiol., *14:*742, 1966.

# Chapter 45

## MICROBIOLOGY OF
## DAIRY PRODUCTS

### 45.1 NORMAL FLORA OF MILK

Milk secreted into the udder of healthy cows is sterile. It has a pH of about 6.8. Some saprophytic bacteria of the outside environment, such as species of Micrococcaceae, Bacillaceae, Escherichieae, Corynebacteriaceae and Lactobacillaceae, are able to grow a short way up into the milk duct of the teat, so that the first milk drawn usually contains from hundreds to thousands per milliliter. This milk should be discarded. Except in cases in which extra precautions are taken at the time of milking (Figs. 45.1, 45.2, 45.3), the milk receives contributions of organisms from the pail or mechanical milker and other dairy utensils (Fig. 45.4), from soil and dust in the air, from the flanks, tail and udder of the cow, and from the hands of milkers. Yeasts, molds and numerous other saprophytes find their way into the milk. These constitute the *normal flora* of market milk.

The presence of these nonpathogenic bacteria in milk is usually not a serious matter, but if they are allowed to multiply they can and will cause the milk to sour quickly, putrefy, or develop undesirable flavors or conditions like bitter milk (*Streptococcus cremoris*), blue milk (*Pseudomonas syncyanea*), red milk (*Serratia marcescens*), ropy (slimy) milk (*Alcaligenes viscolactis, Klebsiella aerogenes* and others). Their presence in very large numbers shows the milk to be stale or dirty. Entrance of these organisms into milk in large numbers can be prevented only by clean handling and routine *effective* sanitization of milk-handling equipment. Their development can be retarded by prompt refrigeration and by pasteurization.

**Pasteurization.** *Pasteurization* consists in holding the milk in tanks at 145° F. (63° C.) for 30 minutes ("low-temperature holding" or LTH) and immediately refrigerating. *Disinfection* of the milk is accomplished; *not* sterilization. In many dairies the same result is achieved by heating the milk rapidly in a tube or in thin layers between metal plates, to 71.6° to 80° C. and holding at that temperature for 15 to 30

**Figure 45.1** Sanitary milk production. Note the cleanliness of the cows, the absence of dung and straw, the good lighting, ventilation and milking machines. (Courtesy of the DeLaval Separator Company.)

**Figure 45.2** A two-unit, barn-type combine milker. Milk is conveyed, *directly from the cow's udders* in a completely enclosed glass, plastic or stainless steel pipe, through a filter and into a refrigerated bulk cooler. The milk is never open to contamination from the air or environment. After milking, the assembled units are connected with a manifold washer in the milk room. Detergent is placed in a special compartment in the automatic washer. By pressing a button the entire system is pre-rinsed, washed and rinsed again automatically. Surely a far cry from the romantic (but insanitary) "pretty milk-maid"! (Courtesy DeLaval Separator Company.)

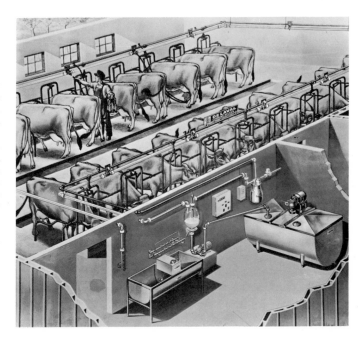

**Figure 45.3** Bottling milk in a sanitary dairy. All of the piping can be demounted in a few minutes for steam sterilization and the floors and walls hosed down. In some plants light, transparent, plastic tubing is used. The bottles in this picture have been steam sterilized just before filling. (Dodd's Alderney Dairy, Buffalo, N. Y. Courtesy of Cherry-Burrell Corp.)

**Figure 45.4** Conditions contributing to high bacterial counts in milk. Milk cooler open to dust and dirt; not readily cleaned. (Photo courtesy of Communicable Disease Center, U. S. Public Health Service, Atlanta, Ga.)

seconds, then cooling. These high-temperature-short-time (HTST or *flash*) methods save time and money and are effective so far as sanitation of milk is concerned.

## 45.2  CHANGES IN FLORA OF MILK

Since milk is an excellent medium for bacterial growth, the numbers of bacteria in it increase steadily the longer it stands, even if pasteurized and refrigerated. Even if milk is refrigerated so that growth of thermophiles and heat-resistant sporeformers is retarded, psychrophilic species will grow. Under storage at 3° C. some of these can soon cause discoloring, ropiness, off-flavors and other undesirable conditions. Common dairy psychrophiles are *Pseudomonas, Achromobacter, Alcaligenes, Flavobacterium* and *Micrococcus* species. Not all are killed by pasteurization and the survivors can multiply rapidly.

It is important that refrigeration be at very near 0° C. Much commercial refrigeration is at about 10° C., a temperature ideal for many psychrophiles. The temperature of the average household refrigerator (not freezer) is about 5° C. At best, such refrigeration is effective for not much over 24 hours.

**Raw Milk.** If allowed to stand at about 22° C., the flora in raw market milk rapidly undergo a series of changes. Numbers of bacteria increase to almost astronomical figures

within 24 hours. Enterobacteriaceae, lactic streptococci (e.g., *S. lactis*), *Micrococcus,* some sporeformers such as *Bacillus polymyxa* and other species of saprophytes that thrive at a pH near neutrality grow rapidly and dominate the picture at first. The lactose is fermented. As acidity increases, these species are inhibited. The aciduric lactic organisms then gain the ascendancy, especially *Lactobacillus* and species of *Leuconostoc.* Many *Clostridium* species will also ferment the lactose, but the presence of large numbers of *Clostridium* spores in fresh milk is not usual and indicates excessive contamination of the milk with soil or dung.

When the acidity reaches a pH of about 4.7, curdling occurs. The curd shrinks and settles out. Eventually, organisms capable of attacking lactic acid develop, especially aciduric yeasts and molds growing on the surface. These lower the acidity of the milk by destroying the acid and by producing alkaline products of protein decomposition: amines, ammonia and the like. Since the carbohydrates (lactose) have been decomposed by this time, fermentation does not reoccur.

Organisms capable of hydrolyzing the fat and casein now thrive: eucaryotic fungi, Bacillaceae, both aerobic and anaerobic, Pseudomonadaceae and many other lipolytic and proteolytic saprophytes. As the oxidation-reduction potential of the milk is reduced, species of *Clostridium* and other anaerobes, both obligate and facultative, gain the ascendancy and the odors (ammonia, odoriferous amines, mercaptans, hydrogen sulfide, rancid odors) and effects of putrefaction become evident. The casein is hydrolyzed; the milk is darkened (Fig. 45.5). After the situation has somewhat stabilized, a more prolonged decomposition continues, mainly by eucaryotic fungi and various microbial enzymes.

**Pasteurized Milk.** Pasteurized milk does not promptly undergo souring because many of the lactose-fermenting species, being nonsporeformers, are killed by the heat of the process. The milk may then undergo *sweet curdling* caused by rennet formation by bacteria, especially proteolytic streptococci and aerobic sporeformers (*Bacillus*). Often pasteurized milk does not sour, but the casein undergoes digestion and, later, putrefaction by the proteolytic enterococci, sporeformers and other thermoduric, proteolytic saprophytes that survive pasteurization.

**Significance of Coliform Organisms in Milk.** Coliform organisms are always present in market milk *before* pasteurization. They are derived from

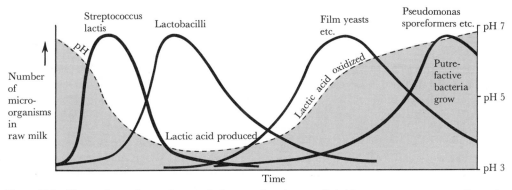

**Figure 45.5** Changes in numbers and types of microorganisms in raw milk held at summer temperature. For explanation see text. Note the initial decline in pH (increase in acidity) during fermentation of the lactose, with later rise in pH as the resulting lactic acid is metabolized and alkaline products of casein putrefaction accumulate. (From Carpenter: Microbiology.)

hay, soil, dust, dung and utensils. They do not necessarily indicate human fecal contamination. However, these organisms do not survive in milk in significant numbers if pasteurization is properly carried out. It is possible to detect coliforms in milk by methods similar to those used for determining coliforms in water. Plating the milk in desoxycholate-lactose agar or violet-red bile agar (both selective media) are especially recommended. Red colonies may be counted as coliforms and transferred for *completed test* if desired. The details for all important laboratory procedures in connection with dairy products are to be found in "Standard Methods for the Examination of Dairy Products" (see supplementary reading).

Unless almost-surgical precautions are used, a few coliform organisms gain entrance to milk *after* pasteurization, during cooling or bottling. Small numbers are of little significance and are not inimical to health, but their numbers give a good indication as to post-pasteurization cleanliness and refrigeration or staleness. Coliform organisms are particularly undesirable in milk to be used for cheese, since they cause rapid souring, gassy fermentation, and undesirable odors and flavors in cheese and other products made from the milk.

If considerable numbers of coliforms (more than about 1 to 5 per milliliter) are found in pasteurized milk it is evident that: (a) the milk has not been properly pasteurized; or (b) it has been excessively contaminated after pasteurization by unclean conditions, possibly by sewage, feces or dung; or (c) the milk has been held unduly long above about 15° C. after pasteurization; or (d) raw milk was mixed with it after pasteurization.

**The Phosphatase Test.** The presence of

excessive numbers of coliform bacteria in pasteurized milk suggests staleness or improper pasteurization or illegal adulteration with raw milk. Concerning pasteurization, more definite and accurate information can rapidly be obtained by means of the *phosphatase test.*

This test is based on the destruction by pasteurization of the heat-sensitive enzyme, *phosphatase,* normally present in fresh milk. The test for presence or absence of phosphatase is based on the power of phosphatase to liberate phenol from phosphoric-phenyl ester added to a sample of the milk.

In this test, 0.5 ml. of milk sample is added to 5.0 ml. of *buffered substrate* (disodium phenyl phosphate buffered with $NaHCO_3 \cdot Na_2CO_3 \cdot 2H_2O$) and held at 40° C. for 15 minutes. If the milk is unpasteurized or insufficiently pasteurized, the phosphatase enzyme normally present in the milk will be active and will decompose the added phenyl phosphate, liberating phenol. The phenol turns blue if 2,6-dichloroquinone-chloroimide (CQC), with $CuSO_4$ as catalyst, is added to the mixture. The appearance of blue color indicates the presence of free phenol liberated by undestroyed phosphatase in the milk. The color of the tested sample of milk is then compared with the color of standards containing known amounts of phenol and treated with the same reagent. When milk is pasteurized at 143° F. for 30 minutes, 96 per cent of the enzyme is destroyed. Only a trace of blue color should appear. Heating above 145° F. for 30 minutes insures complete inactivation of the phosphatase. No blue color should develop.

When milk has been underheated (in respect to either temperature or time) or when there is an admixture of raw milk afterward, the phosphatase will be present in larger amounts than when the milk is properly processed, and a definite blue color appears in the phosphatase test.

The phosphatase test can be made quantitative by comparing color with known standards. This test will detect 0.5 per cent raw milk mixed with pasteurized milk, or one degree below standard temperature, or five minutes of underheating during pasteurization. Color values (in the Sharer rapid method) greater than 0.5 $\mu$g of phenol per ml. of milk indicate progressive degrees of improper handling of milk.

SANITARY SIGNIFICANCE OF PHOSPHATASE TEST. In pasteurization, *Mycobacterium tuberculosis* (the most resistant of the nonsporeforming pathogens commonly found in milk) is destroyed

more quickly than phosphatase. Therefore, a heat treatment adequate to inactivate the enzyme likewise kills this organism and all other common pathogenic microorganisms (Fig. 45.6). A sample of milk that does not have more phosphatase present than the standard allows can be regarded as both safely pasteurized and free from subsequent contamination with raw milk.

*Sources of Error.* In some cases the phosphatase seems to become reactivated after proper pasteurization.

Certain bacteria can give falsely positive results in properly pasteurized milk because they produce a thermostable phosphatase before pasteurization. This remains active even after proper pasteurization.

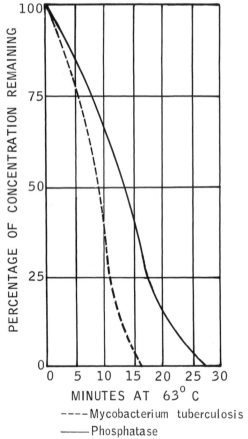

Figure 45.6 Representative comparative time-concentration curves for destruction of pathogenic bacteria (here represented by *Mycobacterium tuberculosis*) (------) and phosphatase (———) in milk during pasteurization at 63° C. Ordinates show approximate percentages of original concentrations or numbers remaining at 63° C. after minutes numbered on abscissa. Note that at all times destruction of the bacteria is more rapid and extensive than destruction of the phosphatase.

## 45.3   ENUMERATION OF BACTERIA IN MILK

In order to have some measure of the conditions under which milk has been produced and handled and to have a legal control over its sanitary quality, health departments and dairymen have set up various standards by which to judge milk. Important among these standards is the number of bacteria present.

**Plate Colony Count.** Numbers may be determined by one or more of several methods, legally recognized procedures for which are detailed in literature cited. One of these, the plate (colony) count, is closely analogous to the plate-count procedure described in Chapter 4.

For counting bacteria in milk the plates may be incubated at 32° or 35° C. for 48 hours for routine work, or at 7° C. for 7 to 10 days to enumerate psychrophiles; at 55° C. for 48 hours to enumerate thermophiles. The plating medium officially recognized for all of these, as well as for enumerating the bacteria in drinking water and widely used for counting bacteria in other materials (e.g., foods), contains: agar, 1.5 per cent; yeast extract, 2.5 per cent; protein digest, 5.0 per cent; glucose, 1 per cent. This medium is generally called *Standard Methods Agar* and must conform in bacteriological quality to that of a standard lot of medium specified by the American Public Health Association in 1963.

**Direct (Breed) Count.** Bacteria may also be enumerated by the direct microscopic examination of milk in a smear. The smear is prepared by spreading exactly 0.01 ml. of the sample on a slide over an area of exactly one square centimeter (100 mm.$^2$). After staining with specially prepared methylene-blue solutions designed to remove fat globules, the smear is examined by means of a microscope calibrated with a stage micrometer so that the field is exactly 0.206 mm. in diameter. Such a field represents approximately 1/300,000 ml. of milk. The number of bacteria seen in it must therefore be multiplied by the reciprocal of this fraction (the *microscopic factor* or MF) to determine the numbers of bacteria per milliliter:

$$MF = \frac{10,000}{\pi r^2}$$

Numerous large *clumps* of bacteria indicate unclean utensils. Many *pus cells* indicate infected udders. Streptococci and staphylococci indicate mastitis (Fig. 45.7). It is common practice to report results in terms of *clump counts* and, in reporting, to translate the microscopic observations directly into such terms as "good," "bad" and "mastitis." The method is quick and inexpensive. It is applied mainly to unpasteurized milk, since heating causes many of the bacteria to die and lose their staining properties.

**Numerical Relationship Between Counts.** The *total* direct microscopic count is usually five to ten or more times as high as the plate count. This is because the total direct count enumerates individual cells, even those in clumps, and

also dead bacteria. As in the plate count applied to water and soil, the plate count applied to milk enumerates only live bacteria capable of developing in the medium and under the environmental conditions used. In the plate count each clump, even though it may contain scores of live cells, counts only as a single bacterium since each clump forms only one colony. The plate count is usually closer to the clump count than to the total direct count.

## 45.4  QUALITY AND OXIDATION-REDUCTION POTENTIAL

**The Reduction Test.** Most actively growing bacteria cause a lowered oxidation-reduction (O-R) potential in their medium. The presence in milk of large enough numbers of growing bacteria to produce a significantly lowered O-R potential can be detected by the use of methylene blue because, with a lowering of the O-R potential to about −0.01 volt, this dye becomes colorless. The reduction (so-called "*reductase*") test is used principally with raw milk, and furnishes a rough but useful approximation of the number and kinds of living bacteria present. In performing the test, 10 ml. of milk sample are pipetted into a sterile tube and 1 ml.

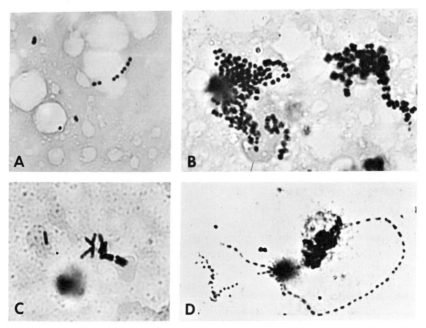

**Figure 45.7** Examples and probable sources of microorganisms detectable by direct microscopic examination of milk: *A*, cocci, milk probably improperly refrigerated; *B*, large masses of bacteria, improperly cleaned milk-handling utensils; *C*, spore-forming bacilli, probably from soil and dust contamination; *D*, pyogenic streptococci and a pus cell from cow with mastitis. (From Foster et al.: Dairy Microbiology. Prentice-Hall, Inc.)

of a standard methylene blue solution (final concentration about 1:250,000) is added. The tube is closed with a rubber stopper and slowly inverted three times to mix. It is placed at 35.0° C. in the water bath immediately. At the end of each hour during the test the tube is inverted once. Observations are made after 30 minutes, 1 hour, and later.

MBRT. The *methylene-blue reduction time* (MBRT) is the interval between the placing of the tubes in the water bath at 35.0° C. and the disappearance of the blue color from the milk.

The shorter the MBRT, the greater the number of active bacteria in the milk and the lower its bacteriological quality. However, MBRT does not give an accurate *count* of bacteria present; only an overall measure of its bacteriological quality. Milk with an MBRT of 30 minutes is of very poor quality; an MBRT of six hours is very good.

RESAZURIN. A dye related to methylene blue, resazurin undergoes a *series* of color changes depending on O-R potential changes, whereas methylene blue changes only from blue to colorless. Resazurin, therefore, permits readings of *degrees* of reduction at shorter intervals than does methylene blue. In one procedure (the *1-hour test*), color of the milk, initially blue, is compared after one hour at 37° C. with several exactly described (*Munsell*) color standards designated as 5P7/4 (mauve), PBP7/5.5 (purple), and so on. Milk showing no greater change during the hour than from blue to PBP7/5.5 is grade 1; to PRP7/8 (lavender), grade 2; and so on to grade 4, complete decolorization. In the *triple-reading* or *three-hour* test, three successive readings are made at one-hour intervals to see how long it takes to reach the color 5P7/4. High grade (acceptable) milk requires at least three hours (resazurin reduction time, or RRT, three hours).

## 45.5  FACTORS AFFECTING BACTERIOLOGICAL QUALITY

**Bacteriophages in Milk.** A factor of importance, especially to manufacturers of dairy products that depend on early, rapid and luxuriant growth of certain bacteria such as *Streptococcus lactis,* is the presence of bacteriophage lytic for that species. These phages are common in dust in and around dairies. They are known to interfere with many sorts of dairy work (cheese-making) that is dependent on bacterial growth. Very rigid aseptic technique in preparing and handling the pure *starter* cultures is necessary to eliminate the phages. Steel filters

with triple layers of fiberglass have been successfully used to remove phages from air of dairy laboratories and work rooms.

**Antibiotics and Disinfectants.** Another important factor in bacteriological studies of milk is the possibility that the results have been influenced by (1) preservatives illegally added; (2) residues of disinfectants used to sanitize the dairy equipment; (3) antibiotics or other drugs used to control udder infections, and otherwise administered to cattle. Antibiotics, disinfectants and preservatives can interfere with growth of the bacteria used in the manufacture of cheese and butter, cultured milks (e.g., yoghurt), and in such bacteriological controls as reduction tests and plate counts. In most manufacturing procedures, uninhibited growth of *S. cremoris, Leuconostoc citrovorum, Streptococcus lactis, Lactobacillus* species and other bacteria is essential.

Penicillin is especially undesirable in milk because it can produce severe allergic reactions in persons hypersensitive to it.

## 45.6  GRADES OF MILK

The actual numbers of bacteria permissible in milks of various grades vary in different cities. A good guide is the standard milk ordinance and code of the Public Health Service of the U. S. Department of Health, Education and Welfare. Various localities may have somewhat different standards.

**Grade A Raw Milk for Pasteurization.** Grade A raw milk for pasteurization is raw milk from properly supervised producer dairies conforming to standards of sanitation of workers, cattle, premises and equipment as prescribed in the ordinance. Cattle and personnel must be free from diseases transmissible in milk. The bacterial plate count or the microscopic clump count of the milk, as delivered to the pasteurizing plant for pasteurization, shall not exceed 200,000 organisms per milliliter as determined by standard methods of the American Public Health Association or must have a MBRT of less than 5.5 hours or RRT of less than 2.75 hours.

**Grade A Pasteurized Milk.** In all cases Grade A pasteurized milk shall show efficient pasteurization as evidenced by satisfactory phosphatase test, and at no time after pasteurization and before delivery shall the milk have a bacterial plate count exceeding 30,000 per milliliter, or a coliform count exceeding 10 per milliliter, as determined by Standard Methods of the American Public Health Association.

**Grade B Pasteurized Milk.** Grade B pasteurized milk is pasteurized milk that does not meet the bacterial-count standard for grade A pasteurized milk, and certain other sanitary requirements. Such milk may be used in some commercial processes.

Most communities now permit the sale only of grade A milk, pasteurized.

**Criteria of Good Milk.** *Quality* tests such as bacterial enumerations and reduction tests, as well as others, have a distinct value and usefulness from the standpoint of *cleanliness* but not necessarily with regard to *infection*. The present status of microbiology of milk was well summarized by Robertson, who said:

None of the routine laboratory procedures for estimating the number of bacteria in milk will determine whether or not infectious bacteria are present. The best assurance of freedom from infectious bacteria is that provided by proper pasteurization of the milk. The best assurance of pasteurization is that demonstrated by a satisfactory phosphatase test on the bottled pasteurized milk. The best assurance of freedom from recontamination in freshly bottled milk after pasteurization is a satisfactory coliform test in 1.0 ml. portions of the bottled product.

**Certified Milk.** If milk is to be offered for sale unpasteurized, it is often required that it be produced only under very carefully supervised conditions. The American Association of Medical Milk Commissions has established rules and regulations concerning veterinary inspection of cows, especially for tuberculosis, brucellosis and infectious mastitis, and sanitation of barns and utensils. These very rigid regulations are often used by health departments and milk dealers in certifying qualified farms to produce such milk. It is usually called *Certified milk* or *baby milk.* The use of certified milk has much to recommend it, especially its cleanliness. The coliform standard for Certified milk—raw, is 10 per milliliter; for certified, pasteurized, 1 per milliliter. It is said to contain a larger proportion of certain vitamins essential for infants than milk which has been heated.

Most cities and states, as well as the A.A.M.M.C., require that all persons occupied in preparing Certified milk, or, indeed, any food for the public, be examined periodically for typhoid, paratyphoid and dysentery bacilli. Examinations for presence of organisms that cause diphtheria, tuberculosis, scarlet fever and other transmissible diseases are also required for Certified milk handlers.

## 45.7 CONCENTRATED AND DRIED MILKS

Milks from which part or all of the water has been withdrawn are termed *concentrated* or *dried.* Assuming that approved standards of cleanliness, freshness, sanitation and chemical content (fat, solids and so on) have been met in selecting the milk to be dehydrated, the microbiological quality of the finished product is determined largely by: (a) temperatures and time of storage (if any) prior to processing; (b) times and temperatures of processing; (c) cleanliness of the apparatus and final containers; (d) time and temperature of final processing of canned milks.

**Evaporated Milk.** The raw milk is first cooled and may be clarified. Fat and solids contents are "adjusted" to meet required standards. The milk is then heated to boiling or nearly so (94 to 100° C.) for about 20 minutes. This kills all but the most heat-resistant microorganisms. Water is driven off *in vacuo* at about 55° C., a temperature which favors development of undesirable thermophiles, e.g., *Bacillus stearothermophilus* and which therefore requires careful bacteriological control.

After homogenization, the product is cooled and canned. It is "commercially sterilized" at about 117° C. for about 15 minutes. Spoilage problems can result from inadequate heating and subsequent storage at unduly high temperatures that favor growth of spores of thermophilic molds and Bacillaceae.

**Sweetened Condensed Milk.** Milk can be doubly preserved by the addition of about 20 per cent of sucrose or glucose, or both, to whole milk, and by subsequent heating at temperatures near boiling and by partial dehydration as with evaporated milk.

**Nonfat Dried Milk.** Nonfat dried milk is prepared by preliminary steps similar to those used for evaporated milk. The fat is removed by high-speed cream separators. The water is partly removed by preliminary heating (about 85° C.) and then by: (a) spraying the milk as a mist into a current of hot (about 120° C.) air in a closed chamber; or (b) by spreading the milk as a thin film on hot rollers or drums—at about 145° C. if no vacuum is used, or at less than 100° C. in a vacuum chamber.

The dried *flakes* from hot drums or the *powder* from sprayed milk are packaged to prevent access of moisture. Dried milks should be kept dry and cool at all times or they may spoil since they are not sterile. As previously pointed out, dry heat is an inefficient sterilant. Microorganisms surviving the process are mainly Bacillaceae and thermoduric streptococci, lactobacilli, micrococci and species of *Microbacterium.* Nonsporing pathogens are eliminated. The presence of coliform bacteria or of pathogenic streptococci or other heat-sensitive microorganisms is of the same sinister significance that it is in pasteurized whole milk.

RECONSTITUTION.   In reconstituting dried or evaporated milk it is clearly desirable to use clean, cool and hygienically acceptable water and utensils. The reconstituted milk should be kept and handled under the same conditions of sanitation and refrigeration as are recommended for whole milk.

STANDARDS OF QUALITY.   Quality standards for dewatered milks are similar to those for whole milk, bearing in mind the changes in flora caused by heating. The standards are established by the U. S. Department of Agriculture, The American Dry Milk Institute and the Evaporated Milk Association (Evaporated Milk Industry Sanitary Standards Code, Chicago, Ill.). Standards for various grades of dried milk, for example, are 50,000 per gram for "extra" quality and 100,000 per gram for "standard" quality. Counting procedures are the same as for fresh milk after the dried milk is reconstituted with sterile water.

## 45.8   SOME MANUFACTURED DAIRY PRODUCTS

Market milk contains numerous species of microorganisms in varying numbers whose uncontrolled action is too unreliable to serve as a basis for commercial operations requiring uniformity of product. Pure-culture inocula (called *mother* or *stock cultures*) of constant properties are essential to continued success in this highly competitive field. For these purposes *Lyophilized* ("freeze-dried"), or other pure, stock cultures of desired organisms may be maintained in the dairy if a competent bacteriologist and adequate laboratory facilities are available. Otherwise it is best to obtain stock cultures from dairy-supply houses. Cultures of species of lactic streptococci, *Leuconostoc* and *Lactobacillus* are used especially.

**Starter Cultures.**   In practice mother cultures in about 2 per cent volume are added as nearly aseptically as possible to about 600 ml. of sterile or very-low-count milk (previously heated 30 minutes at about 88° C. and cooled to 21° C.), and incubated. The lactic organisms soon outgrow other species, if any are present. This culture is called a *starter*. It may be used to inoculate a tank-size batch of milk or cream for butter or cheese, or to inoculate a still larger lot of starter.

Fresh, high-quality (low-count) pasteurized milk is brought *quickly* to the desired incubating temperature. A large, *pre-emptive,* virtually pure, starter inoculum of vigorously growing young cells of the desired lactic organism is added and thoroughly mixed with the milk or cream. Before the other bacteria in the milk have time to recover from their previous refrigeration or pasteurization and overcome their lag phase, the acidity quickly produced by the actively metabolizing added lactic starter suppresses them.

### BUTTER

Butter is generally made by churning cream that has been soured by lactic acid bacteria.

Two species of bacteria, each with a distinct function, are added together to the cream simultaneously. *Leuconostoc citrovorum* is depended on for flavor, *Streptococcus cremoris* or *S. lactis* is selected primarily for *rapid,* initial lactic acid production. If high acidity (pH 4.3) is not produced promptly, numerous undesirable contaminants may grow excessively. When the pH reaches about 4.3 *Leuconostoc* ceases growth, but its enzymes attack the citrates in the milk and produce diacetyl. This substance gives butter and similar products their characteristic buttery flavor and aroma. Neither *S. cremoris* nor *Leuconostoc* alone can produce the desired result in commercial practice.

### CHEESE

Cheeses may be divided into three general types: (a) soft- or cottage-type cheese, and cream cheese (these are eaten in a fresh or unripened state); (b) hard- or rennet-curd cheese, including Roquefort, American cheddar-type ("rat-bait"), Edam, and Swiss (these are *ripened* by the enzymes and slow growth of bacteria or molds or both, which cause some, but not extensive proteolysis); (c) soft or semisoft rennet-curd cheese, of which Camembert, Limburger and Liederkranz are types (these are ripened by proteolytic and lipolytic organisms which soften the curd and give it flavors). The hardness of cheese depends to some extent on moisture and fat content as well as on heating and acidity of the curd, draining, salting and conditions of storage. A list of common cheeses is given in Table 45.1.

**Soft, Acid-Curd Cheese.**   In making cottage cheese, starters containing mixtures of *Leuconostoc citrovorum, L. dextranicum, S. lactis* and the like are added to pasteurized milk. These ferment the

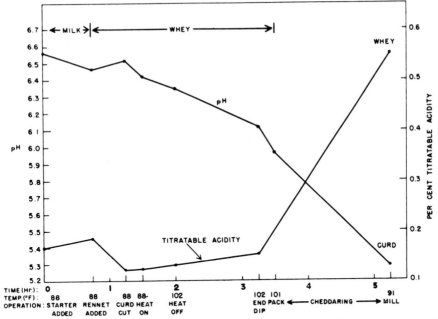

**Figure 45.8**  Cheddar cheese: changes in temperature and in acidity as measured by determination of pH and by titration of total acid, during successive early phases, from addition of starter (low left) to milling (lower right); about 5 hours in all. At the time starter is added at 88° F. the acidity is low (pH 6.58; titrable acidity 0.18 per cent). As lactose is fermented acidity quickly increases. At pH about 6.46, rennet is added and the curd forms. It is soon cut, heated, and the whey is drawn off (dipped). Cheddaring and milling then proceed. Further increases in acidity occur during the ripening process. (From Brown and Price: J. Dairy Sc., vol. 17.)

lactose, *Leuconostoc* adding flavor and aroma. The lactic acid coagulates the casein. Rennet may be added to hasten the coagulation and make the curd firmer. The curd is cut into small cubes. To firm the curd and separate it from the

**TABLE 45.1  TYPES OF NATURAL\* CHEESE**

| Representative Cheeses | Distinctive Organisms in Ripening Flora |
|---|---|
| **Soft:** | |
| Cottage | } not ripened |
| Cream | |
| Liederkranz | *Strep. liquefaciens, Brevibacterium* |
| Camembert | *Penicillium camemberti, Brevibacterium* |
| **Semisoft:** | |
| Blue (or Bleu) | } *Penicillium* strains such as |
| Roquefort | *P. roqueforti* |
| Gorgonzola | |
| **Hard** | |
| Swiss | *Propionibacter* species |
| Cheddar | Lactic group, *Geotrichum* |
| Parmesan | Lactic group (brine cured) |

\*Not processed artificially. (Pasteurized and processed cheeses and cheese spreads are not included since they are made almost entirely from the natural cheeses such as those listed above.)

whey, the mass is heated slowly to about 50° C. and held so for 30 minutes. Water is added; the curd settles. The water, with the whey, is drained off and the curd is pushed into heaps to drain. It is washed a second time with water and drained. About 0.5 per cent salt is added. Just before packaging many manufacturers add a little cream.

**Hard-Curd Cheese.**  In the preliminary stages, nearly all natural (i.e., not "processed") cheeses are much alike. Differences result from different methods of treating the curd: degree of acidity, addition of different amounts of salt, special ripening microorganisms, moisture, temperature and humidity of ripening and other factors (Fig. 45.8).

For yellow cheeses of the Cheddar type, color is added. After a slight acidity has developed, rennet is added to make an elastic, rubbery curd which is later cut into pieces about one inch in diameter (Fig. 45.9) and warmed to about 35° C. The curd becomes firmer and the whey separates and is drained off and may be used for stock feed. The clumped masses of firm curd are chopped (*milled*) again, and piled up to press out whey (Fig. 45.10). This is called *cheddaring* in Cheddar cheese making. The curd is again milled, and then is salted, drained and pressed in hoops to cure. Curing of Cheddar

**Figure 45.9** Making cheddar-type cheese. Liquid milk becomes curd and whey after starter and rennet are added. The milk forms into soft curd much like "junket." This is firmed by heating gently. When it has reached the correct firmness, it is cut into small cubes (one-fourth inch) by special wire knives. The whey is slowly expelled from these cubes as the curd and whey are heated while slowly agitated by revolving paddles. The cubes of coagulated casein are then washed with water and drained. The picture shows the cutting operation. (Courtesy of Kraft-Phenix Cheese Corporation.)

cheese proceeds at about 15° C. It becomes "sharper" with aging.

Curing or Ripening of Hard Cheeses. During the curing process of Cheddar and other hard cheeses, various microorganisms, the varieties depending on the kind of cheese, continue a slow fermentative, lipolytic and proteolytic action, the products of these processes yielding the characteristic flavors, textures and aromas of various cheeses. Prominent among these flavors are diacetyl, lactic, butyric, caproic and acetic acids, and various amines, as well as various esters such as those that give flavors to ripe fruit juices. In addition, since many of these organisms synthesize vitamins, especially nicotinic acid and vitamins of the B complex, the nutritive value of the cured (or ripened) cheeses is increased.

Gas formers such as species of *Clostridium* and *Escherichiae* are undesirable because they produce gassy cheeses (Fig. 45.11) and off flavors; they may be especially active in the early

stages. They generally occur in milk of poor quality.

Swiss cheese is heated to 50° C. after cutting the curd. Starters therefore usually contain the *thermoduric* lactics: *Streptococcus thermophilis* and *Lactobacillus bulgaricus* or *L. lactis,* as well as *Propionibacterium shermanii* and *P. freudenreichii.*

The cheese is soaked in 23 per cent brine for some days at 13° C. Propionibacteria are then favored by incubation at 22° C. Later the cheese is ripened for months at about 13° C.

The "eyes" in Swiss cheese are a result of the production of carbon dioxide by species of *Propionibacterium,* while its bitter-sweet flavor is caused in part by the formation of glycerol, propionic and succinic acids by *Propionibacterium* species while ripening.

Semisoft cheese, such as Roquefort, Gorgonzola or Blue (or *Bleu*), contains much fat and as high as 5 per cent salt and relatively little moisture. The high salt content prevents continued growth of most bacteria, as does the low ripening temperature (7° to 8° C.) and humidity (60 per cent). A species of mold (*Penicillium roqueforti*) is introduced by the inocula-

**Figure 45.10** Making cheddar-type cheese. When cheddaring (firming and draining) is complete (judged by the firmness of the curd, its texture and acidity) the curd is milled (cut into small pieces) in preparation for salting and pressing. About one and one-half pounds of salt are used to 100 pounds of curd. After salting, the curd is placed in cheesecloth or cellophane-lined "hoops" of the desired size and shape for pressing. (Courtesy of Kraft-Phenix Cheese Corporation.)

**Figure 45.11**  Defects in cheeses due to gas-forming (aerogenic) micro-organisms. *A* and *B*, Gas formed by *Klebsiella aerogenes* in early ripening of Cheddar cheeses (*A*, yellow; *B*, white). (Courtesy of The Borden Co.) *C*, Gas formed late in ripening of Provolone, an Italian cheese similar to Cheddar. Compare with "stormy fermentation," Figure 32.7. *D*, Gas formed by a lactose-fermenting yeast in early ripening of Brick cheese. (*C* and *D* from Foster et al.: Dairy Microbiology, Prentice-Hall, Inc.)

tion of spores into the milk or into the curd as it is put into hoops for ripening. The mold grows in the interior, producing the masses of blue-green conidia and the sharp flavor so characteristic of this type of cheese. As the mold is aerobic, perforations are made in the cheese to aerate the interior.

**Soft Cheeses.**  Limburger, Liederkranz and Camembert cheeses are cured mainly by the growth of organisms in a red-orange, slimy coating on the outer surface. Numbers of microorganisms in this slime sometimes exceed 10 billion per gram. In Limburger cheese, yeasts (*Geotrichum* species) begin to grow on the surface after subsidence of the initial acidity caused by lactic organisms. They persist in the surface slime for about a week. *Brevibacterium linens* and *B. erythrogenes* then grow all over the surface, forming a reddish brown coating, or *"smear,"* commonly seen on soft and semisoft cheese (Brick, Camembert). Camembert cheese is sometimes inoculated on the outer surface (or before curd-formation) with a pure culture of the mold, *P. camemberti.* The enzymes of the various micrococci, yeasts or molds in the slime penetrate into the interior of the cheese, producing the flavors, softening, and the famous aroma of Limburger and similar cheese.

## 45.9  FERMENTED MILK BEVERAGES

In certain countries lactobacilli have been used for centuries in combination with certain yeasts and streptococci to produce foods of fermented milk. The *yoghurt* of eastern central Europe (now available in all grocery stores), the *busa* of Turkestan, the *kefir* of the Cossacks, the *koumiss* of central Asia and the *leben* of Egypt are examples of these. Formerly, the microbial nature of these processes was unknown. In all of these fermented milks lactobacilli act in company with other microorganisms: yeasts, lactic streptococci and various rods. For example, kefir, made from milk of various domestic animals, is prepared by putting *kefir grains* (small, cauliflower-like masses) into the milk. These grains consist of dried masses of lactobacilli (*L. brevis*), yeasts (*Sacch. delbruckii*), *Streptococcus lactis* and probably other lactic organisms held together in a matrix of coagulated casein and bacterial polysaccharide gum. The kefir grains increase in size and break apart as the fermentation proceeds. The combined growth of the mixed flora yields a characteristically flavored, soured milk containing small amounts of alcohol. The kefir grains are found in the bottom of the vessels of fermented milk.

YOGHURT. In the United States this is made of pasteurized milk thickened by rennet or addition of dried milk, and soured by species of *Lactobacillus.*

ACIDOPHILUS MILK. Milk soured by *Lactobacillus acidophilus* is thought by some to have medicinal properties in the intestinal tract. *Bulgarian buttermilk,* a similar beverage, is prepared with pure-culture starters of *Lactobacillus bulgaricus.*

BUTTERMILK. Much of the product commonly sold in the United States as buttermilk is in reality pasteurized skim or whole milk soured mainly by *Streptococcus cremoris* with *Leuconostoc citrovorum* and then beaten so as to produce a smooth, creamy beverage. It is a pleasant, nourishing drink. Addition of 0.15 per cent of citric acid to the milk results in formation of increased flavor because diacetyl is produced by *Leuconostoc citrovorum.*

## SUPPLEMENTARY READING

American Association of Medical Milk Commissions: Methods and Standards for the Production of Certified Milk. Am. Assn. of Med. Milk. Com., New York. 1962.

A. P. H. A. Coordinating Committee on Laboratory Methods: Standardization of plating media. Am. J. Pub. Health, *53*:1305, 1963.

Edwards, J. L., Busta, F. F., and Speck, M. L.: Thermal inactivation characteristics of *Bacillus subtilis* spores at ultrahigh temperatures. Appl. Microbiol, *13*:851, 1965.

Foster, E. M., Nelson, F. E., Speck, M. L., Doetsch, R. N., and Olson, J. C.: Dairy Microbiology. Prentice-Hall, Inc., Englewood Cliffs, N. J. 1957.

Gordon, Jr., D. F., and Speck, M. L.: Bitter peptide isolated from milk cultures of *Streptococcus cremoris.* Appl. Microbiol., *13*:537, 1965.

Hammer, B. W., and Bable, F. J.: Dairy Bacteriology, 4th ed. John Wiley & Sons, Inc., New York. 1957.

Koberger, J. A., Speck, M. L., and Aurand, L. W.: Identification of growth stimulants for *Streptococcus lactis.* J. Bact., *85*:1051, 1963.

la Riviere, J. W. M.: Studies on the kefir grain. Proc. Soc. Gen. Microbiol., *31*:v, 1963.

Macaulay, D. M., Hawirko, R. Z., and James, N.: Effect of pasteurization on survival of certain psychrophilic bacteria. Appl. Microbiol., *11*:90, 1963.

Milk Ordinance and Code, U. S. Public Health Service Publication No. 229, Washington, D. C., 1953.

Srinivasan, R. A., Iyengar, M. K. K., Babbar, I. J., Chakravorty, S. C., Dudani, A. T., and Iya, K. K.: Milk-clotting enzymes from microorganisms. Appl. Microbiol., *12*:475, 1964.

Standard Methods for the Examination of Dairy Products, 12th ed. Am. Pub. Health Assn., New York. 1967.

Washam, C. J., Black, C. H., Sandine, W. E., and Elliker, P. R.: Evaluation of filters for removal of bacteriophages from air. Appl. Microbiol., *14*:497, 1966.

# Chapter 46

## MICROBIOLOGY OF FOODS

The modern human dietary includes a wide variety of substances from many sources. Much of it is subject to natural contamination by many different kinds of microorganisms, including some that are dangerous pathogens, and it is modified with many additives (antimicrobial preservatives, hygroscopic agents, colors, flavors) and by various preparative processes involving many species of microorganisms; consequently, the microbiology of foods is an exceedingly complex subject.

### 46.1 CLASSES OF FOODS

Since water and dairy products are dealt with elsewhere, they will not be included here. Other common foods may be grouped as follows:

1. Fresh foods (e.g., meats, vegetables, fruits and fish)
2. Foods preserved by:
   a. Drying
   b. Canning
   c. Pickling, brining, salting or fermenting
   d. Low temperatures, especially rapid freezing
   e. Antimicrobial substances
3. Breads
4. Eggs

For purposes of this discussion fresh foods may be defined as those recently harvested or prepared, that are in their natural or original state, not affected by any means of artificial preservation excepting refrigeration (not freezing) for limited periods, and unchanged by effects of holding for sale or use beyond *slight* wilting or drying. Foods still edible but held so long that perceptibly undesirable changes in volume, weight, color, flavor, odor, appearance or other

properties of fresh products have occurred may be classed as stale. An *accurate* definition of *fresh* and *stale* is very difficult indeed, as are chemical or bacteriological determinations of these conditions. We shall use the terms in their commonly accepted meanings.

Foods may also be classified on the basis of stability:

1. *Perishable* foods such as meat and fish
2. *Semiperishable* foods such as potatoes
3. *Stable* foods such as cereals, flour and sugar.

Of course, any stable or semistable foods that become over-moist or water-soaked are no longer stable.

We may divide microorganisms of foods into three general groups on a functional basis:

1. Those causing spoilage or *undesirable* changes in the food
2. Those producing *desirable* changes
3. Those producing *disease*

Attempts to combat undesirable microorganisms or to encourage desirable microorganisms in food are the basis of industries and research in this country involving billions of dollars annually.

AUTOLYTIC ENZYMES. In any discussion of the stability of foods, autolysis must be considered. When cells die, certain incompletely understood intracellular enzymic processes act within a few hours to disintegrate the cells. Such self-disintegration is called *autolysis*. Autolysis proceeds best under conditions optimal for enzymic action: pH, temperature and so on.

Many meats undergo autolysis. Venison and poultry are often "hung" until tender (i.e., until some autolysis has taken place). Beef is more tender after a ripening period in refrigerators, partly due to autolysis. Autolysis may cause the uninitiated housewife to wonder why the pound of liver she bought in the butchershop seemed to melt away to a half pound as she drove home on a warm summer day. Since conditions for autolysis and microbial growth are parallel to a great extent, autolysis under market conditions is usually accompanied by microbial action unless foods are sterile. Autolysis will occur even in sterile foods if the autolytic enzymes have not been destroyed by heat.

Leafy vegetables (lettuce, spinach, endive), bananas and other fruits are made very soft during autolysis, especially in warm weather. Loss of weight, color, flavor and nutritive value result during excessive autolysis. Decomposition by yeasts, molds and bacteria can advance rapidly when over-autolysis has prepared the way. Hence in preserving foods, efforts are made to (1) prevent autolysis beyond a certain desirable *ripening* point; (2) to prevent decomposition by microorganisms. Usually the same preservative measures are effective against both. For example, in preparation of vegetables for preservation by freezing, autolytic enzymes, as well as some of the superficial microorganisms, are partly destroyed by *blanching* or scalding for a few minutes before packing.

## 46.2 FRESH FOODS

### MEAT

When an animal dies of natural causes (disease or age), before death there is a short period (the agonal or moribund state) during which there is a collapse of the defensive mechanisms which normally prevent invasion of the blood (and thence of the tissues) by microorganisms in the gastrointestinal tract, respiratory tract, skin and other body surfaces. Examination of muscle, liver and other tissues of such an animal (and especially lymph nodes which arrest bacteria coming from such sources) immediately after death reveals the presence, often in considerable numbers, of microorganisms characteristic of the intestine, respiratory tract and so on. These include species of *Clostridium*, Enterobacteriaceae, *Micrococcus*, fecal and respiratory streptococci; *Proteus, Pseudomonas*, and the like. Meat from such an animal will spoil quickly.

If a healthy animal is *suddenly* killed, as in the abattoir by a blow on the head, relatively little postmortem invasion of the blood and tissues occurs. Cutting a large vessel with a sharp, clean knife, as in killing hogs, probably introduces very few microorganisms. If the animal is then immediately dismembered in a cleanly manner, as is done in well-conducted abattoirs, relatively few organisms are to be found in the depths of solid tissues; spoilage must proceed mainly on the surface.

**Surface Flora of Meat.** Meat becomes contaminated immediately upon exposure in the abattoir. Dust from hides and hair, bacteria on gloves, hands and cutting and handling instruments, all contribute to this. The principal damage done by such organisms is to cause decomposition of organic substances in the surface tissues unless preventive and preservative measures include prompt hanging in refrigerators under ultraviolet light.

The microorganisms involved in surface decomposition and spoilage of meat and other protein foods include saprophytes of the genera *Pseudomonas, Bacillus* and *Micrococcus,* various Actinomycetales, yeasts and molds, *Achromobacter, Proteus,* enterococci, *Clostridium, Corynebacterium, Escherichia* and *Aerobacter.* Some psychrophilic microorganisms cause unsightly but harmless blackening, greening, or other discoloration during refrigeration and may produce undesirable tastes and odors, such as rancidity owing to decomposition of fats.

**Antibiotics in Meat.** Spoilage of fresh meat may be prevented for days and even weeks by intravenous injection of antibiotics just before or after killing. Broad-spectrum antibiotics such as chloramphenicol and the tetracycline group appear to give good results. The antibiotic is distributed throughout the tissues by the blood before the animal is killed. The method has proven of value in the tropics and in situations in which refrigeration is not feasible. Such use of antibiotics, however, is a source of some controversy. Probably *legal* residues of tetracyclines are not harmful. The use of penicillin is generally frowned upon because it is highly allergenic. Antibiotics in *any* materials can interfere greatly with bacteriological examinations. Such use of antibiotics is properly restricted to very special situations.

ANTIBIOTIC-RESISTANT ORGANISMS IN FOODS. A serious problem in the use of antibiotics for preservation of foods of any sort concerns the development of antibiotic-resistant species. Antibiotic-resistant pathogens (e.g., *Salmonella*) capable of infecting man as well as animals are developed by the continuous use of antibiotics; the various spoilage saprophytes also become resistant.

**Ground Meat.** The flora of freshly ground meat is much richer in numbers and types of microorganisms than that of large pieces of meat such as roasts, because in the ordinary processes of preparing ground meat, the meat is cut into small pieces, scraps are used and the surface contamination is thoroughly mixed with the meat as it is ground. It is also usually warmed somewhat. The microorganisms present in the product are those found initially on the surface and, in addition, molds, yeasts, sporeformers, Actinomycetales and others from the grinding machine, hands, implements and dust. Unless effectively refrigerated the microorganisms grow throughout the whole mass and the meat spoils rapidly.

BACTERIAL COUNT. Bacteriological standards for ground meat are difficult to establish and to evaluate. According to some workers, using a medium like that used for enumerating bacteria in milk, incubated at 32° C., an aerobic plate count of 10 million organisms per gram of meat is a reasonable maximum. Occasional counts in ground meat of market quality may run into the billions per gram, and this is exclusive of anaerobes, molds, and other organisms that do not grow under the cultural conditions provided.

## BACTERIA IN OTHER COMMINUTED FOODS

The basic principles that apply to ground meats hold true also for products such as separated, fresh, crab meat; "shucked"* shellfish; flaked, fresh fish; ground horseradish; chopped spinach; salad mixtures; cole-slaw, and the like. The more foods are handled and the more they are chopped, ground or grated (*comminuted*), the more the surface microorganisms are mixed with the interior and with richly nutritive sap or juice, and the heavier the inoculation. Such foods must be kept refrigerated at all times, and never sold if more than 24 hours old.

As in preservation of ground meats, admixture of antibiotics to initially reasonably fresh, clean products holds spoilage in check for many days, even without refrigeration. The acidity of products such as slaw and horseradish, mixed with vinegar or citric acid (lemon juice), tends to retard spoilage.

## POULTRY, FISH AND SHELLFISH

**Poultry.** In 1955 the Food and Drug Administration (FDA) approved the use of not over 10 parts per million (ppm) of chlortetra-

cycline (CTC) or oxytetracycline (OTC) in the ice-slush used for chilling eviscerated birds. No part of the finished product may contain over 7 ppm. If the birds are fresh-killed, clean and promptly eviscerated, the *"shelf life"** of the antibiotic-treated products is considerably extended. The advisability of the use of antibiotics for such purposes has been questioned and is now very carefully controlled.

Standards of hygiene and cleanliness surrounding the processing of antibiotic-treated poultry are stringent and are prescribed by the FDA and the Poultry Inspection Branch, U.S. Department of Agriculture. These requirements are necessary to prevent the substitution of cheap and easy antibiotic treatment for expensive and laborious cleanliness and sanitation.

**Fish.** As is true of the flesh of mammals, the deep tissues of freshly killed, healthy fish are sterile or nearly so. Autolysis is slow in fish muscle. It is common practice on commercial fish boats or landing places to gut fish immediately and pack them in ice. The surfaces become contaminated with a variety of bacteria from the skin, scales and intestines of the fish, the decks and cutting boards, and other environmental sources including ice and wash water in tanks.

**Influence of Refrigeration Temperatures.** Failure or delay of refrigeration is one of the commonest causes of spoilage of any nonsterile food. Another is overlong holding at refrigerator temperatures several degrees *above* zero instead of *at* or *below* 0°. Bacterial spoilage of many refrigerated foods may occur twice as rapidly at 5° C. as at −1° C. At temperatures above 5° C. psychrophiles grow well. Many microorganisms not definitely classed as psychrophiles can also grow to a significant extent at low temperatures. Maximum numbers of live bacterial cells accumulate *slowly* at the lower temperature. When the refrigerated products are afterward gradually warmed for use, these enormous active populations (along with their accumulated enzymes, and other growth products) act very rapidly indeed to effect spoilage.

Psychrophilic organisms commonly associated with spoilage of recently caught fish include species of *Pseudomonas, Achromobacter,* coliforms, and sometimes *Clostridium.* Usually present but less active in spoilage are *Micrococcus, Flavobacterium* and *Corynebacterium.*

**Antibiotics in Fish.** Chlorinated water, ice

---

*Removed from the shell.

*Period during which the product remains exposed for sale, frozen or not, in an apparently fresh, wholesome and acceptable condition.

with calcium chloride, and sodium nitrite have been much used to preserve fresh fish. Admixture of antibiotics to the flaked ice in which freshly caught fish are packed keeps the product, if cleanly prepared, in a perfectly fresh state, even unrefrigerated, for days.

In 1959 the FDA permitted the use of chlortetracycline in raw, whole or gutted fish, shucked scallops and unpeeled shrimp, to a maximum concentration of 5 ppm in any part of the product. The same remarks apply to the use of antibiotics in fish as to their uses in meat and poultry (see foregoing paragraphs).

**Shellfish.**   Under market conditions shellfish are often rather heavily contaminated with dirt from the shells and from benches at which *shucking* (removal of shells) is done. The flora includes marine species similar to those found on fish, organisms from soil and from equipment used in handling. If the water in which they have grown has a rich bacterial flora, the shell liquor may contain considerable numbers of various harmless bacteria.

Oysters, mussels and some other shellfish fatten on sewage, and have long been known as vectors of typhoid fever if taken from polluted waters. Typhoid bacilli may live for two weeks or longer in live and in shucked oysters. Formerly common, typhoid due to shellfish is now very rare. Uncooked shellfish are vectors of enteric viruses, especially that of epidemic hepatitis, and they should be regarded with suspicion in respect to polio and other viruses. In the United States, state and government supervision of the shellfish beds has virtually removed infected shellfish from the market. It has recently been shown that fluids inside the shells of steamed clams may not always reach temperatures high enough to inactivate the heat-stable virus of epidemic hepatitis.

Among the bacteria that may be present in shellfish are the coliform group. These are not harmful per se, but represent potentially dangerous sewage pollution. Tests for the coliform group of bacteria in shell liquor, or in the liquid around shucked shellfish, are made in much the same manner as tests are made for this group in drinking water. The results are expressed in a similar manner. However, coliforms in shellfish may be entirely nonsewage in origin if the shellfish are taken from clean beds. Details of procedure may be found in "Recommended Procedures for the Bacteriological Examination of Sea Water and Shellfish," published (1962) by the American Public Health Association.

Oysters to be offered for sale raw are generally *floated* (allowed to remain for some hours or days) in clean chlorinated water. In the process they pass a large volume of the clean water through and around their bodies and thus greatly reduce their bacterial content.

### FRUITS AND VEGETABLES

The principles underlying the microbiology of fresh meat and fish products apply equally to fresh vegetables and fruits. That is to say, the internal tissues of whole, healthy plants and fruits contain very few bacteria, but contamination of the exterior surfaces by microorganisms from the soil, hands and packages occurs. Vegetables growing in the soil, such as root crops, have adhering to them soil saprophytes such as species of *Bacillus, Pseudomonas* and many others, depending on the nature of the soil. These soil organisms are usually held in check by washing, drying, exposure of the surfaces of the vegetables to sunlight, and by refrigeration.

Intact vegetable skins free from superficial water resist invasion of microorganisms for considerable periods, especially if kept in a cool, dry place. Nonsucculent vegetables with whole skins, such as turnips and potatoes, will stand storage better than soft, succulent, nonacid vegetables and fruits like lettuce, asparagus, spinach and ripe peaches, the juices of which offer good pabulum to microorganisms. Such soft vegetables soon autolyze and then decay. Invasion and decomposition are retarded by gentle handling and storage under cool, dry conditions.

### 46.3   EGGS AND EGG PRODUCTS

These may be considered under two general headings: (a) shell eggs (fresh or storage); (b) egg products such as liquid eggs; eggs that are frozen, dried or whole; egg whites and yolks; and eggs that are salted, plain, sugared, desugared, or fermented.

### SHELL EGGS

As soon as an egg is laid, the outer surface becomes contaminated. If, as is the practice in many large-scale poultry plants, the eggs are laid by clean, healthy hens on a clean wire frame and automatically collected immediately, contamination is at a minimum. The sanitary and keeping qualities of such eggs (and of commercial egg products derived from them) are clearly superior to those of eggs laid in damp, mud-and-feces-fouled straw nests and collected perhaps once a day (or every two or three days!).

Surface microorganisms are prevented from entering the egg for some days largely by the dried, mucilaginous surface coat, a sort of natural varnish.

Molds and some bacteria can grow on the outer mucinous coating if eggs are stored in humid atmospheres (above 70 per cent saturation) at ordinary climatic temperatures. The microorganisms eventually penetrate the shell and contaminate the interior. These give the eggs "off" odors and tastes and unsightly appearance. Eventually the mucinous protective film is entirely decomposed and the interior of the eggs is overwhelmingly invaded, with consequent decay.

The flora of stale or bad eggs is largely of fecal and soil origin and includes the various saprophytes listed elsewhere.

**Pseudomonas and Pyoverdine.**   Early spoilage of eggs stored at 15° C. is often due to *Pseudomonas,* especially *P. fluorescens* and *P. ovalis* from soil or dirty wash water. These bacteria impart "musty" tastes and odors to so-called *fresh* eggs long before overt, late-stage decomposition develops. These bacteria produce a fluorescent pigment called *pyoverdine* that can readily be detected by the ingenious expedient of examining eggs, shell or liquid, or extracts of liquid products, in ultraviolet light. Higher than normal fluorescence indicates heavy growth of *Pseudomonas* and usually other bacteria, incipient spoilage and low commercial quality.

**Infection of Eggs.**   Eggs may contain pathogenic bacteria when laid, even though the hen *seems* healthy. *Salmonella* species are commonly found. These bacteria have at times caused serious outbreaks of gastroenteritis. *Salmonella* may be detected by means of selective cultivation and fluorescent-antibody staining.

### EGG PRODUCTS

In commerce, the best (freshest) eggs are sold in the shell, while second or lower grade eggs are used for liquid, frozen or dried products. Plate or direct microscopic counts of such egg products may run from a million to a billion or more per gram. This does not necessarily make the eggs unfit for use in cooking, any

more than high bacterial counts destroy the commercial value of lower grades of milk. The problem is one of profit and loss. Egg products are a picnic for microorganisms, just as are milk, crabmeat and ground meat. If the egg products are not promptly frozen, refrigerated or dried, the heavy initial contamination quickly ruins them.

**Liquid Eggs.**   Egg whites are often sold separately. To improve their keeping quality they (and some other food products) are often heavily inoculated with the nonproteolytic *Escherichia coli* or, better, with *Saccharomyces cerevisiae.* The whites are held at about 28° C. for 24 to 48 hours. Glucose in the whites, main source of energy for putrefactive organisms, is thus promptly removed by fermentation with nonputrefactive *E. coli* or yeast. The whites must be initially clean or they will spoil during the intentional fermentation.

## 46.4   BREAD

The better grades of bakers' bread are produced by allowing bakers' yeast (varieties of *Saccharomyces cerevisiae*) to ferment sugars (glucose, maltose, sucrose) in a mixture (*dough*) consisting mainly of flour and water (or milk), with some salt. In commercial baking softening and hygroscopic agents, and flavoring, raisins, caraway seeds, vitamins and shortening are commonly added. Small amounts of cane sugar are often included in home bread making, both for flavor and to stimulate fermentation.

The dough is a soggy, plastic mass at first. *S. cerevisiae* does not attack the starch in flour. However, the necessary amylases and proteinases from the grains are present in the flour. These enzymes hydrolyze the starch and proteins of the dough. Sometimes *malt* (Chapter 47; *Beer*) is added to aid this process. The products of the hydrolysis support growth of the yeast. Early growth of lactobacilli, derived from the grains, gives the dough an initial acidity which helps suppress undesirable organisms and favors yeast. The lactobacilli and yeast also contribute to the flavor and aroma of the bread.

The yeast, or *leaven* (L. *levare* = to raise), produces carbon dioxide, water and ethanol. The gas causes the bread to rise and gives it its foamy texture. Baking drives off the alcohol and partly dries and *sets* (firms) the bread.

**Leavens.**   An important phase of the work of the microbiologist in some bakeries is the preparation of leavens. Many bakeries maintain their own leavens as trade secrets. The leaven may consist of a pure culture of a selected strain of yeast cultivated massively in aerated wort made of malted grains (Chapter 47) or other starch derivatives. Many tons of yeast in dried, compressed cakes are prepared in commerce daily for use by brewers, bakers and in the home.

Leaven may also consist of a mixture of pure cultures of *aerogenic* (gas-producing) bacteria: *Aerobacter cloacae* (subgroup A), the hetero-fermentative *Lactobacillus brevis* and *Leuconostoc*, as well as yeasts. *Clostridium* species are undesirable in leaven because they produce rancid flavors. Bacterial leavens are used to prepare bread made of sour dough (sauerteig), and "self-rising" or salt-rising breads. Such leavens often consist of previous lots of sour dough and are fortuitous mixtures; the standby of the old-time prospector, or "sourdough," of Alaska.

**Microorganisms in Bread.**   Most organisms in bread, aside from those added as leaven, appear to come originally from the flour or meal and include the familiar list of the environmental saprophytes. Bacterial counts of flour range from a few hundred thousands to several millions per gram. These organisms, especially molds, can cause spoilage in the stored product, especially under humid conditions.

During ordinary baking most of the vegetative forms of molds, yeasts and bacteria are killed. Heat-resistant bacterial spores and conidia of molds may survive. Temperatures inside the loaf of baking bread rarely rise much above 80° C.

ROPY BREAD.   If bread is made with ingredients containing large numbers of spores of slime-forming species of *Bacillus* (*B. polymyxa* and *B. pumilis,* some of these can survive baking and may grow in the bread, producing a mucinous slime. When the bread is broken apart this slime is drawn into long threads, resulting in a defective product called *ropy bread*. These difficulties with bacterial spores may be largely eliminated by cleanliness and modern methods of inducing germination of spores before baking (Chapter 31).

Moldy bread is usually the result of extraneous contamination of cut surfaces or crust by hands, dust and knives, followed by holding under humid conditions at household temperatures. Slight surface growth of mold gives bread a musty odor and taste; some species of mold produce toxins (aflatoxin).

**Bread in the Kitchen.**   Since bread is not sterile it should be cooled promptly after baking. The wise housewife keeps bread in the refrigerator in warm, humid weather. Wrapping bread in waxed paper helps keep the bread clean and prevents drying out, but conserves a humid atmosphere and favors growth of molds and bacteria, even if refrigerated.

Nonsporeforming pathogenic bacteria cannot survive proper baking of bread but may be introduced by unsanitary handling after baking.

## 46.5   SOME FERMENTED FOODS

As noted elsewhere, soil and plants harbor, among many other microorganisms, numerous species of lactic-acid bacteria such as *Lactobacillus, Leuconostoc* and *Pediococcus*. These can ferment the carbohydrates and metabolize the other nutrients in the tissues, sap and juices of green plants. This is the basis of the making of several kinds of fermented plant foods: ensilage for cattle; sauerkraut and pickles for humans. The methods of preparing each kind of food differ somewhat in form, but the principles and microorganisms are identical, or very similar, in all three processes. The preparation of ensilage for cattle is representative.

**Ensilage.**   Finely chopped, partly mature plants such as corn stalks or alfalfa are tightly packed in tall cylindrical tanks (*silos*). Microorganisms of many kinds start to grow in the plant juices and ferment the carbohydrates. As fermentation proceeds, the material becomes warm and acid. The heat can be reduced if the rate of oxidation is decreased (exclusion of free oxygen) by tight packing. Oxygen is used up rapidly so that molds and other strict aerobes soon cease growth. Only facultative and strict anaerobes continue.

In the first stages probably the Enterobacteriaceae and other rapidly growing nonaciduric but fermentative microorganisms predominate. These are undesirable since many produce gas and unpleasant flavors. As acidity increases they subside, and the more aciduric homofermentative lactic-acid bacteria predominate. These produce more lactic acid with small amounts of other products of fermentation (diacetyl and other volatile substances) which give an aroma and flavor to ensilage that is relished by cattle. The last stages of the fermentation and final increase in acidity are caused by the very acidophilic and aciduric lactobacilli, e.g., *L. delbrueckii* and *L. plantarum.*

After three or four weeks, the process slows and the fermented mass gradually cools. Carbon dioxide is produced during the fermentation process and often settles in the lower part of silos, so that a person ignorant of this may die if he stays in the depths of a poorly ventilated silo.

It has been suggested that a desirable type of fermentation in silos may be facilitated by introducing cultures of various fermentative bacteria, such as *Streptococcus lactis* or *Lactobacillus* sp., as the material is packed. Under natural conditions various other organisms are doubtless involved, including the bacteria of the soil. In some sections of the country molasses is added to promote fermentation by the acid-formers, and to improve palatability.

If too much soil is introduced with the fodder, undesirable and excessive putrefactive processes may spoil the product. For example, butyric-acid organisms such as *Clostridium butyricum* get in and ruin the silage by producing butyric acid, which makes it rancid. The action of such organisms constitutes a "disease" of silage. *Cl. botulinum,* a soil anaerobe forming a deadly exotoxin, has also at times caused much damage to livestock by its growth in silos.

**Sauerkraut.** In the production of this savory delicacy pure cultures of lactobacilli are sometimes used to aid the process. Commonly, however, the fermentation is allowed to proceed naturally. Salt is placed between layers of shredded cabbage as it is packed in large crocks or barrels. The salt inhibits undesirable bacteria and draws out the juices of the cabbage. Wooden frames are placed on the cabbage to keep it submerged (anaerobic). Except for the salt, sauerkraut is analogous to silage. Only facultative, anaerobic, aciduric and acidophilic and thermoduric forms not sensitive to salinities of two per cent or higher can survive. During the first two to five days species of *Leuconostoc,* especially *L. mesenteroides,* are common. Acids, esters and diacetyl give pleasant aromas and flavors. Temperatures near 70° F. favor the best fermentations. Fermentation is complete in two to three months.

**Pickles.** Fermentation by mixtures of organisms normally present, in a manner analogous to the manufacture of ensilage and sauerkraut, is part of the processing of pickles, ripe olives and the like. The process is made very selective by progressively increasing salt concentrations up to 30 per cent.

The action of the lactic acid, brine and microbial metabolism change the color, consistency and flavor of the cucumbers, olives, etc. In making pickles, after 8 to 10 weeks the vat is emptied and the pickles, now called *salt stock,* are packed in fluid containing vinegar, sugar and various flavorings, spices, dill, and so on.

Slimeforming organisms such as *Leuconostoc mesenteroides;* sporeforming bacilli; pectinase-formers that destroy vegetable tissues; organisms that destroy lactic acid; molds and other hydrolytic species may ruin the pickles if temperatures remain long near 20° C. or if salinity is too low. Stock to be used for dill pickles (low in acid and salt) is particularly liable to such spoilage. Methods of prevention of spoilage with organic acids are discussed on page 577.

## 46.6  PRESERVATION OF FOODS

Methods of food preservation are of two general classes: (1) *Bactericidal* or *sterilizing* methods, involving canning and such processes as making jams, jellies, and preserves (i.e., heating processes). The use of highly penetrating, microbicidal, ionizing radiations will also probably take its place among these methods in the future. (2) *Bacteriostatic* methods include: drying, freezing, refrigeration at temperatures slightly above freezing, various types of pickling, brining, salting, smoking, the use of antibiotics as already described, and other preservatives such as various organic acids.

Modern home or commercial canners have to consider not only the killing of bacteria likely to cause spoilage or disease but also the effect of the processing on palatability and appearance of the food. If canned foods are processed long enough they can be absolutely sterilized. This may require such prolonged heating in steam under pressure (autoclaving) (especially of nonacid foods) that the foods become mushy and discolored and have bitter flavors. Prolonged heating also adds to the cost of canning. The aim of the canner, then, is to heat as little as possible, consistent with safety from food poisoning and loss from spoilage.

From the standpoint of food poisoning the only organism likely to resist autoclaving is *Clostridium botulinum.* Even the most resistant spores of this species are killed by heating at 121° C. for 20 minutes at pH 7.0.

Acidity greatly reduces the time and temperature necessary to preserve foods by heat even though they may contain resistant spores. Canned tomatoes, rhubarb and acid fruits (pH 3.5 to 4.5), for example, require only a few minutes at 100° C. to preserve them. On the contrary, nearly neutral materials such as meats, corn, spinach and beans require much longer periods depending on solidity and size of packs, and preheating. The cans are often preheated to 100° C. and sealed in a vacuum (Table 46.1).

**TABLE 46.1 ACIDITY (pH) RANGE OF SOME REPRESENTATIVE FOODS**

| Range of acidity | pH | Examples in order of acidity |
|---|---|---|
| Very acid | 2.5 to 3.5 | Lemons<br>Cranberries<br>Rhubarb<br>Grapes<br>Pineapples |
| Moderately acid | 3.6 to 4.5 | Oranges<br>Apples<br>Tomatoes<br>Pears |
| Slightly acid | 4.6 to 6.8 | Carrots<br>Squash<br>Spinach<br>Fish<br>Beef<br>Poultry and eggs<br>Corn<br>Shellfish |

The effectiveness of expert canning is well illustrated by the history of several cans of meat prepared in London several years after the process of canning was devised by Appert, in 1805 in Paris, at the request by Napoleon Bonaparte for a means of preserving foods for his troops. A can of roast veal prepared in London and dated 1823 was carried the next year on the expedition of H.M.S. *Fury* (Sir Edward Parry, R.N., Captain) in search of a Northwest Passage. The *Fury* was crushed in the ice and was abandoned, with stores including the can in question, for four years in the arctic. The *Fury* was visited by another ship in 1829 and the stores were brought back to London. When the can was opened, in 1958, after 125 years, the meat was found in good, unspoiled condition although the fat had emulsified somewhat. Also in 1958, a can of plum pudding prepared in London in 1900 and kept in South Africa was found on opening to be in excellent, unspoiled condition.

**Commercially Sterile Foods.** Canned foods may contain spores of organisms that are viable but fail to grow under ordinary conditions of storage. These foods may be said to be *virtually sterile* or *preserved by heating* or *commercially sterile*. For example, spores of nonpathogenic *Bacillus stearothermophilus* (designated in the trade as No. 1518) and *Clostridium thermosaccharolyticum* (No. 3814) generally withstand ordinary processing. The spores of these species are among the most heat-resistant of all. They are often used to test the efficacy of heating. Both can cause sour spoilage of canned goods. However, being obligate thermophils, they do not grow unless the food is stored in a *very* warm place (55° to 70° C.). Under ordinary conditions of storage the food is, from a practical standpoint, sterile. In any case, care must be taken to eliminate the spores of *Clostridium botulinum,* cause of deadly botulism (Chapter 32).

## PRESERVATION BY FREEZING

Frozen foods represent one of the greatest money-exchange items in the American dietary. These foods may be classified for microbiological purposes as (1) uncooked and (2) precooked.

**Uncooked Frozen Foods.** These are fresh foods to be eaten raw (e.g., frozen berries) or to be cooked (e.g., frozen steaks). At the time of freezing, fresh foods have on or in them the original microbial flora plus any that are added during handling, packaging or processing. Factors affecting the microbial content of uncooked frozen foods include: freshness, condition at time of freezing, pH, preliminary processing, packaging, time and temperature of frozen storage, kind of food (protein, starch, comminuted). If foods are dirty or have been held long at room temperatures prior to freezing, they may be on the verge of spoilage at the time of freezing and the microbial counts may be very high. However, since freezing and storage at −25° C. soon destroys many bacteria, low (deceptively favorable) plate counts may be obtained with long-frozen food that was initially of low quality. In general, storage at higher temperatures (0° C. to −10° C.) is more bactericidal, especially in acid foods such as orange juice, than storage at lower temperatures: −25° C.* in freezer lockers to −75° C. in carbon dioxide ice.

*Vacuum drying* after nearly instantaneous freezing ("freeze-drying") (analogous to *Lyophilization* used to preserve viruses, bacteria, etc, Chapter 19) appears to offer practical usefulness in the preservation of foods.

As with milk, a direct microscopic count on frozen foods reveals much concerning initial numbers of now-dead bacteria. Microorganisms that will not grow in ordinary plate-count media are revealed. The same is applicable to foods preserved by any of the methods described farther on. High microscopic count and low plate count suggests food of initially poor bacterial quality.

**Precooked Frozen Foods.** Some precooked frozen foods, such as certain "TV dinners," are mixtures of cooked or partly cooked components

---

*The approximate temperature of the home freezing locker.

that are not further cooked before packaging and freezing. Some of these foods are meant to be oven-baked before serving. Others, such as meat pies, are said to be ready to eat after mere warming. Bacterial counts on cleanly produced, promptly frozen, cooked foods are relatively low. Excessively high bacterial counts, especially high direct microscopic counts, indicate staleness or dirtiness of ingredients or processing.

Baking meat pies (a representative pre-cooked food) does not necessarily sterilize them. Commercial-size meat pies held at 425° F. for 40 minutes have very low counts but the same temperature for 20 minutes is wholly inadequate and may, by merely warming the interior, actually incubate the pathogens in the pies.

**Sanitation in Frozen Foods.** Virtually all frozen foods are subject to some sort of contamination before freezing. The usual environmental saprophytes are found. Since many foods contain animal products, and are handled by people, fecal streptococci, coliforms and staphylococci are frequently found. The full sanitary significance of these indicator organisms in frozen foods is not yet fully clarified, but they are generally regarded with suspicion.

As indicators, enterococci tend to persist in contaminated frozen foods, while the coliforms tend to diminish in numbers and disappear with continued frozen storage.

**Thawing of Frozen Foods.** Freezing during preparation and thawing for use should be completed within two to four hours under ordinary conditions. Most frozen foods remain wholesome so long as they remain frozen. On thawing, frozen foods undergo rapid deterioration because the natural resistance of fully active tissues is reduced or absent. Autolysis occurs and microbial decomposition can set in with little delay at room temperature. Pathogens can grow at summer temperatures (70° to 100° F.).

Interruptions to electric current supplying frozen-food lockers may cause serious spoilage if long enough for frozen foods to thaw. Indeed, food refrozen after being thawed without the consumer's knowledge may be a very dangerous product. Large masses of ice in the bottom of the package suggest that thawing and refreezing have occurred.

**General Rule.** A sure means of making any food, canned, frozen or otherwise, safe from infectious organisms and from botulinal (but *not* staphylococcal) toxin is to heat all of it to 100° C. for at least 15 minutes just before eating.

As a matter of experience of over three decades, food poisoning (botulinal or staphylococcal) and food infection (salmonellosis, shigel-losis) due to *commercially* prepared foods are rare (but by no means unknown!) in the United States.

## CHEMICAL PRESERVATIVES

*Several organic acids* and their salts: acetic, lactic, benzoic, salicylic, butyric, caproic, sorbic and others, have marked microbistatic and microbicidal action. As previously indicated, the effectiveness of these acids is dependent mainly on the toxic action of the *undissociated* acid or salt. Two factors that diminish dissociation of these acids or their salts are salinity and low pH. The higher the salinity and the lower the pH the more effective these organic acids are as preservatives. Undesirable *yeasts* and *molds* in brined or fermented pickles, in sauerkraut, and in unfermented acid products, such as fresh apple juice and tomato catsup, are well controlled by the addition of 0.05 per cent to 0.10 per cent sodium benzoate or sorbic acid (or sorbate). *Bacterial* growth, desirable or undesirable, is not significantly affected by sorbate.

*Sodium nitrate or nitrite,* or mixtures of these, are commonly added to sodium chloride in mixtures for curing meats (corned beef, ham). Whether the nitrates or nitrites have any bactericidal or bacteriostatic action per se seems to be undecided, but meat packers find less spoilage when these salts are used. They appear to have an adjuvant action in acid solutions (most cured meats are acid, pH near 5.8) and on the preservative effect of sodium chloride. Nitrites and nitrates are particularly desired because they give good red color to meat.

*Sulfur dioxide* has a bleaching effect desired in some fruits and also suppresses growth of yeasts and molds. It is applied as a gas to treat drying fruits and is also used in molasses.

## OTHER METHODS OF PRESERVATION

**High Osmotic Pressures.** The salting and brining of fish, corning of beef and sugar-curing of hams and brining of green olives are examples of the use of solutions of high osmotic pressure for food preservation. Salt concentrations of 20 to 30 per cent are commonly used in brines; 50 to 70 per cent of sugar, in sugar syrups. Their preservative action depends almost entirely on their withdrawal of water from microorganisms. Other uses of sugar are in the making of jams and jellies. Heating of jams and jellies greatly reduces the initial count of microorganisms and enhances the effectiveness of sugar.

Dry salt and sugar-cured products will spoil if allowed to stand in very humid atmospheres, since they are not sterile and since sugar and salt are strongly hygroscopic. Spoilage of salted products is sometimes caused by halophilic microorganisms in the brines or salt. Clean ingredients and equipment help prevent losses due to spoilage. Molds and yeasts are causes of early spoilage of sugared and salted products since these fungi grow well in solutions of high osmotic pressure.

**Drying.** Drying of foods is another time-tested means of withdrawing water from spoilage microorganisms and their environment. Drying is largely microbistatic in effect; therefore, dried foods are not sterile and will decompose promptly if kept warm in humid atmospheres.

**Smoking.** Meats and fish to be smoked are usually first salt-cured to prevent rapid deterioration, since smoke curing is slow. Modern "streamlined" injection processes preserve and flavor more rapidly than salt or smoke curing. The preservative factors in wood smoke are various cresols, a mixture of formic, acetic and other organic acids and alcohol ("pyroligneous" acid), and formaldehyde, all of which are bactericidal or bacteriostatic substances. These are gradually absorbed in small quantities by the tissues exposed to the smoke. The meat is thus cured and rendered impervious to the action of most microorganisms, as well as given an agreeable aromatic flavor. Kept dry, the meat is preserved almost indefinitely. In warm, humid weather it may become moldy and rancid, especially on the surface.

**Radiations.** As pointed out elsewhere, streams of electrons (cathode rays) under sufficient potential (1 million volts or more) are potentially lethal ionizing radiations. Beta rays and gamma rays from radioactive cobalt and other wastes of atomic research have similar properties.

Fresh perishable foods (as well as culture media, surgical supplies and drugs) in packages, e.g., plastics, that can be readily penetrated by such rays can be sterilized *without heat* and kept in their moist, "fresh" condition with *no refrigeration.* The possibility of keeping foods fresh without refrigeration, whether by antibiotics or irradiation or other means, obviously offers enormous advantages.

The necessary amounts of radiation are expensive and produce undesirable changes in flavor, color, consistency, and possibly in vitamin and other nutrient content in many foods. However, nonsterilizing amounts of radiation can be used economically as a preliminary treatment. Spores are sensitized to heat by radiation. The use of irradiation for pasteurizing (not sterilizing) as a means of reducing spoilage is still in the experimental stage.

## 46.7  MICROBIOLOGICAL EXAMINATION OF FOODS

**Quantitative Microbiology of Food.** Estimating the total numbers of bacteria in milk, water, ground meat, vegetables, frozen foods and the like involves basically the same procedures. The main differences lie in methods of collecting, preparing and measuring the sample. These steps are guided by the nature of the material. Fluids are diluted and plated directly, as is milk. In examining solid foods such as meat or vegetables, washings, swabbings or scrapings from measured surfaces may be collected and shaken in measured diluting fluid. Deep samples of solid foods are cut from within after sterilizing the surface with a hot spatula.

**Colony Counts.** Any solid material is first weighed and then comminuted in a Waring blendor or similar device to get the microorganisms of the sample of food *into a fluid suspension.* This can then be diluted and put into Petri plates with "Standard Methods" agar for colony counting. The diluted sample must not be too cloudy or contain visible particles since particles confuse colony enumeration. For inoculation into tubes of broth, clarity of inoculum is not so essential. Highly acid products should be neutralized.

**Direct Microscopic Count.** The direct microscopic examination is very useful, both quantitatively and qualitatively.

It is made in much the same manner as the Breed count for milk. High microscopic counts and low plate counts on a food generally indicate that an initially poor product has been treated in some microbicidal manner or that the organisms seen will not grow in the medium provided for the plate count. Numbers of yeasts and molds and of other special morphological types that do not grow on the routine media may also be estimated in the direct count.

**Qualitative Microbiology of Food.** Methods of examining water or milk for the coliform group or for fecal streptococci typify *qualitative* procedures in examining foods for these groups. Tubes of selective broths (for determining MPN) or of selective plating medium (for colony counts) may be used. The same sorts of media and procedures are used, with minor modifications, as for milk.

In several dried and frozen foods, fecal streptococci appear to be a more dependable indicator of fecal contamination than coliforms. The coliform organisms are so ubiquitous that their presence in many foods does not accurately indicate fecal pollution at all. Further, they do not survive in preserved foods, especially acid foods, as do the enterococci.

In adapting microbiological procedures to the examination of foods the nature of the medium used, the temperature (thermophilic, mesophilic or psychrophilic) and conditions of incubation (aerobic or anaerobic), and other factors (acidity, salinity) must be modified to suit the flora. For example, if a plate count of yeasts and molds is desired, plate with acidified potato-dextrose agar (pH 3.5) or with malt agar (pH 3.5). For lactic acid bacteria, use orange-juice agar (pH 5.5). Other special media for coliforms and staphylococci are suggested in the literature cited. Numbers of bacterial spores may be estimated (not accurately counted) by heating the material to 90° C. for 10 minutes before plating. Other selective procedures will occur to the ingenious microbiologist and can be adapted to various problems.

## 46.8  FOOD SPOILAGE: DOMESTIC

The two principal aims of the domestic kitchen director are much the same as those of the commercial food handler: (a) prevention of spoilage; (b) prevention of food infection and food poisoning.

**Prevention of Spoilage.** The housewife relies mainly on low temperatures, osmotic pressure (e.g., in jams or jellies), and on heating for preservation of foods. As a domestic economist she is interested in saving from spoilage those foods bought in quantities at lower-than-usual prices, or bought only during weekly or monthly trips to food stores. The culinary expert is also interested in "left-overs." The surest mark of high achievement in the art and economics of the kitchen is the skillful and appetizing use of foods that are kept from one meal to another—the pot of good soup (excellent bacteriological medium!) that is saved for tomorrow's dinner, the left-over porridge or bread for pudding, and so on. All are valuable assets to the resourceful domestic economist. But they are also subject to spoilage by microorganisms.

The household refrigerators or freezing cabinets offer the readiest means for saving foods. When these places are overcrowded or unavailable, spoilage can be retarded by reheating con-taminated foods in covered vessels and *not opening* the vessels until more of the food is needed. For example, the pot of soup or other nonacid food may be brought to a boil for a few minutes in a vessel with a good dust-tight cover. The heat kills any vegetative forms of microorganisms and the spores of wild yeasts and molds that might have gotten in while it was cool and uncovered. A good many bacterial spores will be killed also, but some will survive. However, these probably will not grow sufficiently to cause spoilage for 18 hours or more. If the soup should be brought to a boil the next day, the cover not having been removed in the meanwhile, virtual fractional sterilization has been accomplished and the food should keep for some time.

With solid foods not immersed in water, such as a roast of meat, spoilage tends to occur mainly on the surfaces. Much of this is introduced by utensils. Clean utensils introduce less contamination than soiled ones. If the cooled roast is reheated in a very hot oven for a few minutes after the meal, so as to cook only the exterior, and is left in the oven without opening the door, thus avoiding recontamination from the air, surface growth is definitely checked and the meat may remain good for some days, depending on the extent and depth to which initial contamination was introduced. In reheating food in this manner it is desirable to use a self-basting roaster or other covered dish to prevent drying out of the food.

If food is not reheated it should be promptly placed in an efficient refrigerator. It is always poor practice to allow perishable food, including milk, to stand in the warm kitchen overnight—incubating microorganisms into the millions, possibly forming large amounts of toxin—and then put it in the refrigerator next morning. This is locking the barn after the horse is stolen. When feasible cooking of moist foods that have stood more than about 2 hours at temperatures above 15 to 20° C. is desirable.

**Prevention of Infection.** With respect to infection of foods with enteric pathogens the "four F's" are easily borne in mind and are particularly pertinent:

$$\text{Feces} \underset{\searrow \text{Flies}}{\overset{\nearrow \text{Fingers} \searrow}{}} \text{Foods.}$$

With respect to respiratory pathogens, one may remember the "four S's":

$$\text{Saliva} \underset{\searrow \text{Strep.}}{\overset{\nearrow \text{Staph.} \searrow}{}} \text{Sickness.}$$

Proper attention to handwashing after toilet and after nose-blowing is an easy and effective prophylactic against respiratory and enteric organisms. Most bacterial pathogens of the enteric tract and of the respiratory tract can grow luxuriantly in common nonacid foods.

## 46.9 INDUSTRIAL FOOD SPOILAGE

Industrial spoilage of foods may be classified as of the general type or of the specific type.

**General Spoilage.** This is a result of growth of a heterogeneous mixture of various types. Contamination with mixtures of organisms found in soil, dust, decks of fishing boats, floors of slaughter houses, canneries and dairies is really the most difficult to control. It cannot be dealt with by means of a single, specific measure designed especially to eliminate one particular source of difficulty such as a single contaminated piece of machinery. It can be eradicated only by measures of general cleanliness. These may involve expensive manpower, steam and hot water, general disinfection on a very wide scale, and costly measures against continuous reintroduction of dirt.

**Specific Spoilage.** This often presents very challenging detective problems in diagnosis of "diseases" of food products analogous to Pasteur's "diseases" of wine and beer.

Sometimes conditions in food manufacturing or preserving processes become especially favorable to the luxuriant growth of a single species of organism. This can then dominate the flora of a given food, or of a preserving or pickling fluid, and may produce some striking alteration of taste, odor, pigment, sliminess, or the like. A good example is ropy bread caused by the use of flour heavily contaminated with spores of a slime-producing *Bacillus* species. Butter sometimes acquires a rancid, fishy or oily taste or odor because of the growth in it of large numbers of some particular organism, such as *Pseudomonas fluorescens*, which hydrolyzes fat or produces other bad-smelling and bad-tasting compounds. Perhaps a single dirty churn may have heavily seeded the whole lot of butter. Sometimes a red, blue or yellow or other color is imparted to milk or fish by heavy growth in it of a *Serratia* species, a *Pseudomonas* or a *Flavobacterium*. Orange juice sometimes acquires a buttery flavor because of certain diacetyl-producing species of *Lactobacillus*. Various spottings,

ammoniacal decompositions and peculiar types of fermentation are produced under special circumstances and by specific organisms. These spoilages are usually owing to the use of a stale product to begin with, or to a dirty tank, an implement or a particular lot of a preservative heavily contaminated with some organism that can grow in the particular food or circumstances involved. Usually the control of such specific types of spoilage is not too difficult once the organism is isolated and its growth peculiarities and source studied.

## SUPPLEMENTARY READING

Anellis, A., Grecz, N., Huber, D. A., Berkowitz, D., Schneider, M. D., and Simon, M.: Radiation sterilization of bacon for military feeding. Appl. Microbiol., *13*:37, 1965.

Burkwall, M. K., and Hartman, P. A.: Comparison of direct plating media for the isolation and enumeration of enterococci in certain frozen foods. Appl. Microbiol., *12*:18, 1964.

Cliver, D. O.: Food associated viruses. Health Lab. Sci., *4*:213, 1967.

Etchells, J. L., Costilow, R. N., Anderson, T. E., and Bell, T. A.: Pure culture fermentation of brined cucumbers. Appl. Microbiol., *12*:523, 1964.

Frazier, W. C.: Food Microbiology. 2nd ed. McGraw-Hill Book Co., New York. 1967.

Haglund, J. R., Ayres, J. C., Paton, A. M., Kraft, A. A., and Quinn, L. Y.: Detection of *Salmonella* in eggs and egg products with fluorescent antibody. Appl. Microbiol., *12*:447, 1964.

Hobbs, B. C.: Contamination of meat supplies. I and II. Monthly Bull. Min. of Health Pub. Health Lab. Serv., *24*:123, 1965.

Huhtanen, C. N., and Pensack, J. M.: Gnotobiotic silage. Appl. Microbiol., *11*:529, 1963.

Ingram, M., and Roberts, T. A., editors: Botulism 1966. Chapman & Hall, London. 1967.

Peterson, A. C., Black, J. G., and Gunderson, M. F.: Staphylococci in competition. V. Effect of eggs, eggs plus carbohydrates, and lipids on staphylococcal growth. Appl. Microbiol., *12*:83, 1964.

Sharf, J. M., editor: Recommended Methods for the Microbiological Examination of Foods. 2nd ed. Amer. Pub. Health Assn., New York. 1966.

Stumbo, C. R.: Thermobacteriology in Food Processing. *In:* Food Sciences and Technology, Vol. 2. Academic Press, New York. 1965.

Surkiewicz, B. F.: Bacteriological survey of the frozen prepared foods Industry. I. Frozen cream-type pies. Appl. Microbiol., *14*:21, 1966.

Williams, Jr., L. P., and Newell, K. W.: Patterns of *Salmonella* excretion in market swine. Amer. J. Pub. Health, *57*:466, 1967.

York, G. K., and Vaughn, R. H.: Mechanisms in the inhibition of microorganisms by sorbic acid. J. Bact., *88*:411, 1964.

# Chapter 47

## INDUSTRIAL MICROBIOLOGY

Today microorganisms and their enzymes are the basis of industries grossing billions of dollars annually. Several are listed in Tables 47.1 and 47.2. Industrial processes based on microbial action are of several general types. Microorganisms may be cultivated:

A. In food products (e.g., fermented vegetable products and dairy products) for the purpose of *producing certain flavors, consistencies* and *nutritive values* in the products (Chapter 46);

B. In media where they decompose (ferment) various substrates (usually carbohydrates), *the products of the fermentation* (various alcohols, organic solvents, lactic, acetic and citric acids) being recovered, purified and sold;

C. In flavored nutritive solutions, notably fruit juices and extracts of grains that are fermented, the entire culture fluid (after clarification and processing) then becoming *beverages such as beer and wine;*

D. In contact with a specific substance such as a sex hormone (the chemical group of *steroids*) so that a single, specific enzyme of the microorganisms brings about a *specific transformation of the substrate molecule* into a molecule of another desired substance;

E. In media so that the *enzymes* or other substances that the organisms *synthesize* (amylase, protease, antibiotic) may be collected, purified and sold for commercial or medical use.

In addition to these uses, *organisms themselves* (principally yeasts, some algae) are sometimes cultivated *for use as food.* Such food products are generally used as feed for poultry and livestock. This is not as yet a large industry in the United States, where other foods are plentiful. However, in view of enormously increasing populations, the possibilities are being seriously considered and studied experimentally. As mentioned previously cultivation of certain eucaryotic algae. in waste materials as a source of oxygen and food in space and prolonged submarine travel is also under experimentation.

Microorganisms are sometimes used for *special industrial purposes* such as removal of certain sulfur compounds from petroleum, and for vitamin assay. These have highly specialized applications.

The *uncontrolled actions* of fortuitous *mixtures of microorganisms* in processes such as retting of flax, preparing hides for leather, and coffee-bean hulling are time-honored practices. They are now being replaced in more advanced industries by processes in which purified cultures or enzymes of the *effective* species in the mixtures are used under carefully controlled conditions. Since the older processes are not scientifically designed they are not discussed further here.

## 47.1 DEVELOPING AN INDUSTRIAL PROCESS

In developing an industrial process based upon the action of microorganisms many details must be given consideration. Important among these are the type of culture needed, cultural conditions and the adaptability of the organism to large-scale production.

**Purity and Nature of Cultures.** It must be ascertained whether absolutely pure cultures must be used, or whether the mere predominance of one organism is sufficient. This may be a deciding factor, as the cost of preparing and maintaining pure cultures and sterile apparatus throughout a process is relatively high.

**Cultural Conditions.** The organism must be able to grow well in the medium to be used

**TABLE 47.1   SOME MICROORGANISMS IMPORTANT IN INDUSTRY**

| Microorganisms | Raw Materials (Substrates) | Commercially Valuable Products | Nature of the Process |
|---|---|---|---|
| **Bacteria:** | | | |
| *Clostridium aceto-butylicum; Cl. sac-charoacetoperbutyl-icum* | Carbohydrate mashes; molasses | Butanol, acetone, ethanol, vitamin B$_2$ (riboflavin) | Fermentation |
| *Lactobacillus delbrueckii* | Various wastes containing glucose or lactose | Lactic acid | Fermentation |
| *Bacillus subtilis* | Various organic wastes of dairies, canneries | Amylase, protease | Aerobic or aerated tanks; synthesis |
| *Bacillus polymyxa* | Carbohydrate mashes | 2-3-butanediol | Aerobic; metabolic waste |
| *Leuconostoc mesenteroides* | Waste carbohydrate mashes | Dextran | Fermentation |
| *Leuconostoc citrovorum* | Dairy wastes with citrate | Diacetyl | Fermentation |
| *Acetobacter* sp. | Alcoholic liquors | Acetic acid (vinegar) | Aerobic; oxidation |
| *Acetobacter suboxydans* | Yeast extract with glucose, sorbitol, glycerol | Dihydroxyacetone, 5-ketogluconic acid, sorbose | Aerobic; metabolic wastes |
| *Streptomyces* sp. | Corn-steep liquor | Antibiotics | Aerobic; synthesis |
| **Yeasts and molds:** | | | |
| *Saccharomyces cerevisiae* | Various mashes of grain, molasses | Industrial alcohol, alcoholic beverages | Fermentation |
| *Aspergillus niger* | Carbohydrate mashes | Citric acid | Aerobic dissim; aerated tanks |
| *Penicillium notatum* | Corn-steep liquor | Penicillin | ” |
| *Rhizopus nigricans* | Corn-steep liquor and progesterone | 11α-hydroxyprogesterone | Aerobic; hydroxylation |
| *Curvularia lunata* | ” | Corticosterone | Aerobic; dihydroxylation |
| *Fusarium moniliforme* | Corn-steep liquor | Gibberellin | Aerobic; synthesis |

**TABLE 47.2   SOME INDUSTRIAL ENZYMES; THEIR SOURCES AND APPLICATIONS**

| Types of Enzymes | Source Microorganisms | Typical Industrial Applications or Products |
|---|---|---|
| Amylases (starch hydrolysis) | Malt, *Aspergillus* sp., *Bacillus* sp. | Bread; beer; whiskey; textile fibers; preparation of glucose syrups |
| Proteases (protein hydrolysis) | *Aspergillus* sp., *Bacillus* sp. | Clarifying (*chillproofing*) beer; whiskey making, leather, baking bread and crackers, meat tenderizers |
| Pectinases (hydrolysis of pectin) | *Aspergillus* sp. | Clarification of fruit juices |
| Glucose oxidase | *Penicillium notatum* | (1) Removal of glucose from eggs to be dried, to prevent fermentation; (2) removal of oxygen from canned fruits, dried milk, and other products subject to oxygen spoilage |
| Invertase | *Saccharomyces cerevisiae* | Preparation of soft-center candies (cordial cherries) |

and under the conditions of the process. This necessitates exact studies and careful control of *optimum* conditions of aerobiosis or anaerobiosis, temperature, nutrition and pH. Appropriate adjustments of the process and apparatus must be made to provide the necessary conditions.

**Productive Mutants.** The organisms selected must be such as will produce the desired substance(s) or results in the medium under the conditions furnished, in amounts sufficient to yield a profit. Some firms have "pet" strains of microorganisms that excel in producing certain products, such as butyl alcohol, certain antibiotics or itaconic acid, that they have "developed" (selected mutants) for these purposes. It has been found possible to induce industrially valuable mutations in microorganisms by ultraviolet radiations (Chapter 15). Where sexual processes are known to occur, the breeding of yeasts and molds for similar purposes is analogous to breeding of farm animals for special purposes.

**Medium or Raw Material.** The substrate or medium should support luxuriant growth of the organism to be used and it must be available constantly at costs compatible with profit. Expensive handling machinery may be needed for some substrates.

An important item is the possible necessity of a preliminary treatment such as liming of very acid yeast slops, distillery wastes, molasses and whey. Some substrates, such as sawdust or fiber, may need preliminary "digestion" with hot acid or alkali to hydrolyze them to fermentable substances. This all adds to the expense and time.

**Nature of the Process.** The more complicated and exacting the system of cultural details and preliminary heatings, dilutings and digestions, as well as the type of machinery (cracking stills, tanks, pumps) to handle the end- and by-products and the final wastes, the greater will be the cost and therefore the less the commercial practicability of any process. Any time-consuming aging or ripening process eats into profits. Sometimes, very desirable end- or by-products may be found in commercial fermentations, yet the cost of their recovery may be prohibitive.

**Preliminary Experimentation.** The microbiologist working with 10-ml. test-tube cultures may find many valuable things. When attempts are made to reproduce the test-tube experiments on a 100,000-gallon factory scale, however, the laboratory discoveries often fail to yield the promised result. Any process developed in the experimental laboratory must next prove its worth in the factory. A small-sized model, or pilot plant, is usually tried after the preliminary laboratory work. All may depend on such a seemingly far-removed detail as international relations. These may affect the cost of importation of some raw product essential to the process under investigation. Then the industrialist turns to home resources, goes to Washington, or *employs a resourceful microbiologist!*

The whole matter is a complex of microbiology, chemistry, engineering and economics. Only the microbiology can be discussed here. Many chemical and microbiological processes in use at present are patented and secret, and specific strains of bacteria, yeasts and molds, which are zealously guarded, are often carefully developed in the laboratories of manufacturing concerns. As a result of continuous and intensive industrial research, methods change or are superseded frequently.

## 47.2   TYPES OF FERMENTATION PROCESSES

Industrial fermentation processes may be divided into two main types: (1) batch fermentation and (2) continuous process. There are various combinations and modifications of these.

**Batch Fermentations.** A tank or fermentor is filled with the prepared *mash* (material to be fermented, e.g., diluted molasses, comminuted potatoes, digested corn cobs). The proper adjustments of pH, temperature, nutritive supplements and so on are made. In a pure-culture process, the mash is steam-sterilized, the entire fermentation tank sometimes being the autoclave. The inoculum, a *pure culture,* is added from a separate pure-culture apparatus. The fermentation proceeds. Some pressure may be maintained within the tank to prevent inward leakage of contamination and sometimes to maintain increased tension of special gasses. After the proper time, the contents of the fermentor are drawn off for further processing, the fermentor is cleaned, and the process begins over again. Each fermentation is a discontinuous process divided into *batches.*

**The Continuous-Growth Process.** In continuous-growth processes, the substrate is fed into a container continuously at a fixed rate. The cells grow (or enzymes act) continuously as the material passes through the apparatus. The organisms and process are said to be in a *steady state* or condition of *homeostasis.* The product or fully fermented mash is drawn off continuously. The engineering arrangements may be complex, permitting aeration, cooling or heating, adjustment of pH or addition of nutrients continuously during the process. There must also be means of controlling rate of growth, phase of growth curve, and removal of dead organisms. The culture must remain pure and must not undergo any variation.

One may conceive of such a process as taking place in a long pipe (actually it may be a rotating conical tank or series of connected tanks). At one end the prepared mash enters. It at once encounters the growing organisms. These act on the substrate as it flows through the system. At the stage at which the valuable product of the fermentation is at its maximum concentration, the fluid is drawn into receiving vessels for further processing (e.g., distillation). The animal alimentary tract may be thought of as a natural, continuous-growth process.

**Submerged Aerobic Cultures.** Many industrial processes, casually called "fermentations," are carried on by strictly aerobic microorganisms: for example, production of penicillin by *Penicillium notatum,* a strictly aerobic mold. In older aerobic processes it was necessary to furnish large surfaces of culture media exposed to air. The limitations of space, difficulties from contamination, and expense of hand labor can well be imagined, though little expense for power equipment was necessary. Now it is common commercial practice to carry on such "fermentations" in closed tanks with *submerged cultures.* Aerobic conditions are maintained by constant agitation of the contents of the tank with an *impeller* and constant *aeration* by forcing sterilized air through a porous *diffuser.* The flow of air through the tank removes gases such as ammonia and carbon dioxide. In each sort of process very careful adjustments of O-R potentials, mechanical agitation, ratio of dissolved oxygen to other ingredients in the medium, and pH are necessary. This is one of the many fascinating and potentially very lucrative fields for research in industrial microbiology (Fig. 47.1).

## 47.3   INDUSTRIAL ETHYL ALCOHOL MANUFACTURE

Much industrial ethyl alcohol is now made from by-products of *cracking* petroleum to make gasoline. However, the manufacture of ethyl alcohol from fermentation by yeasts is still an important industry. It serves to illustrate industrial fermentation processes in general. Crude molasses is often used as mash. It generally requires only to be diluted and the pH adjusted (usually with sulfuric acid) to 4.5. This pH is favorable to the yeast and unfavorable to many bacteria. A source of nitrogen such as ammonium

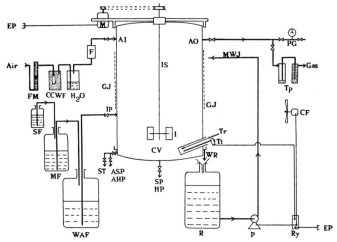

**Figure 47.1**   An example of an experimental laboratory pilot plant devised to obtain dense growths of *Brucella* sp. for immunization of cattle. The basic principles of submerged aerated growth are well illustrated, as is a typical pilot-plant setup. At left of the main tank (CV) are apparatuses for admitting sterilized air, and medium seeded with pure culture. At right of the tank are devices for controlling temperature of the culture tank. The various parts are: AI, air inlet; AO, air outlet; AHP, alternate harvesting point; ASP, alternate sampling point; CCWF, part of air filter; CF; cooling fan; CV, culture vessel; EP, electric plug; F, Seitz filter; FM, flow meter; GJ, gauze jacket; HP, harvesting point; I, impeller; IS, impeller shaft; IP, medium inlet point; M, motor; MF, medium flask; MWJ, multiple water jets; P, pump; PG, pressure gauge; R, reservoir; Ry, relay; SF, seed flask; SP, sampling point; ST, steam inlet point; Tp, trap; Tr, thermometer; Tt, thermostat; WAF, water and antifoam flask; WR, water return. (From van Drimmelen: Appl. Microbiol., vol. 6.)

sulfate or ammonium phosphate is usually added. The final solution is a richly nutrient carbohydrate culture medium or *mash*.

This is rather heavily inoculated with an aciduric and alcohol-resistant strain of yeast, the variety depending on the conditions under which the fermentation is to proceed and the exact end products desired. A good strain of *Saccharomyces cerevisiae* is commonly used. The inoculum comes from a large tank of carefully maintained pure culture, previously inoculated from a smaller seed tank, and the latter from a flask or tube of culture in the laboratory. At present stainless steel continuous-culture apparatus is available for maintaining constantly large amounts (many gallons) of *pure* cultures of inoculum.

The maintenance of purity of the inoculum is a responsibility of the microbiologist, and woe betide him if some sporeformer, *Lactobacillus,* wild yeast or bacteriophage gets in and ruins 100,000 gallons of mash! The mash and all of the machinery are generally sterilized before the inoculation and then cooled. The microbiologist is kept busy at every stage of the process, making cultural and microscopic examinations of the water, mash and apparatus to detect and eliminate contamination.

In the batch process, much used for this purpose, fermentation in enormous tanks (Fig. 47.2) is allowed to continue for about 48 hours at a carefully controlled temperature of about 25° C. until the yeast stops growing because of the concentration of alcohol and other products. Aeration with filtered air is used at first to promote rapid growth, but anaerobiosis is soon established to promote fermentation and alcohol accumulation, and prevent its oxidation to carbon dioxide and water.

The fermented mash contains the crude alcohol or *high wine,* as it is called. This is usually a mixture of ethyl alcohol and a small amount of glycerol with *fusel oil.* The last contains amyl, isoamyl, propyl, butyl and other alcohols with acetic, butyric and other acids, as well as various esters. The high wine is driven off from the mash or *beer* by heat, and further purified by fractional distillation, which is a problem in chemical engineering.

The chemical reactions involved in the fermentation are complex; the principal stages follow the Embden-Meyerhof scheme. The overall reaction in the production of alcohol from glucose is:

$$C_6H_{12}O_6 \xrightarrow{\text{yeast}} 2C_2H_5OH + 2CO_2.$$

The chief constituents of fusel oil are probably derived from the action of the yeasts on amino acids in the mash. The large amounts of carbon dioxide evolved are purified and compressed in tanks or made into solid carbon dioxide. Part of this may be used for cooling the fermentation vats.

## 47.4   ALCOHOLIC BEVERAGE INDUSTRIES

### WHISKEY

In principle the production of alcoholic distilled beverages is similar to the production of industrial ethyl alcohol. Refinements are intro-

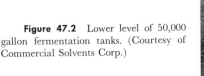

**Figure 47.2** Lower level of 50,000 gallon fermentation tanks. (Courtesy of Commercial Solvents Corp.)

duced in beverage production with respect to flavor, aroma, color and sanitation that are not necessary in the making of industrial alcohol.

There are four general types of distilled liquor: brandy, from fermented fruit juices; rum, from fermented molasses; whiskey, from fermented mashes made with single types of grains; neutral spirits, from fermented mash of mixed grains. In making whiskey and neutral spirits the grain, mixed with water, is autoclaved, cooled, diluted, and 1 per cent barley *malt* (aqueous extract of sprouted barley; see next section on beer) is added to hydrolyze the starch and proteins of the grain. The "mashing," or hydrolysis, proceeds in a special tank at about 65° C. for about 30 minutes. The mash is then pumped to the fermentation tanks. Here, as in beer-making, it is heavily inoculated with a starter of selected yeast, which has been cultivated in a mash previously made somewhat acid (pH 4.0) with lactobacilli. Fermentation is complete in about 72 hours, as in industrial alcohol production. The mash is then removed to the distillery and the ethanol, with various by-products, is recovered.

### BEER

This time-honored and popular beverage is one of the class of malt liquors: stout, porter, ale and others. In preparing beer, grain, usually barley, is kept moist for two or three days to induce sprouting, or *malting*. Amylase enzymes that are released in the malt grains during the sprouting process hydrolyze the starches of the grains to simple sugars, mainly maltose and dextrins. Malting (Ger. *malz* = to soften) is necessary since brewer's yeast does not produce amylase and therefore cannot directly attack the starch of the grain. At the same time proteases in the malt grains convert proteins in the grains and flour to soluble nitrogenous foods.

The sprouts are removed mechanically and the *malt grains* are dried. They are later crushed and soaked, or *mashed*, in warm water. The aqueous extract of these malt grains and flour, prepared at just the time when there are maximum amounts of maltose, dextrins and protein derivatives, constitutes a rich nutrient medium. It is called *beer wort*. The beer wort is now drained off and heated to kill contaminating microorganisms. Hops* are added for additional

---

*The hop vine, *Humulus lupulus*, is cultivated for the papery scales of the female flower, which are dried and powdered for use.

antibacterial (stabilizing) effect, color, flavor and aroma.

After cooling, a large inoculum of pure culture of *Saccharomyces cerevisiae* (brewer's yeast or *"barm"*) is added to the wort. This is called *"pitching."* Rival brewers maintain very special strains of yeast for this process. The inoculated wort is aerated at first to stimulate *rapid growth* of yeast; anaerobic conditions prevail later on to favor *fermentation,* when carbon dioxide and 3 to 6 per cent ethanol are produced. After fermentation is complete, the beer is clarified ("chill-proofed"; see Table 47.2), and pasteurized and otherwise processed and aged (lagered*).

Unless scrupulous care is taken, many contaminants (*Pediococcus, Lactobacillus*) will grow vigorously in beer wort, producing buttery flavor, turbidity and "off" flavors. It was in the study of such spoilages, or "diseases," of beer and wines that Pasteur first became famous and developed *pasteurization* to prevent them. He was one of the first industrial microbiologists.

### WINE

The term wine is broadly used to include any properly fermented juice of ripe fruits, or extracts of certain vegetable products such as dandelions and palm shoots. The juices or extracts contain glucose and fructose in concentrations of from 12 to 30 per cent. Fermentation of these sugars by various species of yeasts produces carbon dioxide and ethanol up to concentrations of 7 to 15 per cent, the alcoholic content depending on the kind of juice and yeast involved and the conditions of fermentation. In Europe the fermentation is produced mainly by *wild* yeasts, i.e., those brought to the fruits (largely by insects) from soil or other fruits. Yeasts similar to the species called *Saccharomyces ellipsoideus* are common in such wines.

Although other organisms are usually present, the yeasts soon predominate in the fermenting juice under suitable conditions. Tartaric, malic and other acids, as well as tannin and other substances, including added sulfur dioxide in commercial wine, tend to inhibit growth of many undesirable organisms in the juices.

Even though practices may differ in different wineries, basically they are similar (Fig. 47.3). Commonly in modern American commercial practice, sterilized fruit juices are in-

---

*Ger. *lager* = to be stored; i.e., to age.

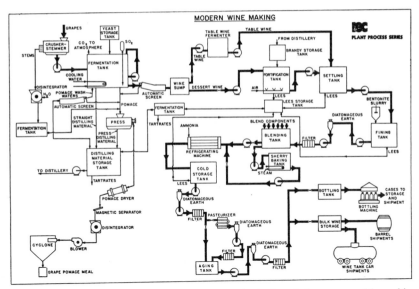

**Figure 47.3**   Modern winemaking. At upper left is shown the beginning of the process, with crushing and stemming of the grapes. The juice passes to a fermentation tank, where SO₂ and yeast are added. (White wines are made with juice only; the juice with skins and seeds is made into red wines.) During fermentation, temperature is controlled with water coils. After initial fermentation the wine settles and clarifies in a wine sump or tank. The fermented juice is then carried through various processes, depending on the type of wine being made. It may be further fermented for table wine or fortified with brandy for dessert wine. It is later clarified by settling, the lees or sediment being piped off for other uses. The clarified wine is then "fined" by filtration and adsorption with diatomaceous earth and passage through other filters; blended, cooled, clarified, pasteurized, aged and dispensed. These processes differ in mechanical details in every winery. (From Hull, Kite and Auerbach: Ind. and Eng. Chem., Oct., 1951, p. 2182.)

oculated with a pure culture of a desirable species of yeast. The preparation and maintenance of the yeast inocula are the special tasks of the microbiologist.

The inoculated juice is, as in beer-making, at first aerated to promote active and pre-emptive growth of yeast. Were this to continue, only carbon dioxide and water and massive growth of yeast cells would result. As soon as a good growth of yeast has occurred, the aeration is stopped and the fermentation proceeds anaerobically, so that ethanol, in concentrations of from 7 to 15 per cent (vol.) is produced. The new wine is placed in large casks to settle, clarify and age.

Spoilage by alcohol-oxidizing species of *Acetobacter,* molds and other *aerobic* microorganisms may occur if conditions are not anaerobic and the reaction not sufficiently acid.

## PRODUCTION OF BUTANOL

The production of butanol is outlined as an example of an industrial fermentation based on a species of bacterium.

As is true of industrial ethanol production,

much butanol is now derived as a by-product of petroleum "cracking." However, the biological process is still used to some extent and illustrates important microbiological principles. There are numerous species of *Clostridium* that ferment carbohydrates with the production of butyl alcohol and other materials of value in drugs, paints, synthetic rubber, explosives and plastics. Some species produce isopropyl alcohol and acetone as well. Important among these organisms are *Cl. acetobutylicum* and *Cl. felsineum.* The name of another species suggests its potentialities as an industrial agent: *Clostridium amylosaccharo-butylpropylicum!*

Many wastes are rich in fermentable carbohydrates, e.g., cannery refuse. Complete sterilization of all apparatus is essential. Conditions cannot be kept as acid (and antibacterial) as they are in yeast fermentations because *Clostridium* has its optimum pH near 7.2. Particularly troublesome contaminants are species of *Lactobacillus.* An organism called *B. volutans,* a gram-positive, nonsporeforming rod (possibly a species of *Lactobacillus?*), is also especially dangerous.

Fermentation proceeds anaerobically for about three days. Normally butyl alcohol, acetone and ethyl alcohol, with carbon dioxide and hydrogen in large amounts, predominate when *Cl. acetobutylicum* acts in a mash rich in glucose. Other substances may occur in smaller amounts. Riboflavin (a vitamin of the B complex) is a valuable constituent of the residue after distillation of the fermented mash. Butyl and isopropyl (rubbing) alcohols are important among the volatile fermentation products of a related species, *Cl. butylicum.*

The successive reactions in the production of butanol and various side-products from glucose are as follows:

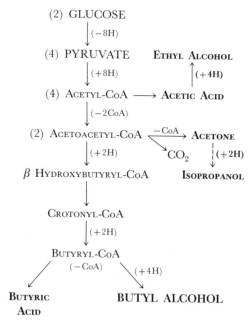

(After Jawetz, Melnick, and Adelberg: Review of Medical Microbiology, 6th ed. Lange Medical Publications, Los Altos, Calif.)

Lactic acid is commonly produced from lactose or glucose by species of homofermentative lactic acid bacteria, notably *Streptococcus lactis* or *Lactobacillus delbrueckii*:

$$C_{12}H_{22}O_{11} + H_2O \longrightarrow 2C_6H_{12}O_6 \longrightarrow$$
*Lactose*                       *Glucose*
                                *and*
                                *Galactose*

$$4C_3H_4O_3 \xrightarrow{(+4H_2)} 4CH_3 \cdot CHOH \cdot COOH$$
*Pyruvate*                        *Lactic acid*

See also Figure 9.5.

Heterofermentative species of lactobacilli like *L. buchneri* produce lactic acid and several by-products:

GLUCOSE $\longrightarrow$ GLUCOSE-6-P $\xrightarrow{(-2H)}$ 6-P-GLUCONATE

$\xrightarrow{(-2H)} \searrow -CO_2$

D-XYLULOSE-5-P $\longleftarrow$ RIBULOSE-5-P

ACETYL-P    3-P-GLYCERALDEHYDE

$\downarrow (-2H)$

ACETIC ACID    PYRUVATE

$\downarrow (+4H)$    $\downarrow (+2H)$

ETHYL ALCOHOL    LACTIC ACID

(After Jawetz, Melnick, and Adelberg: Review of Medical Microbiology, 6th ed. Lange Medical Publications, Los Altos, Calif.)

## PRODUCTION OF VINEGAR

Acetic acid is almost entirely responsible for the sour taste of vinegar. Indeed, a slightly sweetened, three per cent, aqueous solution of acetic acid makes a reasonable substitute for vinegar.

The occurrence of vinegar in fermented fruit juices was known to the ancients, although they had no knowledge of its cause. The bacteria involved were called *Mycoderma aceti* in 1862 by Pasteur.

The acid of natural vinegar is derived from alcohol by the oxidative action of bacteria of the Family Pseudomonadaceae (Genus *Acetobacter*). Pleasant flavors of natural vinegar are given by traces of various esters like ethyl acetate, and by alcohol, sugars, glycerin and volatile oils produced in small amounts by microbial action. Flavors are also derived from the fermented fruit juice, malt, or other alcoholic liquor (wine, beer, hard cider) from which the vinegar was made.

In commercial vinegar-making by biological methods, preliminary fermentation of fruit juices to produce the necessary alcohol is often carried out by means of *Saccharomyces cerevisiae* (brewers' yeast). The *Acetobacter* then utilize the alcohol as a source of energy, oxidizing it to acetic acid in the presence of air. They utilize other substances in the fermented liquor as foods. The alcoholic fluid is aerated as much as possible by various devices. In vinegar "generators" the alcoholic liquor trickles over the surface of aerated shavings, coke, gravel or other finely divided material (Fig. 47.4) inoculated with *Acetobacter*. Such an arrangement is called a

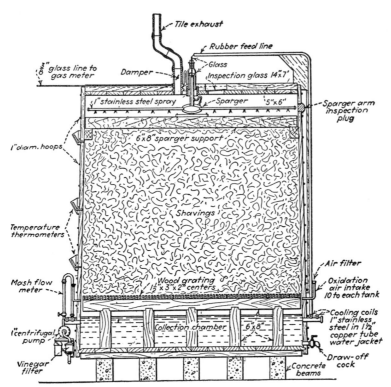

**Figure 47.4** Cross section of the Frings vinegar generator. The alcoholic liquor is sprayed over the shavings by the rotating stainless steel spray (sparger) near the top. Note the thermometers, cooling coils and air intakes. (Hansen: Food Industries, vol. 7.)

*two-phase continuous process;* one phase is the down-trickling alcoholic liquor, the other phase is the column of coke or other material covered with growth of *Acetobacter* (see also *trickling filters,* Chapter 42).

**Genus Acetobacter.** These are nonspore-forming, polar or peritrichous flagellate, gram-negative rods about 0.5 by 8.0 $\mu$, although species vary in size. Branching involution forms and large swollen cells frequently occur, especially in *mother-of-vinegar,* the gummy or slimy growth-phase of the organisms sometimes seen in natural vinegar or sour cider. Various species are found in souring fruits and vegetables. A species of historical interest is *Acetobacter* (*Mycoderma*) *aceti,* originally used by Pasteur to demonstrate the biological nature of vinegar formation. In practice, several species of *Acetobacter* usually act jointly. The alcoholic and acidic nature of the process suppresses most contaminants. The over-all reactions probably are as follows:

$$C_2H_5OH + \tfrac{1}{2}O_2 \longrightarrow CH_3CHO + H_2O$$
$$\textit{Alcohol} \qquad\qquad\qquad \textit{Acetaldehyde}$$

$$CH_3CHO + \tfrac{1}{2}O_2 \longrightarrow CH_3COOH$$
$$\qquad\qquad\qquad\qquad \textit{Acetic acid}$$

In a generator such as that shown in Figure 47.4, the rapid oxidation of alcohol by the organisms produces so much heat that careful control of the internal temperature by cooling coils is necessary.

## 47.5  FOODS FROM WASTES

In the paper-pulp industry, wood chips are cooked for 6 to 18 hours at 60° C. in solutions of calcium bisulfite with free sulfur dioxide. The waste *sulfite liquor,* after the cooking process and removal of the wood fibers for paper, contains much valuable wood sugar (largely *xylose*) and other extractives. These form a good nutrient for asporogenous yeast or *Torula.*

The nutrients in such a medium may be turned into masses of yeast by adjustment of pH to about 5.0, removal of $SO_2$, aeration, addition of nitrogen and phosphorus as $(NH_4)2HPO_4$ and $NH_4OH$, and inoculation with *Torulopsis utilis. Aerobic* growth is induced in aerated vats so that alcohol is not produced. The separation, drying and pressing of the resulting yeast growth are mechanical details

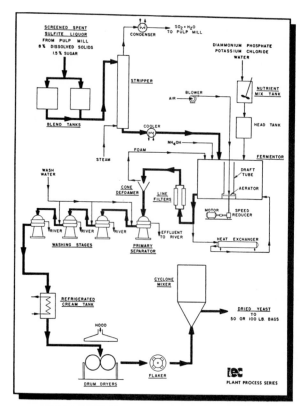

**Figure 47.5**   Paper-mill waste to stock-feed. The blended pulp-mill liquors are heated in a "stripper" to drive off $SO_2$ and $H_2O$, cooled and piped to the fermentation tank. Nitrogen and phosphorus are added as ammonium phosphate and as $NH_4OH$. The yeast culture in the fermentor is aerated to promote maximum growth. The yeast culture is then filtered and passed through a series of centrifuges and other washing and concentrating devices. As "cream" it is finally cooled, dried and packed for shipment. (From Inskeep, Wiley, Holderby and Hughes: Ind. and Eng. Chem., Aug., 1951, p. 1702.)

(Fig. 47.5). Yields of up to 50 per cent of the total reducing sugar consumed, in terms of dry torula, are obtainable. (At present, attempts are being made to cultivate yeasts on petroleum wastes.) The yeast cells are rich in proteins, fats and vitamins. These are fed to stock or poultry and thus turned into meat and dairy products. Surely the transformation of a knotty old pine slab into a succulent pork chop or a fried egg is modern magic!

**Amino Acid Production.**   Not only may yeasts serve as foods themselves, but some species, especially *Saccharomyces cerevisiae* and *Torula utilis,* while growing can synthesize large amounts of various amino acids, e.g., L-lysine. This is an expensive amino acid widely used to "fortify" many familiar foodstuffs. It is requisite that the growth medium for the yeast contain L-adipic acid or its derivatives. The yeasts use the adipic acid derivatives as *precursors* (i.e., as

the molecular raw material) for their synthesis of L-lysine.

**Hydrocarbons for Protein.**   Various hydrocarbon (petroleum) wastes are metabolizable by certain yeasts, eucaryotic fungi and also by some bacteria, e.g., *Bacillus* spp., especially thermophilic species. One difficulty (or possibly a source of profit?) is the production of large amounts of heat by biooxidation of hydrocarbons. The proteins produced in the process are of high nutritive value and the method is potentially profitable.

## 47.6   STEROID TRANSFORMATIONS

In ancient legend sorcerers, by means of their wands, changed beautiful princesses into graceful swans. Today's wizard changes one substance into another, but the sorcerer is now the microbiologist and the sorcerer's wand is replaced by much more potent microorganisms, e.g., *Penicillium, Rhizopus, Streptomyces.* An outstanding example of the use of microorganisms to change one substance into another is the transformation of the steroids. Steroids are physiologically active compounds of complex structure (hormones) (Fig. 47.6) and are represented by cholesterol, ergosterol or vitamin D, sex hormones such as testosterone and progesterone, and the adrenal steroids such as corticosterone and its derivative, cortisone. Microbial transformations of these compounds differ basically from industrial fermentations previously described. In industrial fermentation the alcohol or other product results from the action of numerous enzyme systems in the overall metabolism of a substrate, such as the sugar in molasses. The same product might be made with any of several different microorganisms that ferment saccharose or glucose. In steroid transformation one particular form of molecule is changed into another by the action of a single, specific enzyme. The requisite enzyme may be present in only a single species of microorganism. Many steroid derivatives thus obtained are of immense value in the treatment of various disease conditions or in the development of other hormones. On a commercial scale, many are at present available *only* through the action of certain specific microorganisms.

A single example will illustrate the type and importance of these transformations. Corticosterone, an important hormone from the cortex of the adrenal gland of mammals, was originally obtainable only from animals. It had a wide use in the treatment of shock and other prostrating

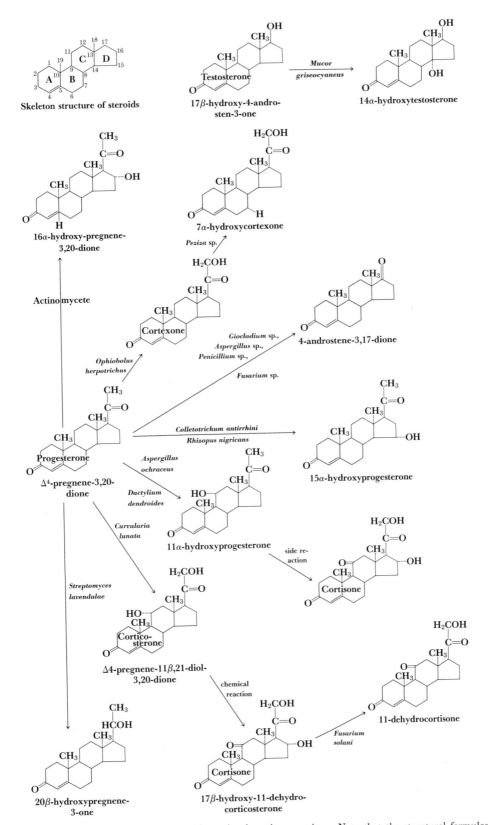

**Figure 47.6** Some examples of steroid transformation by microorganisms. Note that the structural formulas of all are basically alike, differing only in the presence or absence, or molecular position, of OH, H, CH₃, O, etc. Organisms that effect the transformations shown are named. An example of stepwise transformation is given: from progesterone, with *Curvularia lunata* to *corticosterone*; from *corticosterone* to cortisone by chemical alteration. The numbers 11, 15, etc., refer to positions in the molecule shown diagrammatically at the upper left of the figure. Note that several fungi, among them the familiar molds *Penicillium*, *Rhizopus* and *Aspergillus*, as well as certain mold-like bacteria, *Streptomyces* and an actinomycete, perform steroid transformations.

conditions. A still more valuable derivative was made by chemical, and later by microbiological, transformation of the corticosterone molecule. One of these alterations was the introduction by microbial action of an ⁻OH group into the 11 position in the corticosterone molecule (Fig. 47.6). The resulting compound is the now-familiar cortisone, widely used in treating arthritis and many other inflammatory conditions.

The sex hormones, testosterone, estradiol and progesterone, are closely related in molecular structure to corticosterone and cortisone. They differ only in the nature and location of attached side groups, especially ⁻OH and ⁻CO · CH₂OH. These groups may be added or withdrawn or shifted about on a practical scale only through the action of certain specific microorganisms. Some of these transformations are indicated in Figure 47.6. The resulting compounds are often of much greater value than the natural hormone or steroid from which they are derived.

Similar transformations can be brought about in other kinds of molecules, e.g., various alkaloids.

## 47.7   ENZYMES OF MICROORGANISMS IN INDUSTRY

Knowledge that many of the essential chemical changes that occur in microbiological processes are entirely enzymic led to attempts to separate and concentrate the purified enzymes themselves on a commercial scale. The production of microbial enzymes for industrial use is a considerable industry in itself. The enzymes are derived mainly from molds, yeasts and bacteria already familiar to us. A few of the more widely used organisms, their enzymes and their uses, are listed in Table 47.2.

**Mold-Bran Process.** For obtaining enzymes from *Aspergillus* and *Penicillium*, the *mold-bran* process is often used. To provide an extensive aerated surface, flaky or fibrous material, commonly wheat bran, is moistened with a nutrient medium of composition and pH appropriate to the mold being cultivated and the enzyme desired. The nutrient bran is sterilized, spread out in shallow trays and inoculated with the mold conidia. The trays are incubated in carefully air-conditioned cabinets. After sufficient growth the moldy bran is thoroughly extracted with water or other solvent to remove the enzyme. This fluid may be filtered, centrifuged, con-

centrated and the enzyme precipitated and dried for sale.

For bacterial enzymes the desired species of *Bacillus* is generally cultivated on the surface of broad, shallow layers of liquid medium. This is often prepared from inexpensive cannery or dairy refuse (e.g., whey) rich in organic matter. After incubation the bacteria are removed by filtration or centrifugation, and the enzyme is extracted and processed as indicated above.

The submerged culture process may be used in enzyme production by molds or bacteria, in much the same manner as in antibiotic production.

**Gibberellin (Gibberellic Acid).** This sensationally effective plant-growth stimulant, now available in every garden-supply house, was discovered by Kurosawa, in Japan in 1926. Analogous to penicillin, it is a waste product of a mold, *Fusarium moniliforme*, or *Gibberella fujikuroi*, and is a mixture of gibberellins. In nature the mold grows in young rice plants and causes the "overgrowth disease," *bakanae*. A pest in rice paddies, the mold and its *gibberellin* are welcomed by agriculturalists and gardeners. Gibberellin is produced on a commercial scale by submerged aerated growth in media and by methods similar to those used in producing penicillin (Chapter 22).

## 47.8   MICROBIOLOGICAL ASSAY

Microbiological assay is a highly specialized application of the fact that certain organisms lack certain specific synthetic powers, i.e., are auxotrophs. *Lactobacillus plantarum*, for example, is unable to synthesize nicotinic acid ("niacin"). We may furnish the organism with a medium that is complete and satisfactory in all other respects but if niacin is lacking, absolutely no growth occurs. (Humans are no better off; without niacin they die of pellagra.) If a minute amount (say, 0.01 microgram) per milliliter of niacin is added to the medium for *L. plantarum*, some growth will occur. More growth will occur in the presence of more of the missing factor. Up to the point of satiation or acidification, growth bears a linear relationship to the amount of the specific growth factor added.

For example, to assay the nicotinic acid content of fresh green beans, we prepare a medium for *L. plantarum* that is complete in all respects except niacin. This we omit. We now prepare two series (A and B) of 10 sterile tubes each. Each tube receives 10 ml. of the niacin-

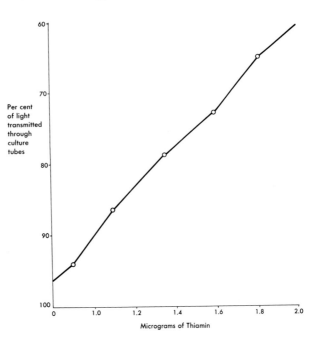

**Figure 47.7** Representative curve obtained with a series of "standard" tubes for microbiological assay of thiamin with *Lactobacillus casei.* A similar form of curve would be obtained in any assay by this method, such as that described for niacin (*L. plantarum*) in the text. Slight deviations from the theoretical straight line are due to slight technical errors. Growth was measured photoelectrically: increasing growth (turbidity) reduced the amount of light transmitted through the culture tubes.

deficient medium. To each tube in series A we add known and graded amounts of pure niacin. To each tube in series B we add graded amounts of bean extract, niacin content unknown. All tubes are now inoculated with carefully washed (niacin-*free!*) cells of *Lactobacillus plantarum.* Accurate, photometric measurements are then made of the growths (turbidities) obtained in the cultures (Fig. 47.7). If the medium contains glucose, titrations of acidity instead of turbidity may be used as a measure of growth (Fig. 47.8). By comparing growths in series A and B it is possible to estimate closely the concentration of niacin in the green beans. This method of estimation of growth factors is spoken of as *microbiological assay.*

Although the basic principle of all microbiological assays is the same, there are other methods of measuring the growth (or other physiological) response. These affect the cultural

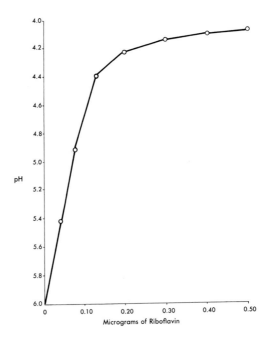

**Figure 47.8** Representative curve obtained in the assay of a food substance for riboflavin content by measurement of pH. This is the "standard" curve used as the basis for measurement of the "unknowns." Note the linear relationship between growth of the test organism (*Lactobacillus arabinosus*) as measured by pH, and amount of riboflavin in the first part of the curve. In the later parts of the curve acidity inhibits unlimited response of the organism to the larger amounts of riboflavin.

methods used. A commonly used procedure is the measurement of carbon dioxide produced by fermentation of sugar in the test medium. Yeast is routinely used in the microbiological assay of *thiamine* (vitamin $B_1$) by this method. In *pyridoxine* (vitamin $B_6$) assays, the mold *Neurospora* is the test organism. After sufficient incubation the culture is steamed and the entire mycelium of *Neurospora* is removed from the culture medium, dried and weighed. Dry weight is directly proportional to concentration of pyridoxine in the sample of material being assayed. Another assay procedure depends on the spheroplast-producing power of the assayed substance.

Certain organisms lend themselves very well to such assay procedures. *Lactobacillus casei* and *L. arabinosus* are easy to cultivate, relatively hardy, harmless and wholly dependent upon several growth-factors including various amino acids, riboflavin, biotin, pantothenic acid and nicotinic acid. Other organisms may be used for assay of other substances, for example, *Streptococcus lactis* for folic acid. Ultraviolet-induced, synthetically deficient auxotrophs of molds, yeasts and bacteria are extremely valuable in assay work.

Even though the basic principle of microbiological assay is easily understood, the technological details are often exceedingly complex and filled with pitfalls. Many obscure factors affect the test organisms, and they may also undergo mutation and other changes without notice. Mutational and other injuries may be held to a minimum by storage of the stock cultures in containers with liquid nitrogen at $-196°$ C. ($-321°$ F.). Temperature, pH and presence or absence of air may be of critical importance. For example, under *aerobic* conditions, *Lactobacillus lactis* will *die* before it will grow without vitamin $B_{12}$! *Anaerobically*, it sneers at vitamin $B_{12}$! There are many other examples. We may smile, but knowledge of this and many other peculiarities is essential to successful assay procedures.

## 47.9  INDUSTRIAL SPOILAGE

In contrast with the useful activities of bacteria, a word may be said of their destructive action. Several causes of industrial spoilage (e.g., "diseases" of fermentations) have been mentioned in this chapter and in the chapters on soil, food, and water bacteria. Species of *Micrococcus, Alkaligenes, Flavobacterium, Serratia, Clos-*

*tridium,* coliform organisms, yeasts and molds are common causes of spoilage.

Each type of product is attacked by certain species of microorganisms that can metabolize the substance especially well. For example, spoilage of cellulosic products such as lumber; telephone poles; paper; sisal, jute and flax fibers; tobacco and cotton is brought about by cellulose decomposers such as molds, various species of *Clostridium, Cellulomonas, Cytophaga* and many other such organisms of the soil. Fermentable substances such as syrups and beverages are attacked by yeasts, lactobacilli, organisms of the coli-aerogenes group and various environmental bacteria including the Genus *Clostridium*. Spoilage of proteins such as meats, fish, milk and so on results from the action of proteolytic species such as *Pseudomonas, Bacillus, Proteus, Micrococcus, Clostridium* and many others. Petroleum hydrocarbons are attacked by certain soil bacteria, as already mentioned, and rubber insulation of vital communication wires is attacked by bacteria and eucaryotic fungi.

Lactobacilli and *Leuconostoc* species have already been noted as particular villains in the acid-food, fermentation and distillery industries. Species of both can ruin fruit or vegetable juice or various industrial mashes (beer and wine) during processing. They produce a buttermilk flavor. Pasteur found *Lactobacillus* and *Leuconostoc* causing "diseases" of beers and wines. They are just as active today. Lactobacilli also discolor meats, especially producing greenish discoloration (oxidized porphyrins) of cured hams and sausages.

The slimy dextran- or levan-forming species, such as *Leuconostoc mesenteroides* and *L. dextranicum* and some lactobacilli and micrococci, produce slimy and ropy conditions in a great variety of human endeavors: sugar refineries, pickle brines, dairy products, ham-curing cellars, and the like. These organisms prefer acidified products such as partly fermented foods, mashes and citrus juice. Examples of several of these types of spoilage have been given in discussions of the various products.

Development of undesirable flavors in fatty products such as butter, especially rancidity, is due in great part to the formation of butyric acid as a result of lipolysis. It is caused by species of *Aspergillus* and other molds, *Pseudomonas* species and streptococci related to *Str. liquefaciens*. These difficulties do not arise when clean equipment, clean milk and proper precautions to avoid contamination are used.

Proteolytic organisms such as *Str. liquefaciens* are responsible for undesirable bitter flavors and early spoilage of cheeses and other protein prod-ucts. Gas production is usually caused by coli-forms and *Clostridium;* putrefaction or digestion by *Clostridium, Pseudomonas* and *Bacillus.* Such conditions result mainly from dirty milk or other food equipment, or careless handling.

Included among other sabotage activities of bacteria are corrosion of the inside of struc-tural aluminum alloys used in fuel tanks of jet-fuel aircraft. Pitting and scaling of the metal occurs beneath heavy, slimy growths of hydro-carbon-utilizing bacteria such as species of *Pseudomonas* and *Desulfovibrio* (see sulfate reduc-tion). Some species of molds are also involved. Bacteria of the Genera *Mycobacterium* and *No-cardia,* among others, are also implicated in the deterioration of bituminous products, including asphalt highways and asphalt coatings and pipe-linings. The microorganisms seem to utilize the high-viscosity hydrocarbons and resins in asphalt.

**Prevention of Spoilage.**   This, in each in-stance, is a problem that can be solved only by careful examination of the process involved to find: (a) the nature of the organism(s) involved; (b) where the contamination is getting in, and (c) then devising means of excluding it. It is im-possible to lay down a blanket rule for industrial spoilage in general. Everything depends on maintaining conditions unfavorable to, or ex-cluding by asepsis, organisms that can grow on or in the particular product involved. This may involve complete steam sterilization of fermen-tation equipment (tanks, pipes, pumps); drying; refrigeration; aeration; the use of inhibitory salt, sugar or acid concentrations; radiation with ultraviolet light; exposure to sunlight; treat-ment with substances such as creosote, sodium benzoate and the like. In some processes specific antibiotics may be used, as penicillin and tetra-cyclines in alcoholic fermentation of molasses.

## SUPPLEMENTARY READING

Charney, W., and Herzog, H.: Microbiological Transforma-tion of Steroids. Academic Press, New York. 1967.

Dawson, R. C.: Potential for increasing food production through microbiology. Bact. Rev., *29*:251, 1965.

Diendoerfer, F. H., Mateles, R. I., and Humphrey, A. E.: Microbiological Progress Report. 1961 Fermentation process review. Appl. Microbiol., *11*:273, 1963.

Eyssen, H., Swaelen, E., Kowszyk-Gindifer, Z., and Par-mentier, G.: Nucleotide requirements of *Lactobacillus acidophilus* variants isolated from the crops of chicks. Ant. Leeuw., *31*:241, 1965.

Freed, M.: Methods of Vitamin Assay. Interscience Pub-lishers, New York. 1966.

Gafford, R. D., and Richardson, D. E.: Mass algal culture in space operations. J. Biochem. Microbiol. Tech. Eng., *II*:299, 1960.

Gaucher, T. A., Benoit, R. J., and Bialecki, A.: Mass prop-agation of algae for photosynthetic gas exchange. J. Biochem. Microbiol. Tech. Eng., *II*:339, 1960.

Hartman, R. E., Krause, E. F., Andres, W. W., and Patter-son, E. L.: Microbial hydroxylation of indole alka-loids. Appl. Microbiol., *12*:138, 1964.

Hedrick, H. G., Miller, C. E., Halkias, J. E., and Hilde-brand, J. E.: Selection of a microbiological corrosion system for studying effects on structural aluminum alloys. Appl. Microbiol., *12*:197, 1964.

Holström, B.: Production of streptokinase in continuous culture. Appl. Microbiol., *16*:73, 1968.

Iizuka, H., and Naito, A.: Microbial Transformation of Steroids, Alkaloids, and Other Organic Compounds. University Park Press, Baltimore. 1968.

Koda, C. K., editor: Developments in Industrial Micro-biology. Vol. 8. Amer. Inst. Biol. Sciences, Washington, D. C. 1967.

Long, S. K., and Patrick, R.: Production of 2,3-butylene glycol from citrus wastes. II. The *Bacillus polymyxa* fermentation. Appl. Microbiol., *13*:973, 1965.

Lüthi, H. R., Stoyla, B., and Moyer, J. C.: Continuous production of flor sherry from New York State wines. Appl. Microbiol., *13*:511, 1956.

Mateles, R. I., Baruah, J. N., and Tannenbaum, S. R.: Growth of a thermophilic bacterium on hydrocarbons: a new source of single-cell protein. Science, *157*:1322, 1967.

Starr, M. P., editor: Global Impacts of Applied Microbiology. John Wiley & Sons, New York. 1965.

Traxler, R. W., Proteau, P. R., and Traxler, R. N.: Action of microorganisms on bituminous materials. I. Effect of bacteria on asphalt viscosity. Appl. Microbiol., *13*:838, 1965.

Tsuji, K.: Liquid nitrogen preservation of *Saccharomyces carlsbergensis* and its use in a rapid biological assay of vitamin $B_6$ (pyridoxine). Appl. Microbiol., *14*:456, 1966.

Umbreit, W. W., editor: Advances in Applied Microbiology. Vol. 10. Academic Press, New York. 1968.

Zacharias, B., and Björklund, M.: Continuous production of *Clostridium tetani* toxin. Appl. Microbiol., *16*:69, 1968.

# *Index*